(2601) 62732 A

PHYSIOLOGICAL REVIEWS · OCTOBER 1959

Supplement no. 3

EFFECTS OF COLD ON MAN

AN ANNOTATED BIBLIOGRAPHY, 1938–1951

By

WAVE ELAINE CULVER

The Library of Congress

Published by

THE AMERICAN PHYSIOLOGICAL SOCIETY

PRINTED IN THE UNITED STATES OF AMERICA
BY WAVERLY PRESS, INC., BALTIMORE, MARYLAND

CONTENTS

PREFACE

THIS BIBLIOGRAPHY was prepared in the Bibliography Section[1] of the Science and Technology Division, Library of Congress, upon the request of the Biological Sciences Division of the Office of Naval Research.[2] Its purpose is to give a comprehensive coverage of the literature from 1938 through 1951 on the physiological effects of cold on man and prophylactic methods of dealing with the various cold injuries, especially frostbite, immersion foot, and trench foot. It includes the effects of cold on the various warm-blooded animals used in experimental laboratories and in other studies simulating conditions of human existence. No *in vitro* studies are included, however.

The references are from a wide range of physiological, medical, and other scientific journals and monographs, the selection of materials having been done on a liberal basis. Unpublished reports on government-sponsored research are not included in the present compilation.[3] Each reference is accompanied by an annotation, which is usually fairly informative, but no critical evaluation of the information has been attempted. A slight unevenness in some of the material has been caused by the economic necessity of incorporating some of the annotations prepared before 1952 when the scope of the annotations was widened to present informative abstracts.

In the earlier stages of the bibliography, it was decided to use only translated titles of papers written in languages other than English. This policy has been continued in work done later, but in each case the original language of the reference is indicated in brackets following the title.

All the references except a few, mostly in Russian and Japanese, which are marked with an asterisk (*), have been verified in the original. The author index contains not only the senior author and all secondary authors for each reference, but also the editors of compiled works and a few translators, as well as any persons indicated as contributing information in a discussion following the presentation of a paper.

Form of entry. Titles of journals are in general abbreviated the way they appear in the Current List of Medical Literature, published by the National Library of Medicine of the U. S. Department of Health, Education and Welfare and in other publications of the National Library of Medicine.[4] The journal title is followed

---

[1] Formerly part of the Technical Information Division.

[2] Under Government Order NAonr 30-58, and previous contracts; publication is supported in part by the U.S. Army Medical Research and Development Command, Office of the Surgeon General.

[3] Annotated references to unclassified reports on effects of cold on man are included in *The Polar Bibliography*, a series being compiled by the Library of Congress for the Department of Defense.

[4] List of abbreviations for serial publications referred to in the Index-Catalogue of the Library of the Surgeon General's Office, U.S. Army, Volume X, Fourth Series. Washington, D. C.; Government Printing Office, 1948. 138 pages.

by the volume number, the month and day of the imprint (if not available, the issue number in parentheses), the year, and, following a colon, the inclusive pagination of the article. In the case of monographs, the title is followed by the place of publication, the publisher, the date of imprint and the pagination.

Arrangement. The references are arranged by a rather detailed subject classification. The major headings of the classification may be seen from the table of contents. At the end of each sub-heading of the classification there is a generous listing of cross-references, by item number, to papers entered in other categories. In order to avoid too many minor subheadings, references which are otherwise not indicated under a specialized heading are grouped under a heading of General.

Acknowledgements. While only one author's name appears on the title page, there have been, in a sense, many collaborators. We wish to acknowledge the contributions of Mr. Morris C. Leikind, Mr. Jack Weiner, and Mrs. Helen Williams Silbernagel to the early work on the bibliography. The assistance of Dr. Ludmila Kassianoff, in the translation of considerable Russian material, is gratefully acknowledged, as well as the occasional aid of Mrs. Elizabeth Petrov with this language. Our thanks are due to Dr. Roman Kenk for continuing constructive criticism and editorial assistance. For aid in the preparation of the manuscript and in the reading of the proof, we owe our thanks also to Mrs. Doris Yates, Miss Mercedes Cain, and Mr. Leroy Davis. For the excellent services extended to us throughout the work on the bibliography, we are deeply grateful to the National Library of Medicine, and several other libraries in the Washington, D. C., area. Particular thanks are due to Dr. Frederick A. Fuhrman of Stanford University, who kindly reviewed the bibliography and contributed some additional references.

Washington, D. C.
April, 1959

BIBLIOGRAPHY

I. TEMPERATURE REGULATION

A. General

1. Anon. Bodily temperature and flying. *Flight Surgeon Topics, v. 2 (1), 1938: 14.*

Comment is made on a letter from Dr. R. GREENE raising the question of whether or not the slight rise in temperature from no apparent cause, which is sometimes found on routine examination of passengers arriving by airplane from foreign ports, could be caused by an interference with the physiological heat-regulating centers by the flight.

2. Adolph, E. F. Some differences in response to low temperatures between warm-blooded and cold-blooded vertebrates. *Am. J. Physiol., v. 166, July 1, 1951: 92–103.*

Studies of pulse rate, breath rate, and oxygen consumption were made on hamsters, rats, cats, and mice, in relation to body temperature, and the results compared with similar known facts about cold-blooded vertebrates. These relations were quite different in the various species, and studies on isolated tissues showed certain species differences to be inherent in the tissues. Although nervous system and hormonal influences were noted, especially in homeotherms, it is concluded that the pattern of homeothermy extends to many or all parts of the physiological organization and is not limited to a region of the central nervous system.

3. Aschoff, J. Physiology of temperature regulation [In German]. *In: FIAT review of German Science, 1939–1946. Pt. II, Physiology; Section XII, p. 77–110. Wiesbaden, Office of Military Government for Germany, Field Information Agencies Technical, 1948.*

In this general review of German research during World War II, the physiology of temperature regulation is discussed under the following headings: Generalized Climatic Effects (metabolism, circulation and respiration, body temperature, disturbances of regulation); The Inner Gradient (temperature topography, heat retention of the body, heat exchange); Climatic Extremes (warm, cold, both local and generalized); and Central Nervous Regulation. The extensive bibliography of this review appears on pages 106–110.

4. Barbour, H. G. The development of homeothermy in animals. *In: American Institute of Physics. Temperature, its measurement and control in science and industry, p. 436–445. New York, Reinhold, 1941.*

This is a general discussion of the development of temperature regulation in animals and the physiology of heat production and heat dissipation, including the role of the hypothalamus, the behavior of water in the body, and the significance of the endocrine glands in temperature control.

5. Bazett, H. C. The regulation of body temperatures. *In: Physiology of heat regulation and the science of clothing, p. 109–192. Ed. by L. H. Newburgh. Philadelphia, Saunders, 1949.*

This is a review of the physiological mechanisms involved in the regulation of body temperature. It includes an outline of an hypothesis of heat regulation; the control of the body temperature by the nervous system (including the role of the endocrine system); and the time sequence of adjustments to heat and cold. 171 refs.

5

6. **Bazett, H. C.** Blood temperature and its control. *Am. J. M. Sc., v. 218, Nov. 1949: 483–492.*

Catheterization of the radial artery has shown temperatures as low as 21.5°C in a room of 9° to 10.5°C, and of 31.1°C in a brachial artery in a room of 13.3°C. Heat loss from the arteries can be explained as the reheating of the cooled blood in the veins due to the close physical association of the peripheral arteries with the veins. Regulation of this circulatory variation appears to depend on at least three mechanisms: direct reaction of blood vessels to temperature levels; reflex responses to thermal sensations; and the reaction of two reciprocal centers in the hypothalamus to temperature levels to which they are exposed, through which the temperature of the blood supplying them is regulated. However, the hypothalamic central control of body temperature by the two centers fails to account for regulation of central body temperature at higher levels during exercise. Since peripheral control can be ruled out, it is still felt that this control is through some alteration in the hypothalamic centers.

7. **Brody, S.** How animals react to air conditions. *Heating Piping, v. 12, Oct. 1940: 584, 592.*

This article, excerpted from a paper presented at a meeting of the American Society of Agricultural Engineers, discusses some aspects of temperature regulation in animals. At temperatures below thermal neutrality the animal keeps warm first by physical methods not involving increase in heat production, and then by chemical methods which do involve heat production. Most farm animals can withstand low temperatures without much energy expenditure because of the insulation afforded by hair, wool, or subcutaneous fat, and because their winter feeds are high in heat-producing properties. At low environmental temperatures, heat dissipation is mostly (up to 70%) by radiation of infrared waves and the humidity of the environment is not a major factor. In general the adaptive powers of animals to cold are very much greater than they are to heat; this is particularly true of the non-sweating, furry, relatively large animals such as sheep, cattle, and dogs. It is therefore not as difficult or important to protect an animal from cold as from heat.

8. **Burton, A. C.** Temperature regulation. *Annual Rev. Physiol., v. 1, 1939: 109–130.*

This general review includes a discussion of the constancy of body temperature, the development of its regulatory mechanism, temperature receptors and sensation, physical and chemical regulation, shivering and thermal muscular tone, and acclimatization. 153 refs.

9. **Burton, A. C.** The operating characteristics of the human thermoregulatory mechanism. *In: American Institute of Physics. Temperature, its measurement and control in science and industry, p. 522–528. New York, Reinhold, 1941.*

This study is concerned only with the thermoregulatory mechanisms operating in the range of "comfortable" temperatures, where neither sweating nor shivering are called into play. The central nervous system regulates body temperature in response to impulses from the temperature receptors by the adjustment of the blood flow of the peripheral tissues through vasoconstriction and vasodilatation of the blood vessels. The thermoregulatory center in the brain is described as having a direct sensitivity to the temperature of the blood, so that the amount of vasomotor discharge resulting from a given stimulation is dependent upon the deep body temperature.

10. **Cannon, W. B.** The wisdom of the body. *New York, Norton, 1939. 312 p.*

Chapter XII (p. 177–201) deals with The Constancy of Body Temperature. The mean body temperature of a normal healthy human is 98.6°F, with an average low reading of 97.3°F at 4:00 A.M. and an average high reading of 99.1°F at 4:00 P.M. The role of metabolism; influence of endocrine functioning; importance of various physiological mechanisms for heat loss and heat conservation; and the functioning of the thermal regulatory centers in the diencephalon, are discussed in relation to this constancy of body temperature.

11. Cier, J. Heat regulation [In French]. *Presse méd., v. 57, (suppl. 47) July 20, 1949: 688B, 688E.*

Temperature regulation is discussed in great detail, with liberal reference to findings of earlier workers, both as to its physical and chemical aspects. Included is considerable discussion of the role of endocrine factors in chemical thermoregulation and of the location and action of thermal-sensitive regulatory areas in the hypothalamus.

12. DuBois, E. F. The temperature of the human body in health and disease. *In: American Institute of Physics. Temperature, its measurement and control in science and industry, p. 24–40. New York, Reinhold, 1941.*

The author discusses the range of normal internal body temperatures. The average rectal temperature according to most authors is 37.0 °C with a variation of 0.4 ° to 1.4 °C. The author mentions different factors which affect body temperature, such as age, time of day, environmental temperature, etc., and discusses each. He notes that the heat-regulating center is located in the hypothalamus and explains the balance mechanism which exists between various factors affecting heat loss and heat gain.

13. Evans, J. P., and R. E. Wilson. A comparison of differential measurements of skin temperature using a radiometer, resistance thermometer, and thermocouples. *J. Laborat. Clin. M., v. 38, Oct. 1951: 557–560.*

A comparison was made of measurements of skin temperature using either a radiometer, a resistance thermometer, or thermocouples. It is concluded that a comparatively simple arrangement of thermocouples may be used under normal conditions in hospitals to determine temperature differences with the same precision as that of the radiometer. By using two similar thermocouple junctions applied to the skin in the same manner, the effects of several variables (including the method for fastening the junctions, the pressure which they exert, and the disturbance of the circulation in the region) are considerably decreased.

14. Giaja, J. Homeothermy and thermoregulation [In French]. *(Actualités scientifiques et industrielles, nos. 576, 577). Paris, Hermann, 1938. 70 + 76 p.*

Fascicle I, Homeothermy (p. 1–70) consists of two parts and contains the following subject headings: The Fact of Homeothermy; Endogenous and Exogenous Homeothermy; The Significance of Homeothermy; The Thermal Environment; The Temperature Level in Homeotherms; The Critical Low Temperature; The Critical High Temperature; The Area of Adaptability in Homeotherms; Basal Metabolism—Outline of the Mechanism of Homeothermy; Basis of Comparison in the Study of the Laws of Bioenergy among Various Species, Basal Metabolism in Homeotherms.

Fascicle II, Thermoregulation (p. 1–76) contains the following subject headings: Chemical Thermoregulation; Chemical Thermoregulation as Influenced by Acclimatization; Metabolism at its Peak (Thermogenetic Potential); Physical Temperature Regulation; Chemical Metabolism and Temperature Regulation; Alcohol and Heat Production; Temperature Regulation and Development; Disorders of Temperature Regulation; The Nervous System and Temperature Regulation; The Endocrine Secretions and Temperature Regulation; and Temperature Regulation and Civilization. The bibliography for both fascicles (204 references) is on pages 67–73.

15. Gotsev, T., and A. Ivanov. Psychogenic elevation of body temperature in healthy persons [In English, summaries in English and Russian]. *Acta physiol. hung., v. 1 (1) 1950: 53–62.*

The body temperature (by axilla) of each of a group of 1068 college students immediately after taking final examinations in their studies was found to be between 37 °C and 38.4 °C in all but a few cases. In the greater number of cases the temperature was 37.5 °C; in only 6.8% of the group was the temperature below 37 °C. In 135 cases where the temperature was taken before and after the examination, a certain number who exhibited no elevation after the examination had had an elevated temperature before the examination. Students who were unsuccessful in the examinations had lower temperatures. In similar studies of a group of students attending the examinations only as listeners, no temperatures above 37°C were recorded. The cause of the psychogenic elevation of temperatures is said to be the result of a general increase in metabolism resulting from the vegetative excitation and an increase of adrenal secretion.

16.   **Grant, R.** Physiological effects of heat and cold. *Annual Rev. Physiol., v. 13, 1951: 75–98.*

A review of the current status of thermophysiology with detailed discussion of the theories of thermoregulation (its disturbances; neural and vascular aspects) and of regional temperature differences. There is also a section on hypothermia. 118 refs.

17.   **Guéniot, M.** Physiological discussion. Temperature regulation [In French]. *Sem. hôp. Paris, v. 25, Oct. 30, 1949: 3320–3326.*

The physiology of temperature regulation is discussed under the following, and other, topic headings: poikilotherms and homeotherms; elements of the thermo-regulatory mechanism; thermal equilibrium and normal temperature; thermal conduction and its protective role; protection against cold or against heat; endocrine, or nervous, mechanisms of temperature regulation; capacity of resistance as a function of regulation; and disturbances of regulation.

18.   **Hardy, J. D.** Physiological responses to heat and cold. *Annual Rev. Physiol., v. 12, 1950: 119–144.*

The literature from July 1947 to June 1949, pertinent to human responses to thermal stress, is reviewed. Included are sections on new methods for measuring temperature, responses to cold (including some findings on limits of exposure to cold), measurements of blood and tissue temperature, vascular responses to thermal stimuli, studies in thermal sensation, and temperature regulation. 119 refs.

19.   **Herrington, L. P., and A. P. Gagge.** Temperature regulation. *Annual Rev. Physiol., v. 5, 1943: 295–320.*

This is a general review of the literature for 1941–1942 on temperature regulation. Included are studies on hypothermia, central and peripheral factors in regulation, physical and chemical aspects of temperature regulation, and information on acclimatization. 105 refs.

20.   **Herrington, L. P.** The range of physiological response to climatic heat and cold. *In: Physiology of heat regulation and the science of clothing, p. 262–276. Ed. by L. H. Newburgh. Philadelphia and London, Saunders, 1949.*

The physiological factors and mechanisms involved in maintaining the stability of the deep internal temperature of the body and the physiological cost of these processes are discussed. Many studies have suggested that the lower limit of deep body temperature beyond which recovery is impossible, is about 25°C. Reports of experiments at the German concentration camp of Dachau confirm this supposition in that the lowest rectal temperature at death, following immersion in ice water, was 25°C and the highest, 29.2°C. The quantitatively important adjustments to cold stress are increased food consumption and adequate clothing, reactions which are voluntary and in this sense radically different from the adjustments to heat.

21.   **König, F.** Blood temperature and heat regulation [In German]. *Pflügers Arch., v. 246, June 2, 1943: 693–708.*

The mechanisms of temperature regulation in warm-blooded animals serve to hold the deep body temperature constant. Experiments in lowering body temperature were carried out and their effects on thermoregulation were studied. Cooling the hand by dipping it in cold water reduced sweating; cooling the face with ice was found to raise the metabolism.

The author concludes that reflexes due to reaction to cold were evoked by the lowering of the blood temperature.

22. **Lee, D. H. K.** Heat and cold. *Annual Rev. Physiol., v. 10, 1948: 365–386.*

This review covers 231 papers published between July 1946 and June 1947. Under the section on cold are discussed temperature regulating mechanisms in the human body; relation of nutrition to exposure to cold; clothing; acclimatization; and tolerance to cold. 231 refs.

23. **Macco, G. di.** Functional study of thermoregulation center [Abstract, in Italian]. *Boll. Soc. ital. biol. sper., v. 21, July 1946: 323.*

Study of the function of the thermoregulatory center brings out the multiplicity and complexity of the factors which intervene in such regulation. The physical aspects of thermal regulation are under the control of the orthosympathetic system; the chemical aspects are under the parasympathetic and closely tied to the phenomenon of reactive hyperemia. In the hyperthermic state one sees a sinusoidal type of curve resulting from a plotting of changes in rectal temperature. In hypothermia, there is great individual variation of body temperature due to the variable reactivity of the autonomic nervous system.

24. **Martin, E. E., and J. P. Henry.** The effects of time and temperature upon tolerance to positive acceleration. *J. Aviat. M., v. 22, Oct. 1951: 382–390.*

Studies were made of the effect of positive acceleration on eleven subjects using the human centrifuge with the subjects unprotected or wearing anti-G suits and with the unit permitting a temperature variation from 15° to 55°C. Results indicated that as long as the subject's heat regulating mechanism was functioning successfully and the subject was not near fainting or heat collapse he would not show significant impairment of G-tolerance when in the upright seated position. A comparison of physiological responses to acceleration in the shivering and sweating states show that the subject's powers of compensation were being called on more severely when he was hot.

25. **Metz, B.** Contribution to the study of the excitability of the thermoregulatory mechanism [In French]. *Strasbourg, Müh-LeRoux, 1949. 70 p.*

A continuous record of cloacal and of muscle temperature and of the consumption of oxygen, was made in a detailed study on pigeons. Lowering the environmental temperature from 20°C to 5°C brought about a decided rise in heat production and of the deep-body, or core, temperature like that occurring during muscular work, with the core temperature stabilizing at a level higher than original level. Lowering the environmental temperature from 30°C to 15°C brought about similar rises in heat production, but core temperature stabilized at a level lower than the original one. A transitory lowering of the core temperature preceded slightly that of the gaseous exchange when the environmental temperature changed from 29°C to 33°C. Raising the temperature from 25°C to 45°C brought about a decided rise in core temperature and polypnea. The author interprets his results as that of a central thermal stimulation and peripheral thermal stimulation interacting in homeothermic regulation.

26. **Missenard, A.** Man and his climatic environment [In German]. *Stuttgart, Deutsche Verlags-Anstalt, [1938] 221 p.*

In Chapter 2, The Effects of Cold and Heat (p. 31–67), is included an account of the physiology of temperature regulation; the effects of temperature on animals, microorganisms, and man; and the resistance to heat and cold.

27. **Niederhäusern, A. de.** Thermoregulation at low temperatures [In Italian]. *Policlinico, Sez. med., v. 46, June 1939: 314–336.*

The literature on thermoregulation is considered with special reference to the protection of the organism against cold. Discussed also are the roles of the autonomic nervous system, the thyroid, and the adrenal glands in the maintenance of a constant body temperature in mammals at low ambient temperatures.

28.   Palmes, E. D., and C. R. Park. An improved mounting for thermocouples for the measurement of the surface temperature of the body. *J. Laborat. Clin. M., v. 33, Aug. 1948: 1044–1046.*

Thermocouples which are technically easy to use in measuring the skin temperatures of the body, are apt to give inaccurate measures primarily because of the type of mounting used. A new type of mounting, made on a 1 x 3 inch rectangle of copper window screen (16 mesh, wire diameter 0.01 inch), is described which has allowed skin temperature to be determined with much greater accuracy than previously.

29.   Porter, H. B. Report of effects of flight on body temperature. *Flight Surgeon Topics, v. 2 (2), 1938: 86–87.*

An extensive series of thermometer readings of body temperature of flying crews was made following airplane flight under very varied conditions. Of 100 determinations made, only 6 remained the same on readings at two different times. Temperatures were elevated from the initial reading in 68 instances, and lowered in 24. The rise consisted of one or more tenths of a degree and occurred primarily in the morning, rising from subnormal to normal. Of the 68 which were elevated, only 4 passed above normal and this did not occur when checked again on later flights. The temperatures which were found to have dropped occurred primarily during the afternoon flights; the drops never went into the subnormal range. It is concluded that flight had no direct effect on body temperature.

30.   Prouty, L. R., and J. D. Hardy. Temperature determinations. *In: Biophysical research methods, p. 131–173. Ed. by F. M. Uber. New York, Interscience, 1950.*

This is a general account of temperature scales and temperature-measuring devices and techniques, with special reference to the measurement of thermal phenomena in biological systems.

31.   Randall, W. C. Alterations in response to changing body temperature following artificial fever and chilling. *Proc. Soc. Exp. Biol., N. Y., v. 52, Mar. 1943: 240–242.*

Young and adult domestic fowl were placed in a cold room (10°C) or wrapped in a heating blanket (about 55°C). During the resulting changes in body temperature, alterations in breathing rate were recorded, as well as the onset of either shivering or panting. Alteration of the temperature regulating mechanism of the fowl was shown by a lowered panting temperature following a maintained reduction of body temperature. Reflex inhibition of panting on application of cold to the skin was also demonstrated.

32.   Rein, H. F. Introduction to human physiology. *Berlin, Springer, 1949. 560 p.*

In Chapter 5, The Warmth Regulation of Humans (p. 170–182), the following topics are discussed briefly: some of the processes of heat retention; normal body temperatures; diurnal range of temperature; maintenance of normal body temperature during sleep or anesthesia; role of the circulatory system; regulation of heat loss through radiation, convection, and evaporation; and the warmth regulatory centers of the diencephalon.

33.   Rietz, E. Heat regulation in man [In Swedish]. *Nord hyg. tskr., v. 23 (12), 1942: 409–414.*

During general cooling the skin temperature drops as the body temperature does, being most pronounced in the arms, then the legs, the head, and the torso. Central nervous system control of body temperature is maintained through sympathetic nervous system control of the peripheral blood vessels of the skin. In cold this occurs as a dilatation of the blood vessels. Heat is then transferred from the deeper to the more superficial areas of the body. An increase in metabolism is part of the body's effort to compensate for a temperature decrease. In severe cooling this is often augmented by the reflex muscular activity of shivering which the individual is unable to control.

34. **Scholander, P. F., R. Hock, V. Walters, F. Johnson, and L. Irving.** Heat regulation in some arctic and tropical mammals and birds. *Biol. Bull., Woods Hole, v. 99, Oct. 1950: 237–258.*

Animal experiments are described which show that down to a certain environmental temperature the body temperature was maintained without increase in metabolic rate by increasing the insulation (physical heat regulation). Below the critical temperature an increase in heat production was necessary (metabolic heat regulation). Results are analyzed with reference to temperature regulation in man.

35. **Scott, J. C., and H. C. Bazett.** Temperature regulation. *Annual Rev. Physiol., v. 3, 1941: 107–130.*

The literature from August 1938 to July 1940 on temperature regulation, is reviewed. Discussions are included on the role of the central nervous system in thermal control; of receptors and sensation; physical and chemical regulation; adaptation to external temperature; and a short section on hypothermia. 123 refs.

36. **Slonim, A. D., and O. P. Shcherbakova.** Physiology of thermoregulation in the lower monkeys [In Russian]. *Arkh. biol. nauk, v. 55 (3), 1939: 3–19.*

The mechanisms of temperature regulation in several of the lower monkeys were compared and the results related to temperature regulation in man. The baboons observed showed a marked capacity for thermoregulation; the *Macacus* species were more subject to the influence of environmental temperature changes.

37. **Thauer, R.** The mechanism of thermoregulation [In German]. *Erg. Physiol., v. 41, 1939: 607–805.*

General review of the literature on the problem of temperature regulation. Included are sections on physical temperature regulation, chemical temperature regulation, and the role of the nervous and endocrine systems in the control of body temperature. The subject of hypothermia is discussed on pages 801–805. The bibliography is found on pages 609–638.

38. **Thauer, R., and K. Wezler.** Temperature-regulation adjustment of the organism in changing climatic conditions (temperature, humidity, and wind velocity). II. Circulation and gas metabolism of man in different external temperatures [In German]. *Luftfahrtmedizin, v. 7 (2–3), 1942: 237–259.*

Circulatory changes (such as blood pressure; heart rate, beat and minute volume; total arterial and peripheral resistance), changes in gas metabolism (oxygen usage; tidal air and respiratory frequency), and some of the other phases of temperature regulation were studied with subjects in a controlled temperature chamber. These functions were measured and represented diagrammatically plotted against time and the outside temperature (temperature range of 15° to 50°C).

39. **Wezler, K., and R. Thauer.** Thermal regulatory transposition in organisms through changing climatic conditions (temperature, humidity, wind velocity) [In German]. *Luftfahrtmedizin, v. 7, 1943: 228–236.*

A climatic chamber for use in thermoregulatory tests is described. The temperature and relative humidity are regulated automatically and can be kept constant at any level between −6° and 55°C and 30% to 95% respectively. The installation consists of a test chamber containing the physiological apparatus, and an adjacent compartment containing the switch system for automatic regulation of climatic conditions. Diagrams are included.

40. **Wezler, K., and G. Neuroth.** Coordination of physical and chemical heat regulation [In German]. *Zschr. ges. exp. Med., v. 115 (1–2), 1949: 127–205.*

Six persons, ages 21 to 27 years, were exposed to temperature changes from 5° to 50°C. Studies were made of respiratory exchanges, circulatory changes, body and rectal temperatures, and any changes in red blood cell counts, hemoglobin amounts, blood cell volume, serum refraction, and of water elimination. It is concluded that there is a definite relation between physical and chemical heat regulation.

41. Winslow, C. E. A., and L. P. Herrington. Temperature and human life. *Princeton, Princeton University Press, 1949. 272 p.*

The physiology of human temperature regulation is discussed under the following chapter headings: Production of heat in the life process; Avenues of heat loss from the body; The adaptations of the human body to varying thermal conditions; The thermal protective influence of clothing; The objectives of air conditioning; Methods of air conditiong; The influence of climate and season upon health. 151 refs.

42. Wurmser, R. Energy expenditure, basal metabolism, thermoregulation (January 1937–January 1938) [In French]. *Paris, Hermann & Cie, 1938. 34p.*

In this literature review there is a short section on heat regulation (p. 18–27). Various experimental findings are discussed briefly under the topic headings of body temperature, various factors of heat regulation, nervous regulation, insensible perspiration, hormonal regulation, humoral regulation, metabolites intervening in thermal regulation, and techniques of respiratory exchange measurement. There is a bibliography of 114 items on pages 29–34.

43.   Yaglou, C. P. Thermometry. *In: Physiology of heat regulation and the science of clothing, 70-77. Ed. by L. H. Newburgh. Philadelphia, Saunders, 1949.*

The techniques and instrumentation of measuring environmental and body temperatures under varying conditions, are discussed.

See also items: 673, 807, 823, 849, 1061, 1097, 1107, 1110, 1116, 1249, 1300, 1699, 1712, 1722, 1816, 1979.

B. Normal Range of Body Temperature

44. Bazett, H. C. Theory of reflex controls to explain regulation of body temperature at rest and during exercise. *J. Appl. Physiol., v. 4, Oct. 1951: 245–262.*

The apparently paradoxical relationship of the mechanisms of temperature regulation at rest in a warm environment and during work is discussed. The first condition is said to impose its load as heat of external origin, the second as that of internal origin. Evidence and logic are recounted which led the author to believe that reflex responses to both heat and cold exist and that the dermal receptors mediating these reflex responses are stimulated by temperature gradients. The author cites evidence for his belief that a second heat receptor (in addition to the established superficial receptors, Ruffini's and Krause's, for heat and cold respectively) lies deeper at the level of the subcutaneous junction and that these deeper receptors are affected by internal heat from working muscles. The theory assumes that the superficial heat receptor is concerned with vascular readjustments induced by external heat and the deeper heat receptor is concerned with sweating and is stimulated readily by internally produced heat. The apparent relationship of sweating to skin temperature is then due to thermal gradients. The relationships of blood flow and temperature affecting these changes in exercise and at rest are discussed.

45. Bessemans, A. General tissue temperatures of the normal rabbit. *Ann. Physiol., Par., v. 14 (5), 1938: 944-970.*

Body temperature of rabbits is relatively unstable, with a wide individual variation. The average buccal temperature of 10 normal rabbits, in a resting state, was 39.11 °C; rectal temperature, 39.56°C. Rectal temperature was found to rise with activity and during the period of digestion following eating, and to fall slightly with inactivity. A great deviation was found between the different organs and tissues of the same animal both during normal and hyperthermic conditions. These deviations of temperature should be considered as a factor in any study involving rabbits. 221 refs.

46. Brody, S. Bioenergetics and growth. *New York, Reinhold, 1945. 284 p.*

In Chapter II on Homeothermy, temperature in life processes, and productive efficiency, the author discusses, among other subjects, the range of normal body temperatures of several species of homeothermic animals and of man; effect of environmental temperature ($-10°$ to $40°$C) on various activities; age changes in homeothermy; and the changes in metabolism during acclimatization.

47. Day, R. Regulation of body temperature during sleep. *Am. J. Dis. Child., v. 61, Apr. 1941: 734–745.*

Measurements of rectal temperature, cutaneous temperature, and rate of weight loss (by evaporation) were made simultaneously and continuously on 9 children (5 months to 4 years old), at different environmental temperatures during the course of 96 afternoon naps. Rectal temperature always fell slightly at first and then quickly levelled off; cutaneous temperature and rate of weight loss rose at first and then fell. The author speculates on the possibility of a "setting" of the physiological thermostat for a lower level of body temperature during sleep and that the fall in body temperature is not the result merely of passive relaxation.

48. De Felice, F. Temperature variations during physical training in man [In Italian]. *Boll. Soc. ital. biol. sper., v. 27, July–Aug. 1951: 1258–1260.*

Studies on two subjects were made on the changes in body temperature immediately after, and one hour after, going through a set of physical exercises each day for a period of 40–41 days. The exercise, which consisted of the rapid ascending of stairs of 94 steps over a period of 3 minutes, brought about no significant variation of the daily buccal temperature at rest during the course of the experiment and only slight lowering (usually in the early days of the experiment) or slight rising (usually in the latter days of the experiment) after the exercise period. It is thought to be probable that exercise of such brief duration and modified intensity had not brought about muscular activity of sufficient degree to account for the slight changes in body temperature, but that these were instead due to individual variations.

49. DuBois, E. F. The many different temperatures of human body and its parts. *West. J. Surg., v. 59, Sept. 1951: 476–490.*

The great differences in temperature which exist between different areas of the body and the great variability that exists among individuals in their body temperature, are discussed in view of experimental and clinical findings. Chart XI shows the range of temperatures (rectal temperature, 96° to 104°F; oral temperature, 35.5° to about 38.7°C) that may be found in perfectly healthy persons. Chart XII includes patients and persons subjected to environmental extremes of heat and cold. Men have survived with internal temperatures in the range of 75° to 114°F.

50. Franckevicius, B. Daily variations of blood sugar and of body temperature of the dog (1944) [Abstract, in German]. *Wien. tierärztl. Mschr., v. 34, Feb. 1947: 122–123.*

Studies were made of the daily variation of the blood sugar level and of the rectal temperature of dogs. The dogs were kept at an outside temperature of 18.2°C with a minimum of movement, and were fed only once a day. The daily rectal temperature varied only about 0.7°–1.0°C with a maximum between the 22nd and 24th hours, a slight rise about 2 hours after feeding, and a minimum at the 7th hour. The daily variation of the blood sugar level was very slight with the variations paralleling those of the body temperature. Movement, eating, and various psychic influences were some of the factors which tended to disrupt this parallellism.

51. Friedman, M. H. F., and I. F. Bennett. The rectal temperature of a group of mongrel dogs [Abstract]. *Fed. Proc., Balt., v. 2, Mar. 1943: 13.*

Rectal temperatures of 22 dogs kept in air-conditioned quarters (about 74°F), and fed Purina dog chow daily and fresh meat several times per week, were found to have rectal temperatures ranging from 100.2° to 103.8°F, with an average of 102.0°F. Eighty-five dogs kept in quarters which were not air-conditioned and fed Purina chow only, had rectal temperatures ranging from 99.9° to 104.8°F, averaging 102.0°F. In neither of these two groups did the sex of the dogs or whether they were a long- or short-haired breed, significantly change the readings. Rectal temperatures recorded periodically throughout the course of an academic year, showed various degrees of individual variation for a group of 6 female dogs. The widest range was 99.9° to 102.8°F; the narrowest was 100.2° to 100.7°F.

52. Goldberg, H. S. The study of the normal temperature of school children aged 2 to 5 years. *J. Am. Osteopath. Ass., v. 49, May 1950: 461–462.*

The average daily rectal temperature of a group of 47 healthy, nursery school children (aged 2 to 5 years), was found to be 99.7° ± 0.38°F. Although there was considerable variation in temperatures, less than 1 per cent exceeded the 99.4°–100.4°F range. Temperatures decreased slightly with age; some slight differences were noted between boys and girls and between the various months of the year (August through April). None of these changes was significant.

53. Goodell, H., D. F. Graham, H. G. Wolff. Changes in body heat regulation associated with varying life situations and emotional states. *In: Life stress and bodily diseases. Proc. Ass. Res. Nerv. Ment. Dis., 1949. Res. Publ., v. 29, 1949: 418–432.*

The thermal adaptation during a uniform burden of work, on the part of 3 adults, was slower during periods of stress associated with feelings of hostility, tension, and of being pushed, than it was when such feelings were minimal or absent.

54. Hart, J. S. Calorimetric determination of average body temperature of small mammals and its variation with environmental conditions. *Canad. J. Zool., v. 29, June 1951: 224–233. Also preliminary note:* Average body temperature in mice. *Science, v. 113, Mar. 23, 1951: 325–326.*

A method is described for determining the average body temperature of small mammals (mice) by placing them immediately after killing in a Dewar flask containing 100 g water (water temperature, 20.5°C; room temperature 20°C), recording the temperature rise, and making a small correction due to heat exchange of colorimeter with its surrounding average body temperatures. Post-mortem heat production did not appear to contribute appreciably to the results. Average body temperatures were usually about 2°C lower than rectal temperatures except during lethal chilling when average temperatures were frequently higher. Rise in average body temperature produced by activity increased with environmental temperature (0°, 10°, 20°, 30°C), but it occasionally was lower during activity than during rest at cold air temperatures.

55. Horvath, S. M., and H. Golden. Observations on men performing a standard amount of work in low ambient temperatures. *J. Clin. Invest., v. 26, Mar. 1947: 311–319.*

Five subjects, wearing light or heavy clothing, were subjected to very cold environments while on a treadmill. Energy expenditure increased 10%. Loss of body heat was greater with light-weight clothing than with heavy clothing.

56. Horvath, S. M., H. Menduke, and G. M. Piersol. Oral and rectal temperatures of man. *J. Am. M. Ass., v. 144, Dec. 30, 1950: 1562–1565.*

A study was made of rectal and oral temperatures of a group of 38 healthy young women and 16 healthy young men, for a period of 29 consecutive days. The mean morning rectal temperature for women was both higher and more variable than that for men. For both men and women the mean morning rectal temperature was significantly lower than the mean evening rectal temperature. In any specific person there was no single constant rectal-oral difference over his range of body temperature. There was found no single "normal temperature" value for all persons; neither is there a single "normal range" of temperature for all persons.

57. Kendeigh, S. C. Body temperatures of small mammals. *J. Mammal., v. 26, Feb. 23, 1945: 86–87.*

A study of the body temperatures was made of several small mammals including the white-footed mouse, chipmunk, short-tailed shrew, and smoky shrew. A compilation of data on the body temperatures of 5 adult and 5 young mice (*Peromyscus maniculatus gracilis*) of both sexes, indicated that the average temperature ranged from 36.9° to 39.5°C; the maximum ranged from 38.1° to 42.3°C; and the lowest normal from 35.0° to 38.8°C. The variation of temperature between periods of excitement and periods of quiet varied greatly (in 2 observed cases, 2° to 4°C) within a period of 5 minutes. The standard or basal temperature, with the mouse at rest, appeared to lie between 35° and 36°C. Four mice exposed to cold when caught in traps. did not survive body temperatures of 32.7°, 32.5°, 30.5° and 25.5°C but one other survived after the body temperature had fallen to 23.4°C. Insufficient data are available to demonstrate possible differences between sexes and ages.

58. Kleitman, N., and A. Ramsaroop. Body temperature and cutaneous sensitivity to tingling and pain [Abstract]. *Fed. Proc., Balt., v. 5, Feb. 1946: 56.*

Tetanizing current was delivered from an inductorium to the volar surface of the terminal phalange of the middle finger of each of two subjects, and the threshold of tingling and pain was determined in an ascending manner. Tests, comprised of 8 series of trials, were conducted during forenoon periods of 6 hours. In each series, during the 5 minutes of testing, there was a gradual rise in sensitivity to tingling. This was also true of pain but only when sensitivity was low. The results obtained also showed a direct relationship between sensitivity to tingling and pain and the oral temperature at the time of testing. As the temperature rose during the forenoon (from a mean of 97.5° to 98.29°F in one subject and 97.81° to 98.96°F in the other), the cutaneous sensitivity also increased. When relaxing in a sitting position for one hour caused a fall in body temperature, there was a corresponding decrease in sensitivity.

59. Kleitman, N., and D. P. Jackson. Body temperature and performance under different routines. *J. Appl. Physiol., v. 3, Dec. 1950: 309–328.*

Diurnal body temperature curves changed, within a few days, to conform to a variety of experimental activity schedules; no change occurred on a rotating activity routine. In general, the higher the body temperature the better was the performance. When the group was divided into two sections, the section having the higher and less variable daily mean body temperature also had the better performance scores in the Link Trainer operation and consumed over three times as much coffee as did the other section.

60. Lee, R. C. The rectal temperature of the normal rabbit. *Am. J. Physiol., v. 125, Mar. 1, 1939: 521–529.*

Limits of normal rectal temperature in four breeds of rabbits were found to be from 38.4° to 41.1°C, and the average normal temperature was 39.6°C. When the animal was adjusted to the temperature for 24 hours or more, over a range of 32° to 10°C, the environmental temperature did not influence the rectal temperature. In sudden changes of air temperature from 10° to 28°C, and from 16° to 28°C, the rabbits showed no greater variation in rectal temperature than was shown by these same rabbits at a constant temperature of 28°C. Rabbits could not adjust their temperature-regulating mechanism immediately when they were exposed either temporarily, or for 1 to 3 hours, to environmental temperatures at 32°C, and high rectal temperatures frequently resulted.

61. Lee, R. C. Basal metabolism of the adult rabbit and prerequisites for its measurement. *J. Nutrit., v. 18, Nov. 1939: 473–488.*

Since there is apt to be a wide variation in rectal temperatures of rabbits under different experimental conditions, in studies of their basal metabolic rates rabbits should be chosen which are in a good nutritive state with rectal temperatures of 38.4°–41.1°C. To aid in obtaining this uniformity, rabbits should be fasted for 24–72 hours prior to the measurement, should have been living at an environmental temperature above 20° but not above 32°C, and should be kept at an environment of thermic neutrality (28°–32°C) for 24 hours or longer immediately before, and during, the tests.

62. **MacLean, D. L., and R. C. Partridge.** Seasonal changes in the body's response to ventilative conditions. *J. Indust. Hyg., v. 22, June 1940: 244–250.*

Four subjects were exposed to 67° E. T. (effective temperature) and to 72° E. T.—previously found to be the temperature of greatest comfort in winter and in summer respectively—for periods of 1½ hours daily for 2 weeks during the winter and for 2 weeks during the summer. Tests were made under the same conditions of diet and exercise, while wearing the same clothing. Recordings of oral and skin temperature, heart rate, metabolic rate, and weight loss were made. The most significant difference appeared to be a higher metabolic rate in winter than in summer. Otherwise comfort differences between winter and summer are probably due to clothing, dietary, and other environmental changes and are not due to a seasonal change in the body *per se.*

*63. **Maksimov, S. V., and ÎA. S. Smelkov.** Physiological fluctuations of temperature in the extremities and their significance for the prevention of frostbite [In Russian]. *Voen. med. zh., Moskva, Apr.–May 1946: 23–28.*

"*Contains* an account of temperature fluctuations of the upper and lower extremities between breakfast and lunch, as affected by meals, by drinking tea or hot water, by warming the abdomen; also, the effect of warming or moving one extremity on the temperature fluctuations of the other extremities. Practical recommendations are made for use in the field, on the basis of these observations. Bibliography (4 items)."—Arctic Bibl., v. 4, 1954: 652.

64. **Mellette, H. C., B. K. Hutt, S. I. Askovitz, and S. M. Horvath.** Diurnal variations of body temperatures. *J. Appl. Physiol., v. 3, May 1951: 665–675.*

Continuous rectal temperatures were recorded for 11 male and 11 female subjects for a total of 42 12-hour periods, between the hours of 6 P.M. and 6 A.M. These hours were chosen after four 24-hour observation periods had shown that almost all maximum and minimum temperatures had occurred during the night hours. Maxima for males were found to average 38.32°C (100.98°F) at 8.49 P.M., and for females 38.36°C (101.05°F) at 10.49 P.M.; minima for males 36.83°C (98.29°F) at 6.04 A.M., and for females 37.16°C (98.89°F) at 4.48 A.M. With the exception of the levels of the maxima, the values were significantly different between the two sexes. One male showed a total range of only 0.70°C (1.26°F) throughout the night, while one female showed as much as 2.08°C (3.74°F). The mean rate of fall from evening to morning was 0.12°C/hour (0.22°F) for males and 0.06°C (0.11°F) for females.

65. **Metz, B., and P. Andlauer.** Nyctohemeral rhythm of temperature in man [In French]. *C. rend. Soc. biol., Par., v. 143, Sept. 1949: 1234–1236.*

A study was made of changes of rectal temperature, of cutaneous temperature, and of energy metabolism during a 24-hour period. A drop in rectal temperature in the subject was shown to be preceded by a drop in skin temperature. The gains and losses of heat are related to these cyclic variations of cutaneous and rectal temperature but could not be explained quantitatively by the variations of energy metabolism which of themselves did not follow a rhythmic pattern.

66. **Metz, B., and J. Schwartz.** Studies of the nyctothermal variations of rectal temperature, of urinary flow, and of ordinary excretion of 17-ketosteroids in man. *Compt. rend. Soc. biol., Par., v. 143, Sept. 1949: 1237–1239.*

Studies were made on four subjects of the fluctuations in body temperature, urinary output, and of the 17-ketosteroids in the urine, over a 24-hour period. Urinary output, and the 17-

---

* Original not seen.

ketosteroid content of the urine, varied in somewhat parallel fashion with that of the body temperature, both being decreased when the body temperature was lowest at night, increasing during the following morning, and decreasing during the afternoon. But the results did not justify any conclusions of similarity of mechanism regulating the secretion of hormone precursors of the body and that regulating the cyclic variation of thermoregulation.

67. Mullin, F. J. Development of the diurnal temperature and motility patterns in a baby [Abstract]. *Am. J. Physiol., v. 126, July 1, 1939: P589.*

Body temperature of a child was measured every two hours for four or five successive days each month, from the time of birth until the age of fifteen months. Whereas the diurnal cycle spread over only one degree F at birth, this spread was three degrees by the eleventh month. The development of this spread was manifested as a progressive lowering of the minimum temperature level at night with little or no change in the maximum temperature of the daytime. From the sixth month on, the temperature curve became increasingly regular with less variation at the same period on successive days.

68. Nielsen, M. The regulation of body temperature in muscular work [In German]. *Scand. Arch. Physiol., v. 79, Oct. 1938: 193–230.*

Continuous recordings were made of the changes in rectal and skin temperatures of three test subjects at various environmental temperatures during periods of physical work. In a room temperature of 22°–23°C with constant humidity and air currents, the rectal temperature increased with the intensity of the work while the skin temperature showed little change. At environmental temperatures of 8°–29°C work efficiency appeared to be independent of the temperature. Heat loss by convection and radiation was greater during work than the entire heat production during rest. After further studies involving heat loss changes from convection and radiation during work under various conditions, it was decided that the degree of—definitely not a lack of—heat regulation during muscular work can be established only after these factors have been taken into consideration. These factors are much more difficult to evaluate when a wide range of environmental temperatures is involved.

69. Nussbaumer, J. The normal body temperature of horses with consideration of various factors. [In German, summaries in German, French, Italian, and English]. *Schweiz. Arch. Tierh., v. 93 (1), 1951: 22–45.*

The chief cause of fluctuations of the normal body temperature (37.5° to 38.0°C) of three horses was found to be the ingestion of food or water. Cooling the air within the stable suppressed this rise in body temperature. A specific rhythm of temperature fluctuation did not exist. When body temperature measurements were made continuously day and night, the temperature rise was found to begin 1 to 2 hours before feeding; this was more pronounced in the mare than in the stallion. The body temperature of the mare was about 0.2°C higher than that of the stallion, while that of the gelding was only a little above that of the mare.

70. Petrides, G. A. Body temperature data for the cottontail rabbit. *J. Mammal., v. 28, Nov. 1947: 400–401.*

The average of 18 recordings of rectal temperatures of a group of cottontail rabbits was found to be 101.6°F, with a range of 97.7° to 105.0°F. The author does not believe that this average temperature is the normal body temperature for the species, but that this would probably be found to be somewhat lower depending on the activity and environment of the animals studied.

71. Porter, E. G., and M. M. H. Gibson-Hill. Observations of normal temperatures in Singapore school girls [In English]. *Med. J. Malaya, v. 5, Mar. 1951: 213–219.*

Oral temperatures, using ordinary clinical thermometers, were taken of each of a group of 4,463 school girls in Singapore between the ages of 6 and 20 years. In the age group of 6–10 years, the mean temperature was 99.5°F; in the 10–14 year group, 99.3°F; and in the 14–20 year group, 99.1 °F. For all the age groups the majority fell within the limits of 98.9°–100°F. Temperatures of over 100°F and up to 100.8°F with no pathological significance were not uncommon. The average normal resting temperature of the group of girls was thus considerably higher than the usually accepted 98.4°F.

72.   Ratcliff, J. D. A new way to sleep. *Science Digest, v. 23, Mar. 1948: 1–6.*

In discussing the role of oscillating beds as an aid to the problem sleeper, human beings are said to be unimpressive sleepers when compared with some of the animals but that man comes uncomfortably close to a deathlike state during periods of deep slumber. During deep sleep the heart action slows as does the breathing; body temperature drops to subnormal levels; the muscles relax, including those of the blood vessel walls thereby reducing blood pressure and draining some of the blood from the brain. At the end of an 8-hour sleeping period the body is said to be producing only enough energy to maintain absolutely essential functions.

73.   Reimann, H. A. Hypothermia; subnormal temperature and its relation to neurocirculatory asthenia (soldier's heart). *J. Am. M. Ass., v. 115, November 9, 1940: 1606–1609.*

In a study of nine patients with chronic subnormal temperatures, signs and symptoms of vagotonia, similar to those described in neurocirculatory asthenia (soldier's heart), were found to be present.

74.   Rodbard, S. Weight and body temperature. *Science, v. 111, Apr. 28, 1950: 465–466.*

A plotting of body temperatures of birds against the logarithm of the average weight of the adult of the species gave a linear relationship. Birds of 1 kg had a body temperature of about 41.5°C; for each tenfold decrease in weight the body temperature increased about 1.5°C. A similar plotting of data on large mammals gave approximately the same linear slope. However, for small mammals, weighing less than 1 kg, different slopes were obtained and for each tenfold decrease in weight the body temperature decreased by about 1.5°C.

75.   Schreider, E. Anatomical factors of body-heat regulation. *Nature, Lond. v. 167, May 19, 1951: 823–824.*

Of two groups of young adult men, the group with the lower weight-surface ratio gained heat at a slower rate and had a delayed and weak sweat reaction after exposure to a dry bulb temperature of 36°C for 30 minutes.

76.   Ware, A. G., R. M. Hill, and F. H. Schultz. The effect of interference with respiration on the control of body temperature in white rats and New Zealand rabbits. *Am. J. Physiol., v. 149, June 1947: 657–666.*

Hypothermia was induced in rats and rabbits by wrapping the thorax and abdomen tightly enough to interfere with respiration and then exposing them to temperatures of 2° to 4°C. It was found that rats could regain normal body temperatures even in a cold room after unwrapping. Baby rats showed an ability to return to normal temperature from as low as 5°C. The oxygen and carbon dioxide contents of the blood of 12 rabbits were measured and a fall in oxygen content parallel to the fall in body temperature was observed.

77.   Wright, S. Notes on experiments illustrating normal temperature regulation in young men. *Brit. M. J., 1949 (v.1), Apr. 9: 610–613.*

In a series of tests by medical students on variations of their own body temperatures, it was found that "half-minute" thermometers, read at half minute intervals, took from 3–4 minutes before a steady maximum reading was obtained for the mouth and 5–7 minutes for the axilla and groin. The latter recordings were, of course, 1°F lower than for the mouth. Drinking one liter of ice-cold water, either as fast as possible or over a 12-minute period, brought a fall in mouth temperature from 97.8° to 95°F (36.55° to 35°C) or less, with the temperature remaining below normal for from 8 to 20 minutes until the oral mucosa was warmed by the circulating blood. Exposure, unclothed, to a moderately cold environment (60°F; 15.5°C) for 20 minutes usually brought about less than 1°F drop in body temperature, owing to compensatory mechanisms coming into play. Only slightly greater lowering of the temperature was caused by cold baths (56°F; 13.3°C), with the temperature remaining at the lower level for from 9 to 13 minutes, and then rising to normal usually within 30 minutes from the termination of the bath.

See also items: 132, 209, 304, 312, 314, 447, 1288.

C. Age Factors in Temperature Regulation

78. Antoshkina, E. D. Ontogenetic development of temperature regulation. I. Development of temperature regulation in rats raised under normal conditions. II. Development of temperature regulation in rats raised at high or at low temperatures [In Russian, summary in German]. *Fiziol. zh., SSSR, v. 26 (1), 1939: 3–29.*

The development of the temperature-regulating mechanism was studied in normal rats aged from 1 day to 1½ months at temperatures of from 5° to 35°C. The chemical heat-regulating mechanism reached its maximum in 3 weeks to 1 month and the physical heat-regulating mechanism in about the same time.

79. Bornschein, H., and W. Auerswald. Thermal-difference findings on the question of the physiological asymmetry of the skin temperature of the trunk of the body in childhood [In German]. *Österr. Zschr. Kinderh., v. 2 (1), 1948: 1–5.*

When a graph was made of the differences in the skin temperatures of similar points on the right and left sides of the trunk of the body of each of a group of 20 young children (ages 3 to 6 years), 16 were found to have a slightly higher skin temperature of the right side. A group of 20 young men (ages 20 to 30 years) showed little difference between skin temperatures of similar areas of the right and left side. Some of the possible reasons for this asymmetry in the very young are discussed.

80. Brody, E. B. Development of homeothermy in suckling rats. *Am. J. Physiol., v. 139, June 1, 1943: 230–232.*

Homeothermy in white rats, as shown by the maintenance of a body temperature of 37°C in an environmental temperature of 15°C, was practically complete at the weaning age of 22 days. Curves were made showing body weight, degree of homeothermy, and heat production, from birth to 25 days of age. Irregularities in the latter two curves occurred at about the ninth day, at the same time that shivering and other muscular reflexes to cold were apparent. The author states that the age curve of the development of homeothermy probably reflects in part the functional development of the heat-regulating center of the hypothalamus.

81. Day, R. Respiratory metabolism in infancy and in childhood. XXVII. Regulation of body temperature of premature infants. *Am. J. Dis. Child., v. 65, Mar. 1943: 376–398.*

Heat production, heat loss by radiation and conduction, heat loss by evaporation, skin temperature, and rectal temperature were determined in 25 premature (2.258 g average weight) male babies who were a week or more old and thriving. In warm air, the chief defect in temperature regulation in the group was the inadequacy of sweat production. Vasodilatation was similar quantitatively to that of adults. In cool air, the infants were handicapped by a large surface area in proportion to body weight and a feeble musculature. There was no evident defect in vasoconstriction. The presence or absence of so-called chemical regulation could not be stated from this work.

82.   Erbslöh, J., and F. Seibert. Influence of adrenal cortical hormone on the thermoregulation of the newborn [In Germany]. *Zschr. Geburtsh.*, *v. 133, 1950: 172–181.*

Temperature regulation was studied in the newborn child, with or without adrenocortical hormone injections being given. Observations on 12 infants indicated that the average body temperature before birth was 37.4°C. Within 4–5 minutes post partum, the body temperature had dropped an average of 0.6°C, and within 1½ hours had reached its minimum of 35.2°C. This minimum temperature persisted for 3.6 hours, then increased to normal (36.6°–37.1°C) after 14 hours. The infants were not bathed, which accounts for slightly higher minimal temperature than had previously been reported in the literature. When the infants were bathed at the time of birth, the body temperature remained below 36°C for over 16 hours. In the first days of life there was great thermolability, which stabilized only after 4–5 days. Injection of 2.5–5 mg DCA [Percorten] immediately after birth (12 cases) and repeated during the next 3–4 days, brought about very little change in the initial temperature drop. However, in the following days the temperature became much more stable than it had been in the un- treated infants. Injection of 5 mg DCA to the mother 1½ hours before delivery (12 cases) diminished the initial temperature drop of the newborn infant considerably (minimum 35.9°C, lasting 3 hours), and accelerated the return to normal temperature, which was reached after 6 hours. These results indicate a thermoregulatory influence by action on the thermoregula- tory center in the brain by means of the nervous pathways.

83.   Friedfeld, L. Heat reaction states in the aged. *Geriatrics, v. 4, July–Aug. 1949: 211–216.*

Lessened capacity for body heat regulation appears to accompany old age, as indicated by the rise in the number of deaths in the older age group, attributable directly or indirectly to the heat during periods of high environmental temperature.

84.   Gernez, M. L. Research on physiological hypothermia of the newborn at term; variations with the environmental temperature [In French]. *Bull. Féd. soc. gyn. obst. fr., v. 3 (1), 1951: 100–101.*

The temperature of the infant at the moment of birth was almost always just a bit higher (37.2°C) than that of the mother (36.8°C). The temperature immediately dropped, in the first 5 or 10 minutes, reaching the lowest 30 to 60 minutes later, then gradually raised to a normal of about 37°C in 24 to 48 hours after birth. The early drop of temperature was lowest (34.7°C) when the environmental temperature was low (15° to 19°C), and was least low (36.3°C) when the environmental temperature was high (30° to 36°C).

85.   Gernez, M. L. Favorable effect of immediate warming of the newborn on physiological hypothermia at birth [In French]. *Bull. Fed. soc. gyn. obst. fr., v. 3 (4) 1951: 627–628.*

The body temperature of new-born infants of full-term (about 2,800 g) was found to drop approximately 2.2°C and that of premature infants (about 1,800 g) approximately 2.4°C within the first 30 minutes following birth when the infants were kept in a room at a tem- perature of 20°–24°C. When the infants were warmed for 20–30 minutes at a temperature of 37°–38°C immediately after birth, the body temperature drop was much less (1° and 0.8°C respectively) and the temperature increased to approximately 37°C by the end of the first 24 hours without the irregularities which were seen in the infants which were not warmed.

86.   Grislain, J. R. Thermoregulation and incubators for premature infants [In French]. *Sem. hôp. Paris, v. 27, Oct. 10, 1951: 2955–2958.*

At birth the body temperature of the full-term infant was identical with that of the mother (37°C), but the temperature quickly dropped 1 or 2 degrees despite the infants being wrapped in warm blankets. About 6 to 8 hours usually elapsed before the temperature of 37°C was regained. Within a day or two infants who were warmly wrapped could tolerate easily an environment of 18°C. Although the thermal regulation of the full-term newborn infant is not good, that of the premature infant is very poor. For the latter group, and a few of the others, a heated incubator is a necessity. Some of the factors involved in design and operation of incubators are discussed.

87.   Herlitz, G. Studies on the consensual reaction of the blood vessels of the skin of the newborn to the effect of cold [In German]. *Acta paediat., Upps., v. 30 (4), 1943: 434–448.*

Newborn babies were exposed for a short period, without clothing, to a room temperature of 19.5°–25°C. Simultaneous measurement of skin temperature of the forehead and of the abdomen did not show changes in the same direction—the former area remained almost constant in temperature while the abdomen temperature was slightly lowered. Consensual reaction to cold, as it is found in the adult, had evidently not yet developed in the infant.

88.   Hill, R. M. The control of body temperature in white rats. *Am. J. Physiol., v. 149, June 1947: 650–656.*

In white rats the maximum resistance to cold appears between the 61st and 300th day of normal life. Better nutrition was found to result in an earlier development of the temperature-regulating mechanism.

89.   Holtkamp, D. E., R. M. Hill, B. B. Longwell, E. K. Rutledge, and A. R. Buchanan. Failure of adrenal cortical hormones to protect against cold in young normal and adrenalectomized rats. *Am. J. Physiol., v. 156, Mar. 1949: 368–376.*

Adrenal cortical hormones give no protection against decrease of body temperature in rats under 16 days of age when exposed to a cold environment. These hormones give effective protection in older rats indicating that the mechanism for defense against cold is not developed before the 16th day.

90.   Howell, T. H. Normal temperatures in old age. *Lancet, Lond., v. 254, Apr. 3, 1948: 517–518.*

Mouth and axilla temperatures of a group of 326 old men (65 to 95 years old) showed a considerable variation, with both temperature readings being lowered as the age increased. Mouth temperatures showed a range of 5°F (95.2°–100.2°F); axillary temperatures of 4.4°F (95.0°–99.4°F). In a group of young persons, mouth temperatures showed a range of 3.0°F (95.6°–98.6°F); axillary temperatures of 3.6°F (95.0°–98.6°F). In general the temperature readings of the older group were considerably lower than those of the young persons.

91.   Kendeigh, S. C. The relation of metabolism to the development of temperature regulation in birds. *J. Exp. Zool., v. 82, Dec. 1939: 419–438.*

Nestling house wrens were kept at room temperatures of 35°C and periodically exposed to air temperatures of 0° to 40°C, from the time of hatching until they were 15 days old. Body temperatures were found to drop, on exposure to low environmental temperatures, until an age of 15 days. Beginning with the 3rd day this drop in body temperature became daily less rapid with the development of temperature regulation. Variations in CO_2 production, water vaporization, rate of heart beat, and muscular activity were also studied.

92.   König, F. Skin temperature measurements in men over 60 years of age [In German]. *Zschr.ges. exp. Med., v. 107, 1939: 98–105.*

The skin temperature of each of a group of men over 62 years of age was measured in various body regions by means of thermocouple. The men were resting undressed at a normal room temperature for a period of 10 minutes. The average rectal temperature was 36.9°C., the average skin temperature (from all the skin regions), 32.2°C. No decrease in skin temperature could be observed under such conditions in men up to 80 years of age or older. However, if the room temperature was higher, the skin temperature would rise; if it was lower, the skin temperature would decrease. It is concluded that the human skin remains an independent thermoregulatory agent even in old age.

93. Krag, C. L., and W. B. Kountz. Stability of body function in the aged. I. Effect of exposure of the body to cold. *J. Geront., v. 5, July 1950: 227–235.*

Elderly persons, who were somewhat debilitated but not bedridden or suffering from any acute illness, were exposed unclothed and motionless to temperatures of from 5° to 15°C for from 45 to 120 minutes. When compared to healthy young persons acting as controls, the aged group were less able to maintain their body temperature although the onset of the increase of oxygen consumption was earlier in the aged. It is inferred that the mechanism of prevention of heat loss, such as contraction of skin vessels, is less efficient in the old than in the young.

94. Lelong, M., A. Rossier, and J. Michelin. Total caloric ration of premature infants in its relation to thermoregulation [In French]. *Arch. fr. pédiat., v. 6 (2), 1949: 113–128.*

Experiences with premature babies maintained at an environmental temperature of 37°C and in sterile surroundings, indicated that they prospered on 100–110 cal/kg/day. It is of utmost importance to reduce for such newborn babies the need to struggle against the cold since such a baby can not possibly, physiologically, compensate by increased calorie intake and increased metabolism.

95. Lookeren Campagne, G. J. van. Low body temperature of the newborn [In Dutch, summaries in Dutch, French, German, and English]. *Ned. tschr. geneesk., v. 85, Mar. 29, 1941: 1346–1349.*

A case of low body temperature (29.10°–31.4°C) in a newborn child is discussed. The condition was thought to be primarily due to little control over the cooling of the body, with poor nutrition being a secondary cause.

96. Okumura, R. On the heat-regulating ability of young rabbits. I. Heat-regulating ability in young rabbits which were a varying number of days old [In Japanese, with German summary]. *Fol. pharm. jap., v. 26, 1938: 61–70.*

Baby rabbits were taken from the warm nest after birth and put into a well-ventilated warm box at 20°C. Body temperatures fell strikingly during the first day of their lives and then began to rise; the carbon dioxide liberation was greatly increased. Eight or 10 days after birth, the body temperature was only a little lowered but the CO_2 liberation was still high. Reactions of body temperature to veratrine and to tetra-hydro-beta-naphthylamine were also studied.

97. Peremislova, A. A. On the thermal regulation in early childhood [In Russian]. *Pediatriïa, Moskva, 1940 (4): 7–10.*

In a study of 50 children (8 months to 2 years of age), skin temperature was measured by thermocouple simultaneously at several locations on the body. The rectal temperature was found to vary quite widely, fluctuating from 0.3° to 3.2°C, and was almost always 0.3° to 1.6°C higher than that of the axilla. The most constant temperature was in the axilla, fluctuating only from 0.1° to 0.3°C. The lowest temperatures were on the skin of the foot and shin. Because of the constancy of the axilla temperature, and because the rectal temperature was found not always to agree with the physiological state of the child, the use of axilla temperature is recommended for use in clinical practice.

98. Roberts, J. E., B. E. Robinson, and A. R. Buchanan. Oxygen consumption correlated with the thermal reactions of young rats to ergotoxine. *Am. J. Physiol., v. 156, Jan. 1, 1949: 170–176.*

Young rats, up to 20 to 28 days old, reacted to administration of ergotoxine by the production of hypothermic states; older rats became hypothermic. These responses of older rats were closely correlated with increase of O_2 consumption, and were such that a direct stimulation of metabolism was indicated. Evidence would point to this metabolic stimulation being mediated through the action of ergotoxine on the thermoregulatory centers of the hypothalamus. The hypothermia of young rats, before development of heat regulation, is thought to be due to unselective stimulation of heat production and heat loss centers, with the latter predominating.

99. Rolleston, H. Fuel rationing and the aged. *Med. Press & Circ., Lond., v. 208, July 15, 1942: 41–42.*

The author discusses fuel rationing as it affects the older, often ill, person who is particularly liable to suffer from cold. Contrary to earlier reports it is now known that the internal temperature is almost constant at all ages. Diminished vascularity of the skin may be correlated with the fall in the metabolic rate in the old age and to the decrease in thyroid secretion.

100. Salhanick, H. A., and J. L. Starr. Resistance to cold and anoxia by young rats [Abstract]. *Anat. Rec., v. 105, Nov. 1949: 562.*

Newborn rats exposed to 3°C become torpid, with a lowering of body temperature, with cessation of circulatory and respiratory movements, and a diminution of oxygen uptake nearing zero. Animals one or to days old could survive for nine hours, but as they grew older (up to 12 days) ability to survive decreased. Until the homeothermic system began to develop, resistance to cold was found to parallel resistance to anoxia.

101. Veldkamp, A. L. Extremely low body temperature in infants [In Dutch, summaries in Dutch, English, and French]. *Ned. tschr. geneesk., v. 90, Mar. 16–23, 1946: 209–210.*

The author discusses the several instances each year from 1940 through 1945, when infants had been found to have very low body temperatures (between 23° and 30°C). In 1941 in a group of 14, he had found three with temperatures of 29.5°, 29.7° and 27.3°C; the latter child was less than 8 weeks old. These occurrences did not seem to depend on cold weather since many were seen when the weather was relatively mild. The infants were treated with warm baths (30°C), kept in warm beds, and given Adrenalin as a stimulant. The prognosis was considered to be good when the temperature began to rise following treatment.

102. Zhila, E. S. Studies on the comparative physiology of heat regulation. The heat regulation of newborn animals (rodents, carnivores, and primates) [In Russian]. *Fiziol. zh. SSSR, v. 28, 1940: 335–349.*

Species differences of thermoregulation were studied in guinea-pigs 12 hours after birth, and in dogs, jackals, cats, and monkeys 10–12 days after birth. Respiratory exchanges were measured and rectal temperatures were recorded. Lowered metabolism was found to be more pronounced in newborn animals than in the adult of the same species (the greatest decrease in guinea-pigs, was 4.3% per degree of cooling in the range of 20°–30°C). If taken from a position close to the mother's warm body to an environmental temperature of 12°–14°C, the body temperature of kittens dropped from 36.0° to 25.5°C; at 20°C the body temperature rose to 32°C; and at 30°C it approached the body temperature near the mother. Normal body temperature for a particular species is established before reduction of the chemical thermoregulation to normal. In early development the species differences of chemical thermoregulation, which are characteristic for the adult species or the climate it inhabits, are absent.

See also items: 67, 213, 370, 415, 416, 472, 521, 791, 793, 799, 839, 944, 992, 1112.

D. *Temperature Gradients and Distribution*

103. Anon. Arctic conditions reproduced in Army research laboratory for testing clothing and equipment. *Heat. and Ventilating, v. 40, July 1943: 69.*

The cold room of the Climatic Research Laboratory of the U. S. Army Quartermaster Department, maintained in Lawrence, Massachusetts, has facilities for obtaining temperatures as low as −90°F. It is equipped with a treadmill to provide a means of exercise for the soldiers, with a fan to simulate arctic winds, and artificial snow-makers made from atomizers. In tests of a down-filled sleeping bag weighing 12 pounds, temperature recordings were made using 23 thermocouples attached to various parts of the sleeping bag and to the skin of the subject. When a temperature of −12°F prevailed outside, +10°F existed between the inner and outer bag, 78°F outside the subject's underwear, and 92°F on his skin. This amounts to a temperature gradient of 104°F in about 3 inches of space.

104. Adolph, E. F., and G. W. Molnar. Temperature gradients in men exposed to cold [Abstract]. *Fed. Proc., Balt.,* v. 5, pt. 2, Mar. 1946: 1.

Lightly-clothed men were exposed to dry outdoor cold for periods of 1½ hours. Even in the presence of large heat losses, temperature differences between deep tissues and body surface were maintained. Shivering was a major factor in heat production.

105. Aschoff, J. Basic experiments in temperature regulation. Comparison of various conditions of heat penetration in a dummy and in the hand [In German]. *Pflügers Arch.,* v. 247, (4–5), 1944: 480–496.

Comparative measurements of heat conductivity were made on a dummy glass hand and on the normal hands of a test subject. It was found that the right hand of the subject had an 8% higher specific conductivity than the left, indicating a larger blood flow in the right. A thin layer of vaseline on the hand reduced conductivity.

106. Auerswald, W., and H. Bornschein. The topography of temperature in the human skin and its relation to age and sex [In German]. *Zschr. phys. Ther., Bäder-u. Klimaheilk.,* v. 1, 1948: 107–113. Abstract, in German, *in: Wetter u. Leben,* v. 1, Oct. 1948: 218.

Reports extensive observations which contribute to the knowledge of human surface temperature. Observations were made on 50 men between 20 and 30 years of age, 50 women between 20 and 30, 50 children between 3 and 6, and 50 children between 7 and 10. Temperatures were recorded in a uniform room temperature of 25°C and 50–60% humidity at not less than 4-hour intervals. Temperatures in approximately 114 body locations were observed for each subject, so that an over-all picture of human surface temperature was obtained. The mean temperature of the different regions of the body and the median distributions are set forth in detail in tables arranged according to the different groups of subjects. High temperatures were noted with greatest frequency on the forehead and throat, as compared with the temperature of the trunk; women had an average of 0.5° to 0.75°C lower surface temperature. The often-reported difference between the right and left halves of the body was not substantiated by the evidence.

107. Barcroft, H., and O. G. Edholm. Temperature and blood flow in the human forearm. *J. Physiol., Lond.,* v. 104, Apr. 15, 1946: 366–376.

Measurements were made of forearm temperatures under varying conditions to establish normal values. Temperature readings on the arm exposed to air were: 27.9°C for the skin, 28.5°C for subcutaneous tissue, 30.7°C for deep muscle. When immersed in a water bath of varying temperatures, the subcutaneous temperature ranged from 14.6°C in a bath of 12°C, to 38.7°C in a bath of 41°C. The corresponding readings for deep muscle were 18.6° and 37.8°C.

108. Batinkov, E. L. Effect of the ingestion of cold and hot water upon the course of thermal changes in the stomach and intestine [In Russian, summaries in Russian and English]. *Fiziol. zh. SSSR,* v. 27, 1939: 108–114.

Thermocouple recordings were made with test subjects after introduction of a tube into the digestive tract. The temperature of the esophagus was found to be 0.1°–0.4°C higher than that of the oral cavity; that of the duodenum somewhat lower (0.05°–0.4°C) than that of the stomach, except in cases of gastritis, cholecystitis, or duodenitis when the intraduodenal temperature was higher. In the normal stomach the temperature was equal or slightly higher than that in the esophagus; in the distended stomach, the temperature was frequently lower than that in the esophagus. A 200–300 cc amount of water of a determined temperature was ingested; a second such portion was ingested when the temperature of the stomach had returned to its original level. Either hot or cold water passed from the stomach to the duodenum only when the temperature of the water had become approximately equal to the temperature of the surrounding organs. Hot water was retained in the stomach for a longer period than cold water.

109. Bazett, H. C. The effect of temperature on the skin. *J. Invest. Derm. v. 1, Dec. 1938: 413–425.*

The author states that the temperature of the skin is varied according to the external environment to which it is exposed and the vascular adjustments in the subjacent areas. He discusses in detail those vascular changes.

110. Bazett, H. C., L. Love, E. S. Mendelson, and L. H. Peterson. Arterial temperatures in man [Abstract]. *Fed. Proc., Balt., v. 6, Mar. 1947: 76.*

Temperature measurements made with needle thermocouples inserted into the brachial and radial arteries show that precooling of arterial blood occurred during transit to the periphery because of the proximity of cooled blood returning through the veins.

111. Bazett, H. C., L. Love, M. Newton, L. Eisenberg, R. Day, and R. E. Forster, II. Temperature changes in blood flowing in arteries and veins in man. *J. Appl. Physiol., v. 1, July 1948: 3–19.*

Measurements of temperature in the brachial, radial, and common iliac arteries were made. It was found that the temperature of the blood in transit in the arteries is not uniform. Cooling of arterial blood in transit in the limbs is dependent on rewarming of cold blood returning in adjacent veins. Temperatures as low as 21.5 °C for the radial artery and 31.1 °C for the brachial artery have been recorded without the subject feeling cold.

112. Benjamin, J. M., Jr., and S. M. Horvath. Temperature measurement inside the body using a thermistor. *Science, v. 109, June 10, 1949: 592–593.*

Using a thermistor, temperature measurements at several places inside the body of a dog were found to range from 96.5 °F (two inches within the thigh muscle) to 99.0 °F (in the coronary sinus and right ventricle). The temperature of the thigh surface was 92.8 °F and the rectal temperature was 99.1 °F. The knee joint temperature of two normal adult males was found to be 90.3 ° and 91.2 °F when skin temperatures were 84 °F.

113. Bierman, W. Conductive cooling of living human tissue. *Proc. Soc. Exp. Biol., N. Y., v. 42, Nov. 1939: 518–520.*

The author found it possible to cause a substantial lowering of the temperature of tissues in the human body at a distance from the point at which cold was applied.

114. Bierman, W., and M. Friedlander. The penetrative effect of cold. *Arch. Phys. Ther., v. 21, Oct. 1940: 585–592.*

Experiments were performed on human subjects and on animals to investigate the effects of regional applications of cold, locally and in its remote and systemic effects. It was found that conductive cooling has profound effects on deep local, distant local, and systemic temperatures of the human body.

115. Eichna, L. W. Thermal gradients during varying body temperatures, with particular reference to changes during application of external cold in patients with non-infectious fevers. *Arch. Phys. M., v. 29, Nov. 1948: 687–697.*

Application of ice to skin of subjects with non-infectious fevers brought about a prompt fall in the temperature of the superficial tissue (skin and subcutaneous) but little or no change in rectal temperature. Greater and more rapid falls in rectal temperature followed immediately after the cessation of peripheral cooling. Apparently because of vasoconstriction, peripheral cooling extracts heat for a short period largely or solely from peripheral tissues and this heat loss is not available to cool the deeper tissues until there is a greater increase of blood flow in the cooled skin after the cooling agent has been removed.

116. Eichna, L. W., A. R. Berger, and B. Rader. Comparison of intracardiac and intravascular temperatures with rectal temperature [Abstract]. *Fed. Proc., Balt., v. 8, Mar. 1949: 40.*

Data obtained by thermal couple readings—in some cases with the thermal couple introduced by cardiac catheterization—were obtained on a group of 12 afebrile patients. Within the pulmonary artery, right ventricle, right atrium and femoral artery the temperatures were usually identical and averaged slightly less (0.2°C) than the rectal temperature. Within the superior vena cava the temperature was lower than in the right heart, and in the subclavian vein its average value was 0.48°C below rectal temperature. Within the inferior vena cava the temperatures were variable and the average approximated closely that of the right heart. The temperatures deep in the hepatic vein and high in the internal jugular vein were considerably above the values in veins into which these vessels drain and the hepatic and internal jugular vein temperatures equalled the rectal temperature. These data are said to demonstrate that the thermal gradients within parts of the vascular tree indicate sites of increased heat formation at rest (liver, brain), and suggest that femoral arterial temperature is perhaps a more desirable index of "mixed" deep tissue temperature than the usually accepted rectal temperature.

117. Eichna, L. W. Thermal gradients in man; comparison of temperatures in the femoral artery and femoral vein with rectal temperatures. *Arch. Phys. M., v. 30, Sept. 1949: 584–593.*

Simultaneous measurements were made of the rectal temperature and of the temperature of the blood in the femoral artery and femoral vein, of 13 normal subjects and of 6 with elevated rectal temperatures. The femoral artery temperatures were generally lower than the rectal temperatures in both the normal (by 0.3°C) and in the febrile (by 0.6°C) groups. When the rectal temperatures were either increased or decreased—in one instance from 41.7°C to 36.1°C by application of cooling agents to the skin—the femoral artery temperature and rectal temperature at times moved in parallel fashion and at other times deviated from each other owing to a lag and even a movement in the opposite direction of the rectal temperature. These differences were not found to be great enough to be of clinical significance, but were sufficient to question the validity of technics which assume that rectal temperature is a measure of the temperature of the inflowing blood.

118. Eichna, L. W., A. R. Berger, B. Rader, and W. H. Becker. Comparison of intravascular temperatures with rectal temperatures in man. *J. Clin. Invest. v. 30, Apr. 1951: 353–359.*

Intracardiac, intramuscular, and rectal temperatures were measured potentiometrically, using thermocouples, in 24 afebrile subjects. These measurements indicated that there was a gradient of increasing temperature in the larger veins as they approached the heart; temperatures within the right heart and pulmonary artery were the same as the temperature high in the femoral artery; rectal temperature exceeded intracardiac and deep intravascular temperatures by a small but significant amount; temperatures in the veins draining the liver and brain were higher than the temperatures of veins into which they drained, and they equalled rectal temperatures. In afebrile subjects, the differences between rectal and intracardiac temperatures were not of such magnitude as to be of clinical importance; during fever, preliminary observations suggest that rectal temperature may exceed intracardiac temperature by a significant amount, up to 0.8°C in one patient.

119. Eisenberg, L., and H. C. Bazett. Further observations on intravascular temperature in man [Abstract]. *Fed. Proc., Balt., v. 7, March 1948: 30–31.*

Intravascular temperatures were determined by the insertion of fine wire thermocouples, enclosed in plastic catheters, into the lumen of several different arteries and veins in man.

Simultaneous determinations of six intravascular, as well as cutaneous and rectal temperatures, were made. Under steady conditions, central vascular and rectal temperatures did not differ markedly but during periods of environmental change there was significant deviation between these temperatures.

120. Fay, T., and G. C. Henney. Correlation of body segmental temperature and its relation to the location of carcinomatous metastasis. *Surg., Gyn. Obst., v. 66, Feb. 15, 1938: 512–524.*

Segmental body temperatures were found to vary individually but there was usually a striking elevation of temperature in the region of the breast segment. The incidence of metastatic malignancy was also found to be almost entirely within these same zones of elevated temperature, with few instances of metastases in the distal portions of the extremities. Refrigeration of these metastatic areas, in hopeless and far advanced cases, brought about relief of pain in most instances and disappearance of metastatic lesions in a few cases.

121. Glaser, E. M. The effects of cooling and warming on the vital capacity, forearm and hand volume, and skin temperature of man. *J. Physiol., Lond., v. 109, Sept. 15, 1949: 421–429.*

Experiments suggest that a redistribution of blood between the internal organs and the periphery may be one of the mechanisms for adapting to temperature changes. Thus cooling by immersion lowers the vital capacity, with blood going to the lungs. Warming results in an opposite effect.

122. Grayson, J. Observations on the temperature of the human rectum. *Brit. M. J., (no. 4744), Dec. 8, 1951: 1379–1382.*

Simultaneous recording of rectal temperature and rectal blood flow showed that external stimuli of heat and of cold (exposure of abdominal wall of fully covered subject to a room temperature of 18°C, or immersion of right hand and forearm of covered subject in water of 7°–9°C) caused changes in rectal temperature coincident with changes in rectal blood flow. Rectal temperature, although a useful clinical indicator, is not truly representative of the temperature at which the body's tissues function. The fact that it can be influenced by blood-flow changes indicates that it is not even the highest temperature in the body but is simply one stage in the temperature gradient which exists between the organs of heat production and the organs of heat dissipation.

123. Hegnauer, A. H. Temperature gradients in dogs in immersion hypothermia [Abstract]. *Fed. Proc., Balt., v. 8, Mar. 1949: 71.*

Experimental immersion hypothermia in dogs is reported, with description of a method for reducing body temperature. Temperatures of various body areas were recorded continuously. Under the conditions of the method, there occurred not only core to surface but also cerebral to rectal temperature gradients.

124. Heidelmann, G. Differential regulation of the skin temperature of different parts of the hands; a contribution on segmental pathology [In German]. *Zschr. Kreislaufforsch., v. 40, Jan. 1951: 31–39.*

Studies were made of the skin temperatures of the hand and of the foot of healthy subjects and of some who were ill. The normal temperature of various fingers of one hand, and between the corresponding fingers of both hands, showed considerable differences in 12 of the 50 subjects. After cooling of the hands for 5 minutes (water at 15°C), the duration of rewarming of the fingers differed noticeably in 20% of the subjects. After injection of 1000 mg of a sympathicolytic drug (tetraethylammoniumbromide) the differences in temperature of the fingers were greater (up to 10°C). Two groups of temperature measurements, which were not always constant, were observed: the thumb and 2nd finger, or the 3rd, 4th and 5th fingers. The 2 fingers on the ulnar side warmed more quickly; on the radial side, much more slowly than before. The differences were usually bilateral, but of unequal strength; they were never opposed. The differences were mostly found in patients with organic or functional diseases of the heart or aorta, but they existed also in healthy subjects. The probable cause is seen in segment-conditioned innervation differences. The above results are of pathognomic importance in segmental pathology.

125. Hemingway, A. Rectal temperature patterns of dogs during peripheral vasodilatation and vasoconstriction [Abstract]. *Am. J. Physiol., v. 155, Dec. 1948: 442.*

Dogs were suspended in a hammock at an environmental temperature of 15°–17°C and, after 30 to 45 minutes, the hind legs were first immersed in water at 44°–45°C and then in cold water. In some instances, a sharp fall in rectal temperature occurred on cutaneous vasodilatation; in other instances, a rising rectal temperature occurred with vasodilatation.

126. Hensel, H. The intracutaneous temperature changes with the action of outside temperature stimulation. *Pflügers Arch., v. 252 (2), 1950: 146–164.*

The author describes a method for measuring intracutaneous temperature changes directly by means of extremely fine thermoelements inserted through very thin injection cannulas using the volar side of the human underarm. The depth of insertion of the cannula was governed by specially constructed micrometer gauges. It was found that the temperature gradient, at various depth levels up to 1.5 mm at a room temperature of 22°C, was between 0.2°C/mm and 0.5°C/mm. The steepness of the gradient varied with the outside temperature and the vasomotor mechanisms within definite limits. The results obtained agree well with known theoretical estimates.

127. Horvath, S. M., A. Rubin, and E. L. Foltz. Thermal gradients in the vascular system. *Am. J. Physiol., v. 161, May 1950: 316–322.*

Marked temperature differences were observed in dogs not only in the peripheral blood but also in that draining from the inner organs of the body. Blood temperature is dependent both on the temperature of tissues through which it passes and also on that of other blood with which it mixes. Studies were made of the temperature of blood simultaneously at such sites as the coronary sinus and renal vein, in relation to the temperature of other areas and to physiological functioning.

128. Jäger, A. The temperature of the kidney of the dog [In German]. *Zbl. Chir., v. 76 (17), 1951: 1182–1184.*

By use of surgical techniques, needle electrodes were inserted under narcosis into the kidneys of dogs. There were slight differences in temperature (in the range of 0.02°–0.05°C) between the interior and the surface of the kidneys; these differences were more pronounced when there were greater variations in the rectal temperature. In a scattered number of readings, the interior temperatures were noted as being slightly warmer than the surface ones. Giving of a diuretic (Euphyllin, subcutaneously) brought about a rise in body temperature and a similar one in kidney temperature with the difference between the interior and surface temperatures not measurable. Drinking of 1 liter of milk of room temperature brought about, within about 10 minutes, a decrease of the interior and surface temperatures of the kidney from just under 39°C to about 38.2°C and 38.41°C respectively. After drinking of ½ liter of cold [°C not given] liquid the temperature of the left kidney was lowered by 0.5°C or more and a greater output of urine was attained in the first hour. During the first minutes the greatest differences between the interior and exterior temperatures were noted. The effect of large amounts of cold liquid in the stomach on the differences in temperature and the rate of excretion of urine of the two kidneys was noted. In considering the relation of such findings to man, the anatomically more intraperitoneal position of the kidneys in the dog and the body-weight difference (1:25) should be taken into account. It is known by studies involving dye excretion, etc., that in man the drinking of cold liquids does cause a difference in the rate of excretion of the two kidneys.

129. Larson, W. P., M. Levine, R. N. Bieter, and W. F. McLimans. Study of mouse temperatures, with reference to the effect of temperature on sulfanilamide therapy [Abstract]. *J. Bact., Balt., v. 39, Jan. 1940: 45.*

By accurate measurement it was found that the subcutaneous temperatures of mice vary considerably from the temperature of the environment. At a room temperature of 70°F (21°C), the average tissue temperature for the mice was 100.6°F (38.1°C). At 98°F (36.7°C) it was 104°F (40°C).

130. **Lippross, O., and W. Schega.** On the physiology of tissue temperature [In German]. *Münch. med. Wschr., v. 88, Apr. 18, 1941: 445–449.*

Experiments were performed on resting subjects recording the temperature of various tissues and organs with a highly sensitive thermoelectrical apparatus. Temperatures were recorded of the heart, liver, mouth, rectum, arm pit, calf of leg, hands, feet, and various muscles. In one series of measurements on a 55-year old man, the mouth temperature was found to be 36.8°C and the rectal temperature 37.3°C. Measurements of major muscle and other areas on the right side of the body were the same as, or slightly lower than, those on the left side. The greatest variation was that of the trapezius muscle (38.8°C on the left; 38.2°C on the right) and the gluteus maximus (38.1°C; 37.9°C). The influence of work on muscle temperature was determined by temporarily tieing off with a tourniquet the circulation of both arms and then leaving one at rest while exercising the other to exhaustion and taking continuous temperature readings of each arm. The temperature of the resting arm fell faster and, after release of the tourniquet, rose more slowly than that of the working arm.

131. **Lowenbach, H.** Hypoxemia and the temperature of the hypothalamus of the cat. *J. Neuropath., v. 10, Jan. 1951: 67–76.*

Temperature measurements in different regions of the brain and in various parts of the circulatory system, were made on cats under anesthesia. The temperature of the hypothalamus rose when the carotid arteries were occluded and fell when circulation was restored; in the cerebral cortex and areas near to it, the temperature changes were exactly opposite to the above. Asphyxia, either gradual or sudden, produced similar effects but the temperature in the superficial areas of the brain increased instead of falling.

132. **Mali, J. W. H.** Temperature of the body surface. [In Dutch, summaries in Dutch, French, German, and English]. *Ned. tschr. geneesk., v. 95, May 26, 1951: 1544–1555.*

By means of a thermocouple, body surface temperatures at 24 different locations on the skin were measured on a group of 189 men and women during the course of the day and at environmental temperatures varying from 18° to 25°C. Average body surface temperature, calculated according to Pjleiderer's method, was found to be lower in women than in men. It varied with changes of 1°C environmental temperature, as well as during the course of the day; the range of variation of the temperature was 3.7°C in 502 measurements.

133. **Marshak, M. E.** Temperature changes in the inner organs caused by warming and cooling the animal. II. [In Russian, summaries in Russian and English]. *Arkh. biol. nauk, v. 55 (3), 1939: 20–28.*

The effect of short periods of cold or of heat on the temperature of inner organs of narcotized dogs was studied by use of a temperature chamber and of thermocouples inserted into the liver and pancreas. Cooling of the chamber to 0°C caused a rise in temperature of the organs of 1°–1.5°C; this rise was retained for a period of time when the chamber was reheated. Heating of the chamber to 30°–33°C was followed by a gradual drop of the temperature of the organs; cooling of the chamber to the original temperature was followed by a prompt recovery of the temperature of the organs. The temperature of the rectum did not change in a number of the experiments, with either cooling or heating. In some of the cooling experiments the rectal temperature changed in the direction of the inner organs but more slowly and less pronouncedly. It is concluded from the above data that the temperature curve of the inner organs reflects the changes in heat production of those organs.

134. **Masuzawa, H.** Experimental studies of the temperature in various tissues and organs of the rabbit [In Japanese, with German summary]. *Okayama Igakkai Zasshi, v. 52, Apr. 1940: 772–780.*

Temperature was measured in various organs of rabbits. The liver was the warmest place in the body, possibly because of its protected location; the kidney was next warmest. The skin temperature of the upper arm and upper leg were lower than those of the subcutaneous layer of the corresponding areas. A distinct temperature rise occurred in muscle tissue when the muscle was working. Injection of a cholagogue (histamine, Adrenalin, and "choleretin") brought about a temperature rise in the region of the gall bladder corresponding to that of the warm bile.

135.   Mead, J., and C. L. Bonmarito. Reliability of rectal temperatures as an index of internal body temperature. *J. Appl. Physiol.*, v. 2, Aug. *1949: 97–109.*

Rectal temperatures near the tip of a flexible catheter inserted 8 inches through the external anal sphincter were usually lower than the temperatures recorded simultaneously at intermediate points along the catheter and the differences were greatest in individuals whose body temperatures were falling. X-ray films and experimental data suggest to the author that this lowering of temperature was caused by the cooled blood from the surface of the body passing through the veins in the pelvic wall adjacent to the catheter tip. The positioning of the device for recording internal temperatures therefore becomes important.

136.   Neuroth, G. The role of skin temperature in heat regulation [In German.] *Pflügers Arch.*, v. *250 (3), 1948: 396–413.*

Changes in skin temperature were studied in a young man with regard to thermoregulation at 5° to 50°C environmental temperatures and various degrees of relative humidity. Results showed that the average skin temperature at 5° to 50°C varied from 22° to 40°C. Cold stimulation at 15° to 5°C decreased the skin temperature but this decrease was not uniform. Three temperature groups may be distinguished: (1) the forehead, chest and epigastrium, (2) the arms and shin, and (3) the backs of the hands and feet. The greatest differences among these values were obtained after 3 hours at room temperature of 8.2°C or after 2 hours 15 minutes at 15°C or 12.0°C, where a new mechanism of thermoregulation had set in. The skin temperature decreased more rapidly as the environmental temperature became cooler. At 15°C there were, after two hours, periodical cold shivers, followed by a temporary rise in skin temperature (peripheral vasodilatation), except in the backs of the hands and feet, where the temperature remained unchanged. In moderate cold the decrease in skin temperature is believed to be a thermoregulatory action, which limits the heat loss. In severe cold the physical thermoregulation becomes inadequate and chemical regulation sets in. This moment is outwardly manifested by goose pimples and shivering, and occurs at an average skin temperature of 26.5°C. At 5°C, after 1 hour 45 minutes, there was a general temporary increase in skin temperature, followed by a continued decrease; the greatest drop occurred in the extremities.

137.   Pennes, H. H. Analysis of tissue and arterial blood temperatures in the resting human forearm. *J. Appl. Physiol.*, v. *1, Aug. 1948: 93–122.*

Skin temperature in the arm was determined with reference to the presence of temperature gradients and to the effects of blood flow on the proximal forearm. Simultaneous rectal and brachial blood temperature and deep forearm tissue temperature were measured. The blood flow acted as a warming agent not only to the superficial tissues but to all the forearm tissue between the skin and axis of the limb. Distribution of the tissue temperatures at various depths were determined and the theory of heat was applied to evaluate the effects of local heat production and circulation.

138.   Razgha, A. von, and L. Szelyonka. Temperature topography of the human skin [Abstract, in German]. *Zschr. ges. exp. Med.*, v. *110, 1942: 643.*

Measurements were made of the skin temperature of 49 subjects, arranged in 3 groups according to their exposure to environmental temperatures of 20°–23°C. In all cases the highest and most constant skin temperature was found to be that of the forehead (slightly above 35°C). The temperature of the thorax region was approximately 1°C lower than that of the rectum. The temperatures of the extremities were much lower, that of the toes being the lowest, occasionally being lower than the room temperature, and showing the greatest degree of individual variation. The little finger was usually 2°C cooler than the first finger, indicating that the vasomotor tonus increases gradually from the 1st to the 5th finger. Transversally, the skin temperatures were usually symmetrical. However, a temperature asymmetry of over 1°C (maximum, 6.1°C) was very often found in one to three body regions. These asymmetries occurred most frequently in the toes, and next most frequently in the fingers; they had a temporary character, occurring repeatedly only in 6 subjects out of the 49. In the trunk the asymmetries were never over 1°C. In a colder atmosphere the frequency of the temperature asymmetries increased. The temperature decrease of the skin at lower environmental temperatures was greatest in the first quarter-hour; it ceased in the fingers after half an hour but continued in the feet even after the end of the experimental hour. The behavior of the skin temperature of the extremities suggests that the skin vasomotor tonus of the limbs is of special importance in thermoregulation.

139.   Reader, S. R., and H. M. Whyte. Tissue temperature gradients. *J. Appl. Physiol.*, v. 4, Nov. 1951: 396–402.

Detailed studies of temperature gradients were made, by using needle thermocouples inserted vertical to the skin surface to measure deep tissue temperatures, on two subjects. One subject was fully clothed at an environmental temperature of 24°C, while the other subject was nude at an environmental temperature of 22.2°C. There was a wide variation in the depth of gradients and the range of temperatures encountered. Temperature plateaux were reached in most sites at depths varying from 20 to 37 mm, but in some places constant temperatures had not been reached at a depth of 40 mm. In general, gradients extended deeper in the limbs than in the trunk and were greater in the cold than in the warm subject. The highest temperature was 36.8°C in the lumbar and gluteal regions of the warm subject, and the coldest deep temperature was 32.7°C at a depth of 37 mm in the calf of the leg of the cold subject. In no instance was there found a deep temperature equal to that of the rectal which was 37.3°C in the warm subject and 36.8°C in the other. In general, deep muscle temperatures were lower the further the site was from the center of the body. Gradients in the lumbar region were measured in a large series of subjects and the effects of localized heating and cooling were observed.

140.   Rubin, A., S. M. Horvath, and H. C. Mellette. Effect of fecal bacterial activity on rectal temperature of man. *Proc. Soc. Exp. Biol., N. Y.*, v. 76, Feb. 1951: 410–411.

It seemed possible that the elevation in rectal temperature over that of other parts of the body might be due in part to the normal bacterial activity in the rectum and rectosigmoid. However, in 5 normal healthy adults given succinylsulfathiazole orally until there was a marked decrease in the number of bacteria present in their feces, there were no significant changes in their rectal temperatures.

141.   Scheurer, O. The temperature of human skin [In German]. *Erg. inn. Med. Kinderh.*, v. 59, 1940: 753–820.

A detailed review of the literature on temperature of the skin is given, including the changes following exposure to cold; after drinking cooled liquids; after smoking; and the influence of hormones on changes in skin temperature.

142.   Sheard, C., M. M. D. Williams, G. M. Roth, and B. T. Horton. The role of the extremities in the dissipation of heat from the body in various atmospheric and physiological conditions. *Tr. Am. Soc. Heat. Ventil. Engin.*, v. 45, 1939: 135–152.

The results are presented of recent investigations on the changes in temperature of the fingers and toes and the relative roles of the upper and lower extremities in the dissipation of heat from the body, under various controlled environmental conditions (temperature range of 18° to 34°C). At an atmospheric temperature of 25°C and 40% relative humidity, the forehead, thorax, and upper part of the legs are 7° to 10°C warmer than the toes and lie approximately within the range of 32° to 34°C. In normally reacting subjects, as the temperature of the room is increased, the regulation and dissipation of heat is accomplished initially by the hands and lower portions of the arms (since normal vasoconstriction of the lower extremities is present). This is followed by a regulatory control on the part of the feet and lower portions of the legs when the room temperature reaches 25°C. Finally, at temperatures of 28°–32°C, the temperature of the fingers and toes closely approximate the temperature of the forehead, thorax, legs and arms. At temperatures exceeding about 31°–32°C, maximal vasodilatation of peripheral blood vessels will be maintained, and the internal temperature of the body will be kept approximately constant by changes in secretion of sweat in order to balance the heat received from the environment.

143.   Sheard, C. Temperature of the skin and thermal regulation of the body. *In: Medical physics [v. 1], p. 1523–1555.* Ed. by O. GLASSER. *Chicago, Year Book, 1944.*

Information on the role of the skin in the regulation of body temperature, is reviewed in detail. The zones of physiological response in relation to various environmental temperatures, both high and low, are discussed (p. 1525–1526). Both internal and external causes of low and high skin temperature are outlined in a chart (p. 1526), and are discussed. Also discussed are: skin temperature of extremities under various physical and physiological conditions (p. 1539); and rates of cooling and warming of the extremities (p. 1547). 116 refs.

144.   Wyndham, C. H., and D. K. C. MacDonald. Human immersion and survival in cold water. *Nature, Lond., v. 167, April 21, 1951: 649–650.*

Heat losses from the human body immersed in cold water could be balanced by exercise. If the rate of heat production (due to exercise) exceeded the loss, the temperature of the deep tissues rose. This, in turn, produced an increase in the surface temperature of the hands and feet. The authors regard the deep and superficial tissues as relatively independent from each other in their thermal behavior; a rise in temperature of the deep tissues, above control levels, results in decreased resistance to heat flow between deep and superficial tissues.

145.   Zselyonka, L. The average skin temperature of healthy people with particular reference to the bath effect [In German]. *Balneologe, v. 9, Dec. 1942: 369–373.*

Skin temperature measurements were made on persons with different amounts of clothing while in a room where the air temperature was 20°C, floor temperature was 16°C, and wall temperature was 18°–19°C. It was found that the average skin temperature of the right half of the body was higher than that of the left and that the temperature difference between the two halves of the body was higher in the extremities.

See also items 44, 87, 150, 249, 330, 343, 349, 359, 371, 469, 505, 535, 542, 549, 663, 846, 860, 1075, 1123, 1125, 1182, 1205, 1213, 1229, 1291, 1316, 1319, 1326, 1579.

E. Heat Balance
(includes also role of insulation in temperature regulation)

146.   Anon. Copper man used for tests on heated clothing. *Textile World, v. 95, Feb. 1945: 157.*

A "copper man" has been constructed in the average proportions of Army Air Force flyers, heated electrically to simulate the human temperature system. It has been used to test electrically-heated flying suits, gloves, shoes, and casualty blankets at low temperatures and predetermined wind velocities. The normal heat loss for a human being in a state of comfort is about 75 watts. The copper of the dummy figure has been finished in a semi-lustrous black which has about the same heat-radiation factor as the skin.

147.   Adolph, E. F. Physiological regulations. *Lancaster, Pa., Cattell Press, 1943. 502 p.*

Chapter XIV (p. 301–322) deals with heat regulation. The subject is discussed under the headings of Maintenance in man, Heat loads (man), Recoveries (man), Heat exchanges of rabbit, and Comparisons among species. The heat loads given as increments in Calories per kilogram of body weight or increments of rectal temperature × 0.83, can be imposed either by walking in the heat or by drinking cold water. Various studies of heat load in relation to heat exchange are cited.

148. Akert, K., and F. Kesselring. Shivering from cold as an effect of stimulation of the central nervous system [In German, summaries in German and English]. *Helvet. physiol. pharm. acta, v. 9 (3) 1951: 290–295.*

This study of shivering in cats, elicited by electrical stimulation of the brain, is based on material assembled by W. R. HESS. A detailed account is given of the histological location of the brain areas which give positive reactions.

149. Aschoff, J. Basic experiments in temperature regulation; comparative values in the estimation of heat loss in water. *Pflügers Arch., v. 247 (4–5) 1944: 469–479.*

Some of the equations used, and the equipment involved, in a study to obtain a cooling curve for a body in a flow calorimeter, are discussed. A hollow glass hand filled with heated water is used as the test object. A normal hand was similarly studied as a control in some of the tests.

150. Aschoff, J. The rise in the rectal temperature by local cooling of the body surface [In German]. *Pflügers Arch., v. 248, Aug. 15, 1944: 149–157.*

Heat exchange in hands immersed in water at 13°C was studied, with the surprising result that the local increase in cold does not increase the heat loss but lowers it 120 cal/min. This effect is due to vasoconstriction in the hand and a decrease in heat transfer. A concurrent increase in rectal temperature was observed.

151. Bazett, H. C., E. S. Mendelson, L. Love, and B. Libet. Precooling of blood in the arteries, effective heat capacity and evaporative cooling as factors modifying cooling of the extremities. *J. Appl. Physiol., v. 1, Aug. 1948: 169–182.*

The role of arterial precooling (resulting from proximity to veins carrying blood from chilled areas), and the role of heat capacity in the cooling of hands and feet were studied further. Paradoxical variations observed in surface temperature were attributed to arterial precooling. In measuring tolerance to cold, both vasomotor reactions and heat capacity were found to be important factors. Evaporative heat loss was found to constitute a large proportion of the total loss, particularly at environmental temperatures near freezing. Types of gloves and boots were tested for protection against evaporative loss.

152. Beal, R. W. Low-temperature properties of man. *J. Soc. automot. Engrs., v. 58, Dec. 1950: 46–47.*

A study of the efficiency of man and machines in the Arctic is made. The effect of cold on both man and machines is expressed in terms of "windchill factor," which is the rate at which a body gives up heat under various combinations of temperature and wind velocity. At temperatures below zero the efficiency of man falls 2% for every degree fall in the environmental temperature. Windchill values (expressed by a system of arbitrary units) of 1400–2400 require the wearing of extremely bulky clothing. Hence the design of machines for arctic use should allow for the adequate spacing of nuts, levers, pedals, and other parts that a bulkily-dressed man must reach and operate.

153. Belding, H. S., G. E. Folk, W. H. Forbes, and R. C. Darling. Secretion and evaporation of sweat in cold weather [Abstract]. *Fed. Proc., Balt., v. 4, March 1945: 7.*

A good part of the sweat which is excreted by the body, during periods of exercise in cold environments, is recondensed in the clothing contributing more heat to the body and resulting in further sweating in an attempt to cool the skin. At rest periods the moisture remaining in the clothing is slowly re-evaporated increasing the heat loss when the storing of heat is essential.

On this information and subsequent experimentation is based the suggestion that men, during work at low temperatures, "undress" somewhat to avoid excessive sweating.

154. Belding, H. S., H. D. Russell, and R. C. Darling. Factors maintaining heat balance of the clothed man at different grades of activity in the cold [Abstract]. *Fed. Proc., Balt., v. 5, Feb. 1946: 7–8.*

Men, dressed in a standard arctic uniform, were exposed for two-hour periods to an environmental temperature of 0°F while seated, standing, walking, or climbing. Data were collected and studies were made of energy production and body heat debt, as well as energy loss by evaporation from the lungs and skin, by warming the inspired air, by work, and by convection and radiation through the clothing. At all levels of activity most of the heat was lost by convection and radiation. The calculation of body heat loss by sweating was complicated by the fact that most of the sweat remained in the clothing. However, evidence exists that most of this had been evaporated at the skin and later recondensed, so it was possible to say that the heat of vaporization of all the sweat minus the effective condensation equalled the body heat loss by sweating. It was found that the net efficiency of the sweat for body cooling never exceeded 60 per cent and only attained this figure when sweating was moderate.

155. Belding, H. S., H. D. Russell, R. C. Darling, and G. E. Folk. Thermal responses and efficiency of sweating when men are dressed in arctic clothing and exposed to extreme cold. *Am. J. Physiol., v. 149, Apr. 1947: 204–222.*

Men dressed in arctic uniform were exposed to low temperatures. Data were obtained on sweating, moisture uptake of clothing, energy expenditure, pulmonary ventilation, skin and rectal temperatures, and comfort.

156. Belding, H. S. Protection against dry cold. *In: Physiology of heat regulation and the science of clothing, p. 351–367. Ed. by* L. H. NEWBURGH. *Philadelphia, Saunders, 1949.*

The author finds that requirements for protection from dry cold are determined by metabolic level, duration of exposure, temperature, wind, sunshine, and altitude. Factors influencing the thermal insulation properties of clothing are analyzed.

157. Benedict, F. G. Vital energetics, a study in comparative basal metabolism. *(Carnegie Institution of Washington, publication no. 503). Washington, Carnegie Inst., 1938. 215 p.*

This is a study of life processes in the energy transformations of animal life as expressed in the form of heat. The study is almost entirely concerned with heat production, since heat production is the essential feature of life. The paths of heat loss are also considered, as a means of throwing light upon the mechanism of maintaining the balance between thermogenesis and thermolysis, the result of which is—with warm-blooded animals in general—an extraordinarily uniform body or cell temperature. Heat production is the measure of the intensity of life processes; and it can be measured with great precision. Data are compared on the heat production of animals of various forms, including cold-blooded, warm-blooded, and heterothermic, or hibernating, animals. The discussion is confined to the higher forms of life in which adaptation to various conditions of temperature and vegetation may be noted. There are numerous footnote references.

158. Black, A., and R. W. Swift. The critical temperature for the albino rat as affected by feeding. *J. Nutrit., v. 25, Feb. 10, 1943: 127–136.*

At environmental temperatures below 25°C, the curves of heat production for rats receiving feed were the same as for fasting rats. The percentage of total heat eliminated as water vapor was constant at temperatures from 12° to 32°C.

159. Brobeck, J. R. Regulation of energy exchange. *Annual Rev. Physiol., v. 10, 1948: 315–28.*

This review on the subject of energy exchange covers the period from July 1, 1945 to June 30, 1947, and has a short section on Body Temperature (p. 318–319). There is an extensive bibliography of 197 items of which items numbered 83 to 142 apply to the section on body temperature.

*160. **Brumshtein, V. I.** Loss of moisture at different temperatures in persons at rest [In Russian]. *Gig. & san., Moskva, Dec. 1950 (12): 12–18.*

"*Contains* a study on two men and two women exposed to temperatures of 5.3° to 30.6°C., and a varying relative humidity. The loss of moisture was lower in the women than in the men under similar conditions; a gradual decrease of evaporation up to a temperature of 15°–18°C. was noticed, followed by an increase at a further rise of the air temperature (up to 32°C.); the more layers of clothing worn, the higher was the loss of moisture."—Arctic Bibl., v. 4, 1954: 158.

161. **Brunt, D.** The reactions of the human body to its physical environment. *Q.J.R. Meteor. Soc., Lond., v. 69, Apr. 1943: 77–114.*

This is a general discussion of the problem of how the body reacts to various climatic conditions. Heat production in the human body and its regulation in response to both hot and cold environments are discussed.

162. **Brunt, D.** Some physical aspects of the heat balance of the human body. *Proc. Phys. Soc., Lond., v. 59, Sept. 1, 1947: 713–726.*

The author discusses the physiological aspects of heat balance in man at varying temperatures, and expresses these in terms of equations and by the use of graphs.

163. **Büttner, K.** Physical bioclimatology; problems and methods [In German]. *Leipzig, Akademische Verlagsgesellschaft, 1938. 155 p.*

Part 2 (p. 68–138) is entitled Heat Economy. Physiological temperature regulation is discussed in Part 2 under the headings: the constituents of heat economy; energy increase through combustion processes in the body; heat retention; warmth transport within the body; heat loss through conduction, convection, and radiation; skin temperature; combined effects of wind, radiation, and temperature; warmth and water loss of the skin through evaporation; warmth loss through respiration; combined effects of air temperature, moisture, and wind; humidity; neutral thermic temperature; and clothing. The bibliography for Part 2 (92 refs.) covers pages 144–147.

164. **Canny, A. J., and C. J. Martin.** The influence of air movement and atmospheric conditions on the heat loss from a cylindrical moist body. *J. Hyg., Lond., v. 39, Jan. 1939: 60–89.*

Studies were made of heat losses not as related to the internal body temperature but to a consideration of the molecular layer boundary of the body—or evaporating surface—in relation to the external conditions particularly those of air movements. Some formulae are suggested and experiments carried out using them. The authors recognize and discuss some of the difficulties of using these formulae, obtained partly by use of a cylindrical dummy body, in connection with human or animal bodies.

165. **Chassin, J. L., and G. W. Hinton.** Hyperpyrexia following thoracolumbar sympathectomy; report of two cases occurring during heat wave. *J. Am. M. Ass., v. 140, July 9, 1949: 873–875.*

The author presents two cases of hyperpyrexia due to extreme environmental heat in patients who had undergone extensive thoracolumbar sympathectomy. Failure of heat dissipation in these persons was said to be caused by abolition of the sweating mechanism resulting from the sympathectomy.

---

* Original not seen.

166. Corlette, C. E. On the calculation of heat and moisture dissipated from the body by respiration, with a table designed to make calculation easy at any temperature, any humidity, and any pressure of the air. *Med. J. Australia, 1942 (v.1), Sept. 5: 198–203.*

In order to calculate the heat loss for any temperature, humidity, and atmospheric pressure, a key table is given which covers a temperature range of −50°C to +55°C (−58°F to +131°F). Several examples are given to explain the method of calculation, using this table.

167. Court, A. Wind chill. *Bull. Am. Meteor. Soc., v. 29, Dec. 1948: 487–493.*

The wind-chill formula derived by Siple is only one of several attempting to express the dry convective cooling-power of the atmosphere. It is, however, the only one to be based on experiments at very low temperatures. Experiments were conducted in the Antarctic during 1940 and involved the rate of freezing of water in a small plastic cylinder at various temperatures and wind speeds. The formula, which does not include any of the later theoretical considerations, is expressed as

$$H = (\sqrt{100\,V} + 10.45 - V)\,(33\text{-}t_a).$$

Wind speed, V, is expressed in meters/second; temperature, t_a (Centigrade), in kilocalories/square meter of exposed surface/hour/degree C of temperature difference between the surface and the air. Some of the merits and limitations of any formula for human convective heat loss, or wind chill, are discussed.

168. Cowles, R. B. Fur and feathers; a response to falling temperature. *Science, v. 103, Jan. 18, 1946: 74–75.*

At the present time it would seem to be generally conceded that the appearance of fur and feathers in birds and man came in response to a need for some mechanism of heat conservation and that mutations in the direction of these dermal coverings survived owing to the advantages of heat or energy conservation conferred upon the possessor of these new insulating features. The author gives his basic reasons, phylogenetic and embryonic, for believing this concept of thermal regulation in present warm-blooded species is not correct.

169. Day, R. Regional heat loss. *In: Physiology of heat regulation and the science of clothing, p. 240–261. Ed. by* L. H. Newburgh. *Philadelphia, 1949.*

Observations are reported on regional variations in blood flow and skin temperature. Heat loss from the lungs was also measured and analyzed.

170. DuBois, E. F. The mechanism of heat loss and temperature regulation. *Ann. Int. Med., v. 12, Sept. 1938: 388–395.*

Temperature regulation in man is maintained as a balance between heat production (exercise, shivering, moderate activity, disease, higher basal metabolic rate, etc.) and heat loss (sweating, panting, increased skin circulation, change in temperature gradient, cooler environment, decrease of clothing, increase of air movement, increase of radiation surface, etc.). Although there are a good many local adjustments in all parts of the body the finer control of temperature regulation is in the hypothalamus. In febrile disease this thermo-regulator seems to be "set" at a higher temperature. In the text there are given several charts, with some discussion, concerning various aspects of temperature regulation, such as (1) skin temperature and rectal temperature during violent exercise and the period of rest following it; (2) heat loss and heat production of 2 unclothed men at temperatures from 22° to 35° C; and (3) the temperature curve during a malarial chill.

171. DuBois, E. F. Heat loss from the human body. *Harvey Lect., Balt., Series 34, 1938–1939: 88–123. Also in: Bull. N. York Acad. M., v. 15, 2nd ser., Mar. 1939: 143–173.*

Temperature regulation as a balance between factors of heat loss versus heat production is discussed in detail. Included are the author's own experiments on heat loss and heat production in subjects during violent exercise, during a chill, drinking of alcohol, drinking of cold water, exposure to air currents from a fan, work in warm and humid air, and with the body naked or lightly clothed.

172. **DuBois, E. F.** Fever and the regulation of body temperature. (*American Lecture Series, publication no. 13*). *Springfield, Ill., Thomas, 1948. 68 p.*

Recent research in the physiology of thermal balance is reviewed, including the effects of exercise and chilling, heat production and heat loss, the efficient adaptation of women to environmental temperatures as compared with that of men, and the mechanisms of chemical temperature regulation. Injuries due to cold and heat, use of protective clothing, and the therapeutic uses of cold—both local and generalized—are also considered. The physiological role of fever is discussed on pages 40–57. The concluding section (p. 57–62) is entitled "The Thermoregulatory Apparatus." 52 refs.

173. **Forster, R. E., II, B. G. Ferris, Jr., and R. Day.** The relationship between total heat exchange and blood flow in the hand at various ambient temperatures. *Am. J. Physiol., v. 146, July 1946: 600–609.*

Measurements were made of blood flow and heat loss when the entire body was exposed to ambient temperatures of from 15° to 38°C. Hand blood flow rates as low as 0.15 cc/100 cc of hand tissue were recorded after exposure of the body to cold for several hours.

174. **Frantz, J. A., and J. L. A. Roth.** Metabolic balances in the cold environment: II. Energy exchanges [Abstract]. *Fed. Proc., Balt., v. 7, Mar. 1948: 35–36.*

Energy exchange data was obtained on human subjects living for nine days, at 32°C, in order to evaluate U.S.A.F. emergency rations. Fasting at this temperature for six days gave control data. Clothing and sleeping bags were adequate to maintain normal body temperatures. It was seen that there was a progressive limitation of voluntary activity among the fasting subjects. During low-temperature exposure there was an increase in the metabolic cost in performing a standard work load. In ability to perform tasks, work capacity, and maintenance of body comfort in the fasting and non-fasting subjects, adequacy of clothing was more important than food for survival at low temperatures.

175. **Gagge, A. P., C. E. A. Winslow, and L. P. Herrington.** The influence of clothing on the physiological reactions of the human body to varying environmental temperatures. *Am. J. Physiol., v. 124, Oct. 1938: 30–50.*

A normally-clothed subject is able to tolerate a difference of 8°C between skin and environmental temperature before body cooling sets in at 25°C. Between 25° and 29°C the thermal equilibrium of the clothed body is maintained by vasomotor regulation. Above 29°C evaporative regulation sets in.

176. **Gagge, A. P., A. C. Burton, and H. C. Bazett.** A practical system of units for the description of the heat exchange of man with his environment. *Science, v. 94, Nov. 7, 1941: 428–430.*

A formula is developed to describe the heat exchange of man with his environment, using the practical units, *met* and *clo*, to make possible a system of physical units which will be equally understandable to the engineer, physician, and physiologist. The proposed thermal activity may be defined as 50 calories per hour per square meter of the surface area of the individual (or 18.5 BTU/hr/sq ft). This is approximately the metabolism of a subject resting in a sitting position under conditions of thermal comfort. This unit may be utilized by any of the groups, regardless of the other systems of units employed. The unit for thermal insulation, the *clo*, of clothing is logically the amount of insulation necessary to maintain in comfort such a sitting-resting subject in a normally ventilated room (air movement 20 ft/min or 10 cm/sec) at a temperature of 70°F or 21°C, and a humidity of the air which is less than 50%. Since thermal equilibrium has been maintained, the insulating value of 1 *clo* can be expressed and defined in terms of the common system of units.

177. Glaser, E. M., and R. V. Holmes Jones. Initiation of shivering by cooled blood returning from the lower limbs. *J. Physiol., Lond., v. 114, July 31, 1951: 277–282.*

When the lower limbs of young men were immersed without movement in cold water (7°–12.5°C) for periods up to 85 minutes, no shivering occurred. However, if the limbs were exercised during or after immersion, shivering always followed within 4 to 17 minutes regardless of the extent of previous cooling. Shivering could be induced—after the limbs were cooled and resting—by a reactive hyperemia of the limb caused by application and then release of a tourniquet, by vasovagal attack of emotional origin, and by injection of Adrenalin. The author concludes that increasing the blood flow through the muscles of the cold limbs causes more cooled blood to pass from those limbs to the rest of the body and that this in turn activates some center or receptors of shivering.

178. Greenfield, A. D. M., J. T. Shepherd, and R. F. Whelan. The loss of heat from the hands and from the fingers immersed in cold water. *J. Physiol., Lond., v. 112, Feb. 20, 1951: 459–475.*

During immersion of fingers or a hand in cold water (o° to 6°C), the heat loss from the circulating blood was calculated by comparison of the heat loss when the circulation was free and when it was arrested. Heat loss was very slight during the first 5 minutes of immersion, then rose rapidly reaching average values of 200 cal/100 ml/min for the hand, 877 cal/100 ml/min for the fingers, and 2200 cal/100 ml/min for the distal 2.8 cm of the index finger. Heat loss was lower when the subject was generally cold and higher when he was hot. Returning venous blood during cold vasodilatation was found to reduce the temperature of the skin overlying veins proximal to the immersed part by as much as 10°C in 4 minutes. With both hands immersed, the esophageal temperature was found to fall 0.55°C in 8 minutes.

179. Greenfield, A. D. M., G. A. Kernohan, R. J. Marshall, J. T. Shepherd, and R. F. Whelan. Heat loss from toes and forefeet during immersion in cold water. *J. Appl. Physiol., v. 4, July 1951: 37–45.*

When the toes of a comfortably-warm subject are immersed in a water-bath at 0°–6°C there was almost complete arrest of circulation followed by a vasodilatation and then by alternating periods of vasoconstriction and vasodilatation. The average internal temperature of the toes was 12°–14°C. Similar but smaller responses followed immersion at 6°–12°C, but there was no initial arrest of the circulation and no vasodilatation at 12°–15°C. If the subject was heated, the heat loss to water at 0°–6°C was about doubled; if cooled, it was reduced. In a heated subject, the blood flow during cold vasodilatation was probably as great as that in the opposite toes in water at 28°–29.4°C; in a comfortable subject, the flood flow during cold vasodilatation was only about one half as great as in the heated subject.

180. Hall, G. E. Protective clothing for RCAF air crew. *Canad. Text. J., v. 59, Dec. 4, 1942: 32–34, 37–39.*

Clothing for aircrew personnel must be designed with specially constructed materials which will be relatively cool under hot ground conditions and at the same time be warm at the sub-zero temperatures of high altitudes. The clothing must be non-bulky because of the limitations of space, allow freedom of movement to operate instruments even though the individual airmen must remain in a restricted area, and be easily discarded in case of fire or other emergency. The degree of thermal insulation for different parts of the body varies considerably. The trunk, particularly the back, requires the greatest thermal insulation and should be kept a few degrees warmer than the hands or feet. If the hands and feet are kept warmer than the trunk of the body, a vasodilatation occurs which produces excess sweating over the whole body. This may facilitate a decrease in body temperature and bring about marked fatigue. Protection by clothing and equipment from wind, noise, glare, cold, etc., can do much to minimize aircrew fatigue. However, the factor of personal confidence in the protective clothing is a major one and must also be met.

181. Hall, V. E., and P. B. Goldstone. The influence of epinephrine on shivering and on metabolism in the cold. *J. Pharm. Exp. Ther., v. 68, Feb. 1940: 247–251.*

Epinephrine, in excess of the rate of physiological secretion in response to cold, acted to reduce the total metabolism by decreasing the amount of oxygen consumed and abolished shivering in chilled, anesthetized cats. Depression by epinephrine of the central motor mechanism is thought to be the reason for these changes.

182. Hall, V. E., F. P. Attardo, and J. H. Perryman. Influence of dinitrophenol on body temperature threshold for thermal polypnea. *Proc. Soc. Exp. Biol., N. Y., v. 69, Dec. 1948: 413–415.*

Dinitrophenol (DNP) in doses of 10 to 20 mg/kg did not prevent the occurrence of thermal polypnea in rabbits but it did significantly increase the rectal temperature at which such polypnea appeared. It is suggested that DNP depresses both heat and cold defense mechanisms by a nonspecific toxic action. It does not appear to sensitize the heat defense mechanism which had been postulated as the possible mode of action.

183. Hardy, J. D., and E. F. DuBois. Basal metabolism, radiation, convection and vaporization at temperatures of 22° to 35°C. *J. Nutrit., v. 15, May 1938: 477–497.*

At temperatures of 22° to 35°C, the average temperature of the skin of two normal, naked, men was midway between that of the air and the internal parts of the body. At lower temperatures, the surface cooled rapidly and heat loss exceeded heat production. Radiation accounted for 70% of heat loss at 22° to 26°C, but this percentage fell rapidly as skin cooled. Vaporization dissipated 18% to 30% at lower air temperatures but accounted for 100% at 35°C. Convection accounted for 15%. Basal metabolism was level at air temperatures of 22° to 35°C and rose after about 2 hours, followed by a shaking chill. At higher temperatures, sweating took care of heat loss, and radiation and convection were abolished.

184. Hardy, J. D., A. T. Milhorat, and E. F. DuBois. The effect of exercise and chills on heat loss from the nude body. *J. Nutrit., v. 16, Nov. 10, 1938: 477–492.*

When naked men were kept in a calorimeter at 22°C, their rectal temperature fell 0.2° to 0.5°C in 2 to 3 hours. The average surface temperature fell 30°C and shivering began; exercise served to stave off chills.

185. Hardy, J. D., and G. F. Soderstrom. Heat loss from the nude body and peripheral blood flow at temperatures of 22°C to 35°C. *J. Nutrit., v. 16, Nov. 10, 1938: 493–509.*

This is a detailed study of the laws of heat transfer as applied to heat loss from the nude human body. Data obtained in a calorimeter were compared with figures obtained by similar measurements of heat transfer performed on a blackened cylinder resembling the shape of the human trunk.

186. Hardy, J. D., and A. T. Milhorat. Basal heat loss and production in women at temperatures from 23° to 36°C. *Proc. Soc. Exp. Biol., N. Y., v. 41, May 1939: 94–98.*

A calorimeter study was made of the effect of environmental temperature (23° to 36°C) on the heat loss of 3 women subjects, with information on average skin temperature, rectal temperature, heat loss, heat production, vaporization, conduction, and the cooling constant of Newton's law. Comparison of the data with those previously reported for male subjects indicated that while the rectal temperatures and the Newton's cooling constants were identical, there were significant differences in other responses. The women did not begin to sweat until the calorimeter temperature was 2 degrees above the threshold for sweating in men and the amount of sweating was less. Apparently a thicker insulating layer of superficial tissue accounts for the lower skin temperature of the women in the cold. Heat production was similar up to 27.5°C but the women then showed a significant decrease at temperatures above this level.

187. Hardy, J. D., and E. F. DuBois. Differences between men and women in their response to heat and cold. *Proc. Nat. Acad. Sc. U. S., v. 26, June 15, 1940: 389–398.*

Women were found to have a physiological advantage in their adjustment to controlled changes in thermal environment (range of 22° to 35°C) over that of men. The comfort zone— in which heat loss and heat production are equal—extends over a range of about 6°C for women and only 2°–3°C for men. Women have generally a thicker layer of subcutaneous fat for insulation against cold. They also have a slightly better adaptation of skin temperature to meet thermal changes in the environment; they usually sweat much less quickly in a warm environment than men do.

188. Hardy, J. D., A. T. Milhorat, and E. F. DuBois. Heat loss and heat production in women under basal conditions at temperatures from 23° to 35°C. *In: American Institute of Physics. Temperature, its measurement and control in science and industry, p. 529–536. New York, Reinhold, 1941.*

Studies on heat loss and heat production in young women under various environmental temperatures reveal a significant difference in response as compared with similar measurements on young men.

189. Hardy, J. D., and E. F. DuBois. The significance of the average temperature of the skin. *In: American Institute of Physics. Temperature, its measurement and control in science and industry, p. 537–543. New York, Reinhold, 1941.*

The average temperature of the total area of the skin—as contrasted with earlier emphasis on temperatures of fingers and toes—was studied in its relation to heat loss in three zones of environmental temperatures. In temperatures cooler than 28°C, heat loss by radiation and convection exceeded heat production. In temperatures of 28.5°–30.5°C, regulation was entirely by vasomotor means, and heat loss and heat production were nearly equal. In temperatures higher than 30.5°C, evaporative regulation of temperature was in effect and sweating and increases in skin circulation were noted.

190. Hardy, J. D., A. T. Milhorat, and E. F. DuBois. Basal metabolism and heat loss of young women at temperatures from 22° to 35°C. *J. Nutrit., v. 21, Apr. 1941: 383–404.*

Calorimeter studies of heat loss and heat production, at environmental temperatures of 22° to 36°C, were made of a group of 8 women and the results compared with similar ones obtained earlier with 2 men. In general there were slight differences in every single factor of temperature regulation and in all respects women had the physiological advantage, especially in the warmer comfort zone. Sweating was less marked in the women and did not begin until the environmental temperatures were higher than was the case for men. The conductance of the peripheral tissues for women was about 20% lower than that for men, in the cold experiments, representing 20% more insulation against cold.

191. Hardy, J. D., and H. Goodell. Thermoregulatory phenomena associated with exposure to warm and cold environments [Abstract]. *Fed. Proc., Balt., v. 6, Mar. 1947: 122.*

Each of a group of 20 medical students was exposed for 3 hours to an environmental temperature of 31°C, and for 4 hours to a temperature of 16°–18°C. In the cold room, temporary rise in rectal temperature was observed, but no change in metabolism occurred until shivering began. This was accompanied by a temporary rise in metabolism, a rise in skin temperature, a rise in peripheral blood flow, and increased heat loss.

192. Hardy, J. D. Heat transfer. *In: Physiology of heat regulation and the science of clothing, p. 78–108. Ed. by* L. H. NEWBURGH. *Philadelphia, Saunders, 1949.*

Enumerated are 7 measurements with regard to man and 9 measurements with regard to his environment which are required to formulate an equation for heat exchange between a man and his environment. This is expressed in kilogram calories per hour.

193. Hensel, H. Shivering produced by carbon dioxide inhalation during exposure to cold [In German]. *Pflügers Arch., v. 252 (1), 1949: 107–110.*

When subjects were exposed nude to an environmental temperature of 10 °C while breathing normal air, even those quite sensitive to shivering did not begin to shiver very seriously until the close of the hour. However, when the subjects were breathing atmospheric air with a 3% carbon dioxide content, an extraordinarily strong shivering reaction began almost immediately on exposure. When the body was kept warm by use of blankets or clothing, shivering did not occur. This heightened effect on shivering could be demonstrated, with a latency of 15 seconds, when the subject breathed carbon dioxide over a period of 1 minute or less, and disappeared on discontinuation of the carbon dioxide.

194. Hensel, H. A flow calorimeter for different parts of the body [In German]. *Zschr. ges. exp. Med., v. 117 (6), 1951: 586–597.*

A new apparatus for the measurement of heat loss by the skin is described. It represents an improved flow calorimeter, and can be applied as a skin thermometer at any part of the body, registering continuously. It consists of a flat, box-shaped, measuring chamber through which flows a stream of water of constant temperature. The temperature of the inflowing and outflowing water is constantly registered thermoelectrically. The heat loss from the measured skin surface can easily be determined from the difference of these temperatures, and the rapidity of the flow. The measuring chamber and the thermal measuring system are isolated to avoid loss of heat to the outside air. The method is appropriate for exact and sensitive quantitative registration of vasomotor processes at all parts of the body.

195. Herrington, L. P. The heat regulation of small laboratory animals at various environmental temperatures. *Am. J. Physiol., v. 129, Apr. 1, 1940: 123–139.*

This is a study on reactions to various environmental temperatures, showing that the metabolic increment with decrease in environmental temperature is species-specific and very regular.

196. Herrington, L. P. Heat production and thermal conductance in small laboratory animals at various temperatures. *In: American Institute of Physics. Temperature, its measurement and control in science and industry, p. 446–452. New York, Reinhold, 1941.*

Observations on heat production and conductance in mice, rats, and guinea pigs, are reported. It was found that at low temperatures increased heat production never compensated fully for increased heat loss so that lower average body temperatures resulted in all three species.

197. Herrington, L. P. The range of physiological response to climatic heat and cold. *In: Physiology of heat regulation and the science of clothing, p. 262–276. Ed. by* L. H. NEWBURGH. *Philadelphia, Saunders, 1949.*

A review and analysis is made of the physiological factors and mechanisms involved in maintaining the stability of the deep internal temperature of the body and the physiological cost of these processes. 48 refs.

198. Herrington, L. P. The role of the piliary system in mammals and its relation to the thermal environment. *Ann. N. York Acad. Sc., v. 53, Mar. 1951:* 600–607.

Piliary (hair) development is of major importance within mammalian species in conjunction with chemical regulation in providing thermal protection, increasing in importance as the size of the animal increases. The author urges further study of the role of the piliary system by species of animal, and the construction of a standard biological scale of temperature. Otherwise no inter-species comparisons of endocrine or metabolic reactions can be said to be fully controlled with respect to the important metabolic stimuli associated with habitat temperature.

199. Hill, L. Effects of clothing and fuel shortage on health. *Nature, Lond., v. 150, Nov. 7, 1942:* 536–538.

The author states that hair, feathers, fur, and clothes protect the body from heat loss not by their substance as such but by the air which is entangled in the meshes of the fibers. Air which is warmed to body temperature and kept stationary acts as an insulator, preventing heat loss. The author discusses the role of clothing among primitive, and other, peoples; during exercise; in unheated rooms; and under varied conditions of humidity and air movement.

200. Horvath, S. M., H. Golden, and J. Wagar. Some observations on men sitting quietly in extreme cold. *J. Clin. Invest., v. 25, Sept. 1946:* 709–716.

Observations were made on the metabolic rate, and on skin and rectal temperatures, of men dressed in arctic uniforms sitting quietly in a cold environment ranging from 1.1° to −40°C. It was observed that heat production in the cold was above basal values, the fall in rectal temperature was moderate, and the hands and feet suffered the greatest heat loss.

201. Horvath, S. M. Ventilation of clothing and tolerance of man to low environmental temperatures. *J. Indust. Hyg., v. 30, Mar. 1948:* 133–139.

Human subjects were exercised on a treadmill in a wind tunnel at −23°C at wind velocities varying from 0 to 9.6 miles per hour. It was found that accumulated moisture in the clothes lowered tolerance to cold if worn the next day without being dried. The use of front-opening outer garments provided ventilation and prevented accumulation of moisture during work.

202. Inouye, T., N. Glickman, and R. W. Keeton. Dynamics of evaporative heat loss for a rapidly cooling human body [Abstract]. *Fed. Proc., Balt., v. 8, Mar. 1949:* 80.

Six healthy young men, who had previously been exposed to a hot environment (37°C) for periods of 1 or 2 hours, were placed in a room of comfortable temperature (24.4°C) and the dynamics of evaporative heat loss of their rapidly cooling bodies were studied. Observations included weight loss and skin temperatures obtained at frequent intervals during the course of 1 hour. Under dynamic conditions, available moisture in the cotton union suit worn by the subject and on his skin was found to adequately express wettedness, as used in the equation governing evaporative heat loss. For subjects under rapidly changing physiological conditions, the amount of evaporative heat loss was found to be proportional to the gradient of water vapor pressure between the skin and the ambient environment, to the amount of available moisture on the skin and in the union suit, and to surface area and time.

203. Karapetian, A. E., and IŪ. N. Livshitz. On the importance of lowering the heat loss in the struggle against overcooling [Abstract, in Russian]. *Sovet. med. ref. Obozr., fiziol., 1949 (3):* 10.

In an effort to discover possible means of reducing the heat loss in the foot to a minimum, an inner sole whose lower side was covered with foil, was placed in one shoe, and in the other a regular inner sole made of cardboard and paper. The skin temperature of the foot and big toe was measured by a thermocouple attached to the foot, and the feet, within the shoe, placed on the snow. The temperature of the foot, under which a foil-protected sole had been placed, was found to be 2.2°C higher than that of the other foot. During prolonged exposure the temperature decreased evenly over the whole surface of the foot. Foil is a preserver of radiated body heat, but is not very satisfactory as insulation because of its great heat conductivity. The most appropriate material for such insulation would be a white shining material whose reflexion coefficient would be close that of foil but whose thermoconductivity would be minimal.

204. Kottke, F. J., J. S. Phalen, and M. B. Visscher. Effect of breathing high oxygen mixtures on human metabolism during shivering [Abstract]. *Fed. Proc., Balt., v. 3, Mar. 1944: 26–27.*

It was found that the onset of shivering in nude subjects exposed to cold (10°C) could be delayed by causing the men to breathe air with a high oxygen concentration.

205. Ladell, W. S. S. Thermal comfort in temperate climates. *Practicioner, Lond., v. 163, Aug. 1949: 141–150.*

The chief means by which temperature is regulated is the adjustment of the heat loss mechanism. Heat loss by conduction, and also by convection, is much greater in water than in air so that a naked man can survive for at least 4 hours in air at 34°F (1.1°C), but immersion in water may cause fatal chilling in less than half an hour (item 821). Body temperature is greatly dependent upon the vascular and nervous systems, with the centers for heat control located in the hypothalamus. The differences in the metabolic rate and in the state of the capillary blood vessels, cause considerable differences in response to temperature of either the old or very young compared with those of the normal adult. The heat-regulating centers of the hypothalamic area are known to be depressed by fatigue, during sleep, and during anesthesia.

206. Lee, R. C., N. F. Colovos, and E. G. Ritzman. Skin temperatures of the pig, the goat, and the sheep under winter conditions. *J. Nutrit., v. 21, Apr. 1941: 321–326.*

Measurements of skin temperature were made of 2 sheep, a pig, and a goat at environmental temperatures between −12°C and +21°C. The protective coats of the ewe, the ram, and the goat enabled them to maintain their skin temperatures within relatively narrow ranges (near 30°C) despite large differences in environmental temperature, but the poorer external protection of the pig did not provide such uniformity. The skin temperature of the sheep was also warmer than that of the goat, under all conditions.

207. Love, L. Heat loss and blood flow of the feet under hot and cold conditions. *J. Appl. Physiol., v. 1, July 1948: 20–34.*

Studies were made of heat loss, blood flow, and skin temperature of the feet of two subjects living at 33°C and at 21°C for periods of 2 to 7 days, in both summer and winter. At the cooler temperature, no progressive changes in skin temperature were found. Exposure to the colder temperature reduced the ability of the foot to lose heat by vaporization during a subsequent period in the warmer temperature. This was associated with a decrease in the amount of heat lost by each volume of blood flowing through the foot. It was estimated that the foot, with an area of about 5% of that of the total body area, lost 6.5% of the total heat in the warmer temperature and only 3.5% in the colder temperature.

208. McAdams, W. H. Heat transmission. 2nd ed. *New York, McGraw-Hill, 1942. 459 p.*

The fundamental aspects of heat transmission are discussed in this book. Although the material is limited exclusively to non-living systems, much of the physical chemistry and physics discussed can be applied to living organisms. The following are a few of the topics presented: steady conduction, methods of heat transfer, transient conduction, radiation, black bodies, and convection. Examples and problems accompany each chapter.

209. MacDonald, D. K. C., and C. H. Wyndham. Heat transfer in man. *J. Appl. Physiol., v. 3, Dec. 1950: 342–364.*

The subjects were clad in cold-weather clothing and exposed to an ambient temperature of 0° to −10°C at rest for 2 hours followed by 1 hour of standardized work activity. At work the rate of metabolic heat production was nearly three times as great as it had been at rest. The rectal temperature at rest fell rapidly during the first hour and then less so to reach a new equilibrium in about two hours; it rose with commencement of work and reached a new equilibrium in about one hour. Skin temperature fell rapidly in the first hour and then more slowly in the second hour; when work commenced it continued slowly to fall initially despite a rising rectal temperature. Between 20 and 30 minutes after work commenced, the skin temperature rose precipitously and by the end of an hour it had reached the control level observed at the beginning of the experiment.

210.   Mali, J. W. H. Possible role of heat metabolism in erythroderma [In Dutch, summaries in Dutch, French, German and English]. *Ned. tschr. geneesk.,* v. 95, June 2, 1951: 1608–1615.

A study of skin temperatures of patients with erythrodermia would appear to justify the assumption of increased local loss of heat, from which heat production necessarily results. But it seemed unlikely that the increased metabolism in some erythrodermias should be of etiological or primary importance with regard to its origin.

*211.   Malysheva, A. E. Cooling of the organism through local activity of cold surfaces [In Russian]. *Gig. & san., Moskva, 1950 (2): 22–26.*

"*Contains* a study of the effects of cold surfaces (walls) on four male subjects, aged 18–24 years, with the upper part of their bodies unclothed and their backs at a distance of 10 cm from a cold wall; this procedure caused a drop in temperature of the exposed part and also of the skin of the nose, hands, fingers, toes, and of the mucosa of the nose."—Arctic Bibl., v. 4, 1954: 809.

212.   Masamichi, R. The effect of severe cold on the human body [In Japanese]. *Seppyo, v. 5, 1943: 211–215.*

"The heat-loss rate of the human body in northern Manchuria at temperatures of −20° to −30°C was measured with an alcohol Kata-thermometer. The heat-loss rate is expressed empirically in terms of temperature and wind. The physiological reactions to frostbite are described. Acclimatization to cold and resistance to frostbite are effective when the numerical product of temperature and wind velocity is low, but becomes ineffective when the number exceeds a critical value. Death from cold exposure is discussed, and some dietetic relationships are reviewed. Ten minutes of vigorous exercise daily in the open without clothing are recommended practices to increase cold endurance. (Abstract by Ukitirô Nakaya)."—SIPRE Report 12, v. 3, Jan. 1953: 195.

213.   Medvedeva, N. B. Thermoconductibility in the skin of rats [In Ukranian, with French summary]. *Med. Zh. Akad. nauk URSR, v. 9, 1939: 129–145.*

Changes in the thermoconductivity of the skin (determined by the "micro-Christiansen" apparatus) and the coefficient of inner heat conductibility (calculated by a formula) were studied in rats during their development and growth. Studies were done in relation to hair covering and to water or fat content of the skin, both in fur-covered and naked animals during the summer and the winter. In the summer, the thermoconductibility of 1 to 18-day old rats was found, in general, to be very high with a sharp decrease on the 16th day after which it increased again. The thermoconductibility of the naked and of the hair-covered skin differ very little from one another at this stage, the decrease being due to thermo-protecting factors in the skin itself. In the winter, 1-day to 2-year old rats were tested. The conductibility in the first day of life was found to be higher than it had been in similar animals in the summer, but dropped to the level of the summer groups on the 8th to 10th day. In the animals without fur, the skin showed a maximal conductibility on the 13th day, then a gradual decline after the first month. This decline was somewhat slower than in the fur-protected animals, in which the decrease started after the 20th day, indicating the importance of the hair covering. The water content of the skin was the same in both seasons; the fat layer was thicker in the winter. The

---

* Original not seen.

increase in thermoconductibility in the adult rat coincided with a thinning of the fat layer; however, there was no direct relationship between the fat content and thermoconductibility. Therefore, it must be assumed that in the winter as in the summer, a great part in the change of thermoconductibility is played by the structural (histological and colloidal) changes in the skin.

214.   Metz, B. Man and cold. *Strasbourg méd., v. 1, May 1950: 303–321.*

A considerable review of the literature is given on the physiological, and a few of the other, mechanisms for protecting man from exposure to cold. Some of the topics dealt with are: methods of exchange of heat between the organism and the environment; physiological means of combating cold; physical thermoregulation; chemical thermoregulation; hypothermia; and the physiological hygiene of cold (including acclimatization, selection of subjects resistant to cold, clothing, and diet. 52 refs.

215.   Mills, C. A., and C. Ogle. Ease of body heat loss as a basic developmental and functional factor in warm-blooded animals. *Am. J. Physiol., v. 125, Jan. 1, 1939: 36–40.*

Three-week-old mice were placed in rooms of varied temperatures (32° to 92°F) and humidities (up to 70% relative humidity), and were observed for 4 months. Room 1 had moist heat; Room 2, mosit heat with radiant cooling; Room 3, cold air with radiant heat; and Room 4 was air-cooled. Fastest growth and earliest sexual development occurred in mice kept in Room 2 rather than in Room 4 where best results had been expected. Suppression of growth took place in Rooms 1 and 3. Good health was maintained in all groups. Human subjects found Room 1 distinctly uncomfortable, but were comfortable in Room 2 which had high heat and high humidity but which also had facilities for radiant cooling. Room 3 was comfortable as soon as heaters were turned on but with both heaters and coolers working, it was soon found to be uncomfortably hot even though air temperatures were only 70° to 76°F. Room 4 was found to be cool but comfortable. The usual partition of heat loss between conduction, convection and radiation was not a physiological condition since the avenue of heat loss was found to be unimportant.

216.   Mills, C. A. Influence of environmental temperatures on warm-blooded animals. *Ann. N. York Acad. Sci., v. 46, June 1945: 97–105.*

A discussion of experimental work indicating that ease of heat loss plays an important role in many vital functions of warm-blooded animals, such as: growth rate, speed of development, fertility, dietary requirements for certain vitamins, storage and mobilization of glycogen, resistance to infection, and incidence of cancer and leukemia. Cold environment was found to increase the incidence of spontaneous tumors, whereas a hot environment increased the incidence of chemically induced tumors and the "takes" of subcutaneously transplanted experimental ones. Storage of liver glycogen was less in a hot environment; the ability to use stored glycogen was impaired in a cold environment.

217.   Mills, C. A. Temperature dominance over human life. *Science, v. 110, Sept. 16, 1949: 267–271.*

Proper ease of heat loss is said to produce a fast-growing, early-maturing individual of keen mentality and one much less susceptible to infectious disease. The author discusses these factors in relation to climatic conditions in various geographical areas and relates the northward shift of world power to the present millennium of warmth.

218.   Molnar, G. W., and E. F. Adolph. Heat exchanges of man in cold outdoor environments [Abstract]. *Fed. Proc., Balt., v. 5, pt. 2, Feb. 1946: 74.*

Men in shorts were exposed to outdoor temperatures for from one to four hours. Heat production and heat loss were measured in shade and sunshine. In the shade subjects cooled about 15 Cal/hr/°C at air temperatures below 30°C. In sunshine, cooling at the same rate occurred only at air temperatures below 25°C. Position did not affect the results.

219. Murlin, J.. R. Skin temperature, its measurement and significance for energy metabolism [In English]. *Erg. Physiol.*, *v. 42, 1939: 153–227.*

This review of information on skin temperature has sections on methods of measurement; on factors, both external and internal, determining skin temperature; on the significance of skin temperature for partition of heat losses with respect to conduction, convection, evaporation, and radiation; and on the significance of skin temperature for direct calorimetry. Equations for use in the various determinations are given throughout the reference. 185 refs.

220. Nelbach, J. H., and L. P. Herrington. A note on the hygroscopic properties of clothing in relation to human heat loss. *Science*, *v. 95, Apr. 10, 1942: 387–388.*

To study the hygroscopic properties of clothing in relation to human heat loss, a garment was tested over a temperature range from 45° to 90°F, at both a high (77%) and a low (30%) relative humidity. A series of graphs show the results of nineteen different exposures and represent gains and losses of weight in the suit for the first six hours. The significant effect of garment moisture gain or loss on skin temperature and heat balance may be illustrated from the magnitude of the weight changes in the first hour of exposure. One conclusion to be drawn from the graphs is that relative humidity influences the weight change far more than temperature although the effect of a 10°C rise in temperature is observable for comparable relative humidities.

221. Ogata, K., and M. Hayama. Physiological studies of the amount of the loss of heat due to the respiratory ventilation [Abstract, in English]. *Proc. Jap. Physiol. Soc., 22nd Annual Meet., Mar. 27–29, 1943: 6–7. (Jap. J. M. Sc., Biophysics, v. 9, 1944).*

The temperature of expired air, in environmental temperatures of 36.9°C to −15.4°C, was measured. This air temperature was influenced by the combination of several factors, such as frequency and depth of respiration, volume of respiratory exchange, amount of heat loss due to respiratory ventilation, and the environmental air temperature. Other studies were made on heat production and on heat loss from the body; effect of local and generalized warming; warming the body while breathing cold air; and the use of a mask to protect against cold.

222. Ogden, L. W., and W. H. Rees. Measurement of temperature and relative humidity on skin and clothing of human subject. *Textile Inst. J., v. 38, Nov. 1947: T371–T386.*

A method is described for measuring temperature and relative humidity at the skin surface and between various layers of garments of a clothed human subject. Continuous values of temperature and relative humidity may be obtained with the subject undergoing various degrees of activity. At rest in a comfortable state the trunk temperature was about 33°C and the relative humidity of the skin about 30–40%. By use of a standard test-garment of known resistance to flow of heat and of water vapour, the rate of flow of each through clothing may be calculated. Under certain conditions the results may be applied to body metabolism. The metabolism of a sitting and resting subject was found to be 58 watts per square meter or 50 kilocalories per square meter per hour.

223. Palmes, E. D. An apparatus and method for the continuous measurement of evaporative water loss from human subjects. *Rev. Sc. Instruments, v. 19, Oct. 1948: 711–717.*

An apparatus and method are described for the continuous measurement and recording of evaporative heat loss from humans. An infra-red gas analyzer is used to measure the difference in water vapor concentration in a stream of air before and after it has passed over the body of the subject enclosed in a sealed chamber. The method has the advantage of producing a continuous and almost instantaneous record. It should be applicable to problems of thermal balance and studies of physiological mechanisms which control the rate of evaporative water loss.

224. Perera, G. A. Clinical and physiologic characteristics of chill. *Arch. Int. M., v. 68, Aug. 1941: 241–260.*

The chill which accompanies disease and the role of cold-induced shivering in temperature regulation, are described. A chill is accompanied by an increase in metabolism and a rise in heat production, causing a rise in body temperature.

225. Pfleiderer, H. Meteorophysiology of heat economy [Abstract, in German]. *Verh. Deut. Ges. inn. Med., v. 47, 1938: 492–500.*

The heat-regulating responses of the body with respect to the temperature of the surrounding air are discussed. Also described are the temperature-control functions of the skin and of the endocrine system.

226. Pinson, E. A., and E. F. Adolph. Heat exchange during recovery from experimental deficit of body heat. *Am. J. Physiol., v. 136, Mar. 1, 1942: 105–114.*

Four men sat unclothed in air at 31°C (relative humidity of 20–30%). After drinking 1.5 liters of ice-water (1°–3°C) their bodies became cooler by 0.72 Cal/kg. Heat exchanges were measured during recovery; 85% of this heat debt was paid off within 200 minutes. Half of the heat regained came from reduction in loss by vaporization, the other half came from reduction in loss by radiation and convection. After drinking ice-water, water diuresis was sometimes delayed. Pulse frequency was diminished. No shivering occurred. At a lower environmental temperature of 28°C, recovery was slower.

227. Pi-Suñer, J. The mobilization of water in thermal regulation [In Spanish]. *Ciencia, Méx., v. 1 (6), 1940: 245–253.*

Several aspects of the mobilization of water in thermal regulation, are reviewed by the author, under such subject headings as: exchange in active and passive hypothermia; external temperature and acclimatization; perspiration and evaporation; insensible perspiration; modification of thermal curve after ingestion of water; and, central regulation of temperature.

228. Prouty, L. R. Heat loss and heat production of cats at different environmental temperatures [Abstract]. *Fed. Proc., Balt., v. 8, Mar. 1949: 128–129.*

Studies of shaved, unanesthetized cats in environments of 19°–39°C showed that the cat is a poor subject for the study of human temperature regulation, since man can alter peripheral thermal conductance 5- or 6-fold, while the cat must rely on its fur. In the cold and without fur, the rectal temperature of the cat drops to 35°C, then falls precipitously until death results. At 20° to 24°C, heat loss became 16% greater than heat production. At 38.5°C heat production was 75% greater than heat loss.

229. Randall, W. C. Factors influencing the temperature regulation of birds. *Am. J. Physiol., v. 139, May 1943: 56–63.*

Chicks exposed to an environmental temperature of 10°C exhibit early periodic muscle tremors, vasoconstriction, and an increased respiratory and heart rate. On continued exposure, shivering declines progressively in intensity.

230. Reed, H. E. Climatic control keeps our soldiers warm. *Textile World, v. 94, Nov. 1944: 113–117.*

Protective clothing requirements are discussed in terms of Clo units, each unit of which has ¼-inch insulation value. The Clo unit gives an objective means of measuring the adequacy of clothing. It can be determined in either of two ways: by use of the original formula for measuring the amount of heat lost by the human body through the clothing, or by a straight physical measurement of the resistance which the clothing offers to the transfer of heat. Use of the formula requires considerable metabolic testing of human or dummy subjects in a cold-chamber laboratory. It is not only possible to determine the temperature at which any given Clo value will keep a man comfortable indefinitely but also how long he can withstand the cold if his clothing is insufficient. Also, given the temperature and the length of time of exposure to it, the required Clo value for a suit may be determined. A chart is given showing the approximate efficiency of 1-inch or 2-inch Clo values for several areas of the body.

231. Rees, W. H. The protective value of clothing. *Textile Inst. J., v. 37, July 1946: P132–P153.*

Some of the physiological aspects of protection of the individual against a warm or cold environment, are discussed. Although the deep body temperature is about 37°C at an ordinary room temperature of 20°C, the skin temperature of the trunk will be about 33°C and that of the exposed face and hands about 30°C. Loss of heat from the body to its surroundings takes place by means of radiation, convection, and evaporation of water from the skin and lungs. Insensible perspiration accounts for about 25% of the total loss of heat; 36% of this is lost from the lungs and 64% from the skin. For resting man under normal conditions metabolism has been found to be 58 watts per square meter of body surface or roughly 105 watts for the average size man. For women this figure is roughly 81 watts. Various theoretical considerations for the design of clothing to prevent this flow of heat from the body to its surroundings, are discussed. One of the most important changes in military clothing during World War II has been the abandonment of wool for outer garments in combat clothing. Under severe climatic conditions wool garments did not prevent penetration of wind and had a high moisture absorption quality. The added weight then tended also to fatigue the wearer. Wool is still used for inner clothing under a light-weight, wind-and-water-resistant, close-knit cotton outer garment.

232. Reifferscheid, M. Behavior of heat loss and circulation during anesthesia and operation [In German]. *Arch. klin. Chir., v. 268 (1), 1951: 84–102.*

A highly sensitive thermometric system was devised to measure heat losses from skin, muscle, and deep body areas. These measures, together with blood pressure changes, were used as a warning system against circulatory collapse in a state of shock. Patients under anesthesia during surgery were observed with the aid of this system. The author was unable to confirm earlier experimental findings of others that lack of a rise in skin temperature, before the fall of temperature began, soon after entering the narcotic state was an unfavorable prognosis.

233. Satorius, F., R. Mänicke, and A. Gemecke. Studies on heat dissipation and individual behavior of the skin temperature in clinically healthy persons [In German]. *Arch. Hyg., Münch., v. 119 (5–6), 1938: 271–288.*

Studies were made of the changes in forehead skin temperature of 19 healthy young persons, at environmental temperatures of 9°, 13°, and 18°–22°C in still and slightly moving air. Skin temperatures changed by 2° to 6°C under the various conditions. The minimum of change appeared at 20°C; this was related to the beginning of sweating.

234. Sauberer, F. The chilling index, an approximate measure of the heat exchange of the human body with its environment [In German]. *Wetter u. Leben, v. 1, Aug. 1948: 154–155.*

Thermal sensations in man are not, as is often supposed, dependent only on the temperature of the surrounding air. As a warm-blooded animal, man produces a certain excess of heat, which is continually given off. If the heat loss is great, one experiences chilling; if it is less, if it is lacking altogether, or if heat is added, one experiences warmth or heat. The measurement of heat exchange with the environment must take into account radiation, convection, and evaporation. A table is given which shows a "chilling index" in mg/cal/cm²/ sec at temperatures of −30° to +34°C and wind velocities of 1–11 (Beaufort scale).

235. Scholander, P. F., V. Walters, R. Hock, and L. Irving. Body insulation of some arctic and tropical mammals and birds. *Biol. Bull., Woods Hole, v. 99, Oct. 1950: 225–236.*

Measurements of insulation were made on the raw skin of 16 arctic and 16 tropical mammals. The insulation of the fur correlated well with its thickness. Small-bodied arctic animals had less insulation than the larger ones and were quite similar to tropical animals. Body size, from the fox to the moose, did not correlate closely with insulation. The blubber of the whale insulated about as well in ice water as in 0°C air; the fur of the polar bear in ice water is a very poor insulator since the skin becomes wet and there is no blubber; the fur of the beaver insulates slightly in ice water since it retains an insulating layer of air next to the skin.

236. Schweisheimer, W. Wet textiles in warm and cold weather. *Rayon Text· Month., v. 29, Aug. 1948: 71–72.*

The author quotes from the findings of other workers, stating that smooth linen and cotton textiles are completely devoid of air when wet and act as conductors of heat from the body. Woolen materials, even when wet, contain more than 60% of air. The relative chilling effects produced by wet fabrics is related to the extent of contact between skin and fabric. Wool feels warmer than cotton since the crimped and springy woolen fibers do not touch the skin in as many places as cotton fabric of the same construction. And the larger layer of air between the skin and wool fabric reduced heat loss from the body.

237. Siple, P. A. General principles governing selection of clothing for cold climates, (U.S. Antarctic Service Expedition, 1939–41). *Proc. Am. Philos. Soc., v. 89, Apr. 1945: 200–234.*

The physiological characteristics of thermal output and regulation of the body are discussed. The thermal properties necessary for clothing of suitable insulation value in cold climates are outlined.

238. Spealman, C. R. A characteristic of human temperature regulation. *Proc. Soc. Exp. Biol., N. Y., v. 60 (1), 1945: 11–12.*

When human subjects were immersed in water at 20°, 25°, and 30°C, deep body temperature became stabilized at 36°C. At this temperature the thermoregulatory mechanism initiated shivering to prevent further body cooling.

239. Spealman, C. R. Physiologic adjustments to cold. *In: Physiology of heat regulation and the science of clothing, p. 232–239. Ed. by* L. H. NEWBURGH. *Philadelphia, Saunders, 1949.*

The author discusses the physiological mechanisms of heat loss and heat production; the effects of acute exposure to cold, including vasoconstriction and shivering; and the effects of chronic exposure to cold, including endocrine and metabolic adaptation.

240. Spealman, C. R. Water. *In: Physiology of heat regulation and the science of clothing, p. 370–374. Ed. by* L. H. NEWBURGH. *Philadelphia, Saunders, 1949.*

The discussion is concerned with the physiology of heat loss in water and the problem of protecting men immersed in water from the fatal effects of hypothermia by means of protective clothing.

241. Suzuki, S. Experimental study of abnormal temperature conditions. I. Experimental study on cold-resistance properties of clothing from the standpoint of gas metabolism [In Japanese, summary in English]. *Kosei Kagaku, v. 2, Sept. 1941: 260–287.*

Subjects were exposed to various degrees of cold in a number of different clothing assemblies. The oxygen consumption curve in each case appeared to correlate with the amount of clothing worn.

242. **Suzuki, S.** Experimental study on abnormal temperature conditions. III. Experimental study on cold-resistance properties of clothing from the standpoint of gas metabolism [In Japanese, with English summary]. *Kosei Kagaku, v. 2, Dec. 1941: 444–467.*

No significant changes in gaseous metabolism were noted when subjects, in various types of clothing, were exposed to temperatures ranging from 0°C to −40°C.

243. **Swift, R. W., and R. M. Forbes.** The heat production of the fasting rat in relation to the environmental temperature. *J. Nutrit., v. 18, Sept. 10, 1939: 307–318.*

Heat production of the albino rat in the post-absorptive state was determined in 122 eighthour periods of measurement at temperatures ranging from 7.5° to 35°C. The critical temperature for the fasting rat was found to be 30°C. Percentage of total heat eliminated increased from 7.9% to 59.2%, with the rise in environmental temperature from 7.5°C to 35°C, although the absolute amount of heat eliminated was practically constant up to 31°C, with a definite increase taking place above that temperature.

244. **Tournade, A., R. Raynaud, and G. Chardon.** Acetylcholine and thermal shivering. *C. rend. Soc. biol., Par., v. 130, Jan. 26, 1939: 1307–1309.*

In the chilled dog, intravenous injection of acetylcholine suppressed temporarily the thermal shivering. Adrenaline secreted in abundance by the adrenal glands of the animal—after treatment with atropine—before receiving an intravenous injection of acetylcholine, appeared to give further aid in the suppression of trembling.

245. **Whyte, H. M.** Measurement of heat from skin. *J. Appl. Physiol., v. 4, Oct. 1951: 263–269.*

A simple heat-flow meter is described which consists of a piece of rubber (4 x 4 x 0.15 cm) with thermocouples placed at the center points on both sides, and connected through a switch to a galvanometer. Heat flow is indicated by the temperature drop across the rubber which is placed on the skin. Recordings from the lumbar area suggest that a linear relationship exists between heat loss and difference in temperature between skin and air, even when the skin is exposed to radiant heat. The meter is influenced by the nature of the skin surface and so can not be used successfully for comparing different areas of the body. It can be used to advantage for making comparative measurement in one region and for the estimation of thermal conductance and blood flow of the skin.

246. **Winslow, C. E. A., A. P. Gagge, and L. P. Herrington.** The influence of air movement upon heat losses from the clothed human body. *Am. J. Physiol., v. 127, Oct. 1, 1939: 505–518.*

The influence of air movement upon heat loss from the human body was studied in experiments in which the subjects were exposed for 200 minutes to the following three conditions: (A) temperature, 16.1°C; air movement, 4.6 cm/sec; (B) 19.2°C; 34 cm/sec; (C) 22.8°C; 264 cm/sec. The conditions of series A removed least heat from the body, those of series B the most. The skin temperature of the trunk fell 0.5°C; head temperature, 1°C; skin temperature of the upper extremities, 3°C; skin temperature of the lower extremities, 2°C; and rectal temperature, 0.25°C.

247. **Winslow, C. E. A.** Man's heat exchange with his thermal environment. *In: American Institute of Physics. Temperature, its measurement and control in science and industry. p. 509–521. New York, Reinhold, 1941.*

Physiological heat exchange is discussed under the following headings: heat production in the body; avenues of heat loss from the body; methods of partitional calorimetry; avenues of heat loss under varying environmental conditions; evaporative heat loss; convective heat interchange; radiative heat interchange; storage; physiological control of peripheral blood flow; physiological control of metabolism; physiological control of sweat secretion; physiological adaptation to varying environmental calorie-demand; upper limits of evaporative regulation; significance of the results reviewed above.

248. Yaglou, C. P. Thermal insulation of clothing. *Heating Piping, v. 20, Sept. 1948: 107–110.*

The two principal methods of evaluating insulation of clothing are discussed as they were used for evaluating over-all insulation of cold-weather clothing. Subjects wearing the clothes to be tested were exposed to a suitable temperature in a refrigerated room for 2 or 3 hours until the body cooling rate became nearly steady. The heat-loss-method for evaluating insulation of clothing employed the use of various physiological and physical observations, including skin temperature, rectal temperature, humidity, air movement, air temperature, etc. The temperature-gradient-method required the measurement of gradients on at least fifteen areas of the body using thermocouples sewed into the clothing. Results obtained by the two methods differed by 10–30% probably due to the difficulty of estimating the body heat debt on exposure to cold and partly due to inability to take all major factors into account. Because the adequacy of cold weather apparel depends on insulation obtained over critical body areas, the temperature gradient method, which permits evaluation of insulation over different parts of the body, has an advantage.

249. Young, A. C., L. D. Carlson, and H. L. Burns. Regional heat loss by temperature gradient calorimetry [Abstract]. *Fed. Proc., Balt., v. 9, Mar. 1950: 140.*

Field tests at northern latitudes were made with special suits to test heat loss from various areas of the body, as well as total heat loss, in both unacclimatized and acclimatized (local) persons. Under similar conditions of exposure, the heat loss from peripheral regions of acclimatized persons was maintained at a higher level than that of unacclimatized persons. Results of the total heat losses of the two groups are not given.

250. Zvereva, N., and A. Volkova. Contribution to the methods of studying the thermoregulatory reaction in man. II. Effect of various temperatures and of physiological strain on water secretion by the skin [In Russian]. *Bull. biol. méd. exp. URSS, v. 6 (4), 1938: 486–489.*

The influence of temperature changes on the secretory function was studied in humans by the modified Galeotti method. By this method a cap with tightly adjusting rubber edges was placed on the skin of the epigastric region, a stream of moisture-free air was passed in, and the humidity absorbed by the air was measured. A two-hour exposure at 12 °C was followed by a two-hour exposure at 25 °C, and vice-versa. No essential differences were found in the rate of water secretion when the skin was exposed to cold or heat at the start of experimentation. However, the differences were great after sudden transition to the opposite state following a preliminary exposure to heat or cold. After transition from heat to cold the secretion was increased; after transition from cold to heat it was decreased. It is concluded that sweat secretion by the skin is dependent not only on the new temperature to which the body is exposed but on the preceding thermal influences as well. Since the rate of water secretion by the skin is closely connected with thermoregulation, it is assumed that the above method can be used as an indicator of thermoregulation.

See also items: 144, 334, 347, 358, 361, 367, 663, 821, 829, 833, 884, 985, 1112, 1121, 1126, 1448, 1461, 1531, 1741.

F. Role of Central Nervous System

251. Abe, K., and T. Tachihara. On the location of the temperature-regulating center. II. Actual puncture of the corpus striatum [In Japanese]. *Nippon Yakurigaku Zasshi, v. 40, Mar. 20, 1944: 17–19.*

Description is given of the puncture of the corpus striatum, or of the thalamus, by which an increase in body temperature is produced in some animals.

252. Amin, N. On the dissociation of heat and cold sensory paths in the spinal cord; investigation of case [In English]. *J. R. Egypt. M. Ass., v. 29, May–June 1946: 173–179.*

A case of gradually developing myelitis of the lower dorsal region of the spinal cord, is described in which an area of the skin responded to heat and touch but not to cold and pain. It was shown, therefore, that the heat and cold sensory nerve paths are separated in the spinal cord.

253. Barbour, H. G. Hypothalamic control of water movement in response to environmental temperature. In: The hypothalamus and central levels of autonomic function. *Proc. Ass. Res. Nerv. Ment. Dis., 1940. Res. Publ., v. 20, 1939: 449–485.*

In experiments performed on cats, regulation of body temperature against cold and power to respond to cold by increased osmotic pressure were shown to be centered in the posterior hypothalamus. In experiments on monkeys, water-shifting responses to cold were found to be mediated through the anterior hypothalamic nuclei. The anterior and posterior hypothalami were confirmed respectively as centers for regulation against heat and cold. The anterior hypothalamus was shown to be the seat of the osmotic pressure and specific gravity responses to environmental temperature.

254. Barbour, H. G. Relation of anterior and posterior hypothalamic nuclei to anhydremic responses to cold in monkeys. *Am. J. Physiol., v. 126, July 1939: 425–426.*

It is concluded that in the monkey the water-shifting responses to cold are mediated through the anterior hypothalamic nuclei. The anterior and posterior hypothalami have been confirmed as centers for the regulation against heat and cold respectively.

255. Beaton, L. E., W. A. McKinley, C. M. Berry, and S. W. Ranson. Localization of cerebral center activating heat-loss mechanisms in monkeys. *J. Neurophysiol., v. 4, Sept. 1941: 478–485.*

Local heating of the brain of monkeys, by use of low-voltage, high-frequency current passed between electrodes oriented in the brain, led to the identification—in the preoptic region of the telencephalon between the anterior commissure and the optic chiasma—of a reactive area for temperature control. This area is normally activated by the rising temperature of the blood when the animal is overheated, and in turn activates the mechanisms of heat-loss.

256. Beaton, L. E., C. R. Leininger, and W. A. McKinley. Thermoregulatory pathways in the cat brain stem. *J. Neurophysiol., v. 6, Jan. 1943: 29–35.*

Brain-stem pathways subserving temperature regulation in the cat have been investigated by examining the animal's reaction to a cold (34°F) or hot (120°F) environment, 2 to 5 weeks after producing bilateral lesions at anterior and caudal midbrain, and at pontile levels. Pathways for heat-loss functions appear to be concentrated in the intermediate and lateral part of the dorsal tegmentum at each of the levels studied.

257. Beattie, J. Functional aspects of the hypothalamus. *In: The hypothalamus; morphological, functional, clinical and surgical aspects, p. 70–83. Edinburgh, Oliver and Boyd, 1938.*

In this lecture of the Henderson Trust Series given at The University of Edinburgh in 1936, the author discusses the role of the hypothalamus in body reactions to cold under the following topic headings: shivering, respiration, basal metabolism, pilomotor effects, water metabolism, and effects on bladder and stomach. He describes the results of his own experimental work and that of other investigators.

258. **Biggart, J. H.** The contribution of pathology to our knowledge of the internal environment. *Ulster M. J., v. 17, May 1948: 1–19.*

In this review the author discusses the regulatory roles of the hypothalamus in man, and cites earlier experimental findings and information regarding hypothalamic lesions affecting temperature regulation.

259. **Blair, J. R., and A. D. Keller.** Complete and permanent elimination of the hypothalamic thermogenic mechanism without affecting the adequacy of the heat loss mechanism. *J. Neuropath., v. 5, July 1946: 240–256.*

When the caudal connections of the entire hypothalamic gray matter were severed, the dog was unable to prevent a fall in rectal temperature at ordinary or cool environmental temperatures. Considerable of the ability was retained if only a small part of the caudal gray matter was left undisturbed. Evidence would indicate that at the hypothalamic level there are separate neural elements for shivering and non-shivering thermogenic functions. Some animals retained their control over heat loss but not over heat maintenance at higher environmental temperatures when there was some intact gray matter caudally; in other animals, heat loss was impaired and heat maintenance considerably retained.

260. **Bonvallet, M., and P. Dell.** Description of a technique of transection or crushing of the spinal cord and the transection of the cerebral trunk without general anesthesia, in the dog [In French]. *C. rend. Soc. biol., Par., v. 140, Apr. 1946: 246–248.*

The authors discuss their methods for experimental transection or destruction of the spinal cord, or of decerebration, of dogs, interfering very little with the animal's regulation of body temperature.

261. **Bonvallet, M., and P. Dell.** Thermal regulation of the hypophysectomized dog with a spinal resection [In French]. *C. rend. Soc. biol., Par., v. 140, Dec. 1946: 942–945.*

Dogs which had been subjected to simple hypophysectomy and later to spinal resection (at C_7–C_8 level), were found to be unable to maintain their normal body temperature. In one instance a dog which had been hypophysectomized 6 weeks earlier and then subjected to a resection, experienced a rectal temperature drop from 38° to 36.3°C within ½ hour, at a room temperature of 22°C. An intact animal after a similar procedure, experienced only a slight and transitory rise of rectal temperature (40.5°C) with a return to the pre-operative normal of 39.7°C. This limited number of experiments presents evidence of the necessity of an intact endocrine system in the maintenance of temperature regulation in the dog after spinal resection, and of the intact spinal cord in the hypophysectomized dog. The insufficiency of thermal regulation in the dog both hypophysectomized and with spinal resection is said to be the direct result of the progressive degeneration of the thyroid and adrenal glands following hypophysectomy. In the hypophysectomized dog without spinal resection this insufficiency is compensated for by the use of other thermal regulatory mechanisms—such as shivering—under nervous system control.

262. **Bonvallet, M., P. Dell, F. S. Stutinsky, and M. Beauvallet.** Role of the supraoptico-hypophyseal system in the control of the metabolism of water on the course of the reactions of thermal regulation [In French]. *C. rend. Soc. biol., Par., v. 142, July 1948: 937–941.*

Studies were made of the decrease in diuresis, provoked by ingestion of 300 cm³ of water, by normal animals as the environmental temperature increased (10° to 25° to 40° C). In the same animals one month after an experimental hypothalamic lesion (to interrupt the nerve fascia of the supraoptic-hypophyseal area) a very small urinary output, similar for all environmental temperatures, could be provoked by a similar ingestion of water. In hypophysectomized animals who were suffering a marked diabetes insipidus, the diuresis provoked was of similar magnitude but in reverse order (being greatest at the highest temperature) from that of normal animals. The authors conclude that there exists a regulation, in the supraoptic area, of water metabolism mediated through the neurohypophysis and its secretions, in connection with the normal regulation of temperature by the hypothalamus.

263. **Bonvallet, M., P. Dell, and F. S. Stutinsky.** Observations concerning the physiology of the anterior hypothalamus (water metabolism, physical thermoregulation, emotional behavior). *Rapports de Association des physiologistes de langue française, Montpellier, 31 May–1, 2 June 1949: 133A–135A (J. physiol. path. gen., v. 41 (2, fasc. 1), 1949).*

Various experimental findings including those on dogs with experimental brain lesions, lead the author to conclude that differences in water distribution between the blood serum and the tissue fluids, in renal and thermoregulatory functioning during temperature changes, are a direct result of the phenomenon of physical temperature regulation. These activities are regulated by the functioning of the supraoptico-hypophyseal area of the brain.

264. **Bonvallet, M., and E. Morel.** Season variations of the composition of the blood of the dog. Role of the supra-optic postpituitary system [In French]. *C. rend. Soc. biol., Par, v. 144, Mar. 1950: 383–386.*

Continuous studies on a group of normal dogs indicated the existence of an important seasonal variation in the blood hematocrit. Variations in serum proteins paralleled those of the hematocrit; in effect, the density of the serum was greater in November through January, was less in May, and greater again in July. These results confirm those of earlier workers who also noted the marked increase in density of the plasma during the winter. Enervation of the neurohypophysis, as a consequence of a hypothalamic sectioning of the fiber bundles of the supra-optic posthypophysis, altered this seasonal variation. It is concluded that these studies have indicated a new example of the synergism manifested at the level of the hypothalamus between the centers for regulation of water metabolism and the thermal regulatory centers. It appears probable that, although previous experimental findings are lacking on this subject, the seasonal variations of the blood composition and mass are an effect to facilitate certain reactions assuring the maintenance of the central temperature of the homeothermic subject to wide variations of environmental temperature and constitute a veritable regulation. This regulation, like that of renal secretion, is a function of the variations of environmental temperature, and, perhaps in part—thanks to this renal regulation—functions as an intermediary of the secretion of the posterior lobe of the pituitary, without hypothalamic control.

265. **Brenning, R., and E. Hultman.** How does the warming of the brain by short wave treatment affect the warmth regulation of man? [In German]. *Upsala läk. fören. förh., v. 47 (5–6), 1942: 305–312.*

Temperature regulation was studied following short wave radiation (diathermy) directed toward the hypothalamic area of the head. Neither rectal temperature nor mouth temperature was influenced in any uniform way. Respiratory frequency increased and the volume of the inspiration decreased. Blood vessels of the skin dilated through central nervous impulse. In several instances, sweating occurred. Oxygen consumption was not changed in any uniform way during the course of the experiment or one-half hour later.

266. **Brobeck, J. R.** Mechanism of the development of obesity in animals with hypothalamic lesions. *Physiol. Rev., v. 26, Oct. 1946: 541–559.*

Injuries of the hypothalamus are discussed, in which consumption of abnormally large amounts of food without similar high levels of work output and heat production, result in large amounts of stored energy and in obesity. From these studies and others of injuries to the hypothalamus—especially those effecting temperature regulation—the author states that it would seem that the hypothalamus normally participates in the maintenance of the overall energy equilibrium, and that the control of food intake, work output, and body temperature may be correlated and integrated within this portion of the diencephalon.

267. **Brooks, C.** The regulation of body temperature. *Med. J. Australia, 1948 (v. 1), Feb. 21: 221–227.*

The physiological factors in temperature regulation are discussed, together with review of the information on the two areas of the hypothalamus which are thought to govern heat dissipation and heat production respectively. From these regions impulses pass to the hypophysis and the motor nerves which control the effector organs involved in activities essential to temperature regulation.

268. **Buchanan, A. R., and R. M. Hill.** Temperature regulation in albino rats correlated with determinations of myelin density in the hypothalamus. *Proc. Soc. Exp. Biol., N. Y., v. 66, Dec. 1947: 602–608.*

Studies of temperature regulation in rats 6–7 days old while exposed to cold (5°–8°C), correlated with the post-mortem examination of the hypothalami, led the authors to believe that myelination in the hypothalamus is one of the factors concerned in temperature regulation.

269. **Buchanan, A. R., and R. M. Hill.** Myelination of the hypothalamus and its relation to thermoregulation in the hamster. *Proc. Soc. Exp. Biol., N. Y., v. 71, 1949: 126–129.*

Temperature regulation in cold environments (5°–8°C) is acquired by hamsters at ages ranging from 30–44 days. Photometrical determination of myelination in the caudal hypothalamus shows that myelination reaches its height at the time thermoregulation becomes fully developed. It is thought, accordingly, that myelination of hypothalamic neurons may be essential to functional maturation of the hypothalamus.

270. **Buck, C. W., H. C. Carscallen, and G. E. Hobbs.** Temperature regulation in schizophrenia. I. Comparison of schizophrenic and normal subjects. II. Analysis by duration of psychosis. *Arch. Neur. Psychiat., Chic., v. 64, Dec. 1950: 828–842.*

Temperature regulation was found to be disturbed in schizophrenics, particularly in the early and acute stage of the disease. Although rectal temperature response to hot baths was quite similar in the two groups, the response to cold baths was very different in the schizophrenics when compared with the normals. The patients showed a significantly lower value for the mean daily range of temperature and for the day-night differential, and a much wider variation in the time of day of both the maximum and minimum temperature. These results agree with the assumption that temperature regulation in the schizophrenic is modified by dysfunction at the cortical or hypothalamic level.

271. **Buck, C. W., H. C. Carscallen, and G. E. Hobbs.** Effect of prefrontal lobotomy on temperature regulation in schizophrenic patients. *Arch. Neur. Psychiat., Chic., v. 65, Feb. 1951: 197–205.*

The temperature regulation of 40 schizophrenic patients, which had been quite irregular, was found to be closer to the normal following lobotomy. The change was greatest in the patients with early psychoses who had shown the greatest irregularity. It is suggested that the preoperative abnormality of regulation resulted from the disturbing influence of the prefrontal cortex on the lower autonomic centers.

272. **Cate, J., ten.** The influence of the central nervous system on warmth regulation [In German]. *Ned. tschr. geneesk., v. 86, 1942: 638–644.*

This is a review article on the role of the central nervous system, especially the hypothalamic area, in temperature regulation.

273. Chatfield, P. O. and C. P. Lyman. Circulatory changes during process of arousal in the hibernating hamster. *Am. J. Physiol., v. 163, Dec. 1950: 566–574.*

During arousal from hibernation of the hamster, the following phenomena were observed: increase of heart rate, increase of velocity of conduction of cardiac impulse, increase in blood pressure, cutaneous vasoconstriction differential between the fore and hind part of the body, activation of the somatic muscular system, and great increase in oxygen consumption. Observation of these phenomena and others lead to the hypothesis that the process of arousal is essentially a mass activation of the centers of the hypothalamus which govern heat production and conservation and which give rise to maximal functional activity of the sympathico-adrenal and somatic motor systems.

274. Chatonnet, J. Thermogenesis and thermoregulation in the dog in the absence of the principal controlling nerves [In French]. *J. physiol., Par., v. 43 (4), 1951: 678–680.*

Experiments on dogs with the spinal cord severed at the dorsal, lumbar, or sacral levels confirmed the findings of other workers that the dogs continued to possess a considerable thermoregulatory ability under conditions of not too severe cold. In the current experiments, some of the dogs were given a high-level medullary resection with bilateral severing also of the brachial plexus and cervical plexus to eliminate as much as possible the intervention of shivering. Only the muscles of the nape of the neck and of the face retained their nerve connections. Tests in a cold room ($-10\,°C$) led to a continuing lowering of rectal temperature and heat production was increased only about 1.5 to 2 times that of basal rate. Animals with a simple medullary resection under the same conditions experienced a decided increase in metabolic rate. It is thought that the trouble is connected uniquely with the suppression of shivering through the anterior pathway and not to the concomitant cutaneous anesthesia; in effect the sensibility to cold of the face and that of the centers themselves are sufficient to provoke a rise in the metabolic rate to the level of moderate cold. The thermogenetic power of shivering appears very great since it is shivering of a very restricted area which assures the very effective temperature regulation of the dog.

275. Chatonnet, J. Thermogenesis of re-warming in the dog in absence of the spinal cord [In French]. *C. rend. Soc. biol., Par., v. 145, Aug. 1951: 1181–1182.*

Dogs, which had had their spinal cords crushed at the level of D1, were confined in a thermal chamber ($-15°$ to $35\,°C$) with observations being made over a period of 20 to 90 days on their ability to regulate their body temperature. Following gas exchange studies a curve was determined for heat production in calories/kg/hr as a function of the ambient temperature. Basal metabolism was found to have increased about 20 to 30 %; neutral thermal temperature was, in general, higher. In the cold there was a great increase in heat production. This transection of the spinal cord, by excluding vasomotor functioning, eliminated the peripheral vasoconstriction in response to cold, and hence thermoregulation by chemical factors played a major role. The exclusion of the adrenaline component did not seem to seriously affect regulation at these temperatures.

276. Chatonnet, J. Importance of shivering in the thermogenesis in a dog with spinal cord destruction [In French]. *C. rend. Soc. biol., Par., v. 145, Oct. 1951: 1538–1540.*

The author continues with his earlier experiments on dogs (same journal, p. 1181–1182). In the current experiments dogs were subjected not only to spinal resection but to bilateral severance of the cervical plexus, the brachial plexus, and motor nerves so that the paralysis obtained was almost complete leaving only the masticator muscles and those at the nape of the neck. The metabolic rate is at first elevated, reaches a plateau with a maximum of 1.5 to 2 times that of the basal metabolic rate, and then decreases. When subjected to a cold environment for an hour or less, the rectal temperature lowers very quickly by $2°–5\,°C$ and then maintains more or less the same level as that of animals with only a medullary resection. Thermal regulation is fairly satisfactory at normal environmental temperatures but is not adequate in severe cold. It is, however, the total capacity of thermogenesis which is diminished not an impairment of the regulatory apparatus. The cutaneous anesthesia which is the result of the surgery does not seem to suppress the temperature regulation; the very important sensitivity of the area of the muzzle continues to exist. The capacity to produce heat even at an environmental temperature of $-10\,°C$ is remarkable when one considers the importance of the loss of all adrenal secretory functioning and of shivering in all but the small area of the head and the nape of the neck. Results of other workers are mentioned and the question is raised whether the suppression of shivering under control by the anterior brain is sufficient to explain the difference in behavior of animals with a cervical, from that of a thoracic, resection of the spinal column. It is known that thermal shivering affects in a preferential manner the anterior portion of the body.

277. **Clark, G., H. W. Magoun, and S. W. Ranson.** Hypothalamic regulation of body temperature. *J. Neurophysiol.*, *v. 2.*, *Jan. 1939: 61–80.*

Marked disturbances of the temperature-regulating mechanism in cats was noted when the hypothalamus was subjected to extensive experimental injury.

278. **Clark, G., H. W. Magoun, and S. W. Ranson.** Temperature regulation in cats with thalamic lesions. *J. Neurophysiol.*, *v. 2*, *May 1939: 202–207.*

Experimental lesions were made bilaterally in the medial nuclei of the thalamus of the diencephalon in each of 9 cats. These injuries to the thalamus caused no obvious disturbance of temperature regulation when the cats were exposed to heat ($104\,°F$) or cold ($40\,°F$). Thermal and decorticate panting were not eliminated by destruction of the caudo-dorsal portion of the medial thalamus. At the level of the mammillary bodies, descending paths from the hypothalamus which are concerned with temperature regulation were located near the ventral surface of the brain. Although the hypothalamus has been shown to play an important part in temperature regulation, the remainder of the diencephalon, including the thalamus, would not appear to participate in this function.

279. **Clark, G.** Temperature regulation in chronic cervical cats. *Am. J. Physiol.*, *v. 130*, *Oct. 1940: 712–722.*

Cats with the lower cervical cord transected, were unable to make the adjustments necessary for maintaining a normal body temperature when a sudden fall in environmental temperature occurred. These animals were, however, able to make a limited slow adjustment to cold, a sort of acclimatization, which was lost when the animals were again kept in a warmer environment. The adjustment was probably due to an increase in metabolic rate.

280. **Davison, C.** Disturbances of temperature regulation in man; a clinicopathologic study. In: The hypothalamus and central levels of autonomic function. *Proc. Ass. Res. Nerv. Ment. Dis.*, *1939*. *Res. Publ.*, *v. 20*, *1940: 774–823.*

Clinical data is given on temperature disturbances observed in 10 cases of hypothalamic tumor. In 4 patients exhibiting hyperthermia, the lesions were in the rostral part of the hypothalamus and involved bilaterally the nerve cells of the lateral parts. In 1 patient exhibiting hyperthermia, the caudal hypothalamus was affected, and there was a possible involvement of the descending hypothalamic pathways or compression of the rostral and lateral hypothalamic area. In 4 cases exhibiting hypothermia, the lesions extended to the caudal part of the hypothalamus and involved bilaterally the nerve cells of the lateral parts. In the 10th case the tumor affected the entire hypothalamic region, and the patient exhibited poikilothermy.

281. **Delgado, J. M. R., and R. B. Livingston.** Some respiratory, vascular and thermal responses to stimulation of orbital surface of frontal lobe. *J. Neurophysiol.*, *v. 11*, *Jan. 1948: 39–55.*

Electrical stimulation of the surgically exposed orbital surface of the frontal lobe of the brain of dogs or monkeys resulted in certain blood pressure, respiratory, and thermal responses. Thermal excitation of the cortex of the orbital surface resulted in a rapid rise of $6\,°–8\,°F$ in the temperature of the extremities.

282.   Dott, N. M. Surgical aspects of the hypothalamus. *In: The hypothalamus; morphological, functional, clinical, and surgical aspects, p. 174–177. Edinburgh, Oliver and Boyd, 1938.*

In this lecture of the Henderson Trust Series, given at The University of Edinburgh in 1936, the author discusses regulation of body temperature. He cites two cases of hyperthermia which were associated with lesions of the hypothalamus. Patients with typical hypothalamic hyperthermia evidenced both increased heat-production and deficient heat-loss. Since the high metabolic rate continued in hyperthermia, although artificial methods of body cooling reduced the body temperature to normal, treatment was unsatisfactory. Hypothalamic hypothermia, on the other hand, was satisfactorily treated by artificial heating and by administration of Pituitrin.

283.   Forster, R. E., II, and T. B. Ferguson. Relationship between hypothalamic temperature and thermoregulatory effectors in unanesthetized cat [Abstract]. *Fed. Proc., Balt., v. 10, Mar. 1951: 44.*

Variations of hypothalamic temperature were studied in each of a group of 8 cats after a small thermistor on the end of a glass needle was permanently affixed in the hypothalamus. Hypothalamic temperature varied from 0.52°C above to 1.2°C below rectal temperature and showed many irregular non-rhythmic variations. Deep peritoneal sodium pentobarbital anesthesia eliminated small variations in temperature and rendered the animal relatively poikilothermic. Rest tended to lower temperature; exercise or excitement to increase it. Data from further observation and experimentation, appear to be consistent with the hypothesis that, in most unanesthetized cats, panting is primarily controlled by hypothalamic temperature while thermoregulatory vasomotor reactions, within the limits of the test, are not.

284.   Frankl, V. E. On the genesis of temperature increases after encephalography [In German]. *Wien. klin. Wschr., v. 60, Mar. 12, 1948: 166.*

Two main theories are advanced to account for the rise in body temperature which occurs following encephalography: the one being that the rise of temperature is merely an artificial, aseptic, symptom resulting from the manipulation of the meninges; the other, that it is because of a direct stimulation of the heat-producing center in the area of the third ventricle through the filling with air involved in the techniques. Investigation of patients at a neurological clinic indicated that there was no fever reaction following the air filling of only the subarachnoid space but that in all cases air filling of only the ventricle brought about a temperature rise. In a discussion following this short paper, it was stated that the findings of another investigator did not follow such a clear-cut pattern.

285.   Fulton, J. F. Physiology of the nervous system. 3rd ed., revised. *New York, Oxford Univ., 1949. 667p.*

The role of the hypothalamus in heat regulation (p. 250–253) is discussed. Since the mechanisms of heat production are activated by the posterior hypothalamus, it follows that they are primarily governed by adrenergically innervated (sympathetic) structures coupled with the somatically-controlled shivering reflex. Heat loss, on the other hand, is primarily governed by cholinergic (parasympathetic) mechanisms including sweating, vasodilatation, etc., coupled with the somatic reaction of panting. The function of maintaining the temperature of the body at a constant level is thus made possible through the operation of a series of highly integrated reactions involving the entire nervous system, i.e., both divisions of the autonomic system and somatic reflexes of shivering and panting. The focal center of this complex integration lies in the hypothalamus but is influenced by all levels of the cerebro-spinal axis.

286.   Gastaldi, E. The thermoregulatory centers. Clinical data [In Italian]. *Nevrasse, Tor., v. 1, Sept.–Oct. 1940: 341–358* [Abstracts in Italian, German, French, and English, in: *Med. sper., Tor., v. 8(2), 1941: 105–106.*]

Clinical findings indicated that the localization of brain tumors which had previously been known to interfere with the thermoregulatory centers, usually had been found to be in the diencephalon-hypophyseal area.

287. **Geurra (Perez-Carral), F., and J. R. Brobeck.** The hypothalamic control of aspirin antipyresis in the monkey. *J. Pharm. Exper. Ther., v. 80, Mar. 1944: 209–216.*

A marked lability of temperature regulation appeared in monkeys after anterior and anterolateral lesions had been made surgically in the hypothalamus. This instable state, which was temporary, was especially evident in febrile animals and in response to a hot environment. The lesions did not alter the rate of decline of fever produced by yeast injection or by aspirin administration. With bilateral lesions well localized in the anterior and lateral regions of the hypothalamus, the monkey experienced a hypothermia lasting several days or even weeks. It is noted that Ranson rarely found such a reaction after this type of lesion but found it frequently after posterior lesions.

288. **Hermann, H., G. Morin, and P. Galy.** Efficacy of thermoregulation in the course of chilling of the "spinal" dog [In French]. *C. rend. Soc. biol., Par., v. 127, Mar. 21, 1938: 1491–1492.*

Normal rectal temperature was maintained for 90 minutes in an environmental temperature of $7°–12°C$ by dogs with the spinal cord transected but with the vagus nerves untouched. When the vagus nerves were transected, the temperature dropped $1°C$ but rose to normal on transfer of the animals to normal room temperature.

289. **Hermann, H., F. Jourdan, G. Morin, and J. Vial.** Preservation of the thermoregulatory reaction in spinal-resected dogs, bistellectomized then bi-vagotomized [In French]. *C. rend. Soc. biol., Par., v. 132, May 15, 1939: 11–12.*

In a normal environmental temperature ($18°–21°C$), with a spinal resection and with a right side vagotomy—in spite of the exclusion of the stellate ganglions and of the right pneumogastric—but before left cervical vagotomy, dogs so treated behaved in a similar manner to dogs with only a spinal resection. The day after the spinal resection the dogs were infirm with some impairment of rewarming ability. This difference in rewarming was noted following exposure to cold ($10°–2.5°C$ for 36–70 minutes). Left vagal resection, about 89 days following spinal resection, brought about death after a brief delay because of acute difficulties of swallowing. In two instances on the first and second day after left vagal resection, rewarming was done and the general state of the animals was good demonstrating that the final vagal resection did not immediately bring a modification of the animal's aptitude to protect itself against cold exposure. These findings are said to confirm those with spinal resected and vagotomized dogs, and, because of the added stellectomy, to indicate that the thermoregulatory capacities which survive after spinal resection can not be attributed to the persistence of nervous pathways by means of these ganglia or to the bringing into play of extra-medullary means.

290. **Hermann, H., G. Morin, and J. Vial.** Thermal equilibrium and thermo-regulation on the first days following spinal cord destruction in the dog [In French]. *C. rend. Soc. biol., Par., v. 36, 1942: 228–230.*

A short time after experimental surgical resection of the spinal cord at a dorsal, lumbar, or sacral level, either guinea pigs or dogs were found to be able to maintain their thermal equilibrium at ordinary laboratory temperatures; they experienced difficulties only when exposed to severe cold. However, in the first days after a resection, an acute insufficiency in temperature regulation was noted. This period was comprised of two variable, but always distinct, phases. The initial phase, which in general extended over the first 24–36 hours after the resection, was characterized by an almost total failure of temperature regulation. It was necessary to place the dogs in a warming cabinet at a temperature ($37°–39°C$) of approximately thermal neutrality. In the second phase, the capacity to resist cold was gradually increased and use of the warming chamber was unnecessary if the laboratory temperature was in the vicinity of $20°C$. Two theories were postulated to explain this phenomenon, which rarely lasts more than 3 days; that a supplementary mechanism for temperature regulation is in the process of developing, or that the period of thermal instability is that needed for dissipation of shock. Experimental findings tend to favor the latter explanation but do not exclude possible intervention with the central regulation of temperature.

291. Hess, W. R. Vegetative functioning and the diencephalon [In German, English summary]. *Helv. physiol. pharm. acta., Suppl. IV, 1947: 1–65.*

Experimental findings in cats and a detailed study of the physiological functioning of the diencephalon, as mediated by the sympathetic and parasympathetic nervous system, are discussed. Some study is made of the hypothalamus in its role of temperature regulation.

292. Issekutz, B., Jr. The temperature regulation after severing of the cervical spinal cord [In German]. *Pflügers Arch., v. 247 (2–3), 1943: 204–221.*

Changes in temperature regulation were studied in dogs with the cervical spinal cord severed at the C-VIII level. Metabolism of the hind legs was studied by means of blood flow and the arterio-venous oxygen differences in blood vessels in the legs. Cooling the nose and neck of the dogs by means of ice bags, 2–3 days after severing of the spinal cord, decreased the metabolism of the leg. Direct cooling of the leg by means of cold and wet cloths (13°–14°C) increased the metabolism of the leg. Two or three days after spinal resection the latter reaction had disappeared, but it reappeared 3–5 days later. Cooling of one leg only increased the metabolism of the other leg after rectal temperature had dropped 0.5°–1.0°C. The same reaction appeared after destruction of the lumbo-sacral cord. The author concludes that after these spinal cord resections the regulation of temperature is accomplished by those connections (vago sympathetic, N. Vertebrales) between the central nervous system and the peripheral which are still in existence.

293. Issekutz, B., Jr., G. Hetényi, H. Nagy, and M. Lung. Temperature regulation of the denervated limb [In English]. *Hungar. acta physiol., v. 2 (1–4), 1949: 93–103.*

The denervated limb of dogs, whose thoracic spinal cord was transected, showed an increase of the metabolic rate of 30–50%, when the upper part of the body was cooled by application of ice to the neck and chest. This increase could be abolished by narcotics and it was concluded that the remaining temperature regulation had been established by excitation of the temperature-regulating center. The humoral temperature regulation was found to represent only about 10% of the total capacity of the chemical temperature-regulation.

294. Keller, A. D. Separation in the brain stem of the mechanisms of heat loss from those of heat production. *J. Neurophysiol., v. 1, Nov. 1938: 543–557.*

From his experimental findings on dogs and cats, the author states that the structural elements in the cephalic brain stem subserving the mechanisms of heat loss and heat production have separate anatomical locations, the former extending further caudally than does the latter. Although activation of the mechanisms of heat loss and heat production are quite independent, a reciprocal innervation exists between the two.

295. Keller, A. D., and J. R. Blair. Further observations on the distribution at the level of the pons of descending nerve fibers subserving heat regulating functions. *Am. J. Physiol., v. 147, Nov. 1, 1946: 500–508.*

The heat regulating functions were studied in dogs in which the brain stem, approximately at the level of the pons, had been severed by a lateral hemisection. Both the heat loss and heat maintenance function were preserved if the hemisection was made on one side only. No asymmetry could be detected between the two sides of the body in caliber of the blood vessels or in shivering. Extension of the transection toward the opposite side abolished heat maintenance before it affected the heat loss function, indicating that the heat loss fibers are more lateral in distribution than are the heat maintenance fibers. Application of a second hemisection on the opposite side eliminated heat regulation completely and permanently. These results suggest that there is no subsidiary medullary heat regulating center in the medulla.

296. Keller, A. D. Descending nerve fibers subserving heat maintenance functions coursing with the cerebrospinal tracts through the pons. *Am. J. Physiol., v. 154, July 1, 1948: 82–86.*

When the dorsal brain stem of dogs was transected at the level of the pons, except for the pyramidal bundles as they become exteriorized at the caudal extent of the pons, it was found that the heat-maintaining mechanism—tested against environmental temperatures of 3° to 10°C—was not eliminated.

297. Kleyntjens, F. Studies on the physiopathology of the thermoregulatory centers [In French]. *C. rend. Soc. biol., Par., v. 132, June 24, 1939: 55–59.*

Studies were made of changes in thermal responses of rabbits after they had undergone surgically-produced punctures of the diencephalon. Immediately following surgery, there was a diminution of the respiratory rate. A generalized and violent shivering began and persisted throughout the 4-hour period of one experiment; the rectal temperature rose rapidly and the respiratory rate then increased. Vasoconstriction and shivering occurred despite a high temperature. Thermal polypnea did not begin until after an exposure to cold of 10 minutes and ceased after return to earlier environmental temperature. The acute vasodilatation provoked by cold was noted in the immediate high rise of the cutaneous temperature. Injections of calcium chloride at the site of the puncture brought about an immediate vasodilatation, a muscular hypotonia, and a rapid decrease in rectal temperature. The hyperthermic reactions described, similar to those following injection of a pyretic (antityphus vaccine), are thought to be caused by nervous excitation of the hypothalamus since they can be controlled by nervous system depressant drugs. The lessening or lack of a thermolytic response (despite the distinct elevation of the central temperature) from the neighboring area of the diencephalon is postulated as being brought about by the subordination of this synergistic center to that bringing about thermogenesis and caloric retention.

298. McCrum, W. R., and W. R. Ingram. The effect of morphine on cats with hypothalamic lesions. *J. Neuropath., v. 10, Apr. 1951: 190–203.*

Cats showed a loss of temperature control and manifested a chronic somnolence after they had been treated to produce experimental lesions in the caudal area of the hypothalamus, and in the upper tegmentum. Their response to injection of morphine was greatly altered; hyperthermia and hyperactivity did not appear.

299. Magoun, H. W., F. Harrison, J. R. Brobeck, and S. W. Ranson. Activation of heat loss mechanisms by local heating of the brain. *J. Neurophysiol., v. 1, Mar. 1938: 101–114.*

Extensive experimental exploration of the forebrain and midbrain of the cat—by use of low-voltage, high-frequency current passing between electrodes oriented with the Horsley-Clarke apparatus—led to the identification of specific areas of the brain which are reactive to local heating. These areas were found to be in the telencephalon and in the diencephalon (in the dorsal part of the hypothalamus and the ventral part of the thalamus). The results are interpreted as indicating that these areas contain structures which help to regulate the body temperature, by loss of heat, through their activation by the rising temperature of the blood.

300. Mansfeld, G., and E. Mészáros. On the absence of thermoregulation independent of the thermoregulatory center [In German]. *Arch. exp. Path., Berl., v. 196 (6), 1940: 609–622.*

Experimental study was made to establish whether an independent thermoregulation existed apart from the thermal centers of the hypothalamic area. The spinal cord of rabbits was resected at the neck or in the thoracic region. Measurements were made of the body temperature and respiratory exchanges at various environmental temperatures. At normal room temperature, both groups of surgically-treated animals preserved their normal body temperature. A cooling of the room to 15°–16°C, however, induced a decrease in body temperature by 2.5° to 3.5°C; at a room temperature of 4°C, by 5.5°–6°C in a few hours in both groups of animals. Cooling or warming of the lower half of the body did not induce any thermoregulatory regulation in either group, even when the body temperature decreased to 34°C; in the controls the oxygen consumption increased by 70–80%. This excludes the existence of a chemical thermoregulation independent of the central nervous system. Cooling of the whole body at a room temperature of 15°–18°C increased oxygen consumption, showing a very active chemical thermoregulation in the non-denervated half of the body. In animals with a cervical resection, a 24-hour period of fasting induced in all the cases a drop of body temperature to 28°C (limit of endurance) at room temperature; feeding restored the body temperature to normal in a few hours. The body temperature of such animals is therefore entirely dependent upon feeding. It was found that in the animals with a thoracic resection the oxygen consumption had greatly increased after the operation, showing a permanent increase in heat production, while in the animals with cervical resection it remained unchanged. These findings were also verified in dogs. Thyroidectomy induced a gradual decrease in oxygen consumption in the group with thoracic resections but not in the other. It is concluded that a cerebrospinal resection below the first thoracic vertebra induces a powerful increase in oxygen consumption, which is independent from heat loss, not related to thermoregulation, and is abolished by thyroidectomy. Cervical resection severs the thyroid innervation. Thoracic resection of the spinal cord severs only the inhibiting thyroid nerves, so that an uninhibited thyroid action raises combustion and simulates a thermoregulation that is independent of central innervation.

301. Miller, H. R. Central autonomic regulations in health and disease with special reference to the hypothalamus. *N. Y., Grune & Stratton, 1942. 430p.*

The role of the autonomic nervous system in the regulation of body temperature is discussed. Included in the discussion is the role of the hypothalamus in governing temperature control. Evidence is drawn from experimental and clinical cases of hyperthermia and hypothermia. The relationship of the hypothalamus to sweating, metabolic rate, circulation, and other phenomena is outlined. References concerned with the possible role of other parts of the brain (cortex, and other areas of the third ventricle) in temperature regulation are considered. There is some discussion of the relationship of pharmacodynamic substances such as chloral hydrate, isopral, Luminal, Nembutal, and Veronal to temperature regulation and the hypothalamus.

302. Morin, G. Efficacy of thermoregulation in the course of chilling of the guinea pig with the spinal cord transected [In French]. *C. rend. Soc. biol., Par., v. 127, Mar. 21, 1938: 1498–1500.*

Temperature regulation of guinea pigs was shown to be abolished when the spinal cord was transected at the thoraco-lumbar or sacral levels.

303. Popova, N. A. The role of the hypothalamic area in the thermoregulation of the adult and growing body [In Russian]. *Kharkov, Institut i T͡Sentral'nyĭ Psikhonefrologischesiĭ, 1940. 183 p.*

In order to determine and localize the thermoregulatory function of the hypothalamus, several of its parts corresponding to histologically-determined centers were destroyed surgically in 25 dogs. After autopsy, the brains were examined histologically at the site of injury. A similar study was conducted on 47 puppies at various stages of development. Histological studies were also done, after death and autopsy, on the brains of 20 human embryos of various stages of development and on infants up to 6 months of age. The thermoregulatory function was also studied in 31 children from 3 months to 6 years of age; the skin-visceral apparatus (perspiration, reflex dermographism, and pilomotor reflex) in 100 children from a few days to 1½ years of age. Observations affirmed the role of the hypothalamic region in thermoregulation and established the absence of localized thermoregulatory "centers" in any limited portion of it. Destruction of the caudal portion of the hypothalamus produces a hypothermic reaction; of the rostral portion, a hyperthermic. Isolated injury to the central gray matter of the hypothalamic region (when the nuclei are preserved) disrupts thermoregulation. Histological studies of the brain showed that the development of the hypothalamic region is completed in puppies only in the second month, which accounts for the lack of thermo-regulation up to this age. In humans, as in the dog, the cells of the hypothalamic nuclei develop before the cells of the central gray matter, which remain immature even in 6 months-old infants. Up to the second or third year, a child remains thermolabile; the pilomotor reflex appears only at the age of $1\frac{1}{2}$ years.

304. Ranson, S. W., C. Fisher, and W. R. Ingram. Hypothalamic regulation of temperature in the monkey. *Arch. Neur. Psychiat.*, *Chic.*, *v. 38, Sept. 1938: 445–466.*

Monkeys were found not to possess a very stable or efficient temperature-regulating mecha-nism, the rectal temperature varying, under normal laboratory conditions, from 100° to 101.5°F, and increasing very rapidly as a result of emotional excitement or of struggling. At moderately low environmental temperatures (64 to 68°F) a slight drop occurred in rectal temperatures; however, at higher than average environmental temperatures, the rectal temperature quickly rose, with temperatures of 102°F and above causing a dangerous rise in rectal temperature. Experimental lesions of the hypothalamus, made by the Horsley Clarke stereotaxic instrument, caused either transient hyperthermia or more prolonged hypothermia in the monkeys. In animals with hyperthermia, the lesions were confined to the rostral part of the hypothalamus; with hypothermia, the lesions were observed to extend backward to the level of the mammillary nuclei. Monkeys which had recovered sufficiently from hypo-thermia to maintain normal body temperatures under normal temperatures—often not until a month after the operation—were still unable to compensate normally at high or low room temperatures.

305. Ranson, S. W. and H. W. Magoun. The hypothalamus [In English]. *Ergeb. der Physiol.*, *v. 41, 1939: 56–163.*

This comprehensive review article on the hypothalamus has a section on Temperature Regulation (p. 142–163) which is part of and is listed in the table of contents under Lesions in the Hypothalamus. The authors discuss experimental findings of themselves and other workers; explain the neural anatomy of the areas involved; and conclude that the hypo-thalamus and the preoptic regions of the brain play leading roles in the regulation of body temperature. 308 refs.

306. Ranson, S. W. The hypothalamus as a thermostat regulating body tem-perature. *Psychosomat. M.*, *v. 1, Oct. 1939: 486–495.*

Observations on the impairment of temperature regulation caused by experimental hypo-thalamic lesions in cats led to the conclusion that the center at the base of the brain which controls temperature regulation has separate areas for control of heat loss and of heat gain.

307. Ranson, S. W., G. Clark, and H. W. Magoun. The effect of hypothalamic lesions on fever induced by intravenous injection of typhoid-paratyphoid vac-cine. *J. Laborat. Clin. M.*, *v. 25, Nov. 1939: 160–168.*

Normal cats respond to intravenous injection of typhoid-paratyphoid vaccine with a cyclic response in which first the heat-preservation mechanism then the heat-loss mechanism pre-dominates. In none of the 21 cats with chronic lesions of the hypothalamus, who were similarly injected, was there any increase in the heighth or steepness of the slope of the fever curve; twelve of these cats showed marked and prolonged falls (3° to 11°F) lasting for 20 or more hours. Such a hypothermic reaction did not prevent the animals from giving a febrile reaction to injection with other material. The authors state that the part of the heat-loss mechanism which is activated by the injection of the vaccine does not lie in the hypothalamus but some-where caudal to it.

308. Ranson, S. W. Regulation of body temperature. In: The hypothalamus and central levels of autonomic function. *Proc. Ass. Res. Nerv. Ment. Dis., 1939. Res. Publ.*, *v. 20, 1940: 342–399.*

The hypothalamus is the center of integration of the control, by the central nervous system, of the body temperature. Although all of the brain in front of the hypothalamus can be re-

moved in experimental animals without affecting this regulation, the removal of the hypothalamus practically abolishes this control. Injury to the hypothalamus also greatly impairs
this control since the various areas regulate the caliber of the cutaneous blood vessels, the
erection of hair, the ability to pant, or, quite possibly, the ability to sweat. Interrupting the
descending pathways from the hypothalamus to the sympathetic nervous system by transection
of the cervical spinal cord almost abolishes this control. A supplementary very slow adjustment,
apparently hormonal in nature, enables such experimental animals to maintain normal body
temperature within fairly normal limits of environmental temperature.

309.   Riddoch, G. Clinical aspects of hypothalamic derangement. *In: The hypothalamus; morphological, functional, clinical, and surgical aspects, p. 109–111. Edinburgh, Oliver and Boyd, 1938.*

In this lecture of the Henderson Trust Series, given at The University of Edinburgh in 1936,
the author states that the regulation of body temperature is controlled through the central
nervous system. He discusses the disorders of thermal regulation which occur following damage
to the hypothalamus in both warm-blooded animals and man. He notes that both hyperthermia and hypothermia can be associated with lesions of the diencephalon.

310.   Rodbard, S. Body temperature-arterial pressure relationship as a basis for
physiological interpretation of diurnal rhythm [Abstract]. *Fed. Proc., Balt., v. 6,
Mar. 1947: 191.*

A direct relationship appears to exist between variations of the temperature and of the systemic arterial pressure in both poikilotherms and homoiotherms, with the relationship apparently under control of the temperature regulation centers of the brain.

311.   Rodbard, S. Body temperature, blood pressure, and hypothalamus. *Science.,
v. 108, Oct. 1, 1948: 413–415.*

Further studies of a relationship between body temperature and blood pressure in various
species of animals, including birds and mammals, indicate that the relationship depends on
the central nervous system and suggest that it may be but a portion of a more general integration.

312.   Rof Carballo, J. Thermal dysfunction [In Spanish]. *Rev. clín. españ., v. 28,
Jan. 15, 1948: 1–13.*

The author discusses 33 cases of continuous or intermittent thermal regulatory dysfunction
which were observed for periods of several months to several years. This dysfunction was sometimes combined with neurocirculatory asthenia and anxiety states. Alterations of endocrine
states, spastic colitis, migraines, and various neuroses were also frequently observed. There
was a complete lack of any biological signs of infection. Anomalies in the diurnal temperature
rhythm were observed. The condition is thought to be a disturbance in the integration of the
temperature regulation centers located in the area of the hypothalamus. The condition was
generally resistant to anti-pyretics; hydrotherapy was often used successfully.

313.   Rosenthal, F. E. Cooling drugs and cooling centres. *J. Pharm. Exp. Ther.,
v. 71, Apr. 1941: 305–314.*

Solutions of picrotoxin or aconitine injected into the infundibular region of the brain of
rabbits—at the probable site of the heat-regulating centers—produced a decided fall in rectal
temperature, accompanied by cardiac symptoms indicating vagal stimulation. The results
also give further support to the theory of the existence of separate centers in the hypothalamic
area for heat-lowering and heat-raising functions.

314.   Serota, H. M. Temperature changes in the cortex and hypothalamus during sleep. *J. Neurophysiol., v. 2, Jan. 1939: 42–47.*

The temperature decrease of the hypothalamus during sleep was shown to be due to lowered
cellular metabolism rather than to any marked change in blood flow. This might indicate that

sleep is associated with a decreased rather than an increased activity of the hypothalamic "sleep center". Absolute temperatures fluctuate during the waking state, sometimes in a semi-rhythmic manner, and the positive temperature difference between the hypothalamus and cortex increases in irregular fashion with activity.

315. Solnitzky, O. C. The hypothalamus; its structure, functions and clinical syndromes. *Bull. Georgetown Univ. M. Cent., v. 2, Feb.–Mar. 1949: 161–174.*

The hypothalamus is the great correlating center of the autonomic nervous system and as such integrates all the autonomic activities of the brain stem and spinal cord for maintaining homeostasis, one of the functions of which is that of temperature regulation. This is carried out by two mechanisms, one for heat maintenance which is regulated through the sympathetic system; the other for heat dissipation which is regulated through the parasympathetic system. The center for heat maintenance is located in the caudal part of the pars tuberalis, and prevents hypothermia by heat conservation (by peripheral vasoconstriction, rise in blood pressure, increase in heart rate, and/or increase in respiratory rate), or by increase in heat production (by elevation of the metabolic rate, or increase in activity of voluntary striated muscles to produce shivering or voluntary movements). The heat dissipation center is located in the anterior part of the hypothalamus and prevents hyperthermia by sweating, peripheral vaso-dilatation, and/or diminution of metabolic activities.

316. Stoll, W. A. Relation of the hypothalamus to temperature regulation [In German]. *Helvet. physiol. pharm. acta, v. 1, Jan. 1943: 329–357,* and [*abstract section*] *p. C24–C25.*

The efficiency of thermal regulation in cats was shown by the lack of any significant change from the normal rectal temperatures (38.7°C, morning; 39.0°C evening) on exposure to environmental temperature of 10° to 25°C, -2° to 10°C, and 25° to 40°C and higher. No temperature variation could be determined in the liver of anesthetized animals. Electric coagulation of areas of the brain in the region of the hypothalamus rendered the animals virtually poikilothermic, with some deaths; some animals gained partial recovery of temperature regulatory functions after a period of time. The author concludes that temperature regulation is, for the most part, under the influence of the hypothalamus.

317. Ström, G. Influence of local thermal stimulation of hypothalamus of cat on cutaneous blood flow and respiratory rate [In English]. *Acta physiol. scand., v. 20, Suppl. 70, 1950: 47–76.*

Local cooling (down to 31–36°C) of the anterior or posterior hypothalamus of cats did not cause any change in the cutaneous blood flow, whereas heating of the anterior hypothalamus caused cutaneous vasodilatation and caused an increase in respiratory rate. Hypothalamic cooling was not observed to cause shivering. The author feels that negative results cannot be taken as proof that cold-sensitive structures in the hypothalamus regulating cutaneous blood flow do not exist, and that the anesthesia might have made such structures less sensitive to cooling. 75 refs.

318. Sunderman, F. W., and W. Haymaker. Hypothermia and elevated serum magnesium in patient with facial hemangioma extending into the hypothalamus. *Am. J. M. Sc., v. 213, May 1947: 562–571.*

An infant with facial hemangioma had a persistent hypothermia, lowered metabolism, and increase in concentration of serum magnesium. At autopsy it was found that the hemangioma had become highly virulent and spread into the intracranial cavity. The hypothermia in the case was ascribed to damage of the ventromedial nucleus and the consequent interruption of fibers which descend the brain stem as part of the autonomic nervous system.

319. Thauer, R. Heat center and heat regulation [In German]. *Klin. Wschr., v. 20, Sept. 27, 1941: 969–973.*

This is a discussion of some of the experimental findings on the subject of control centers in the hypothalamus and their function in temperature regulation. The topic is considered under the headings of the classical theory, newer research, and interpretation of the findings in the light of newer research.

320. Turner, M. L. Hereditary obesity and temperature regulation. *Am. J. Physiol., v. 152, Jan. 1948: 197–204.*

The adequacy of body temperature regulation, at environmental temperatures of 5° to 40°C, was studied in hereditarily obese yellow mice and in normally thin yellow mice. The obese mice had a less adequate adjustment to temperature changes, the body temperature often varying almost directly with the environmental temperature. In view of the similarities of experimentally produced hypothalamic obesity and hereditary obesity, it is postulated that the yellow gene responsible for over-weight is concerned also with hypothalamic function.

321. Urwitz, S. Contribution to literature of thermoregulation, with special reference to two infants with deformity of brain [In English]. *Acta paediat., Upps., v. 33, 1946: 158–168.*

Clinical report is made of two infants with hydrocephalus in whom temperature-regulation was not functioning. In both, post mortem examination revealed the presence of meningo-encephalitis embracing, among other parts, the mid-brain. In one instance, the skull cavity was found to be almost filled with fluid and with only rudiments of a brain, demonstrating that in this almost decerebrated human being vital processes had proceeded quite normally at body temperatures of 31°C for at least 14 days.

322. Von Euler, C. Slow "temperature potentials" in the hypothalamus. *J. Cellul. Physiol., v. 36, Dec. 1950: 333–350.*

By means of glass capillaries, slow changes of action potential were recorded from the anterior hypothalamus and were found to be synchronous with artificially induced variations of the brain temperature. There was also a direct correlation found between these potentials and the occurrence of panting. Potential changes due to heat amounted to a maximum of 0.5–1.0 mV per 0.1°C.

See also items: 4, 80, 181, 351, 356, 360, 398, 409, 429, 470, 472, 473, 502, 506, 514.

G. *Temperature Sense*

323. Chagas, C., G. Mortara, and F. Borges Sampaio. Some studies on thermal sensitivity [In Portugese, with English summary]. *An. Acad. brasil cienc., v. 19, Mar. 31, 1947: 71–102.*

A detailed statistical analysis is made of a preliminary study of the responses, in groups of 68 individuals, to a short questionnaire on their temperature sensations correlated with the known temperature conditions of that period. The principal types of individual sensitivity were revealed as a tendency to hyperthermia, hypothermia, hyperesthesia, and hypoesthesia. A high degree of correlation was found between thermal sensation and the mean temperature for the day which is stated to clearly show the influence of prior experience upon sensation.

324. Christensen, W. R. Effect of physical characteristics of fabrics upon physiological heat load and subjective reactions. *J. Indust. Hyg., v. 30, July 1948: 251–255.*

In a series of tests on nine cotton fabrics, coolness, skin sensation and drag were established as the most important criteria in determining the subjective acceptability of a uniform. Of these, coolness and type of tactile sensation imparted by the fabric, were of major importance.

Subjective appraisal of heat load, however, was found to be quite inconsistent when compared with objective results. It appeared that test subjects were unable to segregate clearly the sensation of coolness and other subjective stimuli.

325. **Ferderber, M. B., and F. C. Houghten.** Effective temperature scale; a measure of human comfort in environmental temperature. *J. Am. M. Ass., v. 116, Feb. 8, 1941: 474-477.*

The term "effective temperature index" is used as a relative index of the atmospheric conditions felt by the human body in response to the physical factors of the air. It takes into account not only air temperature but also moisture content and movement of the air, as they affect heat transfer between the body and surrounding surfaces.

326. **Lee, W. Y.** Physiological reactions to a changing environment. III. Occurrence of "cold shock" [In English]. *Chin. M. J., v. 67, May 1949: 252-256.*

The severity of the unpleasant chilling effect, "cold shock", experienced when the subject goes from a hot (74° and 98.2°F) to a cooled but comfortable (58° and 77°F) environment, is not so much due to the exact temperature as to the magnitude of the change. These experiments indicate that an unpleasant cooling sensation occurs when the magnitude of the change is greater than 18°F.

327. **Munro, A. F., and F. A. Chrenko.** The effects of air temperature and velocity and of various flooring materials on the thermal sensations and skin temperature of the feet. *J. Hyg., Lond., v. 46, Dec. 1948: 451-465.*

Thermal sensation on the sole of the shod foot, whether resting on concrete or on cork, was not significantly different at air temperatures of 55°F. Changes in skin temperature, under similar conditions, did not occur at 65°F during the course of an hour; there was, however, a positive correlation between skin temperature and a feeling of warmth. With bare feet, the changes in skin temperature and sensations of warmth corresponded approximately to the thermal conductivities of the floor materials. Movement of air across the top of the foot had little effect on thermal comfort of the foot. In general, air temperature is the dominant factor influencing thermal comfort of the feet but there are air temperatures below which a floor of high conductivity is undesirable.

328. **Nielsen, M.** Studies on the relation between sensations of comfort, degree of heating, and physiological reactions of sedentary workingmen [In Danish, summary in English]. *(Contribution # 3 from the Committee for the Study of Domestic Heating, Copenhagen) Copenhagen, Teknologisk Instituts Forlag, 1947. 82 p.*

The sensations of thermal comfort were recorded by each test subject in each of three groups (4 young men, 4 young women, and 4 old men) every half hour during the experimental period of 3 hours and 40 minutes while the room temperature was varied from 28.5° to 11°C. Continuous recordings were also made of temperatures of various areas of the body including the mouth, trunk, and rectum. From the experimental results it is concluded that sensations of "uncomfortably cold" are mainly due to cooling of the extremities, particularly the lower extremities, with the temperature of the trunk of minor importance. The physiological significance of cold feet is discussed and it is emphasized that a considerable lowering may be a harmful symptom involving the risk of reflex vasoconstriction in other parts of the body. The rapid fall in mouth temperature which was noted in several instances on exposure to the coldest environment, may be explained as a result of such a reflex. In some instances the foot temperatures of about 15°C which were recorded are approaching values at which Lewis (item 1772) has indicated that direct harmful effects to tissues might be expected. A complete lack of any indications of adaptation to either hot or cold, together with the fact that the character of the sensations of "uncomfortably cold" and the pure skin temperature were not the same, appear to indicate that other sensations than skin temperature sensation contribute to the building up of the sensations of comfort.

*329 **Oikawa, S.** Some hygienical notes on snow [In Japanese]. *Seppyo, v. 2, 1940: 9–11.*

"Light is reflected at a ratio of approximately 30% by an old snow cover of 0.5 density, and at 90% by new snow of 0.1 density. Reflectivity decreases in contaminated snow. A layer of firm snow, 10 cm thick, prevents light transmission. Skin temperatures of persons standing on snow at 0°–4°C, ranged from about 19°C–25°C. The air temperature in a snow cave is about 0°C with humidity nearly 100%. A person feels uncomfortably cold under these conditions. (Abstract by Ukitiro Nakaya)."—SIPRE Report 12, v. 3, Jan. 1953: 207.

330. **Stozhkova, N. F.** Skin temperature and air temperature underneath the clothing as indicators of thermal sensation during the action of low temperatures [In Russian]. *In: Trudy iubileĭnoĭ nauchnoĭ sessii Instituta Gigieny Truda i Professional'nykh Zabolevaniĭ (Leningrad, iiunia 15–19, 1939), p. 158–159. Leningrad, 1940.*

Skin temperature and air temperature underneath the clothing were measured in a large number of subjects and compared to the thermal sensation. Under normal conditions these temperatures proved to be rather constant. In generalized cooling, the sensation of cold was accompanied by a decrease in skin temperature especially of the extremities. The skin temperature of the torso, if well protected by clothing, may remain at a normal or even slightly higher temperature level, in spite of a strong general cold sensation. In cooling of the entire naked body surface, the temperatures of the forehead and torso decrease comparatively little; the temperature of the extremities, especially of the distal portions, decreases as the surrounding temperature of the air decreases and the sensation of general cold is increased. After return to room temperature, the rise of the forehead and torso skin temperature to their initial values is much more rapid than is the sensation of comfort. The latter occurs only after the skin temperature of the distal extremities has reached its normal level. The difference in the temperature of the extremities and of the torso during prolonged generalized cooling increased with the increase of cold sensation, and may therefore serve as an indicator for the comfort sensation. The temperature of the air underneath the clothing in the torso region was measured at comfort temperature with habitual light clothing, and at 0°–9°C with warm clothing, after the appearance of pronounced general cold sensation. Results showed that the temperature of air underneath the clothing in the torso region was never below that which corresponded to the comfort sensation at room temperature, in many cases it was even higher. It may therefore be assumed that sufficiently intense and prolonged cold influence on insufficiently protected parts of the skin, such as hands and feet, can induce a a strong sensation of general cold, even if the torso is kept at normal or slightly higher temperature.

331. **Yaglou, C. P.** Indices of comfort. *In: Physiology of heat regulation and the science of clothing, p. 277–287. Ed. by* L. H. NEWBURGH. *Philadelphia, Saunders, 1949.*

This is a discussion of "effective temperature" (which combines air temperature, humidity, and air movement in a single sensory scale of warmth); "operative temperature" (which combines air temperature, reflected radiation, and air movement); the index of physiological effect; and the thermal acceptance ratio.

See also items: 252, 1132, 1177, 1180, 2629.

H. Circulatory Aspects

332. **Aschoff, J.** On the dilatation by cold of the extremities of men in ice water [In German]. *Pflügers Arch., v. 248, Aug. 15, 1944: 183–196.*

The effects of local cooling of the hand in ice water are reviewed. After a period of 30 minutes a marked dilatation is observed, beginning with the finger tip and extending to the

---

*Original not seen.

body. The importance of the arteriovenous anastomoses in this reaction is described, and the role of the extremities with respect to physiological temperature regulation is discussed.

333. Aschoff, J. On the interference of circulation and temperature regulatory processes in the extremities of men [In German]. *Pflügers Arch., v. 248, Aug. 15, 1944: 197–207.*

Evidence is presented that temperature- and blood-pressure-regulating mechanisms exist in human extremities.

334. Aschoff, J., and F. Kaempffer. On the passage of heat through the skin and its changes with vasoconstriction [In German]. *Pflügers Arch., v. 249, Mar. 1, 1947: 112–124.*

One hand of a subject was immersed in a flowing water bath at 12.5°C and changes in heat loss were measured by use of a flow calorimeter. A hollow glass hand of the same general over-all area, and filled with fluid of hand temperature (32°C), was used as a physical control. With the water bath at 12.5°C, vasoconstriction started immediately but, in most cases, was not lasting. In other experiments, not reported in detail, a more definite pattern of vasoconstriction followed by vasodilatation was seen when the temperature of the water was in the range ot 15°C to 25°C. Also in a few experiments with water at 10°C, the vasoconstriction was found to be lasting. The results of the experiments are expressed in various equations and tabulations. It is shown that the difference in behavior of the hand, as contrasted to the physical control body, was to be attributed to vasoconstriction which within the first 10 minutes following cold stimulus brought about a lessening of the means of heat transport. Use of a Recklinghausen cuff on the upper arm to cut off circulation for a short period, brought about no great changes in the cooling curve.

335. Aschoff, J. The upper extremity in the service of physical temperature regulation [In German]. *Pflügers Arch., v. 249, July 2, 1947: 148–166.*

Studies made with a flow calorimeter to determine skin circulation in the upper extremity showed an increase from the proximal to the distal parts. Heat transfer values were found to be higher in the upper extremity than in the trunk.

336.   Bintakys, F. On the question of vasomotor thermoregulation; thermometric alterations of exposed body parts of iso-, hypo-, and hyperthermic dogs and men and their significance [In German; summaries in German and English]. *Contributions of Baltic University, No. 50. Hamburg-Pinneberg, [Baltic University], 1947. 123 p.*

Ears of rabbits, or the fingers of human subjects, were exposed to an environment or to a water bath where the temperatures were lower (in the range of 12°–18°C) or higher than the average comfortable environmental temperature. Changes in temperature in the areas were measured by thermocouple. The thermal fluctuations, or rhythmic contractions of the blood vessels, were found to depend both on the surrounding temperature and on the thermal influences from distant parts of the body. In the rabbit ears there was a long latent period until the appearance of vasomotor reactions when there was only the inner temperature, or temperature of the blood, to act on the thermoregulatory centers. In lesser changes from an isothermic condition, the changes were dependent on reflex action from thermal receptors; in greater deviations from isothermic conditions, the inner temperature, or temperature of the blood, had a decisive influence on the thermoregulatory center and repressed the impulses of the distant thermoreceptors. The cold receptors are of greater importance than are those for warmth; the latter are easily dominated by the temperature of the blood. The thermoregulatory centers respond more quickly to stimuli from the cold receptors to produce consensual vasomotor reactions than the centers do to stimuli from warmth receptors. Grant's assumption [R. T. Grant. Heart, v. 19, 1930] that the anastomoses of the arteries and veins are open in the hyperthermic condition and closed in the hypothermic condition has been indirectly confirmed. The results of experiments with rabbits and on human subjects correspond quite closely.

337.   Burton, A. C., and R. M. Taylor. Rhythmic fluctuations of sympathetic tone and their modification by temperature and by psychic influences [Abstract]. *Proc. Am. Physiol. Soc., 51st Ann. Meet., Apr. 26–29, 1939: P453–P454. (Am. J. Physiol., v. 126, July 1, 1939).*

Plethysmographic studies were made of blood flow in the fingers. Periodic constrictions, in addition to the regular ones of respiratory origin, occurred every 30 to 60 seconds. These were simultaneous in all digits of the body. They were accompanied by cardiac acceleration and a rise in blood pressure. They represent a rhythmic mass discharge of the sympathetic nervous system. Constrictions were also observed which were of psychic origin. As temperature rose, the average period between these constrictions increased. Amplitude of the fluctuations were small when environmental temperature was low; largest in a comfortable environmental temperature; and less again in the higher environmental temperatures. It is concluded that physical regulation of body temperature is achieved not by a constant level of peripheral blood flow but by a modification of fluctuations in blood flow. Observations, following comparison of changes in skin temperature with those of blood flow, would indicate that afferent temperature impulses merely modify a rhythm which is an intrinsic property of the temperature-regulating center.

338.   Burton, A. C. The range and variability of the blood flow in the human fingers and the vasomotor regulation of body temperature. *Am. J. Physiol., v. 127, Oct. 1939: 437–453.*

A plethysmographic method of recording volume pulsations was adapted to the instantaneous measurement of blood flow in the finger. The range of blood flow in the fingers is from 0.5 to 1.0 cc up to 80 to 90 cc/min/100 cc tissue. The tremendous range of flow, made possible by arterio-venous anastomoses, represents not a metabolic need but a mechanism for temperature regulation by elimination of body heat. The marked fluctuations which occur are rhythmic in character with two main components, one a respiratory fluctuation of small amplitude and the other a slower rhythm of periodic constrictions of large amplitude. Since these are simultaneous in the digits of all extremities and are accompanied by cardiac acceleration and rise of blood pressure, a rhythmic fluctuation of the activity of the entire peripheral sympathetic system acting as a whole is indicated. A third group of constrictions due to pain, startle, or emotional stimuli are sometimes also present. The rhythm is decidedly altered by the conditions of temperature regulation.

339. Burton, A. C. Blood flow, temperature, and color of the skin. *Am. Ass. Adv. Sc., Publ. no. 13, 1940: 308–312.*

Some of the characteristics of the blood flow in the skin are noted together with some information on how the temperature and color of the skin reflect these characteristics. Some of methods used to demonstrate blood flow are discussed. Blood flow has been studied by direct microscopic observation and measurement of the changes in volume or in pulsation volume of the vessels of the skin by oscillometric techniques; and by actual determination of flow by the pressure plethysmograph in an appendage where most of the flow must be to the skin. In this brief review the author attempts only to emphasize the complexity of the interpretation of various methods available for blood flow of the human skin and agrees with Lewis (1937) that each of methods discussed has both distinct values and limitations which tend to disappear when various methods are used in judicious combination.

340.   Burton, A. C., and R. M. Taylor. A study of the adjustment of peripheral vascular tone to the requirements of the regulation of body temperature. *Am. J. Physiol., v. 129, June 1940: 565–577.*

The reflex adjustment of the blood flow in peripheral vessels in accordance with the requirements of temperature regulation is a continuous process which consists in the modification of a vascular tone, which is intrinsically rhythmical in character.

341. **Cacioppo, F., and V. Bevilotti.** Vagus and thermal regulation. IV. Gas exchange and body temperature of vagotomized, plucked pigeons exposed to low temperature [In Italian]. *Soc. ital. biol. sper.*, *v. 22, 1946: 174–175.*

In vagotomized plucked pigeons exposed to environmental temperatures of 2°–3°C for 1–2 hours, the cloacal temperature dropped 10°–12°C and it was not possible to save the animal. Normal plucked animals similarly exposed for 2 hours had a cloacal temperature drop of 4°–5°C, then returned to a normal level soon after their return to an environmental temperature of 24°–26°C. Vagotomized plucked animals had a great variation in their quantitative response with respect to gaseous metabolism during similar exposure; normal plucked animals had an elevation in metabolism quite similar to normal animals before plucking. The thermal regulatory mechanism appeared, therefore, to be greatly disturbed following vagotomy.

342. **Cooper, K. E., and K. McK. Kerslake.** Vasodilatation in response to heating the skin [Abstract]. *Proc. Physiol. Soc., Lond., Dec. 17–18, 1948: 40P. (J. Physiol., Lond., v. 108, 1949).*

Experimental results give further support to the hypothesis that a generalized vasodilatation takes place in response to afferent nervous stimuli arising in locally heated areas of the skin. This vasodilatation was found to be associated with a fall in mouth and rectal temperatures.

343. **Danielson, R. N., and F. W. Kinard.** Effects of temperature of local baths on deep muscle temperature. *J. Appl. Physiol., v. 4, Nov. 1951: 373–377.*

Immersion of the limb of the dog in a water bath at a temperature higher or lower than that of the extremity leads to a prompt and marked change in the deep muscle temperature of the limb in the direction of the bath temperature. Bath temperatures used were 15°, 25°, 35°, and 45°C. The change in muscle temperature was enhanced by occlusion of the circulation. Rectal temperature was affected in the same direction but to a lesser extent when the circulation was intact, but was unaffected when the circulation was occluded. At an elevated bath temperature, irreversible damage to tissues could be produced when there was interference with the circulation, although no damage appeared under similar conditions when the circulation was intact.

344. **Duthie, J. J. R., and R. M. I. Mackay.** Vasomotor reflexes in the control of body temperature in man. I. Reflex vasodilatation in response to a rise in skin temperature in man. *Brain, Lond., v. 63, Dec. 1940: 295–312.*

Heat applied to one limb, after arresting its circulation, can sometimes give rise to reflex vasodilatation in the other, unheated, limb; the reactions may arise from stimulation of nerve endings in the walls of blood vessels in the skin. The authors advance the hypothesis that these vasomotor reflexes from the skin may be the mechanism for maintaining a constant internal temperature when the changes are not too great, but that when changes are greater, the changes in blood temperature activate the thermo-sensitive centers of temperature control in the hypothalamus.

345. **Duthie, J. J. R., and R. M. I. Mackay.** Vasomotor reflexes in the control of body temperature in man. II. Vascular responses to warming of patients with various nerve lesions, with special reference to afferent pathways. *Brain, Lond., v. 63, Dec. 1940: 312–320.*

Preganglionic sympathectomy interrupts the vasoconstrictor fibers to the limbs but does not seem to interfere with the course of the nervous elements carrying the afferent impulses from the skin and concerned with production of reflex vasodilatation; nor does it, in case of a rise in internal temperature, interfere with the increased heat elimination by vasodilatation of the peripheral vessels.

346. Ebbecke, U. The facial reflex of the trigeminal nerve as a heat-protective reflex (wind and weather reflex) of the head [In German]. *Klin. Wschr., v. 23, May 1944: 141–145.*

The author discusses the special mechanism for keeping constant the temperature of the head. When subjects dipped their faces into cold or warm water, strongly individual swallowing reflexes were noted. Some subjects demonstrated an uncontrollable fear reaction at immersing their faces in water and displayed immediately a bradycardia. True bradycardia is explained by the restriction of blood flow making rapid heart movement unnecessary since less blood is moved over a smaller area. The author finds the facial reflex a skin-cold reflex but of a much higher order than other reflexes; its effects on reflexive heightening of oxygen consumption and carbon dioxide production are quantitatively much greater. The reflexes of the trigeminal nerve, stimulated by the cold water on the facial skin, eye ball, or nasal mucous membrane, are coordinated through the mediation of higher brain centers to help maintain a constant temperature pattern for the head.

347. Ferris, B. G., Jr., R. E. Forster, II., E. L. Pillion, and W. R. Christensen. Control of peripheral blood flow; responses in the human hand when extremities are warmed. *Am. J. Physiol., v. 150, Aug. 1947: 304–314.*

The blood flow in the hands of two men was studied at ambient temperatures ranging from 16.4° to 30.2°C. One hand was heated to various levels of skin temperature, and alterations in the blood flow and skin temperature of the opposite hand were recorded. When a steady state was reached at 21°C, the blood flow in the hand was found to be dependent on the body's need to reduce heat dissipation.

348. Fetcher, E. S., J. F. Hall, and H. G. Shaub. The skin temperature of an extremity as a measure of its blood flow. *Science, v. 110, Oct. 21, 1949: 422–423.*

If skin temperature is to be used as a valid measure of blood flow, the authors state that the area of the body being investigated must lose heat at a rate of more than 240 Cal/hr/m² for good correspondence between the flow and skin temperature changes.

349. Fløystrup, A., and A. P. Skouby. Investigation upon the mechanism of indirect warming [In English]. *Acta med. scand., v. 136, (6), 1950: 466–472.*

Ten subjects were tested at a room temperature of 18°–20°C with one leg encased in a box at 1°C, and with the tissue temperature of the great toe measured under the following conditions: while parts of the upper limbs were heated in water of 43°C; while hands were heated during simultaneous cooling of the forearm or neck with icebags; and while circulation was occluded, or not, from heated limbs by the use of an Esmarch bandage. In no instance did a rise in temperature of the toe occur during occlusion demonstrating that the indirect heating produced in the toe was due to the heat assimilated through the hands and not to nervous impulses. Studies were also made of the difference in the latent period from the beginning of the warming of the upper part of the body until the temperature of the toe began to rise.

350. Freeman, H. Skin and body temperature of schizophrenic and normal subjects under varying environmental conditions. *Arch. Neur. Psychiat., Chic., v. 42, Oct. 1939: 724–734.*

Changes of skin and rectal temperatures of normal and schizophrenic individuals were studied under varying environmental conditions (15° to 44°C). Exposure to cold (15°C) for two hours resulted consistently in greater cooling of the skin of patients over the normal controls; exposure to heat (44°C), or to high humidity, resulted in no differences. Rectal temperatures remained normal throughout. It is concluded that the greater reactivity of schizophrenic subjects to cold implies a dysfunction of the neural mechanism controlling vasoconstrictor tone; vasodilatation may, however, be normal.

351. Friedman, M. Hyperthermia as a manifestation of stress. *In: Life stress and bodily disease. Proc. Ass. Res. Nerv. Ment. Dis., 1949. Res. Publ., v. 29, 1950: 433–444.*

Observations have demonstrated that neurogenic hyperthermia is a phenomenon that spontaneously erupts in patients exhibiting a particular type of autonomic instability primarily characterized by sympathetic over-reactivity to internal and external stress. These patients are uncomfortable in any type of thermal environment which varies even slightly from a relatively narrow temperature range of 70° to 80°F. That this intolerance to external temperature changes is not a psychic phonomenon but an expression of a fundamental autonomic derangement was evidenced when two such patients lost control of their temperature regulation when subjected to temperature-raising apparatus. Because the hypothalamus has been found to be concerned not only with temperature control but also with the integration of all autonomic activities, the conclusion is drawn that the neurogenic fever is a result of disturbed hypothalamic activity.

352. Gollwitzer-Meier, K. Consensual hypothermia of extremities in normal persons and in patients with nerve lesions due to gunshot wounds [In German]. *Deut. med. Wschr., v. 72, Mar. 14, 1947: 103–105.*

The mechanical vascular engorgement of one arm, by use of a constrictive band, brings about a consensual vascular constriction and a consensual hypothermia of the skin of the other arm. Nervous control of the blood vessel reaction was demonstrated to be involved in the consensual reactions.

353. Grayson, J. The sensitivity of the cold and warmth vaso-constrictor responses [Abstract]. *Proc. Physiol. Soc., Lond., Feb. 18, 1950: 39P. (J. Physiol., Lond., v. 111, Oct. 16, 1950.)*

Cutaneous vasoconstriction which was known to occur reflexly on exposure to environments colder or warmer than the body (Grayson, J., J. Physiol., Lond., v. 109, Aug. 1, 1949: 53) was eliminated so far as cold stimulus was concerned, by wrapping the subject in blankets. When the right index finger alone was left uncovered, the skin temperature of the finger rose in every case to about 35°C without a rise in the rectal temperature. Subsequent exposure of the head and one arm usually produced less than 2°C drop in finger temperature. Vasoconstrictor responses followed the exposure of the trunk or limbs to temperatures above or below 37°C. In 3 apparently healthy subjects there was a marked hypersensitivity of the cold constrictor response; in these cases exposure of the head alone always caused the skin temperature to fall rapidly to 20° or 25°C.

354. Greenfield, A. D. M., J. T. Shepherd, and R. F. Whelan. The average internal temperature of fingers immersed in cold water. *Clin. Sc., Lond., v. 9, Aug. 31, 1950: 349–354.*

By calorimetric methods at water bath temperatures of 0°–4°C, the average internal temperature of the forefinger of various subjects was found to be between 20° and 30°C, at the height of the vasodilatation due to cold.

355. Hemingway, A., and C. W. Lillehei. Thermal cutaneous vasomotor response in dogs. *Am. J. Physiol., v. 162, Aug. 1, 1950: 301–307.*

Dogs were suspended in a hammock with their hind legs placed in a cool water bath of the same temperature as the testing room (15° to 18°C). After a period of 30 to 90 minutes, the cool water was replaced by warm water (45°C) until a well defined vasodilatation had occurred. The warm water was then replaced by cool water. As measured by skin temperature, the magnitude of thermal cutaneous vasomotor response was greatest at the ear and least at the trunk with the foreleg being intermediate between the two. Vasodilatation was transitory with vasoconstriction occurring with long periods of immersion. The sharp drop in rectal temperature, which often accompanied the vasodilatation, was "paradoxical" if explained by the "central" theory of temperature regulation. Sympathectomy and surgical anesthesia

were each found to abolish the thermal cutaneous vasomotor response. The response of one
ear showed a slight lag from that of the other, similar to that found in paired extremities of
man. This and other findings lead to the assumption that the response in the dog is identical
with that of man.

356. Hyndman, O. R., and J. Wolkin. The autonomic mechanism of heat conservation and dissipation. II. Effects of cooling the body. A comparison of
peripheral and central vasomotor responses to cold. *Am. Heart J., v. 23, Jan.
1942: 43–58.*

Reactions to cold were studied in human subjects who had had various operations on
their sympathetic nervous system. Observations were made before and after the patient was
placed in a refrigerator for various periods of time. Skin and mouth temperature, blood
pressure, pulse rate, onset of shivering, and appearance of skin were recorded. Results indicate the importance of the peripheral vascular response to changes in temperature, and of
the central mechanisms in extreme temperature changes.

357. Isaakian, L. A. On the cortical mechanism of thermoregulation in some
mammal orders [In Russian]. *In: Opyt izucheniia reguliatsii fiziologicheskikh
funktsii, Moskva & Leningrad, 1949, p. 21–39.*

A study was made of the effect of cortical influences on the chemical thermoregulation
and body temperature in various mammal species (primate monkeys, dogs, white rats, guinea
pigs, jerboas, and dormice) by the method of conditioned reflexes. The animals were kept
at 15°–16°C and a series of studies made of their gaseous metabolism at 22°–26°C or at
8°–14°C for 3–4 hours, over a period of several months. Results showed that the mechanism
of conditioned reflexes in chemical thermoregulation differs according to the stage of phylogeny;
thus the physiological significance and biological role of chemical thermoregulation in the
various orders was not the same. In the carnivores the temporary connections for chemical
thermoregulation are formed rapidly, completely change the metabolic reaction, and gradually
disappear in 4–6 days; in the lower monkeys (hamadryl and macacus) the temporary connections are established on the basis of fluctuating values, and their extinction proceeds more
slowly and in waves (indicating possible inhibition); in rodents the unconditioned reaction of
chemical thermoregulation is rather pronounced, but temporary cortical connections, as
in the primates or in the carnivores, could not be observed. The thermoregulatory function
is probably completely determined by cortical impulses of the principle of temporary
connections; namely, in the relation of the unconditioned and conditioned components of chemical thermoregulation, the leading role belongs to the conditioned reflex.

358. Keller, A. D. The role of circulation in the physiology of heat regulation.
Phys. Ther. Rev., v. 30, Dec. 1950: 511–519.

Dogs were exposed to various environmental temperatures, both cold (3°C) and hot (37–
38°C). In exposure to only moderately adverse environmental conditions, heat conservation
or heat dissipation was achieved almost entirely by circulatory adjustments. Only when the
limits of circulatory adjustments were reached, did the non-circulatory mechanisms for heat
gain or heat loss come into play.

359. Lehmann, G. The nasal reflex of L. Hill and its significance in the knowledge of thermoregulation by the skin reflex [In German]. *Arbeitsphysiol., v. 10
(4), 1939: 418–435.*

Experiments on the effect of infrared irradiation of the skin around the entrance to the
nostrils on the capillaries of the nose led to the theory that an increase in the temperature
gradient of the skin causes dilatation and a decrease causes contraction, not only in the mucous
membrane of the nose but in the unstimulated epidermis of other areas as well. These reflexes are of significance in the study of temperature regulation.

360. Lunn, V. Experimental studies on electro-shock treatment. II. Variations in skin temperature following electric convulsion therapy [In English]. *Acta psychiat. neur., scand., v. 26 (1), 1951: 7–48.*

Observations on the initial fall in skin temperature, the changing of color in the extremities, and the rise in blood pressure immediately following electroshock are interpreted as action of the latter on the function of diencephalic vasomotor centers resulting in a general contraction of arterioles and a simultaneous opening of the arteriovenous anastomoses.

361. McDonough, F. K. Homeostasis in the sympathectomized dog. *Am. J. Physiol., v. 125, Mar. 1, 1939: 530–546.*

The response to cold of normal dogs exposed to environmental temperatures of 3.5° to 6.0°C for 2 or 3 hours, was a slight temporary rise in rectal temperature succeeded by a fall to the initial level or a bit lower. Dogs exposed to similar cold environment within 6 weeks following sympathectomy, responded with a slight decrease in body temperature. Both responded to cold by shivering but in the sympathectomized dogs shivering began earlier, was more pronounced, and lasted after removal from the cold room. In discussing the greater ability of sympathectomized dogs to withstand cold over that reported for sympathectomized cats, the author concludes that the sympathetic system appears to be less important for dogs and shivering seems more important.

362. Martinez, C., and M. B. Visscher. Some observations on general skin temperature responses to local heating of human subjects in a cold environment. *Am. J. Physiol., v. 144, Oct. 1945: 724–734.*

Skin temperature measurements were made on 9 humans exposed to local heating while maintained in a cold environment (16.7°C). Immersion of the forearms in water at 43° to 44°C produced a larger rise in skin temperature in all locations except the back.

363. Nielsen, M., L. P. Herrington, and C. E. A. Winslow. The effect of posture upon peripheral circulation. *Am. J. Physiol., v. 127, Oct. 1, 1939: 573–580.*

A passive change of body posture on a tilting table from the horizontal to a feet-down position (45° from horizontal) produced a peripheral vasoconstriction. Except under the most severe conditions of the tests, both fingers and toes changed in the opposite direction from the general skin temperature. The author states that this might possibly involve a protective mechanism against local chilling.

364. O'Keeffe, A. T., R. Warren, and R. C. Hill. Alterations in skin temperature of the toes during lumbar sympathectomy. *Surgical Forum, American College of Surgeons 36th Clinical Congress, Philadelphia, October 1950: 391–394.*

The temperature of the skin of the big toe fell from 3° to 5°F for 5 to 10 minutes, in the first 12 of 19 patients observed, while the patients were undergoing lumbar sympathectomy to relieve arterial spasm of the extremity. In the other 7 patients procaine was injected into the lumbar chain before its removal and the temperature fell in only three cases. In two of the three the temperature fall was thought to be due to the trauma of the injection rather than to the manipulation of the chain.

365. Ponugaeva, A. G., and O. I. Margolina. The cortical mechanism of chemical thermoregulation in man [In Russian]. *In: Opvt izucheniia reguliatsii fiziologicheskikh funktsii, Moskva & Leningrad, 1949, p. 40–47.*

Investigation was made into existing relationships of the human body to natural environmental conditions. Studies were made of the gaseous metabolism and body temperature of conductors working on freight trains (who are constantly exposed to outdoor temperatures) immediately upon arrival at the station, and after 20 minutes of subsequent rest, both in the winter and in the summer. The results indicated that the start, exclusion, or continuance of chemical thermoregulation is realized in man with the participation of the cerebral cortex. The firmly-conditioned connections which are established in the cortex during habitual work can direct the flow of the oxidation processes in the human body and thus determine the body reaction to exterior changes. It is believed that continued action of low temperatures has varied influences on the body, and that professional workers (conductors) showed greater changes in chemical thermoregulatory reactions than did the non-professional control subjects. The chemical thermoregulation, which is little developed in man as compared to animals, can become very important in professional workers under continued conditions of low temperature.

366. Ponugaeva, A. G., and O. I. Margolina. Chemical thermoregulation in man at low environmental temperatures [In Russian]. *In: Opyt izucheniĩa reguliãtsii fiziologicheskikh funkt̄sĩ, Moskva & Leningrad, 1949, p. 48–56.*

Studies were made to determine the influence of temperatures below 0°C on the course of oxidation processes, and the condition of the thermoregulatory function, at various seasons in laborers working in refrigerator chambers (−6° to −18°C) during long periods of time and in other laborers working at normal temperatures. Observations revealed a more stable body temperature and a higher oxygen consumption (greater chemical thermoregulation) in the group working habitually at low temperatures than in the control group. The metabolic changes at low temperatures depended somewhat on the body position in that lying down while working was not accompanied by an increase in the oxidation processes. In non-acclimatized (non-professional) subjects sudden intense cooling induced more intense oxidation processes in the summer; after moderate cooling, in the winter. The above data indicate that at low temperatures the thermoregulatory mechanisms are of a complex reflex nature; the interrelations between the chemical and physical thermoregulations are determined by the cortex in response to extero- and interoceptive stimulations. During more intense cooling the metabolic reactions are determined only by unconditioned reflexes.

367. Ponugaeva, A. G. Peculiarities of thermoregulation during heat loss by radiation [In Russian]. *In: Opyt izucheniĩa reguliãtsii fiziologicheskikh funkt̄sĩ, Moskva & Leningrad, 1949, p. 57–64.*

Assuming that various methods of heat loss have different physiological effects, depending on the cortical mechanisms which are involved, an experimental study was made in adult and young rats, guinea pigs, and white mice. The animals were placed, for a period of 7 hours, in a space formed by three metal cases each of which was cooled by running water. Meteorological conditions were determined by Assman's psychometer and by means of a dry catathermometer. Results showed that the exposure of the animals in front of cooled metal walls induced a drop in body temperature (up to 2°C at 11.8°C; 0.4° to 0.5°C at 22°C) with the temperature of the air remaining the same (11° to 23°C). During convection cooling, the body temperature changed very little. In young rats, however, no difference was found in the reaction to cooling by convection or by radiation. Rats having partly injured cerebral hemispheres showed greater differences in body temperatures during heat loss from radiation or convection than did the normals. The above data indicate a complex reflex mechanism of thermoregulation in response to cooling, depending on the function of the cerebral cortex.

368. Rapaport, S. I., E. S. Fetcher, H. G. Shaub, and J. F. Hall. Control of blood flow to the extremities at low ambient temperatures. *J. Appl. Physiol., v. 2, Aug. 1949: 61–71.*

Observations were made on four young healthy subjects, during a period of two hours in a cold room at temperatures of 0°, −20°, or −30°F, to study the extent of autonomic control of blood flow to the hands and feet. It was questioned whether the blood flow to the hands and feet at low ambient temperatures was regulated by the thermal state of the body as a whole or by the known direct constricting effect of cold upon their blood vessels. It is concluded that the blood flow to the extremities under these conditions is primarily determined by the thermal state of the body as a whole. Vasoconstrictive effects were subordinate to autonomic control. Therefore, the temperature of the extremities can be made nearly independent of the ambient temperature and of insulation, over a wide temperature range;

and dependent primarily upon the thermal state of the rest of the body. Under conditions comparable to these experiments, artificial application of heat to the extremities is unnecessary for comfort.

369. Riemerschmid, G., and O. Scheurer. The action of bathing parts of the body on the skin temperature [In German]. *Zschr. ges. exp. Med., v. 107, 1940: 373–390.*

The effect of baths of the hand and arm at various temperatures (11°, 33°, 41°C, and alternating 41°/11°C) on the peripheral blood circulation and on skin temperature was tested on both arms and one leg at an environmental temperature of 25°C. The skin temperature was also checked over the entire undressed body. It was found that the integral skin temperature (average figure of the surface temperature of the entire body) remained constant after the local bath for indifferent temperature stimulation only; for either cold or hot baths it decreased gradually for about an hour. At the end of one hour the skin temperature curves were usually back to normal, except for cold stimulations during 10 minutes (at 11°C), which induced a temporary increase of integral skin temperature, followed by a continued decrease (of 0.35°C) during the following 60 minutes. After 1 minute of cold stimulation, the temperature decreased for over 50 minutes, then began to rise again. Cold arm-baths (1–10 minutes) do not noticeably influence the skin temperature of the trunk. In the extremities all thermal stimulation, but especially the cold baths, induce a vascular contraction (drop in skin temperature); this was most pronounced in the non-stimulated hand and forearm. It may be assumed that this contraction is caused by two independent reactions, of which one is of central nervous, the other of segmental, origin. Alternating hot and cold baths induced an increased skin temperature in the trunk; the decrease in the contralateral hand and arm was soon followed by a temperature rise above the initial level. Individual values in all thermal skin reactions were subject to daily variations. It is concluded that a favorable vascular skin reaction is of great importance for the final reaction after cold stimulation. Alternating hot and cold baths exert the most favorable influence on the local and general vascular reaction.

370. Rozovskaía, E. I. Heat regulating reflex in children [In Russian]. *Pediatriía, Moskva, 1947 (6): 29–36.*

Thermoregulation was studied in 44 children (2–12 years of age) in a series of 106 tests, determined by Shcherbak's thermoregulatory reflex method (stimulation of the skin receptors by hot arm-baths inducing increased heat production and increased heat loss). Body temperature, blood pressure, pulse rate, and white dermographism were measured before, during, and 30 and 60 minutes after the bath. The main role in this reflex is played by the autonomic nervous system, which determines the character of the temperature reaction, so that this reflex is in effect a functional test for the autonomic nervous system. Results, indicating that this reflex differs in children from that in adults, are given in detail. In the smallest children these differences appear especially in the second phase of temperature reaction, i.e. in heat loss (often increased or variously altered), and in increased blood pressure (instead of the decrease noted in adults), which was shown to be due to predominance of sympathicotonic influence. In the older children a decrease in body temperature is characteristic (instead of the increase noted in adults), that is the thermoregulating reflex is decreased, absent, or even distorted. These facts are due to a predominance of parasympathetic influences.

371. Scheurer, O., and G. Riemerschmid. On the effect of cigarette smoking on the skin temperature [In German]. *Zschr. ges. exp. Med., v. 107 (3), 1940: 391–392.*

Measurements were made of the skin temperature of the finger tips and of nine areas of the body of 5 healthy, undressed, subjects at a room temperature of 25°C, before and after smoking cigarettes. After smoking, the temperature of the finger tips decreased 2°–7°C; the minimum level occurred after 10 minutes. The effect was more pronounced when the smoke was inhaled. The back of the hand and of the foot also showed a temperature decrease from 1°–3°C (maximum 4.6°C on the hand; 3.9°C on the foot). The lower arm temperature decreased by 0.5°–1.5°C. The skin temperature of other areas of the body were not noticeably changed.

372. Sheard, C., M. M. D. Williams, and B. T. Horton. Skin temperatures of the extremities under various environmental and physiological conditions. *In: American Institute of Physics. Temperature, its measurement and control in science and industry, p. 557–570. New York, Reinhold, 1941.*

The effects are analyzed of environmental temperatures of 18°–34°C upon: the results of posture on the skin temperatures of the extremities; the relationship between basal metabolic rates and the temperatures of the toes; the thermal changes produced in the extremities by the ingestion of food; changes in the temperatures of the fingers and toes and the relative roles of the upper and lower extremities in the regulation of the dissipation of heat; the effects of changes in relative humidity on the skin temperatures of the extremities.

373. Trauner, L. On the cold problem [In German, summaries in German, French, and English]. *Ars medici, Basel, v. 39 (6), 1949: 357–365.*

The common cold, either alone or as a symptom of other conditions, has a third factor in its origin beyond the infectious agent—climatic conditions relationship. This factor is that of damage to the vegetative centers of the brain having to do with temperature regulation. Dihydroergotamine-Sandoz (DHE 45), a sympathicolytic drug, was found to be successful if administered early, in cutting short the colds and alleviating pronouncedly protracted colds. The author suggests that, analogous to rheumatic diseases, an important pathogenic factor in colds is a "sympathetic allergy."

374. Wezler, K., and R. Thauer. The role of the circulation in heat regulation [In German]. *Zschr. ges. exp. Med., v. 112, 1943: 345–379.*

Changes in the physical blood circulation were analysed in 4 healthy adults at different temperatures (6°–50°C) and humidities (50%–90%), over periods of three hours. Results showed that circulatory changes (the major component of physical thermoregulation) do not coincide with the changes in gaseous metabolism. Oxygen consumption varied little from the normal within a "comfortable" temperature range, but increased at temperatures above 35°C and below 22°C. There was, however, no similarly indifferent circulatory zone at comfortable temperatures, but constant variations occurred to constitute physical thermoregulation. A change to a lowered temperature did not at first noticeably affect chemical thermoregulation, but affected physical thermoregulation immediately. The blood circulation was reduced with the decrease of room temperature from 35°C and was again stimulated below 15°C. The skin circulation constantly adapts to new temperature levels. The volume/minutes of the heart varied with each slight temperature change even within the comfort zone. After cooling to 15°C the peripheral vascular contraction was followed by an increased general flow resistance; an increased blood pressure, and a reduction in the number of heart beats and heart output. However, this adaptation of physical thermoregulation did not suffice completely to keep the body temperature constant. as a drop of over 1°C was noted in 3 out of 4 subjects. Effective chemical thermoregulation apparently starts when vasoconstriction cannot go much further. Below 15°C a greatly augmented oxygen consumption set in rather briskly together with a strong shivering, which restimulated the circulation. Vasodilatation in the shivering muscles led to a decrease in the general peripheral flow resistance, and to an augmented volume/minute through increased frequency and heart output; the diastolic blood pressure, which had its maximum during the greatest circulatory throttling, decreased again noticeably. At this point the body temperature began to rise, so that at 6°C the lowering which had occurred at 15°C was almost compensated. The pulse rate began to decrease almost before the body temperature, sometimes even below 50/minutes. In general, however, its minimum coincides with the lowest body temperature. The diastolic pressure at this point was maximal, while the frequency of the heart beat was at its lowest. As the diastolic pressure decreased again beyond its maximum, the frequency increased. It is suggested that the pulse rate is a reflex of the pressoreceptors.

375. Wyndham, C. H., and W. G. Wilson-Dickson. Physiological responses of hands and feet to cold in relation to body temperature. *J. Appl. Physiol., v. 4, Sept. 1951: 199–207.*

During rest periods, when there was usually a general body cooling, the hands and feet of test subjects, in full protective clothing, showed marked cooling during exposure for 3 hour intervals at an ambient temperature of $-12\,°C$. Comparative light physical activity quickly caused rewarming of the hands and feet. Reflex control of blood flow appears to exert a dominating effect on extremity temperatures in cold. There was evidently some reinforcement of the vasodilator effect in short exposures with the body heavily clad and body temperature raised by vigorous work, since even bare hands did not cool.

See also items: 109, 110, 121, 122, 135, 137, 138, 143, 165, 173, 175, 177, 179, 194, 207, 246, 291, 292, 336, 348, 369, 439, 499, 520, 1131, 1280, 1236, 1299, 1399, 2084.

I. Role of Hormones

376. Ask-Upmark, E. The parathyroids and the body temperature [In English]. *Acta med. scand., v. 96 (5–6), 1938: 481–500.*

Knowledge, especially clinical, of the role of the parathyroid glands in their relation to body temperature, is reviewed. Four cases of hyperthyroidism are described with regard to variations in body temperature which was usually above normal. In one patient, however, body temperature was sub-normal; after removal of a parathyroid adenoma the temperature approached normal but with marked differences between the morning and evening levels.

377. Balogh, L., S. Donhoffer, P. Jilly, and G. Mestýan. The effect of goitrogens on oxygen consumption and body temperature of albino rats [In Hungarian, summaries in English and Russian]. *Kísérl. Orvostud., v. 2 (1), 1950: 51–61.*

Administration of a single dose of methylthiouracil, especially in normal rats, brought about greater variation, with an increase of shorter or longer duration, of metabolic rate than in the pre-experimental period. In acute experiments with aminothiazole, the rate of metabolism and degree of body temperature were lowered, sometimes after a short initial rise. This lowering of temperature and of metabolic rate were especially pronounced in hypophysectomized or thyroidectomized rats.

378. Balogh, L., I. Barka, S. Donhoffer, P. Jilly, and G. Mestýan. The acute action of antithyroid agents on the body temperature and the oxygen consumption of the rat and analysis of its mechanism [In English, summaries in English and Russian]. *Acta physiol. hung., v. 2 (3–4), 1951: 343–362.*

Subcutaneous administration of a single dose of the antithyroid agents aminothiazole and methylthiouracil, or of sulfonamides, was followed by a rapid fall of body temperature and O_2 consumption in rats which were normal, thyroidectomized, or hypophysectomized. The same dose of aminothiazole administered within a day or two was either less effective or brought about no changes in body temperature and O_2 consumption. The acute action of aminothiazole was not affected by administration of physiological doses of thyroxine, nor was the O_2 consumption inhibited by dinitrophenol. Resection of the cervical cord abolished the effect of aminothiazole on body temperature and brought about a rise of O_2 consumption instead of a fall. Following bilateral electrolytic lesions of the hypothalamus 16 out of 34 animals failed to respond in the usual manner to aminothiazole. It is concluded that the action of antithyroid agents on body temperature and O_2 consumption is mediated through a central nervous mechanism in which the hypothalamus plays an essential role and that both the areas for heat loss and heat gain are affected.

379. Berde, B. On hormonal warmth regulation [In German, summary in English]. *Experientia, Basel, v. 2, Dec. 15, 1946: 498–500.*

The body temperature of thyroidectomized guinea pigs, when placed in an environmental temperature of $34°–35\,°C$, rose higher and for a longer period than did that of normal guinea pigs. Administration of thyroxin increased both the rise and duration of body temperature. It is concluded that the original temperature rise is not due to thyroxin deficiency but to a lack of thermothyrin A, an antagonistic hormone of the thyroid. Administration of methyl-thiouracil to normal guinea pigs gave results similar to those of thyroidectomy, and demonstrated that thiouracil inhibits not only thyroxin production but the formation of thermothyrin A as well.

380.   Berde, B. Behavior of the temperature of the thyroidectomized animals in a hot environment [In English]. *Hungar. acta physiol., v. 1 (2–3), 1947: 52–61.*

Thyroidectomized animals, exposed to environmental temperatures of 27° to 41°C, were less well able to stand a higher than average temperature than were the normal animals. The fact that thyroxin did not improve, but actually worsened this situation, lends further support to the theory that an antagonistic hormone, thermothyrin A, called the cooling hormone—which is normally produced by the thyroid in a hot environment—is also absent in these animals.

381.   Berde, B. New data on the question of hormonal thermoregulation [In English]. *Hungar. acta physiol., v. 1 (2–3), 1947: 62–66.*

The body temperature of guinea pigs or rabbits, treated with methylthiouracil, rises more rapidly and higher than does that of normal animals in a higher than average environmental temperature. Experimental results would indicate that thiouracil derivatives not only suspend the synthesis of thyroxin but bring about a more general inhibition to impede the production of thermothyrin A, the hormone believed responsible for cooling.

382.   Berde, B. Restitution of the reduced heat tolerance of thyroidectomized animals with thermothyrin [In English, summary in German]. *Experientia, Basel, v. 3, Dec. 15, 1947: 500–501.*

The reduced tolerance to heat of thyroidectomized animals, which could not be corrected by administration of thyroxin, as found previously by the author (item 379), can be improved by administration of thermothyrin.

383.   Berde, B. Temperature regulation and the endocrine system [In German]. *Zschr. Vitamin & Forsch., Wien, v. 4, Aug. 1951: 338–376.*

This extensive review of the literature between 1939 and 1949 deals with the role of the endocrine system in temperature regulation. Following the short introduction, the subject is considered under the following headings: epiphysis, hypophysis, thyroid, parathyroid, thymus, pancreas, adrenal cortex, adrenal medulla, testis, and ovary, as well as true hibernation. Under the heading of the hypophysis (p. 340–341), cold is considered in its effect on hypophysectomy, in the regulatory action of the hypophysis, and in relation to the nerve connections of the hypophysis. Under the heading of the thyroid (p. 345–352), there is discussion of the histological and histochemical alterations following cold exposure, or thyroidectomy, of thyroid feeding, of thyroxin, and of the nerve pathways of the thyroid. There are short sections on the effect of cold on the pancreas (p. 356), the adrenal cortex (p. 358–360), the adrenal medulla (p. 361–363), and the ovary (p. 367–368). A bibliography (p. 372–376) of 248 items is appended, including some few 1950 and 1951 references.

384.   Bonanno, A. M. The spleen and thermoregulation [In Italian, summaries in Italian and French]. *Bol. Ist. sieroter. Milan, v. 18 (6), 1939: 427–434.*

The author cites two cases of serious hyperthermia following splenectomies, and then reports results of some experimental work provoking febrile reactions in rabbits 24 hours, 15 days, and 30 days after splenectomy had been performed on them. He concludes that there is a real influence by the spleen on thermoregulation but the mechanism of action is unknown.

385. **Bonvallet, M., P. Dell, and F. S. Stutinsky.** The role of the hypophysis and of the supraoptico-hypophyseal tract in thermogenetic responses [In French]. *Discussions des rapports et communications, Seizieme reunion, Lausanne, 6, 7 et 8 Avril 1948: 123A–126A (J. physiol. path. gen., v. 40, 1948).*

The persistence of homeothermy, following experimental intervention at the cervical medulla of animals, is explained on the basis of the direct activity of the hypophysis without any hypothalamic control. The presence of intact supraoptico-hypophyseal connections is necessary in this situation. Following this and earlier studies on the complex hypothalmo-hypophyseal relationship, the authors suggest that a hypophyseal hormone intervenes in some unknown manner in thermogenetic reactions.

386. **Cate, J. ten.** The significance of thyroxin on warmth regulation [In Dutch]. *Ned. tschr. geneesk., v. 90, Feb. 2–9, 1946: 81–82.*

Changes in body temperature of thyroidectomized, and normal, rats were studied following treatment with tetrahydro-β-naphthylamine or quinine. It is concluded that thyroxin is involved in the antipyretic action of quinine and, through its action directly on cellular metabolism, plays a role in body temperature regulation.

387. **Dal Pozzo, G.** Thymectomy and exposure to severe cold [In Italian, summaries in Italian, German, French, and English]. *Riv. pat. sper., v. 29, Nov.-Dec. 1942: 117–130.*

Rabbits were exposed to an environmental temperature below 20°C after removal of the thymus gland. It was found that the body temperature decrease was accentuated; blood sugar increase was greater; blood volume was increased while plasma proteins decreased; and the weight of the liver was greater than in control animals.

388. **Donhoffer, S., G. Mestyán, and L. Balogh.** Acute action of goitrogenic agents on the body temperature and oxygen consumption of the rat. *Nature, Lond., v. 166, Oct. 28, 1950: 737–738.*

Observations during experimentation with rats indicated that the acute action of goitrogenic agents on oxygen consumption was of central nervous origin involving the hypothalamus. However, effects on body temperature and on oxygen consumption could be abolished together or separately by hypothalamic lesions which did not severely impair temperature regulation.

389. **Fazio, F.** Adrenal capsule and thermal regulation. II. Action of medullary hormone on the resistance to cold of the rat, after adrenalectomy [In Italian]. *Boll. Soc. ital. biol. sper., v. 15, 1940: 496–497.*

Changes of metabolic rate and of rectal temperature were studied in normal and in adrenalectomized rats exposed to cold (3°–4°C). The author concludes that Adrenalin given to an adrenalectomized rat restores to the animal its ability to increase its metabolic rate in the cold, and protects it from an excessive loss of body heat.

390. **Frommel, E., and F. Vallette.** Influence of thyroxin on the body temperature of guinea pigs previously injected with dinitrophenol. *Arch. sc., Genève, v. 3 (1), 1950: 54–56.*

Guinea pigs which were given intramuscular injections of thyroxin (1 mg/kg, each of 4 days) previous to those of dinitrophenol (0.025 g/kg) reacted with a more pronounced rise of temperature (42.8°C) than did those given dinitrophenol only (40.1°C; normal temperature about 38°C). The effect of dinitrophenol was found to be the same as that established earlier for apomorphine except that the active principle of the thyroid gland excites metabolism and respiration while alkaloids reduce them. In the first case an increased, and in the latter a reduced, respiratory effect resulted, demonstrating the important influence of respiration in the regulation of body temperature.

391. Gergely, J. An account of the role of the thyroid and the nervous system in chemical heat regulation [In German]. *Arch. exp. Path., Berl., v. 202, 1943: 597–608.*

Heat regulating ability was considerably impaired in white rats with the thyroid gland removed, as shown by only a slight increase in the oxygen consumption on exposure to cold (water bath, 7°–15°C) and by the greater fall in body temperature. Athyroid animals, given thyroxin, acted much like normal animals. The author concludes that heat regulation is a function primarily of the nervous system; thyroxin aids this regulation by means of its central as well as peripheral action.

392. Giaja, J. Temperature regulation and the thyroid hormone [In French]. *Riv. biol., v. 33 (20), 1942: 158–163.*

Prolonged administration of a thyroid preparation to rats increased greatly their basal metabolism at normal room temperatures and still further increased it at lowered environmental temperatures (16° and 1.5°C) over that of untreated rats. Under conditions of reduced barometric pressure the consumption of oxygen decreased and it was possible to show that of the extra oxidation following thyroid administration, part was due to a basal oxidation independent of the lowered oxygen tension and the other part appeared as a type of temperature regulation whose intensity was a function of lowered oxygen tension.

393. Grant, R. Thermoregulatory thresholds in thyroidectomized rabbits [Abstract]. *Fed. Proc., Balt., v. 10, Mar. 1951: 54.*

The effects of high environmental temperature on rectal temperature, respiratory rate, ear hyperemia, and oxygen consumption were studied in male rabbits before and after thyroidectomy. Heat tolerance was decidedly improved; rectal temperature rose less and more slowly and stabilization of rectal temperature could be achieved at higher environmental temperatures. Decrease of oxygen consumption, of both normal and thyroidectomized animals, was due to decreased random activity and presumably accounted for the animal's ability to stabilize rectal temperatures in hot environments despite saturation of heat loss mechanisms. It is said that these results do not necessarily contradict the existence of thermothyrins but do contradict the improbable postulation that thyroidectomized animals are less resistant to high environmental temperatures. A general dulling of thermostatic responses by reactions involving polypnea and of shivering is suggested as the explanation.

394. [Greene, R.] Discussion on peripheral vascular lesions. *Proc. Roy. Soc. Med., v. 37, Aug. 1944: 625–627.*

In this general discussion on peripheral vascular lesions, Dr. Greene gave some information on the relationship between the thyroid gland's role in temperature regulation and the effects of cold. Some clinical evidence, including 2 detailed case histories, are presented in order to draw attention to the fact that lowered thyroid activity commonly produces not merely cold extremities but the very cold and cyanosed extremities which are sometimes labelled acrocyanosis. This spasm of vessels which was intended to protect the body in general against the effects of hypothermia may be so exaggerated that actual gangrene may occur even at normal temperatures. There is justification to assume the slight unrecognized degrees of hypothyroidism and hypothyrokinesis are likely to increase the liability to frostbite and immersion foot, as well as other peripheral vascular disorders.

395. Hemingway, A., T. Rasmussen, A. T. Rasmussen, and H. Wikoff. Effect of cutting the pituitary stalk on physiological temperature regulation. *Endocrinology, v. 27 (2): 1940: 212–218.*

Physical temperature-regulatory responses, such as panting, shivering, vasoconstriction, and vasodilation, were found to function normally but at thresholds elevated by 0.5° to 2.0°C in dogs when the pituitary stalk was cut. Cutting the stalk also caused an increase in rectal and skin temperatures.

396. Herrath, E. von. The spleen and heat regulation [In German]. *Anat. Anz.*, *v. 91, Feb. 1941: 20–31.*

A review of the experimental findings and interpretations of the role of the spleen in heat regulation, which suggests the possibility that the spleen may produce some regulatory substance, possibly in close metabolic association with the thyroid. Further study of these relations is needed. 22 refs.

397. Macco, G. di. Parathyroid and numbing cold. Experimental research [In Italian, summaries in Italian, French, English and German]. *Ormoni, v. 1, Nov. 1939: 873–884.*

Rabbits, with the parathyroid glands removed, were found to suffer a more rapid lowering of body temperature and a lower temperature at the time of death than did normal rabbits when exposed to a low environmental temperature. This is explained on the basis that the parathyroid gland functions—as the thyroid does—to activate the thermoregulatory center to increase body temperature in an attempt to combat the heat loss.

398. Mansfeld, G., and E. Mészáros. The effect of thyroxin on physical temperature regulation [In German]. *Arch. exp. Path., Berl., v. 196 (6), 1940: 567–572.*

The effect of thyroxin on the drop in temperature caused by Novocain was studied in guinea pigs by thermoelectric measurements of skin temperature and of inner body temperature with regard to the question whether or not the effect was due to central or peripheral factors. It was evident that the body temperature drop from Novocain was due to increased loss of heat through the skin. Pretreatment of the animals with thyroxin was found to hinder the vascular dilatation usually produced in the skin by Novocain; the internal body temperature was not altered by Novocain. The inner temperature could also be maintained at a normal level under Novocain treatment by keeping the animal in a warm environment; the Novocain action caused the skin temperature to rise. Since it had been shown that the thyroxin-Novocain antagonism could be abolished by resection of the spinal cord (at D_5–D_8), and by administration of ergotamine, it is concluded that thyroxin counteracts increased heat loss by stimulating a vasomotor center for the skin whose nervous paths run from the cord below D_5. Hence the final mechanism of its action is a physical (decreased heat loss) regulation of temperature, rather than a chemical, metabolic (decreased heat formation) mechanism.

399. Mansfeld, G. Humoral transferability in chemical heat regulation [In German]. *Arch. exp. Path., Berl., v. 196 (6), 1940: 573–589.*

Rabbits, both before and after thyroidectomy, were subjected to a fall in body temperature of 2° or 3°C when placed in front of an electric fan following their immersion in cold water. Some of the animals were then dried, and after their body temperature had risen 0.5° to 1.0°C, they were bled. Others of the animals were placed in a heating cabinet (31°–33°C) for 3–4 hours until their body temperatures were higher than normal. The blood serum of the cooled (donor) animal was injected intravenously into other (recipient) rabbits. The oxygen consumption of muscle or liver slices from the recipient animals, was studied by use of the Warburg apparatus. In discussing the role of the thyroid gland in chemical regulation, it was concluded that in heat regulation against a cold environment a substance had been released into the blood which could be transferred in the blood serum to another animal bringing about a rise in the rate of combustion in denervated skeletal muscle from the recipient animal without a latent period such as that for thyroxin. This activity could only be observed when the thyroid of the donor animal was active. Intravenous injections of thyroxin in a donor animal produced blood sera which in similar transfer experiments brought about some similar changes, after a lapse of 24 hours, in oxidation of liver slices to those of the "cold" sera. Hence it was concluded that during cold exposure thyroxin is given off into the blood. Presence of a functional hypophysis—but not the presence of an adrenal gland—in the donor animal was necessary to obtain active sera following exposure to cold or treatment with thyroxin. Hence thyroxin, released in response to cold, must cause the pituitary to bring about an increase of muscle oxidation by the giving off of a promptly-acting substance which is humorally transferred;

thyroxin itself only produces increased combustion in vegetative organs, such as liver, after a latent period of 24 hours. In the spring the transfer of activity could not be demonstrated with either the "cold" sera or with that from thyroxin-treated animals. In response to heating, rabbits gave off into the blood a substance which by similar transfer experiments was shown to decrease combustion in the denervated skeletal muscle of other animals. A functional thyroid —but not an intact hypophysis—was necessary for this activity to be observed.

400. Mansfeld, G., and E. Mészáros. Further research in humoral transferability in chemical heat regulation [In German]. *Arch. exp. Path., Berl., v. 196 (6), 1940: 590–597.*

Blood serum from dogs whose body temperature had been raised above the usual level by immersion in hot baths, was found on transfer to other (recipient) dogs to lower the oxygen uptake of such dogs about 20–30% (as tested by gaseous metabolism apparatus employing a cannula technique). The lowest values were reached in 3–5 hours. After hypophysectomy of the heated donor, its serum remained active; after thyroidectomy, it was inactive. Sera from dogs taken during the cold weather of the winter, following treatment as above, showed a similar activity but when taken during the spring was inactive. These differences are explained on the basis that the oxygen spared by the oxidation-checking substance present in such sera was probably used for glycogen formation in the months of greatest glycogen impoverishment. The dog "heat serum" could be deproteinized by alcohol and such deproteinized serum still affected the gaseous metabolism in the expected manner in rats. Dog "cold serum" likewise was still effective after deproteinization. Hence the content of these humoral carrier substances, concerned in body temperature regulation, could be determined in rats without the interference which might occur from the foreign proteins of the dog's blood.

401. Mansfeld, G. The active principle of the oxidation-inhibiting thyroid function [In French]. *Arch. exp. Path., Berl., v. 196 (6), 1940: 598–608.*

Following repeated alkaline hydrolysis and acid precipitation of thyroid gland tissue, there was released an active principle which was similar to that produced normally in animals during the winter. Experiments using 3–5 diiodothyrosin, or iodothyreopeptone, indicated that they did not possess this ability to alter the oxygen consumption of tissue. The new chemically isolated material thermothyrin was found to have the same or similar reactions depending on the environmental temperature of the experiment, as had been demonstrated earlier with the transfused "cold" or "hot" sera. The thermothyrin was found also to be made up of two distinct oxidation-limiting components, one (thermothyrin A) was acid-soluble; the other (thermothyrin B) was precipitated in a solution of pH 5.

402. Mansfeld, G. Hormonal factors of chemical thermo-regulation and two hitherto unknown hormones of the thyroid [In German]. *Schweiz. med. Wschr., v. 72, Nov. 4, 1942: 1267–1273.*

The presence in the blood serum and the physiological functioning of two hitherto unknown hormones of the thyroid gland—thermothyrin A and thermothyrin B—are discussed. These two hormones have an antagonistic action to that of thyroxin and cause, in the normal animal, a decrease in basal metabolism tending to bring about a storing of glycogen. In regulation against cold the thyroid gland delivers to the blood the thyroxin which activates the hypophysis to produce an increased combustion in the resting muscle. During regulation against overwarming, combustion-inhibiting substances are produced by the thyroid. Studies of materials taken from the thyroid led to the isolation of two oxidation-inhibiting crystalline substances: acid-soluble thermothyrin A and acid-insoluble thermothyrin B, the first of which could also be isolated from the blood.

403. Mansfeld, G. Hormonal and nervous factors in regulation of body temperature [In English, German summary]. *Experientia, Basel, v. 3, Oct. 1947: 398–403.*

The ability of rabbits—with cervical transection of the spinal cord—to maintain body temperature at a moderately low environmental temperature was found to be due exclusively to excessive combustion of foodstuffs. In animals with thoracic transection a constant rise of the rate of metabolism was observed which was independent of external temperature and which was due to hyperfunction of the thyroid gland. These differences would appear to be due ultimately to interference with the innervation. The importance of hormonal thermoregulation is said to lie in the fact that by increasing heat production it tends to raise blood temperature; this maintains the blood temperature above the level that elicits shivering. It was found to be unimportant which part of the body was cooled, since the sensory nerves of the skin had nothing to do with this mechanism of shivering.

404. Mansfeld, G. The thyroid glands and their action. *London, Frederick Muller, Ltd., 1949. 157 pp. (Translated by* ERWIN PULAY. *Original published in German by Benno Schwabe & Co., Basle, 1943, under the title, "Die Hormone der Schilddrüse und ihre Wirkungen.")*

Chapter X (p. 84–94), is entitled The Role of the Thyroid Gland and the Pituitary Gland in Heat Regulation against Cold. As a result of the influence of cold, the thyroid gland produces thyroxin which in turn causes the formation, with the aid of the hypophysis, of an additional active substance the so-called heating hormone. This substance can be transferred with the serum and can immediately cause increased combustion in the resting muscles, without tremor of the muscles, and thus intervenes in the process of chemical heat regulation. When in excessive cold the thyroxin can no longer prevent tremor of the muscles it appears to aid in the efficacy of the trembling in heat formation. Thyroxin performs another function, that of the promotion of heat formation in the inner organs lasting many days. This belated effect of thyroxin may well be of importance for adaptation to cold surroundings. Chapter XV (p. 110–114), and the next several chapters, deal with the role of the thyroid gland in regulation of the body temperature against over-heating. In this regulation it releases to the blood serum an active substance which diminishes combustion in the muscles. In contrast to the active substance in the cold sera, this substance in the warm sera is not under the influence of the hypophysis. In these chapters are discussed some of the effects of the active substances—thermothyrins A and B—their differences and seasonal differences in reaction in thyroidectomized animals, their seasonal differences in presence and quantity in the sera, and the importance of the thyroid gland colloid in their action.

405. Maqsood, M. Influence of the thyroid on body temperature of growing animals. *Nature, Lond., v. 167, Mar. 3, 1951: 356.*

Because of its regulation of about 40% of body metabolism, the thyroid hormone is said to play a major role in regulation of body temperature. The author studied the effects of known levels of thyroidal stimulation and inhibition on the rectal temperatures of growing male rabbits and of rams.

406. Martinović, P., and J. Giaja. Hypophysectomy and thermoregulation [In French]. *Bull. Acad. serbe sc., v. 1 (1), 1950: 125–128.*

Hypophysectomized rats have a well developed chemical thermoregulation. They differ from the normal rats by the relatively elevated temperature at which they produce their greatest body heat. Heat loss is vigorously augmented in the hypophysectomized animal.

407. Mészáros, E. Thermoelectrical studies on the role of the thyroid in heat regulation [Abstract, in German]. *Ber. ges. Physiol., v. 114, Oct. 1939: 671.*

Thermoelectrical measurements of the skin and rectal temperature of subjects showed that the temperature drop induced by Novocain was initiated by a marked increase in skin temperature. The initial temperature decrease of 3°–4°C was reduced to less than half, due to stimulated skin circulation. In animals pretreated by thyroxin, the Novocain injection did not stimulate the blood circulation in the skin, and the body temperature remained constant. If, however, the temperature drop after Novocain is averted by warming the abdominal cavity instead of by thyroxin, the skin is warmed considerably. It is concluded that the Novocain-antagonistic thyroxin effect, which acts upon the central nervous system, induces a throttling of the heat loss, and is separate from the thyroxin effect, related to heat production, which acts on the peripheral nerves.

408. Morin, G. Thermogenesis of rewarming in the dog in the absence of adrenal secretion [In French]. *C. rend. Soc. biol.*, *Par.*, v. *136*, *June 1942: 543–544.*

Evaluations of heat production, by measurement of respiratory exchanges in a closed chamber, were made on 4 dogs over a 2–3 week period following various kinds of surgical intervention to decrease or exclude the secretion from the adrenal medulla. The enervation of the medullary portion of the adrenal glands did not prevent the increase of oxygen utilization in the dog in repose and while fasting, when exposed for 1–3 hours at temperatures from 18° to 3°C. Thermogenesis was increased in similar fashion in the dogs deprived of their adrenaline-producing ability whether by ablation or by curettage; the dogs rewarmed in similar manner. However, the increase in heat production under the influence of cold was of the same magnitude in the operated animals as in the controls of similar size and with a comparable growth of fur. These findings are of significance in that under the conditions of intensity and duration of cold employed in the experiments, the regulatory reaction noted was not sensibly modified by the apparent results of the absence of the adrenal secretion. This is in agreement with other researchers using decapsulated mammals, on the role of the medullary adrenal in thermal regulation; it does not exclude the possibility that the intervention of the adrenal gland in response to cold exposure, is a factor in over-all endocrine balance.

409. Morin, G. Action of Adrenalin on the thermogenesis of the dog with spinal resection [In French]. *C. rend. Soc. biol.*, *Par.*, v. *136*, *June 1942: 811–812.*

Heat production, as measured by respiratory exchange in a closed chamber, was studied in dogs after intramuscular administration of Adrenalin. The dogs had earlier been subjected to dorsal, lumbar, or sacral resection of the spinal cord, and a short period had elapsed for recovery from shock and for stabilization of temperature regulation in an environment of 18°–26°C. Under these conditions, Adrenalin in doses of 25–200 γ/kg injected into the pad of a hind paw, brought about an increase in thermogenesis. Heat production attained a maximum value in the first hour after the injection and returned to the initial level in the second or third hour. The percentage increase, and the duration of the metabolic stimulation, was proportional to the quantity of the hormone administered. For example, doses of 25, 50, and 100 γ/kg raised the metabolism 23, 32, and 43%, respectively. The regularity of the results was in contrast to results obtained under similar conditions with normal dogs; the agitation produced by the injection, which is always somewhat painful, rendered the interpretation of results difficult. The results are said to confirm the calorigenic action of Adrenalin and to contribute to the evidence of its peripheral action.

410. Morin, G. On the thermogenesis of rewarming in the dog in the presence and in the absence of medullary adrenal secretions and of the thyroid [In French]. *C. rend. Soc. biol.*, *Par.*, v. *137*, *Jan. 1943: 539–540.*

This is a continuation of the author's previous experiments on the increase in heat production, despite the previous exclusion of adrenal secretion, on exposure of the non-anesthetized dog to cold. In the current experiments, respiratory exchanges of two dogs were studied by use of a closed chamber. One dog had previously had an adrenalectomy on the right side and the adrenal of the left side enervated and the medullary portion removed by curettage; the other dog was thyroidectomized. When the environmental temperature was lowered, but not in excess of 10°C (to produce an environmental temperature of 20° to 14°C), the increase in heat production continued as a secondary measure with the exposure to cold; less frequently the curve of oxygen consumption exhibited alternating oscillations. The results of these experiments, as in previous studies, indicate that the behavior of heat production in rewarming varies as a function of the degree of cooling obtained, and the behavior is not apparently modified by the absence of the thyroid and medullary adrenal secretions.

411. Morin, G. Adrenal medulla and temperature regulation. I. Calorigenic action of adrenaline; demonstration; significance [In French]. *Rev. canad. biol.*, v. *5* (*2*), *1946: 121–134.*

Adrenalin injected into the hind leg muscle of a dog, in a temperature around thermal neutrality, increased heat production. Heat production was a function of the dosage. However, in dosages of 200 to 800 micrograms per kg this increase was not sufficient to overcome the thermoregulatory mechanisms to produce hyperthermia. The author concludes that adrenalinic extra-heat is usable by homeothermic animals in the warming up thermogenesis.

412. Morin, G. The adrenal medulla and temperature regulation. II. Reaction of adrenal secretion to cold [In French, summaries in French and English]. *Rev. canad. biol.*, v. 5 (4), 1946: 388–399.

Unanesthetized dogs were exposed to a cold environment (about 15°–16°C) for periods up to 1½ hours. An increase in adrenaline secretion and use was indicated by the acceleration of the heart action, the extrinsic innervation having been eliminated by surgical vagotomy and stellectomy.

413. Morin, G. Adrenal medulla and temperature regulation. III. Thermogenesis of re-warming in the absence of adrenaline secretion [In French, English summary]. *Rev. canad. biol.*, v. 6 (5), 1947: 715–723.

Indirect calorimetric measurements of respiratory exchanges in a confined chamber, at an environmental temperature of 16°C., did not reveal any notable changes following denervation or destruction of the adrenal medulla of dogs. The author explains that these seemingly negative results are not in conflict with those previously reported—in which intense cold stimulated adrenaline production to give the extra heat needed—since it may be that the eventual changes were beyond the range of the method, or because other regulations compensated for the removed secretion.

414. Nielsen, E. T. Thermo-electric measurement of the body temperature of mice and fishes [In English]. *Acta med. skand.*, Suppl. 90, 1938: 169–189.

Variations of body temperature, as indicated by thermo-electric measurements, concurrent with changes of environmental temperature, were studied in mice (both normal and injected with insulin), mice sucklings, and the fish *Lebistes*. Temperature regulation was usually capable of keeping the body temperature within the range of 17° to 40°C; outside this range the animal died. When the temperature regulation was working well, insulin given to mice with a body temperature of 35°–36°C would cause a fall in body temperature; injection of sugar would stop the fall. Insulin given during lowered or falling body temperatures indicated that a lowered temperature may perhaps cause a slower (mean reaction time for onset of convulsion was 60 minutes as against 50 for normal mice) reaction, without such a deadly effect. It was shown that the differences in body temperature could not be responsible for the differences in insulin sensitivity between these animals, the latter finding having been previously reported.

415. Pintér, S., and J. Méhes. Contributions to hormonal heat regulation during the younger years. I [In German]. *Zschr. Vitamin Forsch.*, Wien, v. 2 (3–4), 1948–1949: 195–204.

"Warmed" sera was obtained from a (donor) child after a rise of the rectal temperature of 1.3°–1.5°C following a hot bath, and was injected into a (recipient) rat. Such sera taken from either a healthy child or one suffering from severe hypothyroidism, did not decrease or alter in any other way, the basal metabolism of the rat. In similar experiments with young animals (14–43 day old dogs or 60–98 day old rabbits), the "warmed" sera did not decrease the basal metabolism of the rat; in some of the younger dogs the metabolism was increased. The "warmed" sera of adult dogs and rabbits invariably brought about a decrease in basal metabolism. At the age at which puberty occurred and the atrophy of the thymus gland began (about 90–98 days of age) in rabbits, their "warmed" sera did not alter the metabolism of the rats. The reason for this difference in the action of the sera of the young or adult animals is presumed to lie either in a quantitative difference in the thermothyrin formation by the thyroid, or in a different integration relationship of the endocrine glands—or in the presence or absence of the thymus—before and after sexual maturity.

416. Pintér, S., and J. Méhes. Contribution to hormonal heat regulation during the younger years. II. Influence of thymectomy and thymus extract on the effect of "warm" sera [In German]. *Zschr. Vitamin Forsch.*, Wien, v. 3 (3–4), 1949–1950: 250–260.

After earlier verification of the fact that neither the serum from normal, nor from heated young rabbits possessed a depressing action on the metabolism of rats, further investigations were carried out to see at what age the depressing factor did appear. Tests with 14 rabbits showed that at the age of 90–110 days all the "warmed" sera induce a 45% increase in metabolism; from 110 to 140 days of age the serum produced no change; from 140 days on, all the sera reduced the metabolism 21.5%. Thymectomy before the age of puberty was followed after 8–10 days by disappearance of the metabolism-stimulating action; however, the depressing action could not be verified because of death of the animals. This action could be restored by injection of a thymus extract (from rabbits or calves) to the thymectomized animals. These experiments show the important role played by the thymus gland in heat regulation.

417. Ring, G. C. Metabolism and body temperature of normal and adrenalectomized rats during exposure to cold. *Am. J. Physiol., v. 122, May 1938: 435–445.*

The rate of temperature increment in rats following exposure to cold was found to be the the same for normal and adrenalectomized rats. In completely adrenalectomized rats, injection of Adrenalin stimulates the basal metabolic rate of animals exposed to cold. Partially adrenalectomized rats show an ability to maintain body temperature.

418. Šahović, K., V. Popović, and M. Anaf. Transplantation of endocrine glands. I. Transplantation of the adrenal; effect of the transplant on thermoregulation [In Serbo-Croatian, summary in French]. *Glas Srpske akad. nauka, odelj. med., v. 204 (4), 1951: 79–85.*

Animals which had had the adrenal gland removed but in which there were successful implants of this gland in the eye, showed a high degree of thermoregulation. Basal metabolism remained unchanged, but peak metabolism was lower than in controls.

419. Šahović, K., V. Popović, and M. Anaf. Contribution to the study of thermoregulation. The role of the adrenal cortex [In Serbo-Croatian, summary in French]. *Glas Srpske akad. nauka, odelj. med., v. 204 (4), 1951: 99–124.*

Ablation of the adrenal gland greatly decreased the thermoregulatory function of the rat. In a group of rats, daily injections of desoxycorticosterone given immediately after ablation of the adrenal capsule made it possible for the animals to exhibit a nearly normal thermoregulatory function. When administration of the hormone was stopped, thermoregulation was impaired and the metabolic quotient was decreased. During administration of the hormone the normal body temperature of the animal was maintained and its weight increased; when administration was stopped, both the body temperature and the weight decreased. The cortex of the adrenal gland plays a major role in the control of thermoregulation.

420. Schaeffer, G., and O. Thibault. Researches on hormonal factors of thermal regulation. Effects of adrenaline on functional change of thyroid activity [In French]. *C. rend. Soc. biol., Par., v. 139, Oct. 13, 1945: 855–856.*

The existence of synergistic thyroxin-adrenaline action, operating in thermal regulation, was demonstrated; thyroid secretion of the rat increased considerably the action of adrenaline, as shown by indirect calorimertic measurements.

421. Schaeffer, G., and O. Thibault. Research on the hormonal factors of thermal regulation. Thermal regulation of the athyroid white rat [In French]. *C. rend. Soc. biol., Par., v. 139, Dec. 8, 1945: 1036–1038.*

After a study of the mechanism of action in relation of thyroxin to oxidative activity of adrenaline, the authors suggest two hypotheses to explain the action: the adrenaline activity is greatly increased in the athyroid rat, or, the sudden increase of metabolic exchange in the reflex thermogenesis of rewarming relies not alone on the medullary adrenal hormone but on another unidentified factor.

422. Schaeffer, G., and O. Thibault. Research on the hormonal factors of temperature regulation. Thermal regulation of the adrenalectomized white rat [In French]. *C. rend. Soc. biol., Par., v. 139, Dec. 8, 1945: 1039–1040.*

Following their studies on hormonal temperature regulation of the adrenalectomized rat, the authors state that there is present another hormone to catalyze the oxidative action of adrenaline, and that they plan to examine the role of the cortical hormones in the reflex thermogenesis of rewarming.

423. Schaeffer, G., and O. Thibault. Studies on hormonal factors of thermal regulation. Thermal regulation in the thyroidectomized and adrenalectomized albino rat [In French]. *C. rend. Soc. biol., Par., v. 140, Feb. 1946: 98–99.*

Rats which had been thyroidectomized and adrenalectomized and then exposed to an environmental temperature of 6°C, underwent a considerable lowering of their body temperature so that after 2 hours the rectal temperature reached 22°C. Even with an increase to 150% in the metabolic rate, the animals could not maintain their normal temperature; an increase to 250% would have been necessary to make up the loss. When the animals were returned to a normal room temperature (28°C), the rectal temperature returned to normal in 5 to 6 hours. In these experiences an environmental temperature of 13°–14°C was the lowest which was compatible with the maintenance of homeothermia; at this temperature an increase in metabolic rate of 150% was sufficient to maintain a normal central temperature. It is concluded that 54% of oxidation is attributable to chemical temperature regulation under control of thyroxin and adrenaline, and 46% to other hormonal functions from which shivering is excluded.

424. Schaeffer, G., and O. Thibault. Studies on hormonal factors of therma regulation. Effects of the injection of cortical hormones on the thermoregulation of the adrenalectomized and thyroidectomized white rat [In French]. *C. rend. Soc. biol., Par., v. 140, Feb. 1946: 100–102.*

The difference in thermal regulation reported in experimental findings with thyroidectomized and adrenalectomized animals may possibly be due to comparisons of reactions at different times following surgery and at different environmental temperatures. In earlier experiments on a group of 150 white rats, adrenalectomized bilaterally, deaths did not occur before the 8th or 9th day; the time of greatest mortality was the 11th day with 79% of the animals having died; one month after surgery only 10% were still alive. In current experiments the rats were both thyroidectomized and adrenalectomized, and then were given synthetic desoxycorticosterone immediately and in continuing doses, while being kept at a room temperature of 28°–30°C. In 12 such animals no signs of cortical deficiency, including no loss of weight, were noted 12 days after surgery; on cessation of medication, deaths began to occur after 3 weeks. However, the hormonal medication of these animals had no effect on heat regulation against exposure to cold since they responded to an environmental temperature of 6°C in the same manner as did a similar group of surgically treated animals which had not been given desoxycorticosterone. Rectal temperatures dropped 7° to 10°C below normal temperatures, and metabolic rats increased 70% to 145%. Following similar experiments with assayed cortical extracts, it is concluded that neither desoxycorticosterone nor the other cortical extracts increased metabolism either directly or indirectly. The author agrees with other workers that in the rare instances where animals have survived double adrenalectomy for more than a month, accessory cortical tissue was present. However, such tissue was without effect in thermal regulation.

425. Schaeffer, G., and O. Thibault. Studies on hormonal factors of thermal regulation. Variation of central temperature of hypophysectomized rat in relation to external temperature [In French]. *C. rend. Soc. biol., Par., v. 140, Oct. 1946: 765–766.*

Groups of rats which had been hypophysectomized were found to experience a mortality of about 50% in the two weeks following surgery, and the remaining rats suffered a loss of about

25% of their weight with a comparable reduction in appetite. After 3 weeks at a room temperature from 23° to 28°C, the rectal temperature of normal rats was approximately 37.3°C; hypophysectomized rats placed in a room of 28°C experienced a progressive decrease of rectal temperature paralleling a decrease in metabolic rate. The rectal temperature of the surgically-treated rats rose to 37.5°C only at an environmental temperature of 35°C. At this higher environmental temperature normal animals succumbed after several days from a strong hyperemia (reaching 40°C). When hypophysectomized animals were taken from the hot room to one at 30°C, their rectal temperatures fell only about 1° after 3½ hours. After several hours at 15°C, rectal temperatures dropped to 28°C or lower. The author concludes that hypophysectomized animals do not react wholly in a homeothermic manner since the rectal temperature drops so little on removal from the hot room to one of normal temperature, and not wholly as poikilothermic since they do experience an increase in metabolic rate at environmental temperatures below 30°C even though that increase is not sufficient to offset the heat loss.

426.   Schaeffer, G. Hormonal factors intervening in chemical regulation of temperature of homeotherms [In French]. *Bull. Acad. nat. méd., Paris, v. 130, ser. 3, Nov. 5–12, 1946: 587–590.*

From studies on rats, in normal (30°C) and low (−7°C) environmental temperatures and in various hormonal states, the author found that 11 calories per kilogram per hour were needed for chemical regulation of body temperature and that 14% of this metabolic total was under the influence of the thyroid gland; 40% under the influence of the adrenal medulla; 28% under the influence of the pituitary (excluding the thyrotropic and adrenotropic hormones); and 18% influenced by unknown factors not connected directly or indirectly with the pituitary.

427.   Scheff-Pfeifer, I. An until-now unknown role of the thyroid gland in heat regulation [Abstract, in German]. *Ber. ges. Physiol., v. 108, 1938: 671.*

Earlier investigations had shown that in guinea pigs, after spinal resection at the level of the 5–8th vertebra, thyroxin administration did not prevent the Novocain-induced drop in temperature during the spring to fall seasons. In the winter, however, thyroxin was effective even after the resection since the thyroxin-stimulated increase of oxidation was approximately three times stronger during the cold season than during the summer. Following thyroidectomy, animals during the summer evidenced a sensitivity to thyroxin similar to that previously shown during the winter. This fact indicates that in the spring the thyroid gland produces a substance which is antagonistic to the oxidation effect of thyroxin. Attempts to isolate chemically this substance have so far not been successful.

428.   Silverman, J. J., and J. E. Wilson. Unusual complication following thyroidectomy; heat-stroke with permanent cerebellar damage. *Ann. Int. M., v. 33 (4), Oct. 1950: 1036–1041.*

Two days after thyroidectomy for a diffuse toxic goiter and during a period of hot weather, a patient developed a fever of 108.4°F and soon thereafter manifested signs of severe cerebellar damage. The authors suggest that the thermoregulatory mechanism, which is very labile during thyrotoxic crisis, may have broken down completely under the added stress of hot weather.

429.   Simonyi, J., and D. Szentgyorgyi. The effect of actedron (phenylisopropylamine) and thyroxin on the body temperature [In English]. *Arch. internat. pharm. dyn., Par., v. 80, July 1949: 1–14.*

The influence of thyroxin on the pyrogenic or antipyretic effects of various drugs, as shown following subcutaneous injection of the drugs into albino rats, gave renewed proof of the central nervous system, thermoregulatory, effect of thyroxin. It was found that thyroxin sensitizes the heating center against pyrogenic substances (including "actedron") and against warmth, while decreasing its sensitiveness against antipyretics.

430. Simpson, S. L. Thyroid and cold sensitivity [Letter to Editor]. *Lancet, Lond., 1947 (v. 1), Mar. 8: 305.*

The author mentions the tolerance to cold seen in patients under thyroid therapy for various disease conditions, and suggests the giving of thyroid preparations in controlled dosage to healthy individuals as a test of its possible use prophylactically in cold exposure.

431. Soumalainen, P., and E. L. Mäkipaja. On the secretion of thermothyrin A in the Finnish steam-bath [In English, summary in German]. *Experientia, Basel, v. 7, Oct. 15, 1951: 384.*

A strong thermothyrin A reaction was obtained from the blood of all subjects after being in a Finnish bath at 75 °C for 15–20 minutes. Since the experiments were carried out in the early winter, thermothyrin B was no longer present in the samples. An aqueous solution of the thermothyrin A crystals, obtained from the blood, injected subcutaneously into the thighs of mice, produced greatly reduced metabolic activity (as judged by the amount of carbon dioxide and water excreted by the mouse in a given period) which was gradually restored to normal. The hormone apparently has a temporarily decreasing effect on metabolism in man also, and is thus a contributing factor in the control of over-heating.

432. Takács, L., and A. Fekete. The effect of methylthiouracil on hormonal thermoregulation in cold environment [In English]. *Hungar. acta physiol., v. 1 (6), 1948: 253–256.*

The blood serum of rabbits exposed to cold (0 °C for 4 hours) was found to increase the oxygen consumption of a skeletal muscle of a rat. After methylthiouracil treatment no such "heating hormone" was demonstrable in the sera. Methylthiouracil appears to have no direct effect upon the hypophysis because thyroxin brings about the production of the pituitary "heating hormone" equally in treated and untreated animals.

433. Thibault, O. Hormonal factors of thermal regulation. Caloric production of the hypophysectomized rat in relation to external temperature [In French]. *C. rend. Soc. biol., Par., v. 140, Dec. 1946: 940–942.*

For normal rats, thermal neutrality (with a rectal temperature maintained at 37.3 °C) was found to be 30 °C; for hypophysectomized rats, it was 35 °C. At an environmental temperature of 35 °C, the metabolic rate of hypophysectomized rats was found to be 3.22 Cal/kg/hr; for normal animals, 5.5 Cal/kg/hr. The author presents a tabulation of the relation of the environmental temperature to the rectal temperature for the normal rat, hypophysectomized rat, thyroidectomized rat, adrenalectomized rat, and the rat both thyroidectomized and adrenalectomized. All but the hypophysectomized rat maintain a normal rectal temperature (37.3 °C) at an environmental temperature of 30 °C. The hypophysectomized animal maintained a normal rectal temperature only when the environmental temperature was 35 °C which was in the zone of hyperthermia for the normal rat. As the environmental temperature decreased the rectal temperature of the hypophysectomized rat likewise decreased in spite of a marked increase in metabolic rate; the normal rat maintained a normal rectal temperature until the environmental temperature was below −5 °C; the thyroidectomized and adrenalectomized animal, until 15 °C; and the rats either thyroidectomized or adrenalectomized, until 0 °C.

434. Thibault, O. Hormonal control of chemical thermoregulation [In French]. *Ann. nutrit. aliment. Par., v. 2 (1), 1948: 89–109.*

Earlier concepts of hormonal factors in thermoregulation, some new trends, and some views of the role of the cortical hormones and of the hypophysis are discussed.

435. Thibault, O. Hormonal factors of chemical regulation of the temperature of homotherms [In French]. *Rev. canad. biol., v. 8, June 1949: 3–131.*

An exhaustive quantitative study was made of the hormonal factors involved in the chemical regulation of temperature in the white rat. Separate and combined ablation of the thyroid and adrenals, or hypophysectomy, were carried out and the role and inter-relation of these glands were studied.

436. Uotila, U. U. On the role of the pituitary stalk in the regulation of the anterior pituitary, with special reference to the thyrotropic hormone. *Endocrinology, v. 25, Oct. 1939: 605–614.*

In animals exposed to cold, the hypothalamus stimulates the secretion of thyrotropic hormone by impulses transmitted through the pituitary stalk.

437. Van Dyke, H. B. The thyrotropic hormone. *In: The physiology and pharmacology of the pituitary body, v. 2, p. 174–197. Chicago, Univ. of Chic., 1939.*

One of the impressive effects of hypophysectomy in mammals is the marked fall in the rate at which heat is produced. A specific substance, the thyrotropic hormone, is secreted only by the anterior pituitary. Normal thyroid function, including its heat-producing ability, is markedly but not completely deficient following hypophysectomy. Morphologically there is atrophy of the epithelium of the thyroid follicles and distention of the latter with dense, non-vacuolated colloids. Following a review of the more current research (since 1935) on the various aspects of the biology of the thyrotropic hormone, it is stated that very little has been produced by way of new factual material since the earlier volume (1936). Effort has mostly been expended in consolidating and extending slightly the knowledge already available. An extensive bibliography, on all aspects of the pituitary gland, is given on pages 298–381.

438. Wertheimer, E., and V. Ben-Tor. Demonstration in vitro of a humoral heat regulation mechanism. *Exp. M. & S., v. 8, May–Nov. 1950: 378–389.*

The diaphragms of rats, which had just previously lived in an environmental temperature of 5°–7°C, excised and incubated in the serum of similarly treated rats, required more glucose and synthesized more glycogen than did diaphragms excised from rats which had lived at environmental temperatures of 28°–30°C. Such increases did not occur when incubation was in Krebs-phosphate-Ringer solution rather than in homologous serum; when the rats were previously treated with thiouracil; or if in addition the rats were returned to room temperature (20°–22°C) for 4 hours. If the cold-treated or heat-treated rats were also adrenalectomized, the diaphragms responded similarly to non-adrenalectomized animals but to a lesser degree.

439. Whitcher, C. E., and F. R. Griffith, Jr. A possible role of the skin in the effect of Adrenalin on body temperature and respiratory metabolism. *Am. J. Physiol., v. 156, Jan. 1949: 114–116.*

The rise in body temperature shown in intact cats after administration of Adrenalin was found to be reduced after removal of the skin. These results would appear to substantiate, in part, the hypothesis that cutaneous vasoconstriction in an intact animal reduces loss of heat through the skin and effects a rise in body temperature.

440. Zummo, C., and G. Sarzana. Adrenal capsule and thermal regulation. I. Action of cortical extract on resistance to cold [In Italian]. *Boll. Soc. ital. biol. Sper., v. 15, 1940: 494–496.*

Adrenalectomized rats, when exposed to environmental temperatures of 3.5° to 4.0°C, had a decreased metabolic rate and lowered rectal temperature from that of normal animals in the same environment. The adrenalectomized rats when treated with cortical extract alone, had a metabolic rate equal to or higher than that of the normal animal but the rectal temperature remained lower than that of the normal animal. From these and other experiments, the authors conclude that both the medullary and cortical functions of the adrenal glands play a necessary and interrelated role in maintaining thermal regulation at low temperatures.

441. Zummo, C., and R. Urso. Adrenal capsule and thermal regulation. III. Action of adrenalin on the gaseous exchange of the rat adrenalectomized and treated with cortical extract [In Italian]. *Boll. Soc. ital. biol. Sper., v. 15, 1940: 498–499.*

Studies were continued on the role of the adrenal capsule in temperature regulation. Changes in oxygen consumption were compared in normal rats given cortical extract, Adrenalin, or both, when exposed to normal (28°C) or to cold (10°C) environmental temperatures. The authors conclude that the stimulating action on metabolism of Adrenalin appears to be aided by the presence in the circulation of cortical hormones.

See also items: 4, 89, 141, 181, 245, 261, 519, 936, 1371, 1376, 1458, 1749.

J. Metabolic Aspects.

442. Brobeck, J. R. Food intake as a mechanism of temperature regulation. *Yale J. Biol.*, v. 20, *July 1948: 545–552.*

Exposure of rats for 18 hours to an environmental temperature of 65°–76°F brought about an increase of food intake, a normal gain in body weight, and an avoidance of hypothermia. If similarly kept at temperatures above 92°F, the food intake was low, water intake was somewhat increased, weight loss was rapid, and fever was experienced. The data indicate that food intake is not necessarily determined by total energy expenditure or by body temperature but appears to be controlled as if it were a mechanism of temperature regulation.

443. Clark, G. The effects of inanition on temperature regulation. *Am. J. Physiol.*, v. 122, *June 1938: 646–649.*

Normal well-nourished cats when placed on an inadequate diet after a preliminary period without food, react normally to cold until the weight loss is considerably more than 30 per cent. Responses to heat are not interfered with by weight losses which cause abnormal responses to cold. The rectal temperatures of cats which have lost more than 30 per cent of their weight under these conditions, are extremely low.

444. Dontcheff, L., and G. Schaeffer. The proteins are not utilized in the reflex thermogenesis of rewarming [In French]. *C. rend. Soc. biol., Par.,* v. 127, *Mar. 11, 1938: 1294–1295.*

Even though the metabolic rate was shown previously to be greatly increased in the cold, it was found that the metabolism of proteins was not under the influence of the hormones associated with cold protection. The reflex mechanism of thermal regulation in rewarming was shown to be mediated through the acceleration of the metabolism of lipids.

445. Fedorov, N. A., and E. I. Shur. The role of the viscera in regulating the temperature of the body of an animal under physiological and pathological conditions. *Am. J. Physiol.*, v. 137, *Aug. 1942: 30–38.*

Thermogenesis in the liver and intestines was studied in normal and in artificially-cooled and -heated animals, as well as in febrile states caused by heterogeneous blood transfusions. Important thermogenesis was found to exist in the intestines. The febrile state caused by heterogeneous transfusion was found to be accompanied by an increase in visceral thermogenesis.

446. Festa, N. Relation of temperature regulation and carbohydrate exchange [In Italian]. *Fol. med., Nap.,* v. 25, *Feb. 15, 1939: 117–125.*

Cold baths lowered the skin temperature but had little or no effect on the internal temperature of normal persons; on the other hand, they caused a pronounced lowering of the internal temperature of diabetic patients even when the skin temperature did not fall correspondingly. These irregularities of behavior noted for the diabetics tended to be minimized when the patient's condition was controlled by insulin.

447. Hiebel, G., and P. Reys. Nyctohemeral rhythm of heat production and specific dynamic action of proteins; study on white rats [In French]. *C. rend. Soc. biol., Par.,* v. 145, *Sept. 1951: 1358–1362.*

Ingestion by rats of protein at the level of 175 mg/100g body weight provoked an increase of heat production of 20% at thermal neutrality. This increase was accompanied by a similar increase in motor activity. The increase was not utilized to prevent the rhythmic periods of reduction of heat production which occur in the normal 24-hour cycle, indicating that the periods of decreased heat production were not due to lapses in the thermoregulation.

448. Hülnhagen, O. On disturbances of heat regulation in acute oxygen deficiency under cold stress [In German]. *Luftfahrtmedizin, v. 9, July 15, 1944: 16–25.*

Measurements were made in a low-pressure chamber on 3 persons subjected to acute oxygen deficiency at altitudes of 5,000 to 7,000 meters and exposed to cold of varying degrees. It was found that under these conditions the heat-regulating mechanism was disturbed and skin and rectal temperatures were lowered.

449. Jitariu, P., A. Koch, and U. Otto. Temperature differences and blood flow measurements in the liver and their use for the estimation of metabolic changes in the organ [In German]. *Pflügers Arch., v. 245 (3), 1942: 317–341.*

Anesthetized cats had ice-water packs or pieces of ice applied to the end of the nose. Rectal temperature was kept as constant as possible by use of heat lamps. Blood flow in the portal vein was measured by Rein's flow meter. Blood pressure in femoral artery and the brachial artery was recorded with a Trendelenburg apparatus. Arteriovenous temperature differences in the hepatic artery and hepatic vein were measured by use of thermoelements; the vein was found to have a temperature 0.2° to 0.6°C higher than the artery. Blood pressure was found to be unaffected; blood flow increased slowly; arteriovenous temperature differences were at first unaffected and then climbed slowly and regularly. It is concluded that the heat production of the liver increased with the cooling of the tip of the nose, and that the liver is very important in physiological heat regulation especially in chemical heat regulation. In a few instances when ice was applied to the abdominal skin, no effects were observed. The anesthesia interfered somewhat with temperature regulation and caused some fall in body temperature.

450. Koskimies, J. On temperature regulation and metabolism in the swift, *Micropus a. apus* L., during fasting [In English, summary in German]. *Experientia, Basel, v. 4, July 15, 1948: 274–276.*

The weight and the body temperature (measured in the throat) of adult and young (4–5 weeks old) swifts were recorded each hour as they were kept in separate glass vessels without food or water. At an environmental temperature of 24°C the survival time of the young birds was about 9 days; the adult birds usually died after a fast of 4 days. The young birds, which weighed more than the adults at the beginning of the experiments, weighed less than the adults at the time of death. The young birds were found to be able to utilize at least half of their total body weight. In the first few days the body temperature of all fasting birds fluctuated in a normal manner. However, birds soon lost the capacity for temperature regulation and reacted like poikilotherms, entering a hunger-coma state. The mechanism of temperature regulation is disturbed more easily in adult birds and the fall of body temperature to a critical limit takes place more rapidly and without as distinct a period of reversible coma. Because the whole metabolic rate is also decreased during this period of coma, the condition can be of great survival value in the cold or when food is lacking.

451. Kramer, K. Chemical heat regulation in extreme cold [Abstract, in German]. *Klin. Wschr., v. 22, Mar. 13, 1943: 242.*

In a report made at the physiological session in St. Johann (Tirol), Austria, on Oct. 4–6, 1942, it was stated that chemical thermoregulation consists of two different mechanisms: (1) conscious and unconscious muscular activity, (2) increased metabolism at rest. Gessler found a rise in basal metabolism at rest of 25% at environmental temperatures below 18°C. Seasonal fluctuations in the basal metabolism indicate variations in the stimulation of the thermal center which parallel the average daily temperatures. Experiments such as those in polar regions, also indicated an increase in basal metabolism with decreasing environmental temperatures. The author's own investigations, made in regard to both above mentioned mechanisms at −20°C environmental temperature with normal clothing have shown increases in metabolism up to 100%, namely of the order of thyrotoxic metabolical changes. However, as long as the involuntary muscular activity (shivering) did not appear, there was no rise in metabolism above 25%. The importance of chemical thermoregulation by means of pure metabolic increase at rest is not yet elucidated. The inadequacy of this increase in great cold is striking.

452. Marčetić, M. Contribution to the study of the chemical thermo-regulation in man [In German]. *Bull. Acad. Roy. Serbe, Sect. B, v. 5, 1939: 91–111.*

Contrary to what had been thought to be the mode of action, it was found that even in short periods of exposure to drastic or weak fluctuations of environmental temperature (20°, then 10°C) men react by an activation of the chemical temperature-regulating mechanism—independent of shivering and of all other muscular activity—to increase the body heat. Men fed protein in abundance, however, when placed in a cold environment in which they would otherwise react with vigorous chemical thermo-regulation, showed little or no such reaction.

453. O'Connor, J. M., and D. K. O'Donovan. The influence of temperature on animal oxidation. *Proc. R. Irish Acad., Sect. B, v. 47, 1942: 251–264.*

It is stated that the known behavior of oxidative metabolism of both reptiles and mammals, at temperatures above those tolerated by the frog, can also be explained by the properties of fatty acids in monomolecular layer.

454. O'Connor, J. M. The influence of fatty acids on the oxygen consumption of the tissues in relation to temperature and the theory of temperature regulation. *Proc. R. Irish Acad., Sect. B, v. 48, 1942: 93–103.*

The skin of the finger was repeatedly treated with various fatty acids (oleic, myristic, palmitic, stearic, and lauric), the finger was immersed in warmed water, and the alteration in the rates of oxidation of the various acids were studied in relation to the theory that the rate of oxidation of the human body is governed by the physical state of the monomolecular layer of the mixed fatty acids. The author interprets this action of fatty acids in view of his theory that normal body temperature is related to the proportion of palmitic acid occurring in the body fat.

455. O'Connor, J. M. The regulation of the body temperature. *Irish J. M. Sc., Sixth series, no. 211, July 1943: 193–218.*

The author gives a historical discussion of the views on the physical principles involved in temperature regulation. He discusses in detail the effect of temperature on oxygen consumption, and states that the intensity of this metabolism is greatly influenced by the surface properties of the higher fatty acids. 60 refs.

456. O'Connor, J. M. The metabolic basis of the constancy of body temperature. *Proc. R. Irish Acad., Sect. B, v. 51, Dec. 1947: 211–222.*

The author had previously found that the increased oxidization of the skin of the finger at higher environmental temperatures decreased momentarily at 30°C and again at 36°C and that the change at these levels had to do with the oxidative disappearance from the monomolecular layer of oleic and of palmitic acid respectively. To further test his theory of the constancy of body temperature, based on fatty acid oxidation unrelated to central nervous control, the author did similar tests on the isolated skin of the frog and obtained similar results.

457. O'Connor, J. M. The control of the body temperature by fatty acid monolayers. *Discuss. Faraday Soc., no. 6 (Sect. on Lipo-proteins), 1949: 160–165.*

The phenomenon of the two temperatures (30° and 36°C) in cold-blooded and in warm-blooded animals respectively where the body temperature falls for a short period as the heat production rises, is based on the oxidative metabolism of a unimolecular layer of fatty acids; the monolayer of oleic and of palmitic acids dissolves out at 30° and 36°C respectively. This is interpreted as the method which continues the regulation of body temperature when the regulatory centers of the hypothalamus are inactivated for some reason. Physical experiments are referred to in which the behavior of a monolayer of palmitic acid *in vitro* would be in agreement with this theory.

458. O'Connor, J. M. Fatty acid and the influence of temperature on the oxygen consumption of animal tissue. *Proc. R. Irish Acad., v. 53 (Sect. B), Feb. 1950: 42–44.*

The skin of the finger was treated with margaric acid instead of the naturally-occurring fatty acids previously tested. Falls in oxygen consumption when the environmental temperature was raised, occurred at 32°, 36°, and 44°C. This is in agreement with the author's theory that the oxidization is involved with a monomolecular layer of mixed body fatty acids, with the falls in oxygen consumption indicating the disappearance from the monomolecular layer of oleic acid at 32°, palmitic acid at 36°, and margaric acid at 44°C.

459. Parvis, D. Ascorbic acid and heat regulation [In Italian, summaries in Italian, German, French and English]. *Vitaminologia. Torino, v. 1, 1941: 33–42.*

Groups of guinea pigs were kept for some hours at 43° to 45°C or at − 10°C. The ascorbic acid content of the brain, adrenals, and liver of the group kept at higher temperatures was considerably reduced as compared with the corresponding organs of controls kept at normal temperature. The animals kept at low temperature also showed a slight loss in ascorbic acid. In animals which died from heat or freezing, the decreases were most marked. No conclusions are drawn as to the real meaning and importance of ascorbic acid in thermoregulation.

460. Ratschow, M., and H. Hasse. Report on the heat regulation in protein-deficient patients [In German]. *Zschr. Kreislaufforsch., v. 37, Apr. 1948: 361–367.*

A study was made of the heat regulation of 25 persons with a known protein-deficiency, during a period when the trunk and not the head or extremities of the subject was enclosed in a warming chamber. There was a great difference noted in the temperature at the beginning of the study between the hands and the feet; the surface temperatures remained low for a considerable time. The final temperatures reached by the extremities, were widely varied. It is suggested that the reason for the great variation in response may not be from a localized circulatory defect, but should be investigated as a change in the over-all hormonal regulation of the vegetative system.

461. Repetto, A. Effects of vitamin B_1 on hepatic homeohypothermia [In Italian]. *Boll. Soc. ital. biol. sper., v. 22, Mar. 1946: 154–156.*

It had previously been known that a lack of vitamin B_1 tends to lead to a hypothermic condition; and that the liver is the depository for vitamin B_1. Following his experiments with vitamin B_1 and observations on both normal persons and on patients with some degree of hepatic insufficiency, the author concludes that variation of the functional tone of the thermal regulatory center is associated with an alteration of liver cell metabolism.

462. Swift, R. W. The effect of feed on the critical temperature for the albino rat. *J. Nutrit., v. 28, Nov. 1944: 359–364.*

Studies of heat production of albino rats, on a high dynamic diet or while fasting, were made at environmental temperatures of 15° to 34°C. The zone of thermal neutrality—where heat loss and heat gain are equal—for fasting rats was found to be from 28° to 33°C; feeding had the effect of lowering both limits of this range by 1°C.

463. Thauer, R., and K. Wezler. Gaseous metabolism during thermoregulation. (First and second chemical thermoregulation) [In German]. *Zschr. ges. exp. Med., v. 112(1), 1943: 95–126.*

The gaseous metabolism of 4 healthy subjects was tested at atmospheric temperatures of 5° to 50°C and at relative humidities of 50% to 90%, over a period of 3 hours by means of a climatic chamber. Measurements were made of oxygen consumption, carbon dioxide production, respiratory quotient, respiratory volume, depth and frequency of respiration, and of body temperature. The dependance of all the values on the external temperature and on the body temperature is represented in diagrams. The results and conclusions refer to the size and gradient of the increased metabolism during the cold, to the width and shape of the so-called metabolically indifferent zone, the absolute metabolic minimum and metabolic rise during overheating. During mild hypothermia there is increased chemical regulation (increased oxidation). The body temperature remains almost constant (35.4°–36.0°C) but the oxygen consumption is greater the lower the surrounding temperature: at 22°C, it was 210–260 cc/min; at 15°C, 260–400 cc/min. Individual variations are considerable (from 30% to 190%). Below 20°C the body temperature decreased noticeably. In men it decreased the more the weaker the chemical thermoregulation (the more the oxidation increase is delayed). In women, the body temperature in cold atmospheres is much higher, in spite of a lower chemical thermo-regulatory participation; the physical thermoregulation appears therefore to be stronger. The respiratory volume per minute increased in direct proportion to oxygen consumption and was determined by it, either in hyperthermia or hypothermia. The respiratory quotient showed no dependence on external temperatures. The depth of each inspiration below 22°C room temperature, was increased; the frequency appeared to be determined by the blood temperature.

464. Van Liere, E. J. Anoxia and heat regulation. *Chicago, University of Chicago Press, 1942. 269 p.*

In a section entitled Anoxia; its Effect on the Body (p. 201–202), various experimental and clinical findings are discussed in which a decrease in body temperature was observed at high altitudes or in a state of anoxia. It was suggested that anoxia might have a direct effect on the heat-regulating mechanism of the body or that it might act indirectly as a consequence of the resultant fatigue or the decrease of the physiological oxidations of the body.

465. Wezler, K., and E. Frank. Chemical heat regulation against cold and heat during oxygen insufficiency [In German]. *Pflügers Arch., v. 250 (3), 1948: 439–464.*

Subjects were exposed, undressed, to the inhalation of mixtures of 12%, 10% or 8% of oxygen with nitrogen, while confined in a climatic chamber, and recordings of various physiological changes were made. As seen in preceding studies, the body temperature of man under anoxic conditions at a comfortable temperature (30°C, 50% relative humidity) decreased at a simulated altitude of 4400 meters (12% oxygen). This decrease was due not only to insufficient heat production but also to a disturbance in physical thermoregulation caused by heat loss through dilatation of the skin vessels. At 7300 meters (8% oxygen) this temperature decrease was greater. In moderate hypoxia (12% or 10% oxygen), the oxygen consumption was slightly increased at all temperatures; in greater hypoxia (8% oxygen), the gaseous exchange was much greater in the cold than it was at comfortable temperatures or in the heat. In a normal atmosphere of 20.8% oxygen, or at 12% oxygen, the body temperature decreased at environmental temperatures of 15°C and rose again at 5°C, because of increasing chemical regulation; in 8% oxygen the decrease in body temperature in a comfortable or a cold environment, was greater. Cheyne-Stokes respiration at 7300 meters (8% oxygen) appeared at 30°C after 90 minutes or at 5°C after 30 minutes. The body temperature at 15°C dropped lower than under either cold stimulation or hypoxia alone, namely by 1.5°C after one hour in 8% oxygen; at 5°C the decrease was similar but mitigated by augmented chemical thermoregulation. It is deducted that though chemical thermoregulation was active, the physical thermoregulation failed to prevent the decrease in body temperature during hypoxia either at 5°C or at 15°C.

See also items: 100, 174, 266, 515, 536, 809, 968, 985, 1377, 1379, 1381, 1383.

K. Effects of Drugs on Temperature Regulation.
(For drug-induced hypothermia, see under Hypothermia, general.)

466. Banno, S. Influence of butyric acid on thermoregulation. Experimental findings [In Italian, summaries in Italian, French, English and German]. *Med. sper., Tor., v. 7, 1940: 225–238.*

Experimental injection of butyric acid into guinea pigs which were kept at a high (52 °C) environmental temperature prevented as much of a rise in rectal temperature as was experienced by the untreated control animals; at a low (−5 °C) environmental temperature the injection brought about a greater lowering of rectal temperature. The author explains these actions on the basis that butyric acid interferes with organic combustion and, therefore, with heat production.

467. Beeson, P. B. Temperature-elevating effect of a substance obtained from polymorphonuclear leukocytes [Abstract]. *J. Clin. Invest., v. 27, July 1948: 524.*

The author started with the hypothesis that some agent, liberated from injured cells, acts on the cerebral thermoregulatory centers and disturbs their function. Four cell types (erythrocytes, lymphocytes, macrophages, and polymorphonuclear leukocytes) of rabbits were tested by re-injection into normal rabbits. Temperature elevations of 2°–3°F resulted from intravenous injection of polymorphonuclear leukocytes—particularly from the supernatant fluid after lysis of the cells—but not from any of the other cells.

468. Beznák, A. B. L., A. G. B. Kovách, and Z. Gáspár-Rády. The effect of histamine on body temperature of normal and of histamine pre-treated guinea pigs, and the mechanism of the changes [In English]. *Arch. biol. hungar., ser. II, v. 18, 1948: 336–352.*

Lowering of the rectal temperature of guinea pigs after intraperitoneal or subcutaneous injections of histamine is thought to be not so much from disturbances of the thermoregulatory center as from changes taking place peripherally in the body. In histamine pre-treated animals, which respond to further histamine with less of a lowering of rectal temperature than do untreated animals, it was found that better oxygenation took place. A slight amount of bronchoconstriction in histamine shock brought about a compensatory increase of the lung ventilation with a greater supply of oxygen to the blood and a rise in body temperature; when the condition was more severe, there was a diminution of oxygen supply and lowering of the body temperature.

469. Birnie, J. H., and J. Grayson. The effect of anesthesia on temperature and liver blood flow in rats [Abstract]. (*Proc. Physiol. Soc., Mar. 9–10, 1951.*) *J. Physiol., Lond., v. 114, Aug. 27, 1951: 30P.*

By means of thermocouples previously implanted by surgical operation, the temperature of the liver of non-anesthetized rats was found to be 38.8°C; of the brain, 38.0°C; and of the peritoneal cavity, 37.7°C. When subjected to anesthesia for 15 minutes there was a relatively similar sharp drop in the temperatures with either ether or pentobarbital sodium (Nembutal). There was a gradual return to normal temperatures within 1½ to 2 hours after discontinuance of ether and slightly longer after pentobarbital sodium. There was a sharp decline in liver blood flow during the period of anesthesia with a prompt return to normal when the administration of the anesthetic was discontinued. The liver temperature continued to decline while the blood flow was returning to normal; this suggests an independence of these two factors.

470. Bruns, E., and F. Hahn. Investigation on the mechanism of action of temperature-lowering substances [In German]. *Arch. exp. Path., Berl., v. 208, 1949: 207–209.*

Study of the anti-pyretic action of several substances (Pyramidon, Veronal, urethane, phenacetin, Cardiazol, and others) alone or in combination, and a discussion of the action of some of them on the central nervous system, is given. Mention is made of the dual structure of the temperature-regulating mechanism in the central nervous system; the system whose stimulation leads to heating but whose impairment leads to temperature-lowering, has a more widespread structure than that system whose stimulation causes cooling.

471. Buchanan, A. R., J. E. Roberts, and B. E. Robinson. Ergotoxine hyper- and hypo-thermia in albino rats. *Proc. Soc. Exp. Biol., N.Y., v. 68, 1948: 143–150.*

Albino rats, given ergotoxine by injection, were found to be unable to adequately regulate their body temperature in environmental temperatures higher or lower than normal. Environments of 28°C or higher, resulted in hyperthermia. Immediate exposure to environmental temperatures of 5°–8°C—or after hyperthermia had been provoked by the higher temperature—resulted in hypothermia. At environmental temperatures of 22° to 25°C a moderate fall or moderate rise occurred in body temperatures.

472. Buchanan, A. R., and J. E. Roberts. Thermal reactions of young albino rats to intraperitoneal injections of ergotoxine. *Am. J. Physiol., v. 155, Oct. 1, 1948: 64–68.*

Rats, kept at an environmental temperature of 30°C, reacted to ergotoxine with varying degrees of hypothermia when they were from 12 to 18 days of age; litter mates of 20 to 30 days of age, however, manifested hyperthermia. The time of change in the reaction coincided with that at which temperature-regulatory ability is known to be attained. The conclusion is reached that both phenomena depend on the maturation of the hypothalamus.

473. Buchanan, A. R., J. A. Witt, J. E. Roberts, and L. C. Massopust, Jr. Peripheral circulatory and metabolic reactions associated with ergotoxine hyper- and hypo-thermia in adult albino rats. *Am. J. Physiol., v. 163, Oct. 1950: 62–69.*

The injection of ergotoxine in experimental rats subjected to cold stress was found to have a marked effect upon the thermoregulatory centers of the hypothalamus and to produce peripheral vasodilatation. Uninjected rats, on the other hand, responded to cold stress by vasoconstriction. The peripheral vasodilatation of ergotoxine-injected rats under cold stress resulted in a marked reduction of body temperature and failure to utilize oxygen at as high a level as control animals. Control animals were able, by means of vasoconstriction and increased metabolism, to maintain normal or near normal body temperatures.

474. Burn, J. H., and N. K. Dutta. Acetylcholine and body temperature. *Nature, Lond., v. 161, Jan. 3, 1948: 18.*

Atropine, Benadryl, Pethidine [Demerol], and quinidine, as well as procaine, lowered the body temperature of mice. The fall was augmented by adrenalectomy. Since a depressant action on acetylcholine is common to all these substances, the authors suggest that maintenance of body temperature depends on a mechanism in which acetylcholine plays a part, and that the adrenal glands support such a mechanism against the depressant substances.

475. Cilento, A. Effect of glycine on the cloacal temperature of normal and vagotomized pigeons [In Italian]. *Boll. Soc. ital. biol. sper., v. 27, July–Aug. 1951: 1300–1303.*

Glycine (25–50 mg), with or without histamine (100γ), was given orally every 10 minutes over a period of 60–70 minutes both to normal and vagotomized pigeons. When given to normal animals, glycine alone produced little change in the cloacal temperature; given with histamine, it was able to prevent the fall in temperature produced by histamine alone. In vagotomized pigeons glycine did not inhibit the hypothermia which resulted from the vagotomy; glycine and histamine together did not appreciably change the cloacal temperature. The hypothermia which is a consequence of vagotomy must therefore be imputed to a factor other than that of increased histamine, either by greater production or less destruction, since the resection of the vagi eliminated such a control of histamine.

476. D'Alessio, A. A specific antithermic effect of paraminosalicylic acid [In Italian, summaries in Italian, French, English, and German]. *Acta med. ital. mal. infett., v. 6, Apr. 1951: 97–100.*

Mild and temporary antithermic effects were observed in guinea pigs which had been given paraminosalicylic acid (PAS). It was demonstrated that the high doses of PAS which were used caused a reduction in the endo-organic oxidative processes but that this would not be the case with the common, clinical, dosages of the drug.

477. DeCourt, P., M. Brunaud, and S. Brunaud. Action of a narcobiotic (chlorpromazine) on the internal temperature of warm-blooded animals subjected to ambient temperatures higher, equal to, or lower than their normal body temperature [In French]. *Comp. rend. Soc. Biol., Par., v. 147, Oct. 1953: 1605–1609.*

Various laboratory animals were given subcutaneous injections of Chlorpromazine (4560 RP) and then kept at room temperatures similar to, higher, or lower than the animal's normal body temperature. The action of the drug did not produce a state similar to that of a poikilothermic, or hibernating animals in which the body temperature of the animal tended to be the same as that of the environmental temperature. The drug brought about a lowering of body temperature by lowering cellular metabolism, and this hypothermic action was independent of the environmental temperature.

478. Dimitrijević, I. N. Influence of ergotamine on the thermogenesis and the thermoregulation of the rat [In French]. *Bull. Acad. Roy. Serbe, sect. B, v. 5, 1939: 63–76.*

When environmental and body temperatures are about equal, there is no noticeable action of erogotamine on the body temperature; at a low environmental temperature (6°–7°C), ergotamine produces a marked drop (4° to 4.7°C) in body temperature. This influence of ergotamine is based on the fact that it depresses the functions of thermoregulation to a level that is equal or less than that of basal metabolism. Ergotamine therefore blocks the need of the animal to increase metabolism to accommodate for the loss of heat in the environment.

479. Dimitrijević, I. N. The influence of ergotamine and adrenaline on the heat production and thermoregulation [In French]. *Bull. Acad. Roy. Serbe, sect. B, v. 5, 1939: 147–169.*

Adrenaline, by its peripheral action, increases thermogenesis; by its central action, it profoundly disturbs and suppresses chemical thermoregulation. Ergotamine likewise suppresses chemical thermoregulation; it has no notable peripheral action. At room temperature, both drugs together produce hyperthermia due to the predominance of the peripheral action of adrenaline in increasing metabolism. At low temperatures, hypothermia is produced because of their combined suppressive action on thermoregulation and because the peripheral action of adrenaline is not sufficient to overcome the effect of environmental cold.

480. Donatelli, L., and G. Noferi. Body temperature and poisoning. II. Acute carbon monoxide poisoning and body temperature [In Italian]. *Rass. neur. vegetat., v. 8, Oct. 1950: 247–265.*

The authors review the literature on the effect of carbon monoxide intoxication on body temperature, both from animal experiments and from clinical findings. Experimentally, a hypothermia usually results but occasionally there is a hyperthermic reaction. The action of carbon monoxide is thought to be either direct or indirect on the thermoregulatory centers. In the latter case, the augmentation of the metabolic rate due to the secondary action on the thyroid or hypophysis produces the hyperthermic state. 54 refs.

481. Dontas, S., and E. Phocas. Experimental research on the influence of sea water on the thermoregulatory centers [In French, Greek summary]. *Prakt. Akad. Athenon*, v. *14*, *Jan. 26, 1939: 83–88.*

Dogs were given intravenous injections of normal and diluted (1:12) sea water (sp. gr. 1027 at 19.9°C) in 150, 200, or 300 cc amounts and were then placed in a hot room at a temperature of 45°C. Body temperatures rose 1.0° to 1.9°C in the animals given normal sea water because of a narcotizing action on the thermoregulatory centers. The temperatures of the dogs given diluted sea water rose only slightly, or fell slightly below normal, because of an excitation of the centers and a resulting antipyretic effect.

482. Ekström, G. A. Note on the influence of small doses of Nembutal upon the temperature regulation in cats [In English]. *Acta physiol. scand.*, v. *22*, *June 1951: 345–347.*

Cats anesthetized with small doses of Nembutal (30 mg/kg) were, in most instances, able to maintain their normal body temperature either at normal room temperature (22°C) or at room temperatures of 30°–40°C. There was usually an initial short drop within the first 50 minutes, followed by a return to normal and often a very slight rise. The anesthesia was sufficient to prevent spontaneous movements and to permit minor surgical procedures. Anesthetized dogs, under the same conditions, were never able to keep their normal body temperature but they lost and regained heat more slowly than the cats.

483. Friederici, L., H. K. Fukas, and W. Klante. Oxygen consumption, rectal temperature, and synthesis of phosphatides during ether anesthesia in rats [In German]. *Beitr. klin. Chir.*, v. *183*, *1951: 362–370.*

Study was made of the gaseous exchange and body temperature, as well as of the liver and kidney functions, in rats during narcosis. The oxygen consumption was measured after 12 hours of starvation, the rectal temperature by means of thermo-element; inhalation anesthesia using ether was maintained over a period of 7 hours; and radioactive phosphorus (P^{32}) was injected subcutaneously 15 minutes later to serve as an indicator of phosphatide synthesis. The body temperature after narcosis showed a close relationship to the oxygen consumption; it decreased 32.9%, while oxygen consumption decreased 36.7%. The degree of temperature drop was found to depend on the following factors: the primary one was the decrease of heat production which is closely related to oxygen consumption; the heat loss, which depends on the exposed surface and the heat capacity of the body; and the environmental temperature. The synthesis of phosphatides decreased by 47.5% in the liver and 21.5% in the kidneys.

484. Grant, R. Influence of environmental temperature on the metabolic response to injected pyrogens. *Am. J. Physiol.*, v. *155*, *Dec. 1948: 440.*

Rabbits which had been shorn of their fur and exposed to an environmental temperature of 0°C maintained constant rectal temperatures with strong shivering. Their oxygen consumption was increased 120%. When injected with a pyrogen such as typhoid-paratyphoid vaccine they showed an elevated temperature which was followed by hypothermia and the elimination of shivering. The fall of temperature was checked, in the third hour after injection, by resumption of shivering.

485. Grant, R., and M. E. Robbins. Effect of ethyl carbamate on temperature regulation. *Fed. Proc., Balt.*, v. *8*, *Mar. 1949: 59–60.*

Rabbits anesthetized with urethane (ethyl carbamate) were found to have a rapid drop in body temperature—resulting from decreased heat production—, vasodilatation in the ears, and, in a few cases, polypnea. After body temperature had fallen 1° to 3°C polypnea ceased, vasoconstriction occurred, and the fall of temperature was retarded. Warming restored the vasodilatation and incited polypnea usually at subnormal rectal temperatures. Various reasons are given for believing that, despite this evidence, urethane lowered the temperature thresholds for activation of thermoregulatory mechanisms and its action was probably not upon the primary centers of thermoregulation.

486. Green, H. D., N. D. Nickerson, R. N. Lewis, and B. L. Brofman. Consecutive changes in cutaneous blood flow, temperature, metabolism, and hematocrit readings during prolonged anesthesia with morphine and barbital. *Am. J. Physiol., v. 140, Nov. 1943: 177–189.*

Anesthesia with morphine caused an immediate and frequently maximal increase in cutaneous blood flow of the patient, and a decline in the average normal rectal temperature (38.5°C) to 34°–37°C. These changes were often followed in 1 to 3 hours by a sharp reduction in cutaneous blood flow. The latter apparently was secondary to the temperature regulating reactions induced by the drop in rectal temperature. Sodium barbital, sodium pentobarbital, and chloralose caused a similar initial increase in cutaneous blood flow and a drop of 0.5° to 1.5°C in rectal temperature and a subsequent decrease of cutaneous blood flow; and in addition, induced an increase of oxygen consumption, often associated with shivering; and a rise of rectal temperature to 38.6°–40.3°C within 3 to 11 hours. Anesthesia with morphine plus barbital accentuated the initial drop of rectal temperature.

487. Gyermek, L. Action of histamine on gas metabolism and body temperature [In German]. *Arch. exp. Path., Berl., v. 209 (4–5), 1950: 456–464.*

The influence of histamine on body temperature and oxygen consumption was studied in rats at various environmental temperatures. The gaseous exchange and body temperature of urethane-anesthetised animals were measured continuously in the Issekutz apparatus, before and after the histamine injection. The whole apparatus containing the animals was then immersed in a water bath at 30°, 20°, or 24°C. At 30°C, after injection (subcutaneously) of 8 mg/100 g of histamine, the oxygen consumption and the body temperature were both increased. At 20°C, the body temperature was lowered, while the oxygen consumption remained unchanged. At 24°C, there was no change in body temperature but oxygen consumption was increased slightly. Subcutaneous injection of 0.05 mg/100 g Adrenalin had an effect similar to that of histamine under the above temperature with similarly narcotized rats. Adrenalin lowered body temperature at 20°C, but less than the histamine had done. In the summer, oxygen consumption was not increased at 30°C, indicating that the influence of histamine on the metabolism changes with the seasons. Similar seasonal variations were observed for Adrenalin.

488. Hahn, F. Different effects of Coramine and Cardiazol upon the body temperature of the rabbit [In German]. *Klin. Wschr., v. 21, May 16, 1942: 460–461.*

A short report is given of the effects of subcutaneous administration of Coramine and Cardiazol on the body temperature of rabbits. A dosage of Coramine between 60% and 80% of that producing convulsion, induced a rise in body temperature of from 1° to 2°C. A significant muscular trembling was produced by the Coramine. The author suggests further tests of the therapeutic effects of the drugs with humans or animals while undergoing a raising or lowering of normal body temperature.

489. Hahn, F. The effect of certain analeptics (Cardiazol, Coramine, "Neospiran," and "Cycliton") on the body temperature of normal and narcotized rabbits [In German]. *Arch. exp. Path., Berl., v. 202, 1943: 165–193.*

The effects of Cardiazol, Coramine, "Neospiran," and "Cycliton" upon the body temperature and respiration of normal and narcotized rabbits were observed with reference to environmental temperatures (4°–30°C).

490. Hall, V. E., R. Grant, and J. Field. The influence of substances affecting body temperature on thermal polypnea [Abstract]. *Fed. Proc., Balt., v. 7, Mar. 1948: 48–49.*

In a study of substances affecting body temperature in rabbits, it appears that magnesium chloride reduces the body temperature level at which heat defense mechanisms are activated.

491. Hall, V. E., and F. A. Ellis. Mechanism of magnesium hypothermia in the rabbit [Abstract]. *Fed. Proc., Balt., v. 9, Mar. 1950: 55.*

Magnesium chloride (2.5 mm/kg) given intraperitoneally to unanesthetized rabbits in an environmental temperature of 28°C caused a body temperature fall of 0.32°C. Since the oxygen consumption was not appreciably altered, the reduction in body temperature was attributed not to a reduction in heat production but to increased heat loss through cutaneous vasodilatation and polypnea. The same dose of magnesium chloride given at an environmental temperature of 0°C, brought about a temperature drop of 1.62°C. The oxygen consumption which had been about double that in the 28°C environment, was reduced 29.9%. Neither polypnea nor vasodilatation occurred at the low temperature, making it appear that the fall in body temperature was due to a reduction in heat production. It is assumed that the magnesium salt interfered with the nervous mechanisms of temperature regulation.

492. Heagy, F. C., and A. C. Burton. The effect of magnesium on body temperature in the dog [Abstract]. *Fed. Proc., Balt., v. 6, Mar. 1947: 126.*

Vasodilatation and paralysis of the neuromuscular junction are known pharmacological peripheral actions of magnesium. When magnesium chloride was injected intravenously into unanesthetized dogs which were attempting to regulate their body temperature against cold by shivering, there was little effect on temperature unless the dose was a large one and caused a paralytic action. In such cases shivering ceased and body temperatures fell.

493. Heagy, F. C., and A. C. Burton. Effect of intravenous injection of magnesium chloride on the body temperature of the anesthetized dog, with some observations on magnesium levels and body temperature in man. *Am. J. Physiol., v. 152, Feb. 1, 1948: 407-416.*

When dogs were wrapped in a special "blanket" through which warm or cold water was circulated, and then received magnesium chloride by injection, there was a decrease in rectal temperature regardless of the temperature of the environment. In a cold environment, the effect was produced by a decrease in shivering and of voluntary motor activity without vasodilatation; in a comfortable environment, either by panting or by vasodilatation or a combination of these and probably by a decrease in muscular tone in some cases; and in a warm environment, by increase in panting. There was a general depression of the nervous system, but the effect on the temperature-regulating center is not clear.

In clinical observations on human subjects, the changes in magnesium level with body temperature were too small to be of physiological importance.

494. Hemingway, A. The effect of morphine on the skin and rectal temperature of dogs as related to thermal polypnea. *J. Pharm. Exp. Ther., v. 63, Aug. 1938: 414-420.*

Under morphine anesthesia, panting in dogs can occur even when the skin and rectal temperatures have been reduced, or before these temperatures have been raised to the usual threshold level for panting. Morphine is thought to sensitize that portion of the hypothalamus which controls panting either in response to direct heat or to impulses arising from heated skin.

495. Hemingway, A. Rate of recovery of temperature-regulating responses after ether anesthesia. *Am. J. Physiol., v. 152, Mar. 1, 1948: 663-670.*

When anesthetized and unanesthetized dogs were subjected to a cold environment (10°C) neither shivering nor peripheral vasoconstriction were interferred with by the anesthesia, but the finer regulation of body temperature was impaired to the extent that rectal temperatures could not be maintained. Within 2 or 3 hours after cessation of anesthesia, the responses had returned to normal.

496. Herrmann, J. B. Effects of certain drugs on temperature regulation and changes in their toxicity in rats exposed to cold. *J. Pharm. Exp. Ther.*, v. 72, *June 1941: 130–137.*

Morphine, paraldehyde, and Nembutal produced a temporary fall in the body temperature of rats, exposed to cold of 3°C, which did not occur in the undrugged rat. The toxicity of these drugs for rats is increased at low temperatures.

497. Hill, R. M., and E. K. Rutledge. Effect of autolyzed yeast, yeast nucleic acid, and related substances on body temperatures of rats. *Proc. Soc. Exp. Biol.*, N. Y., v. 71, May 1949: 9–11.

Subcutaneous injection of 2 cc of a yeast autolysate into young adult white rats produced a significant rise in body temperature while a similar intraperitoneal injection produced a significant fall. Similar results were produced with a solution of the magnesium salt of yeast nucleic acid. No effect on body temperature by either route of injection was found using adenine, uracil, xanthine, or allantoin. Guanine brought about a slight lowering of body temperature by intraperitoneal route but none by subcutaneous.

498. Hill, R. M., and E. K. Rutledge. Effects of injection of large molecular and particulate substance on body temperature of rats. *Proc. Soc. Exp. Biol.*, N. Y., v. 72, Nov. 1949: 310–315.

Subcutaneous injections of particulate matter, including India ink, blood, charcoal, carmine, or trypan blue, as well as intramuscular injection of carmine, resulted in a rise in body temperature in rats. Following intraperitoneal injection of the same substances, a fall in body temperature occurred. Measurement of blood cell volume and plasma protein concentration did not indicate that the animals were in shock. Peptone solutions and ox bile produced mild hypothermia when injected intraperitoneally; ox bile caused severe shock. The cause of the fall in body temperature (following intraperitoneal injection of the particulate substances) would appear to lie in some interference with the normal functioning of the reticuloendothelial system.

499. Horwitz, O., H. Montgomery, E. D. Longaker, and A. Saÿen. Effects of vasodilator drugs and other procedures on digital cutaneous blood flow, cardiac output, blood pressure, pulse rate, body temperature, and metabolic rate. *Am. J. M. Sc.*, v. 218, Dec. 1949: 669–682.

Heat, alcohol, moderate doses of Priscoline, and food caused selective vasodilatation of the skin of fingers and toes in varying degrees. Mecholyl and Etamon caused widespread vasodilatation, unselective for skin of fingers and toes. Drugs causing the greater increases in cutaneous blood flow were found to cause the greater decreases in body temperature.

500. Issekutz, B., and F. Kövari. On the action of Novocain in metabolism [In German]. *Arch. exp. Path. Lpz.*, v. 200, 1942: 156–166.

Novacain modified the chemical temperature regulation in guinea pigs, decreasing the metabolism and causing a lowering of body temperature. Thyroxin hindered this action but could not wholly prevent it.

501. Issekutz, B., Jr., I. Lichtneckert, and H. Nagy. Effect of capsaicin and histamine on heat regulation [In English]. *Arch. internat. pharm. dyn.*, Par., v. 81, *Jan. 1950: 35–46.*

In calorimetric experiments on the mouse, capsaicin or small doses (30–50 γ/g) of histamine produced a fall in rectal temperature. This effect seemed to be caused by an excitation of the terminal heat receptors which reflexly set up a stimulation of the temperature regulating centers to bring about cooling. This resulted in a decrease in metabolic rate, a dilatation of blood vessels of the skin, and a decrease in rectal temperature. If the action had been on the cooling center directly, the reaction of the blood vessels would have been a contraction. In the temperature decrease from large doses (100 γ/g) of histamine, the author mentions that the shock which is brought about plays a decisive part.

502. Issekutz, B., Jr., I. Lichtneckert, and M. Winter. Effect of histamine, capsaicin and procaine on heat-regulation [In English]. *Arch. internat. pharm. dyn., Par., v. 83, July 1950: 319–326.*

Thyroxin, which checked the temperature-decreasing effect of procaine, was often ineffective against the temperature-decreasing effect of capsaicin. Transection of the spinal cord of the guinea pigs at the 3rd thoracic segment did not influence the effect of capsaicin. Pyribenzamine (PBA) reduced the cooling action of histamine in mice, and checked it completely in guinea pigs, but did not affect the decrease, in either animal, caused by capsaicin or procaine. The conclusion is drawn that procaine reduces body temperature by inhibition of the heat center; capsaicin by stimulation of the cooling center.

503. Kuhn, R. A., and K. Henkel. Decrease of body temperature by means of adenylthiomethylpentose [In German]. *Zschr. phys. Chem., v. 269, 1941: 41–46.*

Experimental study was made in guinea pigs to determine whether the decrease in body temperature (1°–2°C) which follows injection of adenylthiomethylpentose is specific for this substance, or whether other adenyl compounds or derivates from adenylthiomethylpentose have the same action. Pronounced results were obtained only with adenylthiomethylpentose and its chlorine hydrates. Distinct, but less active, was the temperature-lowering action of hypoxanthylthiomethylpentose, which the author had isolated from the adenyl compound by means of nitrous acid. The chemical properties of these substances are described.

504. LaGrutta, G. Action of histamine and antihistamine on body temperature of the normal and vagotomized pigeon [In Italian]. *Boll. Soc. ital. biol. sper., v. 27, Jan–Feb. 1951: 74–77.*

When histamine was administered to normal pigeons the cloacal temperature dropped, varying from a minimum of 0.5°C to a maximum of 1.9°C, over a 20 minute period. Vagotomized pigeons had no significant temperature change on administration of histamine. When vagotomized pigeons were given an antihistaminic substance before administration of histamine, there was some temperature drop but in contrast to the findings of di Macco, (item 508) they did not react like the normal animals. The author suggests several possible means of action to explain the phenomenon.

505. Linder, F., and J. Vollmar. Clinical experiences with the synthetic analgesic, 1-methyl-4-(3-hydroxyphenyl)-4 piperidyl ethyl ketone; comparative studies on its effect on respiration, circulation, and heat regulation [In German]. *Klin. Wschr., v. 28, Oct. 15, 1950: 675–681.*

A clinical study of the relief of pre- and post-operative pain was made with 220 patients using the analgesic drug Cliradon (Ciba 7115; hydrochloride of 1-methyl-4-oxyphenyl-piperidin-4-ethyl ketone), which is related to Dolantin. Ampoules, suppositories, and tablets were used, in a dosage range of 5 to 15 mg. Respiratory, circulatory, and temperature-regulatory changes were noted and recordings made of skin temperature changes of the brow, finger, and big toes. It was found that Cliradon brought about changes in the heat regulatory functions—as did parallel studies with morphine and Polamidon—which were indicated by a temperature rise of the upper extremities, a lowering of the lower extremities, and no change of the temperature of the brow.

506. Logaras, G. The action of bromides on the body temperature in pyrogen test [In English, Greek summary]. *Prakt. Akad. athen., v. 25, May 4, 1950: 288–295.*

During the course of routine testing for pyrogens, it was found that parenteral solutions containing calcium bromide or potassium bromide produced some antipyretic effect, tending to lower the body temperature of rats or rabbits. This antipyretic effect was enhanced by the presence of calcium ions which did not of themselves cause the effect. Experiments show that the depressant action of the bromide ion in lowering body temperature could be abolished by diluting the solution to be tested 1:5 or 1:10 with pyrogen-free water. The action of the bromide ion on the central nervous system is known to be one of depression.

507. Macco, G. di. Histaminic and antihistaminic hypothermia [In Italian]. *Boll. Soc. ital. biol. sper., v. 25, 1949: 150–151.*

Histamine, given by either subcutaneous or intramuscular injection, always produced a fall in the rectal temperature of guinea pigs. Anti-histaminic substances produced a slight preliminary fall in rectal temperature of short duration, followed by a rise in temperature. The injection of histamine, after the giving of an antihistaminic, caused a negligible drop, then a rise, in rectal temperature. It thus appeared that the hypothermia produced in guinea pigs by the action of histamine was counteracted by pre-treatment with an antihistaminic (e.g., dimethylaminoethylbenzylaniline).

508. Macco, G. di. Histaminic and antihistaminic hypothermia [In Italian, summaries in Italian, English, French, and German]. *Pat. sper., Tor., v. 38, 1950: 189–191.*

Histamine, given by subcutaneous or intramuscular injection, produces a lowered rectal temperature in guinea pigs. The antihistaminic substance, dimethylaminoethylbenzylaniline, produced a slight transitory hypothermia; if given before histamine, it attenuated or abolished the hypothermia produced by histamine alone.

509. Pfeiffer, C. C., L. Schlann, and L. Meduna. Hypothermic agents. III. Effect in man [Abstract]. *Fed. Proc., Balt., v. 9, Mar. 1950: 307–308.*

The body temperature of the rabbit, dog, or of man is not lowered by 4-amyl N-benzohydryl pyridinium bromide (B-45) even in large doses and regardless of the route of administration. Privine (alpha naphthyl methyl imidazoline HCl), which is relatively ineffective in lowering the body temperature of rats and mice, is extremely effective in lowering the body temperature of higher mammals, including man. It is suggested that lower mammals maintain body temperature through an acetylcholine-like substance, but in higher mammals this is accomplished by the imidazoline groups of histamine, histidine, or an unknown compound.

510. Pick, E. F., and S. Feitelberg. Thermogenetic action of Adrenalin and Benzedrine on the brain [In English]. *Arch. internat. pharm. dyn., Par., v. 77 (2), 1948: 219–225.*

Injections of Adrenalin and of Benzedrine were made, under anesthesia, into the right femoral vein of cats. The thermogenetic action of these drugs on the brain was found to be independent of their peripheral vasoconstrictor effect.

511. Roberts, J. E., L. C. Massopust, Jr., and A. R. Buchanan. Effects in albino rats of dihydrogenated derivatives of the dimethylpyruvic acid group of ergot alkaloids as manifested by thermal reactions and oxygen utilization. *J. Pharm. Exp. Ther., v. 100, Sept. 1950: 51–58.*

Report is made of the effects of intraperitoneal injection of the dihydrogenated derivatives of the three natural dimethylpyruvic acid alkaloids of ergot (dihydroergocristine, dihydroergokryptine, and dihydroergocornine) on metabolism, peripheral circulation, and body temperature in albino rats. Rats after being given an injection of these substances, and maintained at an environmental temperature of 27.4°–28.6°C, exhibited a mild hypothermia, a peripheral vasodilatation, and depressed oxygen consumption.

512. Rothlin, E. The pharmacology of the natural and dihydrogenated alkaloids of ergot [In English, summaries in English, French, German, and Italian]. *Bull. Schweiz. Akad. med. Wiss., v. 2, Sept. 21, 1946: 249–273.*

Both ergotamine and dihydroergotamine act on the central nervous system to depress the body temperature when given in small doses; in large, especially toxic, doses ergotamine raises the body temperature while dihydroergotamine lowers it. Actions on the body temperature of other alkaloids in this group are also discussed.

513. Scheurer, O., and W. Hugo. The effects of cardiovascular agents on skin temperature [In German]. *Münch. med. Wschr., v. 89, Oct. 23, 1942: 907–911.*

Various cardiovascular drugs were given intravenously to both normal subjects and to patients with some cardiovascular impairment. Strophanthin produced a rise in the skin temperature of the normal subjects and a greater one in the patient group. Strophanthin combined with grape sugar resulted in a long-lasting rise of temperature while the sugar alone caused a slight warming. Sympatol produced an immediate cooling of the skin, then a warming, and again a moderate cooling. Sympatol given by mouth gave less pronounced reactions. Cardiazol, given in any manner, resulted in heightened peripheral blood flow and higher skin temperatures. Results were most rapid after intravenous injection and slowest after oral administration. Results with Coramine were not uniform but a moderate amount of skin warming occurred. Caffeine produced a step-like rise in skin temperature.

514. Schleinzer, R., and J. Antal. The influence of the most important narcotics used in animal experiments on the respiratory metabolism [In German]. *Pflügers Arch., v. 245, (3), 1941: 361–384.*

Guinea pigs were given various anesthetics (urethane, Evipan, chloralose, Pernoston, and morphine) by intravenous injection. Frequency and depth of respiration and the movement of the animal were recorded as well as changes in the oxygen-carbon dioxide content in the respiratory chamber in which the animals were enclosed. A sudden lowering of the metabolism is attributed to an inhibition of oxidation in all cells of the organism. There is said to be also an interference with centripetal nerve impulse transmission in the lipoid-rich cells of the central nervous system. The higher centers appear to be affected early. Regulatory centers for temperature, circulation, and respiration were hindered thereby. The rise in metabolism after a few hours serves for the removal of incomplete products of combustion and the raising of the lowered body temperature, and also furnishes optimum conditions for the regulatory processes.

515. Szwabowicz, A. The influence of the concentration of alcohol upon temperature, pulse rate, and respiration of rabbits and dogs [In English]. *Acta biol. exp., Warsz., v. 12 (23), 1938: 130–138.*

Administration of warmed ethyl alcohol (0.25 cc/100 g) either orally or rectally to rabbits or dogs caused a decrease of rectal temperature (maximum of about 1.5°C). The temperature then rose above normal before the alcohol had completely disappeared from the blood stream. Respiration and pulse rate (the latter, especially in dogs) were increased, returning to normal at the time of the disappearance of the alcohol from the blood. Intravenously the same quantity of alcohol in rabbits caused a long increase in body temperature above the normal (38.8°C) after an initial short period of decrease (maximum of 2.0°C); in dogs, there was a transient increase in temperature. The respiratory rate was decreased and the pulse rate accelerated. Alcohol was found to have been metabolized, and absent from the blood stream, after about 8 hours in rabbits and about 13 hours in dogs.

516. Thauer, R. The influence of anesthesia on the normal temperature regulation [In German]. *Pflügers Arch., v. 246 (3), 1943: 372–410.*

Rabbits were given drugs (Pernoston, Veronal, Luminal, urethane, or paraldehyde) while being kept in cages allowing very little body movement or while being held immobile, over the test period of 5 hours. Body temperature, rate of respiration, and depth of anesthesia (as observed by tests of reflex actions) were observed at normal outside temperature of 18°–20°C; at temperatures of 0°C, 20°C, or 35°C in a controlled-temperature chamber; or after being given one of several pyretic substances. In different experiments the same degree of anesthesia produced a lowering of rectal temperature of 1.5°C and 3.9°C depending on the length of the anesthesia. In non-anesthetized animals at a temperature of 0°C, rectal temperature dropped 0.1° to 2.0°C, the lowest reading occurring usually after 2 hours, followed by a rise after 4 hours. When the same animals were anesthetized and kept under the same conditions, the rectal temperature after 4 hours dropped approximately 4.6°C lower than in normal animals. The lowering of the rectal temperature was greatly increased unproportionately with the anesthesia. The same dosage in different animals caused quite different degrees of temperature drop indicating the anesthesia acts on a dynamic rather than a static basis and that anesthesia affects the defense-regulatory processes in an unpredictable manner. The apparently differing results obtained from different anesthetics do not necessarily mean that there were differing effects upon heat regulation. No clear conclusions could be drawn from the studies at 0°C since the reactions were so varied, this being contrary to the results expected following the studies done at normal environmental temperatures.

517. Vacirca, F. Amino acids and thermoregulation [In Italian]. *Boll. Soc. ital. biol. sper., v. 21, July 1946: 114–116.*

Intravenous or intraperitoneal injections of alpha amino valeric acid or alpha amino caproic acid in doses of 1–2 g/kg brought about a rise in the rectal temperature of either rabbits or guinea pigs. The highest level was reached after 1 hour and gradually dropped to normal 4 hours after the time of the injection. A dose of 0.2 g/kg did not modify the body temperature. Following administration by either oral or subcutaneous routes, there was no change in temperature even at dosages up to 3.0 g/kg.

518. Zsirai, K. Relation between pyrogenic activity and vitamin C level of the blood [In German]. *Klin. Wschr., v. 21, Jan. 10, 1942: 38–39.*

Studies were made on the effect of a pyrogenic substance (intramuscular injection of sterile milk) on guinea pigs in various states of vitamin C nutrition. The average body temperature of guinea pigs having a vitamin C deficiency was found to be lower (36.7°C) than that of normal guinea pigs (37.2°C); a pyrogenic substance produced less of a rise (37.2°C) in body temperature than it did in normal animals. In contrast, the hypervitaminized animals had a body temperature slightly above average (37.3°C) and the pyrogenic substance produced a greater rise (39.2°C) in temperature. The maximum rise was reached within 1 hour in the scorbutic animals, after 3 to 4 hours in normal animals.

See also items: 82, 96, 98, 182, 390, 398, 407, 414, 542, 813, 814, 960, 997, 1000, 1002, 1004, 1009, 1024, 1042, 1079, 1080, 1081, 1084, 1085, 1531.

L. Effects of Various Agents on Temperature Regulation
(includes humidity, air movement, air pressure, altitude, surgery, hypnosis, and electro-convulsive shock)

519. Altenburger, E., and H. Petzold. The action of nicotine on skin temperature, and the influence exerted upon it by sex hormones [Abstract, in German]. *Klin. Wschr., v. 20, Apr. 19, 1941: 394.*

Experimental study of temperature changes in healthy men under the influence of nicotine at a room temperature of 20°–21°C, showed a decrease of 3°–7.5°C in the temperature of the finger tips after 5 minutes of cigarette smoking. Intramuscular injection of either a folliculin compound (Progynon B) or Testosterone altered the temperature curve obtained after smoking: after a 4-day treatment with Progynon B the temperature decrease was always noticeably diminished (1.5°C, as compared to 7°C without the treatment). Thus, Progynon B largely inhibited the vascular spasm elicited by nicotine. A 4-day treatment with Testosterone had no effect on the nicotine-induced temperature decrease.

520. Bateman, J. B., and C. Sheard. The effect of pressure breathing on the cutaneous temperatures of the extremities. *J. Aviat. M., v. 17, Dec. 1946: 568–578, and 583.*

The data obtained from these series of experiments appear to indicate that the decrease of peripheral blood flow observed by other workers during pressure breathing is a transient phenomenon, which is followed by a slow increase of flow in most normal subjects. The authors are unable to find a completely satisfactory explanation of these changes. A steady increase in intrapulmonary pressure usually gives rise to a transient decrease of cutaneous temperature of the extremities which is succeeded by a slow rise of temperature. From their data the authors feel that the fears expressed by others, that pressure breathing has a deleterious effect on temperature regulation, are unfounded.

521. **Bigler, J. A., and W. O. McQuiston.** Body temperatures during anesthesia in infants and children. *J. Am. M. Ass., v. 146, June 9, 1951: 551–556.*

Temperatures of infants and children vary considerably during surgery. Infants under 6 months of age tend to develop subnormal temperatures which have not proved harmful. In this series, over 62% of the children between the ages of 6 months and 13 years developed fever during surgery unless methods of body cooling were used. Techniques are being perfected to give additional information on physiological changes occurring in hypothermia and hyperthermia in children.

522. **Blood, F. R., R. V. Elliott, and F. E. D'Amour.** The physiology of the rat in extreme anoxia. *Am. J. Physiol., v. 146, June 1, 1946: 319–329.*

The body temperature of anesthetized rats subjected to an anoxia comparable to an elevation of 5,280 feet, fell from the normal ($37°–38°C$) to $32.7°C$; at 40,000 feet, the fall was to $31.2°C$. The body temperature of unanesthetized rats, under comparable conditions, fell to $37.3°$ and $34.1°C$, respectively. The average temperature of the experimental chamber was $23.0°C$ for the anesthetized rats, and $25.0°C$ for the unanesthetized ones.

523. **Brandis, H. J. von.** Relationship between temperature regulation and surgical intervention [In German]. *Arch. klin. Chir., v. 192 (2–3), 1938: 245–327.*

Observations of heat loss and heat gain were made simultaneously and continuously before, during, and after surgical intervention in an attempt to perfect the knowledge of the total picture of temperature regulation during surgery. Deep anesthesia and lumbar anesthesia brought about a significant decrease of the inner body temperature and significant heat loss from peripheral skin areas. This was a depression, not a complete cessation, of temperature regulation since reactivation occurred quickly on rewarming. Effect on temperature regulation varied with the type of anesthesia (deep, spinal, or local) and, generally, within these types it varied according to the size of dosage, toxicity for the individual, physical condition of the patient, and the extent of surgery. In order to avoid surgical shock and circulatory collapse, a light anesthesia and careful surgery are recommended together with supportive circulatory measures and application of warmth to the patient's body. The nature of the temperature regulation with its extraordinary persistence indicates that it possesses a certain predominance over the other vegetatively directed functions, as other workers have already shown from animal experimentation.

524. **Chiucini, G.** Effects of cranial and labyrinth lesions on the body temperature of the pigeon [In Italian]. *Boll. Soc. ital. biol. sper., v. 27, Mar.–Apr. 1951: 648–650.*

During the course of experiments on the effect of streptomycin on the semicircular canals of pigeons, it was found that control animals which had been subjected to labyrinthotomy or labyrinthectomy had experienced a drop in cloacal temperature. This post-operative hypothermic phase, with a decrease in temperature of $0.9°$ to $2.3°C$, lasted for varying periods of from 2 to 10 days.

525. **Eiff, A. W. von.** Effect of hypnosis on temperature sense and heat regulation [In German]. *Zschr. ges. exp. Med., v. 117 (3), 1951: 261–273.*

The question was investigated, whether suggestions of warmth could remove cold sensation and elicit sensations of comfort even under extreme cold stimulation. Experiments were made in a climatic chamber at $11.7°C$ or $1°C$, with 50% relative humidity, on 11 undressed subjects under 2nd degree hypnosis and in a group of non-hypnotized control subjects. The rectal or sublingual and skin temperatures were measured by Hensel's thermointegralgraph.

It was found that thermal sensations and general comfort sensations, without clothing, could be influenced by psychic suggestion, even at 10°C and 0°C. Thus a thermal sensation is induced not only by physical factors but by a certain psychic reaction to the temperature stimulation. The chemical heat regulation can be to a large extent excluded by hypnosis. The assumption that the increased O_2 consumption in cold may be referable to an increase in reflex muscular tonus appears probable. It is stated that there is possibly no chemical thermoregulation in the narrow sense of the word. Physical thermoregulation can be influenced during cold by suggestions of warmth, but it can not be removed.

526. Frank, E., and K. Wezler. Physical heat regulation against cold and heat during oxygen insufficiency [In German]. *Pflügers Arch., v. 250 (3), 1948: 598–622.*

Peripheral vascular resistance was determined in subjects exposed to oxygen lack at various environmental temperatures. With a normal oxygen supply the resistance was at a maximum at 15°C and decreased at both higher and lower temperatures. In hypoxia the resistance was lowered proportionately to the severity of oxygen lack. Pulse rate increased with both hypoxia and degree of cold.

527. Freeman, H., and B. A. Lengyel. The effects of high humidity on skin temperature at cool and warm conditions. *J. Nutrit., v. 17, Jan. 1939: 43–52.*

Subjects in a nude and fasting state were exposed for 3 hours to a low humidity (20%) and to a high humidity (90%), on 2 separate days, at environmental temperatures of 24°C or 32°C. At 24°C the cooling of the skin observed at the low humidity was practically inhibited by high humidity so that the skin temperature rose. At 32°C the heating of the skin found at low humidity was increased by high humidity, especially on the extremities. The increase in skin temperature as a result of high humidity at 32°C was slightly less than at 24°C.

528. Giaja, J. An analysis of heat production in homeotherms as affected by barometric pressure [In French]. *C. rend. Soc. biol., Par., v. 127, Jan. 13–Feb. 15, 1938: 1355–1357.*

Lowered barometric pressure acts on that heat production which is under the influence of chemical thermoregulation but, under the same conditions, it is without effect on basal metabolism. These facts are used in experimental studies of the role of the two sources of heat production in homeotherms.

529. Grigor'ev, N. F. The nervous system on mountain heights [In Russian, with English summary]. *Izv. Akad. nauk SSSR, ser. geogr., 1939: 453–468.*

The effects of altitudes of 2,250, 4,250, and 5,300 meters upon the nervous system were studied in 25 persons on the Elbrus Expedition in 1936. Shifts in thermoregulation and vasomotor disturbances were among the effects noted.

530. Grigor'ev, N. F., G. V. Peshkovskiĭ, and L. N. Shteingauz. On the question of thermoregulation on the heights [In Russian, with English summary]. *Izv. Akad. nauk SSSR, ser. geogr., 1939: 511–522.*

Thermoregulation was studied on the Elbrus Expedition (1937) by measuring skin and mouth temperatures at altitudes of 2,250 and 4,250 meters. Thermoregulation is somewhat disturbed under conditions of high altitude.

531. Hoyt, R., and H. E. Rosvold. Effect of electroconvulsive shock on body temperature of the rat. *Proc. Soc. Exp. Biol., N. Y., v. 78, Nov. 1951: 582–583.*

Hooded rats, housed at a room temperature between 70°–80°F, were subjected to electroconvulsive shock. The normal variation of the rectal temperatures of the rats was shown to be decreased during the periods of shock. It is suggested that electroconvulsive shock may affect the temperature-regulating mechanism of the hypothalamus.

532. Jouck, K. T. Oxygen consumption and heat regulation during oxygen insufficiency [In German]. *Luftfahrtmedizin, v. 9, 1944: 26–32.*

Oxygen consumption and skin and rectal temperatures were studied in healthy young adults (20–22 years of age) at a simulated altitude of 5000 and 7000 meters, for 40–50 minutes at a room temperature of 24°C. Next to the disturbance in gaseous metabolism, which consisted of a very low oxygen absorption at the start and a highly increased absorption at the end of the experiment, the rectal temperature was found to sink (0.2°–0.5°C) in all the tests. The temperature decrease started either simultaneously with the hypoxic inhalation, or after a very short period of latency. The role of pulmonary hyperventilation in this decrease was found to be insignificant. Therefore, even at 5000 meters of simulated altitude and a normal room temperature, a disturbance in heat regulation must be assumed. The skin temperature, measured at the elbow, remained constant in all the tests.

533. Kottke, F. J., J. S. Phalen, C. B. Taylor, M. B. Visscher, and G. T. Evans. Effect of hypoxia upon temperature regulation of mice, dogs, and man. *Am. J. Physiol., v. 153, Apr. 1948: 10–15.*

Hypoxia (250 mm Hg or less) decreased the ability of mice, dogs, and men to control their body temperature during exposure to cold (temperature range, 4°–24°C). The loss of temperature control and fall in body temperature was most marked in the mouse and least marked in man. Hypoxia inhibited shivering in all 3 species studied. In man exposed to cold (11°C) hypoxia suppressed an increased oxygen consumption and increased the dissipation of heat from the skin. Decreased environmental and body temperature favored the survival of mice exposed to progressive hypoxia; between 37° and 20°C, the survival ceiling increased approximately 1000 feet per 1°C of drop in temperature.

534. Léger, L. Cooling of patient during operation [In French]. *Presse méd., v. 54, Dec. 21, 1946: 846.*

The general body cooling of a patient during surgery can be considerable depending on the kind and length of operation, the type of anesthesia used, and the environmental temperature. Hypothermia is caused especially by exposure of the deeper areas of the body to an environmental temperature which is cooler than their normal temperature, and to some interference with vascular flow. To combat this heat-loss the author suggests the use of infrared irradiation of the field of operation, warming of the serum to be used in transfusion, warming of the operating table covering and the covering of the patient, and rapid re-warming of the patient at the close of the operation.

535. Mole, R. H. The relative humidity of the skin. *J. Physiol., Lond., v. 107, Sept. 30, 1948: 399–411.*

The author re-analyzes the experimental data of earlier workers (Winslow, Herrington, and Gagge; Am. J. Physiol., v. 120, 1937: 288), using the variable, rh_s (relative humidity of the skin), to replace w (wettedness of the skin). One of his conclusions is that the relative humidity of the skin (rh_s) depends on the diffusion of water through the skin, on the skin temperature (air temperatures of 14° to 38°C), on the vapor pressure of water in the environment, and on air movement. Also that the temperature gradient from body to skin varies inversely and the gradient from skin to air directly with the humidity of the air.

536. Phillips, N. E., P. A. Saxon, and F. H. Quimby. Effect of humidity and temperature on the survival of albino mice exposed to low atmospheric pressure. *Am. J. Physiol., v. 161, May 1, 1950: 307–311.*

At ambient temperatures of 22° to −20°C, mice survived exposure to a lower atmospheric pressure longer in moist air than in dry air; between 30° and 0°C, their ability to withstand hypoxia increased as the temperature decreased. Evidence is presented that at reduced pressures thermoregulation is lost and the resulting lowering of body temperature lowers metabolism. Likewise increased humidity lowered the energy requirements by reducing the rate of vaporization of moisture from the body. Thus both factors reduced the needs of the animals for oxygen and permitted survival to lower pressures.

537. Piatigorskiĭ, I. V. Effect of erythemic doses of ultraviolet radiation on the thermoregulating functions in infants [In Russian]. *Vopr. pediat., v. 18 (3), 1950: 47–50.*

In healthy children up to 1½ years of age, the thermoregulatory reflexes were found to be of three types: (1) the sympathicotonic (increased heat production with increased heat loss), (2) the vagotonic (small heat production with increased heat loss), and (3) the normotonic (normal heat production and loss). A considerable number of children of this age belong to the sympathicotonic group. Ultraviolet-radiation therapy, especially by the method of fractional dosages of erythemic level, induced a sharp improvement of thermoregulation toward normal.

538. Quimby, F. H., N. E. Phillips, B. B. Cary, and R. Morgan. Effect of humidity on the change in body temperature during exposure to low atmospheric pressures. *Am. J. Physiol., v. 161, May 1, 1950: 312–315.* Also, abstract in: *Am. J. Physiol., v. 155, Dec. 1948: 462.*

The fall in body temperatures of rats at reduced atmospheric pressures is significantly less in moist air than in dry air. These results are interpreted as due to the heat conserved by absence of evaporation from respiratory and body surfaces.

539. Rein, H., and U. Otto. Carbon dioxide in the role of adjustment of the circulatory system [In German]. *Pflügers Arch., v. 243 (3), 1940: 303–328.*

Using tracheal intubation and a fan, air with a definite concentration of carbon dioxide was introduced directly into the respiratory tract of anesthetized dogs. Studies on the biceps muscle of the leg were made of blood flow, blood pressure, and of arterial and venous temperature differences. It was found that levels of carbon dioxide which did not have any effect whatever on blood pressure or on respiration, caused a slowing of the blood circulation in the resting muscle but had no effect on the working muscle. High levels of carbon dioxide brought the working muscle to a stop and seriously slowed blood circulation there. When the leg of the dog was packed tightly in cellulose and therefore heat loss mechanisms were activated, the vasoconstrictor action of low levels of carbon dioxide were greatly diminished. High levels of carbon dioxide called forth a vasoconstriction in the vessels of the leg, but the final result was usually, instead, a reactive hyperemia. The vasomotor reaction activated by carbon dioxide was always found to be more effective than the nervous reflex, one of the circulatory self-regulatory reflexes. The latter were never able to cancel the effects of carbon dioxide. A lowering of the arterial-venous temperature differences was seen in the resting muscle with the lower levels of carbon dioxide. This may be explained on the basis of a decreased metabolic rate. During the period of activation of heat loss mechanisms, this lowering was less significant. The heat loss of muscle was not caused by changes in the blood flow since it mostly precedes the changes and was often covered up by them.

540. Scano, A., and P. D'Arcangelo. Resistance to low barometric pressure; maximum resistance of rabbits in relation to amount and velocity of decompression, behavior of respiration, gas exchange, and low temperature [In Italian, summaries in Italian, English, French, Spanish, and German]. *Riv. med. aeronaut., v. 14, July–Sept. 1951: 573–579.*

In rabbits exposed to barometric decompression, oxygen consumption and carbon dioxide elimination appeared to decrease progressively from a simulated altitude of 5,000 meters upward. Pulmonary ventilation and tidal volume, after showing the increase in agreement with the progressing decompression, decreased sharply above 10,000 meters. During the decompression, the inner body temperature decreased markedly. Above 7,000 meters there was a decrease in cardiac rate. The maximum tolerance of the rabbits appeared to be less than in an earlier experimental group in which the decompression rate was greater.

541. Verzár, F. Complete acclimatization to high altitudes [In German, summaries in German, French, Italian and English]. *Bull. Schweiz. Akad. med. Wiss., v. 7, Jan. 1951: 26–38.*

At the low environmental temperature and low atmospheric pressure which are found at 3000 or 4000 meters of altitude in the Andes, body temperature falls and shivering begins in subjects on arrival, before any acclimatization has taken place. Laboratory tests on guinea pigs have shown that at environmental temperatures of either 29–30 °C or 8–10 °C, body temperatures fall at lowered atmospheric pressures, the decrease being greater at the lower temperature.

542. Walther, J., F. W. Bishop, and S. L. Warren. The temperature pattern of laboratory animals in normal and febrile states. *In: American Institute of Physics. Temperature; its measurement and control in science and industry, p. 474–486. N. Y., Reinhold, 1941.*

Many observations concerning the temperatures in various parts of the body of normal laboratory animals, and the influence of some chemical and physical agents on these temperatures, are presented. In general, the body of the animal seems to be better able to withstand a fall of 10 °C rectal temperature than it does a rise of 6 °C (from 36 ° to 42 °C). In a cold state, the shrinkage of tissues, the increase in viscosity of the blood, and other reactions, are apparently better tolerated than the dehydration and other phenomena resulting from attempts of the body to cool itself while in the heated state. It is concluded that there is no constant and fixed normal temperature within the body. Under "normal" conditions, the rectal temperature in all the common laboratory animals fluctuates near 36.5 °C ± 0.5 °C. Some of the deep viscera, including the brain, are often higher than this by 0.2 ° to 1.2 °C, and superficial areas are considerably lower. Many factors, both exterior and interior, influence observations made on the animals. The temperature of the viscera probably depend a good deal upon their intrinsic metabolic activity at the moment. The results of the use of various chemical and physical agents are discussed and several are shown by temperature curves. Anesthetics, in general, cause disturbances in the superficial temperature and result in a general reduction of the whole body temperature. Depending considerably on the method used to create and maintain the elevated temperatures, in febrile states the usual temperature relationships may be modified or even reversed.

543. Winslow, C. E. A., L. P. Herrington, and A. P. Gagge. Reactions of the clothed human body to variations in atmospheric humidity. *Am. J. Physiol., v. 124, Dec. 1, 1938: 692–703.*

Sweat secretion and wetted area are minimal in body cooling in environmental temperatures below 25 °C. Humidity in this temperature range has little appreciable influence upon physiological reactions.

See also items: 392, 1067, 1538.

II. RESISTANCE TO COLD

A. Resistance, General

544. Anon. Medical problems of flying in the stratosphere. *J. Am. M. Ass., v. 117, Sept., 27, 1941: 1110.*

One of the medical problems of flying at great heights is that of extreme cold. More than 80% of the men tested were unable to withstand the lowered oxygen pressure and the temperature of −56.5 °C found at altitudes of 36,000 feet. Symptoms which occurred in high altitude flying were noted.

545. Anon. Survival in the Arctic. *In: Survival; a manual for aircraft crews forced down in all parts of the world—including hints on living off the land, building shelters, traveling, protection against disease, saving life and limb, p. 1–32. Washington, D. C. Airlines War Training Institute, [1943.]*

Lists are given of equipment which should be available to each individual as an aid in survival in case the airplane is forced down in the Arctic. Also given are suggestions for supplies to be carried on the person, and of those needed for signaling devices, fishing kits, winter clothing, food, and for a first-aid kit. Detailed information is given on how to signal, to build a fire, build a shelter, to provide drinking water, and on the what species of local animals and plants are available for food. Frostbite of the face, hands and feet should be avoided by keeping them protected as much as possible, keeping beards cut and clothing as loose and non-constricting as possible. Frostbitten areas are best warmed with body heat by holding a hand cupped against the face or by holding a frost-bitten hand, with mitten removed, inside the shirt next to the body. They should never be rubbed because of the danger of additional tissue damage and of infection.

546. Anon. Operation windchill. *Bull. U. S. Army M. Dep., v. 8, Jan. 1948: 6.*

Operation Windchill was undertaken as an exhaustive experiment to determine what might happen to the physical and psychological well-being of soldiers suddenly transported by air from warm climates (McDill Field, Florida) to a sub-arctic cold area. Within a matter of 15 hours the group of 32 Air Force soldiers, ages 18–22 years, were set down amid snow and ice in zero temperatures to set up a bivouac—a situation similar to that which would have been encountered had they crashed in the Arctic. Before leaving Florida extensive physiological tests had been made, including basal metabolic rate, blood pressure, sulfur content of red blood cells, vitamin C content of blood cells and plasma, extensive chemical tests of urine, and an analysis of body fats. Soon after arriving at the arctic base, these tests were repeated in order to study physiological changes that accompany day-to-day acclimatization to cold and their individual variations. Although much has been discovered in tests under simulated conditions, much remains to be explored as to psychological reactions and their effects on physical well-being. No results of the tests are given in this short note.

547. Anon. Army trains personnel for arctic survival. *Refrig. Eng., v. 56, Aug. 1948: 142–143.*

Information is given on the activities of the Arctic Indoctrination School in Alaska, set up by the Alaskan Air Command of the Air Force. Groups of personnel are given one day of classroom instruction and outdoor demonstration at the school, followed by experiences of living first on the frozen tundra—surviving on parachute rations—and then in a snow cave or ice house out on the ice pack. During indoctrination the student learns the cardinal rules for survival in the arctic: to keep dry and prevent excess perspiration; not to waste energy in violent exercise; and not to allow any body surface to become exposed. In emergency shelters the dangers of carbon monoxide accumulation and poisoning is stressed, together with its prevention.

548. Anon. Thermal standards in industry. *(American Public Health Association Yearbook, 15th, 1949–1950). Am. J. Pub. Health, (Part II), v. 40, May 1950: 131–143.*

In this report of the Committee on Atmospheric Comfort, short sections appear on the Limits of Tolerance to Cold (p. 138) and on Control of Occupational Cold Hazards (p. 139). The limit of endurance of an inactive person, even if warmly clothed, is less than 6 hours at 10°; about 4 hours at −10°; 1½ hours at −40°; and 25 minutes at −70°F. Endurance limits depend largely on insulation of clothing and amount of physical activity. Healthy, acclimatized, persons can withstand fairly low daily work temperatures if extremities are well protected. Fingers and toes cool quickly and set the limit of endurance for the rest of the body. Disappearance of pain should be considered as a warning sign since the areas become painful, then numb, and finally frostbitten as exposure continues. Rewarming in hot air (70°–100°F) is effective but slow; almost instant relief is given by rewarming in a hot water (90°–100°F) bath.

549. Armstrong, H. G. Physical factors in flight. *In: Principles and practice of aviation medicine, 2nd edit., p. 187–200. Baltimore, Williams & Wilkins, 1943.*

In this chapter on the physical factors in flight there is a short section on Cold (p. 189–192). The author states that for all practical purposes the atmospheric temperature falls about 2°C for each 1,000 feet of ascent until 35,000 feet are reached after which it remains practically constant at −55°C at least up to 80,000 and possibly beyond. Winter flying clothing in open cockpit airplanes, in addition to being somewhat of a physical and mental handicap, is generally ineffective at temperatures below 10°F. Hands and feet are the first to be affected, then back, chest, abdomen, and legs in that order; discomfort changes to pain and generalized shivering; voluntary muscular action becomes sluggish and finally some frostbite of tissues occurs; the emotional and mental states, meanwhile, deteriorate. A table of estimated loss of pilot efficiency from cold environments (50° to −40°F) in open aircraft is given on page 191, and it is indicated that there are three principal temperatures at which efficiency drops very rapidly. At 30° to 40°F, heavy clothing is first needed and the efficiency loss from the use of heavy gloves is equal to all the rest of the extra heavy clothing combined. At −10°F, vision is markedly reduced by frosting of the goggles. At −20° to −40°F, mental and physical reactions account for the further loss.

550. Back, E. H. Medical aspects of a wartime Antarctic Expedition: 1944–1946 (Operation Tabarin). *J. R. Nav. M. Serv., v. 33, July 1947: 193–197.*

Report is made of the medical aspects of a stay of nearly two years on the Falkland Islands in the Antarctic by a wartime expedition from the United Kingdom. Vitamin tablets containing 50 mg ascorbic acid were taken daily when at the base, while compound vitamin tablets of 75 mg of C, plus B complex, were taken on sledge journeys; there was no indication of true deficiency disease among the personnel although fresh food was available for only short periods. Frostbite of the feet occurred among the personnel of sledge parties but in general was only superficial. From this and similar experiences, the author concludes that from the point of view of health and morale two years is the maximum that any man should spend in the Arctic or Antarctic at one time.

551. Bader, M. E., J. Mead, and M. E. Pillion. Individual differences in vascular responses and their relationship to cold tolerance. *J. Appl. Physiol., v. 2, May 1950: 608–618.*

Although some correlation could be demonstrated between digital vascular response to immersion of the finger in cold water and the individual's cold tolerance in general, individual exceptions to the pattern were numerous. Hence the cold immersion response of the individual could not be considered as a specific indication of his response to cold stress. None of the other physiological indices—such as differences in pulse volume, blood pressure, and sensation of pain—in which consistent variations among individuals were found, showed any marked relationship to cold tolerance. Individuals who experienced only a transient reduction of finger-blood flow during immersion of feet in ice water, had, in general, a lower incidence of frost bite. Men, following exposure to cold stress on a field bivouac, experienced less pain and had smaller blood pressure rises on immersion of feet in ice water.

552. Brody, S. Temperature factors in animal production. *In: American Institute of Physics. Temperature, its measurement and control in science and industry, p. 462–473. New York, Reinhold, 1941.*

The author discusses warm-blooded animals in relation to their ability to withstand high temperatures and, on this basis, divides them into sweating animals (men, horses, mules) and non-sweating animals (cattle, sheep, swine, dogs, cats, rabbits). Farm animals, especially of the non-sweating class, are much less sensitive to declining temperatures and their efficiency and comfort are not reduced by temperatures as low as 0°F.

553. Büttner, K. The heat economy of the human organism and protection against cold in aircraft. [*In German*]. *In: Jahrbuch 1941 der Deutschen Luftfahrtforschung, Section III, p. 83–90. München u. Berlin, R. Oldenbourg,* [*1941*].

This is a report on the establishment of a quantitative basis for the temperature relations between occupants and aircraft in order to develop more effective means of protecting fliers against cold.

554. Critchley, M. Problems of naval warfare under climatic extremes. *Brit. M. J., 1945 (v. 2), Aug. 4, Aug. 11, and Aug. 18: 145–148, 173–177, and 208–212. Also, in Spanish, in: Rev. san. mil. argent., v. 45, July 1946, Aug. 1946, and Sept. 1946: 886–903, 1009–1014, and 1118–1126.*

This is the publication of the two Croonian Lectures delivered to the Royal College of Physicians, July 10 and 12, 1945. Lecture I deals mainly wits the modifications of environment and dress which have been evolved to meet the contingencies of cold, and Lecture II with the human side of the problems. The author states that naval personnel exposed to arctic cold and immobilized for several hours often find the bulky clothing to be tiring and burdensome; high wind makes hearing difficult; lacrimation and smarting impair visual acuity; poor light and fatigue may produce visual illusions; pain of intense cold produces a general sensation of distress; attention becomes distracted; perception and performance are dulled and slowed; and irritability or a mood of depression often results. Somnolence is common and may become overwhelming especially when one returns to warmth. Big persons tend to endure cold better than small, and a generous amount of subcutaneous fat, but not enough to involve circulatory strain, is an advantage. Degree of cutaneous pigmentation does not appear to influence resistance to cold. In neuroses among arctic personnel, depression is the dominant symptom rather than irritability or forgetfulness as in the tropical neuroses.

555. Critchley, M. Effects of climatic extremes. *Brit. J. Indust. M., v. 4, July 1947: 164–190.*

This is a discussion of the problem of climate and human survival. Partial contents include: measurements of environmental conditions; thermal comfort; psychological efficiency in the cold; physiological responses to cold (with a review of major research under 2 headings, "Knowledge before 1939" and "After 1939"); acclimatization; morbid effects of cold; psychological effects of prolonged residence in the cold; and effects of sudden change from one climatic extreme to another.

556. Desmarais, A., and L. P. Dugal. Influence of Adrenalin and Arterenol administration on the hypertrophy of the adrenal cortex during exposure to cold [In French]. *Canad. J. M. Sc., v. 29, June 1951: 104–107.*

Injections of Adrenalin or Arterenol had no effect on the hypertrophy of the adrenal cortex during the exposure of white rats to cold (0°C). However, injection of Adrenalin in the rats seemed to decrease the mortality from cold exposure.

557. Dorfman, R. I., R. A. Shipley, S. Schiller, and B. N. Horwitt. Studies on the "cold test" as a method for the assay of adrenal cortical steroids. *Endocrinology, v. 38, 1946: 165–177.*

A method of bioassay of urinary cortin is discussed, based on the survival time on exposure to cold (5.6° to 7.0°C) of adrenalectomized rats given the unknown urine either orally or subcutaneously. These survival times were compared with those of similar animals given a solution of known cortin concentration, used as a standard.

558. Eisberg, H. B., and J. E. Owens. Fundamentals of arctic and cold weather medicine and dentistry. *Research Division, Bureau of Medicine and Surgery, U. S. Navy Department, Washington, D. C.* [*Washington, D. C., Government Printing Office, 1949*]. *204 p.*

In discussing the clothing requirements for personnel in an extremely cold environment (p. 77–82), the "layer principle" is an attempt to provide the individual with possibilities of varying his clothing according to activity and changes of temperature. A chart of the values necessary for protection at a given temperature at different energy expenditure levels is given on page 80. In discussing rations a chart on page 84 shows the caloric consumption increase as the temperature is decreased. A 25% increase from that in the table of normal requirements of the Bureau of Supplies and Accounts Manual, is thought to be adequate for any naval vessel operating at sea under cold conditions. Some directions for preparation of pemmican, and for a survival and trail ration, are given on pages 90–92. In the section on hypothermia (p. 125–128), the localized cold injuries such as immersion foot, immersion hand, and frost-bite, are also discussed. Some of the physiological changes in deep hypothermia and hypothermic death are mentioned, based somewhat on the experiences at Camp Dachau. Death usually occurred at body temperatures between 77° and 79°F. Resuscitation was attempted by rapid rewarming by means of hot baths, also by rewarming by light cradle, heated sleeping bags, energetic massage, packing in blankets, or diathermy of the heart. None of the latter group were too successful. The nude body is unable to maintain an adequate thermal balance in water below 68°F; only 1 man out of 10 survived following immersion in water at 29°F for one-half hour. In treatment of severe immersion cases immediate rewarming is essential. Since facilities for hot baths and the number necessary may not be available, hot showers or the conversion of shower spaces into steam rooms for steam baths, may be used. Inhalation of 100% oxygen is indicated when available since tissues are usually anoxic in direct proportion to the severity of their cold trauma. Plasma should be used also in direct proportion to the degree of shock experienced. Infectious sequelae may be avoided by routine administration of antibiotics as soon as the immediate resuscitation has been performed. The patient suffering from immersion foot or immersion hand should be placed in bed and warmed by hot drinks and heat applied to the body only. The injured area should not be heated, and during the hyperemic phase should be cooled by means of ice bags or cooling cabinets. Systemic administration of penicillin and other antibiotics is recommended as well as the giving of tetanus anti-toxin and a tetanus booster shot. Similar treatment to that above should be used in treating frostbite cases. In addition, heparin used in the first 48 hours has prevented gangrene and other frostbite damage. In the latter half of the book, entitled Arctic and Cold Weather Dentistry (p. 169–204), it is concluded that though a few dental problems do arise, or are aggravated into an acute state by exposure to cold weather, cold does not appear to be the etiological factor. Rather there is a chronic dental condition or disease which is lying more or less dormant and cold may be the stimulus to irritating these malconditions to fulminate, or it increases the magnitude of symptoms already present and disregarded by the patient.

559.   Ershoff, B. H. Effect of thiouracil feeding on resistance to low environmental temperature. *Endocrinology, v. 43, July 1948: 36–39.*

Rats which were fed thiouracil until they were in a hypothyroid state, survived exposure to a cold environment (2° to 3.5°C) for an average of only 5.7 days. All of the similarly treated animals, who were in addition given thyroxin, survived for the entire 28 days of the experimental period; all of the control animals, without thiouracil or thyroxin administration, also survived for the entire period.

560.   Fernández Rodríquez, E. The organism versus cold [In Spanish]. *Rev. pract., Valencia, v. 4, Dec. 1948: 561–565.*

In various internal and external ways the organism adapts itself to maintain a homeothermic inner state. In a colder climate the plumage, pelt, or clothing aid in defense against cold. Man is aided also by a diet rich in fats and by the use of braziers or stoves for heating interiors of houses. Debilitated persons and those inclined to a scrofulous state, are especially susceptible to cold. These conditions are characteristic of the pathogenesis of erythema pernio, commonly called sabañón. Continued cold has an effect on the formed elements of the blood causing their agglutination and producing clots and emboli. A state of continued vasodilatation brings about a characteristic condition with blood plasma release and edema. The muscular system suffers also from the effects of low temperature bringing about a tonic reaction of the myofibrils. This produces a muscle contracture diminishing both the volume need of circulating blood and decreasing heat loss by radiation. Muscles in such a condition produce an involuntary motion said to be like castanets. Death from cold is preceded by quiescence of all functioning, a somnolence which deepens into unconsciousness and the final sleep of death.

561.   Grupp, G. W. Man and materials in the polar regions. *Proc. U. S. Nav. Inst., v. 75, Aug. 1949: 865–871.*

Results of studies done at Point Barrow, Alaska, on the effects of constant cold on man, materials, and machines, are reported. It has been found that work performance of human beings declines with temperatures below 0°F and that coldness is productive of apathy, lethargy, slowness, and clumsiness. Higher caloric intake (about 5,900 calories) is necessary in a very cold climate. Polar region clothing should fit loosely, and should be kept dry and clean to retain insulating properties. To survive in the polar regions, human beings should be cooperative, dependable, robust, self-reliant, and versatile, and not of the morbid or nervous type.

562.   Horvath, S. M., F. A. Hitchcock, and F. A. Hartman. Response to cold after reduction of adrenal tissue. *Am. J. Physiol., v. 121, Jan. 1938: 178–184.*

Unilaterally adrenalectomized albino rats, exposed to an environmental temperature of 4°C for from 2 to 72 hours, had an increase in heat production (measured at 29°C) of only about 7% as compared to 22% for normal animals. The maximum heat production was attained more slowly and was lower in the rats with reduced adrenal tissue. Colonic temperatures of both groups of rats remained practically unchanged at environmental temperatures of either 4° or 29°C.

563.   Horvath, S. M. Response to cold following double adrenalectomy. *Endocrinology, v. 23, Aug. 1938: 223–227.*

The heat production of bilaterally adrenalectomized rats kept at 4°C was measured and compared with normal rats kept at the same temperature. In the adrenalectomized animals heat production went up 79%, whereas in normal rats it increased 176%.

564.   Horvath, S. M., G. E. Folk, F. N. Craig, and W. Fleischmann. Survival time of various warm-blooded animals in extreme cold. *Science, v. 107, Feb. 13, 1948: 171–172.*

Survival time and body temperatures of various adult animals at an ambient temperature of −35°C, without food, was found to be: mice, 0.4 hour; Wistar rats, 0.75 to 1.6; albino rats, 2.0; New Zealand white rabbits, 3.5 to 6.5; white Leghorn hens, 3.3 to 29.5; and Army carrier pigeons, 22 to 48 hours. For the latter three groups the survival time varied greatly with the body weight of the animals. The lowest temperatures at which various animals could maintain body temperature for 1 hour was: pigeons, −85°C; chickens, −50°C; rabbits, −45°C; and white rats, −25°C.

565.   Knoblauch, F. J. Medical problems in cold weather operations. *Mil. Surgeon, v. 102, Apr. 1948: 283–285.*

Medical and other problems are greatly magnified when it is considered that minor physical effort in the Arctic may become tremendously laborious with the greater part of a man's total energy output being used up in the effort to survive in the cold. Newer and faster methods of casualty location and evacuation must be used since survival time without aid is markedly shortened in the severe cold.

566.   Krasner, B. Medical service with Exercise Snowdrop. *Bull. U. S. Army M. Dep., v. 8, Aug. 1948: 629–635.*

The services provided by a medical detachment from a Parachute Infantry Regiment to an Airborne Battalion Combat Team during Exercise Snowdrop in the Arctic, are discussed. In the period of Oct. 22, 1947 to Feb. 6, 1948, the total of 879 men treated on sick call varied from what would be expected at Fort Bragg, North Carolina, only in the low number of upper respiratory infections seen, and the number of injuries encountered during skiing many of which occurred during off-duty hours. Despite operations under field conditions of −25°F, only 13 cases of frostbite were reported in the combat team; in many of these carelessness was a

contributing factor. The only cases of severe frostbite occurred during a 3-day battalion problem; 4 of these required hospitalization. Men from temperate climates found greater difficulty
adjusting to arctic operations than did those from New England and the Northwestern states.
Clothing used during the exercise was generally adequate but frequently bulky and cumber-
some. Availability of dry boots and socks became imperative in such cold. No cases of trench
foot occurred but this condition is said to be seen very seldom at temperatures below zero. A
place to warm up periodically was essential since efficiency decreased with decreasing cold
until the primary concern of the individual soldier was to keep warm and not to carrying out
his mission. Without some type of heated shelter for treatment of casualties there was danger of
cold injury to both the patient and the aid man. In the cold, adhesive tape would not stick,
metal instruments could not be handled with or without mittens, and all liquid medications,
except alcoholic ones, froze solid. Since no solution to the latter problem has been found,
bottles should be only partially filled to prevent breakage on expanding, and individual
ingenuity used to thaw them. The effect of shock is known to be aggravated by cold. A Jane-
way shelter heated by Yukon stoves or Nelson heaters was found to be satisfactory. Tracked
vehicles like the weazel were found to be necessary for evacuation of casualties and the moving
of equipment.

567. **Kure, M.** Experimental studies on the human resistance function against
cold (Preliminary report) [In Japanese]. *Kosei Kagaku, v. 6 (3–4), 1947: 10–13.*
English summary, by S. Go, *p. 31–32.*

Studies were made to determine the effects of environmental cold (−10°C) upon experimental subjects as indicated by any changes in blood pressure, pulse rate, body temperature,
pH of saliva, amount and composition of urine, shivering, and sensory perception. The effectiveness of warming by use of a pocket stove was compared with the administration of ephedrine and with the consumption of alcohol and sugar. Alcohol and sugar (0.5 g/kg body weight)
produced the greatest resistance to cold.

568. **Lange, K., M. M. A. Gold, D. Weiner, and M. Kramer.** Factors influencing resistance to cold environments. *Bull. U. S. Army M. Dep., v. 8, Nov.
1948: 849–859.*

Rabbits restricted in their activity and kept at −20°C showed a markedly shortened survival time as compared with unrestricted controls kept at the same temperature. Superficial
anesthesia—somewhat comparable to sleep—resulted in a much more rapid loss of heat than
in controls. Inebriating doses of alcohol reduced survival time, while treatment with thyroid
hormone for several days before exposure resulted in prolongation of survival time.

569. **Liversidge, D.** Living in the Arctic. *Discovery, Lond., v. 10, May 1949:
141–144.*

A report is made of tests done in the Arctic by a British Royal Naval task force on efficiency
of clothing, responses of clothed body to cold, protection of body extremities from cold, performance and accuracy while wearing arctic clothing, and palatability of a new type
pemmican. Manipulative ability of the hands of men working for short periods of time without
gloves at below freezing temperatures deteriorated greatly but with considerable individual
variation. After running a mile in arctic clothing, the runner suffered no serious effects from
the cold and high wind velocity when he immediately ran a second mile clothed only in shorts
and vest. Without protective clothing, immersion in arctic waters results in unconsciousness
in 5 minutes and death within 20. Whether fighting or working, a man must have 4,000 calories
or more of food daily, and it must be palatable to assure that all is eaten. Normally the limit
of fat a person can consume is about 150 grams but persons in the Arctic become accustomed to
eating about 300 grams of fat.

570. **Neumann, R.** Observations on the psychological and physical reactions of
troops in subarctic climate of northern Norway, north of 70° latitude [In
German]. *Deut. Militärarzt, v. 6, Sept. 1947: 555–557.*

The author discusses the incidence of various illnesses which occurred, during the winters
of 1939–1941, in troops quartered in a subarctic area of northern Norway. The illnesses most

often occurring were respiratory infections, grippe, and occasional digestive upsets. There were a few scattered incidences of frostbite injuries of 1st or 2nd degree but none of 3rd. There were no psychotic incidents and only an occasional nerve inflammation (including sciatica). The two deaths which occurred were attributable to causes other than cold. The daily diet was of 4000 calories, containing an abundance of protein. No vitamin tablets were issued but cod liver oil was taken daily at breakfast. Beer and schnapps were to be had only occasionally. Books and movies were provided.

571. Ogata, K., M. Takeuti, S. Masaki, and H. Matumoto. Studies on the influence of the exposure to cold upon the regulation of human temperature, with some remarks on the build and native place [Abstract, in English]. *Jap. J. M. Sc., Biophysics, Mar. 1943: 5* *

Nine Japanese medical students were exposed, in groups of two, to temperatures of $-10°$ to $-18°C$, for a period of 50 minutes. Decided individual differences in the rate of oxygen consumption and the type of variation of skin temperature were noted but correlation of these findings to body build and native place of residence were not possible. However, it was noted that of the men who kept their rectal temperature higher than their initial one during exposure to cold, 7 were of portly build. This group generally had lower skin temperature than the other 2 who were of slender build.

572. Perla, D., and J. Marmorstorn. Natural resistance and clinical medicine. *Boston, Little Brown, 1941. 1344 p.*

In Section IX, Chapter 41, The Effect of Cold and Heat on Resistance (p. 1165–1178), is discussed the effect of sudden or prolonged chilling or overheating upon the defensive mechanisms of animals and men. Chapter 42, The Effect of Weather and Season on the Incidence of Infection and Resistance (p. 1179–1205), takes up the physiological adaptation of organism to climatic variations. In Chapter 41 is also given an analysis of the effect of temperature on the production of antibodies and resistance to infections.

573. Sacks, J. G. Psychological reactions to winter arctic conditions. *U. S. Armed Forces M. J., v. 2, Feb. 1951: 309–311.*

The observations summarized in the article were made over a 2-month period during the winter of 1948–49 while accompanying an Army Medical Test Team to an arctic area. It was found that the severity of the cold and wind was not the chief cause of complaint but rather that it was important from a psychological viewpoint because of its intensification of the isolation. Tenseness and irritability were seen at times among the soldiers who complained about the living conditions, lack of recreational facilities, and frustration met in attempting to perform unfamiliar tasks in the severe cold. Personality type, in itself, did not appear to be related to the good or poor adjustment; emotional problems encountered did not appear to be different from those in field conditions under other climatic extremes. Among American troops in Alaska, over a 2-year period, the incidence of neuropsychiatric conditions is cited as being lower than in any other Army theatre outside the continental limits of the U.S.

574. Shackleton, E. Arctic journeys; the story of the Oxford University Ellesmere land expedition, 1934–35. *New York, Farrar and Rinehart, 1938. 372p.*

This is a popularized account of Oxford University Exploration Club's journey to Ellesmere Land and points north during 1934–1935. Ellesmere is across Smith Sound from Greenland and is situated approximately 200–300 miles south of the North Pole. Detailed accounts of the winter clothing, food rations, morale, native wild life, and the construction of igloos are given. The party did not experience any frostbite. They attribute this to the extreme care taken in the selection of clothing. In order to avoid the freezing of feet after the the feet perspired, they wore woolen socks, sheepskin inner linings, sealskin boots, and bearskin or deerskin overshoes. The damp socks were removed from the feet only after the return to camp.

575. Shelesnyak, M. C. Some problems of human ecology in polar regions. *Science, v. 106, Oct. 31, 1947: 405–409.*

This is an outline of possible research in the field of human biology, primarily in the Arctic, for the purpose of inviting comment and of indicating the directions which such studies might take. There is discussion of the problems of selection and special training of personnel, including psychological evaluation of persons who have lived there successfully and re-evaluation of the factors involved in instability from the isolation of the Arctic. Some of the factors of the environment which have not been investigated are: the effect of meteorological factors on man; the abnormally low threshold level for sound; effects of humidity, fog, wind, water currents, and barometric pressure; effects of solar radiation on the eyes, skin, and body temperature; nutritional requirements; water and mineral balance and vitamin requirements.

576. Shoji, R., T. Fujimoto, and M. Yoshimura. On the ability of adaptation of man to the winter atmosphere in Manchoukou. III [Abstract, in English]. *Jap. J. M. Sc., Biophysics, v. 8, Mar. 1943: 99*.*

By use of an empirical formula for "freezing point", as function of temperature below zero and of wind velocity, a study was made of reactions to cold atmosphere of Japanese and of Manchurian farmers. At the equilibrium state of body temperature, no differences were found, except in oxygen consumption, which in the Japanese showed a higher level than it did in the Manchurians.

577. Stefansson, V. Arctic manual. (Prepared under direction of the Chief of the Air Corps, United States Army.) *New York, Macmillan, 1944. 556 p.*

The manual is a detailed and practical discussion of those underlying facts and principles which would be most useful to a person who wanted to live or travel in the Arctic, but with special reference to the needs of the Army. A section dealing with protection from visible and invisible perspiration (p. 271–281), gives detailed information on avoiding overheating, excessive condensation, freezing and melting of moisture in the clothing and bedding. Ordinary visible perspiration occurring from exertion or too-warm clothing, combines with the invisible perspiration and the two condense somewhere in or on the clothing as hoarfrost. Hoarfrost can easily be shaken or beaten from clothing. In Chapter 10, Health, Accident, and Disease (p. 281–319), it is stated that although frostbite can not be entirely prevented it can be avoided by suitable clothing and proper procedures. Small areas of frostbite of the face can be thawed by placing the palm of the uncovered hand over the area for a few moments; hands or wrists can be warmed by withdrawing the hand inside the clothing, removing the mitten, and warming the hand against the body. Frostbitten feet are difficult to cope with if you are alone in the open. If warmer or more footgear are available, this can be put on, or the foot can sometimes be warmed by the body heat of a sled dog. Immediate return to camp is indicated if feasible. Thawing rather rapidly, without friction, with the use of soft, slushy, snow—also for anesthetic reasons in case of pain—is recommended. Immunity or susceptibility to frostbite is individual rather than racial. In a discussion of the differences in disease incidence in the Arctic from those of warmer climates, it is stated that when small parties are isolated from all other human beings, the members recover from their head colds and do not catch more despite the intense cold and sudden changes from cold to warm. The successful use of an all-meat diet is discussed, as is the danger of carbon monoxide poisoning from interference with ventilation of the shelters which are heated by stoves and braziers.

578. Vignes, H. The struggle against the cold [In French]. *Biol. méd., Par., v. 31, Jan.–Feb. 1941: 1–35.*

Injury from cold is stated to be primarily a physical-chemical phenomenon modifying the colloids of the cells, the less severe states of which are reversible. Under individual resistance to cold are discussed obesity, temperament, endocrine status, neuro-vegetative status, and nutrition, as known from experiences in early European wars. The author discusses also true hibernation, false hibernation, and the large quantity of food, especially of fats, in diets of natives of far northern countries.

579. Yoshimura, H., and T. Iida. Studies on the reactivity of skin vessels to extreme cold. I. A point test on the resistance against frostbite [In English]. *Jap. J. Physiol., v. 1, Aug. 31, 1950: 147–159.*

This study is an attempt to devise a test method for determining an individual's resistance to cold injury (item 1308), based on individual variation in vascular reactions of fingers and toes. The middle finger of the test subject was held in ice water for 30 minutes, its skin temperature was measured, and, by comparing it with the curve obtained by plotting the reactions of many subjects, an index of resistance was obtained to be known as a "point test of resistance against frostbite." Under controlled conditions of environmental humidity and temperature, and of pre-test conditions which would effect temperature regulation, the method gave reproducible results at room temperatures of 15 °C to 25 °C. A method was devised to express all results in terms of a standard temperature of 20 °C.

580. Young, E. J. Military hygiene problems encountered in Arctic and Subarctic. *Canad. J. Pub. Health, v. 41, Mar. 1950: 123–127.*

Some of the military hygiene problems encountered in the Arctic and Subarctic are discussed, including those of shelter, food, clothing, disposal of excreta, and occupational hazards peculiar to cold climates. A suitable ration for the Arctic has to be considerably higher in calories than that for temperate zones and sufficiently palatable so that it will all be eaten. Prevention of frostbite is a matter of suitable clothing and training; first aid treatment of minor frostbite of the face is to allow the heat of the hand placed over the area, to warm it; in more severe cases, the area should be warmed very slowly and should never be rubbed with snow.

See also items: 26, 105, 151, 156, 201, 203, 222, 231, 450, 676, 808, 818, 821, 834, 883, 889, 947, 1003, 1108, 1111, 1308, 1332, 1338, 1344, 1345, 1357, 1362, 1370, 1448, 1520, 1558, 1699, 1704, 1710, 1754, 1996, 2002, 2012, 2589.

B. Role of Nutrition in Resistance

581. Anon. U. S. War Department General Staff. Operations in snow and extreme cold. *Basic Field Manual FM 70-15. Washington, D.C., Government Printing Office, 1944. 82 p.*

Chapter 2 summarizes information on problems of food, clothing, and shelter which might confront troops operating in conditions of snow and extreme cold. Rations should include a large percentage of sugars and fats since they are high in heat-producing qualities; the amount of food should be increased. Corn bread provides more heat than wheat bread, and, in case of animals, corn is more heating than oats. Great effort should be made to keep food hot—possibly by first heating the mess gear—and to eat it in a heated tent or shelter. Man can live indefinitely on a diet composed entirely of fresh meat, about 1⅛ pounds of lean meat and ½ pound of fat per man per day, but it must be eaten rare. Clothing should be loose enough not to interfere with circulation and sufficiently porous to prevent moisture from condensing and freezing on the inner surfaces. Since on the inner surfaces of the wrist the blood runs close to the surface, the wrists should be well protected.

582. Anon. Influence of food on body heat. *Heat. & Ventilating, v. 43, Nov. 1946: 79.*

Conscientious objectors assigned to a research hospital at the University of Illinois served as subjects in tests to determine what type of food would be best suited for combat troops in frigid zones. The subjects spent many days in a cold room (−20 °C); tests were given to determine the effect of cold and of diet on their ability to perform, think, see, hear, and coordinate. Results indicated that although the average individual developed more resistance to cold on a high-fat diet, the tests also showed that performance ability was improved by a high-carbohydrate diet. Subjects on a high carbohydrate diet required more food than those on a protein or fat diet, indicating that carbohydrate tended to be expended on the production of body heat. Cold appeared to have little mental effect upon the subjects. Muscular reactions were slower and the performance of even simple tasks was hampered. Adequate amounts of vitamins were found to be essential in resisting cold but excessive amounts had no added effect.

583. Anon. Nutrition surveys in the Arctic. *Bull. U. S. Army M. Dep., v. 9, June 1948: 484.*

Announcement is made of the nutritional surveys in sub-arctic areas being made by the Medical Nutrition Laboratory in Chicago. Ten-day survey of food consumption and actual intake of nutrients by troops subsisting in a post mess were made in the early winter and mid-winter of 1947, and the spring of 1948. Similar surveys in mid-summer and fall will be made to study the differences, if any, in food intake of troops as influenced by seasonal fluctuations in climatic temperatures.

584. Bezançon, F. Influence of sub-standard nutrition on the decrease of resistance of the organism to cold [In French]. *Bull. Acad. méd., Par., v. 124, Jan. 7, 1941: 5–13.*

The restriction of food, especially of fats, during rationing is stated to be not only cruel but dangerous when the person involved must be exposed to cold since it is known that in a cold environment there is a decided increase in the calories needed.

585. Bingham, E. W. The Antarctic expedition from a medical angle. *Med. Press & Circ., Lond., v. 219, Mar. 3, 1948: 185–188.*

In discussing his experiences as a medical officer on several expeditions to the Antarctic, the author comments on the rather high percentage of fat in the diet and his ability to tolerate it well when he had not been able to before when living in a more temperate climate. With correct precautions against it, frostbite could be reduced to being a minor affliction. Slow rewarming, often with only the normal heat of the hand, and no rubbing, was used on frostbitten areas.

586. Bly, C. G., R. E. Johnson, R. M. Kark, C. F. Consolazio, A. Laudani, M. A. Maloney, W. G. Figueroa, and L. E. Imperiale. Survival in the cold. *U. S. Armed Forces M. J., v. 1, June 1950: 615–628.*

Four groups of 8 men each were flown directly from Florida to Canada in the middle of winter and then lived for 12 days in bivouac areas, isolated from one another. They were fed continuously on one of 4 different rations. The calories eaten per man per day on the 4 rations were 1,120; 1,940; 1,650; and 4,850, respectively. The only ration of the 4 which was completely satisfactory for the 12 day period—as to health, good psychological attitude, and nutritional balance—was the diet of 4,850 calories.

587. Butson, A. R. C. Utilization of high-fat diet at low temperatures. *Lancet, Lond., v. 258, May 27, 1950: 993–994.*

Man tolerated well a high-fat diet (295 g fat; 4000 calories) at temperatures around 0°F but not at temperatures around 32°F.

588. Donhoffer, S., and J. Vonotzky. The effect of environmental temperature on food selection. *Am. J. Physiol., v. 150, Aug. 1947: 329–333.*

Mice kept at low temperatures (10°–11°C) showed a marked tendency to increase their consumption of carbohydrates when allowed free selection of foods. Mice kept at higher temperatures (29°–33°C) ingested less calories when similar food mixtures were offered.

589. Dugal, L. P., C. P. Leblond, and M. Thérien. Resistance to extreme temperatures in connection with different diets. *Canad. J. Res., Sect. E, v. 23, Dec. 1945: 244–258.*

Studies are reported on the relative effects of diets rich in fats, proteins, and carbohydrates on resistance to heat and cold. Diets rich in fats were found to be superior to those rich in carbohydrates in developing adaptation and resistance to cold. Diets rich in carbohydrates were more effective in developing resistance to heat than those rich in fats.

590. Duncan, A. C. Diet and disease in the subarctic. *Lancet, Lond., v. 253, Dec. 20, 1947: 919–921.*

After 10 years of general practice in the Yukon, where the temperatures range from full summer heat to 70°F below zero, the author postulates that the absence of several important diseases (rheumatic fever, Bright's disease, toxemias of pregnancy) may be explained by the high protein diet of the inhabitants.

591. Ershoff, B. H. Effect of prolonged exposure to cold on the vitamin A requirement of the rat. *Proc. Soc. Exp. Biol., N. Y., v. 74, July 1950: 586–587.*

Young rats fed a diet deficient in vitamin A were maintained at temperatures of 2°C and 23°C. The animals subjected to cold depleted more rapidly, weighed less at time of depletion, and had a shorter survival time after depletion.

592. Ershoff, B. H. Effects of prolonged exposure to cold on the thiamine requirement of the rat. *Arch. Biochem., N. Y., v. 28, Sept. 1950: 299–304.*

Groups of male adult rats were kept at temperatures of 23°C and at 2°C and fed a basal synthetic ration for 10 days, and then were fed a similar thiamine-deficient ration. Rats in the cold environment survived an average of 27.6 days while those kept in the normal room survived for an average of 64.7 days. In contrast to this, all rats fed a similar pantothenic-acid-deficient ration survived the entire experimental period of 12 weeks.

593. Ershoff, B. H., and H. B. McWilliams. Effects of B vitamins and liver on growth of immature rats maintained at low temperatures. *Proc. Soc. Exp. Biol., N. Y., v. 75, Oct. 1950: 226–229.*

Studies on rats maintained at low temperature and fed a purified diet, showed less resistance to cold as shown by retarded growth and gonadal weight than did rats on a similar diet with supplements of various liver fractions or of the B vitamins. Vitamin B_{12} appears to be the operative protective factor against cold.

594. Ershoff, B. H., and S. M. Greenberg. Effects of a transient vitamin A deficiency on subsequent resistance to cold. *Proc. Soc. Exp. Biol., N. Y., v. 75, Nov. 19, 1950: 604–607.*

A transient deficiency of vitamin A in young rats, although apparently corrected by administration of high doses of the vitamin, caused marked impairment of the ability to withstand cold (environmental temperature, 2° ± 1.5°C).

595. Ershoff, B. H. Beneficial effect of liver feeding on swimming capacity of rats in cold water. *Proc. Soc. Exp. Biol., N. Y., v. 77, July 1951: 488–491.*

Young rats (22–25 days of age) raised to maturity on a diet containing 10% whole liver powder, swam for a significantly longer time in water at 20°C than rats fed a diet supplemented with B vitamins. It was not clear whether the protective effect of liver was due to an unidentified factor or to its content of known nutrients.

596. Ershoff, B. H. Decreased resistance of pyridoxine-deficient rats to cold exposure. *Proc. Soc. Exp. Biol., N. Y., v. 78, Nov. 1951: 385–388.*

Groups of immature rats were fed a purified ration containing all the known B vitamins in synthetic form while other groups were fed a similar diet with pyridoxine omitted. Some of the rats were exposed to cold (2° ± 1.5°C) either from the first day of feeding or after 80 days. In the group exposed to cold from the first day of feeding, mortality was 25.0% of those on the pyridoxine-deficient diet and 18.7% on the non-deficient ration, over a period of 100 days. When the exposure to cold did not begin until after 80 days, these figures, over the 20 day additional period, were 68.8% and 0%.

597. Glickman, N., R. W. Keeton, H. H. Mitchell, and M. K. Fahnestock. The tolerance of man to cold as affected by dietary modifications; high versus low intake of certain water-soluble vitamins. *Am. J. Physiol., v. 146, July 1946: 538–558.*

Experiments were performed on 12 men over 150 days to determine the effect of supplements of the water-soluble vitamins to the diet on their ability to withstand repeated exposures of 8 hours to either intense cold with protective clothing or moderate cold with little clothing. Although some acclimatization was demonstrated, it was concluded that ability to withstand repeated exposure to cold could not be enhanced by increased amounts of vitamins.

598. Gounelle, H. Nutrition and the very cold climate [In French]. *Ann. nutrit., Par., v. 3 (5), 1949: 471–489.*

An average daily intake of 5000 calories appeared to be necessary for a person exposed to outdoor temperature in a very cold climate, preferrably with the energy needs supplied by fats, and with a good source of vitamin C. One ration found satisfactory was made up of 55% lipids, 34% carbohydrates, and 11% proteins. Alcohol, to exercise a stimulating action, was found to be useful as a therapeutic agent but was not incorporated as part of a specific ration composition for defense against exterior cold. Small meals at frequent intervals appeared desirable.

599. Grab, W., and K. Lang. Cold resistance and nutrition. 2. Influence of the addition of vitamins A and B on cold resistance [In German]. *Klin. Wschr., v. 23, June 1944: 230–234.*

No effect on resistance of rats exposed to cold (1 °C) and treated with vitamins A and B, separately, was noted. However, an augmented resistance to cold was shown when both vitamins were administered together.

600. Grab, W., and K. Lang. Cold resistance and nutrition. 4. Influence of vitamin C on cold resistance [In German]. *Klin. Wschr., v. 24–25, Oct. 1–15, 1946: 40–41.*

When guinea pigs deficient in vitamin C were exposed to dry cold at 0 °C, it was found that their resistance to cold was increased by feeding maximal doses of vitamin C.

601. György, P. Environmental temperature and 'rat acrodynia'. *J. Nutrit., v. 16, July 1938: 69–77.*

Acrodynia (induced experimentally by a deficiency of pyridoxine) appeared more quickly in rats exposed to an environmental temperature of 40 °F than in rats kept at a normal room temperature. Peter's eluate (a preparation rich in pyridoxine) cured and prevented the condition in both groups of animals.

602. Hegsted, D. M., and G. S. McPhee. The thiamine requirement of the adult rat and the influence on it of a low environmental temperature. *J. Nutrit., v. 41, May 10, 1950: 127–136.*

In an environmental temperature of 55 °F the thiamine requirement per rat per day was 50% greater than when the animals were kept at 78 °F. The increased food intake (approximately 25% more calories) at the low temperature accounted for much, but may not have accounted for all, of the increased thiamine requirement. The thiamine requirement of the rat, per 1000 non-fat calories consumed, appears to be essentially the same as the requirement of adult human subjects on the same basis.

603. Hunt, M. M. The man who ate bears. *Sc. Illust., N. Y., v. 4, July 1949: 47–48, 60–62.*

This biographical sketch mentions the detailed metabolic study conducted through the Russel Sage Foundation and Bellevue Hospital in 1928, in which the author and an old arctic friend lived for one year on a diet (mainly of meat and water) similar to the bear-meat diet of northern Eskimos. At the end of the period of dieting, doctors found the men to be in perfect health with somewhat more stamina than they had had at the beginning of the experiment.

604. Johnson, R. E., and R. M. Kark. Environment and caloric requirements. *Fed. Proc., Balt., v. 6, Mar. 1947: 138.*

Studies were made of voluntary food intake among groups of soldiers in desert, moist tropics, temperate areas, mountains, and subarctic and arctic areas. A straight line correlation was found between the voluntary caloric intake and decrease of temperature; the colder the climate the more the men wanted to eat.

605. Johnson, R. E., and R. M. Kark. Environment and food intake in man. *Science, v. 105, Apr. 11, 1947: 378-379.*

Studies were made of the average daily, voluntary, caloric intake of American soldiers acclimatized to the desert (92°F) or to the arctic (−30°F). Of 3,100 calories chosen in the hot environment and 4,900 in the cold, the percentage of calories derived from protein was practically constant. The data imply that the same general types of food can be provided for ground troops regardless of environment, but that men in cold climates require greater quantities of food than those in hot temperatures.

606. Kark, R. M., R. R. M. Croome, J. Cawthorpe, D. M. Bell, A. Bryans, R. J. MacBeth, R. E. Johnson, F. C. Consolazio, J. L. Poulin, F. H. L. Taylor, and R. C. Cogswell. Observations on a mobile arctic force. The health, physical fitness and nutrition of exercise "Musk Ox", Feb.–May 1945. *J. Appl. Physiol., v. 1, July 1948: 73-92.*

During the cold weather military exercise "Musk Ox" it was found that tolerance of the men to cold was increased by frequent feedings. An increased percentage of caloric intake supplied by fat also had a favorable influence on cold tolerance.

607. Keeton, R. W., E. H. Lambert, N. Glickman, H. H. Mitchell, J. H. Last, and M. K. Fahnestock. The tolerance of man to cold as affected by dietary modifications; proteins versus carbohydrates, and the effect of variable protective clothing. *Am. J. Physiol., v. 146, Apr. 1946: 66-83.*

The heat increment of a high-protein diet was 50% greater than that of a high-carbohydrate diet during exposure for 6 hours to cool environmental temperatures. Under comfortable temperature conditions the heat increment was 76% higher. The high-carbohydrate diet was shown to be more effective in increasing man's tolerance to intense cold than a high-protein diet. This difference was marked as shown by psychomotor tests even when the men were fully clothed against the cold.

608. Lang, K., and W. Grab. Cold resistance and nutrition [In German]. *Klin. Wschr., v. 23, June 1944: 226-230.*

Experiments on rats to study the relation of diet to the animals' ability to withstand cold (0° to 2°C) showed a direct correlation between the protein content of the diet and resistance to cold.

609. Lang, K., and W. Grab. Cold resistance and nutrition. 3. Influence of fat supply on cold resistance [In German]. *Klin. Wschr., v. 24-25, Oct. 15, 1946: 37-40.*

Rats maintained in dry cold at 0°C were fed a diet of from 10 to 50% fat calorically expressed. Cold resistance was found to decrease with increasing fat content.

610. LeBlond, C. P., L. P. Dugal, and M. Thérien. The food chosen by white rats in the cold and in the heat [Abstract, in French]. *Rev. canad. biol., v. 3, Feb. 1944: 127–129.*

In an experiment of 7 months' duration, rats were kept at environmental temperatures which were either cold (-2°C), hot (32°C), or normal, and allowed their choice of several foods. In the cold the rats chose a diet of about 25% each of protein material and of fats, and 30% of carbohydrates. In the heat, the consumption of glucose increased slowly to nearly 70% and that of fats decreased quickly. Sodium chloride, calcium lactate, and monosodium phosphate were chosen in greater quantity in the cold than in the normal environmental temperature.

611. Lockhart, E. E. Antarctic trial diet. *Proc. Am. Philos. Soc., v. 89 (1), 1945: 235–248.*

This is a report on diets developed for, and used extensively by, sledging parties during the U.S. Antarctic Service Expedition of 1939–1941. A ration was developed, following scientific research and practical experience in the Antarctic, which had the following attributes: more than an adequate supply of nutritious protein; adequate amounts of important minerals and vitamins; a total of at least 5,000 calories per day; weight of about 2 pounds; little fuel required for preparation; good palatability, except for the need to further improve the pemmicans; and with few digestive upsets resulting.

612. Miller, A. J. Physical fitness for strenuous work in relation to the survival situation in a cold environment. *J. Aviat. M., v. 20, Feb. 1949: 65–67, 72.*

Studies were made on 18 young volunteers to determine their ability to work and survive in cold environments (10° to -40°F). During 10 days in a very cold environment with excellent food, subjects maintained and even improved their ability to do strenuous work. In general, those men with the highest physical fitness indices at the beginning of the tests, maintained the highest morale under the varying stressful conditions but undoubtedly these subjects were also the most highly motivated. However, after 6.5 days of starvation in an extremely cold environment, those subjects with the highest physical fitness indices showed the greatest fall. The factor of motivation was a highly important one in evaluating the fitness of men to do strenuous exercise by a test such as was used in this study.

613. Mills, C. A. Environmental temperatures and thiamine requirements. *Am. J. Physiol., v. 133, July 1, 1941: 525–531.*

Optimal thiamine requirements for rats, either per gram of food or per calorie, were found to be twice as high at a 91°F as at a 65°F environmental temperature.

614. Mills, C. A. Environmental temperature and B vitamin requirements. *Arch. Biochem., N. Y., v. 1, Oct. 1942: 73–81.*

Rats kept at an environmental temperature of 91°F required for optimal growth twice as much thiamine and pyridoxine and over five times as much choline as those animals kept at the somewhat cool temperature of 65°–68°F.

615. Mills, C. A. Environmental temperature and B vitamin requirements: riboflavin and pyridoxine. *Arch. Biochem., N. Y., v. 2, June 1943: 159–162.*

Riboflavin and pyridoxine requirements for optimal growth of young rats seem to be the same for both a hot environment (90°–91°F) and a relatively cold environment (68°F). Likewise there were no differences shown in the requirements for inositol, p-aminobenzoic acid, or nicotinic acid. Only thiamine and choline exhibited heightened requirements in tropical heat.

616. Mills, C. A., E. Cottingham, and E. Taylor. The influence of environmental temperature on dietary requirement for thiamine, pyridoxine, nicotinic acid, folic acid, and choline in chicks. *Am. J. Physiol., v. 149, 1947: 376–382.*

The minimum levels of thiamine at which polyneuritis could be avoided in very young chicks were 1 mg/kg at a temperature of 70°F, and 3 mg/kg at 90–91°F. Dietary needs for folic acid, nicotinic acid, pyridoxine, or choline were not found to be significantly different at the two temperatures.

617. Mitchell, H. H., N. Glickman, E. H. Lambert, R. W. Keeton, and M. K. Fahnestock. The tolerance of man to cold as affected by dietary modification: carbohydrate versus fat and the effect of the frequency of meals. *Am. J. Physiol., v. 146, Apr. 1946: 84–96.*

Experiments reported here indicate that diet exerts an important influence on man's ability to resist exposure to intense cold (down to a temperature of −20°C, for 8 hours). High-carbohydrate and especially high-fat-content foods appear to be more effective than high-protein foods. Furthermore, small meals every two hours were shown to be more effective than large meals conventionally spaced four to six hours apart.

618. Mitchell, H. H., B. C. Johnson, T. S. Hamilton, and W. T. Haines. Riboflavin requirement of the growing pig at two environmental temperatures. *J. Nutrit., v. 41, June 1950: 317–337.*

The daily riboflavin requirement of pigs was found to be 1.2 p.p.m. or less at an environmental temperature of 85°F, and approximately 2.3 p.p.m. at 42°F. Preliminary experiments on older pigs revealed a consistently smaller "spill over" of riboflavin in the urine, on the same diet, at 42° than at 85°F. Supplements of protein and of fat added to a diet of natural feeds depressed the output of riboflavin, indicating but not proving, an increased assimilation of protein and fat. Similar tests with a glucose supplement yielded negative results. Since the riboflavin requirement of animals per unit of food seemed to be independent of body size, the above method of expressing the requirement seemed preferable to expressions based on units of body weight.

619. Mitchell, H. H. Physical environment control essential in nutrition studies. *Heating Piping, v. 22, Oct. 1950: 87–90.*

The need for control of the physical environment (temperature, humidity, and other factors) is stressed in nutritional investigations since environmental factors have a considerable effect on the nutritional processes of animals and of man. It is mentioned that the Eskimo of cold climates consumes a high-fat and high-protein diet while the inhabitants of hot Central American countries live on a low-fat and a low-protein diet generally. The author raises the question of whether these differences in food habits prove that in a cold climate the body's requirements for fat and protein foods are increased or whether the differences are a reflection of the availability of the foods eaten.

620. Mitchell, H. H., and M. Edman. Nutrition and climatic stress, with particular reference to man. *Springfield, Ill., Thomas, 1951. 234 p.*

In Chapter 2, Diet in a Cold Environment (p. 9–41), the subjects discussed under the heading of The Physiological Effects of Cold are: basal metabolism; the cold stimulus to metabolism; lower limits of tolerable temperature; sweat secretion (especially the problem of work in arctic clothing); water shifts in response to cold; gastric evacuation time; and pathology of cold. Other headings in this chapter are: the effect of cold on nutrient requirements (animal experiments); the effect of cold on nutrient requirements (experiments on human subjects); the effect of diet on tolerance to cold (animal experiments); the effect of diet on tolerance to cold (experiments and observations on human subjects); thermal balance in the cold as affected by the specific dynamic action of food (experiments on human subjects). An extensive bibliography appears on pages 175–234.

621. Musacchia, X. J. Lipid metabolism in arctic Alaskan birds [Abstract]. *Fed. Proc., Balt., v. 8, Mar. 1949: 116.*

Biochemical analyses were made of the lipid content of the liver and kidneys of 2 species of birds—the Old Squaw, *Clangula hyemalis,* and the Red Phalarope, *Phalaropus fulicarious*—which migrate to arctic Alaska and are abundant there during the summer months. The average amounts of lipids, expressed as percentage of wet weight (the figures being the mean of values obtained from 10 individual birds) are given for both the liver and kidneys for each of the two species. The tables show total lipids, esters (free cholesterol values being obtained by subtracting esters from total lipids), lipid phosphorus, fatty acids, and the relationship of cholesterol/phospholipid, free cholesterol/total cholesterol, and cholesterol/fatty acid.

622. Ogata, K., N. Nasu, K. Harada, and M. Kamota. Influence of a large amount of sodium chloride ingestion on the basal metabolism and on resistance to cold and frostbite [In English]. *Jap. J. Physiol., v. 2, Aug. 1951–July 1952: 303–309.*

Daily ingestion of 50–60 g of sodium chloride by healthy, young Japanese men during a winter in North Manchuria showed that after a few days a gradual rise in basal metabolism took place, with an increase in appetite and an energetic feeling. In this state of high metabolic activity the subjects were more resistant to cold ($-9\,°$C environmental temperature) and frostbite. If the increased salt ingestion was continued very long beyond this favorable reaction period, physiological symptoms of excess (known to occur often at a 30 g/day level of ingestion, in other climates) occurred. In general, the rise in body functions seemed to be associated not with the increased amount of sodium chloride being ingested and excreted but with the amount of sodium chloride held in the body. The maximum amount of sodium chloride which could be retained without symptoms of excess was far greater in late autumn and winter than in the rest of the year.

623. Orth, G. L. Food requirements in the Arctic regions. *Mil. Surgeon, v. 104, Mar. 1949: 204–206.*

Army regulations currently provide for an adjustment of rations to yield a minimum of 4400 calories per man per day whenever the prevailing temperatures in arctic areas are subzero for periods of over one week. Experiences with troops in the cold would indicate that an additional 15–25% should be added under very adverse conditions or for heavy work; physical fitness and morale are best on a varied diet. Lack of sufficient fluids in the diet to maintain a positive water balance is a serious problem; dehydration exhaustion can take place in as little as two days in the Arctic when the air is both cold and dry and when only solid waters are available. Eating of snow or ice can delay this collapse but the amount of water obtainable in this way would not be great because of soreness of mouth and freezing of lips and face. Melting of ice or snow and its storage in large quantities takes large amounts of fuel and time.

624. Roberts, J. M. Falkland Islands dependencies survey. *Brit. M. J., 1949 (v. 2), Oct. 15: 863–864.*

Report is made of a British group of persons living for 14 months at a temporary base on the Falkland Islands in the Antarctic. The average hut temperature for the year was $52\,°$F ($11.1\,°$C), varying from $32\,°$ to $74\,°$F ($0\,°$ to $23.3\,°$C), with an outside temperature averaging $22\,°$F ($-5.5\,°$C) and ranging from $-14\,°$ to $49\,°$F ($-25.5\,°$ to $9.4\,°$C). The diet was regularly supplemented with 50 mg of ascorbic acid daily. In winter, because of the fatigue from even light work, 9,000 I. U. of vitamin A and 1,800 I. U. of vitamin D were added daily for 1 month. The author states that the latter two vitamins seemed to have some good effects although the reason was not entirely clear. Because of the great care taken to avoid them, injuries from frostbite and snow-blindness were never severe.

625.   Roth, G. M., R. D. Williams, and C. Sheard. Skin temperatures of the extremities of persons with induced deficiencies of thiamine, riboflavin, and other components of the B complex. *J. Clin. Invest., v. 23, May 1944: 373–379.*

None of the 8 women with induced thiamine, riboflavine, or vitamin B complex deficiencies showed any degree of vasomotor disturbances as evidenced by measurements of skin temperature and determination of rates of cooling (at environmental temperature of 20°C) or warming (at 32°C) of body tissues. Skin temperatures of the extremities of these subjects measured at the height of vitamin deficiency and after return to a normal level showed a closer correlation with the basal metabolic rate than with the state of vitamin deficiency.

*626.   Sapporo, T. T. Principles of nutritional chemistry at low temperature. *Jap. Ass. Adv. Sci., v. 16, 1942: 566–571.*

Quoted in: Chemical Abstracts, v. 44, Mar. 25, 1950: 2616b.

627.   Sealander, J. A. Survival of Peromyscus in relation to environmental temperature and acclimatization at high and low temperatures. *Am. Midl. Natur., v. 46, Sept. 1951: 257–311.*

Studies are reported for the northern white-footed mouse, *Peromyscus leucopus noveboracensis* and for the prairie deer mouse, *Peromyscus maniculatus bairdii*. When without food or water, winter *noveboracensis* survived longer than summer *noveboracensis* in the range of temperature from −35° to +35°C while summer animals survived longer at 40° to 50°C. The length of survival was directly correlated with the amount of weight lost before death. At very low temperatures neither summer nor winter animals were able to utilize more than a small portion of their surplus weight. The longer survivals of heavy individuals were associated with increased deposits of fat. Visceral fat was used before subcutaneous fat at low temperatures. No evidence was found of any hardening of the subcutaneous fat in cold weather. Laboratory-bred *bairdii* acclimatized at low temperatures survived longer at −20°C than animals acclimatized at high temperatures. At +20°C the reverse was true. At 35°C no decided differences were apparent. On the basis of hair follicle count, pelage of *noveboracensis* was denser in winter than in summer. Regrowth of pelage in animals of either subspecies was most rapid at intermediate temperatures.

628.   Smith, E. D., B. H. Ershoff, R. J. Winzler, and H. J. Deuel, Jr. Effects of B vitamins, liver, and yeast on growth under cold room and room temperature conditions. *J. Nutrit., v. 35, Jan. 1948: 39–48.*

Immature female rats were raised to maturity in a cold room (2°C) on purified rations containing B vitamins as synthetic factors and also as present in whole liver and yeast. Growth was reduced in all rats in the cold room although animals fed liver gained more weight than those fed other diets. Animals fed identical diets at room temperature showed no such effect. Whole liver appears to contain at least one factor distinct from the B vitamins, of which the requirement is greater in animals living under cold room conditions.

629.   Smith, S. Treatment of conditions arising from exposure to extreme cold. *In: Treatment in general medicine, p. 400–410. Ed. by* H. A. REIMANN. *4th ed., v. 4. Philadelphia, Davis, 1948.*

The importance of adequate nutrition in cold climates is stressed. The presence of adequate fat in the diet is especially emphasized, together with the wearing of protective clothing and other adequate prophylactic measures against cold weather. In a section on cold injuries, the author discusses clinical aspects, pathology, and treatment of frostbite, trench foot, immersion foot, and frostbite of the lungs.

630.   Stefansson, V. The diets of explorers. *Mil. Surgeon, v. 95, July 1944: 1–3.*

Several instances are cited where small groups of early explorers, or persons accidentally left behind in the Arctic, have lived for considerable periods of time on the local all-meat diet

---

* Original not seen.

while other groups living on the staple foods of their native countries have died of scurvy and other ills. From his own experiences of living for long periods in the Arctic on a carnivorous diet, the author has found that there appears to be no factual basis for the saying that in order to be healthy on a carnivorous diet you must eat the meat underdone or raw, and that you must eat the organs which are rich in vitamin C. He mentions the fact that on an all-meat diet, the free selection of fat or lean meat brought about a diet ratio of 80% fat to 20% lean. A feeling of dissatisfaction occurs when fat calories are less than 60%, and a constantly uncomfortable feeling occurs with diets of only 20% or 30% fat.

631. Stefansson, V. Pemmican. *Mil. Surgeon, v. 95, Aug. 1944: 89–98.*

The use of pemmican as a staple food by early plains people, fur traders, and arctic explorers is discussed. To produce the usual pemmican, the North American Indian took lean beef, split it in thin sheets, and dried it, usually by exposure to air, and then pounded it to small flakes. Melted very hot fat was added to the meat bits held temporarily in a hide bag which was then partially flattened before the fat was completely hardened. In this manner, without loss of caloric value, three pounds of fresh lean beef and one half pound of fat could be reduced to one pound of the dehydrated product with a corresponding shrinkage in bulk. Pemmican is known to remain unspoiled for months even if moistened by rain. The so-called winter pemmican, as contrasted to summer pemmican, is made in the fall and early winter and is not as well dehydrated and does not keep as well. Several quotations are given from military men, from explorers, and other persons concerning the use of pemmican as a food to be considered for military survival or as emergency rations.

632. Swain, H. L., F. M. Toth, F. C. Consolazio, W. H. Fitzpatrick, D. I. Allen, and C. J. Koehn. Food consumption of soldiers in a subarctic climate (Fort Churchill, Manitoba, Canada, 1947–1948). *J. Nutrit., v. 38, May 1949: 63–72.*

A study of voluntary food intake was made of a 100-man group of garrison troops, the average person of the group being moderately active spending about 3 hours daily in the open at the subarctic installation of Fort Churchill. The caloric intake in the 3 surveys made was inversely correlated with the mean outdoor temperatures prevailing at the time, and was directly correlated with the mean windchill. The percentage of calories furnished by protein, fat, and carbohydrate remained almost constant, averaging 13, 41, and 46% respectively. These values were not significantly different from those reported regularly for troops eating garrison rations at temperate climates. There was no evidence of an increased appetite for fats in the subarctic winter.

633. Templeton, H. A., and B. H. Ershoff. Comparative effects of carbohydrate, protein, and fat when fed as single foods on the survival time of rats under conditions of accelerated metabolism. *Am. J. Physiol., v. 159, Oct. 1, 1949: 33–39.*

The length of time of survival was determined for adult female rats fed purified diets of only sucrose, casein, or margarine fat, under conditions of accelerated metabolism resulting from thyroxin administration or prolonged exposure to low environmental temperature. Rats fed only sucrose or only margarine fat lived significantly longer at an environmental temperature of 2°C than did those fed only casein. At 23°C, no significant differences in survival time were noted on any of the three types of foodstuff.

634. Thérien, M., and L. P. Dugal. Need for ascorbic acid in acclimatization of guinea pigs to cold [In English]. *Rev. canad. biol., v. 6 (3), 1947: 548–551.*

Resistance and adaptation of guinea pigs to cold (+8° to −8°C) were found to depend directly on the quantity of ascorbic acid administered (orally). The amount of food consumed by the animals increased in the cold environment but was similar for each of the groups of animals at that temperature regardless of the level of ascorbic acid being administered.

635. Thérien, M. Contribution to the physiology of acclimatization to cold [In French]. *Laval méd., v. 14, Oct. and Nov., 1949: 1062–1110 and 1192–1257.*

It was found that in the guinea pig the ability to acclimatize to cold is related to the daily intake of ascorbic acid. Reserves of ascorbic acid determine survival time in cold when vitamin C is excluded from the diet.

636. Thérien, M., J. Leblanc, O. Héroux, and L. P. Dugal. Effects of ascorbic acid on several biologic variables normally affected by cold [In French]. *Canad. J. Res., Sect. E, v. 27, Dec. 1949: 349–363.*

The authors found that the "stress" produced by exposure to cold ($-1.5\,°C$) was diminished or abolished in rats or guinea pigs by the giving of massive doses of ascorbic acid. Ascorbic acid produced (1) inhibition of usual thymus atrophy, (2) acceleration of thyroid enlargement, (3) increase in weight of spleen, (4) decreased histamine content of the adrenals, (5) decreased cholesterol content of the adrenals, and (6) prevention of the hypotension usually produced at first by cold, and return of later hypertension to normal.

637. Wohlfeil, ... Opinion with respect to (a) occurrence of freezing injuries, and (b) the spreading of infectious diseases [In German]. *Ber. Arbeitstag. Ost., v. 1, May 1942: 147–149.*

As ways of increasing resistance to cold, the author suggests among others the giving of large amounts of vitamins C, A, D, and B; wearing of protective winter clothing including overshoes and gloves early in the winter; and that no tight-fitting boots or clothing be worn.

See also items: 550, 558, 561, 569, 577, 580, 645, 660, 670, 1118, 1259, 1364, 1442, 1445, 1702, 1744, 1950, 1984, 2582.

C. Acclimatization to Cold

638. Anon. Winter tests. *Bull. U. S. Army M. Dep., v. 6, Nov. 1946: 494–497.*

Winter equipment tests, during 1946–1947, were conducted by Army Ground Forces, in three areas: near Fairbanks, Alaska with Task Force "frigid"; Adak in the Aleutian chain of islands, with Task Force "williwaw"; and near Camp McCoy, Wisconsin, with Task Force "Frost". Basic data was to be obtained on the physiological demands of men in arctic and sub-arctic areas. Some of the areas in which the Medical Department was interested either directly or indirectly were those of: acclimatization; "accustomization" to strange clothing and equipment and to the use of normal equipment under varying conditions; physical efficiency, which is known to decrease with the cold; clothing and shelter; physical and mental casualties typical of extreme cold or wet conditions, especially those of frostbite, freezing, trench foot, and dietary deficiency diseases; collection and evacuation of casualties; hospitalization; sanitation and personal hygiene; and nutrition since in cold regions the caloric requirements are high and cooking is difficult.

639. Anon. The role of lipids in the adaptation of animals to various climates [Abstract]. *Arctic, v. 3, Apr. 1950: 71.*

Studies are being done at the Arctic Research Laboratory, Point Barrow, Alaska, on the role of lipids in the adaptation of animals to climate. About 150 animals of the Arctic are under investigation, including bearded seals, ground squirrels, and various birds, fishes and other marine forms.

640. Adolph, E. F. Acclimatization to heat and cold. *In: Advances in military medicine, p. 488–496. Ed. by E. C. ANDRUS and others. (v. 2) (Science in World War II). Boston, Little Brown, 1948.*

A brief summary account of investigations sponsored by the Committee on Medical Research, Office of Scientific Research and Development, is given. Studies were made on acclimatization to cold, with respect to clothing, diet, and tolerance to cold.

641. Balke, B., H. D. Cremer, K. Kramer, and H. Reichel. Investigation into adaptation to cold [In German]. *Klin. Wschr., v. 23, 1944: 204–210.*

The authors conclude that adaptation to cold is a central nervous system reaction, and is not affected by any real change in blood chemistry.

642. Bass, D. E., D. C. Fainer, R. K. Blaisdell, and F. Daniels, Jr. Adrenal cortical activity and hematological changes in man during cold acclimatization [Abstract]. *Fed. Proc., Balt., v. 10, Mar. 1951: 10.*

Twelve men were exposed nude to an environmental temperature of 60°F for 7¼ hours daily for 12 days, and then, after a 10-day interval, to another 5 days. During cold exposure blood was drawn on the 1st, 4th, 8th, and 11th days before entering the cold at 8:00 A.M. and 4 hours later. Controls were kept at 85°F. Eosinophilic counts at 8:00 A.M. fell significantly below controls on the 4th and 8th days; did not vary on the 4th day or the 11th day of re-exposure; and, in those taken 4 hours after exposure began, did not vary significantly. Uric acid-creatinine ratios, taken from 7:00–8:00 A.M., did not vary throughout, but urine voided from then until noon had higher ratios. Erythrocytes gained water after 4 hours on the 4th day of initial exposure and the 1st day of re-exposure. Morning hematocrits were higher during exposure phases. Hemoconcentration during 4 hours exposure was significantly higher on the 1st than on the 11th day. Evidence of altered adrenal cortical activity was equivocal.

643. Blair, J. R., J. M. Dimitroff, and J. E. Hingeley. Acquired resistance to cold exposure in the rabbit and the rat [Abstract]. *Fed. Proc., Balt., v. 10, Mar. 1951: 15.*

The effect of adaptation to cold upon subsequent resistance was tested on acclimated and unacclimated groups of rabbits and rats. Rabbits were exposed for 20 hours each day for 7 weeks to −29°C and rats for 16 hours each day for 7 weeks to −7°C. The conditioned rabbits tolerated subsequent exposure to −45°C and the conditioned rats exposure to −15°C without hypothermia or frostbite injury. All the unconditioned control animals suffered progressive hypothermia and 2nd or 3rd degree frostbite when subjected to the same degree and duration of cold.

644. Bobrov, N. I. On acclimatization to cold [In Russian]. (Trudy nauchnoĭ sessii posv. 30-letiiu vel. oktiabr. sotsial. revoliutsii). *In: Tr. Voenno-morsk. med. akad. (Leningrad), 1947, p. 369–370.*

Reactions to experimental cooling were studied in 10 subjects. Cooling of the hand, foot, or hip was done with water of 10° or 5°C, for 30 minutes daily for 2 to 2½ months. The following results were obtained: (1) Prolonged and repeated local cooling during 2 months resulted in a diminished reaction of the thermo-receptors of the skin; the drop in local skin temperature after cooling was decreased by 1.5°–2.5°C as compared to the start of the period. (2) Restoration of the local skin temperature to normal proceeded much more quickly at the end of the 2nd month of acclimatization than in the beginning. (3) Acclimatization continued beyond 2 months, did not further diminish the reaction of the thermoreceptors nor did it further shorten the restoration period of the skin temperature. (4) The establishment of a constant local reaction of the skin vessels in response to a determined cold stimulus indicated the appearance of acclimatization to this temperature. (5) In the covered parts (hip, foot) the vessels of the skin, after reaching a determined state of contraction, remained in that state to the end of the period of cold-stimulation; in the uncovered part (hand), however, a reflex hyperemia occurred which increased up to the end of acclimatization. (6) Interruptions in training for one month or more induced a loss of acclimatization, manifested by a greater decrease in skin temperature during cooling.

645. Burton, A. C., J. C. Scott, B. McGlone, and H. C. Bazett. Slow adaptations in the heat exchanges of man to changed climatic conditions. *Am. J. Physiol., v. 129, Apr. 1940: 84–101.*

Subjects were exposed to high or low temperatures in an air-conditioned room to study the effects of slow adaptation to heat or cold upon heat exchanges of the body with its environment, with respect to both the total heat loss and its partition into losses by radiation, convection, and evaporation. In the heat, radiation and convection losses eventually play a greater role; in the cold they decrease. Average calorie intake was significantly greater in cool than in warm conditions; foods chosen were of higher calorie count per gram, and there was a definite appetite increase.

646. Butson, A. R. C. Acclimatization to cold in the Antarctic. *Nature, Lond.,* *v. 163, Jan. 22, 1949: 132–133.*

Observations are given on the cold acclimatization of 11 men with the Falkland Islands Dependencies Survey in the Antarctic.

647. Daniels, F., Jr., D. C. Fainer, C. L. Bonmarito, and D. E. Bass. Acclimatization to cold in man [Abstract]. *Fed. Proc., Balt., v. 10, Mar. 1951: 32–33.*

Men were exposed to a cold environment (60°F) for 12 days, then after an interval of 5 days, to another 10-day period, except for mealtimes and for an hour each morning when they were at rest in an environmental temperature of 85°F. The results of this study, in which a number of physiological responses were measured, agree with the concept that acclimatization is the result of small co-ordinated changes in many responses rather than a striking change in any one function. Indications of reduced physiological strain under continued cold stress were most evident in changed distribution of body heat. Subjective improvement in cold tolerance was present in 11 out of 12 men, and in most of these by the fourth or fifth day. No changes in basal metabolic rate were found.

648. Desmarais, A., L. P. Dugal, and C. P. Leblond. Effect of partial ablation of the liver on resistance of adapted animals to cold [In French]. *Rev. canad. biol., v. 2, Oct. 1943: 453–454.*

Rats adapted to cold and non-adapted rats were exposed to a temperature of −2°C after partial ablation of the liver. It was found that the cold-adapted rats survived longer than the non-adapted animals.

649. Desmarais, A. Differences in the effects of cold environment and of muscular work on adrenal function [Abstract]. *Fed. Proc., Balt., v. 8, Mar. 1949: 34.*

The investigator found that non-adapted, non-adrenalectomized rats were more resistant to cold than adapted, adrenalectomized rats.

650. Desmarais, A., and L. P. Dugal. Peripheral circulation in the rat exposed to cold [In French]. *Rev. canad. biol., v. 9, May 1950: 206–209.*

Peripheral vascular sensitivity to Adrenalin was studied in rats which were maintained in a cold room (0° ± 1°C) for 24 days. The authors noted the usual vasoconstriction immediately on exposure to cold followed by a rapid return to normal by the end of the first day and vasodilatation by the second day. During the process of adaptation to cold they observed patterns of alternating phases of vasoconstriction and vasodilatation.

651. Desmarais, A., and L. P. Dugal. Peripheral circulation and the adrenal gland content of adrenaline and arterenol (noradrenalin) in white rats exposed to cold [In French]. *Canad. J. M. Sc., v. 29, June 1951: 90–99.*

During the period of resistance and acclimatization to cold (10°C and 0°C), the peripheral circulation manifested both vasodilatation and vasoconstriction, with the latter being more prevalent. These changes were not, however, accompanied by parallel fluctuations of the adrenaline and arterenol (noradrenalin) content of the adrenal medulla, but exposure to cold seemed to increase gradually the adrenal gland content of both hormones until adaptation was reached.

652. Dugal, L. P., and M. Thérien. Relation between ascorbic acid content of organs and acclimatization to cold of guinea pig [In French]. *Rev. canad. biol.,* v. 6 (3), 1947: 552–553.

Continuing with their studies on the need for ascorbic acid in the acclimatization of guinea pigs to a cold environment, the authors found that the ascorbic acid content of organs, especially the adrenals, was high in the groups of animals which had adapted well to cold, highest in those individual animals which had adapted best, and was low in those which had not acclimatized successfully.

653. Dugal, L. P., and M. Thérien. Ascorbic acid and acclimatization to cold environment. *Canad. J. Res., Sect. E,* v. 25, June 1947: 111–136.

Rats subjected to long exposure to cold (4° to −4°C) showed a large increase in ascorbic acid content of the tissues. Rats fed vitamin C showed a smaller increase, while in rats unable to adapt to cold, a decrease in ascorbic acid was noted. Guinea pigs, which are unable to synthesize ascorbic acid, require large amounts of vitamin C in order to survive in cold.

654. Eliot, J. W., H. J. Stein, and R. A. Bader. Cross-acclimatization to heat and cold [Abstract]. *Am. J. Physiol.,* v. 155, Dec. 1948: 435.

Three men were exposed to 19 five-hour periods of heat (107°F) and 14 five-hour periods of cold (−20°F), followed by 5 periods of re-exposure to heat. After 5 weeks of rest 3 more exposures to heat were given. It was found that loss of acclimatization to heat was not accelerated by exposure to cold. No difference in the basal metabolic rate was noted during the hot and cold periods. Diuresis was continuous during cold exposure and chloride loss was increased. Hemoconcentration as measured by plasma protein and hematocrit values increased in the cold and decreased during heat.

655. Frazier, R. G. Acclimatization and the effects of cold on the human body as observed at Little America III, on the United States Antarctic Service Expedition 1939–1941. *Proc. Am. Philos. Soc.,* v. 89, Apr. 1945: 249–255.

Observations were made of effects of exposure to cold and ability to acclimatize to low temperatures on members of the U. S. Antarctic expedition during the period 1939–1941. Blood count, blood pressure, respiration, blood sugar, and adrenaline secretion were studied, as well as the incidence of various diseases. Toothache and frostbite resulting from exposure to cold were common. Methods for treatment of frostbite are outlined.

656. Frieboes, [W.] On the necessity for developing resistance to cold in man and domestic animals [In German]. *Arch. Derm. Syph., Berl.,* v. 184, 1943: 58–61.

The necessity for studying means for developing resistance to cold in man and animals is discussed on a theoretical level. The author reports also on certain experiments in this direction undertaken in various German institutes.

657. Giaja, J., and L. Marković. Adaptation to cold and resistance to low atmospheric pressure [In French]. *C. rend. Acad. sc., Par.,* v. 227, July 26, 1948: 296–297.

Groups of 7 rats previously adapted to an environmental temperature of 28°–30°C and a group of 7 other rats adapted to 0°C, were placed in an environmental temperature of 13°–18°C. Heat-adapted rats began to lower their consumption of oxygen when the pressure reached 131 mm (normal, 159 mm), or the corresponding barometric pressure of 623 mm, simulated altitude of 1,500 m, or respiratory quotient of 13.3. For the cold-adapted animals these figures were 106 mm, 504 mm, 3,300 m, or a quotient of 19.7. The difference in the consumption of oxygen of the two groups would indicate that adaptation to cold provides for the increased consumption of O_2—at the reduced O_2 pressure—by the medium of tissue oxidation. Two rats similarly adapted to heat and two to cold, were placed in a chamber at

17°C and the air pressure reduced to a barometric pressure of 250 mm in a space of 10 minutes. The heat-adapted rats promptly died; the cold-adapted ones, although breathing with great difficulty, survived and recovered upon being returned to normal pressure.

658. Glaser, E. M. Acclimatization to heat and cold. *J. Physiol., Lond., v. 110, Dec. 31, 1949: 330–337.*

Experiments performed on six sailors showed that it was possible to demonstrate acclimatization to cold after 3 days spent in a moderately cool environment. This acclimatization may be inhibited by exercise or severe shivering. It was also found that frequent changes of temperature may be useful in promoting adaptation to extremes of climate.

659. Glickman, N. Comparison of physiological adjustments of human beings during summer and winter. *Heating Piping, v. 20, Aug. 1948: 113–119.*

After an exposure for one hour to a comfortable environment, reactions of 4 subjects were the same in summer and in winter. The comfort impression on entering a comfortable room was higher in winter than in summer. After one hour in a hot room, mean skin temperature was the same in winter and summer but rectal temperature increased slightly more in winter. Perspiration was greater in summer, although the time of appearance on the subject was the same. These slight alterations in physiological adjustment are interpreted as giving little evidence of seasonal adaptation in determining responses.

660. Horvath, S. M., A. Freedman, and H. Golden. Acclimatization to extreme cold. *Am. J. Physiol., v. 150, July 1947: 99–108.*

Basal metabolic rates were determined on 5 subjects who spent 3 days at 25°C, 8 days at −29°C, and 3 subsequent days at 25°C. No changes in basal values for heart rate or rectal temperature were noted. During exposure to cold the caloric expenditure while sitting or performing work was higher. The data provide some evidence for possible acclimatization to cold.

661. Hutchinson, F. W. The parodox of acclimatization. *Heat. and Ventilating, v. 39, Feb. 1942: 25–27.*

When a person passes from an environment to which he is accustomed into one colder or warmer, he experiences both "shock" and some acclimatization. The distinction between the two is said to be that "shock" occurs in the relatively brief interval preceding a return to the original equilibrium condition (about 1½ to 3 hours) while acclimatization occurs in the extended period during which the body alters its condition of optimum comfort. The severity of the discomfort, or health hazard, depends on the time required for restoration to control conditions and is, therefore partially determined by the lag or thermal inertia of the body. Acclimatization because of previous exposures to the newer temperature involves a "re-setting" of the thermal mechanisms and produces greater thermal inertia and greater lag. The effect of lag is said to increase with body size, it having been found that heat regulating mechanisms in animals operate with an effectiveness which varies inversely with the mass. Acclimatizing effects are an aggravating influence in air-conditioning operations. If it were not for acclimatization, the discomfort caused by summer temperatures would be greater, but if it were also not for acclimatization the "shock" attendant upon the use of summer cooling would not be as prolonged or as great.

662. Irving, L. A study on climatic adaptation in arctic and tropical mammals and birds. *Proc. Alaskan Sc. Conf., 1950: 85–86.*

A few arctic mammals and birds preserve body temperatures around 37°C even though they are exposed at times to environmental temperatures which may go as low as −60°C. Measurements of heat transfer through the skin of arctic animals showed that insulation varies with fur thickness and increases with the size of the animal. In arctic animals as large as foxes, metabolism remains constant over a range of temperature of 30°C to −50°C.

663. Irving, L. Physiological adaptation to cold in arctic and tropic animals. *Fed. Proc., Balt.,* v. *10, June 1951: 543–545.*

Among arctic animals, the fur thickness increases with size up to that of the arctic white fox. However, in larger animals such as the caribou and polar bear, no marked increase in thickness of fur was found. Insulation of adult arctic animals larger than the arctic fox was sufficient to enable them to maintain normal body temperature in an environmental temperature down to −30°C; it appeared that they did not need to increase basal metabolic heat production until environmental temperature fell below −50°C, and then only slightly. Insulation of animals in the Tropics is so poor that only slight diurnal and other changes cause them to become too cold; well-adjusted arctic animals do not shiver in any winter weather, and there is a wide range of temperature which is tolerable to them. At an environmental temperature of −3°C, the skin temperature of dogs was found to be 33°–37°C; at −19°C, it was 36°C. At −50°C the rectal temperature of sleeping dogs was around 38°C, the skin temperature around 30°C, with immediate subcutaneous temperature a few degrees higher. The subcutaneous temperature of the bare footpads was found to be from 10° to 20°C in temperatures from −30° to −45°C. The temperatures of the muzzle were very low at the surface of the skin and 10°–15°C subcutaneously (2–3 mm below the skin). This temperature was higher nearer the eyes and reached body level on the head just back of the eyes. In an environmental temperature below −46°C, the temperature of the hooves and lower legs of living and freshly shot deer remained at 10°C or even lower. The melting point of fat from the marrow of the hind leg of caribou shot during November, was found to be 15°C for the distal metatarsal bones, and 47°C for the upper femur which is well within the body. This variation could afford the apparent advantage of preserving flexibility in the cold. It is suggested that certain tissues of warm-blooded animals in the Arctic must have in this and other respects a sort of chemical adaptation of their substances to suit them for operation at temperatures lower than that of the mammalian body.

664. Liese, W. On seasonal adaptation in man [In German]. *Deut. med. Wschr.,* v. *68, Sept. 4, 1942: 896–898.*

Seasonal variations in man of the sensitivity of the eye to monochromatic light, of the blood iodine level, of rectal temperature, and of skin temperature, were studied.

665. Lockhart, E. E. Acclimatization in the Antarctic. *Science,* v. *94, Dec. 12, 1941: 550.*

Studies of white men in the Antarctic showed that a sudden temperature change somewhat decreased both the respiration rate and the heart rate. Under typical basal conditions, the pulse rates, respiration rates, blood pressures, and body temperatures of men in the Antarctic are slightly lower than those recorded for temperate climates. Basal metabolism averages are lower but blood sugar levels are slightly above the normal limits found in temperate zones. It is suggested that the acclimatization procedure is begun by the continual pressor action of low temperature and followed by hypo-effects in the endocrine systems involved in metabolism.

666. Marshak, M. E. The vascular reaction of the skin as an index of adaptation to cold stimuli [In Russian, summary in English]. *J. Physiol. USSR,* v. *28 (2–3), 1940: 223–230.*

The vascular reaction of the skin in adult humans is different in different parts of the body. On exposed parts of the body (hands and forehead) restitution of skin temperature after cooling is much more rapid than it is on those parts of the body covered by clothing. Restitution rate in a skin area of the covered part of the body increased after 1–2 months of daily cooling.

667. Miller, A. J. Study of certain blood properties in healthy men transferred from a subtropic to a subarctic environment. *J. Aviat. M.,* v. *20, June 1949: 201–206.*

Blood studies made in 30 subjects who had lived in sub-tropical and later sub-arctic environments (temperature change from 102°F to −40°F) showed no marked changes. No evidence of acclimatization to cold was noted.

*668. Nagaya, N. Basic studies on the adaptation to weather. VI. Seasonal variations of human serum cholinesterase activity [In Japanese]. *Igaku to Seibutsugaku, v. 16, 1950: 334–337.*

Weekly tests were made for 1 year on the serum cholinesterase activity of 377 men and 225 women. Sexual differences were not observed. These activities were weakest in July, August, and September, and moderate in June and October. (cf., Chem. Abstr., v. 45, Feb. 10, 1951: 1180f).

669. Ol'nianskaia, R. P., and A. D. Slonim. On the adaptability of organisms to the very low temperatures of the environment [In Russian]. *Izv. Akad. nauk Kazakh. SSR, ser. biol., 1947 (2): 245–250.*

Detailed observations of respiratory changes and of body temperature, were made in several species of mammals during three winter seasons. Respiration studies were made in chambers at out-of-doors temperature, and alternately, at temperatures of 5° to 20°C. Results showed that the body temperature of the polar animals (polar fox and white hare) at 0°C to −20°C was much more constant than it was in animals inhabiting moderate climates; gaseous exchange showed a very slight rise in polar species and a very pronounced rise in the animals of the moderate climate. The author concludes that this constancy of body temperature in arctic species during continuous exposure to cold is not due to intensified heat production but to the role of a perfect, deep, vascular reaction. Insufficiency of this reaction, rather than insufficiently increased heat production, results in a disturbed heat balance.

670. Pagé, E., and L. M. Babineau. The effect of cold environment on the hibernating gland of the rat [In English]. *Rev. canad. biol., v. 9, May 1950: 202–205.*

Groups of rats were fed various diets (low protein, high fat; medium protein, high fat; medium protein, low fat) while being kept at either room temperature or in a cold room (0° to 2°C). Following adaptation to cold (after 80–90 days), the animals were sacrificed and the weight of the fresh perirenal fat and the interscapular brown fat (hibernating gland) was recorded individually. Some chemical determinations were done on small pools of these fats. High-fat diets were found to favor the accumulation of neutral fat, at least in the abdominal cavity. Rats adapted to cold were leaner and smaller than control rats kept at room temperature. Hypertrophy of the so-called hibernating gland occurred in the cold. The increase in size was due to a higher content of water and non-fat dry matter.

671. Pearse, B. How to live at 35 below. *N. York Times Mag. Suppl., Mar. 13, 1949: 19; 24–25.*

Tests conducted with Army personnel transferred from San Antonio, Texas, to Ladd Field, Alaska, indicated that geographical origin of the individual did not influence his adaptation to cold. However, there was considerable individual variation. Emotional factors were thought to exert an effect by overstimulation of the adrenal gland. Red and white blood cell counts after several months showed practically no difference from counts done in San Antonio. Experimentally, however, a slight and transient increase in blood counts was found to occur on first exposure. Groups of men under field conditions at −35°C for 1 week were allowed diets of 3500, 2000, 1000, and 0 calories (but all had 500 cc of melted snow) daily. The men spent most of the time in sleeping bags and exercised only enough to keep warm. At the end of the experiment all groups were in good condition, but the group without food suffered a 10% loss of weight. To revive persons in shock from exposure to cold, immersion in water at 110–120°F was used; frozen fingers or hands were immersed in water which was only warm.

672. Pinks, R. R. A preliminary investigation of psychological requirements for arctic duty [Abstract]. *Am. Psychologist, v. 5, 1950: 363.*

Experimental psychological tests and questionnaires were used to evaluate the adjustment to arctic duty in a sampling of 110 enlisted airmen, immediately after their transfer to arctic

---

* Original not seen.

stations and during their tour of duty. Four factors bearing on this adjustment were tentatively identified as motivation, emotional stability, personal-social relations, and technical proficiency. The evidence for progressive psychological deterioration with continued duty in the Arctic was very slight. Individual cases of extreme "success" and "failure" could not be readily identified by statistical analysis of the data obtained and an individual-clinical approach was suggested as advisable.

673.   Sarkizov-Serazini, I. M. Principles of body toughening [In Russian]. *Leningrad, Gosudarstvennoe Izdatel'stvo "Fizkul'tura i Sport", 1949. 278 p.*

   In Chapter 6 of this monograph are described the physiological mechanisms of thermoregulation, the effects of low temperatures on the human body, the influence of meteorological factors, the common cold in relation to body acclimatization, and acclimatization by means of aerial baths and contrasting temperatures. Chapters 7–10 describe the influence of water on the body metabolism, nervous and vascular systems, blood, muscles, and thermoregulation, and acclimatization by water-baths and associated therapeutic procedures. Chapters 11–13 treats of mud-baths, climatology and climatotherapy, and paraffinotherapy. Chapter 14, on the prophylaxis of frostbite, outlines the symptoms of lethal hypothermia and of frostbite, and gives advice on the prophylactic use of clothing, food, general hygiene, massage, ointments, collective prophylactic measures (e.g., during army marches) to prevent injuries, and on first aid measures. The latter includes the employment of conservative, slow, rewarming.

674.   Scholander, P. F., R. Hock, V. Walters, and L. Irving. Adaptation to cold in arctic and tropical mammals and birds in relation to body temperature, insulation, and basal metabolic rate. *Biol. Bull., Woods Hole, v. 99, Oct. 1950: 259–271.*

   Three factors in adaptation to cold are analyzed: (1) the body-to-air gradient, (2) the insulation, and (3) the basal metabolic rate.

675.   Sealander, J. A. Physiological and behavior responses of small mammals to changes in air temperature. *Thesis, University of Illinois, 1949. 259 leaves. (Microfilm copy issued as Publication no. 1558 by University Microfilms, Ann Arbor, Michigan, 1949.) Also in: Microfilm abstracts, v. 10 (1), 1950: 134–135.*

   Acclimatization of 2 species of mice to low and high environmental temperatures is discussed. The winter type survived longer than the summer type in the range of temperature from 35 °C to −35 °C, while summer animals survived longer at 40 °C and 50 °C. Mice reared and bred in the laboratory acclimatized to low temperatures and survived much longer at −20 °C than did animals acclimatized at high temperatures. Longer survivals of winter animals were correlated with increased weight in the form of fat.

676.   Sellers, E. A., S. S. You, and N. Thomas. Acclimatization and survival of rats in the cold; effects of clipping, of adrenalectomy and of thyroidectomy. *Am. J. Physiol., v. 165, May 1, 1951: 481–485.*

   Rats exposed to a cold environment (1.5 °C) following clipping of their fur, died within 3 to 23 hours. However, most rats that had been acclimatized by living in the cold environment for 2 or more months before their fur was clipped, survived for 17 days or more and about half of the group were living after 60 days. Rats exposed to cold 3 hours after adrenalectomy, or thyroidectomy (or after feeding propylthiouracil), had an average survival time of 2.4 and 7 days respectively. In rats acclimatized to cold for 2 or 3 months, the survival time after adrenalectomy averaged 12 days and after thyroidectomy varied from 19 to 38 days. The results of these experiments indicate the essential role of the adrenal and thyroid hormones for prolonged survival in a cold environment.

677.   Sellers, E. A., S. Reichman, and N. Thomas. Acclimatization to cold: natural and artificial. *Am. J. Physiol., v. 167, Dec. 1951: 644–650.*

   Groups of rats were adapted to cold by being maintained at a room temperature of 1.5 °C for varying periods of time, then were removed to a warmer area to have their fur clipped, and were returned to the cold environment within 3 hours. The period of survival of the animals was longest when the period of adaptation was from 4 to 6 weeks. Without any period of adaptation, clipped animals died of hypothermia within 24 hours. When the clipped animals were kept at room temperature for 4 days before being returned to the cold, the acclimatization was shown to be only temporary since the period of survival was noticeably decreased. Artificial acclimatization by pre-treatment with various materials, of which a combination of cortisone and thyroxin was best, gave a longer period of survival to these animals than to the unacclimatized control animals, but not as long as for those acclimatized naturally.

678.   Sellers, E. A., S. Reichman, N. Thomas, and S. S. You. Acclimatization to cold in rats: metabolic rates. *Am. J. Physiol., v. 167, Dec. 1951; 651–655.*

After removal of fur by clipping, acclimatized rats survive exposure to cold (1.5 °C.) for long periods, while unacclimatized rats so treated succumb to hypothermia within 24 hours. Ability of the rat to maintain a very high level of heat production, the author believes, is due to changes brought about in the process of acclimatization. Indirect evidence is presented that the increase in oxygen consumption of clipped over unclipped animals is largely due to greater muscular activity.

679.   Selye, H. Experimental evidence supporting the concept of "adaptation energy." *Am. J. Physiol., v. 123, Sept. 1938: 758–765.*

Experimental animals were treated with gradually increasing amounts of Adrenalin, morphine, and atropine; of muscular exercise; or of exposure to cold. It was found that the resistance to such alarming stimuli could be raised so that amounts which would often cause marked thymus involution in normal animals, had little effect on the thymus of these animals. However, stimuli other than that for which the animal had been pre-treated caused a thymus involution usually more severe than that of non-treated animals. Similarly, doses normally lethal were withstood by pre-treated animals but resistance to toxic doses of other than the one to which the animal was adapted, usually went below the normal level. The author concludes that adaptation to any stimulus is acquired at the cost of adaptation energy of which the organism possesses only a limited amount so that its use for adaptation to a certain stimulus of necessity involves a decrease for use in resistance to other stimuli.

680.   Selye, H. The general adaptation syndrome and the diseases of adaptation. *J. Clin. Endocr. Metab., v. 6, Feb. 1946: 117–230.*

A detailed review is given of the literature on the general adaptation syndrome and the diseases of adaptation. Body temperature is known to decrease during the shock phase of the alarm reaction, and is particularly marked in adrenalectomized animals, while fever is probably a counter-shock phenomenon. Defensive endocrine responses aid adaptation to stress (infection, intoxications, nervous commotions, cold, etc.) but the resulting endogenous hormone overdosage may become the cause of certain cardiovascular, renal, and joint diseases. The pituitary gland under conditions of stress, such as exposure to cold, produces an increased amount of corticotrophic hormone, but it is apparently less capable of elaborating the growth hormone, prolactin, or the gonadotropic hormones at the same time and, therefore, functions under the control of these latter hormones are inhibited. 698 refs.

681.   Selye, H. The physiology and pathology of exposure to stress; a treatise based on the concepts of the general-adaptation-syndrome and the diseases of adaptation. *Montreal, Acta Inc., 1950. 822 p.*

This is essentially a review of the physiology and pathology of exposure to stress and of the general-adaptation-syndrome (G-A-S). Among the "alarming stimuli" or stressor agents, which are factors in eliciting the G-A-S, are those of a cold temperature (p. 31), frostbite (p. 32), and cold climatic conditions (p. 50). The references, used liberally as footnotes throughout the text, are assembled alphabetically by author in the 203-page bibliography at the end of the text.

ACCLIMATIZATION 141

682. Shoji, R., T. Kosuge, A. Kawahata, and T. Fujimoto. On the ability of adaptation of man to the winter atmosphere in Manchoukuo. *Proc. Jap. Physiol. Soc., 17th Annual Meet., Apr. 1–4, 1938: 19†–20†. (Jap. J. M. Sc., Biophysics, v. 5, 1938).*

Studies were made of changes in skin temperature, blood pressure, pulse rate, hemoglobin content of blood, respiratory quotient, and sugar concentration of arterial blood as indicators of adaptation to cold environment ($-10°$ to $-20°$C) of a healthy man of 51 years. No chilblains developed following this exposure for 2 or 2½ hours while dressed in ordinary, or minimal, clothing.

683. Singer, C. I. Climate and military preparedness. *J. Am. M. Ass., v. 115, Oct. 26, 1940: 1421–1424.* Similar material in: *Bull. Am. Meteor. Ass., v. 22, May 1941: 191–197.*

Methods are suggested for conditioning soldiers to be able to withstand prolonged climatic exposures, especially cold, associated with physical strain. Some of these suggestions were: barracks be kept not warmer than 65°F; "hydrotherapy", such as cold baths, be used; extensive testing be done of various clothing materials; extensive individual testing be done and individual climatic endurance charts be kept; and optimal diets for each climatic area be ascertained and used.

684. Siple, P. A. Adaptations of the explorer to the climate of Antarctica [Abstract of thesis]. *Clark Univ. Abstr. of Dissert. and Theses, v. 11, 1939: 31–35.*

The material is arranged in three sections: Pt. 1, Climatic Factors of the Antarctic; Pt. 2, The Effect of Climatic Factors upon the Explorer; Pt. 3, Suggested Plans for an Antarctic Expedition, with Special Emphasis on Adaptations to Climatic Factors. Included is data on the role of metabolism in acclimatization and on food and shelter requirements. A convenient index of wind chill is suggested, derived by multiplying the temperature by the wind velocity. Caloric requirements and travel conditions are related to the wind-chill index.

685. Slonim, A. D., and others. Results of the dynamics of physiological functions in man in the Arctic [In Russian]. *In: Opyt izucheniia periodicheskikh izmenenĭ fiziologicheskikh funkt͡sĭ v organizme, p. 207–222. Moskva, 1949.*

Seasonal changes of physiological functions of subjects living in the Murmansk area for 1 to 5 years compared with those of inhabitants of the Baltic coastline, showed: an increase in hemoglobin content in the spring with unchanged erythrocyte count; increased pulmonary ventilation in the spring; increased basal metabolism during the spring-summer period; and increased pulse frequency in the summer. These shifts are the result of direct effect of different factors, such as change of ultraviolet radiation, and of a combination of environmental factors, such as light, muscular activity, etc. Seasonal changes caused by such physical factors as radiant energy or temperature, were not changed by prolonged stay in the Arctic. However, those brought about by the entire complex of environmental and living conditions disappear after a certain number of years.

686. Sullivan, B. J., and X. J. Musacchia. Glycogen content of various Arctic animals [Abstract]. *Anat. Rec., v. 105, Nov. 1949: 576.*

An estimation of the glycogen content of liver, kidney, and muscle tissues from various arctic birds, mammals, fish, and invertebrates, was made. Comparison of these values with those for closely related forms in temperate zones, is contemplated.

687. Thérien, M., and L. P. Dugal. Ascorbic acid and acclimatization of animals to cold environment [Abstract]. *Fed. Proc., Balt., v. 8, Mar. 1949: 156.*

White rats when adapted to cold synthesize ascorbic acid, thus increasing it in the tissues. Guinea pigs, since they are unable to synthesize it, require it in increasing amounts as their body temperature falls. There appears to be a direct relationship between the ascorbic acid content of the adrenals and adaptation to cold, and a preventive effect of ascorbic acid towards the normal hypertrophy of the adrenals in cold exposure.

688.   Vadimova, M. A., and N. A. Popov. A contribution to the reaction of the skin to cooling [In Russian]. *Bull. biol. méd. exp. URSS, v. 6, 1938: 303–306.*

N. A. Popov's hypothesis was verified, according to which the three rates of return to normal temperature following cooling of normally exposed areas of the skin, when plotted on a graph, will lie on a straight line in relation to the abscissa representing the temperature in degrees, and the ordinate representing the time of return to the initial temperature. The experiments were carried out on the skin of the forehead, of the back, and of the chest of the subjects. After an initial measurement of the skin temperature, the region to be tested was covered by a metallic cylinder at temperatures 5°, 10° or 15°C below that of the normal level, and the thermocouple applied. Results showed that, for the skin of the forehead, the figures of the recovery rate to normal temperature lie on a straight line; for the back and for the chest the line represented varied curves (sometimes parabolic), occasionally without a return to the initial level. It is concluded that the position of the 3 points of recovery rate on a straight line is a reliable indicator of acclimatization to cold of a given skin portion, in particular of the habitually exposed regions.

689.   Wilber, C. G., and X. J. Musacchia. Notes on the blood chemistry of various arctic mammals [Abstract]. *Anat. Rec., v. 101, Aug. 1948: 668.*

Analyses of whole blood and serum samples taken from a variety of arctic mammals, including the fox, seal, and reindeer, for the amount of fatty acids, phospholipids, and cholesterol. Values were compared with those of domestic animals and man. Similar studies for arctic mammals which have been acclimatized to temperate climates and men who have been acclimatized to the Arctic, are anticipated.

690.   Wulsin, F. R. Adaptations to climate among non-European peoples. *In: Physiology of heat regulation and the science of clothing, p. 3–69. Ed. by L. H. New-BURGH. Philadelphia, Saunders, 1949.*

Physiological adaptation to cold and the development of types of clothing and shelter which will reduce body heat loss, are discussed. Information is given on adaptation to cold among the circumpolar peoples (Eskimos and tribes of Northeastern Siberia); the peoples of Central Asia; and the naked peoples exposed to cold (Fuegians and Australian aborigines).

691.   You, R. W., and E. A. Sellers. Increased oxygen consumption, and succinoxidase activity of liver tissue after exposure of rats to cold. *Endocrinology, v. 49, Sept. 1951: 374–378.*

After rats have been exposed to a cold environment (1.5°C) for more than 16 days, the oxygen consumption and succinoxidase activity of liver tissue was significantly increased. These findings confirm previous evidence that the metabolic activity of visceral tissues of animals exposed to cold is increased.

See also items: 8, 19, 22, 62, 212, 214, 228, 240, 250, 546, 555, 572, 826, 852, 950, 951, 1011, 1112, 1113, 1114, 1121, 1124, 1142, 1224, 1256, 1327, 1361, 1385, 1402, 1426, 1443, 1444, 1466, 1468, 1475, 1478, 1495, 1535, 1545, 1752, 1754, 1976, 2028, 2161, 2575, 2595.

D. Hypersensitivity to Cold

692.   Abramson, H. A. Whealing response to light and cold with a note on the mechanism and the origin of physical allergies. *Psychosomat. M., v. 10, Mar. 1948: 114–117.*

A detailed case history is given of a patient who experienced welt and hive formation on her body after immersion while swimming in Long Island Sound (water temperature of 70°–

74°F). Wheals could also be formed on the skin when ice was applied to an area of the body. The emotional trauma which the patient was experiencing was thought to contribute to the cold hypersensitivity of the skin. Hypersensitivity was reported by the patient to have ceased as her anxiety state lessened.

693. **Arbesman, C. E., G. F. Koepf, and A. R. Lenzner.** Clinical studies with N'pyridyl, N'benzyl, dimethylethylenediamine monohydrochloride (Pyribenzamine). *J. Allergy, v. 17, Sept. 1946: 275–283.*

Three patients, who on exposure to cold developed urticaria and angioneurotic edema, were relieved of symptoms when treated with the antihistaminic, Pyribenzamine.

694. **Baker, T. W.** Histaminase in the treatment of cold allergy. *J. Am. M. Ass., v. 114, Mar. 23, 1940: 1059–1061.*

Two patients with both local and systemic reaction to cold were successfully treated by combined use of histaminase and a systemic desensitization to cold by repeated immersion of hands in cold water.

695. **Barr, D. P., G. G. Reader, and C. H. Wheeler.** Cryoglobulinemia. I. Report of two cases with discussion of clinical manifestations, incidence, and significance. *Ann. Int. M., v. 32, Jan. 1950: 6–29.*

Extensive clinical study was made of two patients from whom blood samples showed the formation of a heavy flocculent precipitate when the serum was cooled and which dissolved on warming to 37°C. Exposure to cold of one patient, suffering from multiple myeloma, caused numbness, pain, a conspicuous pallor of toes and fingertips, and mottled blanching of skin of ears and face. The other patient, seemingly free of any other pathology, when similarly exposed developed an extensive, purpuric eruption.

696. **Becker, R. M.** Cold hemoglobinuria. *Arch. Int. M., v. 81, May 1948: 630–648.*

Points of differentiation between syphilitic paroxysmal cold hemoglobinuria and cold hemagglutionation paroxysmal hemoglobinuria are discussed.

697. **Benians, T. H. C., and W. R. Feasby.** Raynaud's syndrome with spontaneous hemagglutination. *Lancet, Lond., v. 241, Oct. 25, 1941: 479–480.*

The authors report the presence of extensive cold agglutinins in the sera of two middle-aged women evidencing Raynaud's phenomenon, and suggest a causal relationship between the two conditions.

698. **Bergouignon, ...** The syndrome of hypersensitivity to cold [In French]. *J. méd. Bordeaux, v. 126, Sept. 1949: 446.*

The author reports his observation of a woman patient who for over twenty years had suffered a vasomotor rhinitis on the slightest exposure to cold. One year, in addition to these mucous membrane manifestations, there occurred also an urticaria from cold. Antihistaminic treatment rapidly suppressed all these symptoms.

699. **Bickel, G.** Comments on the treatment of the syndrome of hypersensitivity to cold [In French]. *Schweiz. med. Wschr., v. 78, Dec. 24, 1948: 1260.*

In hypersensitivity to cold, the local reaction of the area exposed to cold may appear as redness, resemble a burn, exhibit a pruritus, or appear as a puffy, more or less massive, urticaria. Generalized symptoms, which usually appear some minutes after exposure, may include some trembling and weakness of the legs, cephalic conditions, congestion of the face, tachycardia, sharp drop in arterial pressure, and a state of syncope. The generalized symptoms usually last only a short time, disappearing within a half hour; the localized reactions often last a day or two. Study of gastric contents during these periods indicates a hyperchlorhydria similar to that following an injection of histamine. Treatment by the author of such patients has been successful using antihistaminics, Neo-antergen or Benadryl given orally, or Antistine intramuscularly.

700. Blanke, K. F. On sudden death in cold baths [In German]. *Deut. Militärarzt., v. 7, Dec. 1942: 735–738.*

Several cases of deaths while swimming in cold water are discussed in which the cause of death was not drowning but was probably the result of an acute allergic reaction to cold.

701. Borges, D. R., and L. A. Sant' Anna. Paroxysmal hemoglobinuria due to cold; study of a case [In Portugese]. *Rev. paul. med., v. 31, Sept. 1947: 128–132.*

A classification is given of the various types of hemoglobinuria. Paroxysmal hemoglobinuria resulting from cold exposure is discussed as to etiology, pathology, and treatment. A case history of a patient, with detailed information on clinical laboratory findings, is given. Intensive anti-luetic treatment as in this case often brings about an alleviation or termination of the hemoglobinuria condition.

702. Braun, H. Skin hemorrhage due to cold injury [In German, summaries in German, Russian, English, and French]. *Derm. Wschr., v. 120 (1), 1949: 1–10.*

The author discusses his observations of a purpura occurring on the legs of 8 patients following unaccustomed exposure to damp and cold. He suggests the term "cold purpura".

703. Calder, R. M. Cold allergy; report of a case. *J. R. Nav. M. Serv., v. 26, 1940: 291–293.*

A case is reported of severe urticaria with systemic collapse following swimming, in which cold was thought to be the causative agent. The patient gave a positive response to the Vaughan test of sensitivity to cold after immersion of the hand and forearm in a water bath at 9°C. The author points out the possible importance of this condition as a cause of drowning.

704. Canella, C. Possibility of resistance to cold of erythrocytes in paroxysmal cold hemoglobinuria; clinicobiologic study of case [In Italian]. *Minerva med., Tor., anno 38 (v. 1) June 23, 1947: 571–577.*

The author discusses a case of paroxysmal hemoglobinuria, in which the attacks were precipitated by exposure to cold, giving detailed serological finds and suggesting that the luetic condition had altered the capillary network so that cold exposure more readily brought about the hemolytic crisis.

705. Chobot, R. A report of the clinical studies on the use of Pyribenzamine in allergic diseases. *J. Allergy, v. 17, Sept. 1946: 325–326.*

In this report, by the Chairman of the Committee on Pharmaceuticals and Medicaments of the American Academy of Allergy, of extensive clinical trials of Pyribenzamine, 2 cases of cold allergy are reported as having shown improvement and 3 cases as not having done so.

706. Deth, S. M. van. Hemolytic syndrome caused by cold [In Dutch, summaries in Dutch, French, German, and English]. *Ned. tschr. geneesk., v. 95, Oct. 1951: 3105–3111.*

Hemolytic syndromes caused by cold, and due to syphilitic cold-hemoglobinuria or to so-called cold-hemagglutination, are discussed. The differences existing between these two hemolytic syndromes caused by cold, are pointed out.

707. Feinberg, S. M., and S. Friedlander. Relief of dermographism and other urticarias of histamine origin by a synthetic benzhydryl alkamine ether. *J. Allergy, v. 16, Nov. 1945: 296–298.*

Although the antihistaminic substance, B-dimethylaminoethyl benzhydryl ether hydrochloride, is known to relieve cold allergy, it did not have any effect in several cases of rhinitis and asthma where the symptoms were precipitated or aggravated by cooler temperatures.

708.   Ferriman, D. G., J. V. Dacie, K. D. Keele, and J. M. Fullerton. The association of Raynaud's phenomena, chronic hemolytic anemia, and the formation of cold antibodies. *Q. J. Med., Oxf., v. 20, July 1951: 275–292.*

Detailed case histories are given of three patients who suffered from Raynaud's disease and chronic hemolytic anemia, both of which were more severe in cold weather. Their sera contained cold agglutinins, cold hemolysins, and incomplete cold antibodies in high titer. Other cases from the literature are cited. The Raynaud's phenomenon is almost certainly due to obstruction of the peripheral circulation caused by auto-hemagglutination *in vivo*; the relative importance of cold agglutinins and cold hemolysins in causing hemolysis *in vivo* is less clear.

709.   Fisher, B. Positive Coombs' test in cold hemoglobinuria. *J. Urol., Balt., v. 64, Dec. 1950: 816–817.*

Episodes of paroxysmal hemoglobinuria, with the passing of dark red urine over a period of 6 hours, following cold exposure, occurred in a 40-year-old negro. These episodes were accompanied by cramping of the hands, headache, and dull aching lumbodorsal pain. Laboratory examinations revealed relatively normal hematological findings, and the Kahn and Kolmer tests and the Donath-Landsteiner reactions were positive. In addition the Coombs test was also positive. The paroxysmal hemolytic reaction could be induced by immersion of the patient's hands and feet in cold water. After intensive antisyphilitic treatment with penicillin, both the Donath-Landsteiner and the Coombs' tests continued to be positive. At a follow-up examination two months later the tests were still positive but exposure to cold in the meantime had not brought on episodes of hemoglobinuria.

710.   Fleming, R. G., and B. L. Heffner. Paroxysmal cold hemoglobinuria; a report of two cases. *North Carolina M. J., v. 9, Mar. 1948: 142–145.*

Following their study of two cases of paroxysmal hemoglobinuria in a short period of time, the authors feel that the low incidence reported for this condition may be due to lack of its detection. The very high percentage of this group showing positive serological reactions for syphilis, in many instances without any other evidence of syphilis, may well be based on false-positive serological reactions.

711.   Forbes, G. B. Autohemagglutination and Raynaud's phenomenon. *Brit. M. J., 1947 (v. 1) May 3: 598–600.*

Some 18 cases on record in the literature are discussed, in which autohemagglutination was associated with symptoms of a peripheral vascular nature. A case report is given of an Army Sergeant whose fingers, tip of nose, and lobes of ears became blue and numb on exposure to cold. The attacks could be precipitated by immersion of the hands in cold water. Clinical tests of blood samples showed true hemagglutination.

712.   Frank, D. E. Metrorrhagia due to allergy to cold [Abstract]. *Ann. Allergy, v. 5, Nov.–Dec. 1947: 574.*

Report of a case of a 16-year-old girl who experienced uterine bleeding of 10 hours' duration, each time after she swam twice weekly in a cold pool. Histamine desensitization injections were not successful. No blood tests or endometrial studies were done. The fact that directly after her menstrual period the patient could tolerate cold relatively well suggested that a secretory phase of the endometrium was necessary to complete the allergic reaction.

713.   Franz, G. Pathologic anatomy of toxic damage following local frostbite [In German]. *Virchows Arch., v. 315 (5–6), 1948: 708–722.*

A young Norwegian seaman, following exposure to severe cold, experienced stiffness, swelling, and weeping of the rims of his ears together with swelling and a slight sloughing of tissue at the tip of the nose. Local treatment gradually brought about relief. There was no known previous history but the patient appeared to be very sensitive to cold exposure. A few months later as a laborer with a shore-side job, another exposure to cold brought about the same, but more severe, symptoms accompanied by a numbness of the legs. Periarteritis nodosa and periarteritis obliterans from cold injury was suspected. Bronchopneumonia ensued with pleural effusion and a high temperature followed by secondary anemia and death. Histological examination following autopsy indicated damage to the heart, kidneys, and brain. The damage is interpreted as the result of a suppurative inflammation. The possibility of an endarteritis far removed from the area damaged by the cold is suggested. Kidney damage appeared to be that of a glomerular nephrosis, but the cardiac finding of a suppurative myocarditis points to a possible nephritic condition.

714. Frouchtman, R. Urticaria a frigore [In Spanish]. *Medicina, Méx.*, v. 27, *June 25, 1947: 278–285.*

The appearance of urticaria on exposure to cold is discussed as an allergic phenomenon involving histamine-like substances. In three cases, the author was able to obtain a passive transfer of the reaction.

715. Gantenberg, R. Diseases due to cold [In German]. *Med. Welt.*, v. 12, Dec. *3, 1938: 1729–1731.*

An individual's susceptibility to diseases due to cold is greatly dependent on the state of the neuro-endocrine system and the capillary and peripheral blood vessel tone. Any functional or morphological dysfunctioning of the blood capillaries also makes the individual more susceptible to bacterial infection and to bacterial allergies, such as the hypersensitivity of the mucous membrane of the respiratory passages. These complex changes may well condition the individual so that an extremely slight degree of chilling will result in rheumatic-like pain and hyperergic inflammation.

716. Gaul, L. E., and G. B. Underwood. Infantile and atopic eczema from injury to skin by overcare and overtreatment. *Am. J. Dis. Child.*, v. 80, Nov. 1950: *739–752.*

Clinical study was made of 18 cases of atopic dermatitis of which 10 had severe symptoms only in cold weather. Vasodilatation following cold exposure, occurring in a cutaneous vascular bed previously injured, often chemically by continuous medication, produced the signs and symptoms of atopic dermatitis.

717. Grifoni, V. The hemolytic disease due to cold (paroxysmal cryohemoglobinuria) [In Italian]. *Riv. Ist. sieroterap. ital.*, sez II, v. 23, Jan.–Mar., Apr.– *June, 1948: 36–68; 121–138.*

The author discusses paroxysmal hemoglobinuria as to clinical picture, pathogenesis, etiology, and pathology. The therapy of the condition is practically non-existent except for anti-luetic medication, (in the instances where a syphilitic condition also exists) and the possibility of gradual acclimatization to the cold.

718. Grifoni, V., and M. Soliani. The fibrinolysis accompanying hemolytic diseases due to cold [In Italian, summaries in Italian, French, and English]. *Riv. Ist. sieroter. ital.*, sez II, v. 23, July–Sept. 1948: 155–159.

Analysis of plasma proteins in the blood of a patient subject to cryoglobinuria, during chilling by immersion of a hand in cold water (5 °C) for 12 minutes, showed a fall in fibrinogen content from the originally high level. This is in accord with the hypothesis that fibrinolysis occurs in the preparatory phase before an attack of hemoglobinuria.

719. Guye, S. C. P. Urticarias from cold [In French]. *Rev. méd. Suisse rom.*, v. *61, Oct. 25, 1941: 695–706.*

The author gives a very short historical review of cases of urticaria caused by cold which have been cited in the literature. He mentions 4 representative cases which he has observed. The etiology of such urticarias is complex but appears to be associated with an infectious or inflammatory condition, an endocrine imbalance, an unstable sympathetic nervous system, or a familial predisposition. Treatment of the conditions is often prolonged and the results are irregular. Desensitization by use of cold baths, and use of various vascular-acting drugs, has often been effective.

720. Guzman, R. Y. A case of allergy to cold; its treatment with histamine [In Spanish]. *Rev. méd. Chile, v. 75, June 1947: 426–428.*

The author discusses a few of the cases cited in the literature, and then presents the case history of a patient with severe urticaria from cold exposure who also gave a pronounced dermal reaction to injection of very dilute solutions of histamine. Treatment of the cold allergy by gradual desensitization to increasing dosages of histamine, was successful.

721. Hanns, A., and A. Sommer. Acrocyanosis, auto-agglutination of erythrocytes, paroxysmal hemoglobinuria. *Strasbourg méd., v. 98, May 5, 1938: 172.*

The authors believe that the phenomenon of hemoglobinuria is easily understandable as a consequence of agglutination and destruction of the red blood cells following exposure to cold. They reserve judgment on whether the syndrome of acrocyanosis has a similar relation to intravascular agglutination.

722. Hansen, P. F., and M. Faber. Raynaud's syndrome originating from reversible precipitation of protein [In English]. *Acta med. scand., v. 129 (1), 1947: 81–100.*

On exposure to cold a woman patient exhibited severe symptoms of Raynaud's disease which were alleviated by application of warmth. Her blood serum, upon cooling, was found to form a gelatinous precipitate which disappeared on warming. The symptoms of Raynaud's syndrome are thought to be caused by the precipitation of these blood proteins on cold exposure.

723. Hoff-Graz, F. Hypersensitivity to cold [In German]. *Zschr. klin. Med., v. 142, July 15, 1943: 726–733.*

A case history is presented of a soldier exposed to extreme cold on the Russo-German front. The subject had developed a strong anaphylactic skin reaction to cold apparently caused by an active, unidentified, substance in the blood.

724. Horton, B. T., and G. M. Roth. Hypersensitiveness to cold with paradoxical adrenaline-like systemic reaction. *Proc. Mayo Clin., v. 14, July 5, 1939: 419–423.*

A case of hypersensitivity to cold, with the usual local response, is reported because the systemic reaction included a sharp rise in blood pressure instead of the drop in pressure usually observed.

725. Hursh, L. M. Human sensitivity to a stardardized cold test. *J. Appl. Physiol., v. 2, Feb. 1950: 425–430.*

An attempt was made to develop a standardized test for measuring human sensitivity to cold. The apparatus consists of 2 glass cylinders, the smaller one (about 5 inches in length) being fitted loosely inside the larger (about 4 inches in length). The inner cylinder is fitted with a cork stopper at each end and the lower one of these has attached to it a small flat piece of carbon dioxide snow. The test was carried out by placing the cylinder against the anterior surface of the forearm of the subject, allowing the carbon dioxide to come in contact with the skin for 2 seconds, and removing it. Any reaction of erythema or wheal formation 5 to 10 minutes following the application, was recorded. The variation in response to the described test by individuals was great and variation in response of the same individual within a 3-month period was equally great. The statistical analysis indicated that all results could be explained by chance alone.

726. Jordan, W. S., Jr., L. Pillemer, and J. H. Dingle. The mechanisms of hemolysis in paroxysmal cold hemoglobinuria. I. The role of complement and its components in the Donath-Landsteiner reaction. *J. Clin. Invest., v. 30, Jan. 1951: 11–21.*

Detailed serological testing of the blood of two patients, suffering from paroxysmal cold hemoglobinuria following exposures to cold, is reported.

727. Jordan, W. S., Jr., L. Pillemer, and J. H. Dingle. The mechanism of hemolysis in paroxysmal cold hemoglobinuria. II. Observations on the behavior and nature of the antibody. *J. Clin. Invest., v. 30, Jan. 1951: 22–30.*

Further biochemical tests are reported on the erythrocytes and sera of two patients who suffered paroxysmal cold hemoglobinuria when exposed to cold.

728. Karády, S. Role of "auto-antigens" in the pathogenesis of physical allergy. *J. Immun., v. 37, Nov. 1939: 457–461.*

Guinea pig serum, exposed to cold (−5°C) or to heat (56°C) for 1½ minutes, was injected into normal guinea pigs. Injection of similarly treated serum into the same animals three weeks later brought about anaphylactic shock, but shock did not occur when the serum injected the second time had been exposed to the opposite physical condition. Shock also occurred when the hind leg of a guinea pig was treated with cold (−5°C) or heat (56°C) and three weeks later the injection was of serum so treated. Similarly, repeated exposure of the leg also brought about shock. In none of the methods of treatment did shock occur when the second injection or treatment had the opposite physical conditioning. The experiments would indicate that the organism's own protein could be altered by the physical agents of hot or cold to acquire antigenic properties.

729. Kile, R. I., and H. A. Rusk. Case of cold urticaria with unusual family history. *J. Am. M. Ass., v. 114, Mar. 23, 1940: 1067–1068.*

A case of cold urticaria with severe systemic manifestations is described, in which 23 of 47 relatives had a medical history of similar cold hypersensitivity which was also unresponsive to therapy. Treatment with a low-sodium diet and potassium chloride brought a rise of the blood-potassium level to normal at the end of the week but there was no subsidence of symptoms.

730. Klaus, F. J. Cold-exertion allergy, a sports-restricting ailment. (Together with a section on the prevention of sudden death in the water) [In German]. *Deut. med. Wschr., v. 67, Aug. 1, 1941: 845–849.*

Cold- or exertion-allergy, which occurred on exposure to cold during strenuous exercise, in a 20-year-old athlete is discussed together with 15 similar cases mentioned in the literature. Development of an exudative pleuritis in the athlete suggests that bacteriological-serological factors may play a role. In several of the cases reported there was either a disease condition or infection present. Because of the danger of severe reaction, persons who are subject to cold- or exertion-allergy are warned not to go into the water unless help is near at hand, for fear of drowning.

731. Kramer, D. W., and P. K. Perilstein. Case report of cold sensitivity with cold hemagglutinins. *Angiology, v. 2, Aug. 1951: 283–292.*

A case of cold sensitivity, with presence of serum hemagglutination, is reported in detail clinically.

732. Kvale, W. F., E. A. Hines, Jr., N. W. Barker, and E. V. Allen. Some diseases of the peripheral arterial circulation. *In:* D. D. Lewis, Practice of surgery, *v. 12, Chapter 5-C, p. 55–154. Hagerstown, Md. Prior Co., 1948.*

In section XI, diseases which primarily are effects of environmental temperature on the vascular system (p. 138–154), information is given on sensitivity to cold and heat; the pernio syndrome; trench foot and immersion foot; and frostbite. Sensitivity to cold is characterized by either a local or a systemic reaction. Either small or extensive areas of urticaria may appear on exposure to cold or cold air; the mucous membrane of the respiratory tract may be affected. The systemic reaction is similar to that following injection of histamine; the pulse rate increases and the blood pressure decreases. Syncope occurs in some cases and may be the cause of the shock or drowning when persons who are excellent swimmers have become involved in difficulties on exposure to cold water. It is said that logically both acute and chronic chilblains, and the wartime conditions of trench foot and immersion foot, may be included in the pernio syndrome since they have as their outstanding feature hyper-reactivity of the peripheral blood vessels to cold; clinical features are also quite similar. But because of differences in the clinical picture of immersion foot, it and trench foot have been classified separately until more is known. Treatment of pernio is usually based on methods to increase the peripheral arterial circulation. In some severer cases, sympathectomy may be helpful. Both trench foot and immersion foot are said to result from changes in peripheral circulation produced by exposure to cold and dampness, together with a mild, usually sterile, inflammatory reaction and trauma. However, immersion foot may result from immersion in cool water, or for longer periods in warm water. Although the conditions are usually considered to be similar if not identical, opinions differ as to whether the immersion foot conditions produced from exposure to cold water or to warm water are the same. Important contributing factors im immersion foot are dependency and immobility of the lower extremities and in some cases vitamin deficiency; these are said to account, probably, for much of the difference in the clinical pictures of chronic pernio and immersion foot. In treatment of either trench foot or immersion foot caused by cold, the patient should be given bed rest with legs elevated, the feet should be kept cool and the body warm, until the hyperemic phase has passed and any ulcers or gangrenous lesions have healed. Sulfa powder to control infection, and opiates to control pain, may be needed. Following this period, passive exercise or light massage with some application of heat, can be used. If vasoconstriction from cold exposure is very severe or prolonged, frostbite is likely to occur. Freezing of the cellular fluids, with crystallization and formation of ice, will cause some degree of tissue necrosis. Quick re-warming, often by the heat of the person's own body—without vigorous rubbing of the part which might cause further trauma—is the usual treatment of mild frostbite of small areas of the body. In frostbite of 2nd and 3rd degree, further trauma should be avoided and aseptic techniques used. Although there is not general agreement as to whether slow or fast re-warming is preferable, the opinion is expressed that judicious elevation of the affected extremity will probably counter-balance the increase in edema which would be likely to occur as the result of the use of heat.

733. Lerner, A. B., and C. J. Watson. Studies of cryoglobulins. I. Unusual purpura associated with the presence of a high concentration of cryoglobulin (cold precipitable serum globulin). *Am. J. M. Sc., v. 214, Oct. 1947: 410–415.*

Purpura and sensitivity to cold are reported in a patient whose serum contained a cold-precipitable protein. Similar cases previously reported in the literature are reviewed and discussed.

734. Lindemayr, W. Problem of "physical allergy" in connection with case of urticaria due to cold. *Arch. Derm. Syph., Chic., v. 193, 1951: 161–169.*

A case history is presented of a boy 15 years of age who developed urticaria on the exposed areas of face and arms on exposure to cold. The urticaria was produced experimentally by cold baths, drinking of cold water, and exposure to cold air. No significant effect on pulse rate, blood pressure, or gastric secretion could be demonstrated upon immersion of an extremity in cold water. The presence of histamine or histamine-like substances could be demonstrated in the skin and antihistamics given to the patient produced some relief. Because of a chronic tonsilitis, tonsilectomy was performed; a short time later the cold allergy was barely noticeable on exposure to cold.

735. Lui, S. H. Chronic hemolytic anemia with erythrocyte fragility to cold and acid. I. Clinical and laboratory data of two cases, with special reference to cell abnormality. *Blood, Balt., v. 6, Feb. 1951: 101–123.*

Two cases histories, including detailed information on laboratory findings, are discussed in which the early diagnosis was of aplastic anemia. In the first case there was a definite history of hemoglobinuria after exposure to cold; in both cases there was positive laboratory evidence of syphilis. Experimental chilling *in vivo* produced hemoglobinuria in the first case but not in the outer; chilling *in vitro*, or the addition of acid, produced an abnormally high degree of hemolysis of the red blood cells in both cases.

736. McGovern, J. P. An unusual case of hypersensitivity to cold complicated by paroxysmal diarrhea. *J. Allergy, v. 19, Nov. 1948: 408–410.*

A case of hypersensitivity to cold exposure is presented with the patient manifesting both local and generalized symptoms, paroxysmal diarrhea being a part of the systemic reaction on several occasions. The patient did not give a hypersensitive response to histamine and the antihistaminic, benadryl hydrochloride, did not modify the reaction to cold.

737. Magrini, A., and V. Giunti. Urticaria due to cold; a case [In Italian, summary in Italian and Esperanto]. *Gior. clin. med., v. 29, May 1948: 435–441.*

A case of urticarial response to cold is discussed in detail including the passive, serum, transfer of the sensitivity to a normal person.

738. Malley, L. K., and M. D. Hickey. Paroxysmal cold hemoglobinuria of nonsyphilitic type. *Lancet, Lond., v. 256, Mar. 5, 1949: 387–390.*

The case history of a patient with paroxysmal cold hemoglobinuria is presented. Blood serum constantly showed the presence of high-titer cold agglutinin and the red cells were abnormally susceptible to mechanical trauma. Hemolysis was produced in the blood by chilling of the patient's upper extremity, without exercise.

739. Mathov, E. Allergy to cold in the respiratory system; characteristics and incidence in the allergic patient; an experimental study. *Ann. Allergy, v. 8, May–June 1950: 366–372.*

In a group of 40 patients suffering from various clinical allergies, 40% claimed allergic symptoms of the respiratory tract on becoming cold or wet. Only 17% of this latter group showed objective symptoms (rhinitis, cough, and asthma) when tested by immersion of a hand in water at 0°C for 10 minutes. However, the eosinophilic index—or count of eosinophils in nasal mucus—before and after the test, correlated well with the 40% figure. This increase in eosinophils would indicate the condition to be due to a mechanism truly allergic and not to a vasomotor reflex. Nearly all patients benefited by antihistamine therapy unless the symptoms were shown to be due to allergies of other causes. The study does not support or deny the theory that histamine or H-substance is liberated in tissues injured by cold.

740. Mathov, E. Allergy to cold as an occupational disease; clinical and experimental study on 100 workmen in a meat-packing factory. *Ann. Allergy, v. 8, May–June 1950: 373–376.* Also published in Spanish, *in: Med. deporte, B. Air., v. 16, May 1951: 4138–4148.*

Fifty-two persons in a group of 100 who worked daily in freezing chambers (−3° to −30°C) experienced various symptoms (rhinitis, asthma, headache, weeping, and cystalgia) when entering the cold area. These conditions could only be detected objectively in 27%. There was not a single case of urticaria. The symptoms were relatively mild and did not prevent working; they appeared in those both with and without histories of allergy; in those working in cold 6 years or only 2 years; those working at −14°C or at −3°C. A positive eosinophilic index was associated with the allergic symptoms in 81.4% of the cases.

741. Moffatt, G. M. Cold auto-hemagglutination. *Canad. M. Ass. J., v. 60, June 1949: 612–614.*

A case is presented of cold hemagglutinins present in the blood of a patient, with a history of illness following cold exposure. The condition was associated with atypical pneumonia and hemolytic anemia.

742. Mullinger, M. A., and A. Bogoch. Cold hypersensitivity. *Canad. M. Ass. J., v. 58, May 1948: 499–501.*

A review of the literature and a discussion of the treatment of cold hypersensitivity is given. A detailed case report is noted of a patient for whom antihistamine therapy was of little value.

743. Notier, V. A., G. M. Roth. Treatment of hypersensitiveness to cold with Benadryl: report of a case. *Proc. Mayo Clin., v. 21, Apr. 17, 1946: 170–175.*

Treatment of a patient who was manifesting typical hypersensitivity to cold, with Benadryl for a period of 48 days did not appear to be particularly effective since the patient reported only about 50% improvement. This improvement began to decrease two weeks after treatment was discontinued.

744. Perry, E. L., and B. T. Horton. Use of Pyribenzamine in prevention of histamine-induced gastric acidity and headache and in treatment of hypersensitiveness to cold. *Am. J. Med. Sc., v. 214, Nov. 1947: 553–558.*

Pyribenzamine was found to be of some value in clinical treatment of 3 patients who had signs and symptoms of hypersensitivity to cold.

745. Peters, G. A., and B. T. Horton. Allergic purpura with special reference to hypersensitiveness to cold. *Proc. Mayo Clin., v. 16, Oct. 1, 1941: 631–636.*

An unusually severe case of purpura and hypersensitivity to cold is reported. The two conditions may or may not have been related but it is highly suggestive that they were. On exposure to cold, or even cool, environment the patient developed hives and complained of arthralgia in his extremities. The ears seemed to cause the most distress; they appeared cyanotic and swelled to a point of becoming gangrenous. Pain was present; the petechial patches desquamated. Testing for cold hypersensitivity by immersion of the hand in cold (10°C) water gave only a mild reaction. Previous treatment with various substances, and current treatment with histamine and then histaminase, gave only slight relief and the patient found it necessary to move to a warm, dry climate.

746. Petersen. W. F. The organic state in the problem of allergy. *Ann. Allergy, v. 3, Sept.–Oct. 1945: 348–359.*

Diurnal and seasonal changes in physiological functioning of the body, are discussed. Since the reactivity of the subject varies greatly, the reaction also varies greatly. The reaction to any allergen, such as cold, is therefore greatly influenced by the season.

747. Přerovský, K. Resultant erythema after warmth and cold [In Czechoslovakian]. *Čas. lék. česk., v. 37–38, Sept. 1939: 1036–1039.*

The intensity of the erythematous reaction of areas of the skin, as an indication of the freeing of histamine from the tissues, was studied using the reaction of the skin to ultraviolet radiation, and to combinations of ultraviolet radiation and such agents as local exposure to cold (16°C), to heat (42°C), to sunlight, to diathermy, and to a period of massage. The periods of treatment were for 15 or 20 minutes. The erythemic reaction was quicker to begin and of greater intensity, within the 5-minute period studied, following cold or massage than it was with heat, sunlight, or diathermy.

748. Rajka, E., and A. Asboth. The question of urticaria from cold [In French]. *Ann. derm. syph., Par., ser. 8, v. 9, 1949: 149–157.*

A case of urticaria, accompanied by severe systemic symptoms on exposure to cold, is described. Urticaria was provoked on the skin and mucous membranes not only at the site of irritation but also along the lymphatic paths without, however, further spread. This gave rise to the assumption that the antibodies are residual in these cells and that if antibodies are present in the blood they are of insufficient quantity to give a more generalized rash. The authors were unable to demonstrate passive transmission of this condition.

749.   Rajka, E., and A. Asboth. Cold urticaria; investigations concerning its pathogenesis. *Ann. Allergy, v. 9, Sept.–Oct. 1951: 642–652.*

Case histories are discussed of 4 subjects in whom cold urticaria could be elicited by exposure of the forearms to cold water (9° or 18°C for 3, 5, or 10 minutes). In all subjects a more or less marked hemoclastic crisis accompanied by a drop of body temperature of a maximum of 1.1°C was produced by the stronger and longer exposure to cold. Synthetic antihistamines relieved the pruritis for approximately two hours and prevented the wheal formation for an hour.

750.   Rayo Planella, G. Cold allergy [In Spanish]. *Rev. méd. Chile, v. 75, June 1947: 418–426.*

Detailed clinical and experimental studies of the hypersensitivity to cold of a 30-year-old patient, are presented. The allergy appeared to be related to the liberation of histamine, or a histamine-like substance, on exposure to cold. Desensitization was achieved by immersion in cold water baths for increasing periods of time.

751.   Renzi, S. de. Heredity of acrocyanosis and of erythema pernio [In Italian]. *Fol. card., Milano, v. 6, Dec. 31, 1947: 248–251.*

The author discusses the hereditary aspects of acrocyanosis and of erythema pernio following exposure to cold and includes 5 hereditary charts showing the incidence through three generations. Acrocyanosis appeared to be a dominant characteristic, but not sex-linked.

752.   Revell, S. T. R., Jr. Paroxysmal hemoglobinuria as a result of cold hemolysin. *Bull. School Med. Univ. Maryland, v. 32, July 1947: 17–22.*

The classification of the hemoglobinurias, the symptomatology and pathology, are reviewed. The case history is given of a patient with paroxysmal hemoglobinuria whose high serum titer, as shown by Kahn or Donath-Landsteiner reactions, was unchanged after penicillin treatment.

753.   Rinkel, H. J. Thermal allergy; clinical evaluation and management. *South. M. J., v. 44, Nov. 1951: 1067–1073.*

The history and treatment is discussed of patients having a typical history of inhalant food, or mold, allergy where the attacks are brought on or intensified by exposure to cold. The typical patient is one with repeated colds and respiratory infections throughout the winter, year after year. Differential diagnosis must be made between true infections; true infections with allergy as a complication; and the allergic response which often is the cause of a "cold".

754.   Rodin, H. H. Sensitivity to cold. *Arch. Derm. Syph., Chic., v. 63, Jan. 1951: 152–155.*

A 4½-year-old girl developed, on exposure to cold for ½ hour, an urticarial breaking out on cheeks, neck, and exposed portions of upper and lower extremities. Family history indicated this dermatosis to be present as a dominant non-sex-linked Mendelian trait, with the condition in the late teens being accompanied by constitutional symptoms such as headache, nausea, and abdominal cramps, in addition to the profuse sweating which had existed from the first.

755.   Rodin, H. H., and S. M. Bluefarb. Cold urticaria. *J. Indiana M. Ass., v. 44, Sept. 1951: 846–847.*

A case of cold urticaria was reported in a 4½-year-old girl in which all laboratory tests (including Coombs' test and cold agglutinins) were essentially negative. Examination of the skin showed numerous edematoids papules and urticarial lesions present on the cheeks, neck, and exposed parts of upper and lower extremities. The eruptions were not pruritic. Lesions occurred within one-half hour after exposure to cold. The child was found to be one of twenty-one cases of cold urticaria occurring in the family within four generations. These findings would indicate the dermatoses to be a dominant, non-sex-linked Mendelian trait. The father of the patient was affected by a similar condition which began at 17 years of age; constitutional symptoms, associated with termination of the attack, consisted of profuse perspiration, headache, nausea, and abdominal cramps and joint pains.

756. Rønnov-Jessen, V. Case of primary atypical pneumonia with hemolytic anemia and cryogangrene presumably caused by cold agglutination; with a survey of the subject [In Danish, English summary]. *Ugeskr. laeger, v. 112, Nov. 1950: 1548–1551.*

A fatal case is reported of primary atypical pneumonia which was complicated by hemolytic anemia and cryogangrene of the finger tips, caused presumably by cold agglutination. Other cases involving high titers of cold agglutinins, are reviewed.

757. Rose, B. Studies on role of histamine in hypersensitivity to cold [Abstract]. *J. Clin. Invest., v. 27, July 1948: 553.*

Histamine content of blood was studied from 8 patients known to be hypersensitive to cold, following administration of histamine and immersion of hands and forearms in ice water before and after administration of antihistamines. In four patients, symptoms of hypersensitivity were not produced nor was the blood histamine altered; in the remaining four patients, there was marked swelling of the immersed areas.

758. Rothschild, J. E. Effects of Benadryl on systemic manifestations of cold hypersensitivity. *J. Allergy, v. 20, Jan. 1949: 62–65.*

The antihistaminic, Benadryl, abolished the effects of cold on the blood pressure, on gastric secretion, and on local tissue reaction in a case of cold hypersensitivity.

759. Savonen, K. Diagnostic significance of the cold agglutination [In English]. *Acta med. scand., v. 138, suppl. 239, 1950: 133–138.*

Studies of the presence of cold agglutinins was undertaken on the sera of 6971 patients picked at random and of 413 normal subjects. High titers of cold agglutinins were found to be a more common occurrence in pneumonias than in other diseases. This is said to indicate that cold agglutination is brought about primarily by an injury to the lung. Although there is some indication that certain forms of pneumonia (primary atypical pneumonia) seem to increase the titer more than others, it was not felt that this was sufficiently absolute to justify a differential diagnosis on the basis of cold agglutinin titers.

760. Schobel, E. Cold hemoglobinuria [In German]. *Österr. Zschr. Kinderh., v. 5 (3), 1950: 299–307.*

The author discusses hemoglobinuria in general, and specifically the case of a 15-month-old child suffering from cold hemoglobinuria in which the condition terminated with the death of the child.

761. Scolari, E. Mechanism of hemolysis in paroxysmal hemoglobinuria due to cold [In Italian]. *Minerva med., Tor., anno 41 (v. 2), (Nov. 24, 1950, suppl.): 1165–1167.*

Paroxysmal hemoglobinuria from cold exposure, together with detailed serological studies of several cases, is discussed.

762. Sherman, W. B., and P. M. Seebohm. Passive transfer of cold urticaria. *J. Allergy, v. 21, Sept. 1950: 414–424.*

A case is described in detail in which the serum of a patient with a marked urticarial reaction to cold, could transmit a passive sensitization to cold to a normal person who was given the donor serum intracutaneously. The reaction could be elicited on the first time of contact of the skin with ice but not on later trials.

763. Siebens, A. A., W. H. Zinkhan, and P. F. Wagley. Observations on mechanisms in paroxysmal hemoglobinuria. *Blood, Balt. v. 3, Dec. 1948: 1367–1380.*

Clinical reports are given of 2 cases of hemoglobinuria following exposure to cold. Both cases, however, gave positive serological tests for syphilis.

764. Skouby, A. P. Studies in acrocyanosis [In English]. *Acta med. scand., v. 134, 1949: 335–345.*

Studies were made of the circulation of the right hand of 20 healthy persons and 15 patients with acrocyanosis, by measuring the tissue temperature of the third finger by thermocouple during local cooling of the hand enclosed in a small chamber at 1 °C. The action of tetra ethyl ammonium bromide (to block synaptic transmission in the autonomic ganglia) and of indirect warming upon the autonomic innervation of the vessels was studied. In normal persons injection of the drug produced within 1–3 minutes an average rise of 12 °C, and a return to normal temperature in 15–20 minutes. No relation existed between the rise in temperature and the dosage, duration of cooling, or the tissue temperature before injection. In patients with acrocyanosis, the rise in temperature was least when tissue temperature was highest before injection, and between 7° and 23 °C the rise failed to appear. A vasoconstriction due to local hypersensitivity to cold, was shown. Indirect warming by placing feet in a water bath of 43 °C, showed that the central autonomic impulses are able to overcome the conscriction where ganglionic blockage was ineffective. The author points out that closure of arterio-venous anastomoses alone can produce the picture seen in acrocyanosis. Fundamental cause may not be the cold; this may be of secondary etiology.

765. Soeroso, ... Cold hemolysis? [In Dutch]. *Med. mbl., Batavia, v. 3, Dec. 1950: 610–612.*

Marked spontaneous hemolysis of a blood specimen, when it was placed in a cold room, is reported. The blood was shown to be free of infection and had not been stored for a long period, but it gave a positive reaction in several serological tests for syphilis. The author was unable to correlate these findings with clinical information to establish whether the patient suffered from paroxysmal cold hemoglobinuria.

766. Sorribes-Santamaria, U. Hypersensitivity to cold and antihistaminics [In Spanish]. *Med. españ., v. 24, July 1950: 17–20.*

Hypersensitivity to cold, accompanied by urticaria and active pruritis, which was treated with an antihistaminic (Antistine) for a prolonged period—in one case well over a year—responded well. No toxic manifestations were seen in the patients, nor were there any appreciable changes in the blood picture.

767. Stats, D., E. Perlman, J. G. M. Bullowa, and R. Goodkind. Electrophoresis and antibody nitrogen determinations of a cold hemagglutinin. *Proc. Soc. Exp. Biol., N.Y., v. 53, June 1943: 188–190.*

Electrophoretic studies were made of samples of serum from a patient who had been previously reported (item 568) as having a gangrenous condition of the tips of the fingers and toes following exposure to cold, and whose blood contained a very high titer of cold hemagglutinins. The cold hemaglutinin was found to have the electrophoretic mobility of gamma globulin. A cold hemaglutinin titer of 1:2560 at 4°C was equivalent to 1.473 mg/ml of antibody nitrogen.

768. Stats, D., and J. G. M. Bullowa. Cold hemagglutination with symmetric gangrene of the tips of the extremities; report of a case. *Arch. Int. M., v. 72, Oct. 1943: 506–517.*

A case is reported of hemagglutination, with eventual gangrene of the toes and fingers, caused by exposure to cold, in the absence of syphilis or evidence of a hemolytic anemia. There is also a review of similar cases reported in the literature.

769. **Stats, D., and L. R. Wasserman.** Cold hemagglutination—an interpretive review. *Medicine, Balt., v. 22, Dec. 1943: 363–424.*

A review is given of the various aspects of hemagglutination from cold or cold exposure, including a tabulation and discussion of the cases reported in the literature. In a section on paroxysmal cold hemoglobinuria (p. 380–387) the authors state that paroxysmal cold hemagglutination, although rare in occurrence, is distinct from the much more common syphilitic paroxysmal cold hemagglutination. 216 refs.

770. **Stevenson, I. P.** Paroxysmal hemoglobinuria; with report of a case. *McGill M. J., v. 12, Oct. 1943: 192–209.*

The author gives a classification for, and some of the symptomatology of, the various kinds of hemoglobinemia and hemoglobinuria. Cold is by far the most important precipitating cause of paroxysmal hemoglobinuria, although the incidence of positive syphilitic reactions is very high in the relatively small number of cases which have been reported in the literature. Antiluetic therapy has been shown often to have benefitted the paroxysmal hemoglobinuria as well.

771. **Stich, W., and E. Korinth.** Investigations on hemolysis in normal and pathological states. Effects of cold, circulatory disorders, and carbonic acid on the blood [in German]. *Zschr. ges. exp. Med., v. 115, Mar. 1950: 452–462.*

In mixtures of normal red blood cells and serum, hemolysis did not occur when the mixture was saturated with carbon dioxide alone but did occur when such saturation was followed by cooling and later rewarming to 37 °C. In similar mixtures of the blood of patients with paroxysmal cold hemoglobinuria or nocturnal hemoglobinuria, hemolysis occurred on saturation with carbon dioxide in either acid or alkaline media. The addition of anticoagulants prevented the hemolysis.

772. **Sussman, R. M., and H. J. Kayden.** Renal insufficiency due to cold hemoglobinuria. *Arch. Int. M., v. 82, Dec. 1948: 598–610.*

Report is made of a fatal case of renal tubular necrosis following twelve attacks of parosysmal cold hemoglobinuria. The pathology is said to reflect both old and recent renal injury apparently due to the hemolytic episodes.

773. **Torp, K. H.** The mechanism of the proximate hypersensitive skin reaction to cold [In English]. *Scand. J. Clin. Lab. Invest., v. 3 (3), 1951: 217–220.*

In addition to the usual reaction of the exposed part, immersion of one hand in a cold water bath (6 °C) for 9–12 minutes brought about a distinct hyperemic zone approximately 2–3 cm wide along the whole course of the cephalic vein and, less markedly, following the basilic vein. After 12 minutes of exposure small wheals, localized at the hair follicles, appeared in the same area. Similar reactions occurred with a second subject when the water bath was maintained at 8 °C. Fluorescein injected intracutaneously near the wrist served to locate the superficial lymphatics but no erythema, itching, or wheals occurred in this area on exposure to cold. It is concluded that in a person hypersensitive to cold, the skin reaction proximal to a cold area is not caused by lymphatic drainage of histamine or histamine-like substances, but that the reaction is localized to the course of the main superficial veins draining the area. Direct measurement of the temperature of the blood in these veins would indicate it to be sufficiently cooled to act as a provocative agent to the surrounding tissue.

774. **Tötterman, L. E.** A contribution to the knowledge of paroxysmal cold hemoglobinuria [In English]. *Acta med. scand., v. 124 (5), 1946: 446–465.*

Detailed clinical description of a case of paroxysmal cold hemoglobinuria precipitated by cold exposure and accompanied by a "cold fit" (clonic jerks of muscles of the extremities and of the lower jaw). No history of venereal disease was given by the patient, but Wasserman and Kahn reactions were found to be positive using the blood and negative using the cerebrospinal fluid.

775. Urbach, E., F. Linneweh, and S. Greenberg. Blood urticaria, including a contribution on metallurgic genesis of cold urticaria. *Arch. Derm. Syph., Chic., v. June 1939: 987–991.*

A case of urticaria following the ingestion of pork blood sausage, of which the animal blood was the causative agent, is discussed. An attack of urticaria, caused by contact with cold water, occurred during the period of food allergy and could be produced again only during or soon after the food allergy period. The terms metallurgy and parallergy are explained, and an attempt is made to explain the physical (cold) allergy on the basis of metallurgy.

776. Urbach, E., M. F. Herrman, and P. M. Gottlieb. Cold allergy and cold pathology. *Arch. Derm. Syph., Chic., v. 43, Feb. 1941: 366–374.*

Different ways are discussed in which hypersensitivity to cold could be brought about: both primary and secondary physical allergy; release of histamine-like substances under influence of physical agent; instability of peripheral neurovascular system in response to local physical agent; and, possibly, disturbances in the central temperature-regulating mechanism such as those caused by previous infectious or febrile diseases. Seventeen cases of urticaria due to exposure to cold air are reported in a family of 28 members in 4 generations.

777. Urbach, E., and P. M. Gottlieb. Physical agents. *In:* Allergy, *p. 467–498. New York, Grune & Stratton, 1943.*

The incidence of so-called cold urticaria is said to be relatively high. In localized conditions, the urticarial manifestations are restricted to the site of direct exposure to cold; in generalized conditions the hypersensitivity may produce urticaria and itching, swelling of the lips and tongue, lacrimation, coughing, pains in areas of the digestive tract, diarrhea, headache, a general feeling of weakness, or general collapse-like reactions. The over-all urticarial swelling seen in bathers renders them so helpless that rescue from drowning is difficult. Their loss of consciousness can probably be explained on the basis of a cerebral edema, resulting from the same mechanism as does their temporary loss of vision. Certain myalgias may prove to be of similar origin. Only by careful and appropriate experimental investigation can it be determined whether the pathogenesis is allergic or pathergic. An instance is cited in which of the 28 members of a family (4 generations), 16 showed a hypersensitivity to cold from birth. In cases where no physical condition is the underlying cause, treatment is suggested by massive intravenous injections of calcium gluconate, or of histamine, or by autodesensitization.

778. Vaughan, W. T. Physical allergy. *In:* Practice of Allergy, *p. 248–259. St. Louis, Mosby, 1939.*

The test for allergic reaction to cold, by the newer methods, involves immersion of one hand and part of the forearm in cold water (9°C) for six minutes followed by a six-minute observation period for local, and for possible systemic, responses. If no symptoms have appeared after this period a tourniquet is applied above the elbow and the procedure repeated. The tourniquet is released after two or three minutes of observation. During immersion the skin blanches; on removal from the water the pallor changes to redness. There is also a slight edema and an increase in local temperature, characteristic of a positive reaction. The systemic positive reaction usually develops in from three to six minutes after removal of the hand from the cold water. In sensitized individuals, various tissue reactions may occur and in some cases constitutional changes occur, with falls in both systolic and diastolic blood pressure, rise in pulse rate, vertigo, or even syncope. Within six to eight minutes the blood pressure and pulse rate return to normal. Because the reflex-like constitutional reaction following exposure to cold may be so severe as to cause syncope, it has been considered to be a factor in the drowning in cold water of good swimmers (Horton et al. J. Am. M. Ass., v. 107, 1936: 1263–1265). In testing for allergic reaction to cold air, a blower-type apparatus is briefly discussed and described.

779. Wagley, P. F., W. H. Zinkham, and A. A. Siebens. Hemolysis in cold hemoglobinuria. *Am. J. Med., v. 2, Apr. 1947: 342–346.*

Detailed serological studies were made on the blood of a patient with paroxysmal hemoglobinuria resulting from cold exposure.

780. Watson, C. J., and A. B. Lerner. The clinical significance of cryoglobulinemia [In English]. *Acta med. scand.*, v. *128, suppl. 196, 1947: 489–494.*

Previous reports of the occurrence of cryoglobulins, any known relation to pathological conditions, and the percentage of protein precipitated when that information was available, are reviewed from the literature, together with a detailed discussion of a case presented by the author. It is concluded that cryoglobulins—which precipitate from serum on cooling and disappear on warming—are present in very variable amounts in the serum of patients with a great variety of diseases but that they do not appear to be present in normal serum. These proteins in large quantities may well relate to patients' symptoms such as purpura, thrombosis, oozing blood from mucous membranes, and sensitivity to cold, but the presence of cryoglobulins should be considered as a non-specific indication of a disease process.

781. White, C. Cold allergy with a case report. *Tufts M. J.*, v. *16, May 1949: 95–98.*

A case is reported of hypersensitivity of the esophageal area to cold food or drink, and of an allergic skin response of the extremities to cold baths or immersion in cold water. Only a partial response to Pyribenzamine could be demonstrated, and treatment by progressive exposure to cold appeared to have failed.

782. Wildführ, G. Effect of low temperature on the alexin and opsinin content of the blood in individuals susceptible to colds [In German, summaries in German, English and French]. *Arch. Hyg., Münch.*, v. *133 (1), 1950: 49–58.*

Following exposure to cold—including outdoor temp of +2° to −5°C, or foot bath of 8°C—the percentage of alexin and opsinin in the blood was found to be decreased considerably in persons sensitive to cold and only slightly so in the others.

783. Winetrobe, M. M. Clinical hematology. 2nd edit. *Philadelphia, Lea & Febiger, 1946. 862 p.*

Under the heading of Agglutination and Hemolysis of Red Corpuscles, cold hemagglutination (p. 123–124) is discussed as a phenomenon in which a mixture of red corpuscles and serum from the same individual exhibits agglutination in the cold (0°–5°C). The phenomenon can be reversed by warming above 20°–30°C or re-established by cooling below 10°–20°C. Cold hemagglutinins have been found in several disease states. It has been suggested that under certain circumstances agglutination may occur in the peripheral circulation. The frequency of Raynaud's syndrome in association with the phenomenon and the occurrence of gangrene following exposure to cold in patients with cold hemagglutinins indicates its pathogenetic importance. Paroxysmal (cold) hemoglobinuria *e frigore* (p. 483–486) is a condition characterized by the sudden passage of hemoglobin in the urine following local or general exposure to cold. The autohemolysin of the patient's own blood unites with the red corpuscles only at a low temperature but destruction of the cells occurs only after the blood is again warmed. Paroxysmal hemoglobinuria is a common manifestation of syphilus, especially of the congenital form. It has been noted in the literature that in a family one child with congenital syphilus suffered attacks of paroxysmal hemoglobinuria while two younger children with no indication of congenital syphilus (including a negative Wasserman reaction) but with a high titer of autohemolysins, did not suffer the attacks. The relationship of the attacks to syphilus is discussed, including the suggestion of a possible altered vasomotor state.

784. Wise, F. Erythema pernio. *Arch. Derm. Syph., Chic.*, v. *57, Mar. 1948: 519–521.*

A clinical case is presented of a woman (age 25) who became nauseous and sleepy when she became chilled. On exposure to cold, her hands became livid in color, her fingers swelled, and erythematous patches turning purple appeared on fingers and palms. Wasserman and Kahn reactions were negative; tuberculin test, with 0.1 cc, was negative. Biopsy section was diagnosed as erythema pernio.

785.   Witherspoon, F. G., C. B. White, J. M. Bazmore, and H. Hailey. Familial urticaria due to cold. *Arch. Derm. Syph., Chic., v. 58, July 1948: 52–55.*

A case of familial urticaria due to cold in a 19-year-old soldier is reported. The syndrome appeared shortly after birth and the attack was brought on in every case by cold, wind, or extreme changes in temperature. Ingestion of cold liquids had no discernible effect. An incidence of an identical syndrome in 24 of 45 members of his family for 4 generations is also reported.

786.   Woofter, A. C., and B. S. Parks. Paroxysmal hemoglobinuria with report of a case. *Ann. Int. M., v. 12, Sept. 1938: 402.*

Report is made of a case of paroxysmal hemoglobinuria on exposure to cold, in which treatment of the syphilitic condition led to prompt disappearance of hemoglobinuria, even though the syphilitic condition worsened.

787.   Yater, W. M., and E. W. Nicklas. Cold allergy: report of an unusual case *Ann. Int. M., v. 15, Oct. 1941: 743–748.*

Clinical study of a patient with cold allergy which was manifested by urticarial reactions which subsided leaving purpuric hemorrhagic areas of the affected—mainly acral—regions. There were no general or constitutional reactions on exposure to cold. The patient did not respond to usual therapeutic methods, such as antihistaminase or desensitazation by gradually cooled and repeated showers, even at the time of urticarial erruption.

788.   Young, L. E. The clinical significance of cold hemagglutinins. *Am. J. M. Sc., v. 211, Jan. 1946: 23–39.*

Examination was made for cold hemagglutins of 1762 specimens of serum collected from 987 persons during a 17-month period. Included in the study were 154 sera from 45 patients with primary atypical pneumonia. Titers of 1:32 or above appeared in 80% of these cases and the development and disappearance of agglutinins in these lower titers was thought to be of significance. No definite relationship between titers and severity of illness could be demonstrated. None of the patients with atypical pneumonia developed complications which could be associated with the presence of cold hemagglutinins even though the antibodies were sometimes present in high titers and were active at room temperature. In 291 patients with respiratory infections other than atypical pneumonia and 521 patients with various other diseases, the titer of cold agglutinins were not usually found to be of any significance. Only 2 of 130 "normal" individuals were found to have borderline titers and in both cases a history of recent pulmonary infection was found.

See also items: 1109, 1152, 1315, 1419, 1589, 1590, 1773, 1796, 1799, 1814, 1998, 2114, 2591, 2614.

III. HYPOTHERMIA

A. General
(includes also induction of hypothermia)

789.   Anon. Deaths from exposure to cold. *Statist. Bull. Metrop. Life Insur., v. 24, Jan. 1943: 8–9.*

This is the latter of two similar statistical reports on deaths, within large life insurance groups in the United States, directly caused by excessive cold. The number of such deaths during the period of 1933 to 1940 averaged 363 annually—at a rate of about 3 per 1,000,000— with a maximum loss of 597 lives in 1936 when there was a period of exceptionally cold weather, and a minimum of 190 lives in 1939. The figure for Canada is about twice as high. Four out of five of these deaths, in the U.S., occurred in males and nearly two-thirds of these were in men over 50 years of age. An earlier analysis had shown that about one-third of the total number had been of persons who were either intoxicated or mentally deranged, and that most of the remainder had been due to injury or infirmity while lost in a storm on a hunting or fishing trip. Very few were due to lack of fuel indoors, despite the shortage of fuel, unless illness or infirmity was also involved.

790. Adolph, E. F. Cold tolerance and cold immersion in infant rats [Abstract]. *Fed. Proc., Balto., v. 7, Mar. 1948: 1.*

Young rats, up to 17 days of age, recovered after refrigeration in oxygen or in air, with body temperatures of 3°–10°C. These temperatures were tolerated for 2.5 hours but not for 3 hours. When immersed in water to the shoulders, however, the rats did not tolerate temperatures below 15°C. Damage occurred during the cooling period. Part of the lethal damage was attributed to hydrostatic pressure about the chest, and part to local anoxia.

791. Adolph, E. F. Tolerance to cold and anoxia in infant rats. *Am. J. Physiol., v. 155, Dec. 1948: 366–377. Advance abstract in: Anat. Rec., v. 101, Aug. 1948: 737–738.*

Infant rats of ages up to 27 days were chilled to known body temperatures with or without immersion. After various periods of exposure, during which all signs of life disappeared in some cases, rewarming was applied until it was ascertained which animals were capable of survival. In an atmosphere of nitrogen, rats survived for 2 hours at 10°C. In oxygen, survival was prolonged greatly at all temperatures up to 12°C. As age increased, tolerance to anoxia disappeared before the loss of tolerance to cold.

792. Adolph, E. F. Lethal limits of cold immersion in adult rats. *Am. J. Physiol., v. 155, Dec. 1948: 378–387. Advance abstract in: Fed. Proc., Balt., v. 7, Mar. 1948: 1.*

Mature rats immersed for 2 hours in water of 14.8°C succumbed to cold. Death occurred whenever the temperature of the head and chest was decreased to 15.1°C. It was found that rates of cooling were not considerations in survival and that no factors were found to modify the lethal temperature. Resistance to cold appears to depend only on delays in the chilling of essential tissues.

793. Adolph, E. F. Responses to hypothermia in several species of infant animals. *Am. J. Physiol., v. 166, July 1, 1951: 75–91.*

Studies of newborn or very young cats, hamsters, rats, mice, guinea pigs, and rabbits showed that the minimum body temperatures from which they could survive was, in all species, higher as the animals became adult. In the cat it changed from 7°C to 18°C; in the hamster, only from 1° to 4°C. The adult pattern of response to hypothermia emerged in several steps at specific ages, being in general slower in the animals which were slower to mature. The heart beat frequency bore diverse relation to body temperature. In general it was linear in adults and exponential in infants; the transition occurred in at least two steps. Isolated heart muscle strips did not follow the pattern of the *in vivo* studies. Breath frequency decreased as temperature decreased in the newborn; then was increased probably in response to the animal's capacity to increase his heat production as a function of temperature regulation.

794. Allen, F. M. Experimental and clinical observations on hypothermia and procaine. *J. Internat. Coll. Surgeons, v. 11, May–June 1498: 278–281.*

In the half of the paper dealing with hypothermia, the author discusses some of the differences in physiological reaction to cold and to shock of the rat in contrast to that of dogs and of men. The recognition of the differences in thermal response of rats from those of men, he believes, should remove the apparent objections to the hypothermic treatment of human burns, injuries, and shock.

*795. **Ar'ev, T. ÎA** Freezing. *In: Entsiklopedicheskiĭ slovar' voennoĭ meditsiny, v. 2, col. 751–753* [In Russian]. *Ed. by* E. T. SMIRNOV. *Moskva, 1947.*

"*Contains* a definition of the term as applied to human beings and information on the critical temperature of hypothermic death, symptoms at various lowered body temperatures, mass occurrences of freezing in peace and war. Successive symptoms during freezing, therapy, and prophylaxis are discussed. Bibliography is given under heading: 'Otomorozhenie' (Frostbite)." —Arctic Bibl., V. 4, 1954: 51.

796. **Ariel, I., F. W. Bishop, and S. L. Warren.** Studies on the effects of hypothermia. I. Acute physical and physiological changes induced by the prolonged hypothermic state in the rabbit. *Cancer Res., v. 3, July 1943: 448–453.*

The reduction of the rectal temperature to between 20° and 10°C is possible but the ability of the rabbits to recover spontaneously was greatly lessened at the lower part of the temperature range. An inanimate state was produced in the animal at rectal temperatures in the range between 15° and 10°C. A pseudo-hibernating, or equilibrium, state can be produced in the rabbit by lowering and maintaining the rectal temperature in the range between 23° and 28°C; spontaneous recovery can be brought about by exposure to room temperature (20° to 25°C) with the fur dry. The presence of a two-week-old Brown-Pearce epithelioma in one animal did not change the reaction of the rabbit to hypothermia.

797. **Barbour, J. H., and M. H. Seevers.** Narcosis induced by carbon dioxide at low environmental temperatures. *J. Pharm. Exp. Ther., v. 78, July 1943: 296–303.*

A reversible state of narcosis having the characteristics of both hibernation and anesthesia, can be induced in the rat and dog by sudden exposure at 5°C to concentrations of carbon dioxide of 5% or more. In this state the rat has a body temperature of 16° to 20°C, a heart rate of 30–100 per minute, and a respiratory rate of 1–20 per minute. A similar state may be induced in rabbits by 20% CO_2 and cold but is not reversible because of fatal pulmonary edema. A somewhat similar but not identical state, as above, may be produced in rats at an environmental temperature of 5°C by either a low or a high O_2 tension.

798. **Bischoff, F.** Conditions required to produce a prolonged hypothermia in the mouse. *Cancer Res., v. 2, May 1942: 370–371.*

In mice maintained at environmental temperatures of 5° to 7°C, with adequate food, the rectal temperature does not fall below 33°C until after 48 hours. At −2° to +5°C the period of increased metabolism is reduced to 2 hours. This results in a loss of body heat which exceeds the animal's capacity for adjustment and a hypothermic state then occurs.

799. **De Boer, B., H. E. Ederstrom.** Lethal hypothermia in dogs of various ages. *Anesthesiology, v. 7, Sept. 1946: 518–521.*

The normal rectal temperature was measured in 121 dogs ranging from 1-day-old to adults. Of these animals 46 were then cooled in a water bath of from 1.5°C to 6°C. It was found that the lethal temperatures varied with the age of the dog, the younger dogs dying at lower temperatures than the older ones, indicating that the minimal viable temperature was lower in infant dogs than in mature ones.

800. **Fay, T.** Observations on prolonged human refrigeration. *N. York State J. M. v. 40, Sept. 15, 1940: 1351–1354.*

In this report of the first observations in general refrigeration in the human being, it was noted that body temperature can be lowered repeatedly to around 80°F over a period up to 8 days without harmful effects.

---

* Original not seen.

801. Freeman, H., and R. F. Nickerson. Skin and body temperatures of normal individuals under cold conditions. *J. Nutrit., v. 15, June 1938: 597–606.*

A study was made of the skin and rectal temperature of ten normal subjects exposed to a temperature of 20°C for 2 hours and of an equal number to 15°C. The greatest fall in skin temperature was in the first hour; the rectal temperature only fell after the first hour.

802. Gagge, A. P., and L. P. Herrington. Physiological effects of heat and cold. *Annual Rev. Physiol., v. 9, 1947: 409–428.*

This review of the literature from July 1945 to July 1946 includes an analysis of the freezing experiments performed on inmates of the Dachau concentration camp in Germany. 91 refs.

803. Gevelt, R. Hypothermia; report of a case [In Norwegian]. *Tskr. Norske laegeforen., v. 66, Oct. 1946: 608–609.*

After exposure to an environmental temperature of about −1.0°C for 7 hours and while in a state of alcoholic intoxication, a man was admitted to the hospital in a deep coma with a rectal temperature too low to be measured by clinical thermometer. He was wrapped in warm wool blankets and after 10 hours was lucid but with a rectal temperature of 28.1°C; he appeared clinically normal by the afternoon of the next day. The author discussed other cases, mentioned in the literature, where the rectal temperatures were in the range from 24.6° to 26.8°C, and where there was survival. He states that rectal temperatures under 20°C are usually fatal; those up to 30°C are questionable as to survival. Usually there is severe headache and mental disorientation on recovery but this was entirely lacking in the case he cites. For therapy he suggests the use of a warm room, warm drinks, and warm baths gradually increasing in warmth up to 37°C. Mention is made of the use of oxygen inhalation to compensate for the lack of available oxygen in the blood because of the poor dissociation of oxyhemoglobin found at very low temperatures.

804. Giaja, J. Hypothermia [In Serbian, French summary]. *Acta med. Iugoslav., v. 3 (1), 1949: 9–33.*

Hypothermia from cold exposure, hypothermia from hypoxia, and the difference in physiological responses of the two are discussed. To produce hypothermia by cold, the ambient temperature must be lowered quite drastically or the animal or man must be immersed in a cold bath. Hypothermia from hypoxia can be obtained at a temperature only slightly lower than a comfortable temperature using a lowering of air, or in some cases oxygen, pressure. By enclosure in a limited volume of atmospheric air, while absorbing the CO_2 formed, homeothermic animals are reduced to a lethargic state with a metabolism similar to that of a poikilothermic animal. In such a manner, rats, cats, and dogs have been cooled to body temperatures of 15°C and have recovered when artificially rewarmed. In progressive asphyxia due to oxygen insufficiency, hypothermia allows the organism to tolerate a lower oxygen tension than do anoxic animals artificially warmed. Other instances are cited such as that of carbon monoxide intoxication and insulin shock, where hypothermia occurs at normal environmental temperatures; and survival from loss of a large amount of blood was observed when artificial warming was not done. These findings lead the author to suggest that, under certain circumstances, hypothermia in homeothermic organisms plays a defensive role.

805. Glaser, E. M. Immersion and survival in cold water. *Nature, Lond., v. 166, Dec. 23, 1950: 1068.*

In controlled experiments it has been found that few men can survive in water of near-freezing temperature for more than 30 minutes and none for more than 1½ hours. The author discusses the discrepancies between these findings and the known instances of survival after accidental immersions for longer periods. He states that healthy men in such a situation, who swim or struggle as hard as they can for as long as they can, have a greater chance of survival than those who try to preserve their strength by clinging to wreckage or floating on lifebelts.

806.   Gohrbandt, E. Generalized cooling [In German]. *Zbl. Chir., v. 70, Oct. 30, 1943: 1553–1557.*

In hypothermia, conditions may vary from minor disturbances of circulation and metabolism to complete paralysis depending upon temperature and length of exposure. Clinical features are described and details of treatment are given based upon the pathological physiology. Rewarming—neither too rapid nor too slow—is advised.

807.   Grant, R. Emotional hypothermia in rabbits. *Am. J. Physiol., v. 160, Feb. 1950: 285–290.*

A reversible hypothermia was induced in rabbits by light restraint and was largely inhibited by exposure to cold. The phenomenon appeared to be due to emotional factors. In experiments carried out at room temperatures of 25°C, the ears became flushed and their temperature rose to the value of the rectal temperature; $5\frac{1}{2}$ hours after restraint began the ear temperature returned to normal (about 39.8°C). At the beginning of the period of restraint, a fast polypnea was established and was active for $1\frac{1}{2}$ hours. In one instance, the temperature fell during this period about 2.5°C. In 51 experiments on 36 animals, at room temperatures of 18° to 30°C, restraint caused activation of heat loss mechanisms and some hypothermia (exceeding 0.5°C in 46 experiments) in 50 cases. Prior exposure to cold (4°C) inhibited the phenomenon almost entirely; exposure after activation of heat loss mechanisms cut short the period but did not prevent the drop in temperature.

808.   Gray, S. W. Respiratory movements of the rat during drowning and the influence of water temperature upon survival after submersion. *Am. J. Physiol., v. 167, Oct. 1951: 95–102.*

Rats, both anesthetized and unanesthetized, showed 4 definite respiratory phases during experimental submersion: a short period of apnea; a period of dyspnea; a long period of anoxic apnea; and a short series of respiratory movements accompanied by neck and facial movements. When the temperature of the water in which they were submerged was 37°C, about 91 seconds elapsed between submersion and terminal gasps; at 1°C this time increased to about 155 seconds. Some increase in survival time also occurred at temperatures above 37°C, with a maximum time of about 102 seconds at 54°C, but above this temperature the time decreased again. Animals with ligated trachea and head not immersed, gave the same response. Epinephrine and ethyl alcohol given orally decreased survival time at low temperatures.

809.   Hill, R. M., A. G. Ware, and F. H. Schultz. A technic for the production of hypothermia in albino rats. *Cancer Res., v. 3, Dec. 1943: 839–840.*

Hypothermia was induced in the rat by wrapping its thorax and abdomen with adhesive tape tightly enough to decrease the frequency and amplitude of respiratory movements thus decreasing the oxygen supply to the tissues and building up the carbon dioxide content of the blood. The authors have been able to maintain rats at rectal temperatures between 25° and 30°C for a week or longer, or intermittently for periods of 10 hours over a much longer period of time. After several days of continuous hypothermia the rats lose their resistance to hypothermia and respond to environmental temperatures in a poikilothermic manner. It has been found that very young rats are much less able to withstand exposure to 4° to 6°C than are mature rats.

810.   Horn, G. Death by super-cooling [In German]. *Ärztl. Wschr., v. 6, Apr. 20, 1951: 376–380.*

Findings at the autopsy of a body following death from accidental immersion in water of 5° to 6°C for 3 hours, led to the report that death was due to the cold rather than to drowning.

811.   Kalow, W. Choleresis induced by synthetic drugs. 4. Poikilothermic study of the anesthetized rat [In German]. *Arch. exp. Path., Berl., v. 210 (4–5), 1950: 336–345.*

Earlier studies of choleresis in rats had shown the dependence of the bile secretion on the body temperature. In the current experiments, the choleretic drugs were injected, in physiological solution, into the femoral vein; bile was collected directly from the hepatic duct. A hypothermic state was obtained in the animals by the injection of 1 gm/kg of urethane. The rectal, liver, and muscle (thigh extensor) temperatures were measured. Results showed that the rate of bile secretion decreased when the temperature of the liver decreased below, or rose above, normal; it was maximal at normal liver temperature ($39°-40°C$). Death through hypothermia occurred at a rectal temperature of $15°C$. The differences in reaction of the various choleretic drugs are explained on the basis that the water-soluble ester has first to be saponified in the body.

812. Kramer, K., and H. Reichel. The limitations of chemical heat regulation [In German]. *Klin. Wschr., v. 23, June 1944: 192–198.*

When dogs were placed in an ice-water bath they promptly began to shiver and their temperature fell. At $30°C$ shivering was at a maximum and the dogs' temperature remained constant for about an hour, after which it decreased to $15°C$ and death ensued.

813. Laborit, H., and P. Huguenard. Artificial hibernation by pharmacodynamic and physical methods in surgery [In French, summaries in French, English, and Spanish]. *J. Chir., par., v. 67, Aug.–Sept. 1951: 631–641.*

The "lytic cocktail" consists of a multiplicity of drugs in small doses which act together on the neurovegetative system to produce a pharmocodynamic hibernation in the patient. In this state the patient is freed of the usual stresses and can be subjected to refrigeration anesthesia for surgical intervention or to treatment of a severe illness even though the patient is in a very poor physical condition. Some of the drugs involved are curare; Diparcol; synthetic antihistamines, especially Phenergan; procaine; and Dolosal.

814. Laborit, H. Artificial hibernation [In French]. *Acta anesth. belg., v. 2, Dec. 1951: 710–715.*

The three main physiological areas of reaction to a "cocktail" of 4560RP (derivative of phenothiazine) combined with low dosage of morphine or of Dolosal are: its action on the diencephalon of the central nervous system to block the thermoregulatory mechanism; action on peripheral nerves at the vegetative reflex arc; and an important lowering of the basal metabolism. Experimental studies are discussed on the lowering of body temperatures, using 4560RP combined with hypothermia by ice refrigeration, producing an artificial state of hibernation. Body temperatures of rats were lowered to $10.4°C$ and the animals successfuly revived. In dogs whose body temperatures were lowered to between $27°-29°C$, it was impossible to produce hemorrhagic shock in the 6–8 hours of the duration of the experiment.

815. Laufman, H. Profound accidental hypothermia. *J. Am. M. Ass., v. 147, Nov. 24, 1951: 1201–1212.*

A detailed analysis is given of the physical condition, physiological findings, therapy, and sequelae of a young Negro woman patient who was brought into a Chicago hospital following accidental hypothermia. She had been found in a nearby alley in a cold-induced coma; 90 minutes after admission rectal temperature was established at $18°C$ ($64.4°F$) by use of a chemical thermometer. The patient was kept at a room temperature of $68°F$ during the early period and no attempts were made to rewarm the patient in order to help prevent secondary shock. Heparin therapy was used for the first two days, followed by Dicumarol. Some time after surgical amputation of both lower legs, the patient was discharged to a convalescent home—6 months after admission—to await fitting of lower limb prostheses. Of the left hand, only the left thumb and the stumps of 4 fingers remained; only the palm of the right hand remained.

816. Lutz, W., and R. von Werz. Vital functions at low body temperature [In German]. *Münch. med. Wschr., v. 93, Jan. 26, 1951: 161–168.*

From experiments on animals performed at a previous time, the author concludes that cold itself is not the damaging agent but that it is the failure of the hemoglobin to release oxygen to the tissues. With lowering of the blood temperature, oxygen was found to be released less easily. Death was delayed in animals which were cooled under conditions of above-normal oxygen pressure. The author states the rational therapy for hypothermia to be the employment of hot baths (40°C), the giving of oxygen and carbon dioxide through a breathing mask, and the use of supportive measures against shock especially if the degree of cooling had been very pronounced.

817. Luyet, B. J., and P. M. Gehenio. Life and death at low temperatures. *Normandy, Mo., Biodynamica, 1940. 341 p.*

This is a general review of the mechanisms of death at low temperatures. Part I, The Lower Limit of Vital Temperatures, contains information on homeotherms (p. 91); Part II, The Physical States of Protoplasm at Low Temperatures; and Part III, Mechanism of Injury and Death by Low Temperatures, includes several theories on the cause of death from cold. The authors not only review the literature but also include considerable original data of their own. Brief lists of references appear at the conclusion of each chapter and a general bibliography is found on p. 296–328.

818. Mazer, M. Medical problems in air-sea rescue. *Air Surgeon Bull., v. 2, Oct. 1945: 348–349.*

The temperature of the water is the main factor in determining the duration of life of individuals immersed in the sea. In the North Sea the water temperature (in the operational area of World War II) in the winter was as low as 39° to 41°F, in summer seldom higher than 60°F. In cold water the flyer loses body heat rapidly, develops shock, and dies either from shock or from unconsciousness with consequent drowning. Immersion for more than 20 to 30 minutes during the winter months was usually fatal. Even with the great efficiency of air-sea rescue existing in 1944, the mortality rate was 42% in a group of 163 men who were immersed for 10 minutes or more in water of 40° to 60°F. Of 103 men rescued from the North Sea and English Channel, 60% were immersed for more than 30 minutes. Very few would probably have survived if immersion had occurred during the winter. The survival rate for ditched airmen who used dinghies was considerably higher than those who did not. Because of the temperature-and-time element neither a large supply of drinking water nor food was essential in the North Sea or English Channel as it was in the South Pacific. The use of a water-proof, quick-donning, exposure suit is discussed.

819. Mellanby, K. Medical experiments on human beings in concentration camps in Nazi Germany. *Brit. M. J., 1947 (v. 1): 148–150.*

The human experimentation carried out on prisoners in concentration camps by the German physicians and medical administrators being tried for War Crimes before Military Tribunal I of the United States at Nuremberg, is discussed. The author quotes from the findings of the International Military Tribunal in which it is stated that the inmates of concentration camps were subjected to cruel experiments; victims were immersed in cold water until their body temperature was reduced to 28°C and death occurred. Other experiments were made to determine how long human beings could survive in freezing water.

820. Mitscherlich, A., and F. Mielke. Experiments with sustained low temperature. *In:* Doctors of infamy, the story of Nazi medical crimes, *p. 20–33. Trans. by* H. NORDEN. *New York, Schuman, 1949.*

Experiments are reported on humans subjected to immersion in water at temperatures of 36.5° and 53.5°F. Body temperatures as low as 79.5°F were recorded. Body temperatures of 82.5°F and lower were found to be lethal. Rapid rewarming was shown to be more effective than slow rewarming. Cause of death was determined to be heart failure.

821. Molnar, G. W. Survival of hypothermia by men immersed in the ocean. *J. Am. M. Ass., v. 131, July 27, 1946: 1046–1050.*

This study attempts to establish how much cooling can be tolerated by men totally immersed in cold water. The literature of shipwreck survival and the rescue records of the Bureau of Medicine and Surgery, U. S. Navy, were examined for data on survival time; data on the human immersion experiments performed on prisoners of the Dachau concentration camp were analyzed. It is concluded that temperatures below 68°F are not tolerated when the rate of heat loss exceeds rate of heat production. When the rectal temperature falls below 95°F, heat production decreases and death results.

822. N., L. H. Physiological responses to immersion in cold water. *Bumed News Lett., Wash., v. 2, Sept. 3, 1943: 5.*

In experiments at the Naval Medical Research Institute, rats immersed in water at 50°–59°F lost consciousness in 20–30 minutes and their rectal temperatures fell to about 70°F. Although human subjects were not kept in cool water long enough to reach a stage of incoordination, immersion in water at 50°F resulted in a fall in rectal temperature of 5° or 6°F per hour. It is assumed from this and other experimental evidence that man is in imminent danger from drowning when his internal temperature falls below 86°F.

823. Rosenstiel, R. Analysis of German studies on hypothermia; results of experiments on man and animals; therapy and prevention [In French]. *Rev. méd. nav., Par., v. 1 (4), 1946: 377–399.*

Some analysis is given of the results of human experimentation by Nazi Doctors during World War II. Some of the subjects discussed are: rewarming (by use of hot baths); the mechanism of death from cold; effects of medical therapy (use of strophanthin, Cardiazol, Coramine, lobeline); preventive measures; and use of life-saving vests. In the preceding sections of the article there is discussion of results of exposure to low temperatures; of recent information on temperature regulation; and of experiments on hypothermia in animals.

824. Sheinis, V. N. Hypothermia; pathology and therapy [In Russian]. *Moskva, Medgiz, 1943. 96 p.*

A study of hypothermia is presented under the following subject headings: etiology, pathological anatomy, pathological physiology, pathogenesis, first aid, and therapy. Among the external signs of lethal hypothermia none can be considered to be pathognomic for death by freezing. The author shares Ar'ev's view that the macro- and micro-pathological structure of the hypothermic human and animal body does not, usually, substantially differ from the normal. Therefore, the main role in the development of hypothermia is played not by easily discernible anatomical factors but by functional changes in biological processes. The pathological physiology is discussed in detail. The temperature changes observed in the organs of the body reflect the course of progressive hypothermia. In experiments with rabbits, the brain varied from this pattern in that there was a 15–20 minute cessation of cooling just before the agony of death began. At a body temperature of 25°C the carbohydrate metabolism was so depressed that chemical thermoregulation ceased and the body passed into a poikilothermic state. It is emphasized that endeavor should be directed toward very rapid rewarming of the body following hypothermia.

825. Shmidt, P. I͡U. Anabiosis. *Moscow-Leningrad, Akademii͡a Nauk SSSR (Nauchno-populiarnai͡a serii͡a), 1948. 375 p.*

A comprehensive survey of experimental data on anabiosis—induced by the effect of low temperatures or dehydration in animals, plants, and cancerous tissues—is presented, including the author's experiments with plants. The monograph is divided into four chapters; the final chapter discusses the effect of low temperature on insects, fish, amphibians, reptiles, and mammals, giving data regarding body temperatures under freezing conditions. N. V. Puchkov (1933) lowered the body temperature of a dog in an ice-water bath under anesthesia to 3°C, then connected its circulatory system to that of a normal dog, raised the bath temperature to 35°C, and applied artificial respiration. The first respiratory movements appeared 2½ hours later; 0.5 cc of Adrenalin was then injected, and heart-beat reappeared. However, after injection of thyroxin, the animal died with a body temperature of 28°C, having survived four hours. N. V. Puchkov's assumption was that the influence of cold increases the thrombin content of the blood, which, after prolonged exposure, leads to blood coagulation. Experiments by N. V. Minin (1940) and I. I. Murygin (1937) showed that hibernating animals are far more resistant to cold than non-hibernating. There is a great lowering of the body temperature during hibernation which greatly reduces metabolism, slows down circulation, and inhibits the action of the nervous system. Hibernation is closely related to the anabiosis of freezing, but much more complicated. Anabiosis is the better tolerated, the drier the environmental atmosphere or body condition. It is suggested that complete anabiosis means complete temporary cessation of life, rather than life latency, as has been shown by G. RAHM's experiments (1924).

826.　Shoji, R., and K. Ogata. On the change in the rectal temperature in man when his body is exposed to extremely cold atmosphere [Abstract, in English]. *Jap. J. M. Sc., Biophysics, v. 6, 1940: 85*–86*.*

The subject exposed his body (clothed in either a winter suit, a set of worsted underwear, or with the upper half of his body naked) to environmental temperatures of −25° to −35°C. Sometimes there was an initial, unexplained, rise in rectal temperature within the first 10 or 15 minutes. The rectal temperature never fell during the first 40 minutes or hour, but lowered usually, by 0.2° to 0.5°C, after 2 hours of exposure. This fall seemed to be the reaction of the temperature regulating center to cold and did not relate to the temperature or to the clothing worn. The significance of the slight fall in rectal temperature within the first 5 or 10 minutes following return to normal room temperature, was not known. Rectal temperature, measured at room temperature during the first week of stay in Manchuria in the winter, fell from 36.5° to 36.0°C which indicated adaptation of the heat regulating centers.

827.　Sillevaerts, C. Second Nüremberg Trial; report of Nazi medical experimentation [In French]. *Bruxelles méd., v. 27, Jan. 12, 1947: 65–70.*

The author reports on the brutal and sadistic use of human beings at the Dachau concentration camp in which they were immersed in a reservoir of water of never more than 3°C until their body temperatures reached 22°C. The time period for this varied from 80 minutes to about 3 hours. The experiment terminated with the death of the subject. Also some persons were exposed nude for several hours in below zero outdoor temperatures and experiments made on rewarming them.

828.　Smith, S. A. Death from cold. *In:* Forensic medicine, *8th ed., p. 247. London, Churchill, 1945.*

Suitably-clothed and well-nourished persons can survive considerable periods of exposure to cold. Older persons or children withstand cold less well than do normal adults. Fatigue, indulgence in alcohol, and even minor degrees of mental depression increase the danger of death from cold. The actual cause of death from cold is unknown. There are no distinctive post-mortem signs either externally or internally; the skin on exposed areas is said to acquire a red florid color in patches and a general pallor elsewhere. When the body is stiff from freezing, it is only after thawing that normal rigor mortis occurs. In severe but not fatal hypothermia the tissues remain in a state of suspended animation; inflammation of the lungs and kidneys are common sequelae of survival. Oxygen is liberated from the blood less readily at low temperatures; the metabolic rate is decreased; vital processes are slowed; and the victim feels fatigued and drowsy, readily falling into a deep sleep which passes into coma and death.

829.　Spealman, C. R. Body cooling of rats, rabbits, and dogs following immersion in water, with a few observations on man. *Am. J. Physiol., v. 146, May 1946: 262–266.*

Rats and rabbits when immersed in water at 30°C and below, cool at a rate dependent upon the temperature difference between the body and the water. Men and large dogs cool in water 15°C or lower but not in water 20°C or above.

830.　Sturkie, P. D. The production of twins in Gallus domesticus. *J. Exp. Zool., v. 101, Feb. 1946: 51–63.*

Hypothermia was induced in hens, by immersion for up to 7 hours, in cold water baths directly after the laying of the previous egg. Chick embryos, which were obtained by 48–72 hour incubations of the next egg laid by these hens, were all retarded in development and there was also a rather high incidence of duplications of the embryo. These latter occurred specially when the hypothermia was induced and terminated before the onset of the first cleavage stage of the ova.

831. **Sturkie, P. D.** Tolerance of adult chickens to hypothermia. *Am. J. Physiol.,* *v. 147, Nov. 1946: 531–536.*

Severe hypothermia was induced in cocks and hens by putting them in water of 6° to 11.7 °C. Lethal body temperatures were 22.8°–23.9 °C and the period of survival was 50–90 minutes.

832. **Veldkamp, A. L.** Serious hypothermias of infants. [In Dutch, summaries in Dutch, English, and French]. *Mschr. kindergeneesk, v. 16, Jan. 1948: 23–28.*

Clinical symptoms—and in some instances autopsy findings—in cases of serious hypothermias of infants are discussed. There is also some discussion of the physiological changes on exposure to extreme cold. It is recommended that slow rewarming be used when the exposure to cold has been of long duration, and that intensive rewarming be done only when the exposure has been sudden and intense.

833. **Wolff, R. C., and K. E. Penrod.** Factors affecting rate of cooling in immersion hypothermia in the dog. *Am. J. Physiol., v. 163, Dec. 1, 1950: 580–584.*

The rectal temperatures of dogs immersed in a water bath (2° to 5 °C), except for head, neck and ventral thorax, were reduced from 39° to 20 °C in an average of 126 minutes (52 to 227 minutes). Some of the factors studied for their effect on rate of cooling were: pre-immersion surgical manipulation, hair covering, shivering, body size, and sex. Relatively slight surgical manipulations were found to decrease the rate of cooling perhaps because of the role of either the adrenal cortex or medulla as a response to stress. Epinephrine is known to increase heat production. The matting in the water of a heavy coat of hair offered considerable protection and slowed the cooling, but short hair appeared to offer no more protection than no hair at all. Although minimal shivering showed a tendency to increase the cooling rate when compared with no shivering, in general it had a significant effect on slowing the cooling rate. There was a definite trend to slower cooling with larger-sized animals but the results were not statistically significant. No differences were found because of sex.

See also items: 16, 19, 20, 21, 33, 35, 37, 49, 72, 76, 77, 123, 212, 214, 228, 241, 318, 330, 399, 471, 473, 477, 478, 479, 504, 522, 524, 560, 569, 673, 1109, 1112, 1115, 1116, 1295, 1413, 1511, 1525, 1699, 1715, 1718, 1730, 1757, 1773, 1913, 1915, 1933, 1947, 1948, 1950, 1958, 1972, 1979, 1982, 1988, 2009, 2245.

B. *Effects on Body Systems and Functions, General*

834. **Anon.** Exposure to cold. *Med. Times, Great Neck, v. 79, Apr. 1951: 192–203.*

The author discusses the physiological responses following exposure to cold, especially under the headings of physiology of heat regulation; hypothermia and its prevention; other cold exposure syndromes (including frostbite); and acclimatization. Of the Dachau experiments (immersing humans in water of 36.5° to 53.5 °F) it is stated that the decline in body temperature from normal to 95 °F was slow but below that level was faster, especially if the cervical region was immersed. Consciousness was impaired below 88 °F; cold narcosis was evident below 85 °F; danger of death existed, and arrhythmical heart action began, below 86 °F; death was inevitable below 82.5 °F; rewarming by total body immersion in hot water was more effective than any other method.

835. Ar'ev, IA. T. On the question of the pathology and clinical treatment of general and local hypothermia [In Russian]. *Klin. med., Moskva, v. 28, Mar. 1950: 15–24.*

An analysis of the pathogenesis of local cold injury and general hypothermia is given, describing the effects of cold on the heart, blood vessels, metabolic system, endocrine system, nervous system, and on temperature regulation. During World War II rapid rewarming was found to be more effective than slow rewarming. The incidence and significance of lethal hypothermia, especially in wartime, is summarized.

836. Behnke, A. R., and C. P. Yaglou. Physiological responses of men to chilling in ice water and to slow and fast rewarming. *J. Appl. Physiol., v. 3, Apr. 1951: 591–602.*

Two nude subjects were immersed in ice water until their toes became numb, and then were rewarmed by exposure to air of 73°–100°F, or to water of 100°–102°F. A third subject, clothed in outdoor winter clothing, was chilled in a cold chamber at a temperature of −20°F for 3 hours, and then rewarmed in air of 100°F, without changing clothes. During cooling in ice water, skin temperature fell rapidly, the subjects experiencing excruciating pains over entire body. Despite a 6-fold increase in metabolism and violent shivering, the rectal, gastric, and oral temperatures fell continually, except for a short initial rise. In rewarming, in air of 70°F–100°F, skin temperatures rose rapidly but deeper temperatures continued falling even more rapidly than during the immersion period and a second cold shock with violent shivering occurred. If rewarming was done more quickly, in a water bath at 100°–105°F, the duration of this violent shivering was greatly shortened.

837. Brokaw, R., and K. E. Penrod. Bromsulphalein removal rates during hypothermia in the dog. *Am. J. Physiol., v. 159, Nov. 1, 1949: 365–368.* Advance abstract in: *Fed. Proc., Balt., v. 8, Mar. 1949: 17.*

Two groups of dogs were held in ice water baths of 2° to 5°C until their rectal temperatures reached 35°C (7 dogs) and 30°C (10 dogs), and then were given bromsulphalein removal tests. Both groups showed a marked retention and slowed removal rate of the dye as indicated by the urine. The disappearance rate curves of the two groups were roughly parallel, with the 30°C group showing the greater delay. Decreased cellular activity or reduced hepatic blood flow or both may be responsible for the slower removal rate.

838. Dill, D. B., and W. H. Forbes. Respiratory and metabolic effects of hypothermia. *Am. J. Physiol., v. 132, April 1941: 685–697.*

Observations were made during experimental hypothermic treatment (rectal temperatures, 38.3° to 25.5°C) of 9 schizophrenic patients. Hypothermia produced, after a short period of time, a state of anesthesia in which certain functions such as those concerned with temperature regulation and acid-base balance, remained moderately effective. Respiratory regulation remained effective even at 25°C. The total metabolic exchange was considerably above the basal level, because of involuntary shivering of voluntary muscle activity and of muscular rigidity of unknown origin. Functions of some vital organs of the body, such as the brain and kidney, were quite possibly decreased in activity.

839. Fairfield, J. Effects of cold on infant rats: body temperatures, oxygen consumption, electrocardiograms. *Am. J. Physiol., v. 155, Dec. 1948: 355–365.*

Newborn white rats up to 17 days old were chilled to 2°, 5°, 10°, or 20°C in an oxygen-filled respirometer immersed in a water bath. The intraperitoneal temperature promptly fell, showing that the rats were too young to maintain body temperature. Rate of the heartbeat and conduction of the cardiac impulse decreased linearly with the decrease in body temperature. In all animals up to 10 days of age at 3°C or lower, metabolic rate reached zero and remained so for as long as 108 minutes, but was followed by complete recovery. Low lethal temperatures indicate that the newborn rat may be regarded as a temporary poikilotherm.

840. **Förster, A.** Death and impairment of health through freezing [In German]. *In: Handwörterbuch der gerichtlichen Medizin und naturwissenschaftlichen Kriminalistik, p. 812–815. Berlin, Springer, 1940.*

In this section of the handbook are mentioned the high incidence of deaths from freezing while in a drunken state; the various gradations of cold injury; the types of skin lesions encountered; the injury of blood vessel innervation from cold; changes in composition of the blood, and in oxyhemoglobin, following cold exposure; lack in the literature of instances of self-destruction by cold; and the tendency of the occasional deaths from cold, in cold countries, to be only in helpless persons or in the very young.

841. **Freud, J.** The influence of low temperature upon the cytology of new born rats [In English]. *Acta brevia neerl., v. 10, 1940: 39–41.* Also, in Dutch, in: *Ned. tschr. geneesk, v. 84, Jan. 6, 1940: 96–98.*

Young rats 4–6 days of age were studied for the effect of chilling on the thyroid, ovary, testicle, and sigmoid intestine. Rats became apneic at an external temperature of 3°–8°C within ½ hour. After 4 hours of chilling, histological changes were observed which led to the conclusions that (1) chilling prevents mitosis or arrests it in the metaphase; and (2) chilled rats were less sensitive to colchicine.

842. **Fujimoto, T.** On the action of cold upon the rabbit [Abstract, in English.] *Jap. J. M. Sc., Biophysics, v. 9, 1944: 75*–76*.*

Changes in gaseous exchange, respiration, circulation, and of blood constituents were estimated in rabbits fixed on their backs and immersed in water of 30°, 20°, 10°C, or in ice water. Both anesthetized and unanesthetized animals showed a rise in gaseous exchange, and in respiratory and circulatory activity at the initial stage, then a gradual fall, while the rectal temperature showed a gradual fall from the beginning and was more rapid in anesthetized than in the unanesthetized animals. In unanesthetized animals no marked change was seen in hemoglobin content, number of red blood cells, or in volume of corpuscles. CO_2 content was reduced markedly to a rectal temperature of 30°C; O_2 content showed an increase throughout the experiment. In anesthetized animals, the gaseous content of arterial blood was the same as in unanesthetized, but the O_2 content of venous blood decreased with the fall in rectal temperature to reach a minimum at 25°C. Animals which had been bled to decrease their total blood volume about 30%, lost their ability to increase heat production to protect against the action of cold. When the blood volume in such animals was restored by transfusion with the shed blood, the ability was restored; when the transfusion was with gum-Ringer solution the ability was only partly restored, and was not restored at all with Ringer solution alone

843. **Gosselin, R. E.** Acute hypothermia in guinea pigs. *Am. J. Physiol., v. 157, Apr. 1949: 103–115.* Advance abstract in: *Fed. Proc., Balt., v. 7, Mar. 1948: 42–43.*

Severe hypothermia was induced in unanesthetized guinea pigs by partial immersion in ice water, and the following measurements were made: colonic temperature, electrocardiograms, ventilation rate (minute respiratory volume), oxygen consumption, and carbon dioxide production. Wide variations in lethal temperatures were noted, some animals recovering after rectal temperatures reached 18°C, others dying at 22°C. The mechanism of hypothermic death is still unknown, but observations indicate that circulatory inadequacy often precedes respiratory failure.

844. **Grosse-Brockhoff, F.** Pathological physiology and therapy of acute hypothermia [Abstract, in German]. *Deut. med. Wschr., v. 69, May 14, 1943: 408.*

Experiments on dogs showed that there may be 3 phases involved in the physiology during cooling (water bath of 5°–10°C): the stimulated phase, the phase of decreased stimulation, and the impairment phase. Death from acute cooling comes from loss of sensitivity of the medullary centers in the brain and of the source of stimulation within the heart. The alteration of blood sugar, lactic acid content, and alkaline reserve play only a subordinate role. The

author expresses his agreement with other workers that lobeline and Coramin used therapeutically give poor results. As a life-saving therapy, rewarming with water baths of 40°C
was best.

845. Grosse-Brockhoff, F., and W. Schoedel. The picture of acute supercooling in animal experiments [In German]. *Arch. exp. Path., Berl.,* v. *201,*
June 12, 1943: 417–442.

Experiments were performed on dogs to determine the mechanism of death by cooling.
Dogs were cooled by immersion in water at 6° to 8°C under morphine-urethane anesthesia.
Simultaneous measurements were made of temperature of skin, brain, and rectum; respiratory
volume; composition of expired and alveolar air; O_2 and CO_2 content of the blood; arterial
and right ventricular blood pressure; femoral blood flow; blood lactic acid; and certain other
factors. Electrocardiograms were taken at intervals. Results were largely negative. No metabolic
effects of sufficient magnitude to cause death were noted. The view that adrenal failure causes
death was not substantiated. Direct effects of cold on the heart were found to be of major
significance, however. Conclusion was reached that while damage to the function of the
medulla and possibly hypoglycemia may play a part, the real cause of death in cooling experiments is heart failure due to direct effect of cold.

846. Haterius, H. O., and G. L. Maison. Experimental hypothermia and rewarming in the dog: recovery after severe reduction in body temperature. *Am.
J. Physiol.,* v. *152, Feb. 1948: 225–232.*

Twenty-one dogs anesthetized with cyclopropane were immersed to the neck in an ice-
water bath (2°–9°C) for an average of 155 minutes and then rewarmed by immersion in water
at 42°–45°C. There was a linear fall in body temperature during the cooling period, a more
pronounced visceral-rectal temperature gradient, a decrease in arterial blood pressure, and
bradycardia. Eight of the animals died.

847. Holzloehner, E., S. Rascher, and E. Finke. Report of 10 October 1942 on
cooling experiments on human beings. *In: Germany (Territory under Allied occupation, 1945– U.S. Zone) Military Tribunals. Trials of war criminals before the Nurenberg
Military Tribunals under Control Council law No. 10, Nurenberg, Oct. 1946–Apr. 1949.
v. 1, p. 226–243. Washington, D. C., Government Printing Office, 1949.*

This is a partial translation of a report on cooling experiments on human beings, signed
by Drs. E. Holzloehner, S. Rascher, and E. Finke, and used as a prosecution exhibit during
the trials of war criminals following World War II. In human beings immersed in a tank of
ice-water (2°–12°C or 35.6°–53.6°F) the rectal temperature decreased gradually to about
35°C (95°F), after which the drop became rapid; some deaths occurred at rectal temperatures
below 30°C. Deaths resulted from heart failure; total irregularity was observed at this temperature in all cases indicating direct damage to the heart. Cardiac damage was due to overloading
of the heart by the marked and regular increase in the viscosity of the blood as well as by the
marked throttling of large peripheral vascular areas; it is also probable that there was a direct
injury to the heart from the cold. The lowering the temperature was more rapid if the neck
was also chilled. Such chilling interferred with the temperature-regulating and vascular
centers. Cerebral edema also appeared. Blood sugar rose as the temperature fell, and blood
sugar did not drop again as long as the body temperature fell, suggesting an intermediary
disturbance of metabolism. Respiration of the individual was made more difficult because of
the rigor of the respiratory musculature. Body temperature continued to fall for more than 15
minutes after removal from the cold water; this may be an explantion of deaths occurring
after successful rescue from cold water. Intense rewarming, preferably by immersion in a hot
bath, was never found to be injurious to the subject. Use of drugs which acted on the peripheral circulation were definitely not helpful; the use of strophanthin is still open to question.
Special protective clothing doubled the survival time over that of subjects who were immersed without protective clothing.

848. Karády, S. The role of the alarm reaction during the formation of food allergy [In German]. *Zschr. ges. exp. Med.*, v. *110 (6), 1942: 617–622.*

Study was made of food allergies in healthy guinea pigs with normally-functioning intestine and liver. A state of alarm reaction, consisting of 3 phases—alarm, resistance, and exhaustion—was induced by cooling or by injections of Formalin or histamine. Cooling of the animals was effected in a refrigerator at 1 °C over a period of 24 hours. Sensitization was induced by oral injection of 2 cc of normal horse serum, repeated after 3 weeks. The anaphylactic shock was elicited in all the animal groups, with one lethal case out of 8 during hypothermia. Twenty minutes after the second administration the body temperature of all the animals had dropped 1 °–2.5 °C. The shock was lightest in the group sensitized by Formalin. The tests showed that the alarm reaction is capable of inducing intestinal sensitization against orally-injected normal horse serum. It is therefore assumed that in healthy individuals also general deteriorating factors, like exhaustion, prolonged stay in cold, trauma, strong X-ray radiation, parenteral overdoses of medicines, etc., can increase the permeability of the gastric and intestinal mucosa, and sensitize the organism against food albumin by damaging the liver function.

849. Kelsey, M. P. Acute exposure of flyers to arctic waters. *Air Surgeon Bull.*, v. *1, Feb. 1944: 7–10.*

Accidental immersion of flyers in a subarctic region where water temperatures ranged from 38° to 52°F are discussed, especially the physiological changes taking place in such a situation. Numbness often came within 5 minutes after immersion, because of cold anesthesia, and shock probably occurred within 10 minutes. Also panic appeared to occur in all but the most stolid, even though this panic was often not remembered accurately, and was the cause of poor judgment. Death probably occurred within 1 to 1½ hours as a result of shock or sooner by drowning if flyer was unconscious and safety equipment did not prevent submergence of face. There is little possibility of swimming as much as a mile in such cold water and handicapped by fairly heavy clothing and equipment.

850. Killian, H. Nature of cold injuries [In German]. *Schweiz. med. Wschr.*, v. *79, Dec. 31, 1949: 1262–1266.*

The four phases which occur in progressive deep hypothermia are discussed. A table is given outlining the various physiological changes which occur during these phases, as they have been discussed in the literature. Injury or death from cooling will not depend on cellular injury but on the failure of some vital organ function. The four phases of circulatory changes which occur in local cold injury, are outlined. Euphyllin, Eupaverin, Padutin, and acetylcholine are some of the medicaments suggested for use in combating the vasospasm resulting from cold exposure. Also suggested is sympathectomy and ganglion block by anesthesia.

851. Laborit, H. Therapeutic generalized hypothermia [In French]. *Presse méd.*, *Par.*, v. *59: May 5, 1951: 606–608.*

In discussing the physiopathology of exposure to cold, or of death from cold, it is stated that there are two stages in the defense against cold. In the earlier period there is an attempt to maintain homeostasis particularly through the neuro-endocrine functions; in the latter period, having exhausted the energy reserves, the defense mechanisms can no longer maintain the body temperature which continues to lower until death ensues. In the process of defense against the cold, various physiological mechanisms are activited: cutaneous vasoconstriction, accelerated cardiac rhythm, intracellular and extracellular fluid changes, accelerated respiration; glycogen mobilization; changes in central nervous system and in endocrine gland functioning. The therapeutic use of generalized cold in cancer cases is discussed. Such a hypothermic state is rendered possible by a pharmacological blocking of the neurovegetative system.

852. Luft, U. C. Cold and protection against cold in high mountains; experience of the Himalayan expedition [In German]. *Zbl. Chir.*, v. *69, Nov. 7, 1942: 1775–1779.*

Prolonged sojourn under low atmospheric pressure has been found to lead to considerable hypothermia, even at room temperature. Shivering was inhibited, and if the body temperature dropped, oxygen supply to the tissues deteriorated with the appearance of pulmonary congestion and edema. Oxygen release in the peripheral parts of the body was prevented more readily and more rapidly at high altitudes than at low. Acclimatization to high altitudes induced an increase in the viscosity of blood with a slowing of circulation. Under the combined effect of high altitude and cold, the stasis stage occurred more quickly and, because of the added lack in oxygen, a hypoxic condition appeared more rapidly. Especially dangerous was the weak subjective sensation of cold and pain and the apathy developing at high altitudes, which brought an awareness of frostbite long after its occurrence. For prophylaxis against cold injuries at high altitudes oxygen inhalation should be added to circulatory stimulation and protective clothing. The author does not believe in the usefulness of rubbing the injured areas with snow. Clothing should consist of many layers permitting a large volume of air to act as insulation, be light-weight and comfortable, wind-tight but not water-tight. Shoes should not be oiled, should have bent soles, and be padded with a removable felt lining.

853. **Meader, R. G., and C. Marshall.** Studies on the electrical potentials of living organisms. II. Effects of low temperatures on normal unanesthetized mice. *Yale J. Biol.*, v. *10*, Mar. *1938: 365–378.*

Effects of low temperatures on 20 mice of two genetic strains were studied. All were able to survive internal temperatures of 8.5°C. Chilling produced initial increase in bodily activity and in respiratory rate, followed by a decrease. The strains were found to differ in pattern of bioelectric potentials, both in the base line and in reaction to chilling.

854. **Müller, E., W. Rotter, G. Carow, and K. F. Kloos.** A study of death from exposure to cold in men cast away at sea [In German]. *Beit. path. Anat.*, v. *108*, Dec. *30, 1943: 551–590.*

The pathological anatomy of 28 men dead from exposure to cold at sea was studied. Findings in cases of varying exposure times were compared. No important pathological changes were seen in the thyroid and pituitary glands or in pancreatic islet tissue. A decrease in liver glycogen and degeneration of the adrenal cortex was observed in those men longest exposed before death. Changes in the heart, kidney, liver, and muscular tissue were also noted.

855. **Muschenheim, C., D. R. Duerschner, J. D. Hardy, and A. M. Stoll.** Hypothermia in experimental infections. III. The effect of hypothermia on resistance to experimental pneumococcus infection. *J. Infect. Dis.*, v. *72*, May–June *1943: 187–196.*

Experimental hypothermia (rectal temperature, 31°–33°C) was induced in rabbits over a period of 4–5 hours by use of a refrigeration unit or cold baths, after the animals had been injected dermally with one of two strains of pneumococcus. It was found that in rabbits injected with a highly virulent strain of Type I pneumococcus, hypothermia decreased the local inflammatory reaction in the area of the injection, but no effect was noted on subsequent bacteremia and death. When a relatively avirulent Type III strain was used, however, induced hypothermia resulted in extreme bacteremia and death, as well as inhibition of the dermal inflammatory reaction. Local chilling at the site of inoculation resulted in inhibition of the dermal inflammation but failed to cause a fatal bacteremia unless the general body temperature was allowed to fall to a low level.

856. **Nei, T., and N. Tada.** Vital reactions from exposure to cold [In English]. *Jap. M. J.*, v. *3*, Apr. *1950: 185–193.*

Rabbits, unanesthetized and fixed in a dorsal position, were exposed for 15 or 30 minutes to a cold environment (−40°C). With the shorter period of exposure, all animals survived and recovered normally within 2 or 3 hours when rewarmed at a room temperature of 15°C; with the longer period of exposure, recovery took at least 10 hours and not all animals survived. On cooling there was an initial rise, followed by a decrease, in body temperature, in pulse rate, and in respiratory rate. On rewarming the body temperature continued to fall for 2 or 3 minutes and then gradually rose. The recovery of heart action was slow, paralleling then the recovery of body temperature. The respiration which had been steady, regular, slow and deep in the latter part of the cooling period, remained the same for the short period of observation during rewarming. Except for a tendency to return to normal about 1 or 2 minutes after exposure, the brain waves were suppressed throughout the cooling period. Despite the speedy recovery of the cortical temperature on rewarming, cortical activity remained in a depressed state for a considerable time.

857.   Nuzie, S. B., and S. L. Nuzie. Preliminary observations in lowering of body temperature. *J. Laborat. Clin. M., v. 26, June 1941: 1423–1426.*

The body temperature of dogs was lowered from the normal (approximately 100.8°F) to 79.5°F by placing the anesthetized animal in an electrically refrigerated unit over a period of six hours. When the refrigeration was discontinued it took a little over twice that period of time for the body temperature to return to normal. When the body temperature was 79.5°F, the respiratory rate decreased to three per minute and the pulse rate dropped to 60 per minute; the respiratory rate was a more reliable indication of the condition of the dog than was the pulse rate. The temperature of the interior of the cabinet was 44°F, with a humidity of 72%, when the body temperature was 79.5°F.

858.   Ranke, O. F. Temperature regulation in chilling [In German]. *Klin. Wschr., v. 22, Feb. 6, 1943: 113–116.*

Experimental findings and clinical observations of the physiological reactions to cold are discussed in detail, including the physiological mechanisms involved in rewarming following hypothermia. Included in the text is a parallel chart, for hypothermia and local cooling, outlining the sequence of some of these physiological changes and some of their interrelations.

859.   Rascher, S. Intermediate report on intense chilling experiments in the Dachau Camp, started on 15 August 1942. *In: Germany (Territory under Allied occupation, 1945– U.S. Zone) Military Tribunals. Trials of war criminals before the Nuernberg Military Tribunals under Control Council law No. 10, Nuernberg, Oct. 1946–Apr. 1949, v. 1, p. 220–221. Washington, D. C., Government Printing Office, 1949.* Also, excerpts from translations, in: Cold endurance tests. *Bull. U.S. Army M. Dept., v. 6, Dec. 1946: 680–681.*

This is a translation, signed by Dr. S. Rascher, of an intermediate report on the intense chilling experiments at Camp Dachau; the translation of the document became a prosecution exhibit during the trials of war criminals following World War II. In the experiments the subject, dressed in flying uniform complete with aviator's helmet and rubber or kapok life jacket, was immersed in water of temperatures from 2.5°C to 12°C. In one series, the occiput (brain stem) protruded above the water; in another series the occiput and back of the head were submerged in the water. Electrical measurements gave low temperature readings of 26.4°C in the stomach and 26.5°C in the rectum; fatalities occurred only when the brain stem and back of the head were also chilled. Autopsies of such fatal cases always revealed large amounts of free blood—up to ½ liter—in the cranial cavity. Extreme dilation of the right chamber of the heart was invariably shown. As soon as the temperature in these experiments reached 28°C the experimental subjects died invariably despite all attempts to revive them. The findings conclusively prove the need of a warming protective device for head and occiput when designing protective clothing of the foam type. Other important autopsy findings, in all cases, were the marked increase in blood viscosity; marked increase of hemoglobin; and increase of leukocytes approximately five-fold; invariable rise of blood sugar to twice its normal value. Auricular fibrillation made its appearance regularly at 30°C. Since after removal from cold water the body temperature continued to drop, rapid rewarming was preferable to slow rewarming in all cases. Rewarming by animal warmth—animal bodies or women's bodies—would be too slow. Pharmaceutical measures are probably unnecessary if the flier is still alive at the time of rescue.

860.   Roger, H. Physiology of the aviator [In French]. *Presse med., v. 48, July 24–27, 1940: 606–609.*

Some of the atmospheric conditions which influence the physiological functioning of the aviator during flight are primarily the lowering of temperature and the lowering of atmospheric pressure. Temperature decreases, in general, 2 °C for each 300 meters of altitude up to 12,000. At this altitude, and up to 24,000 meters, the temperature is approximately −55 °C. At about 2 °C suffering from cold begins. At −13 °C, unless protected by gloves and heated garments, the hands become frosted. At −18 °C the feet and body are chilled and shivering occurs. The body chills in the order of, first the back, then the buttocks, the abdomen, and finally the legs. At −23 °C, shivering is intense and visual acuity is diminished. At −29 °C a physical and mental depression is produced. At −40 °C muscular contracture and apathy are augmented until at −40 °C to −45 °C, a comatous state begins and death ensues.

861. Shoji, R., K. Ogata, T. Fujimoto, S. Yasaki, and K. Aida. On the adaptation of human body to an extremely cold atmosphere. [Abstract, in English]. *Jap. J. M. Sc., Biophysics, v. 6, 1940: 1 **

During the winter of 1938 in Manchuria, the test subject clothed only in ordinary underwear, exposed his body to temperatures from −25° to −35 °C. Various physiological changes were studied, including rectal temperature, blood pressure, pulse rate, lung ventilation and gaseous exchange, and hemoglobin and sugar content of arterial blood. Rectal temperatures began to fall after 1 hour and fell by 0.5° to 0.7 °C after 2 or more hours; blood pressure rose; pulse rate did not usually rise unless the blood pressure remained high for a while. Visual sensitivity suffered no change; auditory sensitivity lowered especially if cold wind blew directly against the ear; tactile discrimination of two points on skin was markedly depressed.

862. Talbott, J. H. Cold exposure; pathologic effects. *In: Medical physics. v. 1. Ed. by* O. GLASSER. *Chicago, Year Book Publishers, 1944. 1744 p.*

In the section on Cold Exposure (p. 244–246), two clinical syndromes follow exposure to a low environmental temperature: those from local exposure sometimes with freezing of an area or extremity, and those from generalized reduction of body temperature. Studies during experimental hypothermia have shown alterations mainly in the cardiovascular-renal systems and in the central nervous system. Some details of the changes in blood composition, are discussed. In recovery from hypothermia it is essential to have a long period for restoration of body temperature. The environmental temperature during early stages of recovery should be just above 32 °F; the rate of restoration should not be greater than 2° or 3 °F per hour. Blood pressure and rectal temperature should be taken frequently; any tendency of systolic pressure to fall below 100 mm Hg should be taken as an indication of too rapid rewarming. Bradycardia below 50 minute or a persistently recurring arrhythmia suggest a more serious state than a fast pulse rate with regular rhythm. Administration of fluids intravenously is desirable although venipuncture may be difficult because of vascular constriction (one or more liters of saline or glucose solution may be given every 4 hours). Vigilance should not be relaxed until the body temperature is normal. A slight hyperemia may follow for a short period. Local damage from exposure to cold varies from simple erythema to thrombosis and gangrene. During exposure, use of tobacco is contraindicated because of its vasoconstrictor action. The vasodilatory effect of small amounts of alcohol gives little help in protection from cold but may be of some help in later treatment; in large quantities, alcohol has an inhibitory effect on the higher brain centers. Sympathetic block may be used for relief of vasospasms and as an aid in establishing a collateral blood supply.

863. Taylor, H. M., and L. Y. Dyrenforth. Chilling of the body surfaces; its relationship to aural and sinus infections. *J. Am. M. Ass., v. 111, Nov. 5, 1938: 1744–1747.*

Cooling of guinea pigs (refrigerator at 59 °F) and man (immersed in 72 °F water or swimming in water at 68.5 °F) indicated that chilling without exercise led to physiological changes within the body. Included are peripheral vasoconstriction, lowered leukocyte response (total and polymorphonuclear), and impairment of phagocytic capabilities of the fixed tissue cells followed chilling. These changes are said to predispose to infection of areas such as the upper respiratory tract, the eustachian tube, and the middle ear.

864. Troedsson, B. S. Experimental lowering of the body temperature of rabbits and its possible application in man. *Arch. Phys. Ther.*, v. 20, Aug. 1939: 501–504.

Hypothermia was induced in anesthetized rabbits by placing them in a cold box at temperatures of 4 °C. Body temperatures below 24 °C resulted in frostbite. Lethal temperatures were found to be about 16 °C. Large amounts of heat were required to restore temperatures to normal. It was found that at reduced temperatures the central nervous system was paralyzed, basal metabolic rate was lowered, and the pulse and respiratory rate were slowed.

865. Walker, S. M. Effect of low temperature on the mechanical response and action potential of rat muscle [Abstract]. *Am. J. Physiol.*, v. 155, Dec. 1948: 475–476.

Anesthetized rats were cooled until the rectal temperature decreased to about 22 °C. The gastrocnemius muscle showed a 50% increase of tension and a 100% increase in contraction and relaxation time. Cooling under the conditions of these experiments produced about 100% increase of the duration of action potentials obtained with belly and tendon leads.

866. Walker, S. M. Potentiation of twitch tension and prolongation of action potential induced by reduction of temperature in rat and frog muscle. *Am. J. Physiol.*, v. 157, June 1, 1949: 429–435.

The triceps surae muscles of 18 rats were cooled by placing the whole rats in a cold room (10 °C) or by placing the legs of 3 rats in a cooling chamber. Cooling of the muscle from 37 ° to 24 °C increased twitch tension about 80 to 90 per cent and the duration of the action potential about 300 per cent. The effect of cooling is apparently not due to change in concentration of plasma potassium, although moderate cooling and treatment with KCl both induced similar changes. Support is given to the theory that cooling prolongs the membrane "breakdown" produced by the passage of an excitation wave along the muscle fiber. A causal relation is suggested between duration of this "breakdown" and increased contraction of muscle fibers.

867. Wayburn, E. Immersion hypothermia. *Arch. Int. M.*, v. 79, Jan. 1947: 77–91.

Immersion hypothermia is a clinical syndrome which was seen among American and British flyers rescued from the North Sea. The clinical picture appears to result from several factors including the coldness of the water, length of exposure, emotional factors, and specific reaction of the person to cold. Chief effects are those on cardiovascular system, nervous system, and on blood. Resemblances of syndrome to experimental hypothermic and clinical shock are discussed. Treatment includes rapid rewarming, reduced activity, administration of warm fluids by mouth, and administration of plasma in severe cases.

868. Werz, R. von. Refuting the texts? On the nature and treatment of general chilling [In German]. *Med. Welt*, v. 20, Apr. 28, 1951: 566–568.

The survival of the young, and intoxicated, Negro woman in Chicago following exposure to severe cold, which caused a drop in body temperature to approximately 18 °C, is discussed as an exception to the textbook statements that human life can not be sustained at that low a temperature. Deaths from severe cooling are due primarily to the lack of available oxygen in the blood rather than to respiratory or cardiac failure. The author states that the oxygen pressure of the blood is decreased drastically as the temperature drops. Therefore, in the therapy of severe cooling, rapid rewarming should be employed, making sure of a sufficient supply of oxygen to the patient. Although alcohol gives a false sense of warmth to the cold sufferer by causing a dilatation of skin blood vessels and by supplying extra calories, the eventual faster heat loss and somewhat narcotizing effect protects the sufferer by reducing him to and maintaining him in a semi-hibernating state where his oxygen needs are less than normal.

869. Woodruff, L. M. Survival of hypothermia by the dog. *Anesthesiology, v. 2, July 1941: 410–420.*

Dogs subjected to hypothermia do not survive long enough for metabolic studies in this state, the average length of survival being 7 hours. No dogs survived with body temperatures below 72°F. Respiratory failure was a frequent cause of death, and was not prevented by oxygen inhalation. Circulatory failure was the cause of death in those dogs not succumbing to respiratory failure. Digitalis prolonged life for some hours.

See also items: 193, 239, 887, 1064, 1066, 1074, 1075, 1084, 1100, 1103, 1136, 1724, 2014, 2017.

C. Nervous System and Sense Organs

870. Cate, J. ten, G. P. M. Horsten, and L. J. Koopman. The influence of the body temperature on the EEG of the rat. *Electroencephalography, Montreal, v. 1, May 1949: 231–234.*

The electroencephalogram of curarized rats remains practically unaltered at rectal temperatures of 32°–39°C; below 30°C, the amplitude gradually decreases; electrical activity of the brain virtually disappears at a rectal temperature of 18°–20°C.

871. Cortesi, C., and G. Marsili-Libelli. Fluctuations in the value of minimum effective stimulus for the motor area in hypothermic animals [In Italian]. *Arch. fisiol., Fir., v. 48 (1–2), 1949: 204–210.*

Guinea pigs were immersed in a water bath until their rectal temperatures were about 22°C. In the hypothermic animals, fluctuations were found in the value of the minimum effective electrical stimulus of the motor area of the cerebral cortex. The electrical excitability of the cortical area showed periodic variations analogous to those observed in ether-chloroform narcosis; excitability decreased rapidly when the rectal temperature of the animals fell below 22°C.

872. Fay, T., and G. W. Smith. Observations on reflex responses during prolonged periods of human refrigeration. *Arch. Neur. Psychiat., Chic., v. 45, Feb. 1941: 215–222.*

Neurological studies were made on 42 patients during a state of induced hypothermia. Deep reflexes increased when the body temperature was between 97° and 85°F. No changes were noted in the abdominal reflex. At 78°F deep tendon, abdominal, gag, and eye reflexes were abolished. Mental faculties were reduced at 93°F, and pain was completely relieved in all but 2 cases.

873. Fulton, J. F. Physiology and high altitude flying: with particular reference to air embolism and the effects of acceleration. *Science, v. 95, Feb. 1942: 207–212.*

Some of the effects of low temperature (p. 208–209) on war time personnel are discussed. Exposure to intense cold sufficient to cause a perceptible lowering of rectal temperature is known to make motor performance slow and inaccurate and to greatly impair cerebral activity (as indicated by ability to solve simple problems or to follow simple directions by radio). The gunner in a bombing plane is most liable of all the crew to suffer seriously from cold since he must often be at his position for several hours exposed to drafts of outside air through the machinegun apertures. At an altitude of 20,000 feet the outside air temperature would be about 25°C below zero. The need for electrically-heated clothing, and for an oxygen mask and line of supply which will not freeze up, is discussed.

874. Girgolav, S. S., and V. S. Levit. Frostbite [In Russian]. *In: Uchebnik chastnoĭ khirurgiĭ, v. 2, p. 484–485. Ed. by* I. S. Babchin, A. N. Bakudev, *and* L. S. Bekerman. *Moskva, Medgiz, 1944.*

This section serves as an introduction to a collection of reports of workers in the field of cryopathology, of the Academy of Medical Science of the USSR, not published in periodicals. Experimental data have shown that necrosis resulting from general body cooling is due not to the slowing down and cessation of chemical reactions in accordance with van't Hoff's law or to exhaustion of energetic resources, but to the weakening or complete cessation of nervous regulation in the tissue areas which are exposed to cold. The entire nervous system is affected. The exceptionally important role played by the central nervous system in hypothermia is revealed in A. A. Kalikhman's work. The disturbances resulting in the tissues are purely functional. The problem consists therefore in determining the character of these functional disturbances. T. A. Achkasova's experiments have shown the reflex nature of the carbo-hydrate metabolic changes which depend not only on the temperature of the tissue but are subject to the regulatory action of the nervous system (manifested in the mobilization of all the body resources, not only those of the cooled area). This constitutes the scientific basis for the therapeutic use of glucose combined with rewarming. The neuro-vascular disturbances arising under the effect of cold, simultaneously with the necrosis or even without apparent necrosis, remain to be studied.

875. Grosse-Brockhoff, F., and W. Schoedel. Changes in the excitability of the respiratory and circulatory centers during rapid cooling [In German]. *Pflügers Arch., v. 246, June 2, 1943: 664–674.*

Dogs under urethane anesthesia were cooled in a water bath of 5°–10°C in order to study the effects of rapid cooling upon the sensitivity of the respiratory and circulatory centers. Maximum sensitivity was observed to exist at a brain temperature of 34.5°C. At 26°C the depressor reflex was no longer detectable. Metabolism reached its maximum at a temperature lower than the temperature of maximum medullary excitability.

876. Haterius, H. O., and A. H. Hegnauer. Consciousness and reflex potenti-alities of dogs during immersion hypothermia [Abstract]. *Fed. Proc., Balt., v. 8, Mar. 1949: 69–70.*

Observations on central nervous system activity in 150 dogs during immersion hypothermia, are reported. The rectal temperature at which consciousness was abolished by cold narcosis—determined by the use of ether or cyclopropane anesthesia, withdrawn periodically—was found to vary from 22.5°–26°C. The lowest temperatures at which spontaneous reflexes under light anesthesia were noted were: shivering at 16°C, vocalization at 17°C, spontaneous respiration at 11.8°–16°C.

877. Horsten, G. P. M. Influence of the body temperature on the EEG [In English]. *Acta brevia neerl., v. 17 (1–4), 1949: 23–25.*

During experimental cooling, the brain of rats showed no marked changes in the electrical activity at rectal temperatures from 37.5°–32°C. When the temperature fell to 30°–29°C, marked changes were observed. The proportion of low frequencies decreased markedly, whereas the amplitude of the higher frequencies appeared to be augmented. With a fall to 28°–27°C, the amplitude decreased; in a majority of cases the low frequencies disappeared completely. At 20°–18°C, the electrical activity of the brain virtually disappeared and the EEG became almost a straight line. If the period of cooling was not too long, the electrical activity could be restored.

878. Kahana, L., W. A. Rosenblith, and R. Galambos. Effect of temperature change on round window response in the hamster. *Am. J. Physiol., v. 163, Nov. 1, 1950: 213–223.*

Hamsters were given barbiturate anesthesia in order to vary their body temperatures over a range of 39° to 18°C, and the changes in electrical response of the cochlea of the ear were studied. The temperature of the cheek pouch was used as a relative measure of the temperature of the cochlea. The electrical responses to acoustic clicks has two components: aural microphonic generated in the cochlea, and action potentials in the auditory nerve. Amplitude of both components decreased when cooling was below 30°C. Neural component declined more rapidly than microphonic and disappeared at a temperature where microphonic was still observable. The latency of the most prominent microphomic component was found to be constant and independent of temperature. As the temperature decreased below 30°C, there was a progressive increase in both latency and duration of the neural component.

879. **Libet, B., J. F. Fazekas, A. M. Meirowsky, E. H. Campbell, and H. E. Himwich.** Control of electrical and oxidative activity of brain by temperature [Abstract]. *Am. J. Physiol.*, v. *129*, *May 1940: 404–405.*

The effects of lowered temperature on the brain of dogs and cats are reported. Electrical activity of cerebral cortex, posterior thalamus, and medulla decreased in frequency and amplitude with cold, but some activity continued in all parts of the brain until the temperature had dropped to 15°C, at which temperature other parts of the body ceased to function. When pentobarbital anesthesia was used, electrical activity was slower at normal body temperature, and ceased at 25°C when death occurred.

880. **Marro, F.** Respiratory effects from bulbar thermic changes and from lobeline in animals in hypothermia. [In Italian, summaries in Italian, English, French, Spanish, and German]. *Riv. med. aeronaut.*, v. *14, July–Sept., 1951: 443–447.*

A progressive general hypothermia does not abolish the reaction of the bulbar respiratory center to changes in the environmental temperature. But the response in severe hypothermia to either a lower or higher temperature is always an increase in respiratory rate, while in the normal animal the rate increases and decreases with rises and falls, respectively, of the temperature. Lobeline increases the rate in all cases but this is more pronounced and prolonged the lower the body temperature of the animal. The fact that bilateral vagotomy abolishes the effect of lobeline at all temperatures, suggests that the drug has a reflex action rather than acting directly on the bulbar respiratory centers.

881. **Marsili-Libelli, G.** Variations in the excitability of the cerebral cortex in the hypothermic guinea pig [In Italian]. *Boll. Soc. ital. biol. sper.*, v. *17, Oct.– Nov. 1942: 553–554.*

The effect of cold upon the excitability of the cerebral cortex was studied in anesthetized guinea pigs immersed in running water of 12°–15°C. Capacity for reaction was found to decline steeply after the rectal temperature had fallen below 20°C.

882. **Marygin, I. I.** The essential nature of anabiosis during hypothermia [Abstract, in Russian]. *Sovet. med. ref. Obozr., fiziol., 1949 (4): 15.*

Bakhmet'ev's data concerning anabiosis were verified and the mechanism of the anabiotic condition studied in frogs, marmots, hedge-hogs, and jerboas. The animals were placed at 0°C and below, for periods of 2 to 8 hours. Results indicate that death under conditions of hypothermia was due to injury of the thermoregulatory center. The primary cause of death is believed to be cold injury to the nervous system, especially to the nervous centers and primarily to those centers regulating blood circulation. Cellular dehydration is a secondary cause of death. The restoration of vital functions is possible only as long as the vital nervous centers have not been affected by the cold. The state of anabiosis is not a cessation of all vital body functions but a condition of lowered functional activity, during hypothermia.

* 883. **Morita, S., and N. Tada.** Experimental studies of the death from cold, especially on the electrocardiogram under alcoholic condition [In Japanese, with English summary]. *Teion-kagaku*, v. *4, 1948: 117–132.*

"An injection of 6cc of 25% alcohol/kg. into the vein of a rabbit raises the body temperature and increases the respiratory rate. The body temperature decreases at a linear rate when the

---

* Original not seen.

alcohol-injected rabbit is exposed to a temperature of −40°C. The body temperature is lowered beyond the critical temperature and survival duration is prolonged. (Authors' abstract)."—SIPRE Report 12, v. 3, Jan. 1953: 200.

884. Perkins, J. F., Jr. The role of the proprioceptors in shivering. *Am. J. Physiol.*, v. 145, Dec. 1946: 264–271.

After being lightly anesthetized, cats had their front feet placed in water baths of 5°–10°C whil oscillographic records were made for analysis of the rate and character of their shivering movements. In most instances shivering started by the time rectal temperature had fallen to 35°–36°C. Simultaneous studies made on normal and on deafferented hind limbs showed movements of the limbs to be rhythmic on the normal side and irregular on the deafferented side. A hemi-decerebellate animal and two animals with severance of one dorsal column shivered normally on both sides. The rate of shivering of a normal muscle could be changed greatly by varying the mechanical resonance of the moving muscle. It is concluded that the rhythmicity and rate of shivering are determined by a mechanism involving the proprioceptors. The rate of shivering in normal muscle is probably close to the resonant frequency of the moving part. A pacemaker action of the shivering center appears unlikely.

885. Rewerts, G. Subjection to cold and cerebral damage [In German]. *Klin. Wschr.*, v. 26 (15–16), 1948: 249–250.

Clinical, and later post mortem, examinations were made of several soldiers who had been exposed for months, under field conditions, to severe cold. From these examinations the author concludes that the cerebral cortex is most sensitive to cold. The damage from long periods of cold exposure at below-threshold levels is shown in the dulling of consciousness which can lead to general psychomotor slowing, symptoms of being imprisoned, of loss of initiative as well as deterioration of the personality. There are also focal symptoms (speech defects and agnostic features), and finally typical symptomatic psychoses of which the most serious is cold idiocy which would appear to be irreversible and often lethal. The brain stem is more resistant but symptoms of damage to the pyramidal-motor system are not rare. The appearance simultaneously of cerebral cortex and brain stem damages results usually in the downfall of vital vegetative functions. The convulsive cold encephalopathies which appear, and likewise the hyperkinetic symptoms on the part of the brain stem, require an immediate decompression of the brain by drainage of some spinal fluid. The cold blindness resulting after 1–2 hours of hypothermia is attributed to an extension of cerebral edema to the papillae. Apoplectiform sicknesses are not rare; they are attributed mainly to cerebral bleeding from vascular wall damage. Cerebral symptoms, such as a daily rhythmic hypotony and bradycardia occurring mostly in the early morning, are explained as cold-actuated. The bradycardia could lead to restriction of cerebral circulation with consequent hypoxemia and damage to cerebral centers. Injury to cerebral nerves can appear. Temperature drops were found to be accompanied by cerebral symptoms. Older persons with less adaptable vascular systems were more inclined to be afflicted with cold encephalopathology. Since protracted exposure to cold can injure the cerebral vascular system, it is to be expected that some cold-injured persons will suffer later from cerebral endangiitis obliterans. Thus, former victims of hypothermia may suffer epileptic attacks and cortex symptoms of various kinds, as well as a variety of injuries to the central nervous system.

886. Rewerts, G. Cold lesions of central nervous system [In German]. *Deut. med. Wschr.*, v. 74, Nov. 11, 1949: 1365–1368.

From the rather rare instances in the literature and from his own experiences, the author presents evidence of injuries to the brain resulting from severe, often fatal, exposure to cold. Autopsy material showed evidence often of cerebral edema, severe arterial and venous hyperemia, and rather often of punctate hemorrhages in the brain stem, the medulla, and around the third ventricle. Clinical symptoms in those who survived, or before death in others, included general psychomotor slowing and various psychotic states. It is argued that these changes are not due to direct injury by cold of the central nervous system, but are due to cerebral hypoxemia caused by a lesion of the capillaries and small cerebral vessels as a result of factors acting by way of the autonomic nervous system.

887.   Rewerts, G. Centrogenic blood flow disturbances of interior organs caused by chilling [In German, summaries in German, English, French, and Italian]. *Acta neuroveget., Wien, v. 2, July 1951: 315–328.*

A survey was made of the literature concerned with the relations between damages to the brain stem and edema of the lungs. According to these findings cerebral trauma may result in extensive damage to the blood circulation with extravasations to the organs of the chest and damage to the mucous membrane of the gastrointestinal tract. These alterations are to be considered as states resulting from injury to the regulatory center for blood circulation located in the hypothalamus. An attempt was made to relate this information to the circulatory anomalies quite regularly observed in the inner organs in cases of death due to cold exposure. These are quite similar to the ones appearing in consequence of brain injuries, to cerebral factors including increase in intracerebral pressure, and to damage to the brain stem. A case of cold exposure (continuously for a month, 10°–15°C) is cited which resulted in a rapidly occurring edema of the lungs with manifestations of encephalopathic symptoms thought to be caused by exposure of the brain stem. Lumbar puncture to relieve spinal fluid pressure brought about a disappearance of both the vehement encephalopathic symptoms and the pulmonary edema.

888.   Swinyard, E. A., and J. E. P. Toman. Effects of alterations in body temperature on properties of convulsive seizures in rats. *Am. J. Physiol., v. 154, Aug. 1, 1948: 207–210.*

Characteristics of experimental convulsive seizures—brought about by the use of electroshock, picrotoxin or Metrazol—were studied in rats whose body temperatures were altered by exposure to extreme environmental temperatures (−8°C, and 55°C). Seizure threshold was increased, seizure duration reduced, and post-seizure recovery hastened by increased body temperature, and conversely changed by decreased body temperature. Test results were plotted for a range of body temperatures of approximately 45° to 20°C.

* 889.   Tanaka, M., and S. Morita. Experimental studies on death from cold [In Japanese, with English summary]. *Teion kagaku, v. 4, 1949: 105–116.*

"The relationship between body temperature and brain waves at −40°C temperature were studied by injecting 6 cc of 25% alcohol/kg. into the veins of rabbits. The body temperatures fell with linear rate. The abdominal temperatures remained 3°–4°C below that of unanesthetized controls. Brain temperatures differed only within 1°C, and brain waves were unchanged. Alcohol appeared to have delayed brain deterioration and the disappearance of the brain waves. It is concluded that the injection of alcohol prolongs the period of survival. (Authors' abstract)."—SIPRE Report 12, v. 3, Jan. 1953: 203.

890.   Vallery-Radot, P., G. Mauric, A. Holtzer, A. Domart, and J. Lemant. Study of the sympathetic nervous system in the course of hypothermia of the rabbit [In French]. *C. rend. Soc. biol., par., v. 137, Feb. 13, 1943: 78–79.*

The effect of Adrenalin and acetylcholine was tested on rabbits during both a hypothermic state and at normal body temperature. Adrenalin injected into hypothermic animals did not raise blood pressure as much as in the animals kept at normal temperature.

See also items: 475, 824, 1076 ,1081, 1086, 1098, 1634.

---

* Original not seen.

C. Circulatory System
(includes also lymph, fluid shifts, and reticulo-endothelial tissue)

891. Barbour, H. G., E. A. McKay, and W. P. Griffith. Water shifts in deep hypothermia. *Am. J. Physiol., v. 140, Oct. 1943: 9–19.*

Monkeys chilled to 23°C and white rats cooled to 16°C were rewarmed at 28°C. While the protective reflexes were operating, there was a gain in intracellular water. With more cooling, so as to cause general neuromuscular depression, the reflex responses disappeared and the water shift was reversed so that extracellular fluid increased and subcutaneous edema appeared. The edematous condition became greater with rewarming.

892. Bigelow, W. G., W. K. Lindsay, and W. F. Greenwood. Hypothermia; its possible role in cardiac surgery; an investigation of factors governing survival in dogs at low body temperatures. *Ann. Surg., v. 132, Nov. 1950: 849–866.*

Dogs were cooled to body temperatures below 20°C. Light anesthesia was used to prevent shivering and artificial respiration was given in studying the possibility of cardiac, rather than respiratory, failure as the cause of hypothermic deaths. Gradual falls of blood pressure, heart rate, and cardiac output were observed as cooling progressed, with comparable rises on rewarming. Intense vasoconstriction was observed grossly and vascular stasis, with erythrocyte agglutination, microscopically. Electrocardiographic studies were done during both cooling and rewarming.

893. Crismon, J. M. Effect of hypothermia on the heart rate, the arterial pressure, and the electrocardiogram of the rat. *Arch. Int. M., v. 74, Oct. 1944: 235–243.*

In rats cooled to lethal levels it was found that the lowered temperature slowed both the heart rate and conduction of the cardiac impulse. Abnormalities of the P wave and complete atrioventricular dissociation were also noted. Respiratory failure appeared only after the arterial pressure had fallen below 70 mm Hg.

894. Crismon, J. M., and H. W. Elliott. Circulatory and respiratory failure in the hypothermic rat and the response to local application of heat to the heart. *Stanford M. Bull., v. 5, Aug. 1947: 115–119.*

The effect of local applications of heat to the heart was studied in rats which had been chilled to a body temperature which was associated with a reduction in arterial pressure, extreme bradycardia, and slowed respiration. Warming of the heart resulted in an increased heart rate, elevation of arterial pressure, and an increased respiratory rate.

895. Eckstein, R. W., D. Book, and D. E. Gregg. Blood viscosity under different experimental conditions and its effect on blood flow. *Am. J. Physiol., v. 135, Feb. 1, 1942: 772–775.*

The viscosity of the blood of normal dogs was studied under various experimental conditions including a fall (38° to 33°C) in body temperature. An average of 1°C drop in body temperature increased viscosity by about 2 per cent. Experiments showed that changes in viscosity altered greatly the facility with which blood flowed through vascular beds of the dog or through perfused organs.

896. Fröhlich, A. The behavior of the white blood cells in generalized cooling [In German]. *Deut. Zschr. gerichtl. Med., v. 30, Nov. 21, 1938: 199–202.*

Rabbits were immersed in ice water at a temperature of 1°C for 8–15 minutes. Body temperatures fell 7°–14°C. The percentages of eosinophils and polymorphonuclear leukocytes in the blood were increased; up to 65% of the leukocytes were injured and distorted.

897.   Giaja, J., and R. Andjus. Cardiac function of chilled mammals [In French].
C. rend. Acad. sc., Par., v. 230, Apr. 3, 1950: 1366–1367.

Rats and rabbits were subjected to cold until their rectal temperatures had fallen to 15°C
and the animals were in a very lethargic, hypoxic, state. The heart of the animal continued
to beat for several hours after opening of the thoracic cavity and cardiac puncture, if the
lungs were supplied with oxygen.

898.   Gonzales, F., and B. J. Luyet. Resumption of heart-beat in chick embryo
frozen in liquid nitrogen. *Biodynamica, Normandy, Mo., v. 7, May 1950: 1–5.*

Chick embryos were removed from the incubated eggs after 40 hours, were slightly dehydrated in a hypertonic solution of ethylene glycol, frozen solid by immersion in liquid nitrogen
at −195°C, and then thawed by immersion in Tyrode's solution at 40°C. The heart resumed
beating and continued to do so for hours after the treatment. Earlier work had indicated
that rapid cooling and thawing, so that solidification was always in the vitreous state and
crystallization was avoided, did little harm to protoplasm.

899.   Grant, R., M. M. Gertler, and K. G. Terroux. Atrial fibrillation induced
by epinephrine in hypothermic dogs. *Am. Heart J., v. 37, June 1949: 1081–1089.*

Dogs, and a few cats, were packed in ice except for their chests, and given epinephrine intravenously. In a few cases, epinephrine was applied directly to the auricles after opening of the
chest surgically. Atrial fibrillation following epinephrine administration occurred at rectal
temperatures from 37° to 25°C. Following stimulation of the vagus nerve during cooling, it
occurred at rectal temperatures from 37.6° to 27.6°C. Epinephrine and vagal stimulation
were found to act synergically to incite atrial fibrillation; epinephrine alone could produce
fibrillation only when the vagus nerves were intact. Spontaneous atrial fibrillation could not
be caused by cooling alone, even at body temperatures as low as 13°C. Since anoxia is known
to favor fibrillation and to sensitize the heart to vagal action, the avoidance of anoxia in these
experiments may have been a big factor in the absence of spontaneous atrial fibrillation from
cold.

900.   Graybiel, A., and C. J. Dawe. Auricular fibrillation following hypothermia, report of a case. *U. S. Armed Forces M. J., v. 1, Apr. 1950: 418–421.*

Auricular fibrillation and various changes in the T wave were among the electrocardiogram
findings on a healthy young man who nearly died following accidental immersion in cold
water. The patient was rewarmed under blankets and given an ounce of alcohol, hot coffee,
and ephedrine (intramuscularly). Re-examination 18 days later showed no abnormalities.

901.   Halpern, B. N., P. Dick, G. Biozzi, and G. Mené. Effect of chilling on
the granulopectic activity of the reticuloendothelial system [In French]. *C.
rend. Soc. biol., Par., v. 145, Apr. 1951: 503–505.*

A series of experiments had been carried out previously on the ability of the reticulo-
endothelial system of white rats to clear their circulating blood of particulate matter following
repeated injections of India ink. In these experiments its was found that an injection with a
quantity (8 mg of carbon) which had never produced intravascular blood clotting in the rat
at normal temperatures, produced in the hypothermic (26°–22°C) rat a highly coagulated
state. Heparinization of a similar group of hypothermic rats and of another group of rats
kept at a room temperature of 37°C, indicated that there was in a hypothermic state a decided
slowing down of the activity of the reticulo-endothelial system, an increase in the rate of
accumulation of carbon particles in the blood, and a very important prolongation of the time
which the particles remained in the blood. For example, in the rat at normal temperature
two minutes after injection, 35% of the particles were "fixed" in the reticuloendothelial
system; after 35 minutes, 90%. In the hypothermic rat these figures were 13% and 29%.

902. **Hegnauer, A. H., and H. O. Haterius.** Pulse rate and blood pressure of dogs in immersion hypothermia [Abstract]. *Fed. Proc., Balt., v. 8, Mar. 1949: 71.*

In 18 anesthetized dogs the pulse rate and blood pressure were plotted against the blood temperature in the right ventricle of the heart during immersion of the dog in an iced bath. A thermocouple was placed in the right ventricle of the heart with continuous recording. The pre-immersion pulse rate was 155. Following an initial abrupt increase and decrease in rate from the moment of immersion to a blood temperature of 36°C, the pulse rate followed a smooth regression curve down to a blood temperature of 15°C, at which point the pulse rate was 15 per minute.

903. **Hegnauer, A. H., W. J. Shriber, H. O. Haterius, J. Flynn, and R. C. Wolff.** Cardiovascular response of the dog to immersion hypothermia. *Am. J. Physiol., v. 161, June 1, 1950: 455–465.*

Anesthetized dogs, tied supine to an animal board, were immersed, except for upper chest, neck, and head, in an iced bath of 2°–5°C. Pules rate, blood pressure, cardiac mechanogram, electrocardiogram, and blood viscosity were recorded. In early stages of hypothermia, the pulse rate reflected the algebraic sum of reflex excitatory and cold depressor influences. In the temperature range of 25° to 14°C, excitation was absent. The decrease in blood pressure was independent of pulse rate until a temperature of approximately 23°C was reached when it was completely dependent. Blood viscosity at 20°C was 2 or 3 times that at normal body temperature and was attributable to hemoconcentration. As other workers had found, the various phases of the cycle in electrocardiograms were prolonged as hypothermia progressed. Prolongation of the systolic and isometric relaxation at 18°C was 5- or 6-fold. The authors suggest that the cause of death in hypothermia is predominantly of cardiac origin, caused by both inadequate coronary flow and lowered metabolic rate.

904. **Hegnauer, A. H., H. D'Amato, and J. Flynn.** Influence of intraventricular catheters on course of immersion hypothermia in dog. *Am. J. Physiol., v. 167, Oct. 1951: 63–68.*

During experimental hypothermia the presence of intraventricular catheters in dogs appeared to initiate idioventricular ectopic beats which in turn precipitated ventricular fibrillation at temperatures above the mean lethal temperature for uncatheterized dogs (about 16.5°C). This sensitivity appeared especially at temperatures below 25°C. The findings from these experiments make untenable the hypothesis previously presented that the ventricular abnormalities observed in catheterized dogs were induced by hypoxia. Breathing 100 per cent oxygen did not influence the temperature of onset of the arrhythmia. Neither intravenous procaine nor a specific adrenergic blocking agent appeared to exercise any control over the idioventricular beats of catheter origin.

905. **Hegnauer, A. H., J. Flynn, and H. D'Amato.** Cardiac physiology in dog during rewarming from deep hypothermia. *Am. J. Physiol., v. 167, Oct. 1951: 69–75.*

Dogs were successfully rewarmed by use of a 45°C bath following cooling to a near-lethal heart temperature of 16.2°C. The changes, such as those of pulse rate and blood pressure, during the rewarming mirror those taking place during cooling. The authors state that, under the conditions studied, the changes taking place are merely brought about by the decreased metabolic rate rather than by any pathological dysfunction.

906. **Hook, W. E., and R. T. Stormont.** Effect of lowered body temperature on heart rate, blood pressure, and the electrocardiogram [Abstract]. *Am. J. Physiol., v. 133, June 1941: 334–335.*

The body temperature of dogs and cats anesthetized with ether or sodium barbital was reduced with crushed ice, and electrocardiograms were made. As body temperature sank from 38° to 18°C, heart rate decreased from 163 to 22 beats/minute and blood pressure from 128 to 31 mm Hg. As the body temperature was reduced, the amount of ether required was gradually decreased until at 22°–20°C ether administration could be discontinued. Below 20°C artificial respiration was frequently necessary to maintain life. Recovery occurred in some animals even when the body temperature had been reduced to as low as 17°C, provided that the animal was warmed by external heat.

907. Lange, K., D. Weiner, and M. M. A. Gold. Studies on the mechanism of cardiac injury in experimental hypothermia. *Ann. Int. M., v. 31, Dec. 1949: 989–1002.*

In experimentally-cooled rabbits a proportional fall in pulse rate was noted, which makes possible the prediction of the precise temperature at which the heart will stop. It was shown that anoxemia is not a factor and that the stoppage is due to the direct effect of cold on the pacemaker of the heart or its governors.

908. Lutz, W. Electrocardiographic observations in the cooling of warm-blooded animals [In German]. *Zschr. Kreislaufforsch., v. 36, Dec. 1944: 625–640.*

Observations of a "retardation curve" resembling that produced by heart block, noted in the electrocardiogram of chilled warm-blooded animals, strengthened the author's theory that the significant damage in cold injury is the result of oxygen deficiency and not the direct effect of cold upon the heart.

909. Lutz, W. On the dependence on temperature of the process of stimulation in the heart [In German]. *Zschr. Kreislaufforsch., v. 37, May 1948: 266–272.*

Studies were made of the dependence of the process of normal cardiac stimulation on temperature changes. The frequency, conduction rapidity (PQ and QRS), and duration (QT) of stimulation were determined in 35 guinea pigs, cooled in a bath at 0°C. The rectal temperature was verified thermoelectrically; the heart temperature was measured directly in 7 cases, by means of a thermoneedle. All the electrocardiographic values were found to have the same relationship to temperature, and could be graphically represented by a hyperbola, or by a straight line, depending on how the process was envisaged. It is concluded that hypothermia induces a slowing down, then a cessation, of the stimulation processes in the heart, without irreversible functional or anatomical damage.

910. Lutz, W. Nature and cause of cardiac arrest during hypothermia [In German]. *Zschr. Kreislaufforsch., v. 37, June 1948: 314–321.*

Earlier studies of the author, and others, had indicated that death from hypothermia (at body temperatures of 15°C or lower) did not result directly from the cold effect itself but from hypoxemia due to displacement of the oxygen dissociation curve. It was found that this hypoxemia could be avoided by the inhalation, during the cooling, of oxygen under pressure. When the heartbeat ceased at body temperatures below 15°C, such administration of oxygen was found to revive the organ, indicating that no severe organic injury had occurred. The stimulation capacity of the heart (or its frequency) ceased at a higher temperature (16°C) than the propagation of stimulation in the heart muscle (13°C), indicating that heart function ceased because of cessation of stimulation. This assumption was verified by stimulating the hearts of 5 guinea pigs electrically, after they had ceased to beat. Results showed that the heart remained capable of stimulation and contraction (the frequency corresponding to the heart's temperature) even after spontaneous death. However, after cooling of the animal slightly below a body temperature of 13°C, this reviving action was found ineffective. The reason for this is seen in a cellular resistance to oxygen diffusion, due to solidification of membrane lipoids and disturbance in cellular permeability.

911. Massik, E. On the action of cold on the peripheral blood picture of infants [In German]. *Acta paediat., Upps., v. 35, suppl. 7, 1948: 1–107.*

When guinea pigs were placed in a cold bath until their normal body temperatures (38°C) were reduced to 27°C, their blood showed a reduction from normal in the number of erythrocytes, polymorphonuclear leukocytes, lymphocytes, and a reduction of the hemoglobin content.

Following a cold bath (9°–17°C, 8–15 minutes) the body temperature of infants (12 days to 5½ months of age), decreased approximately "15.2%," the erythrocyte count and the hemoglobin content were decreased, but the leukocyte, polymorphonuclear leukocyte, and lymphocyte counts rose. The changes in body temperature of the infants, following a cold foot-bath (5°–6°C; 15 mins) were not significant. The erythrocyte count and the hemoglobin percentage decreased and after 3½ hours had not returned to normal. When the infants were fed ice-cold milk or ice-cold barium meal the hemoglobin percentage and erythrocyte count decreased and had not returned to normal after 3½ hours. There was no change in the leukocyte count, whereas the polymorphonuclear leukocytes and lymphocytes decreased. When the barium meal was warmed to 37°C before feeding, the erythrocyte count increased. Neither before or after cold stimuli were any immature erythrocytes or erythroblasts demonstrable.

912. **McCarrell, J. D.** The effects of hyperthermia and hypothermia on cervical lymph flow. *Am. J. Physiol.*, v. 130, July 1940: 34–42.

When three anesthetized and curarized dogs were subjected to low environmental temperatures (10°C), the cervical lymph flow was not significantly altered even when the body temperature was reduced to 25.6°C. There were no appreciable circulatory changes, with the exception of a decreased heart rate. Thoracic duct flow was too variable to permit conclusions. In contrast to these findings, in high environmental temperatures there were marked circulatory changes, increases in cervical lymph flow, and decreases in lymph protein percentages.

913. **Maison, G. L., and H. O. Haterius.** Terminal changes in cardiac activity and in respiration in death from severe hypothermia [Abstract]. *Fed. Proc., Balt.*, v. 6, Mar. 1947: 162.

Under urethane or morphine-urethane anesthesia, and while immersed in water between 5° and 20°C, the rectal temperature of a dog fell 10°C per hour until death occurred at a rectal temperature of 18°–26.5°C. Electrocardiogram patterns showed: (1) ventricular fibrillation, with respiration continuing after the last effective heart activity; (2) sinus rhythm continued until death from heart stand-still; (3) auricular standstill, with the ventricle continuing at a slow rate until death, which apparently resulted from respiratory failure.

914. **Martos, J., J. Nuñez del Carril, R. J. Mora, and E. Ortiz de Landázuri.** Arterial hypertension due to intraperitoneal fluids. I. Effect of cold [In Spanish]. *Rev. clín. españ.*, v. 43, Dec. 15, 1951: 317–325.

Intraperitoneal injection of cold (1°C) serum when the animal was surrounded by ice, gave rise to either of two types of shock. In one, shock came on rapidly and there was hypertensional response; in the other, shock came on slowly and there was no hypertensional response. Hypertensional response did not depend on the presence of kidneys and suprarenal glands; its genesis was vasomotor, being inhibited by Dibenamine. Shock was accompanied by hypertensional response when rectal temperature was about 25°C and the parenchyma of the liver was unimpaired. It would seem that the integrity of the liver plays a role in hypertensional response.

915. **Meidinger, O.** Investigations on death from freezing [In German]. *Zschr. Biol.*, v. 100, Dec. 28, 1940: 361–372.

Experimental cooling, as it is described in the literature, of guinea pigs and rabbits to a lethal or near-lethal level is discussed. Physiological changes, especially those in the rate of heart beat, are discussed in detail. There is also some discussion of the role of hunger in the hypothermic state and of the question of the critical body temperature.

916. **Oppenheimer, M. J., and A. McCravey.** Circulation time in man at low temperatures. *Am. J. Physiol.*, v. 129, May 1940: P434–P435.

Blood circulation time was studied in patients while they were being subjected to refrigeration and were in a hypothermic state. Measurements made on arm, neck, and leg veins, by the sodium cyanide injection method, showed an increased circulation time.

917. Oppenheimer, M. J., and A. McCravey. Pulmonary circulation time in man at low body temperatures. *Proc. Soc. Exp. Biol., N. Y., v. 46, Mar. 1941: 513–519.*

Observations of the effects of hypothermia on pulmonary circulation were made on 14 human subjects suffering from inoperable malignant tumor, whose internal temperature had been reduced to 85°F in experiments with cold therapy. Pulmonary circulation time was lengthened, largely owing to the lowered output of the right ventricle. In 2 of the subjects observed, shivering, which was the result of insufficient depth of anesthesia, produced a shortened circulation time.

918. Prec, O., R. Rosenman, K. Braun, S. Rodbard, and L. N. Katz. The cardiovascular effects of acutely induced hypothermia. *J. Clin. Invest., v. 28, Mar. 1949: 293–300.*

Circulatory changes and cardiac output were studied in dogs during cooling and rewarming. In the early cooling period, oxygen consumption, respiratory and heart rates, blood pressure, and cardiac output were raised by shivering. As cooling proceeded, these effects decreased and hemoconcentration was noted. On rewarming, these effects were reversed. Death when it occurred was caused by vasomotor or respiratory, rather than cardiac, failure.

919. Puchkov, N. V. On the influence of cooling upon the organism [Abstract, in German]. *In: Zbl. allg. Path., v. 81 (8–9), 1943: 289.*

The posterior part of the body—or the hind legs—of rats, mice, and rabbits were cooled in ice and water (0°–2°C). In rats and mice the body temperature decreased to 23°–25°C, in rabbits only to 32°–33°C. During the hypothermic state, the number of leukocytes was found to be considerably decreased in rats and mice. In hypothermic rabbits the leukocyte number changed, either increasing or decreasing. The number of thrombocytes, or blood platelets, was always reduced, sometimes by nine tenths. The coagulation of the blood was always accelerated. Injection of various anticoagulants into the blood diminished to some extent the alterations resulting from hypothermia.

920. Rodbard, S., and M. Tolpin. A relationship between the body temperature and the blood pressure in the chicken. *Am. J. Physiol., v. 151, Dec. 1, 1947: 509–515.*

Interrelationship between body temperature and blood pressure was studied in 22 chickens ranging in age from 6 to 16 weeks. Unanesthetized chickens were cooled by application of ice packs, to reduce the body temperature close to the lower limit of cold tolerance (about 24° to 25°C). They were rewarmed later by radiant heat until they died (about 45° to 46°C). (Normal body temperature was about 41.5°C.) Blood pressure fell during the cooling phase. On rewarming, the blood pressure rose to control level and then fell just prior to death. There was no significant change in blood pressure response to epinephrine from that observed at normal body temperature in either hypothermic or hyperthermic chickens, although the return of pressure to pre-epinephrine level was slower when body temperatures were lowered. The heart rates varied directly with the body temperatures of the animals. It is assumed, as a working hypothesis, that there is a direct control of blood pressure by the brain to maintain the blood supply necessary for body needs.

921. Rodbard, S., and A. Fink. Effect of body temperature change on the circulation time in the chicken. *Am. J. Physiol., v. 152, Feb. 1, 1948: 383–388.*

In six chickens cooled from the normal body temperature (about 41.5°C) to 25.0°C by packing in crushed ice, the circulation time was increased from a normal of about 3 seconds to 10 or 15 seconds. This fall in rate of circulation appeared to be directly related to the fall in body temperature. The regulation of blood pressure appeared to depend on factors other than changes in heart rate, circulation time, or rate of metabolism of peripheral tissues; it probably resides primarily in the central nervous system.

922. Rodbard, S., H. Saiki, and A. Malin. Body fluid redistribution in induced hypothermia and hyperthermia [Abstract]. *Fed. Proc., Balt., v. 6, Mar. 1950: 107.*

Lowering the body temperature of rabbits and chicks to 25 °C brought about a slight increase in hematocrit and specific gravity of the blood. However, plasma and blood volume and thiocyanate space were all reduced 30% below normal levels. Data suggest that induction of hypothermia results in a marked shift of fluid from the plasma and interstitial spaces to the intracellular phase. The fact that the hematocrit and specific gravity do not rise commensurate with the decreased volumes suggests that blood cells and plasma proteins are removed from the circulating plasma and stored. The reverse processes are brought about by rewarming to normal temperature levels.

923. Rodbard, S., H. Saiki, A. Malin, and C. Young. Significance of changes in plasma and extracellular volumes in induced hyperthermia and hypothermia. *Am. J. Physiol., v. 167, Nov. 1951: 485–498.*

Experiments carried out on both rabbits and chicks show that there may be a slight increase in the circulating plasma volume and in the thiocyanate space. During induced hypothermia (reduction of normal body temperature by 12° to 15 °C), there was a striking reduction, by as much as 30%, of these volumes. Previously it had been thought that these later changes were due to the shift of fluid out of the blood or the extracellular space. Results of the current studies would tend to support more recent thinking which suggests that vascular beds may open or close—in response to neurogenic regulatory mechanisms from the central nervous system—to lock away some of the circulating blood.

924. Rosenhain, F. R., and K. E. Penrod. Effect of immersion hypothermia on cardiac output. *Fed. Proc., Balt., v. 8, Mar. 1949: 134.*

Observations on cardiac output, pulse, and O₂ consumption were made on dogs before and after immersion in cold water. Between 35° and 25 °C the measured factors fell in a linear fashion. The cardiac output curve, but not the pulse curve, reflected a peak in O₂ consumption associated with shivering.

925. Rosenstiel, M. German researches on induced hypothermia in animals and in men [In French]. *Presse méd., v. 54, Apr. 20, 1946: 257–258.*

It has been established by German research that the etiology of frostbite is based on a modification of tissue metabolism and that from generalized hypothermia is due to cardiac failure. The most favorable results in reviving hypothermic subjects were obtained by the author by using a 10-minute bath at 50 °C.

926. Shriber, W. J. Effect of hypothermia on cardiodynamics. *Fed. Proc., Balt., v. 8, Mar. 1949: 146.*

Anesthetized dogs were cooled in water baths of 2° to 4 °C. Electrocardiograms and records of intracardiac pressure were made until death. Left ventricular systolic pressure remained constant until rectal temperatures of 25°–23 °C were reached, then fell rapidly. Simultaneously, right auricular systolic pressure rose rapidly. These changes appear to be correlated with cessation of respiration. Hypoxia of cardiac muscle may be a factor in stoppage of the heart.

927. Tolpin, M., and S. Rodbard. The body temperature-arterial pressure relationship in the chicken [Abstract]. *Fed. Proc., Balt., v. 6, Mar. 1947: 215.*

Chickens which were cooled by ice packs were shown to have a fall in arterial pressure and heart rate. Rewarming by radiant heat caused a rise in blood pressure and heart rate until a critical level of about 44 °C was reached. With further increase in temperature the blood pressure fell but the heart rate continued to increase. These findings indicate a definite body temperature-blood pressure relationship in the chicken, independent of heart rate.

928. Tomaszewski, W. Electrocardiographic changes observed in man dying from exposure to cold [In French]. *Arch. mal. coeur, v. 31, May 1938: 525–528.*

Electrocardiograms were made on a man dying from exposure to cold. It was noted that the EKG picture resembled that seen following a lesion of cardiac muscle. The P-R and QRS intervals were prolonged and the S-T segment was decreased.

929. Tomaszewski, W. Electrocardiographic study of animals subjected to refrigeration [In French]. *Arch. mal. coeur, v. 31, July 1938: 730–737.*

Rabbits subjected to artificial refrigeration showed the following electrocardiographic changes: a decrease in cardiac rhythm, an increased auriculo-ventricular conduction, and a prolongation and lowering of the S-T segment. Cold acts directly on the centers of stimulation in the heart.

930. Uttley, K. F. M. Death from cold. *N. Zealand M. J., v. 47, Oct. 1948: 427–434.*

Gross and microscopic findings are given from the autopsy reports on three girls who died from cold exposure. Outstanding feature was congestion of the small blood vessels in the internal organs while the skin and subcutaneous fat were bloodless. There is also included a brief discussion on the local and general effects of cold.

931. Weiner, D., K. Lange, and M. M. A. Gold. Mechanism of cardiac injury in experimental hypothermia [Abstract]. *Fed. Proc., Balt., v. 8, Mar. 1949: 345.*

It was found that rabbits suffering from experimental hypothermia showed a reduction in heart rate directly proportional to the fall in body temperature. The changes in the normal electrocardiogram are given.

932. Wendt, H. J. The spleen under the influence of cold [In German]. *Forsch. Röntgenstrahl., v. 69, May–June 1944: 182–193.*

X-ray examination of rabbits before and after whole body cooling (to rectal temperatures of approximately 30°C, 24–26°C, and 18°–19°C) and after rewarming, showed the spleen to be distinctly and measurably reduced in size by cooling. The decrease in size paralleled the decrease in body temperature to reach a maximum at 24°–26°C rectal temperature. The rise in erythrocyte count and of hemoglobin content of the blood was principally due to the limiting of the blood flow through the spleen; the slight decline in erythrocyte count which followed was attributed to some hemolysis. Blood viscosity increased on cooling. Rewarming the animal brought about a reversal of most of the changes.

933. Werz, R. von. Anoxia as a cause of death from cold [In German]. *Arch. exp. Path., Berl., v. 202, 1943: 561–593.*

Rabbits or cats under narcosis were cooled to the point of death by use of an electric fan while cold water was poured over them. Continuous studies were made of rectal and forehead temperatures; of the alkali reserve, total CO_2, oxygen saturation, and, in some cases, the pH of the blood, and of the oxygen consumption. The author regards as the cardinal point in the question of the role of anoxia in lethal hypothermia, whether the progressive oxygen saturation in the venous blood and slow dissociation of oxyhemoglobin during continued cooling is the cause or the consequence of the simultaneous decrease of oxygen consumption. In hypothermia the arterial oxygen tension decreased more slowly than the oxygen consumption, indicating the presence of anoxia. The failure or inadequacy of the defense processes against hypoxia brings about disturbances of metabolism and damages to such organs as the adrenals, kidneys, liver, and heart until finally manifest anoxia occurs and death results from anoxic respiratory stoppage and secondary circulatory stoppage. On the basis of his theory of death from hypothermia being from anoxia, the author outlines a 4-level system of processes: (1) regulation against heat loss; (2) direct cold effects, because of failure of (1); (3) regulation against cold-caused anoxia; and (4) hypoxic disturbances causing injury, and death, because of failure of (3). He states that the simultaneous course of these processes tends to obscure the true mechanisms of death by cold.

934. Williams, J. R., Jr. The effect of changes in body temperature on peripheral circulatory failure in the mouse [Abstract]. *J. Clin. Invest., v. 21, Sept. 1942: 638.*

The effects of raising (39°-40°C) and lowering (28°-32°C) the body temperature of mice, on the peripheral circulatory failure which was prompted by the intraperitoneal injection of 50% sucrose solution, were studied. Mice kept at the higher temperature appeared more active and in better condition but died in a very short time; those at normal temperature did not appear as "well" clinically but survived a longer time; while those at the lowered temperature appeared to be comatose, cyanotic, and very ill, but they survived longer and a higher percentage ultimately recovered than in either of the other groups. The amount of fluid exuded into the peritoneum was approximately the same in all three of the groups.

See also items: 23, 498, 845, 886, 942, 945, 949, 957, 964, 1018, 1021, 1047, 1062, 1071, 1265, 1589.

E. Endocrine System

935. Ariel, I., and S. L. Warren. Studies on the effect of hypothermia. II. The active role of the thyroid gland in hypothermic states in the rabbit. *Cancer Res., v. 3, July 1943: 454–463.*

When rabbits were chilled by various means and at different rates and periods, profound changes were noted in the thyroid gland. The gland enlarged from 1 to 3 times normal size in most rabbits, and there was microscopic evidence of increased activity. During the period of recovery metabolism was greatly increased. In general it was found that the rabbit's ability to withstand prolonged chilling was partially dependent on the state of activity of the thyroid and its capacity to function over a long period of time in the cold.

936. Büchner, F. The pathology of hypothermia [In German]. *Klin. Wschr., v. 22, Jan. 30, 1943: 89–92.*

The author discusses three grades of hypothermia in humans. There is first a compensation then a decomposition with a relative, and later an absolute, insufficiency of heat regulation. In a person in a compensated or slightly decompensated state and exposed to low environmental temperatures over lengthy periods of time, changes in the thyroid gland are concluded to take place for increasing heat production. In such situations loss of colloids was observed, with a heightening of the epithelial layer. Because of a decrease in lipoid content of the adrenal cortex during a condition of hypothermia, it is concluded that the hormones of the adrenal cortex play a large part in heat regulation.

937. Capitolo, G. Thyroidectomy in numbing cold. Glycemia, variations of water balance, chloremia [In Italian, summaries in Italian, French, German, and English]. *Ormoni, v. 1, Apr. 1939: 291–304.*

Normal rabbits and those which had been thyroidectomized or parathyroidectomized, were exposed to a low ambient temperature until they died. In the animals which had also been surgically treated, there was found, at death, to be an increase in the blood sugar and in the chlorine content of the blood and also a higher content of water in both the tissues and the blood, than there was in the normal rabbits.

938. DeCourcy, C. B., and J. L. DeCourcy. Hypothermia in hyperthyroidism. *Am. J. Surg., v. 77, Feb. 1949: 199–201.*

Animal experimental and human clinical findings on the effect of cold on the thyroid gland are reviewed. In generalized hypothermia, the gland manifests acute hypertrophy with an increase in size of the epithelium and loss of colloid. Local cooling has been used effectively for thyroid crises; its use combined with propylthiouracil or related drugs, is suggested.

939. Driessens, J. Diminution of the amount of adrenal-cortical hormone in guinea pigs drastically chilled [Abstract, in French]. *C. rend. Soc. biol., Par.,* *v. 137, 1943: 255–256.*

Biochemical examination of the adrenal cortex immediately following the death of guinea pigs exposed to temperatures of −20° to −25°C for one to six hours, showed a diminution in the amount of adrenal-cortical hormone.

940. Ershoff, B. H., and O. J. Golub. Effects of prolonged exposure to cold on the serum protein-bound iodine of the rat. *Arch. Biochem., N.Y., v. 30, Jan. 1951: 202–206.*

Groups of male rats, 25–28 days of age, were kept at room temperature (23 °C) and in a refrigerated atmosphere (2°–1.5 °C) for 45 days. Studies of the protein-bound iodine, considered to be a good index of the thyroxin content, in the serum of blood samples from each group showed no significant differences.

941. Gellhorn, E., and J. Feldman. The influence of cold and heat on the vago-insulin and the sympathetico-adrenal systems. *Am. J. Physiol., v. 133, July 1941: 670–675.*

Rats were exposed in test groups to cold by immersion in water of 2°–4°C for 10 min. Normal rats reacted with a hyperglycemia; adreno-demedullated rats reacted with hypoglycemia; and adreno-demedullated-vagotomized rats showed no significant change in blood sugar. It was concluded that cold acts on both vago-insulin and sympathetico-adrenal systems, the effect predominating in the latter.

942. Hartman, F. A., and K. A. Brownell. Response to chilling and recovery in adrenalectomized cats. *Am. J. Physiol., v. 141, July 1944: 651–661.*

Adrenalectomized cats, maintained adrenal extract adequate for laboratory life, were chilled until the rectal temperature was 25 °C and then rewarmed to normal rectal temperature in 5 or 10 hours. The same fall in rectal temperature was produced in a shorter time in adrenalectomized animals than in normal animals. The arterial pressure fell to a lower level in the adrenalectomized cats than in the controls and the increase in blood sugar was usually less in the operated cats than in the normal ones.

943. Hill, R. M., J. E. Roberts, D. E. Holtkamp, B. B. Longwell, and R. W. Whitehead. Critical body temperatures and efficiency of body-temperature control of adult rats during successive cold stresses [In French]. *Rev. canad. biol., v. 10, Dec. 1951: 425–434.*

Both normal and adrenalectomized adult rats, exposed at 4°C without food or water, undergo a fall in body temperature. When 0.9% saline was given in place of drinking water, body temperature regulation was significantly better in the adrenalectomized rats. In general the body temperature curves showed 2 points of accelerated fall in all of the rats; but, although the body temperature at these points were approximately the same, the time elapsing between the beginning of exposure and the first points and between the first and second points was much shorter in the adrenalectomized rats. Because these time intervals were so extended in the group of normal rats, inanition may have superimposed an additional stress on this group.

944. Irwin, E., A. R. Buchanan, B. B. Longwell, D. E. Holtkamp, and R. M. Hill. Ascorbic acid content of adrenal glands of young albino rats after cold and other stresses. *Endocrinology, v. 46, June 1950: 526–535.*

Significant depletions of adrenal ascorbic acid were not obtained in 13-day-old rats subjected to cold (5°C) stress for 3 hours or for 1 hour with an indwelling rectal thermopile. The adrenals of 32-day-old rats, under the same conditions, showed significant depletion of ascorbic acid. The failure of cold stress to produce significant depletions of adrenal ascorbic acid in the 13-day-old rats—even though the rats were shown to experience a sizeable hypothermia and to be capable of participation in the "general alarm reaction" of Selye—was possibly due either to the immaturity of the thermoregulatory mechanism or to the fact that the temperature level was too low for proper enzymatic functioning in the production of corticosteroids.

945. **Malvestio, A.** Effects of unilateral suprarenalectomy in freezing [In Italian, summaries in French, Italian, English, and German]. *Arch. ital. med. sper., v. 3, 1938: 577–592.*

Ten to twenty days after unilateral suprarenalectomy, rabbits were exposed to cold, by immersion in water of −10°C in a room temperature of 17°–19°C, until they died. It was found that the suprarenalectomized animals experienced a more rapid fall in body temperature than the controls did; that they lived longer (av., 161 mins.), however, than did the normal animals (av., 149 mins.); but that at the time of death their rectal temperatures (av., 15.4°C) and the temperatures of various internal organs were lower than similar temperatures (av. rectal temp., 17.4°C) of the normal animals. Immediately after death the gross weights and dry weights of various organs (kidney, spleen, liver, muscle, brain) of the suprarenalectomized animals indicated a remarkable dehydration of the viscera. Also, the water content of the blood decreased at first but toward the close of the cooling period the content of water in the blood was remarkably high.

946. **Turner, M. L.** The effect of thyroxin and dinitrophenol on the thermal responses to cold. *Endocrinology, v. 38, May 1946: 263–269.*

Thyroxin decreased the fall in body temperature usually found in mice subjected for one hour to an environmental temperature of 5°C. Dinitrophenol in doses calorigenically equal to thyroxin had an opposite effect.

947. **Tyslowitz, R., and E. B. Astwood.** The influence of the pituitary and adrenal cortex on resistance to low environmental temperatures. *Am. J. Physiol., v. 136, Mar. 1942: 22–31.*

Hypophysectomized young rats were unable to maintain their body temperature when exposed to 0°C and showed an increasing sensitivity to cold over a period of time. Administration of pituitary extract or purified corticotrophin increased the cold resistance of these animals.

948. **Verzár, F., and V. Vidovic.** Inhibition of thyroid function in severe chilling [Abstract, in German]. *Helvet. physiol. pharm. acta, v. 9, June 1951: C13–C14.*

Rats were cooled until their rectal temperature had dropped to 15°–16°C and then were given an injection of radioactive iodine (I^{131}). The iodine did not collect in the thyroid gland but remained diffused through the whole blood circulation. When the body temperature had risen to above 30°C, in 12–24 hours, the iodine began to collect in the thyroid. In animals which were not cooled the iodine began to collect in the thyroid after 6 hours and was completely collected in 16–24 hours. These experiments show that in the great oxygen deficiency during cooling, the thyroid does not function; in consequence also the oxidation and oxygen need is very slight.

949. **Wada, M., and K. Fuzzi.** Effect of severe cold upon the rate of the denervated heart of non-anaesthetized dogs and the epinephrine secretion [In English]. *Tohoku J. Exp. M., v. 37, Feb. 29, 1940: 505–516.* Also, abstract in English, in: *Jap. J. M. Sc., Biophysics, v. 6, 1940: 116*.*

Two series of dogs with denervated hearts, one series also having had the suprarenals medullated, were cooled by immersion in ice water to below 30°C. The heart rate was first accelerated and then decreased in both sets of animals, along with the fall in body temperature. The magnitude of increase was great and decrease slight in animals with intact suprarenals as compared with demedullated animals. When removed from the ice water, animals with intact adrenals showed a return to basal heart rate at a lower temperature than did the demedullated dogs.

See also items: 557, 676, 980, 1347, 1366, 1367.

F. Metabolic Aspects

950.   Adolph, E. F. Oxygen consumption of hypothermic rats and acclimatization to cold. *Am. J. Physiol., v. 161, June 1, 1950: 359–373.*

Rats were held in cylinders, immersed in water or air of controlled temperatures, through which air was drawn. Oxygen consumption was studied by recording the oxygen pressures of effluent air flowing past the rat. When the cylinder was immersed in cold water, oxygen consumption increased two to two and a half times that at room temperature, and colonic temperature of the rat was decreased. Later the oxygen consumption decreased, and at a colonic temperature of 15 °C it tended toward zero. Pulse rate increased slightly at the beginning of cooling and then declined with colonic temperatures during cooling; oxygen consumption was depressed whenever the body temperature became higher than the colonic temperature. After an exposure at 4° to 10 °C for a week, rats had increased their mean basal oxygen consumption by 11% to 28% (tested at 28° to 32 °C air temperature), indicating their acclimatization to cold. However, the maximum oxygen consumption and the decrease of oxygen consumption with decreases of colonic temperature were not modified by this acclimatization.

951.   Adolph, E. F., and J. W. Lawrow. Acclimatization to cold air; hypothermia and heat production in the golden hamster. *Am. J. Physiol., v. 166, July 1, 1951: 62–74.*

Hamsters immersed in cold water (3 °C) for one hour had colonic temperatures of 3.4 °C or less. In order to study oxygen consumption, another group of hamsters were individually placed in a glass cylinder through which air was flowing and around which cold water (4°–10 °C) was circulated. No differences were found in mean frequency of deaths in the two groups when they were cooled to the same minimal colonic temperatures. Lethal colonic temperature (lethal core temperature) for 50% of the hamsters exposed was 3.8 °C; lethal core temperature of rats is usually 15.1 °C. Heat production, measured as oxygen consumption, was about equal at rest to that of rats. During sudden cooling it increased 6-fold and then diminished as colon temperature fell below 4 °C. Breathing frequency and heart beat frequency bore relations to oxygen consumption which were not constant during cooling. The paralysis of heat production by chilling, and also the rates of heat loss, were less in hamsters than they are in rats. Acclimatization of the hamsters after exposure for 6 days to cold air (4°–6 °C) was shown by increase in minimal oxygen consumption after cooling and the decrease again after 3 weeks of no cooling. No effects of acclimatization were apparent in rate or lower limit of colonic cooling, in maximum oxygen consumption during cooling, or in breathing or heart beat frequency.

952.   Bigelow, W. G., W. K. Lindsay, R. C. Harrison, R. A. Gordon, and W. F. Greenwood. Oxygen transport and utilization in dogs at low body temperatures. *Am. J. Physiol., v. 160, Jan. 1950: 125–137.*

The oxygen consumption of dogs which were cooled, under anesthesia, in a cold room to 18 °C, fell as the body temperature was reduced. In the subsequent rewarming process, oxygen consumption rose; the increase paralleled the temperature rise.

953.   Calogera, E. The behavior of heparin activity in heat shock and in freezing [In Italian, summaries in Italian and French]. *Fol. med., Nap., v. 34, Sept. 1951: 461–471.*

Along with a considerable review of the pertinent literature on blood changes during heat, shock or severe chilling, the author reports his own findings on the heparin activity of the blood of guinea pigs at or near death from heat or cold. In severe cooling, contrary to the expected results, there was little modification of the heparin activity of the blood.

954.   Cremer, H. D., K. Kramer, and H. Reichel. On the chemical changes in the blood during general cooling [In German]. *Klin. Wschr., v. 23, June 1944: 210–212.*

During acute cooling of dogs (by use of an ice bath), a condition of narcosis developed. During the early stages an increased oxygen consumption was accompanied by a heightening of the blood sugar content. This latter reached a maximum in the second phase of cooling, and returned to normal, or in some cases decreased drastically, in the last two phases. Correspondingly, in nearly all cases, the glycogen content of the liver was sharply decreased; that of the skeletal muscles was diminished, especially after long periods of shivering. In view of this accelerated use of hydrocarbons, it is questioned whether the doubtlessly occurring mobilization of the fat reserve might manifest itself in an alteration of the fat content in the blood. However, no alteration was noted on examination of the total fat fraction of the blood. The equilibrium between storage and consumption of fats appeared to be preserved even during periods of strong mobilization. Similar observations were made of lack of change in the blood-protein content, the blood corpuscle volume, and the sodium and chlorine concentrations of the blood.

955. Dybing, F. The blood alcohol curve in hypothermia [In English]. *Acta pharm. tox., Kbh., v. 1, May 5, 1945: 77–81.*

Albino rats were given ethyl alcohol in physiological saline solution, by injection into the femoral vein, and blood samples were taken from the heart every hour for the next 7 or 8 hours. One group of rats was kept at a room temperature of 20 °C; the other group was cooled by refrigeration to rectal temperatures of from 20° to 25 °C, and kept at that temperature by continued refrigeration except for the brief periods while blood samples were obtained. The fall in concentration of ethyl alcohol in the blood was much less in the rats kept in the cold, indicating that the oxidation rate of alcohol was inhibited by hypothermia.

956. Eröz, K., F. Özer, and H. Winterstein. Blood sugar and liver glycogen of cooled mammals [In German, with English summary]. *Arch. internat. pharm. dyn., Gand, v. 88, Oct. 1951: 63–83.*

Groups of guinea pigs, rabbits, and cats under Nembutal anesthesia were kept at a refrigerator temperature of 4 °C until their body temperatures reached 17°–23 °C. Other groups had the spinal cord severed at the level of the 6th cervical vertebra; the body temperature dropped 1°–2 °C above the room temperature within 4–5 hours. Blood and liver biopsy samples were taken to ascertain the blood sugar and liver glycogen levels. Artificial cooling, when muscle reactions were entirely eliminated, provoked a strong hyperglycemia; liver glycogen was unchanged or increased. If muscle shivering occurred, the blood sugar level was not changed in guinea pigs but was increased in cats with a decrease in liver glycogen. Injections of insulin were effective in bringing about a hypoglycemic effect in the cooled animals; injections of Adrenalin were apparently without effect. Hyperglycemia in cooled animals is the effect of the pouring forth of adrenaline by nervous reflex; after extirpation of the adrenal glands or resection of the splanchnic nerves this increase in blood sugar does not occur.

957. Fazekas, J. F., and H. E. Himwich. Effect of hypothermia on cerebral metabolism. *Proc. Soc. Exp. Biol., N. Y., v. 42, Nov. 1939: 537–538.*

Observations made on 9 dogs anesthetized with pentobarbital and packed in ice showed that the cerebral arteriovenous oxygen differences diminish as the rectal temperature falls, despite a slower circulation as evidenced by a decreased heart rate and a prolonged circulation time. Since a lower circulation rate would normally result in an increase in arteriovenous difference, with a constant cerebral metabolism rate, it is concluded that cerebral metabolism decreases as a result of the temperature drop.

958. Fuhrman, F. A., and J. M. Crismon. The influence of acute hypothermia on the rate of oxygen consumption and glycogen content of the liver, and on blood glucose. *Am. J. Physiol., v. 149, June 1947: 552–559.*

Adult white rats were cooled under light anesthesia until their respiration stopped. Studies on liver tissue taken from these rats indicated that oxygen consumption had not been significantly decreased by chilling but that the liver glycogen had been rapidly used. Animals which had been fasted could be chilled to 9.6 °C before respiration stopped; well-fed animals could be cooled only to 14.3 °C. Blood glucose was elevated in animals with ample supplies of carbohydrate while in fasted animals it fell.

959.   Fujimoto, T. On the change in the respiration and the gaseous metabolism of the rabbit caused by cooling the body [Abstract, in English]. *Jap. J. M. Sc., Biophysics, v. 6, 1940: 86*–87*.*

Rabbits were anesthetized with urethane, then each was fixed to a board and "the lower half of its body" was immersed in a water bath of 50 liters at varied temperatures: 30°, 20°, 10°, or 0°C. The body temperature lowered gradually even in the 30°C bath, but fastest in the coldest bath, and continued at a decreasing rate as the body remained in the bath. Lung ventilation and gaseous exchange increased until they reached the highest level when the body temperature was lowered to between 32° and 27°C, then decreased gradually reaching their original levels when the body temperature was approximately 21°C. At 18°C the respiratory function had diminished to about one-half, and at about 13°C the respiratory gas was almost impossible to collect accurately. The author concluded that the animal counteracts a severe loss of body heat by an increase in heat production, but that at a body temperature below 30°C this compensation ceases and the animal gradually dies from cold.

960.   Giaja, J. The defense role of hypothermia [In French]. *Bull. Acad. serbe sc., v. 1 (1), 1950: 107–112.*

Various experimental conditions—such as insulin shock, asphyxia from oxygen lack, or carbon dioxide intoxication—will produce in the rat a more or less profound hypothermia as a consequence of the slowing of the metabolism of the animal. If the rat is warmed, thereby imposing on it an intense increase in metabolism which the animal can not support, the result is often fatal. Hypothermia, in these conditions, can be said to play a protective role, prolonging the life of the animal by slowing the metabolic functioning.

961.   Giaja, J., and M. Stefanović. Relation between hypothermia and glycemia in asphyxia [Abstract, in French]. *C. rend. Acad. sc., Par., v. 232, Feb. 1951: 751–753.*

Asphyxia induced experimentally in rats by confining them in a closed chamber, caused glycemia and glycosuria. When, in addition, the rats were subjected to hypothermia, glycemia occurred in the range of 200 to 290 mg per cent as contrasted to around 100 mg per cent without hypothermia.

962.   Grossman, M. S., and K. E. Penrod. Relationship of hypothermia to high oxygen poisoning. *Am. J. Physiol., v. 156, Feb. 1949: 177–181.*

Rats cooled to rectal temperatures of 20°, 25°, and 30°C were subjected to 5.2 atmospheres of air pressure and 5.8 atmospheres of oxygen tension for 1 hour. Oxygen consumption increased above normal at a rectal temperature of 30°C, rose again at 25°C, but fell off sharply to below normal at rectal temperatures of 20°C. Survival rate of rats exposed to 5.8 atmospheres was so low as to obscure any effects of altered metabolism. A sharp difference was noted in survival of rats exposed to 5.2 atmospheres of air pressure and 5.8 atmospheres of oxygen tension.

963.   Hiestand, W. A., and H. R. Miller. Further observations on factors influencing hypoxic resistance of mice. *Am. J. Physiol., v. 142, Oct. 1944: 310–314.*

Hypoxic resistance of mice was increased in direct proportion as the temperature of the surrounding air was lowered (from 29.5° to 10°C). The explanation of the physiological effect of temperature on hypoxic resistance is probably that the rate of oxygen consumption is lowered by the decrease in metabolic rate accompanying the lowered body temperature.

964.   Levent, R. Cold and metabolism [In French]. *Gaz. hôp., v. 122, Apr. 1949: 215–216.*

Oxygen liberation, from oxyhemoglobin of the blood, was increasingly less as the body temperature was lowered. This was accompanied by some initial increase in the number of red blood cells; cellular fragility was an inconstant factor; the number of white blood cells decreased gradually as temperature decreased below a rectal temperature of 35°C. Severe and brief cooling did not affect the reserve glycogen; in prolonged and less severe cooling the glycogen reserves were depleted and there was a hyperglycemia, followed, with continued cooling, by a terminal hypoglycemia. At the German prison camp at Dachau the height of the hyperglycemia occurred at a rectal temperature of about 27.5 °C and this was also a period of glycosuria. Also the blood viscosity was increased at 35 °C rectal temperature and remained so as temperature was lowered.

965. Lutz, W. Experimental blood cooling of warm-blooded animals. A contribution to the mechanism of death by cold [In German]. *Klin. Wschr., v. 22, Dec. 19, 1943: 727–733.*

The role of oxygen consumption in the death of warm-blooded animals by cold exposure was investigated. It was found that test animals chilled under high oxygen pressure tolerated cold better than the controls. Making allowance for the deaths resulting from the toxic effects of the oxygen, it was concluded that the guinea pig with sufficient oxygen supply could survive a rectal temperature of 15 °C. The author notes that oxygen deficiency is the sole cause of hypothermic death.

966. Lutz, W., and R. von Werz. Death from cold and oxygen deficiency [In German]. *Med. Zschr., v. 1, Jan. 1945: 133–134.*

A lowered oxygen content was observed in the blood of animals cooled for one hour to a body temperature of 16 °C. On rewarming the animal the blood oxygen content rose. Studies on lethal cooling lead to the conclusion that death results from a progressive degradation of cellular metabolism.

967. Malorny, G. Relationship between the gaseous content of body tissues and the body temperature [In German]. *Arch. exp. Path., Berl., v. 208 (2–3), 1949: 205–207.*

A pocket of nitrogen gas was introduced into the body of animals (guinea pigs, rats, or rabbits) either subcutaneously or intraperitoneally. After the diffusion balance had been established, microtonometrical tests were made from these gas samples. The body temperature was altered by hot or cold baths. At a body temperature below 25 °C the initial increase in O_2 tension was followed regularly by a tension drop in the pneumoperitoneum, in some cases to 30% of the initial value; in the subcutaneous bubble, after some delay a severe oxygen insufficiency was noted under conditions of hypothermia. In cases of extreme hypothermia the CO_2 tension usually increased, partly due to insufficient alkalinity in the hemoglobin of the capillaries, and partly to a circulatory deficiency. The oxyhemoglobin was unable to give off its oxygen at low body temperature, and to offer alkaline equivalents for the fixation of CO_2. At a rectal temperature of 20°–24 °C the venous blood of rabbits showed a very diminished oxygen; the arterial oxygen content was usually increased but occasionally was decreased. After a brief increase in blood sugar, hypothermia induced in guinea pigs a pronounced hypoglycemia in the blood, while the lactic acid content doubled or tripled due to the predominance of anaerobic conditions. A pronounced increase in the carbonic acid anhydrase content of the blood was found when hypothermia had lasted 2–6 hours. The increased CO_2 and diminished O_2 tensions in the subcutaneous tissue, and in the peritoneal space, are typical for the occurrence of thermic collapse. All the temperature-conditioned changes proved to be reversible after return to normal conditions and a certain period of latency; the CO_2 tension returned rather rapidly to normal, the O_2 tension after several hours. It was assumed that the gaseous content of the tissues can serve as an indicator for the determination of a state of thermal collapse.

968. Ogata, K., M. Takeuti, M. Masaki, and T. Kiyonaga. Influence of the exposure to cold and the inhalation of cold air on the regulation of body temperature [Abstract, in English]. *Jap. J. Med. Sc., Biophysics, v. 7, 1941: 45*–46*.*

In men exposed to temperatures ranging from -2 °C to -20 °C, increase of metabolism due to cold was reflexively controlled by skin sensations. Fall of body temperature appears to have less influence on rate of O_2 consumption. Alternate exposure to cold and moderate temperature results in an increase of oxygen consumption.

969. Onti, T. Influence of cold upon the blood sugar level in a cat under insulin [In English]. *Tohoku J. Exp. M., v. 41, Oct. 31, 1941: 97–101.*

Insulinized cats (3 to 4 units/kg body weight), were placed in a cold-water bath. The body temperature fell within a half hour from 31 °C to 26.6 °C; blood-sugar level increased; and shivering took place. These phenomena took place in both normal cats and in ones in which the suprarenal medulla had previously been rendered functionless.

970. Penrod, K. E., and F. R. Rosenhain. Blood gas content of dogs during immersion hypothermia [Abstract]. *Fed. Proc., Balt., v. 8, Mar. 1949: 126.*

Studies were made on the blood gas content of dogs breathing air, and on a second series breathing 100% oxygen, before and during immersion in an iced bath. In 7 out of 9 dogs beginning circulatory inadequacy was not yet evident at 20 °C rectal temperature. In the series breathing pure oxygen, 4 of 9 dogs showed some respiratory failure above 25 °C; circulatory impairment was evident in only 1 dog at 25 °C.

971. Penrod, K. E. Oxygen consumption and cooling rates in immersion hypothermia in the dog. *Am. J. Physiol., v. 157, June 1949: 436–444.*

Seven anesthetized dogs were each cooled twice in an ice and water bath to rectal temperatures of 20 °C and then rewarmed in room air at 25° to 28 °C or warm water at 40° to 42 °C. Oxygen consumption and rates of temperature change were recorded continuously. Oxygen consumption varied directly with the shivering response which occurred between 24° to 28 °C rectal temperature.

972. Penrod, K. E. Oxygen partial pressures during hypothermia in the dog [Abstract]. *Fed. Proc., Balt., v. 9, Mar. 1950: 99.*

In studying the role of hypoxia in hypothermic deaths, the comparative values of oxygen consumption, oxygen content of coronary sinus blood, and of internal jugular blood were measured in dogs under hypothermic conditions. No results are given here.

973. Penrod, K. E., and J. Flynn. Cardiac oxygenation during severe hypothermia in dogs. *Am. J. Physiol., v. 164, Jan. 1, 1951: 79–85.*

Coronary blood of dogs was collected by syringe after surgical opening of the chest and puncture of the circumflex artery; simultaneously, arterial blood was taken from the carotid artery. Approximately 15 minutes before drawing of blood, the dogs were connected to a large spirometer by endotracheal tube and the inspired gas was varied from 100% oxygen to very low oxygen in nitrogen. Blood samples (38 °C) were collected at room temperature and after the dogs were immersed in an ice bath to the shoulders; other samples (20 °C) were taken. The samples were tested, by the Van Slyke apparatus, for hemoglobin dissociation and curves were plotted. These curves superimposed on those of earlier workers (Brown and Hill, 1922–23) whose curve for dissociation of blood at 20 °C was obtained after *in vitro* chilling of the sample. No support was found in these studies for the contention that the heart is unable to remove oxygen from the blood when the blood temperature is chilled to 20 °C.

974. Ramazzotti, P. Behavior of glycemia in experimental cooling [In Italian]. *Gior. clin. med., v. 25, Jan. 20, 1944: 76–82.*

Experimental animals, exposed constantly to the intense cold of a water bath, were found to have significant individual fluctuations in their blood sugar concentration after 5 and after 30 minutes. After 3 hours, there was a definite increase in blood sugar concentration in the entire group; after 6 hours, a decrease. The rectal temperature, except for a slight rise within the first few minutes, dropped throughout the experiment.

975. Rodbard, S. Relationship between body temperature and blood sugar in the chicken. *Am. J. Physiol., v. 150, July 1947: 67–69.*

Cooling of chickens, by ice pack, from the normal body temperature of 41.5 °C resulted in a fall in blood sugar which was progressive with cooling and at 25 °C resulted in a value which was 65% of control levels. On rewarming by radiant heat, the value became almost normal at 40°C, then rose on continued warming until at 44°C it was 26% above normal. This was approximately the range of temperature for survival of the animals. Response of blood sugar to body temperature changes lagged by about 30 minutes while blood pressure changes (item 927) had been found to occur within a few seconds of the temperature stimulus.

976. Rodbard, S., and M. S. Goldstein. Neurogenic control of the blood sugar elicited by induced variations in the body temperature of the chick. *Am. J. Physiol., v. 162, July 1, 1950: 175–181.*

Lowering of the body temperature (from 41.5° to 25°C) of the intact chick by packing it in chipped ice for about 90 minutes, brought about a fall in blood sugar level. Rewarming by radiant heat brought a return to normal levels. Abdominal bilateral vagotomy inhibited this thermoglycemic relationship; atropine induced a transient hyperglycemia but did not clearly block it; alloxanization or pancreatectomy did not inhibit it, indicating that the pancreas was not involved. It is assumed that the vagal nuclei operate through some other structure in the abdominal area to effect this fall in blood sugar level induced by hypothermia.

977. Rosenhain, F. R., and K. E. Penrod. Blood gas studies in the hypothermic dog. *Am. J. Physiol., v. 166, July 1951: 55–61.*

Observations were made of the gaseous content of simultaneously drawn arterial and mixed venous blood of dogs during hypothermia. The dogs were immersed to the neck in ice-water (2°–5°C) baths and the determinations of the gaseous content of the blood were made at rectal temperatures between 38° and 20°C while the dogs breathed either room air or 100 percent oxygen. It was observed that the metabolic demands of the animal, though greatly reduced, were adequate until near the point of final collapse. Decline of all functions of the body would appear to be such that death could be precipitated by any of several failures.

978. Rossoni, V. Changes in the blood sugar level in experimental hypothermia [In Italian]. *Ann. ital. chir., v. 25, Feb. 1948: 124–128.*

In hypothermia in rabbits, which was induced by immersing them in ice-cold water for 12 hours, there was a constant hypoglycemia due to an increase in oxidative processes.

979. Russell, J. A., and M. Cappiello. The relationship of temperature and insulin dosage to the rise in plasma amino nitrogen in the eviscerated rat. *Endocrinology, v. 44, Feb. 1949: 127–133.*

The amino nitrogen content of the plasma of eviscerated rats maintained at environmental temperatures of 38°C increased an average of 14 mg/100 cc in 3 hours. At environmental temperatures of 29°C, the increase was reduced to 6 mg/100 cc. From 10 to 50 times as much insulin appears to be required to prevent the increase of the plasma amino nitrogen at body temperature of 38°C as at temperatures below 30°C.

980. Šahović, K., and B. Oreščanin. Contribution to the physiopathology of the hypothermia of homeotherms; effect of deep hypothermia on glycemia; effect of Adrenalin, insulin, and adrenalectomy [In Serbo-Crotian, summary in French]. *Glas Srpske akad. nauka, odelj. med., v. 204 (4), 1951: 87–97.*

A profound hypothermia, accompanied by hypoglycemia (52–54 mg %), occurred in rats upon exposure to a cold environment (2°–4°C). The extent of hypoglycemia was not dependent on the degree of hypothermia but on the duration of exposure to the cold. In animals given Adrenalin while subjected to cold the hypoglycemia produced (45–47 mg %) was similar to that of the normal, untreated, animals. In animals given insulin, while being exposed to cold, the degree of hypoglycemia (27-22-18 mg %) was greater than under either condition alone. Ablation of the adrenal capsule produced in some of the animals a hypoglycemia but without hypothermia; upon exposure to cold the hypoglycemia was found to be in the range of 41-37 mg %. In most of these surgically-treated animals, however, on exposure to cold the range was 69-57 mg %. Again the extent of hypoglycemia did not depend on the degree of hypothermia. Under the conditions of the experiment, the lowest values in hypoglycemic states were obtained under the combined influence of insulin and cold.

981.   Samaras, K. The influence of cold on carbohydrate metabolism [In German]. *Zschr. ges. exp. Med., v. 106, Oct. 10, 1939: 510–520.*

Rats chilled to a body temperature below 22 °C showed an increased blood sugar level.

982.   Sarzana, G. On the energetic material utilized by the pigeon in its defense against lowering of temperature [In Italian]. *Arch. fisiol., Fir., v. 38, 1938–1939: 514–532.*

Metabolic studies were made of pigeons while they were maintained in a neutral thermic (29 °C) environment, or in a cold environment (13° to 3 °C or 7° to 3 °C). Similar studies were made after the pigeons had been fed 4–8 g. of glucose. A comparison of respiratory quotients showed that the average figure for the portion attributable to the cold was 0.82 whether the pigeon had been fasted or had been fed sugar. It would appear from the findings that the increased metabolism of the pigeon during exposure to cold was independent of the nutritional state so far as glucose was concerned, but that it might indicate a slightly increased use of fat.

983.   Staudinger, H., and I. Haenel-Immendörfer. The carbohydrate content under the influence of cold [In German]. *Beit. path. Anat., v. 109, Sept. 28, 1944: 409–436.*

Studies were made of the glycogen content of the heart, liver, muscle, and diaphragm, and of the blood sugar and lactic acid content of the blood of guinea pigs, in order to study the effect of cold on carbohydrate metabolism. The animals were exposed to acute cold by being kept either in a water bath (15 °C) until the body temperature dropped to 22°–24 °C and remained at this level for 5½ hours, or by being kept in a cold room (3°–5 °C) for 6 hours. In chronic exposure to cold, the animals were kept at a room temperature of 17 °C for a long period. Under conditions of acute chilling, the carbohydrate reserves of the body were maintained, but under prolonged cooling they were depleted and hypoglycemia resulted. The glycogen content of the heart was reduced in both types of experiments, owing to the increased activity.

984.   Steadman, L. T., I Ariel, and S. L. Warren. Studies on the effect of hypothermia. IV. The rise of serum magnesium in rabbits during the hypothermic states as shown by the spectrochemical method. *Cancer Res., v. 3, July 1943: 471–474.*

Spectrochemical analyses were made on the blood of rabbits subjected to experimental hypothermia. It was observed that serum magnesium showed a rise of 24% above initial values after the rabbits had been in the hypothermic state (body temperature, 13°–22 °C) for 2 or 5 hours. There did not seem to be any relationship between the serum magnesium levels or their change, and the duration or the level of the low temperature.

985.   Streicher, E., D. B. Hackel, and W. Fleischmann. Effects of extreme cold on the fasting pigeon with a note on the survival of fasting ducks at −40 °C. *Am. J. Physiol., v. 161, May 1, 1950: 300–306.*

Fasting pigeons were able to survive from 48 to 144 hours at −40 °C. The metabolic rate was increased approximately four times the normal resting level, and this increased rate was maintained until the termination of the survival period. The blood glucose levels, as observed at intervals between 1 and 72 hours of exposure, were not significantly different from the levels of pigeons kept at room temperature. The liver glycogen decreased after 8 hours of exposure to cold; at room temperature it did not show a comparable decrease until 24 hours after the fasting was begun. Death was caused more quickly in pigeons who were exposed to winds of 3 m.p.h., in addition to the cold exposure, than it did in pigeons exposed to cold alone. Body temperature of plucked pigeons, placed in the same cold environment, dropped rapidly and death occurred within 20 to 30 minutes. Four fasting ducks, exposed to −40°C, survived from 7 to over 16 days.

986. Sturkie, P. D. Effects of hypothermia upon the specific gravity and proteins of the blood of chickens. *Am. J. Physiol., v. 148, Mar. 1947: 610–613.*

Hypothermia was brought about in white hens by suspending them to the level of the neck in cold water, for periods of ½ to 6¼ hours. At the end of the periods the body temperatures were 36.1°-23.9°C. Plasma proteins before hypothermia averaged 4.308 grams %; after hypothermia, 4.797; and after warming for 1 to 5 hours they averaged the same or slightly lower than the original sample.

987. van Harreveld, A., and D. B. Tyler. The influence of temperature on spinal cord damage caused by asphyxiation. *Am. J. Physiol., v. 142, Aug. 1944: 32–39.*

Ringer's solution was forced, under pressure higher than blood pressure, into the isolated caudal part of the spinal dural cavity of the tails of cats, interrupting the blood circulation in the cord and causing local asphyxiation. The caudal part of the cord and dural cavity had previously been isolated by surgical procedure at the level of Th 10–12. The cord, as indicated by reflex activity, was seriously impaired in animals when the asphyxiation was for a period of 35 minutes at a body temperature of 38°C; in 6 animals there was no flexion reflex, only traces of knee jerk in 1 animal, and tail movement could be elicited only by pinching. In 4 out of 6 animals, when the period of asphyxiation was 120 minutes, with the animal held at a rectal temperature of 27°C, the flexion and tail reflexes were present. Metabolic and histological studies done after sacrifice of the cats 5 days after asphyxiation, also showed more severe damage after 35 minutes asphyxiation at 38°C than after 120 minutes asphyxiation at 27°C.

988. Vinokurov, S. I., and O. Sidorova. The dehydrating capacity of hepatic tissue, and the reduction of dehydro-ascorbic acid, from cooled animals [In Russian, with English summary]. *Biokhem. Zh., v. 19, 1940: 361–367.*

The dehydrating capacity of pieces of hepatic tissue from rats was studied, by Thunberg's method, after the animals had been put into a hypothermic condition by exposure to an environmental temperature of 0° to −11°C. Hypothermia was found to induce a decrease in the dehydrating capacity of the hepatic tissue at the expense of the thermolabile part of the dehydrogenase system. The thermostable part of the system (codehydrogenase) did not change. At the same time the restoration of the dehydro-ascorbic acid in the tissue was also diminished. Further study is needed to determine whether these phenomena are connected by a causal relationship, or whether they are merely coexistent.

989. Williams, J. N., Jr., P. E. Schurr, and C. A. Elvehjem. Influence of chilling and exercise on free amino acid concentrations in rat tissues. *J. Biol. Chem., v. 182, Jan. 1950: 55–59.*

A study of the free (microbiologically available) amino acids in the tissues and body fluids of rats following either exercise or chilling (−5°C for 6 hours) showed the greatest changes to be in the plasma amino acids and the least in the brain tissues. In all of the tissues studied leucine and valine increased during exercise; otherwise, no consistent changes were observed. In general, the effect of chilling tended to be in the same direction as that of exercise but not to be as pronounced.

990. Wolff, R. C., and K. E. Penrod. Effect of altered metabolism on extreme hypothermia in dogs and albino rats [Abstract]. *Fed. Proc., Balt., v. 8, Mar. 1949: 170.*

Studies were made on the metabolism of rats fed propylthiouracil or thyroid extract for varying periods of time. These rats together with controls were cooled by immersion to the shoulders in water of 7°C. The rate of cooling for dogs in a water bath of 4°C, time of rewarming in air and water to 34 °C, and oxygen consumption were measured in six dogs. The results suggest that during immersion in very cold water the metabolic defenses do not give adequate protection.

See also items: 76, 463, 532, 533, 904, 924, 937, 995, 1485, 1543, 1604, 2136.

G. Effects on Drug Action

991. Anon. Delayed morphine poisoning. *Bull. U.S. Army M. Dep.*, no. 74, Mar. *1944: 5.* Also in: *Anesthesiology, v. 5, May 1944: 273.*

In shock or with low blood pressure from other causes, and subsequent chilling, morphine has been found not to be absorbed and to produce no clinical response. Warning is given of administration of a second dose in these circumstances, e.g. under battlefield conditions, since on rewarming or recovery from shock and return of a normal circulatory state an excessive amount of morphine may then be absorbed.

992. Barrows, E. F., and M. Dobbs. Body temperature of mice during anesthesia. *Am. J. Physiol., v. 137, Sept. 1, 1942: 259–262.*

In mice less than 3 weeks old resistance to death by ether or chloroform anesthesia was greater the younger the animals were. Tests at environmental temperatures of 22°, 28°, 35°, or 40°C showed that this resistance increased with the coldness of the environment. No significant differences were observed in two homozygous strains of mice. It is known experimentally that mice do not acquire complete ability to maintain a uniform body temperature against external changes until after the second, and possibly the third, week of life. The observations from this study support the theory that a fall in internal temperature is the principal cause of the slower effectiveness of the anesthetics.

993. Bernardini, R. Experimental studies on the action of sulfur during freezing [In Italian, summaries in Italian, French, English, and German]. *Arch. ital. med. sper., v. 5, 1939: 825–836.*

Rabbits were given sulfur intraperitoneally, both in an oil mixture and as elementary sulfur, before exposure to severe cold. At the death of the animals, subcutaneous temperature and the temperatures of various internal organs and their weights were determined. The duration of life was shortened by treatment with either form of sulfur. The temperatures at death were higher after treatment with the sulfur in oil mixture, than in the normal animals, possibly because an initial slight hyperthermia immediately after treatment interfered with the hypothermia; and lower than normal with elementary sulfur. Neither the degree of decrease of the body temperature nor the levels of the blood sugar concentration varied in either group from those of the normal group.

994. Costanzo, F. Hypothermal reactivity and thionine [In Italian, summaries in Italian, English, French, and German]. *Pat. sper., Tor., v. 35, 1947: 81–96.*

Guinea pigs repeatedly exposed to an environmental temperature of −2°C for 30 minutes, after injection of thionine solution, were found to be more sensitive to the cold. The initial hyperthermic reaction did not occur, the temperature decrease was more pronounced and lower, and the return to normal temperature was slower on return to room temperature than that of untreated guinea pigs. These changes are assumed to be due to the diminution of neuro-vegetative ortho-sympathetic tonus as a result of treatment with thionine.

995. Elliott, H. W., and J. M. Crismon. Increased sensitivity of hypothermic rats to injected potassium and the influence of calcium, digitalis, and glucose on survival. *Am. J. Physiol., v. 151, Dec. 1947: 366–372.*

Both potassium (K) and calcium (Ca) concentrations increased in the blood plasma of rats subjected to hypothermia, but the rise of Ca was smaller than that of K and the Ca/K ratio was reduced. An unfavorable Ca/K ratio may contribute to cardiac failure and death from hypothermia. Intravenous injection of KCl in amounts which produced only transient effects at normal body temperatures, were fatal at body temperatures of 22°–25°C. Injection of CaCl or ouabain and administration of glucose by mouth (previously shown to lower lethal temperature) protected the animals against doses of KCl usually fatal at low temperatures. CaCl injection during cooling permitted survival to lower body temperatures.

996. Fuhrman, F. A., J. M. Crismon, G. J. Fuhrman, and J. Field. The effect of temperature on the inactivation of epinephrine in vivo and in vitro. *J. Pharm. Exp. Ther., v. 80, Apr. 1944: 323–334.*

This is a report of studies on the effect of reduced body temperature on the inactivation of epinephrine. Parallel *in vitro* experiments on the rate of oxidation of epinephrine by amine oxidase at graded temperatures showed that this phenomenon could be described by the Arrhenius equation. *In vivo* experiments were performed on hypothermic cats where the rate of epinephrine inactivation was measured by its effect on the nictitating membrane. It was shown that in the cooled body the rate of inactivation was slowed. The possible clinical implications are discussed.

997. Fuhrman, F. A. The effect of body temperature on drug action. *Physiol. Rev., v. 26, Apr. 1946: 247–274.*

The literature is reviewed on the effect upon drug action in (a) homeotherms at varied levels of environmental temperature, (b) in both homeotherms and poikilotherms at varied body temperatures, and (c) in isolated organs and tissues at graded temperature levels. There is also considerable study of the effect of drugs, such as natural and synthetic hormones, and various anesthetics—which generally suppress the reflex responses to cold—, on temperature regulation. The author restates the opinion of an earlier worker that the action of a drug must be defined as the reaction of the drug and tissues of the body at a certain temperature.

998. Fuhrman, F. A. The effect of body temperature on the duration of barbiturate anaesthesia in mice. *Science, v. 105, Apr. 11, 1947: 387–388.*

Mice treated with barbital, pentobarbital, or Sandoptal injections, and then maintained at temperatures of 35°–37°C, or 25°–27°C, showed a significant increase in the duration of action of both pentobarbital and Sandoptal. The author states that barbiturates which are inactivated in the tissues (pentobarbital and Sandoptal) can be expected to have prolonged action if the body temperature is reduced, while those excreted by the kidney (barbital) will be little affected by changes in body temperature.

999. Grosse-Brockhoff, F., and W. Schoedel. On the effect of analeptics on supercooled animals [In German]. *Arch. exp. Path., Berl., v. 201, June 12, 1943: 443–456.*

The possible therapeutic effects of Cardiazol, Coramine, lobeline, and strychnine were tested on dogs chilled by immersion in cold water for 3 to 7 hours to a body temperature of 30°C. Coramine and lobeline in doses tolerated by normal control animals produced arrhythmia, slowed the heart, and lowered blood pressure. This effect apparently resulted from a heightened sensitivity of the chilled heart to vagus impulses.

1000. Günther, B., and Y. Navarro. Toxicity of caffeine in relation to weight of body and to ambient temperature [In Spanish]. *Rev. Soc. argent. biol., v. 22, May 1946: 35–43.*

The toxicity of caffeine for rats or mice was greatly increased at a low environmental temperature (10°–12°C) over that at a temperature of 30°C. Caffeine is thought to act on temperature regulation causing a loss of heat, even though the animal's metabolism is very intense, and resulting in acute hypothermia and death of the animal.

1001.   Hazard, R., J. Cheymol, and A. Quinquaud. Impairment and reversal of toxic apnea in hypothermia [In French]. *C. rend. Soc. biol., Par., v. 137, Feb. 1943: 85–86.*

At normal body temperatures, a group of hyperthermic chemical substances hindered the apnea caused by Adrenalin and reversed the apnea—to a state of polypnea—caused by yohimbine. When dogs, which were anesthetized with chloralase, were made hypothermic by being packed in ice, the two alkaloids again hindered and reversed respectively the apnea condition, but with considerably different effects on the respiratory rhythm. Given by injection into the renal vein, yohimbine slowed the respiration at a normal temperature level; below 35 °C it provoked a reversal and accelerated the respiratory rate as much as three times. Given following the administration of the hyperthermic, methylene blue, the acceleration was of the same order but began at a lower temperature (just above 23 °C); however, at the lowest level of the experiment (about 21.5 °C), the respiratory rate dropped to 10%. Adrenalin gave quite different results in that apnea was more pronounced as the temperature lowered, and the giving of yohimbine did not reverse the condition for very long periods. The occasional very short periods of polypnea which could be produced disappeared more frequently as body temperature dropped below 30 °C. At any time the polypnea did not continue very long and the rhythm was maintained unchanged. With yohimbine controlling the impairing action of Adrenalin, methylene blue reacts more or less feebly; at about 30 °C, Adrenalin caused stoppages in breathing of long duration such as 80 seconds at 30 °C for a dog weighing 5 kg or 100 seconds in a lighter-weight fox. At lowered body temperatures the reversal of the apnea, or increase of respiratory rate, from yohimbine did not change much when it followed an injection with methylene blue; the apnea from Adrenalin was impaired by yohimbine but persisted after the methylene blue.

1002.   Hemingway, A. The effect of barbital anesthesia on temperature regulation. *Am. J. Physiol., v. 134, Sept. 1941: 350–358.*

In a cool environment of 22 °C and 50% relative himidity, dogs were allowed to rest until shivering and vasoconstriction appeared. Animals were then heated by diathermy until shivering was inhibited and vasodilatation occurred. It was found that amytal and pentobarbital anesthesia suppressed shivering and vasomotor thresholds. Barbital anesthesia in surgical doses was found to suppress responses to cold without entirely inhibiting them.

1003.   Jarisch, A. Effects of medication on cold injuries [In German]. *Klin. Wschr., v. 23, June 1944: 213–215.*

A toxicity of up to 10 times that under normal conditions was found in hypothermic rats for Cardiazol, Coramine, strychnine, and caffeine. The author explains this as resulting from a restriction of the peripheral circulation which causes the substances to be distributed over a smaller body mass; a metabolic slow-down of detoxification in the cooled body; and, most important, to the heightened excitability of the spinal-cord reflexes in cold. The respiratory center was found to be particularly sensitive. Small doses of analeptics were found to have little therapeutic effect on hypothermic rabbits (rectal temperature, 23 °C). Respiration of carbon dioxide (6.3%) was found to be effective. Water of 45°–50 °C was poured over the hypothermic animals and found to cause strong respiration. Muscular rigidity in the intensely cooled underarm of subjects was found to be uninfluenced by aspirin, Pyramidon, antipyrin, muscle adenyl phosphoric acid, and nitrite. Quick heating was found effective in restoring the functioning of muscles. In mice, cold resistance was increased by previous bathing in water at 5 °C until their rectal temperature was 15 °C. Histamine raised the resistance of mice 150% for about 10 days. The author questions the value of cold-protective salves but suggests that the hyperemic action to substances, such as camphor, contained in them may be beneficial.

1004.   Killian, H. Interference of chilling and anaesthesia [In German]. *Arch. klin. Chir., v. 266 (6), 1951: 650–664.*

The interaction of cooling and narcosis, as shown by experimental results of the author and others, is discussed in some detail. Some of the effects on the metabolism and on the circulatory, respiratory, and nervous systems of this interaction are noted. Since the normal protective reactions of the organism against cooling are absent during narcosis, only light narcosis should be used when the body temperature is below normal or until the heart action, circulation, and respiration have returned to approximately normal. The danger of the use of narcotics during hypothermia is emphasized with the warning that this interaction had previously been underestimated.

1005. Leser, A. J., C. H. Thienes, and D. B. Tyler. Effect of low body temperature on toxicity of drugs. *Proc. Soc. Exp. Biol., N. Y., v. 45, Nov. 1940: 682–684.*

Cooling of mice (to body temperatures of 18°–20°C) by use of air currents after the animals were wetted by alcohol or water, brought about an increased mortality following injection of toxic doses of strychnine, nicotine, Amphetamine, cocaine, and procaine. There was no marked difference with Metrazol and morphine. However, in the cooled animals there was a prolongation of the survival time.

1006. Shaw, F. H., and K. J. Shankly. Factors affecting the duration of Nembutal anesthesia in rats. *Austral. J. Exp. Biol., v. 26, Nov. 1948: 481–491.*

A significant difference was shown between the slopes of the regression lines of dosage-response and log dosage-response curves for Nembutal anesthesia at different levels of body temperature (32°C to 40°C; normal, 36°C) of normal adult white rats. It is inferred from the curves that low dosages of Nembutal are more effective at high body temperatures and high dosages at low body temperatures. Tabulations show that a low dosage of Nembutal anesthetized a smaller percentage of the rats at low environmental temperature than the same dose did at higher temperature. For a given dosage of Nembutal the mortality rate varies over a range of temperature. For a dosage of 7.0 mg/100 mg body weight, the lowest mortality was at a temperature of 37.5°–39.0°C, with increased mortality at temperatures down to 32°C and decidedly increased mortality above 39°C.

1007. Stormont, R. T., and W. E. Hook. Effect of convulsants at low body temperature [Abstract]. *J. Pharm. Exp. Ther., v. 72, May 1941: 40.*

Cats, under sodium barbital anesthesia, were kept at a room temperature of 40°C and their body temperatures were reduced to, and maintained at, 20° to 23°C. Picrotoxin, Metrazol, or strychnine was administered intravenously to both the cooled animals and control animals (37° to 39°C, body temperature). The lethal dose of picrotoxin in cooled animals was approximately the same; strychnine was slightly more toxic in cooled animals. In cooled animals convulsions were much less severe but were greatly prolonged; survival time of cooled animals averaged eighteen times that of controls.

1008. Tournade, A., M. Chevillot, and G. Chardon. Exaggeration of the physiologic effects of acetylcholine in the dog under the influence of cold [In French]. *C. rend. Soc. biol., Par., v. 128, May 14, 1938: 166–167.*

The authors found that lowering the body temperature of the dog to about 30° accentuated the heart-slowing effects of intravenous injection of a weak dosage of acetylcholine. The effect is in accord with the theory that the pneumogastric and vasodilatory nerves exercise an inhibitory action upon the heart muscle in the presence of acetylcholine.

1009. Tyler, D. B. Effect of cooling on the mechanism of insulin action. *Proc. Soc. Exp. Biol., N. Y., v. 42, Oct. 1939: 278–280.*

The effects of lethal doses of insulin on the survival period of cooled and non-cooled rabbits and on the effect of temperature on insulin action, were studied. Administration of glucose to hypoglycemic animals resulted in a rise in their body temperature; insulin hypoglycemia was prolonged by cooling the animal; the survival time of rabbits receiving lethal doses of insulin was prolonged by cooling to temperatures below 30°C. In woodchucks, when enough insulin was given to produce hypoglycemia, the animal lost its ability to control temperature and went into "artificial hibernation". The author states that his results give support to a thesis that available glucose is essential for the maintenance of normal body temperature.

See also items: 313, 378, 414, 468, 491, 493, 495, 500, 512, 516, 521, 534, 542, 841, 880, 890, 979, 1530, 2132.

H. Prophylaxis and Therapy

1010. Anon. Cold exposure treatment. *Bull. U.S. Army M. Dep.*, *v. 6, Nov. 1946: 511–512.*

The danger of rapid rewarming of survivor of hypothermia has been disproved. Persons in severe hypothermic states should be rapidly rewarmed, preferably by a warm bath, until the rectal temperature begins to rise; after this time more gradual rewarming is indicated. If the person rescued from cold water immersion and with a rectal temperature below 80.6°F is unconscious but breathing, he should be rescued from the water, placed in a bath of 115°–120°F for 10 minutes, then dried with a towel and placed in warmed blankets. If the temperature does not rise at least 2°F every 10 minutes, the baths should be repeated until the rectal temperature reaches 93°F. If conscious, the survivor should be immersed first in water of 105°–110°F for 10 minutes and then treated as above. Water heated to 115°F is painful to a conscious patient and may cause some scalding in hypothermic persons with rectal temperatures above 91°F. Survivors exposed to moderately cold temperature for relatively long periods should be rewarmed much more slowly, preferably by use of electric blankets or heating pads or light cradles. Massaging is to be avoided. Drugs, such as Strophanthin, digitalis, Metrazol, lobeline, Coramine, and alcohol are of no value and are likely to be harmful. Administration of 100% oxygen at atmospheric pressure should be advantageous in supplying dissolved oxygen independent of that from hemoglobin dissociation in the blood, the latter being retarded by cold. The rationale of the treatment outlined is said to be that blood volume is reduced in cooling by the general constriction of the vascular bed to force fluids into the tissues, and that relaxation of the peripheral vascular bed by warming allows the ready return of the fluids to the circulation.

1011. Anon. Evaluation of methods of rewarming men. *Bull. U.S. Army M. Dep.*, *v. 9, May 1949: 443.*

Studies were made of the relative efficiency of various methods for rewarming men exposed to cold. Tests were made of increasing metabolism, ambient temp., and insulation. Walking at 3.5 miles per hr. on a 6.5% grade was found to be the most effective method; the next best was selective heating of face and hands. Repeated short periods of exposure to environmental cold used in this experiment did not produce evidence of acclimatization to cold in terms of cooling curves.

1012. Ames, A., III, R. S. Griffith, D. A. Goldthwait, M. B. Macht, and H. S. Belding. A study of various methods of rewarming men after exposure to extreme cold [Abstract]. *Fed. Proc., Balt.*, *v. 7, Mar. 1948: 2–3.*

Tests were made of the relative efficiency of rewarming men exposed to 40°F for 1 hour, rewarming for 1 hour, then re-exposing to the low temperature for another hour. Measured by the change in total body heat the various rewarming methods were efficient in the following order: (1) strenuous exercise (2) ambient temperature of 90°F (3) sleeping bag (4) ambient temperature of 40°F (5) moderate exercise (6) irradiation of face (7) irradiation of hands.

1013. Andjus, R. The possibility of resuscitating an adult rat chilled almost to the point of freezing [In French]. *C. rend. Acad. sc., Par.*, *v. 232, Apr. 23, 1951: 1591–1593.*

Rats were cooled by a combination of low environmental temperature (15°C), and of the progressive hypoxia from being kept in a closed space without additional air. Under such conditions, the body temperature dropped to approximately 20°C in about 2 hours; respiration ceased at about 9°C; and the heart ceased to beat at about 6°C. Immediate rewarming of the whole body and artificial respiration did not revive the rats. The author perfected a technique of first rewarming the heart only, by application of the flame-warmed flattened end of a metal probe to the moist skin in the cardiac area of the chest, followed later by insufflation of air and occasionally of carbon dioxide by rubber tube directly into the external nares. This was accompanied by occasional pressure on the chest wall for compression of the thoracic cage. At about 15°C, when respiratory movements had become spontaneous, further rewarming was done by immersion of the whole body in a warm water bath. Rats which had been cooled to temperatures of 7°–9°C have been satisfactorily and permanently revived by this method; rats cooled to about 1°C have been revived but they have survived at most only a few days.

1014. Barbour, H. G., E. A. McKay, and W. P. Griffith. An approach to the use of drugs in hypothermia. *Yale J. Biol., v. 16, Jan. 1944: 231–238.*

Studies were made on the effects of drugs on rats and monkeys chilled to deep hypothermia. In rats chilled to 16°C and monkeys to 23°C, hydration was increased on rewarming to 30°C. Strychnine and caffeine were found to be unsuitable for treatment of deep hypothermia because of edema after large doses. Beta-tetrahydronaphythylamine gave best results in rats. Ephedrine reduced edema faster but was inferior in other respects.

1015. Behnke, A. R. Cold injuries. *Med. Bull. Europ. Command, U.S., v. 8, Nov. 1951: 503–510.*

The author states that cold was by far the most disabling stress in World War II, and brought about the incapacitation of many men. But despite the seriousness of cold injury, research since the war has not produced answers to many of the fundamental questions. The author discusses the question of injury as being directly from the cold or as occurring during or following rewarming. The concept is presented of the "core" of the body responding physiologically quite differently from the skin, hands, and feet. A phenomenon spoken of as "after drop" occurs in which body temperature drops several degrees within the first 20 minutes after removal of the person from the cold water following immersion hypothermia. This drop may reflect the resumption of peripheral blood flow through the cold skin and subcutaneous layers; it may be sufficient to injure the heart and account for the collapse seen in individuals who have been removed from cold water to a comparatively warm environment. Rapid rewarming of the "core" of the body is imperative and can best be done by immersion in a hot bath (40°C or 104°F). However, there may be a decrease in blood volume which would make it inadvisable to divert any large quantities of the blood to the periphery by rapid rewarming. The differential diagnosis of immersion foot and frostbite is discussed as well as some information of rapid versus slow rewarming of frozen feet, and some prophylactic measures.

1016. Binhold, H. Should slow or fast rewarming be applied in cold injury? [In German]. *Deut. mil. ärztl. Zschr., v. 7, Aug. 1942: 491–496.*

Distinction must first be made between total-body cooling and local, smaller body-area, cooling. In total-body cooling, or hypothermia, the person is drowsy, has a slowed respiratory rate and heart action, has a lowered body temperature, and is indolent and apathetic. For such person rewarming should be fast in a dry, warm room, while they are given very warm liquids to drink, and are later put in a warmed bed. Use of too hot a bath is warned against as it may cause a circulatory collapse because of the inability of the inner circulatory mechanisms to adjust quickly enough to the very great skin stimulation. The pathological condition of the involved area is described in each of the three degrees of local cold injury or frostbite. In most of these injuries there is vascular impairment; slow rewarming is recommended to prevent further injury of the area.

1017. Brandis, H. J. von. General and localized cold injury in war. *Lectures on the practice of surgery, v. 27, p. 7–40 [In German]. Stuttgart, F. Enke, 1943.*

Cold injury during war is discussed under the following headings: the temperature regulation of man; temperature regulation and circulation; nervous control of temperature regulation; temperature regulation and influence of cold; the causes, nature, clinical picture, and treatment of hypothermia; the causes, nature, clinical picture, prophylaxis, and treatment of local cold injury; and chilblains. If there is no break in the skin or similar injury, hypothermic patients may be warmed quickly by immersing them in a hot bath of 40°–50°; if there is a broken-skin area, they may be put in a warm room (20°–22°). Intramuscular and intravenous infusions of a physiological solution of 5% grape sugar, may be given. Circulation can be aided by various drugs. In the treatment of local cold injury, very gentle massage, not with snow but with a soft wool cloth, is recommended to help restore circulation. Circulation may be stimulated by alternating hot and cold baths or rhythmic electrical stimulation. Use of powders and salves is sometimes effective.

1018. Callaghan, J. C., and W. G. Bigelow. An electrical artificial pacemaker for standstill of the heart. *Ann. Surg.*, v. *134, July 1951: 8–17.*

By use of a refrigerated blanket, and of intravenous Pentothal sodium to control shivering, dogs were cooled until rectal temperatures were reduced to between 15.8° and 21.5°C. At this low temperature either a complete standstill or extreme slowing of the heart occurred. Electrical stimulation of the heart in the area of the sino-auricular node either externally or internally via an electrode in the superior vena cava, acted as an artificial pacemaker in resuscitation of the animals and control of heart action. Complete survival with no ill effects is reported in a dog whose heart action had been artificially maintained for as long as 30 minutes. It has also been possible to take over control of heart action in hearts beating at normal or at reduced rates, and to increase or decrease the rate at will. The artifical pacemaker is suggested for possible use in instances of cardiac arrest during cardiac surgery in a hypothermic state, and for resuscitation and maintenance of persons in a hypothermic state following exposure to severe cold for short periods.

1019. Cignolini, P. Use of Marconi therapy in cold injury and traumatic hypothermia in the Army during the war [In Italian]. *Gior. med. mil.*, v. *87, July 1939: 676–686.*

Discussion of cold injury and general hypothermia among soldiers, with emphasis on treatment by short-wave therapy.

1020. Cilleuls, J. M. des, and J. G. F. E. Bellon. General accidents due to cold and their prophylaxis in the Army [In French]. *Rev. Serv. san. mil., Par.*, v. *109, Oct. 1938: 479–506.*

Some of the individual factors (amount of subcutaneous fat present; psychic condition; state of fatigue), and meteorological factors (wind, humidity, etc.) involved in deaths from cold are considered. Such deaths in a military situation are usually due to lowered physical resistance as a consequence of food deficiency, lack of sufficient bedding and wearing apparel, or of too great physical strain. The tendency of deaths to occur during the nighttime, is noted. Some of the pathology of the condition is discussed. Preventative measures mentioned are the provision for sufficient extra clothing, bedding, and food, and the shortening of marches and periods of sentry duty.

1021. Crismon, J. M., and H. W. Elliott. Effect of lanatoside C upon the survival of rats subjected to severe hypothermia. *Am. J. Physiol.*, v. *151, Nov. 1947: 221–228.*

The intravenous injection of lanatoside C (a pure digitalis glycoside) into hypothermic white rats improved their ability to withstand cold without circulatory collapse as compared with untreated controls. The minimum lethal temperature was 2° to 5°C lower for treated rats than for controls. Treated rats also showed fewer disturbances of cardiac rhythm and conduction than did untreated chilled animals.

1022. Dorfman, R. I., R. A. Shipley, E. Ross, S. Schiller, and B. N. Horwitt. The relative potencies of adrenal cortical steroids as determined by a cold-protection test and by a glycogen-deposition test. *Endocrinology, v. 38, Mar. 1946: 189–196.*

In tests of protection against a cold environment (5.5°–7.0°C), survival time of adrenalectomized immature rats showed 17-hydroxy-11-dehydrocorticosterone to be the most effective; 11-dehydrocorticosterone, corticosterone, and 11-desoxycorticosterone acetate were less so, in that order. On the basis of the amount of deposition of liver glycogen, 11-dehydrocorticosterone was only ¼ as active as 17-hydroxy-11-dehydrocorticosterone.

1023. Erastov, V. V. Patho-anatomical changes from cooling [Abstract, in German]. *Zbl. allg. Path., v. 81 (8–9), 1943: 289–290.*

Rabbits were cooled in ice water (0°–2°C, 5–15 minutes), warmed at 31°C, and later, on the 5th day, were killed. Half of the animals were injected with Naganol, synanthrin "33", or heparin. Of the 18 animals given the drugs, 14 survived; of 16 not treated, 8 survived. In the animals which were chilled but not treated with the drug, pathological symptoms were as follows: formation of innumerable coagulates in the vessels of all the organs, especially in the lungs; destruction of erythrocytes and leucocytes; increased porosity and damage of the vascular endothelium; infiltration of exudate into the tissues and into the perivascular space and extension of the latter; appearance of erythrocyte diapedesis in the surrounding tissue; venous hyperemia and edema in the organs, especially the lungs; deterioration of the parenchyma cells in the liver and kidney; serous exudate in Bowman's capsule of the kidneys and cylinder formation in the kidney tubules; at a later stage of the process a catarrhal, serous, and even fibrous inflammation of the organs, appeared especially in the lungs. In the rabbits which had been injected with the drugs, the alterations were much less. There was no necrobiosis or necrosis in the epithelium of the liver. The kidney manifested no changes except a slight destruction of erythrocytes. In the lungs the exudate was insignificant. The endothelium of the vessels remained unaltered in most cases, indurations were either absent or very slight.

1024. Gennari, G. The effect of caffeine on passive hypothermia in experimental cooling [In Italian]. *Rendic. Ist. san. pubb., Roma, pt. 2, v. 3, 1940: 515–522.*

Eighteen guinea pigs were subjected to an air temperature of 0°C, and half of these were injected intramuscularly with 5 mg/kg of caffeine. After 90 minutes in the cold chamber, it was found that the rectal temperature of the control animals fell to 27°C, while that of the caffeine-injected animals fell only to 31°C. It was concluded that caffeine increased resistance to cold.

1025. Georgievskiĭ, A. Some problems of first aid on the battlefield in wintertime [In Russian]. *Voen. san. delo, 1939 (11): 5–12.*

As a preventive measure against frostbite injury in wounded soldiers during front-line activity, it is recommended that holes be dug in the snow. Straw or branches of evergreen shrubs can be placed at the bottom, and also used as a primitive "roof" with the branches covered with snow. With this protection from the wind, the wounded can be placed inside and kept warm through additional blankets, sleeping bags, coats from dead soldiers, chemical heaters and hot drinks (hot, sweet tea).

1026. Glaser, E. M. The effects of cooling and of various means of warming on the skin and body temperature of men. *J. Physiol., Lond., v. 109, Sept. 15, 1949: 366–379.*

Young men were chilled (outdoor temperatures of 4°–9°C) and then rewarmed over a 1¾ hour period, under the following conditions: (a) rest at room temperature, (b) a hot drink followed by rest at room temperature, (c) alternate periods of rest and exercise at room temperature, and (d) rest in a warm dry medium. The author concludes that a combination of hot food and drink, coupled with exercise in a warm place, would warm people more effectively than would any one method. However, warming by immersion of whole body in hot water (Alexander, Leo J. Appendix 7, CIOS Report, item #26, file #37, July 1945) probably remains the most efficient single method especially after severe chilling.

1027. Glaser, E. M., G. R. Hervey. Swimming in very cold water [Abstract]. *J. Physiol., Lond., v. 115, 1951: 148.*

Three men of varied swimming ability were observed in an attempt to study whether swimming, when full clothed, might prolong survival in icy water (2°C). All subjects were gasping for breath within 30 seconds after entering the water. The poor swimmer, and the moderate swimmer who was in poor physical condition, had to be taken from the water in less than 2 minutes. The good swimmer became less breathless and was swimming without difficulty when he was asked to leave the water after 9 minutes. Measurements of skin and rectal temperatures did not indicate the very great heat losses which had been anticipated. The entire skin of all the subjects was very painful while they were in the water and became very bright red when they left it.

1028. Grosse-Brockhoff, F., and W. Schoedel. Animal experimental investigations on the question of therapy in supercooling [In German]. *Arch. exp. Path., Berl., v. 201, June 12, 1943: 457–467.*

Experiments on dogs chilled by immersion in cold water while under morphine-urethane anesthesia showed that atropine and intravenous glucose may have some value in treatment for general hypothermia. Adrenalin is contraindicated on the basis of experimental results. Rapid rewarming is the most effective method.

1029. Grosse-Brockhoff, F. General cold injuries [In German]. *In: S. Handloser, Innere Wehrmedizin, p. 541–548. Dresden and Leipzig, Steinkopff, 1944.*

This general account of injuries resulting from cold—including local injury, hypothermia, and death from cold—outlines the clinical picture resulting from varying degrees of exposure. A tabular outline (p. 546–547) lists (1) the symptoms (state of consciousness, reflexes, pulse, respiration); (2) therapies of rapidly occurring (during the first 12 hours of exposure) hypothermia; and (3) therapies of slow (beyond 12 hours) hypothermia. Three phases of the hypothermic state and a state of apparent death are distinguished: (1) body temperature decreased from 36° to 34°C, and a phase of increased excitability; (2) 33° to 26°C, and a phase of waning of excitability; and (3) 25° to 21°C, and a phase of incapacitation. At a body temperature of 20°C a death-like state occurs. In general, therapy during the first phase involves the giving of warm baths (36°C, increased gradually to 40°C), and of hot drinks with grape sugar added in cases of slowly-developing hypothermia. In the second phase, absolute rest is necessary; also hot baths (36°C, increasing every 10 minutes up to 42°C), intravenous injections of 40–60 cc of warmed (37°C) and concentrated (20%) sugar solution if the patient can no longer drink, and subcutaneous injections of Atropine sulfate, are recommended. In slowly-developing hypothermic injury, additional drugs (Strophanthin, desoxycorticosterone acetate, and vitamin B) are recommended. These therapies are, in general, continued during the third phase, so far as the patient's condition warrants it, the sugar solution to be given rectally if intravenous injection becomes difficult.

1030. Grosse-Brockhoff, F. Pathologic physiology and therapy of hypothermia. *In: German aviation medicine, World War II, v. 2, p. 828–842. Washington, D. C., Dept. of the Air Force, [1950].*

This is a review of German work on hypothermia, considering both human and animal data, with emphasis on the pathological physiology and on therapy which is based on physiological principles.

1031. Jaulmes, [C.], and [A. C.] Bénitte. Treatment of hypothermia [In French]. *Méd. aéronaut., v. 5, 1950: 73–74. Also, in French, in: Rev. méd. nav., Par., v. 5 (1), 1950: 131–132.*

Whether hypothermia is caused by immersion in cold water or by exposure to cold air, the physical response to severe cold brings about a rapid numbness both physical and mental, the appearance of a muscle rigidity, thirst, anorexia, headache, and profound fatigue. Skin temperature lowers quickly but the beginning and rate of lowering of the rectal temperature varies greatly according to the individual. The lethal rectal temperature seems to be about 24°C; Anglo-Saxons appear to withstand cold very well but for Germans there is some danger of death at 30°C. Previously deaths had been attributed to the poor oxygen dissociation of oxyhemoglobin; more recently the failure of circulation has had its supporters. Rapid rewarming by hot baths of 50°C is superior to all procedures in acute hypothermia. In therapy alcohol appears useless; Cardiazol [Metrazol], coramine, and lobeline are ineffective; adrenaline is contraindicated; benzedrine given slowly intravenously is a useful adjuvant; inhalation of CO_2 raises the reserve alkalinity of the blood; and spinal puncture relieves the fluid pressure which is always elevated. The authors warn of the great possibility of a secondary collapse within the first few hours after initial treatment.

1032. König, F. Physiological notes on the physical treatment of hypothermic persons [In German]. *Klin. Wschr.*, *v. 22, Jan. 16, 1943: 45–50.*

The author discusses the method of gradual rewarming used in reviving hypothermic persons. Studies were made on the basal metabolism, deep-body or core temperature, and skin temperature of subjects under conditions of work or rest and in various states of nourishment. Cold stimulation was applied by means of pieces of ice to the brow, eating of ice, removal of clothing at a room temperature of 20°C, or at a room temperature of 17.8°C while subjected to a draft of air. The author concludes that warmth-producing and warmth-saving reactions, released by cold stimulation of the skin, are different according to the skin area stimulated, the temperature of the remaining skin, and the core temperature. Heat stimulation of the skin tends to cool the inner body; cold stimulation to warm it. Severe cold stimulation brings about a constriction of peripheral blood flow, cools the skin, and calls forth a strengthened cold reaction. The modification of the sensitivity of the skin by the temperature of the circulating blood helps to modify the over reactivity of the skin and to balance the over-all temperature regulation. In rewarming a hypothermic person, the counteractions released by heat stimulation in the skin must be taken into account. The most effective method for rewarming is a very gradual warming of the periphery.

1033. Komarov, L. V. Effect of separate cooling of the trunk and head in warm-blooded animals during rapid decrease of temperature of the trunk [In Russian]. *Doklady Akad. nauk SSSR, v. 80, Sept. 1951: 281–283.*

The results of a fractional study, dealing with the possibility of obtaining in homothermal animals a deep and stable, incomplete anabiosis (or cold-induced hypobiosis), are presented, with special reference to body temperature and breathing. Under alcohol-ether-chloroform anesthesia each of a group of 22 cats was kept in snow, snow and water, or cold water up to the neck (the body covered with oilcloth), under various conditions of experimentation, all of which induced rapid hypothermia in the body and delayed hypothermia in the head (measured in the mouth). Death (cessation of respiration) occurred only when the rectal temperature dropped below 16°C; in some few cases the temperature was as low as 3.5°C; the average was 12°C. When hypothermia involved the whole body, death occurred at a body temperature of 15°–25°C (average, 19°C). It is assumed that better techniques for higher temperature conservation in the head and medulla (e.g. by ultrahigh-frequency radiation) might permit the lowering of the body temperature still further without causing death.

1034. Lutz, W. New ways of resuscitation after severe exposure to cold [In German]. *Wien. med. Wschr., v. 99, June 25, 1949: 287–289.*

Rewarming by means of a bath, together with artificial respiration when necessary, are recommended in cases of generalized cooling or prolonged immersion in cold water. The paper includes clinical data as well as results of animal experiments.

1035. Lutz, W. Resuscitation after death due to cold [In German]. *Zschr. ges. exp. Med., v. 115, 1950: 615–637.*

Earlier studies by the author and others had shown that death through hypothermia was chiefly due to resulting oxygen insufficiency, as the hemoglobin of the blood becomes unable to release its oxygen to the tissues. In a continuing study guinea pigs were cooled (in ice

water at 0°C, with up to 20 atmospheres of oxygen) until the heart stopped. Before rewarming
of the animals, they were brought under 4 atmospheres of oxygen pressure, artificial respiration was administered, and electrical cardial stimulation was applied. In 9% of the cases
these animals, whose heart-beat had been arrested for 72 minutes and whose body temperature had dropped to 0° or −1°C, could be permanently revived without apparent injury.
The remaining animals died a "late death" after revival due to a condition of shock (manifested by pulmonary edema, hemorrhaged kidneys, gastric ulcer, etc.). Injury was, in general,
roughly proportional to the length of the simulated or "early" death, induced either directly
by the cold or by cessation of blood circulation, or both. Artificial respiration and anti-shock
therapy may in the future permit revival of hypothermic casualties when rapid rewarming
by itself proves inadequate.

1036. Lutz, W. The significance of artificial respiration for resuscitation following hypothermia [In German]. *Wien. Zschr. inn. Med., v. 32, Jan. 1951: 36–41.*

In a study of collapse and heart failure occurring in experimental animals during rewarming from a state of deep hypothermia, artificial respiration (by means of an electrode needle
subcutaneously in the heart region) was given to one group during rewarming and not to
two others. Without artificial respiration, if rewarming began well before heart-failure it was
successful. It was not successful if heart failure had already occurred. But with artificial respiration, even though heart failure had occurred rewarming was successful. Success is said
to be less dependent on the temperature of the respiratory-regulating center than on the improvement of the circulation itself. Artificial respiration provides a tentative aid during the
period of apnea until improvement can occur. It was noted, however, that a day or so after
artificial resuscitation following a heart-stoppage, deaths similar to those from shock occurred
in many of the animals and appeared to depend on the length of time of the stoppage of the
heart. As a therapeutic regime the author recommends, in all cases of severe hypothermia, a
fast rewarming in a hot bath. Artificial respiration should be given if any respiratory difficulties are suspected. In case of continuing fall of body temperature, despite these aids, anti-
shock therapy should be followed, including giving of blood plasma and administration of
anti-histaminic drugs.

1037. Macco, G. di. Hypothermal reactivity and orthosympathicolytics [In
Italian]. *Boll. Soc. ital. biol. sper., v. 20, Sept.–Oct. 1945: 633–634.*

Intramuscular injection of an orthosympathicolytic substance (Stenamine or r-phenyliso-
propylamine) lessened the drop in rectal temperature of the guinea pig on exposure to cold
for 30 minutes. The duration and intensity of the hyperthermic reaction early in the cooling
was accentuated; the duration of the secondary hypothermic reaction immediately on return
of the guinea pig to an ambient temperature of 20°C, was shortened; and the time elapsing
before return of the rectal temperature to normal, after return to room temperature, was
decidedly shortened.

1038. Matthes, M. German air-sea rescue service during World War II. *In:
German aviation medicine, World War II. v. 2, p. 1139–1157. Washington, D. C.,
Dept. of the Air Force, [1950].*

A portion of this chapter is devoted to a review of German work on the medical aspects of
air-sea rescue, with emphasis on the development of protective clothing for prevention of
immersion injury and hypothermia.

1039. N., W. M. Chill in cattle. *Chemist & Druggist, Lond., v. 148, July 5, 1947:
26.*

Two formulas are given of preparations used in treating cattle suffering from chill.

1040. Niedner, F. Pathology and treatment of freezing injury [In German].
Wien. klin. Wschr., v. 56, Dec. 31, 1943: 740–744.

The physiological and pathological effects of cold, and the interruption of vital processes
by cold are described. Hypothermia is considered by the author to be best treated by fast
rewarming of the body and infusion of glucose solution. Local frostbite injury is best treated
with sulfonamide powder. Progynon, and, in severe cases by Novocain block or lumbar
anesthesia.

1041. Orlov, A. V. Active therapy in hypothermia according to clinical observations [In Russian]. *Klin. med., Moskva, v. 29, Dec. 1951: 28–36.*

A study was made of the treatment by rapid rewarming of 73 cases of hypothermia (body temperatures, 32°–26°C), all except one of which were of a second or third stage of severity. Three stages in the clinical aspects of hypothermia are distinguished: the adynamic, the stuporous, and the spastic, or first, second, and third stages. Treatment consisted of the giving of hot baths (36° to 40°C) with under-water soap friction, of intraperitoneal injections of glucose and Adrenalin, and of hot drinks and hot food. Use of alcohol or of calcium chloride was excluded. This therapy proved effective in that only three cases of death and four cases of complications occurred. A most important part in the pathogenesis of hypothermia is played by increasing central paralysis of the sympathetic nervous system, which is one of the main links in the thermoregulatory apparatus. In view of the importance of carbohydrate metabolism in the functioning of the brain, the author concludes that the disturbance of this metabolism and the depression of the nervous system in severe hypothermia form a vicious circle which is the basis of this pathogenesis.

1042. Pagliari, M. Effect of corticosterone, stilbene, and testosterone on histamine hypothermia [In Italian]. *Minerva gin., Tor., v. 2, June 1950: 255.*

No significant change in rectal temperature occurred following subcutaneous injection of testosterone; a slight rise occurred with corticosterone and stilbene. All these hormones—through some not well-defined action attributed to neurovegetative mechanisms in the thermal regulatory centers of the brain—block the fall in rectal temperature usually experienced following subcutaneous injection of histamine.

1043. Rîumshin, I. E. Evacuation of the severely wounded in the winter time [In Russian]. *Vrach. delo, v. 23 (2): 1941: 93–96.*

Evacuation of war-casualties following severe burns, heavy loss of blood, or under conditions of shock, at outdoor temperatures of −30° to −40°C requires a special heating device to avoid the consequences of hypothermia. The chemical heater made in the USSR, although considered superior to those made in other countries, has several disadvantages. To avoid these and produce a constant, even temperature all around the patient's body, an electrical blanket was devised, containing 27 parallel wires. The current is supplied by the battery in the ambulance or directly from the car generator. The blanket uses 50 watts (equivalent to 5 chemical heaters); the temperature within the blanket is 40°–50°C. The device is perfectly safe.

1044. Rossi, R. Experimental research on the action of potassium in numbing cold. [In Italian, summaries in Italian, French, English, and German]. *Med. sper., Tor., v. 7, 1940: 529–542.*

The intraperitoneal injection of KCl-Ringer's solution into rabbits which were kept passive at a low environmental temperature (18°–19°C) appeared to decrease the resistance of the animals to the cold. Although the degree of body cooling was lessened from that of controls which were not given the injection, the duration of life was shortened. The increase of blood sugar was less pronounced. The changes in water balance differed from those of the controls in that the amount in the blood and in muscle tissue was higher while internal organs, particularly the liver, showed a greater dehydration.

*1045. Shamshina, M. On the influence of rapid re-warming on blood pressure and respiration in acute hypothermia [In Russian]. *Biull. eksp. biol. med., v. 15 (1–2), 1943: 60–62.* Translation in: E. Hope. *Frostbite. Translations from the Russian of a collection of sixteen papers published between 1939 and 1944, p. 107–108. Ottawa, Defence Research Board, Canada, 1950.*

Each of a group of rabbits were immersed, except for the head and part of the thorax, in a water-and-snow mixture at 6°–7°C until a hypothermic state developed, when the cold water

---

* Original not seen.

was replaced by warm water (38°–40°C). Within 5–10 minutes the arterial pressure, pulse and respiratory rates had risen. After 1½ hours the rabbits were removed from the bath and appeared well after about another 1–2 hours. However, all the animals had died by the next day. Warning is given that these findings may not apply to humans since the vascular skin reaction in the rabbit is sharply different from the reaction in man. It is mentioned that S. S. GIRGOLAV and his associates had found rapid rewarming to be more effective than gradual rewarming.

1046.   Sheinis, V. N. Experimental data on general hypothermia [In Russian]. *In: Trudy 24-go Vsesoūznogo S''ezda Khirurgov, Kharkov, 1938, p. 196–199. Kharkov, Medgiz, 1939.*

Warm-blooded animals die when the body temperature drops to 18° or 20°C. The direct cause of death is found in the paralysis of the coordinating activities of the nervous system, all other functions being normal. Rapid general rewarming of the body is the decisive factor for the saving of the animal. Warm-blooded animals under conditions of pronounced hypothermia become poikilothermic, therefore temperatures below that of the body will only prolong the effect of cold. Uniform results obtained in mice, guinea pigs, and rabbits in extreme hypothermia, showed that the number of survivals was greater the more rapid and intensive the rewarming. Rapid rewarming restored the animals to normal after 1½ to 2 hours, while the slowly rewarmed animals remained prostrate for a long time and often died. However, rewarming above normal body temperature is harmful, because of the temporarily paralyzed thermoregulation, and may lead to death from overheating. Injection of carbohydrates (concentrated solutions of glucose, etc.) and of hormones (Adrenalin, thyroxin, etc.) to aid the assimilation of these carbohydrates, are necessary for the mobilization of the body resources. Cardiotonic drugs (lobeline, Cardiazol, etc.) is needed to stimulate respiratory and cardiovascular functions.

1047.   Veselkin, P. N. Restoration of cardiac activity and respiration in rabbits following "clinical death" from cooling [In Russian]. *Biull. eksp. biol. med., v. 15 (1–2), 1943: 58–60.*

After 20–30 minutes rabbits packed in ice showed elevated blood pressure, faster and deeper breathing, and great excitement. In 30–40 minutes the pulse, arterial pressure, and respiration fell. At a body temperature of 22°–24°C arterial pressure was near zero, but ventricles continued to beat. At 17°–22°C, respiration failed and the heart beat stopped. When the ice was removed, artificial respiration and rapid rewarming by electric bath, plus arterial injection of 20% glucose and Adrenalin, started the heart beat, assisted by cardiac massage. Respiration was restored in ½ hour or more and rectal temperature sometimes reached 34°–37°C. Death followed the next day, thought to be due to late hypoglycemia and its effects on the central nervous system.

1048.   Weltz, G. A., H. J. Wendt, and H. Ruppin. Rewarming after near-lethal hypothermia [In German]. *Münch. med. Wschr., v. 89, Dec. 25, 1942: 1092–1096.*

A group of guinea pigs was drastically cooled to the point of death (body temperature, 20°C) in a water bath of 4°–17°C for 2 hours. A second group was cooled (body temperature, 20°–25°C) in a water bath of 17°–23°C for 5 hours. The third group remained in a bath of 25°C or higher more than 5 hours; the deaths in this group were credited to exhaustion. In the first group, 80% died within 24 hours following removal from the bath, and some few died later, if no attempts were made to rewarm the animals. Rewarming in a 40°C bath cut the death rate in half; treatment with short-wave radiation was less effective. Intramuscular injections of glucose solution had no therapeutic effect when used either alone or combined with the 40°C bath. In the second group, deaths were 100% if no rewarming was done; rewarming in 40°C baths cut the death rate down slightly more than for the first group and eliminated the few late deaths found in the first group. Intramuscular glucose alone gave excellent results in the second group in cutting down the death rate, and combined with hot baths it was even more effective. This reaction was explained by further studies which showed the blood sugar level to be high in the first hour or two in the cold bath but to drop very low after continued cooling and the extended further time without food. If the animals were not fasted, the blood sugar level after 5 hours of cooling was quite variable but the average value was similar to that for the normal animals. There is some discussion of the application of these findings to the rewarming of humans.

1049. Zarrow, M. Protective action of desoxycorticosterone acetate (adrenal preparation) and progesterone (corpus luteum hormone) in adrenalectomized mice exposed to low temperatures. *Proc. Soc. Exp. Biol., N. Y., v. 50, May 1942: 135–138.*

Desoxycorticosterone acetate and progesterone prolong the life of adrenalectomized mice subjected to a temperature of 6 °C.

See also items: 89, 488, 507, 548, 558, 559, 567, 568, 671, 803, 806, 808, 815, 816, 823, 824, 832, 835, 836, 837, 844, 846, 847, 850, 856, 859, 862, 867, 868, 874, 883, 889, 894, 900, 905, 910, 920, 925, 946, 947, 993, 995, 1003, 1049, 1063, 1079, 1097, 1099, 1103, 1244, 1367, 1890, 2165, 2199, 2209, 2279, 2290, 2299, 2593, 2596, 2733.

I. Clinical Use of Hypothermia
(includes also basic studies on animals)

1050. Anon. Treatment by hypothermia [Editorial]. *Brit. M. J., 1941 (v. 2), Aug. 16: 231–232.*

The lowest internal temperature that man can bear probably lies somewhere between 70 °F and 75 °F and not between 90 °F and 95 °F as it had been thought to be earlier. The author mentions the report of 2 cases by Talbot (item 1097) with rectal temperatures of 74 °F and 75 °F who recovered from cooling. The heat-regulatory mechanism presumably ceases to operate below 75 °F in warm-blooded animals and a continued fall in temperature is like that in a dead animal in similar circumstances. However, in hibernating animals the body temperature may approach 32 °F without causing death.

1051. Anon. Cooling in shock. *J. Am. M. Ass., v. 121, Feb. 6, 1943: 432–433.*

In shock, much of the harm done is attributed to tissue anoxia. Lowered temperatures tend to prevent anoxia by decreasing the oxygen need; raising the temperature has the opposite effect.

1052. Allen, F. M. Resistance of peripheral tissues to asphyxia at various temperatures. *Surg. Gyn. Obst., v. 67, Dec. 1938: 746–751.*

In a series of animal experiments it was found that reduction of the environmental temperature greatly reduced the dangers, in ligation by tourniquet, from both gangrene and shock. Maintenance of the environmental temperature at 2 °C allowed the limbs of the animals to survive asphyxia for more than 50 hours. Raising the temperature only slightly caused the development of fatal shock or gangrene in only a fraction of the time which was tolerated at the low temperature.

1053. Allen, F. M. Surgical considerations of temperature in ligated limbs. *Am. J. Surg., v. 45, Sept. 1939: 459–464.*

Reduction of body temperature had a retarding effect on the development of systemic shock. The incidence of gangrene in ligated extremities was also lessened.

1054. Allen, F. M. The status of refrigeration for military surgery. *Arch. Phys. M., v. 26, Feb. 1945: 92–98.*

The literature on the use of refrigeration in surgery is discussed with special reference to its use by the military. The use of hypothermia in the treatment of frostbite, immersion foot,

and other injuries due to cold is discussed and the importance of local and generalized hypothermia in the treatment of shock is emphasized.

1055. Allen, F. M. Broader aspects of refrigeration anesthesia. *Current Res.
Anesth., v. 24, Mar.–Apr., 1945: 51–65.*

Comparisons are made of effects of cold upon the entire body, upon local areas, and upon
isolated extremities. Isolation of parts of the body by excision or ligation introduces several
changes: usual defense reactions, and injuries resulting from their breakdown, are abolished;
resistance to reduced temperature greatly increased; and the reversal of the usual inverse
law of survival (time of survival is decreased as the degrees of cold are increased) to become
a direct ratio (time of survival is prolonged as the degrees of cold are increased). Applications of these principles to refrigeration anesthesia and therapy are discussed.

1056. Allen, F. M., and F. K. Safford, Jr. New proposals in anesthesia. *Current
Res. Anesth., v. 26, July–Aug. 1947: 133–139.*

Included in the discussion is information on the physiological effects of lowered body temperature, with special reference to the reduction of pain and protection against shock.

1057. Allen, F. M. Discrepant animal and clinical observations on hypothermia
and procaine [Abstract]. *Fed. Proc., Balt., v. 7, March 1948: 268–269.*

General evidence supports reduction of body temperature as a method of treatment for
burns and visceral shock, even though different animal species show great variation in their
reaction to different temperatures.

1058. Allen, F. M. Hypothermic anesthesia. *Current Res. Anesth., v. 29, Mar.–
Apr. 1950: 97–100.*

Anesthesia induced by reduction of body temperature, or hypothermia, requires a minimum of drugs, and has been found to be an aid in increasing resistance to both shock and
asphyxia. The physiological effects of reduced body temperature are discussed with respect
to blood coagulation, resistance to infection, and effects on systemic diseases especially heart
disease.

1059. Antos, R. Influence of hypothermia and hyperthermia on survival time
of dogs in hemorrhagic shock. *Proc. Soc. Exp. Biol., N. Y., v. 56, May 1944:
60–63.*

A group of dogs were submitted to standardized bleeding and reinfusion procedures to
induce irreversible hemorrhagic shock. Some of the animals were kept at room temperatures
ranging from 26° to 33°C (with rectal temperatures varying from 38.8° to 41.7°C), while
others were kept in a cold room with air temperatures of 15° to 20°C with radiating wall
surfaces slightly above that of melting ice. Ice bags were also sometimes applied to hasten
the reduction of body temperature. The rectal temperatures of the group of animals kept in
the cold ranged from 28.3° to 36.7°C. Even though all dogs, except one, of both groups
finally succumbed, the survival period following reinfusion of heparinized blood was definitely
extended for those in a hypothermic state.

1060. Ariel, I., and S. L. Warren. Studies on the effect of hypothermia. III.
The effect of a single short period of hypothermia on the Brown-Pearce rabbit
epithelioma. *Cancer Res., v. 3, July 1943: 464–470.*

Groups of rabbits, at various periods of time following testicular inoculation of suspensions
of Brown-Pearce rabbit epithelioma, were subjected to periods of hypothermia. One group
had their rectal temperatures reduced to 18°C for 6 hours; another to 20°C for 8 hours; and
a third to 30°C for 24 hours. Various changes in the growth curves of the epithelioma occurred, but an analysis of the averages of these curves indicated a definite slowing of growth
during the week following treatment. However, after the second week following treatment
the growth rate was essentially normal. The number of animals succumbing to metastases

was decidedly increased after short periods of hypothermia. Hypothermia as a "cure" for cancer is not considered successful in these experiments.

1061. Barbour, H. G. The physiological effects of cold. *Connecticut M. J., v. 5, Oct. 1941: 719–720.*

A brief summary is given of the physiological effects of cold to provide a basis for its use in the therapy of fever or inflammation, or as anesthetic or stimulant in psychotic and other conditions. Temperature regulation is discussed, particularly its seeming inactivation in the hypothermic state. The effects of hormones and drugs are also considered.

1062. Bergman, H. C., and M. Prinzmetal. Influence of environmental temperature of shock. *Arch. Surg., v. 50, Apr. 1945: 201–206.*

The optimal environmental temperature range for the highest survival of mice from shock following burns was found to be 65° to 71°F. In a hotter environment, an increased mortality in shock was due to a further decrease in the effective circulation and an increase in capillary congestion caused by the toxic factor. Mice in shock kept in a cooler environment had an increased bleeding volume and a reduced degree of capillary atonia, when compared with values obtained in an environment of ordinary room temperature. The cause of the increased mortality in a cold environment is as yet unknown. Environmental temperatures of 37°, 71°, and 98°C had no significant effect on the local fluid loss following burns.

1063. Bigelow, W. G., J. C. Callaghan, and J. A. Hopps. General hypothermia for experimental intracardiac surgery. *Ann. Surg., v. 132, Sept. 1950: 531–537; discussion p. 537–539. Also in: Am. Surg. Ass., v. 68, 1950: 211–217; discussion p. 217–219.*

By lowering the body temperature of dogs to 20°C the heart was excluded from the circulation for periods of 15 minutes with survival of the animal. However, the eventual mortality rate was high and the cause of death was not clearly understood. Periodic electrical stimulation of the phrenic nerve for artificial respiration or of the S-A node area of the heart for restoration of heart action, and of radio frequency in rewarming procedures were also studied.

In discussion following the paper, DR. WILLIAM L. RIKER at Children's Memorial Hospital, Chicago, mentioned the use of a cold-water-filled mattress to keep the body temperature at normal, or lower, during major surgery on children in cyanotic cardiac states. DR. WARFIELD M. FIROR stated that in the tissue laboratory in the Department of Surgery at Johns Hopkins Hospital, a variety of mammalian tissues had been maintained in viable states for periods of 6 weeks at temperatures as low as 28°C. Cell division continued at reduced temperature but cell growth appeared to be altered by not in any way to simulate a change from benign to malignant state. DR. CLARENCE DENNIS mentioned that in Minnesota, in similar work to that reported by the author, the pyruvic acid level of the blood was found to be very high just before these late deaths of the dogs.

1064. Bischoff, F., M. L. Long, and J. J. Rupp. Influence of induced hibernation on mouse sarcoma 180. *Am. J. Cancer, v. 39, June 1940: 241–244.*

Mice were injected with mouse sarcoma 180 and immediately, or after an interval of ten days when the tumor had reached macroscopic size, were subjected to artificial hibernation. This state was produced by exposing the mice suddenly to low environmental temperatures of −2° to −5°C. After the artificial hibernation state was reached, in about two hours, it was maintained by placing the mice in an environmental temperature of approximately 15°C. No permanent effect upon the growth process of sarcoma 180 was noted when mice were kept at a body temperature below 20°C for 7-hour periods on 5 successive days or for a 24-hour period. A temporary retardation of growth, similar to that from caloric restriction, was observed.

1065. Blalock, A., and M. F. Mason. A comparison of the effects of heat and those of cold in the prevention and treatment of shock. *Arch. Surg., v. 42, June 1941: 1054–1059.*

Shock was produced experimentally, under anesthesia, in dogs either by bleeding to remove one-third of the volume of blood or by traumatization of one of the posterior extremities.

About 30 minutes later, heat or cold (by nearly surrounding the body of the animal with rubber bags of crushed ice) was applied to one leg of each of pairs of animals. Significant elevations of temperature decreased the chance of life and shortened the period of survival, causing more disasterous results than did depressions of similar degree. The application of cold did not increase the chance of survival of all animals but it was accompanied by a lengthening of the survival of an animal with a low blood pressure.

1066. Boerema, I., A. Willschut, W. J. H. Schmidt, and L. Broekhuysen. Experimental researches into hypothermia as an aid in the surgery of the heart [In English]. *Arch. chir. neerl., v. 3 (1), 1951: 25–34.*

Dogs were cooled to body temperatures of 25°C or 19°C within 20 to 150 minutes by diverting the blood from a large vein through sealed, sterile, glass tubing, by cooling it and then returning it to the body. By use of such a cooling system it was possible to open the thoracic cavity surgically and to interrupt the circulation for 10 to 15 minutes for intracardiac surgery without causing permanent pathological results. This period was 3 to 4 times as long as that with normal temperatures. If the rewarming rate was slightly slower than that of cooling, there was less chance of shock developing. During the cooling period pulse rate fell in proportion to the temperature; on rewarming it rose proportionately more quickly than the temperature. Blood pressure fell slightly, then rapidly; on rewarming it rose quickly. Rate of respiration decreased rapidly with the depth of respiration diminishing at the same time. When apnea occurred, the body temperature was between 33° and 27°C and it continued until rewarming started. Spontaneous respiration returned at both lower and higher temperatures than the range where apnea occurred. Cessation of spontaneous respiration did not always indicate a rapid development of anoxemia.

1067. Cole, W. H. The treatment of shock with special reference to the use of heat and cold. *Arch. Phys. Ther., v. 24, Nov. 1943: 670–675.*

From a survey of the literature it is concluded that, although it is not indicated that patients in a condition of shock should be subjected to refrigeration, the effect of treatment with cold is often to prolong the life of the experimental animal. Treatment with heat may be definitely harmful. In a condition of shock the patient's temperature, particularly in the extremities, may drop several degrees. This appears to be a protective action on the part of the body and exposure of the patient to room temperature will not elevate the temperature significantly until the patient is out of shock.

1068. Colvin, J. W., and C. A. Mills. Ease of body heat loss and resistance to infection. *Science, v. 90, Sept. 22, 1939: 275–276.*

The authors report the results of a study on mice which were kept at a control room temperature (70°F), in a cold room (65°F), or in a hot room (90°F), and were given cultures of hemolytic streptococcus by injection. Mice from the control room died more quickly than those in the cold room while mice in the hot room died with only one-fourth the amount of the culture which was lethal for the other two groups.

1069. Coulter, J. C. Crymotherapy. *In:* The cyclopedia of medicine, *p. 566– 568. Ed. by* G. M. Piersol *and* E. L. Bortz. *Service volume. Philadelphia, F. A. Davis Co., 1941.*

In a short section on Crymotherapy are discussed the findings of Smith, Fay, and Vaughan on human beings with cancer maintained at reduced body temperatures of 75°–90°F (23.8°– 32.2°C). Previous to this work it was the general impression that any prolonged reduction of body temperature below 94° or 95°F (34.4° or 34.9°C) was inevitably fatal. One clear-cut result of these studies is the successful use of low temperatures in the control of pain.

1070. Duerschner, D. R., C. Muschenheim, and J. D. Hardy. Hypothermia in experimental infections. II. The effect of hypothermia on tuberculin sensitivity in guinea pigs. *J. Infect. Dis., v. 72, May–June 1943: 183–186.*

Guinea pigs subjected to repeated reductions of body temperature were infected subcutaneously with a standard strain of virulent human tubercle bacilli. No apparent inhibitory or promoting effect on the course of infection was noted. A delay in the appearance of skin sensitivity to tuberculin and a lessened degree of sensitivity were, however, observed.

1071.   Duncan, G. W., and A. Blalock. Shock produced by crush injury; effects of the administration of plasma and the local application of cold. *Arch. Surg., v. 45, Aug. 1942: 183–194.*

When blood plasma was administered before experimental crush injuries of the posterior extremities of dogs, the survival rate of the animals was increased (from 1 to 9 out of 19), but there were still large local fluid losses in the area of injury. Local application of ice during the period of crushing resulted in less swelling and a further increase (5 out of 7) in survival rate. If temperature was lowered after crushing had occurred, no favorable influence was obtained. The results would indicate that deaths were due to local fluid loss plus absorption of toxic products. When the crushing was of slight duration, the fluid loss appeared to be the major factor in precipitating peripheral circulatory failure; when crushing was maintained for long periods of time and death following release from crushing was delayed by administration of plasma, it was likely that the ultimate fatal outcome was due mainly to the effects from absorption of toxic products.

1072.   Fay, T. Clinical report and evaluation of low temperature in treatment of cancer. *Proc. Interst. Postgrad. M. Ass. N. America, Cleveland Assembly, 1940 (Cleveland, Ohio): 292–297.*

Clinical responses are discussed to extended periods, from a few hours to 5 or 8 days of both local refrigeration (40°F; 4°–5°C) and of generalized refrigeration (rectal temperatures of 75°–90°F; 23°–32°C) in acute, mostly terminal, cases of cancer. In 5 patients suffering from brain tumor, a metal capsule, through which refrigerating fluids could be circulated, was inserted deep within the tissues of the brain. Prolonged refrigeration of carcinomatous tissue at 40°F, as shown by these studies, and by local refrigeration of other areas of the body, was accompanied by regressive histological tissue changes. It was found that normal brain tissue could tolerate 40°F for 96 days without clinical or biopsy signs of degeneration. General body refrigeration did not induce myocardial degeneration.

1073.   Fay, T. Panel discussion on coma and shock. *Pennsylvania M. J., v. 46, Jan. 1943: 332.*

In the panel discussion on shock, Dr. Fay stated that from experiences of keeping patients chilled to a body temperature of 80°F for from 7 to 10 days without any manifestations of shock, he could not feel that cold *per se* was a cause of shock. He felt that the cold shown by the individual in shock was due to evaporation of fluid from the body surface, and that this loss of fluid was the shock-producing factor. He mentioned that recently patients with severe brain trauma had been kept at a body temperature of 90°F for the first 24 to 48 hours to prevent shock.

1074.   Frank, D. E. Crymotherapy and anaphylaxis. *Ann. Allergy, v. 6, Nov.– Dec. 1948: 667–668, 704.*

Fourteen days after guinea pigs were sensitized by injection of horse serum, the animals were packed in chipped ice until their rectal temperatures had dropped from 38° to 25°C. A second injection of horse serum resulted in the deaths of 5 of the 13 guinea pigs which had been refrigerated, and in the deaths of all of the control animals which had remained at room temperature. On rewarming of the animals with a heating pad, some additional deaths occurred. On autopsy it appeared that refrigeration had caused extreme distention of the entire gastrointestinal tract, including the gall bladder; the liver was enormously enlarged and showed passive congestion; the auricles and tributary veins were moderately engorged; however, the over-all heart size seemed to be normal. Refrigeration appeared to slow anaphylactic symptoms but not significantly to prevent fatalities. It was also shown to delay onset of signs of histamine shock but not prevent those fatalities.

1075. Gerster, J. C. A., C. E. Kossman, C. Reich, A. Bernhard, J. Geiger,
T. K. Davis, M. C. L. McGuinness, H. R. Kenyon, J. F. Dixon, F. Huber,
R. M. Paltauf, and P. K. Sauer. General crymotherapy; a symposium. *Bull.
N. York Acad. M.*, v. 16, May 1940: 312–338.

This symposium is based on comprehensive studies of the various responses of the human
body to cold as they were observed in 4 months' experiences with the use of crymotherapy in
a special 2-bed ward at the Lenox Hill Hospital, New York City. The room was air conditioned
at 55 °F; patients were lightly anesthetized and the torso packed in ice until the rectal temperature reached 90 °F; ice was removed and the patient maintained at rectal temperatures in the
high 80's for periods up to several days. Feeding of glucose and saline was done hourly by
stomach tube. Rewarming to normal rectal temperature, usually in 6–8 hours, was done by
either shutting off the air conditioning or by the use of blankets. The following individual
reports are included:

KOSSMAN, C. E. Cardiovascular aspects, p. 317–320. During decreased body temperature
the pulse rate slowed; blood pressure was variable but usually fell if an abnormally low temperature was maintained for more than 24 hours; blood vessels showed marked and generalized
constriction; T wave, and often the QRS group, showed abnormalities; and auricular fibrillation was common.

REICH, C. Hematology, p. 321. In a patient suffering only from drug addiction, an increase
in hemoglobin, red blood cell count, white blood count—with a rise in the per cent of polymorphonuclear leukocytes—and a decrease in platelets and in sedimentation rate, was found.
Toward the end of 5 days of treatment, the hemoglobin was reduced but returned to normal
when cold treatment was discontinued. Findings were quite similar in carcinomatous patients.

BERNHARD, A. Blood chemistry, p. 322. No significant changes were found following cold
treatment up to 64 hours. The red cell volume was increased in 4 of 11 cases, and in 3 of 11
cases there was a definite fall in sedimentation rate which was re-established after 48 hours.

GEIGER, J. Basal metabolism determinations, p. 323–324. It was concluded that there was
a definite drop in the basal metabolic rate indicating that metabolism was greatly depressed
by continued low body temperatures, in contrast to the increased rate often found in short
periods of exposure to cold.

DAVIS, T. K. Neurological observations, p. 324–325. There was found a transient lack of
plantar responses in 1 patient and transient crossed reflexes in another, indicating a tendency
for pyramidal tracts to lose part of normal control. The pseudoplasticity of the cold extremities
was thought to be local. Patients were semicomatose; comments and replies to questions were
not usually remembered afterward. In no case were there any different findings after treatment
from those of the pre-treatment examination.

McGUINNESS, M. C. L. Temperature observations, p. 326–328. Great variations in skin
temperatures were encountered because of sedation, hourly feedings, almost constant shivering
and tendency of the patients to move. But it was concluded that different parts of the body
cooled at varying degrees with the changes being greater at 78° than at 71 °F. Vasoconstriction
was marked, thus decreasing conductivity of skin and holding blood deeper within the body.

KENYON, H. R. Urologic aspects, p. 328–330. Studies were made only on patients with
severe, usually cancerous, involvements of the urino-genital tract. Some measure of subjective
improvement was found in all cases and in several a considerable alleviation of severe pain.

DIXON, J. F. Pulmonary complications, p. 330–332. Of the 18 patients whose lungs were
shown by x-ray to be clear, only 1 developed pneumonia following treatment and that one as
the result of aspiration.

HUBER, F. Roentgenological examination, p. 332. X-ray examinations of 2 patients with
bone metastases showed definite increase in the size of the previously noted defects, following
crymotherapy.

PAULTAUF, R. M. Biopsies and deaths, p. 332–334. Mention is made of the findings of a
decided degree of necrosis in cancerous tissue of the uterus following 10 days of local crymotherapy (circulating water of 34°C; estimated temperature of uterus, 40°–45°C) with no
change seen in the normal tissue of the surrounding area.

SAUER, P. K. Clinical manifestations (general observations; pain relief; mortality; local
crymotherapy), p. 334–338. In 11 of 17 patients with intractable pain due to carcinoma, the
alleviation of pain was such that no narcotic was necessary for from 24 hours to 8 weeks.

1076.   Gordon, J. B. Experience with refrigeration anesthesia; six supracondylar amputations for arteriosclerotic gangrene. *Am. J. Surg., v. 76, Oct. 1948: 393–397.*

In connection with his experiences using refrigeration anesthesia, the author discusses the reduction of protoplasmic activity of tissue by the lowering of the body temperature, especially the decrease in the conduction of the nerves at lowered temperatures.

1077.   Green, H. D., and G. A. Bergeron. Effects of environmental temperature on the traumatic shock produced by ischemic compression of the extremities. *Surgery, v. 17, Mar. 1945: 404–412.*

Fifteen of 16 anesthetized dogs, subjected to a 6-hour period of ischemic compression of their hind legs and kept in an environmental temperature of 20° to 28°C, died in an average of 6.4 hours after release of compression. Fourteen dogs similarly traumatized, but kept in a cool environment of 9° to 14°C during and for 24 hours after compression, with one exception, lived more than 20 hours; 9 survived indefinitely. This beneficial effect of the cool environment is thought to be due partly to the diminution of damage to tissue during compression and partly to the decreased metabolic demand on the circulation during the critical first 24 hours after compression.

1078.   Hardy, J. D., D. R. Duerschner, and C. Muschenheim. Hypothermia in experimental infections. I. Preliminary observations on tolerance of guinea pigs and rabbits to induced hypothermia. *J. Infect. Dis., v. 72, May–June 1943: 179–182.*

The effect of prolonged hypothermia on experimental infections in rabbits and guinea pigs was studied. Rabbits were able to tolerate continuous hypothermia of 8° to 10°C for as long as 96 hours. While guinea pigs do not tolerate continuous hypothermia for longer than 24 hours, they may be subjected repeatedly to lowered temperature for 24 hours or less for many weeks.

1079.   Huguenard, P. Technic for artificial hypothermia in surgery [In Italian]. *Gior. ital. anest., v. 17, July–Oct. 1951: 295–304.*

Patients in very poor physical conditions were put into a state of pharmacodynamic hibernation by the administration, either oral or intravenous, of combinations of several drugs, including Diparcol, procaine, Phenergan, curare, morphine, and atropine. The stabilization of the neurovegetative system by the lytic action of these drugs can then be followed by spinal anesthesia or by refrigeration anesthesia (packing in ice for 24 to 72 hours) before surgical intervention. Termination of the artificial hypothermia and the lytic state can be brought about quickly by administration of Adrenalin. Of a group of 25 desparately-ill patients treated in this manner, the author reports only 3 deaths.

1080.   Huguenard, P. Artificial hibernation; new practical experiences and latest results [In French]. *Acta anesth. belg., v. 2, Dec. 1951: 716–734.*

Case histories are given of 25 patients who were treated with induced hypothermia before and during surgical intervention. Premedication was with various combinations of nembutal, Phenergan, Gardenal, and Dolosal. On the day of the operation use was made of intramuscular injections of various combinations of morphine, atropine, Phenergan, Dolosal, and Diparcol. Lytic perfusion was applied, preferably slowly by means of a vein, using procaine and amide procaine in a 2% solution combined with 2% 4560 RP. During refrigeration in an ice bath — and combined with the drugs as indicated — the body temperature fell in the range of 36.5° to 30°C, but mostly in the range of 34° to 32°C.

1081. Jaulmes, C., H. Laborit, and A. C. Bénitte. Can one conceive of the application of artificial hibernation to war surgery? [In French]. *Bull. Soc. med. mil. fr., v. 10, Dec. 13, 1951: 196–199.*

The possibility, and some of the advantages, of the use of artificial hibernation during a war or national disaster are discussed. Artificial hibernation consists of two phases: pharmaco-dynamic and physical. The possibility of soldiers and civilians being supplied with a small syringe containing 50 mg of 4560RP [a derivative of phenothiazine] and 100 mg Dolosal for intramuscular self-injection, is suggested. Thus the individual could be protected by pharmaco-dynamic hibernation against shock and greater injury as he awaits further, professional, care and air-lift evacuation especially in case of a large-scale disaster and evacuation. Further, physical cooling, such as that of packing in ice, would not be necessary since the drugs act to block temperature regulation and the individual tends to cool to the level of his environment. In a temperate or cooler climate such cooling, without rewarming, would be sufficient. Some of the advantages which blocking of the vegetative nervous system by artificial hibernation give to the patient are: inhibition of intestinal motility in case of abdominal injury, diminution of oxygen need in thoracic cases, and decrease in cerebral edema formation in injuries of the head.

1082. Jones, A. J., J. Graham, and A. Mueller. Local and general temperature reduction in malignancy. *Am. J. Surg., v. 52, Apr. 1941: 14–23.*

Case histories are given of 14 patients with inoperable and far-advanced cancers who were subjected to local area cold, to hypothermia, or to both. The lowest temperature reached during hypothermic treatment was 77.6°F; the periods of hypothermic treatment varied from 36½ to 120 hours. Local cold was applied for periods ranging from 236 to 792 hours. One death occurred during hypothermic treatment; 8 deaths occurred 3 to 7½ months after treatment; but 3 patients were still living 3½, 4½, and 8 months following treatment. Two patients receiving only local cold treatment died in 1 month and 9 months. All patients complaining of pain were relieved in whole or in part following treatment with cold, either local or general.

1083. Junge, J. M., and S. M. Rosenthal. Effect of environmental temperature upon resistance to pneumococcal infection under sulfadizine therapy, and upon body temperature and oxygen consumption during infection. *J. Immun., v. 58, Mar. 1948: 237–244.*

The resistance of mice to a pneumococcal infection, while under sulfadiazine therapy, was significantly influenced by environmental temperature. The optimum room temperature for increased resistance was in the range of 26°–31°C; resistance was lowered at either 18°C or 37°C. In untreated mice with pneumococcal infection, no febrile response was observed when the animals were maintained at room temperatures of 18°C or 31°C. At 18°C there was a progressive fall in oxygen consumption and in body temperature, as the infection progressed.

1084. Laborit, H. On the subject of artificial hibernation [In French]. *Rev. méd. nav., Par., v. 6, Feb. 1951: 123–129.*

The action of a general anesthetic can be intensified by giving to the patient a combination of several drugs known as a "lytic cocktail". With such preparation the patient will often be able to survive a surgical intervention which would have been fatal in a patient not so treated. Under such treatment there is a lowering of rectal temperature, absence of pain, and shock is not experienced. But a subject so treated has lost touch with the exterior environment, the sense organs can no longer relay their sensations, and the human subject becomes similar to the animal. The neuro-endocrine functioning contributes greatly to our human, social, environment.

1085. Laborit, H. Some new trends in anesthesiology [In French]. *Presse méd., v. 59, Sept. 8, 1951: 1161–1162.*

Among new trends in anesthesiology, the author mentions the use of pharmacodynamic hibernation induced by combinations of drugs together with refrigeration to produce a deep hypothermia and anesthesia. The object of this newer anesthesia technique is not to try to maintain homeostasis but to protect the existence of life by reducing the needs of the tissues while establishing a more slowed-down way of life.

1086. McQuiston, W. O. Anesthetic problems in cardiac surgery in children. *Anesthesiology, v. 10, Sept. 1949: 590–596.*

Hypoxemia, and the resulting brain injury, are the most troublesome complications and most frequent causes of death of young children undergoing surgery for cardiac malformations. Reduction of body temperature and consequently of the oxygen need of the brain for less oxygen, was found to reduce surgical risk. One such operative case, cited as an example, was that of a child of 4 months with a tetralogy of Fallot, whose rectal temperature was reduced to 96.0°C by the use of ice bags, while under cyclopropane anesthesia.

1087. Newman, B. M. Refrigeration for insanity; hibernation at lowered temperatures promises value as a treatment; delayed by the war. *Sc. American, v. 167, Oct. 1942: 160–162.*

The author discusses the work of Talbott and Tillotson who used hypothermia as a method of treatment for schizophrenia. In some cases the clinical course was unaffected; in others improvement was noted for a brief period and reversion to the psychotic stage followed. In some individuals hypothermia resulted in marked improvement as evidenced by their ability to adjust socially.

1088. Parker, J. S., and C. S. Welch. The influence of cooling on the survival of the ischemic extremity. [Abstract]. *Surgical Forum, American College of Surgeons, 36th Clinical Congress, Philadelphia, Oct. 1950: 443.*

Legs of dogs were made ischemic experimentally by transection at a temperature of 40°F. Restoration of the circulation was then made and the survival of the extremity was studied when the animals were kept at various lowered environmental temperatures for periods of 6 to 30 hours. No results are given.

1089. Ricca, R. A., K. Fink, L. I. Katzin, and S. L. Warren. Effect of environmental temperature on experimental traumatic shock in dogs. *J. Clin. Invest. v. 24, Mar. 1945: 127–139.*

With a room temperature of 28°C the outcome of a 5-hour press on the leg of a dog to produce experimental traumatic shock, was fatal in 90% of the cases. Under similar conditions, the local application of ice to the injured limb afforded almost complete protection from death. With a room temperature of 16°C, such an experimental injury was fatal in only a small percentage of the cases, all other conditions remaining the same.

1090. Sénèque, J., M. Roux, and P. Huguenard. On general anesthesia "without anesthetics"; anesthesia by "potentialization" and artificial hibernation. *Mém. Acad. chir., Par., v. 77, June 6 and 13, 1951: 613–620.*

Five typical case histories are presented in which the patients were subjected to surgical intervention after anesthesia had been produced by a "lytic cocktail." With the patient in a neutral vegetative state, a "potentialization" of the effect of the lytic drugs was achieved by applying ice bags to the inner thigh, the precordial region of the chest, the abdomen, and by intravenous injection of cold solutions. The lytic cocktail was composed of a combination of several drugs, including derivatives of Dibenzoparathiazine; Diparcol; Phenergan; atropine; the curares; intravenous procaine; and synthetic analgesics like Dolosal. The results obtained by this system of artificial hibernation, have confirmed the earlier finding that this type of anesthesia is excellent in preventing shock and other postoperative complications. It is recommended as the method of choice especially with seriously-ill patients.

1091.   Smith, L. W., and T. Fay. Temperature factors in cancer and embryonal cell growth. *J. Am. M. Ass., v. 113, Aug. 19, 1939: 653–660.*

The authors correlated the relative infrequency of both primary and metastatic carcinoma of the extremities of the body with the low surface temperatures found in these areas. This observation, together with the evidence for need of optimal temperatures by embryonic cells, led to experiments in refrigeration of cancer patients. Carcinomatous tissues subjected to temperatures of 90°F or below showed degenerative changes, in biopsy specimens, after 72 hours of treatment. Refrigeration of the affected area or maintenance of the patient at a rectal temperature of 81°–90°F for 1–5 days, resulted in considerable relief of pain in terminal cancer cases.

1092.   Smith, L. W. Pathologic changes observed in human tissues subjected to sub-critical temperatures. *Arch. Path., Chic., v. 30, July 1940: 424–439.*

This is a report on the results of 60 autopsies of cancer patients treated by refrigeration. Normal tissues generally showed no changes but tumor tissues regularly showed regressive changes.

1093.   Smith, L. W., and T. Fay. Observations on human beings with cancer, maintained at reduced temperatures of 75°–90° Fahrenheit. *In: American Institute of Physics. Temperature, its measurement and control in science and industry, p. 576–583. New York, Reinhold, 1941.* Also in: *Am. J. Clin. Path., v. 10, 1940: 1–11.*

This report presents observations made on the physiological effects of very low body temperatures maintained in patients suffering from terminal cancer. Relief of pain and reduction of tumor size were achieved in patients kept at temperatures of 74°–90°F for periods of 4–5 days, repeated at week-long intervals 3 or 4 times. Effects upon the blood included a striking leukocytosis and increased viscosity. Circulation was nearly halved in the peripheral vessels; blood chlorides and blood sugar fell; carbon diozide tended to rise. In patients anesthetized with Avertin and barbiturates, renal function was inhibited; in those given "epival" and paraldehyde, fluid balance was maintained. Respiration rate tended to be irregular, with shallow breathing. Basal metabolism was reduced by 6–25%.

1094.   Smith, L. W. Cold treatment. *Clin. Med., v. 49, Aug. 1942: 231–232.*

The author states that chilling of the whole body, for 24 hours or more at lowered environmental temperatures (with Evipal to prevent shivering), until the rectal temperature became about 40°F, produced definite changes in embryonal cells and possibly in malignant cells. Tissue activity may be nearly suspended by use of a tourniquet around a limb and then packing it in ice to keep it at about 35°F for 3 or 4 days. Fibroblasts grow more compactly, with less collagen, at lower temperatures than they do at higher temperatures thus producing smaller, firmer scars and more rapid healing.

1095.   Smith, L. W. The use of cold in medicine. *Ann. Int. M., v. 17, Oct. 1942: 618–636.*

The literature on the biological effects of cold, both local and generalized, on mammalian physiology is reviewed. The physiological changes in a hypothermic state are discussed, especially with regard to the use of a lowered body temperature as a therapeutic or as an anesthetic agent.

1096.   Spradley, J. B., and M. Marin-Foucher. Hypothermia (new treatment of psychiatric disorders). *Dis. Nerv. Syst., v. 10, Aug. 1949: 235–238.*

Effects of hypothermia (rectal temperature of about 90°F) for 48 to 72 hours on mentally ill patients, were studied. Although some of the patients were also having other treatment, a few of the patients showed some improvement after hypothermic treatment.

1097. Talbott, J. H. The physiologic and therapeutic effects of hypothermia. *N. England J. M.*, v. 224, Feb. 13, 1941: 281–288.

A considerable review is given of the literature on the therapeutic use of both general hypothermia and of local cooling. The author notes that in two of his own patients the rectal temperature reached 74°F (remaining below 80°F for more than 10 hours), and 75°F. Heat regulation appears to cease below 75°F and cooling proceeds as it would in a dead body; if rewarming begins soon enough, the heat regulation mechanism is activated again at 75°F. 45 refs.

1098. Talbott, J. H., and K. J. Tillotson. The effects of cold on mental disorders; a study of 10 patients suffering from schizophrenia and treated with hypothermia. *Dis. Nerv. Syst.*, v. 2, Apr. 1941: 116–126.

Ten patients suffering from frank schizophrenia, all of whom had failed to respond to numerous types of therapy, were subjected to hypothermic treatment by use of refrigerated blankets. In 8 of the patients the body temperature was reduced below 85°F, with a minimum of 74.6°F in one patient. A change in the clinical course of the disease was observed in 4 of the patients. Each of these patients was under 30 years of age and had been mentally ill for a relatively short time. A transient period of improvement was experienced by 3 patients between the age of 30 and 45; 2 patients ill for more than 10 years exhibited no improvement. The results suggest that during the first years of schizophrenia irreparable morphological damages do not occur; any alternations of the clinical course during these years may offer considerable hope in treatment of an essentially incurable disease.

1099. Talbott, J. H., W. V. Consolazio, and L. J. Pecora. Hypothermia: report of a case in which the patient died during therapeutic reduction of body temperature, with metabolic and pathologic studies. *Arch. Int. M.*, v. 68, Dec. 1941: 1120–1132.

A patient in a mental hospital subjected to refrigeration therapy died during the rewarming process. Anatomical and biochemical studies were made on the body 4 hours after death. No important structural changes were noted in the tissues following the prolonged hypothermia. Cardiovascular collapse brought about by too rapid rewarming was the immediate cause of death.

1100. Vaughn, A. M. Experimental hibernation of metastatic growths (Preliminary report). *J. Am. M. Ass.*, v. 114, June 8, 1940: 2293–2298.

Six patients, ranging in age from 26 to 52 years, with hopeless metastatic cancer were subjected to hypothermia by being exposed to a room temperature of 60°F for from 9 to 54½ hours. The lowest rectal temperature obtained was 83.2°F. Some physiological tests (basal metabolic rate, blood chemistry determinations, and blood counts) were done at various times before, during, and after the treatment; some tabulations of temperature, pulse, and respirations were made. Pulse and respiration usually run a smooth and even curve until the end of hibernation when the pulse rate becomes very fast. In all but one case, the basal metabolic rate during hibernation was lowered. Blood sugar was high while non-protein nitrogen and urea were decreased. Hemoglobin and red blood corpuscles were increased as would be expected as the result of dehydration. Blood pressure readings were generally lower. Bowels did not function during hibernation; the amount of urine (by catheterization) gradually decreased unless fluids were given. An interesting observation was that the temperature of the urine was usually from 1 to 5 degrees lower than the rectal temperature. Except for the absence of pain for 3 months, and its decrease in the 7 and 8 months since treatment of the 2 patients still living, no other result of value was observed. This relief of pain may have been influenced by the high-voltage roentgen therapy employed before experimental hibernation.

1101. Wakim, K. G., and W. D. Gatch. The effect of external temperature on shock; an experimental study. *J. Am. M. Ass., v. 121, Mar. 20, 1943: 903–907.*

In experimentally-shocked animals (rats, rabbits, dogs, guinea-pigs), the optimal external temperature for survival was in the neighborhood of their normal body temperature. Temperatures below ordinary room temperature and above 45 °C had deleterious effects on these animals. Data would indicate that temperatures of 5 °C, or above 50 °C, have harmful effects even on normal animals.

1102. Whittemore, W. L., J. R. Lisa, and P. K. Sauer. Crymotherapy and its relation to hibernation. *N. York State J. M., v. 40, Nov. 11, 1940: 1563–1566.*

The authors discuss somewhat the physiological differences between true hibernation and the greatly lowered metabolic state due to treatment with cold. They mention the instance of the first artificial lowering of body temperature (to 83°F) of a normal person by keeping him in a brine bath at 40°F for 45 minutes, according to the incident published by JAMES CURRIE in a monograph in London in 1798.

1103. Wright, L. K. Effect of low temperatures on the human body; freezing to induce hibernation. *Refrig. Eng., v. 38, Sept. 1939: 143–144, 167, 192.*

The author discusses the treatment of Drs. Fay and Smith of Philadelphia of cancer, and other, patients by packing the body in chipped ice. When the body temperature was maintained at about 90°–89°F for several days, the patient remained in a sleeping state much like that of a hibernating animal. In this state the pulse beat nearly disappeared, the electrocardiograph alone being able to detect it beating with perfect rhythm; bowels, kidney and digestive organs ceased functioning; and blood analysis showed no waste products. Cancer cell growth was arrested and pain was reduced or eliminated. The patients were aroused by hot applications and hot coffee.

See also items: *794, 813, 838, 851, 855, 938, 1557, 1562, 1577, 1579, 1582, 1590, 1594, 1602, 1621, 1622, 1713.*

IV. PHYSIOLOGICAL EFFECTS OF COLD

A. General

1104. Anon. Science and technology in Japan; a conspectus of Japanese research in environmental physiology and closely related fields. *General Headquarters, Supreme Command for the Allied Powers, Economic and Scientific Section. Report no. 21. Tokyo, 1950. 242 p.*

Information on Japanese research is assembled under the main headings of bibliography of Japanese research in environmental physiology and related fields, with bibliographies on high and low temperatures, 585 citations (p. 2–73); on seasonal changes, 285 citations (p. 74–117); on clothing, 189 citations (p. 118–146); and with research reports on seasonal physiology, 293 citations (p. 146). Some of the subject headings are: frostbite, death from freezing, body temperature regulation, pathology, pharmacology and toxicology, skin temperature, circulation and gas metabolism, nutrition, and clothing. An appendix (p. 206-242) lists the repositories, in Japan, of the journals appearing in the bibliography, giving the original journal name and its translation in English.

1105. Adolph, E. F., and G. W. Molnar. Exchanges of heat and tolerances to cold in men exposed to outdoor weather. *Am. J. Physiol., v. 146, July 1946: 507–537.*

Nearly nude men were exposed to outdoor environments ranging from uncomfortably warm to bitter cold. Responses over periods of 1–4 hours were measured in terms of pulse rates, arterial pressures, deep and superficial temperatures, heat exchanges, ventilation rate, urinary flow, and blood concentration. Effects of exposure to cold may be noted at least 24 hours afterward.

1106.   Ar'ev, T. ÎA. On the temperature of transfused blood and the response of organism to low temperature blood transfusion [In Russian]. *Vest. khir., v. 55, June 1938: 689–701.*

Details are given of the warming of refrigerated blood for transfusion. Blood at temperatures between 2°C and 12°C was transfused into dogs with no harmful effects.

1107.   Brobeck, J. R. Physiology of heat and cold. *Annual Rev. Physiol., v. 8, 1946: 65–88.*

This general review includes discussions of cold stress, immersion foot, therapeutic use of cold, and the mechanism of temperature regulation in relation to diet, hormones, and the central nervous system. 143 refs.

1108.   Byrd, R. E. Alone. *New York, Putnam, 1938. 296 p.*

A vivid account is given of the psychological effects of cold, and of survival under extremely cold conditions, while maintaining an advance weather base alone in the Antarctic during the winter of 1934.

1109.   Carles, L. M. Pathogenic influences in the climate. Elements adverse to man [In French]. *Paris, Masson, 1945. 338 p.*

In the chapter entitled Cold (p. 39–62) is discussed the general effects of environmental cold; the use of cold in cancer therapy; diseases which result from exposure; hypothermia; frostbite; chilblains; abnormal cold sensitivity; and related aspects of cold injury.

1110.   Day, R. The effect of cold on man. (*Review series, v. 1, no. 2*) [*New York*], *Josiah Macy, Jr., Foundation, 1943. 64 p.*

This is a general review of the physiological and pathological effects of cold on man. The author discusses the maintenance of deep body temperature during exposure to cold (elevation of metabolism, control of heat loss, and cooling power of the environment); local reactions to cold (including frostbite, chilblains, and trench foot); and the relatiohship of exposure to cold and the resistance to infection. 231 refs.

1111.   Dureuil, M., and A. R. Ratsimamanga. Effect of sudden changes of temperature on the capacity for enforced work of the normal rat [In French]. *C. rend. Soc. biol., Par., v. 142, June 1948: 720–723.*

Rats were kept at a room temperature of 16°–19°C, and their reactions to enforced labor (lifting a weight attached to the tail) were studied at that temperature and during periods of sudden elevations or lowerings (by 5°–8°C) of that temperature, during a 4-hour period, the tests being repeated at intervals over several weeks. In general, the animals reacted to stimulation by either heat or cold in approximately the same way. About 30% reacted by an immediate betterment of their performance which slowly decreased and returned to the normal level at the end of the third hour. In the second week the results were about the same but a little less pronounced; in the third week there was little reaction to the stimulus. Another 40% reacted very strongly to temperature stimulus during the second week and later dropped to normal. The remaining 30% did not react noticeably to temperature stimulus. The reactions, in general, were characteristic of the alarm phenomenon of Selye. With the exception of some of the animals after the second hour of heat stimulus, all animals presented evidence of shock, such as tachycardia, extreme prostration, and bleeding from the natural orifices. It is suggested that the lack of response in some of the animals was an indication of poor general resistance.

1112.   Field, J., and V. E. Hall. Physiological effects of heat and cold. *Annual Rev. Physiol., v. 6, 1944: 69–94.*

The literature on the physiological effects of heat and cold, published in British and North American journals for the period of Aug. 1, 1942 to Aug. 1, 1943, is reviewed. Discussion is under the following subject headings: (1) effect of temperature, especially of cold, on oxygen uptake of excised tissue; (2) oxygen consumption of intact animals; (3) temperature regulation, its development in newborn; (4) various aspects of heat loss and heat gain; (5) adaptation; (6) hypothermia; and (7) hyperthermia. 129 refs.

1113.   **García Gómez, F. J.** Action of cold on the organism [In Spanish]. *Med. españ., v. 20, Nov. 1948: 359–378.*

This general review on the physiological effects of cold includes discussions of acclimatization, metabolic and hormonal effects, and of neurological, vascular, and hematological responses. The clinico-pathological aspects of frostbite, immersion foot, and trench foot are also included. 23 refs.

1114.   **Gilson, S. B.** Studies on adaptation to cold air in the rat. *Am. J. Physiol., v. 161, Apr. 1, 1950: 87–91.*

Albino rats were studied during protracted exposure to low environmental temperatures (4° to 6°C). Edema and erythema of the hairless areas of the feet appeared after a few hours of exposure but on continued exposure these disappeared. On protracted exposure the animals developed a progressive erythema and gangrene of the tail tip and ear edges. Heightened adrenal activity was indicated by the presence of adrenal enlargement. The animals developed a systolic hypertension after several weeks of cold exposure; it persisted or increased with further exposure; the blood pressure returned to normal on removal to room temperature.

1115.   **Günther, H.** Freezing and cooling. *Mitt. Biochem., v. 47, Mar. 1, 1940: 18–20.*

General discussion of the physiological effects of cold, including the effects of generalized and localized cooling and freezing.

1116.   **Hemingway, A.** Physiological effects of heat and cold. *Annual Rev. Physiol., v. 7, 1945: 163–180.*

This review of the literature for 1944 covers the physiological effects of heat and cold. Included are sections on nervous and hormonal controls of the thermoregulatory mechanisms, effects of cold on the circulation, effects of drugs on recovery from cold exposure, and information on the lowest recoverable body temperature. The etiology, clinico-pathological aspects, and treatment of frostbite are also included.

1117.   **Henschel, A., H. L. Taylor, and A. Keys.** Some responses to hot and cold test meals. *J. Appl. Physiol., v. 2, Oct. 1949: 208–216.*

Gastric motility was not greatly altered by the temperature (−8°, 26°, or 65°C) of a test meal when ingested. Blood sugar concentration was slightly but promptly increased after any test meal was ingested but was significantly greater after a cold meal; skin temperature of a finger dropped as much as 3.5°C after a cold meal and did not return to normal within 50 minutes; blood pressure increased after the larger (400 gram) but not the smaller (100 gram) cold meal; pulse rate increased after the larger test meal; none of the test meals produced significant electrocardiographic responses except for the cycle length.

*1118.   **Masamichi, R.** On the adaptability of the human body to winter coldness in Manchuria [In Japanese]. *Seppyō, v. 2, 1940: 111–114.*

"The effects of low temperatures on the physiological processes of the body were investigated in Manchuria. Experiments were conducted to demonstrate the effects of food on cold endurance. Visual, auditory, and tactile sensations as affected by cold exposure were studied. (Abstract by Ukitiro Nakaya)."—SIPRE Report 12, v. 3, Jan. 1953: 191.

1119.   **Mills, C. A.** Climate makes the man. *New York, Harper, 1942. 320 p.*

This book is a popularized account of experiments and examples drawn from the experience of a medical practitioner-researcher. The cases cited stress the role of the climate on man. The

* Original not seen.

effects of temperature on body heat production, fertility, sex drive, and psychology are discussed in a rather general way.

1120. Narsete, E. M. Some physiologic responses of airmen on long-range flights in the Arctic. *J. Aviat. M., v. 20, Oct. 1949: 336–342.*

Physiologic measurements were made on 50 airmen during long-range flights to the Arctic. Sub-lingual body temperature decreased during flight but returned to normal at the conclusion of the flight. Blood pressure, pulse rate, and respiratory rate all increased during flight, returning to normal when the flight ended. Cold was one of the factors which operated to produce the observed phenomena.

1121. Pathault,.... Influence of cold on the organism. *Gaz. méd. France, v. 46, Mar. 1, 1939: 293–294.*

The effects of cold on the animal and human organism are discussed in general with particular attention to thermoregulation, vasomotor phenomena, and the physical and physiological defenses against cold. Among the latter are the protection offered by clothing, plumage, or fur; the effect of barometric pressure; the upper the lower temperature limits of resistance; and adaptation.

1122. Petersen, W. F. What weather does to man. *Heating Piping, v. 10, Sept. 1938: 595–596, 598.*

Air-conditioning which brings about a temperature change of as much as 20° to 30°F between the hot outdoor temperature and the colder indoor temperature may bring about a considerable metabolic strain and may be quite detrimental to some individuals. On first coming into the cold there is said to be a period of "retreat" to the interior of the body. During this period the skin vessels contract; the blood pressure is increased; blood flow of the interior is greater; blood becomes transiently more alkaline; the K/Ca ratio is increased; and the body cells become less permeable. Within a very short period a stimulation phase ensues; blood vessels are dilated; the blood becomes more acid; the pulse, respiratory, and metabolic rate are increased; and the K/Ca ratio is lowered.

1123. Pugh, L. G. C. Aspects of the physiology of cold. *Physiotherapy, Lond., v. 36, Jan. 1950: 3–7.*

Measurements made on watchkeepers during a cold weather cruise (1949) of the Royal Navy showed that subjects did not feel cold as long as their mean body temperatures were above 35.2°C (95.2°F), and their mean skin temperatures above 32.0°C (89.5°F). They did not feel uncomfortably cold with a heat debt of 30 Cal/m² unless their initial body temperatures had been low. Subjects near shivering had heat debts of 40–50 Cal/m²; the major part of the heat debt arose during the first hour of exposure. The extremities were excluded in calculating these values since once vasoconstriction had taken place, they cooled independently of the rest of the body. The temperature of the toes during the 3-hour periods on deck at temperatures from −3°C (27°F) to −11°C (10°F), fell to between 22°C (72°F) and 15°C (59°F). The subjects were then aware of their feet being cold but the degree of discomfort was not great. Since the subjects were performing dexterity tests with bare hands, the finger temperature sometimes fell to 10°C (50°F). At this low temperature there was numbness of fingers and a 50% reduction in dexterity. When the fall in temperature was rapid, pain was experienced at about 15°C (59°F). If the subject remained comfortably warm, a large fall in temperature was followed by sudden flushing and warming of the skin due to hyperemia. The sensation of cold first evoked on entering a cold environment is thought to be associated with the rate of change of thermal gradients in superficial tissues rather than to skin temperatures as such. Once these changes are over, no further discomfort usually occurs until the body temperature has fallen to a level at which muscle tensing occurs.

1124. Stein, H. J., J. W. Eliot, and R. A. Bader. Physiological reactions to cold and their effects on the retention of acclimatization to heat. *J. Appl. Physiol., v. 1, Feb. 1949: 575–585.*

Measurements of physiological reactions to heat and cold were made in 3 subjects exposed alternately to heat and cold. In heat-acclimatized men, intermittent exposures to cold did not accelerate the de-acclimatization process. Occasional re-exposure to heat, however, proved to be sufficient to maintain heat acclimatization for several months. Successive exposures to cold resulted in more rapid vasoconstriction, as was shown in the more rapid decrease in toe temperatures, but no increase in tolerance to cold was demonstrated. Diuresis and negative chloride balance, which characterized the periods of cold exposure, tended to persist during subsequent re-exposures to heat.

See also items: 18, 620, 642, 673, 682, 685, 713, 817, 858, 898, 1095, 1333, 1558, 1586, 1606, 1611, 1620, 1624, 1626, 1641, 1653, 1698, 1777, 1974, 2007.

B. Integumentary System
(includes also teeth)

1125. Anton, H., and F. Elsässer. The role of the skin temperature in various areas of the body, especially the shoulder, in cooling experiments [In German]. *Arch. Hyg., Münch., v. 120 (2), 1938: 105–128.*

Studies were made of the skin temperature at 24 or more body locations, especially of the upper body, of a young man before and during severe cooling (20°–25°C, then 4°C) of the air temperature of the experimental room for a period of 20 minutes. It was found that the skin temperature about the shoulders, especially in the acromion area and over the deltoid muscle, was considerably lower than on other parts of the body. When the subject wore an especially designed shoulder protector, suitable for wear under regular clothing, this severe cooling of the shoulder area was completely prevented.

1126. Aschoff, J. On the range of the physical temperature regulation [In German]. *Pflügers Arch., v. 249, July 2, 1947: 137–147.*

The effects of various external temperatures on the skin temperature of the hand and finger were studied. A slight decrease in room temperature caused a large drop in skin temperature. Exposure to water of 10°C caused a heat loss of one-third to one-fifth of the initial value.

1127. Bonora, L. Immediate alterations of dental tissues due to continuous refrigeration. *Nova acta stomat., Parma, v. 3, Nov.–Dec. 1951: 65–74* [In Italian]. Also advance paper: Effect of cold on dental and paradental tissue [In Italian]. *Boll. Soc. ital. biol. sper., v. 27, July–Aug. 1951: 1119–1121.*

A small block of ice was applied to an inferior incisor tooth, and the surrounding gingival tissue, of each of a group of rats for 1 minute on three successive days. The temperature of the oral cavity dropped from 34°C to 32°C during the treatment. The temperature of the tissues treated with the ice dropped to the range of −6°C to −10°C. Microscopic evidence of great tissue changes was seen in the gingival mucosa, the paradental tissue, and the dental pulp. Although there was some evidence of reflex vasomotor action involving the Gasserian ganglion, this could not be definitely stated to be the mode of action involved. Using an ethyl choride spray instead of the ice brought about considerably less alteration of the various dental tissues.

1128. Buettner, K. [Büttner, K.] Effects of extreme heat and cold on human skin. II. Surface temperature, pain and heat conductivity in experiments with radiant heat. *J. Appl. Physiol., v. 3, June 1951: 703–713.*

In addition to his studies on threshold of pain, and on heat conductivity of the upper skin, following exposure to infrared radiation, the author studied some of the effects of extremely cold air (−40°C) on bare skin. Pre-cooling the skin seemed to offer an effective protection against overheating.

1129. Dünner, M. Influence of physical factors (atmospheric pressure, temperature) on secretion of sebaceous glands in man [In German, summaries in German, English, and French]. *Dermatologica, Basel, v. 93, 1946: 249–271.*

Low environmental temperature (10°C) was found to cause a decrease in the quantitative secretion of the sebaceous glands and in the sebum-level on the surface of the skin. High temperature (50°C) raised both the activity and the level. Low atmospheric pressure had no immediate influence on either. The sebum-level is dependent on the viscosity of the sebum; the viscosity is strongly influenced by temperature.

1130. Freitag, W. On the effect of cold on the dental system [In German]. *Luftfahrtmedizin, v. 7, Jan. 30, 1943: 335–343.*

In a study of the effects of cold on the teeth of flying personnel, the temperatures in three sections of the oral cavity were measured while subjects were exposed to environmental temperatures of −44° to −46°C. The mouth temperatures ranged from 0° to +28°C. Under the influence of contraction and expansion due to temperature changes, tooth fillings are apt to become loose and the enamel of the teeth may develop fissures, which accounts for an increased incidence of caries in aviators.

1131. Goldby, F., C. S. Hicks, W. J. O'Connor, and D. A. Sinclair. A comparison of the skin temperature and skin circulation of naked whites and Australian aboriginals exposed to similar environmental changes. *Austral. J. Exp. Biol., v. 16, Mar. 1938: 29–37.*

Naked Australian aborigines in the Musgrave Ranges of Central Australia and unclothed whites were studied under the same conditions of atmospheric cooling. Though the skin temperature falls to an equal extent in both races, it was found that the natives appear to have a more effective control of heat loss from the skin by vasoconstriction in response to cold.

1132. Hardy, J. D., H. Goodell, and H. G. Wolff. The influence of skin temperature upon the pain threshold as evoked by thermal radiation. *Science, v. 114, Aug. 10, 1951: 149–150.*

The authors report measurements taken of pain, cold, and warmth thresholds on the back of the hand, the forehead, and other parts of the body. Relationships between these and environmental temperatures, skin temperatures, and the rate of change of skin temperatures, are analyzed.

1133. Harvey, W. Tooth temperature with reference to dental pain while flying. *Brit. Dental J., v. 75, Nov. 5, 1943: 221–228.*

Because some airmen had experienced toothache while flying at high altitudes, experimental subjects were placed in a refrigerated decompression chamber with thermocouples inserted in the fillings of their teeth. In some experiments, oral breathing was maintained throughout; in others, nasal breathing. After 12 minutes in a chamber at −35°C, the lowest tooth temperature recorded in any experiment was 20.4°C. A further drop might have produced pain; presumably no pain was experienced in any experiment. However, when subjects drank cold water (1°C), tooth temperature registered 12°C and definite pain was felt. It is believed that the lips, cheeks, tongue, and saliva protect teeth greatly from cold air.

1134. Hicks, C. S., and W. J. O'Connor. Skin temperature of Australian aboriginals under varying atmospheric conditions. *Austral. J. Exp. Biol., v. 16, Mar. 1938: 1–18.*

The skin temperature of Australian aborigines was measured under natural conditions of exposure to heat and cold and also under controlled conditions. Skin temperatures of natives asleep by the campfire were observed to be 5° below those of whites in bed. When naked blacks and whites were under same environmental conditions, skin temperatures fell to the same extent.

1135. Horwitz, O., G. Pierce, and H. Montgomery. Oxygen tension of tissues by the polarographic method. III. The effect of local heat on the oxygen tension of the skin of extremities. *Circulation, N. Y., v. 4 (1), 1951: 111–115.*

The oxygen tension of the skin of human extremities was measured at skin temperatures from 10° to 50°C. Oxygen tension became very low when skin temperature was lowered to 15°C. In normal extremities oxygen tension increased as the skin temperature rose, with no resulting pain at the higher temperatures; in extremities with occluded arteries, similar effects were noted, but with pain occurring at the higher temperatures.

1136. Koïranskiĭ, B. B. The effect of low temperatures on the body [In Russian]. *In: Trudy iubileĭnoĭ nauchnoĭ sessii Instituta Gigieny Truda i Professional' nykh Zabolevaniĭ (Leningrad, June 15–19, 1939), p. 146–147. Leningrad, 1940.*

Study was made of the skin temperature of the hand, and in particular of the 3rd phalanx of the index finger, during 30 minutes of immersion in a water-bath (at 5°, 10°, or 15°C). The following observations were made. In the first 5 minutes a sharp decrease in skin temperature indicated vascular contraction in the skin. Beginning with the 8th minute or later, acclimatization commenced. After the 10th minute, a wavelike increase in skin temperature set in. A 3-hour cold stimulation at 5°C produced in certain subjects wavelike fluctuations in the skin temperature (corresponding to clearings in the vessels), which started 3–10 minutes after the onset of cooling. Restoration of normal skin temperature after the above cooling proceeded slowly (more rapidly during the first 5–10 minutes), usually with adaptation to the surrounding temperature (21°–23°C). Repeated cold stimulations at 5°C for 30 minutes during 12 weeks progressively produced: a greater decrease in skin temperature; a greater drop of temperature in the 1st, 5th, and 10th minutes; a sharp increase in the wave frequency; an earlier appearance of waves; and a tendency to more rapid restoration of skin temperature. The effect of cold on the exposure of the undressed body to temperatures of 10° to 20°C for 1 hour produced the following results: the degrees of temperature decrease in different parts of the skin were unequal; the higher the initial temperature of the skin region, the lesser would be its cooling, and the more rapid its adaptation. The temperature of the phalanges can serve as an indicator for the general cooling of the body. The changes in skin temperature (i.e., in blood supply) have a general effect on various organs and body systems as well as a local effect. The cooling of only one hand decreased the skin temperature of the other; general cooling of the body induced in experimental animals a decrease in glycogen of the blood, muscles, and liver, and an increase in lactic acid; in rabbits kept 3–3½ months at −8° to −12°C, the general cooling induced hypertrophy of the adrenal glands; the anaphylactic shock was more violent in cooled rabbits than in animals kept at room temperature; a camphor injection after general or local cooling induced a sudden vascular dilatation.

1137. Koïranskiĭ, B. B. Vascular reaction in the skin of the foot in response to local cooling with regard to the etiopathogenesis of the common cold [Abstract, in Russian]. *Sovet. ref. med. Obozr., Fiziol., 1950 (6): 43.*

The vascular reaction of the foot in response to local cold stimulation was studied with a view of elucidating the etiopathogenesis of the common cold. The skin temperature of the right toe was measured in 4 healthy subjects (20 to 30 years of age) at room temperature and then during immersion (in a rubber sock) in cold water of a constant temperature. It was found that an incomplete vascular defense reaction takes place in the cooled skin portion, as the reactive hyperemia remains absent. This lowers the resistance to low temperatures of the cooled tissues. Moreover, the appearance of a general vascular reaction, spreading to various systems and organs, combines with the local reaction to create a state of hypothermia, since the changes have in some cases a disorganizing effect on the normal functions of these organs. These facts explain why the cooling of the foot is often a leading factor in the etiology of the common cold.

1138. Linderholm, H. On the influence of stress by cold on dermal spread [In English]. *Acta physiol. scand., v. 24, Aug. 1951: 163–173.*

The spread in the skin of an intradermally injected hemoglobin solution was inhibited in living rabbits by exposure to cold (2° to 5°C) for 15–16 hours; no inhibition was evidenced when the rabbits were killed immediately before the spreading test. In mice exposed to similar cold conditions for 11 days there was an inhibition in both living and dead animals. The mechanism of the differences in dermal spreading in living and dead animals may be connected with different phases of the general adaptation syndrome—the alarm reaction with eventual changes in the peripheral circulation and the stage of resistance with possible change in the structure of the connective tissue. Specific effects of cold, however, cannot be excluded.

1139. Maslov, A. F. Electrical resistance of the skin on exposure to cold [In Russian, summary in English]. *Fiziol. zh. SSSR, v. 28 (2–3), 1940: 264–270.*

Repeated applications of cold to one hand (immersion in water of 10°C for 15 minutes daily) increased the electrical resistance at the locus of cold application and, in a lesser degree, in the skin of the other hand. The period of restoration after exposure to cold was shortened by repeated applications, indicating an induced adaptation to cold.

1140. Mialhe, C. Pigmentation and sympathectomy; dissociation of sympathetic denervation factor and of thermic factor [In French]. *Ann. derm. syph., Par., v. 78, Nov.–Dec. 1951: 721–727.*

Studies were done with white-furred rabbits with pigmented (dark) extremities in which cold provoked slight pigmentation of the body and heat hindered the coloration of the extremities. Preliminary experiments had shown that following cervical sympathectomy the pigmentation of the area of the ears and across the nose was decreased. Unilaterally sympathectomized animals, maintained at various temperatures for fairly long periods showed that—independent of the transient thermogenic stimulus to increase pigmentation—sympathectomy acted to decrease the pigmentation.

1141. Pellerat, J., and M. Murat. Variations in the histamine content of the skin under the influence of cold and in certain dermatoses. *C. rend. Soc. biol., Par., v. 139, Dec. 1945: 1141–1142.*

If large areas of human skin are chilled, its histamine content drops while blood histamine rises. Certain forms of dermatitis exhibit a similar reaction.

1142. Popov, N. A., M. A. Vadimova, and S. A. Feinstein. The response of the skin to cooling and its alteration under the influence of carbon dioxide baths [In Russian]. *Fiziol. zh. SSSR, v. 30, 1941: 581–588.*

In skin areas acclimated to cold, the relation between the temperature of the skin and the time required for restoration to normal skin temperature obeys a law which is not valid for non-acclimated areas. Non-acclimated areas treated with CO_2 baths react like acclimated areas.

1143. Schindl, K. Skin temperatures under the influence of cold [In German]. *Zschr. ges. exp. Med., v. 113, June 1944: 613–626.*

Measurements were made of the skin temperature of areas of the body exposed to environmental cold when the subjects were either drinkers of alcohol or were abstainers. Skin temperatures were found to be higher and returned to normal more quickly in the subjects who abstained from drinking.

1144. Stray, K. Experimental investigations of the reaction of the skin to cold; contribution to the prophylaxis of freezings [In English]. *Oslo, I kommisjon hos Dybwad, 1943. 216 p. Also, in English, in: Skrifter Norske Videnskaps-Akad. i Oslo. I. Mat.-Naturv. Klasse, No. 3, 1943: 1–216.*

Studies were made of the reaction to cold of the skin of the author and of recruits in the Norwegian Army during the winter of 1940–41. The experimental report is preceded by a review of the literature on the anatomy and physiology of the skin, with special reference to its reactions to cold. Observations include reactions of exposed parts of head and hands to external temperatures, wind velocity, and other factors. Various ointments and powders were tested as to their prophylactic and therapeutic properties. Bibliography, p. 207–216.

See also items: 558, 579, 625, 1176, 1185, 1242, 1282, 1774, 2033, 2079.

C. Muscular and Skeletal Systems

1145. Bing, H. I., A. Carlsten, and S. Christiansen. The effect on muscular temperature produced by cooling normal and ultraviolet radiated skin [In English]. *Acta med. scand., v. 121 (5–6), 1945: 577–591.*

Temperature of the biceps brachii muscle was recorded for 54 subjects before and after local cooling of the skin area above it for 5 minutes. The same amount of cooling produced individual variations of temperature from a very slight amount to 10°–12°C. In general the fall of muscle temperature was found to be due to direct cooling of muscle tissue. However, in cooling of moderate intensity, the blood vessels of the muscle were found to be dilated. Subjects whose skin had previously been treated by ultraviolet radiation were better able to compensate for the increased heat loss indicating that the magnitude of temperature drop might depend upon blood flow of the covering skin and subcutaneous tissue.

1146. Fischer, E. Muscle strength and the weather. *Arch. Phys. M., v. 28, May 1947: 295–300.*

This study would indicate that weather changes represent a factor of significant importance in relation to muscle grip, showing some correlation of grip strength with changes in barometric pressure and with temperature (ranges of 20°–60°F, and 40°–80°F). The record of one subject might be read as showing a decrease in strength during the passing of a warm front and a decrease followed by an increase during the slow passing of a cold front.

1147. Hunter, J. and M. G. Whillans. A study of the effect of cold on joint temperature and mobility. *Canad. J. M. Sc., v. 29, Oct. 1951: 255–262.*

Exposure of the knee joint of the cat to low ambient temperatures (about 32°F, and sub-zero°F) resulted in a lowered joint temperature which was lower than the rectal, muscle, or "average" skin temperature. Exposure to the lowered temperature brought about an increase in the force necessary to start movement at the joint.

1148. Perkins, J. F., Jr., M. C. Li, C. H. Nicholas, W. H. Lassen, and P. E. Gertler. Cooling as a stimulus to smooth muscles. *Am. J. Physiol., v. 163, Oct. 1, 1950: 14–26.*

The eyes of anesthetized cats were enucleated and the cervical sympathetic trunks were severed to eliminate the activity of the autonomic nervous system. Nictating membranes of the eyelids were cooled by application of hollow glass bulbs to the orbits of the eyes. Water of 37°, 10°, or 5 °C was circulated through the bulbs. Cooling, either rapid or slow, stimulated contraction of the membrane. This stimulus was found not to be the same as that elicited by epinephrine. Other smooth muscle preparations, from dogs, rats, and frogs, tested in a similar manner but with the use of a muscle bath, also showed stimulation by cold.

1149. Tuttle, W. W. The effects of decreased temperature on the activity of intact muscle. *J. Laborat. Clin. M., v. 26, Sept. 1941: 1913–1915.*

Local cooling of the intact gastrocnemius muscle of human subjects showed that the lowering of the temperature increased the relaxation time of the muscle 2 or 3 times as much as it did the contraction time.

1150. Wakim, K. G., A. N. Porter, and F. H. Krusen. Influence of physical agents and of certain drugs on intra-articular temperature. *Arch. Phys. M., v. 32, Nov. 1951: 714–721.*

Hot packs and short-wave or microwave diathermy raised the intra-articular temperature of the knee of dogs as well as of the adjacent muscle and subcutaneous tissue, but no significant reflex changes in the contralateral joint were observed. Ice packs markedly reduced the temperatures of the treated knee with only a slight reduction in temperature in the untreated knee. Repeated percutaneous electric stimulation produced no significant change in intra-articular temperature but brought about a temperature rise in the muscular and subcutaneous tissue. Intravenous administration of vasoconstrictor and vasodilator drugs (epinephrine, nitroglycerin, Priscoline, or histamine) produced insignificant changes in the temperature of the joints and adjacent tissue.

1151. Walker, S. M. Failure of potentiation in successive, post-tetanic, and summated twitches in cooled skeletal muscle of the rat. *Am. J. Physiol., v. 166, Aug. 1951: 480–484.*

The *in situ* triceps surae of the rat was stimulated electrically through the cut sciatic nerve with the rat at normal body temperature (37 °C) or with the animal placed in a cooling chamber at about 15 °C so that the muscle temperature was reduced to 29° or 20 °C. At normal body temperature 3 types of potentiation were observed: (1) potentiation in successive responses; (2) posttetanic potentiation; and (3) potentiation resulting from 2 stimuli. It was concluded that the potentiation was due in all cases to an increase of contractile strength in the component muscle fibers. Cooling the muscle to 29° or 20 °C abolished the 3 types of potentiation observed in normal muscle. Some evidence is presented that the failure of potentiation in cooled muscle is not due to fatigue.

1152. Wawersik, F. Von. On the casuistics of paramyotonia [In German]. *Nervenarzt, v. 18, Oct. 1947: 463–466.*

The case history is discussed in detail of a patient suffering from paramyotonia in which the condition was brought on by exposure to cold. The condition is traced, as a dominant inherited factor, through six generations. The muscle tone disorder and cold rigidity begins in childhood in the underarm, hand, and pharyngeal musculature and death eventually comes from muscular hypertrophy.

1153. Wiersma, C. A. G., and G. A. Feigen. Influence of temperature on the distensibility of the pubic ligament. *Proc. Soc. Exp. Biol., N. Y., v. 70, Feb. 1949: 349–351.*

The distensibility of the pubic ligament of guinea pigs was studied both in isolated preparations and intact within the animal, using a constant load but at varied environmental temperatures from 25°–42 °C. In the range of temperature between 30°–40 °C both types of preparation exhibited a marked dependence of stretching on temperature; distension at 30 °C was negligible; above 34 °C it was rapid.

See also items: 560, 866, 1188, 1201, 1282, 1608, 1682.

D. Nervous System and Sense Organs

1154. Abderhalden, E. Sensory systems of the skin [In German]. *In: Lehrbuch der Physiologie. Berlin, Urban & Schwarzenberg, 1944. 409 p.*

Chapter 22 (p. 274–287) is entitled Sensory Systems of the Skin, and deals with both temperature and pain sensations. The anatomy and functioning of the central nervous system and of the nerve pathways in temperature regulation are discussed as well as the localization and functioning of cold and warm spots on the skin. The limits of temperature regulation in man (approximately 16° to 42 °C) and the perception of temperature are discussed, the latter tied to pain perception. The points on the skin of the hand sensitive to heat and cold are mapped, and Krause's end organs and Ruffini's corpuscles for perception of cold and heat respectively, are described.

1155. Bañuelos García, M. Clinical note on medical rhigosis and thalposis [In Spanish]. *Clín. laborat., Zaragoza, v. 50, July 1950: 1–12.*

Cold and warmth perception are discussed, including physiopathology and the clinical symptoms of irregularities of perception and sensation. Three case histories of patients with abnormalities of cold sensation, are given.

1156. Bazett, H. C. Temperature sense in man. *In: American Institute of Physics. Temperature, its measurement and control in science and industry, p. 489–501. New York, Reinhold, 1941.*

The author reports a study of the thermal receptors and the mechanism by which heat and cold stimuli are picked up and transmitted by the nerves to the central nervous system. Problems of measurement, methods of stimulation, and other aspects of experimentation in this area are analyzed.

1157. Bernhard, C. G., and R. Granit. Nerve as model temperature end organ. *J. Gen. Physiol., v. 29, Mar. 20, 1946: 257–265.*

The main stem of the sciatic nerve of decerebrate or anesthetized cats was locally cooled or warmed by a thermode and the discharge recorded from one of the roots. Cooling or heating of the mammalian nerve sets up a discharge, which is preceded by a local temperature potential, the effected region being electronegative relative to a normal portion of the nerve. These local temperature potentials, set up by the nerve itself, are said to serve as "generator potentials" and the mechanism found is regarded as the prototype for temperature end organs.

1158. Bickford, R. G. The fiber dissociation produced by cooling human nerves. *Clin. Sc., Lond., v. 4, Dec. 1939: 159–165.*

Human superficial nerves were cooled to temperatures of 5°C to 15°C producing paralysis. The apparatus for cooling consisted essentially of a metal cooling element made from lead tubing through which a water-ice-salt mixture was circulated, and which was placed in close contact with the skin overlying a nerve. A thermal junction was soldered into the tubing at the point at which it was in contact with the skin. The effects of rapid cooling and the vasomotor paralysis which followed are described. The order of fiber paralysis was found to differ from that produced by asphyxia or cocaine. The recovery of function on rewarming was by stages which reversed those produced by chilling.

1159. Bing, H. I., and A. P. Skouby. The influence of skin temperature on the number of reacting cold spots [In English]. *Acta physiol. scand., v. 18, Aug. 1949: 190–196.*

A study was made of the number of cold spots, in a 6 cm² area of skin on the volar aspect of the forearm of two different subjects, at different skin temperatures on 17 different days over a period of one month. The number of reacting cold spots was found to increase, in one subject, from 17 to 93 in a temperature increase from 25° to 33°C; and, in the other subject, from 13 to 93 from 27.5° to 34.5°C. The cause of this increase in number of spots reacting at higher temperatures is not known, but it is thought possible that the increase in excitability is due to increase in rate of restitutional processes following a previous reaction, or that it improves the conduction of impulses via afferent nerves.

1160. Bing, H. I., and A. P. Skouby. Sensitization of cold receptors by substances with acetylcholine effect [In English]. *Acta physiol. scand., v. 21, Nov. 1950: 286–302.*

The number of cold spots in a given area of the skin of the test subject, was found to increase with the skin temperature, with, however, some areas from which no cold sensation could be released. Localization of reacting cold spots varied somewhat from time to time with constant external conditions and constant skin temperature but in general could be repeated with a slight standard deviation in the number. From studies with acetylcholine and similar substances, it is concluded that the number of cold spots must be due to direct effect of acetylcholine either on the cold receptors or on the nerve fibers connected with them. It is, therefore, possible that the cold spots are regulated by changes in the active acetylcholine content of the skin.

1161. Dubois, R. Meteorosensitivity of nervous system [In French]. *Progr. méd., Par., v. 77, Sept. 10, 1949: 390–394.*

The effect on the nervous system of heat, cold, changes of temperature, light, humidity, wind, rain, storms, snow, and seasonal changes, is discussed. The nervous system adapts, generally, more easily to heat than to cold. Cold affecting the nervous system brings about an increase in infections, such as tetanus. Some of the nervous afflictions which have been attributed to cold are facial paralysis, and neuralgias especially of the sciatic nerve and the brachial plexus. Cold has also been thought to favor the appearance of myotonia and of depressed mental states.

*1162.   Dzidzishvili, N. On the general inhibition and facilitation caused by temperature stimulation of the skin [In Russian]. *Soob. Akad. nauk Gruzinskoi SSR, v. 1 (3), 1940: 217–224.*

Deals with motor responses of rabbits during and after cooling of the skin and their relation to the nervous system. See Biol. Abst., v. 20, 1946; ✳ 19849.

1163.   Ebaugh, F. G., Jr., and R. Thauer. Measurement of cold and warmth thresholds of subjects exposed to environments from 18°C to 38°C [Abstract]. *Fed. Proc., Balt., v. 8, Mar. 1949: 38.*

Sensory thresholds for cold remained constant in air temperatures of 15°C to 25°C but increased with the air temperatures from 25°C until at 38°C the cold threshold was more than twice that of cooler environments. Warmth thresholds remained constant throughout the range of air temperatures studied. It is thought possible that hyperemia of the skin increases the threshold of cold sensation but has no effect on the threshold of warmth sensation.

1164.   Ebaugh, F. G., Jr., and R. Thauer. Influence of various environmental temperatures on cold and warmth thresholds. *J. Appl. Physiol., v. 3, Oct. 1950: 173–182.*

In a study of the effect of different environmental temperatures on the cold and warmth thresholds of human subjects, the average value of the cold threshold at environmental temperatures between 16°C and 24°C was lower than the average value at environmental temperatures between 35°C and 40°C. There was no change in the warmth threshold. The author cites indirect evidence that the rise in the cold threshold at the higher environmental temperatures was associated with vasodilatation of the blood vessels of the skin.

1165.   Ebbecke, U. On a circulatory reflex (trigeminus nerve) arising in the facial skin [In German]. *Pflügers Arch., v. 247 (2–3), 1943: 240–254.*

Trigeminal nerve stimulation was brought about by immersing the face of several subjects in cold water (10°C) for varying periods up to 30 seconds or by blowing cold air against the face. Reflex swallowing, momentary reflex breath stoppage, diminished heart rate, and increased blood pressure due to generalized vasoconstriction, were observed. In certain very susceptible subjects there was a momentary heart stoppage. These reactions are regarded as part of complicated reflex mechanisms in the facial skin having to do with protection against cold.

1166.   Ebbecke, U., and F. Knüchel. The trigeminal, respiratory, swallowing and heart reflex in the rabbit [In German]. *Pflügers Arch., v. 247 (2–3), 1943: 255–263.*

A spray of ice-cooled water was played softly over the nose, mouth, and face of lightly-anesthetized rabbits for several seconds. A breath stoppage, lasting slightly longer than the pouring of the water, a temporary increase in blood pressure, and a swallowing reaction were observed. In one rabbit, ice-cold water sprayed into the nasal opening produced a similar effect but to a lesser degree in both blood pressure and pulse rate and elicited no swallowing reaction. The severing of both vagus nerves at the neck had no effect on the reaction of the facial skin after having cold water played on it. Stimulation of the trigeminus nerve brought about stronger reflex reactions in the rabbits than had been exhibited by humans (item 1165).

---

* Original not seen.

1167.   Esser, A. M. Ancient writings about the eye in snow and frost [In German]. *Klin. Mbl. Augenh., v. 100, Jan. 1938: 100–103.*

The author refers to passages, mostly from the Greek classical writers, on eye injuries from frost and snow. In several of these it is stated that while the feet may become frosted and eventually even gangrenous, the injury to the eyes is not usually from the cold itself but is rather that caused by the glare from the snow which causes "snow blindness." Other references are to excessive lacrimation, and irritation of the eyes by the cold.

1168.   Fay, T. Response of human brain tissue to local refrigeration [Abstract]. *Arch. Neur. Psychiat., Chic., v. 47, Jan. 1942: 189–191.*

Five terminal cases of brain tumor are discussed, in which a metal capsule had been inserted in the brain at a depth of 3–9 cm. Refrigerating solutions were circulated through the hollow capsule to cool the tissue to 40°F and 20°F. Some capsules were retained in the tissue for as long as 210 days. Observations indicated that normal brain tissue can withstand temperatures of 20°F for prolonged periods and that certain regressive changes occur in tumor tissue exposed to 40°F for prolonged periods.

1169.   Fritz, A. The effect of temperature on retinal blood vessels [In French]. *Bull. Soc. belge opht., v. 78, Apr. 30, 1939: 121–126.*

A cold atmosphere tends to bring about a retinal ischemia caused by constriction of the blood vessels. The author states that about two weeks after return to normal temperature, following an exposure to severe cold, a congestive retinal condition with hyperemia may develop. In one instance this resulted in retinal hemorrhage and in another in thrombosis of a vein. This sequence of events he attributes to a neuro-humoral mechanism, acting directly on the retinal circulation through the sympathetic system.

1170.   Fritz, A. The ocular pressure-decreasing action of cold applied to the orbital region [In French]. *Bull. Soc. belge opht., v. 78, Apr. 30, 1939: 127.*

The application of ice for several minutes on the closed eyelids quickly brings about a drop in ocular pressure in the order of 6 to 10 mm Hg. The vasomotor action caused by the cold brings about changes in the production of intraocular fluid.

1171.   Gilmer, B. von H. The relation of cold sensitivity to sweat duct distribution and the neurovascular mechanisms of the skin. *J. Psychol., Provincet., v. 13, Apr. 1942: 307–325.*

Through analysis of biopsy materials two distribution patterns of cutaneous cold spots were discerned. About twice as many cold-sensitive spots were found on sweat duct openings as were found on spots which did not include the mouths of sweat ducts. The relation of these findings to cold sensitivity and neurovascular activity is discussed.

1172.   Gordon, G. The mechanism of the vasomotor reflexes produced by stimulating mammalian sensory nerves. *J. Physiol., Lond., v. 102, June 30, 1943: 95–107.*

Cats, which were under anesthesia or were decerebrated, had the medial popliteal nerve and its extension the posterior tibial surgically exposed from mid-thigh to ankle. The nerve was treated in various ways including cooling (to temperatures between 4° and 10°C) or freezing and was then stimulated electrically. When the nerve was cooled to 4°C, no depressor reflex could be obtained and the pressor reflex was smaller than normal. When the cooling element was removed both reflexes reappeared within a few minutes. Cooling the nerve below 4°C abolished both reflexes. Following freezing and electrical stimulation every 5 minutes, there was no vasomotor response to stimulation at the distal pair of electrodes for the first 10 minutes. A pressor reflex then appeared on strong stimulation and after an hour or more it was larger than that obtained by stimulation of the proximal pair of electrodes. At this stage a weak stimulus distally gave a small pressor reflex and at the proximal electrode gave a large depressor reflex. The effect of cooling or freezing of the sensory nerves resembled that of asphyxia in that the depressor reflex was the first to be abolished by cooling and the last to return on rewarming.

1173. Granit, R., and C. R. Skoglund. The effect of temperature on the artificial synapse formed by the cut end of the mammalian nerve. *J. Neurophysiol.*, *v. 8, May 1945: 211–217.*

Transmission across the artificial synapse—formed by the cut ends of the sciatic nerve of the cat—is facilitated by cooling (16 °C) so that the relayed volleys increase in size. In warming (40.4°) the size is decreased.

1174. Grow, M. C. Preliminary report on effect of cold on oxygen content of the blood. *Mil. Surgeon, v. 86, Mar. 1940: 225–235.*

The author found that mental symptoms, consisting of warped judgment and distortion of the intellect, appear immediately after exposure to severe cold and are the result of anoxia. The use of oxygen and small percentages of carbon dioxide are recommended.

1175. Hardy, J. D. and T. W. Oppel. Stimulation of the cold end organs of the human skin by radiation. *Am. J. Physiol., v. 123, July 1938: 89–90.*

End-organs in the skin responsible for cold sensation were stimulated by cold radiation. It was found that there were more cold end-organs than those for heat but that it required more cold to excite a cold end-organ than heat to stimulate a heat end-organ. It was also found that temperature sensation does not depend on vascular changes in the skin.

1176. Hardy, J. D., and T. W. Oppel. Studies in temperature sensation. IV. The stimulation of cold sensation by radiation. *J. Clin. Invest., v. 17, Nov. 1938: 771–778.*

End-organs in the skin sensitive to cold were tested in six subjects by exposure to cold radiating from a block of CO_2 ice. It was found that cold end-organs are nearer to the skin surface than heat end-organs and that the former are more numerous per unit area than the latter. Cold radiation was found to produce about twice the rate of change in skin temperature, calorie for calorie, as heat radiation. Temperature sensation does not depend upon vascular changes in the skin.

1177. Hensel, H. Temperature perception and intracutaneous temperature changes [In German]. *Pflügers Arch., v. 252, 1950: 165–215.*

Using previously described methods (item 126), the author continued with his investigations of continuously registering intracutaneous temperature changes at exactly measurable depths of layers from 0.06 mm to 2 mm. Temperature stimulation by thermodes containing circulating water of controled temperature (15° to 40 °C) was applied to the hands, fingers, underarm, and feet of subjects. Warm or cold solutions were given intravenously also. Thermal stimulation was also done over small and large areas, with constant and varying temperatures, and over differing periods of duration. The subjects, unaware of the degree or duration of stimulation, were asked to give their estimates of the degree of warmth or cold they had experienced. The author concludes that the findings are not sufficiently explained by any previous theory of temperature perception, several of which he had mentioned earlier in the paper.

1178. Hensel, H., and Y. Zotterman. The response of the cold receptors to constant cooling [In English]. *Acta physiol. scand., v. 22, Apr. 25, 1951: 96–105.*

Cats or dogs were anesthetized and, after surgery of the mandibula to obtain free access to the whole tongue and branches of the lingual nerve, their tongues were pulled forward and fixed on a sheet of cork. Thermal stimulus was applied by a right-angled metal thermode through which tap water at various temperatures could be circulated. Action potentials of the lingual nerve were recorded by a cathode ray oscillograph. Application of an "indifferent" thermode (35°–37 °C) brought a burst of large fast impulses from the pressure and touch receptors. If the thermode was well insulated, there was an absence of all other impulses. When the water was changed from 37° to 18°C, there was an almost immediate decrease of the action potentials; the impulses persisted throughout the hour period of the test although the tongue had reached a constant temperature. Rewarming caused an immediate cessation of the impulses. Contrary to an earlier theory, the results show that thermoreceptors are stimulated not only by changes in temperature but also by constant temperature stimuli.

1179. Hensel, H., and Y. Zotterman. The persisting cold sensation [In English]. *Acta. physiol. scand., v 22, Apr. 25, 1951: 106–113.*

The tongues of anesthetized cats were surgically prepared and the action potentials from the lingual nerves were recorded in the same manner as in previous experiments. When the tongue was warmed from 10°–16°C to less than 22°C, the cold impulses persisted throughout the whole period of warming and even after establishment of a constant temperature of 21°C. When the temperature was raised similarly to more than 22°C, the cold impulses gradually disappeared. The experiments are said to show that the after-sensation of cold is due to a true, adequate stimulation of the cold receptors by the prevailing low temperature, and that below a certain temperature cold impulses are always present, independently of whether the temperature rises or falls. This is in opposition to the almost universally accepted theory of Weber according to which only a rise or fall of temperature is an adequate stimulus for the thermoreceptors.

1180. Hensel, H., and Y. Zotterman. Quantitative relations between the discharge of individual cold-receptors and the temperature [In German]. *Acta physiol. scand., v. 23, Sept. 1951: 291–319.*

A branch of the lingual nerve of the narcotized cat was prepared surgically so that the discharge of single functioning cold fibers of the nerve on the upper surface of the tongue could be studied in relation to temperature. Temperature of the gilded silver thermode was registered by means of microgalvanometers simultaneously with the action potentials. With a completely constant temperature a constant discharge of cold receptors with constant frequency may occur. The frequency of the activity is a function of the temperature: i.e., the cold receptors function here like a thermometer. At very low temperatures (between 0° and 5°C) the constant frequency is low, reaches a maximum of about 10 impulses/second with rising temperature, and sinks to zero value with further temperature rise. The thresholds and maxima of this constant discharge of individual cold fibers are divided over a large temperature area. Single cold receptors can be constantly active even somewhat above the blood temperature. The total discharge frequency of all cold fibers in the entire nerve, obtained by a statistical distribution of the single fibers is, with the range of 20°–40°C, nearly a linear function of the temperature. In temperature changes the discharge frequency depends upon the speed of the changes as well as the temperature as such. There is considerable discussion in the paper of the specificity of cold fibers, peripheral and central thresholds, thermoreceptors and thermoregulation, and the theory of receptor stimulation.

1181. Hensel, H., and Y. Zotterman. The effect of menthol on the thermoreceptors [In English]. *Acta physiol. scand., v. 24, Sept. 1951: 27–34.*

The discharges of the thermal receptors of the lingual nerve of anesthetized cats were recorded with and without the application of menthol solutions while the tongue was being kept under various, exact, temperature conditions. At 40°C there was no discharge of cold receptors until menthol was applied; this discharge ceased when the temperature was raised to 47°C. At 20°C the active discharge from cold receptors was greatly increased by the addition of menthol. No effect on warm receptors was elicited. The threshold concentration for menthol action on the cold receptors was found to lie between 1:1,000,000 and 1:500,000. It is suggested that such action probably indicates the involvement of enzymes.

1182. Hensel, H., and Y. Zotterman. Action potentials of cold fibres and intracutaneous temperature gradient. *J. Neurophysiol., v. 14, Sept. 1951: 377–385.*

Studies were made of the cold impulses from the lingual nerve of a cat when the tongue was cooled either by application of a thermode (at 10°C) to the upper or lower surface of the tongue or by injection of cooled (5° to 10°C) Ringer's solution into the lingual artery. The experiments show that stimulation of the cold receptors does not depend upon the direction or slope of intracutaneous temperature gradient but simply on the cooling of the receptor layer.

1183. Hensel, H., L. Ström, and Y. Zotterman. Electrophysiological measurements of depth of thermoreceptors. *J. Neurophysiol., v. 14, Sept. 1951: 423–429.*

A physiological method for measuring the depth of the cold receptors in the tongue of the cat is described, based on the recording of spike potentials of specific cold fibers in the lingual nerve (during sudden cooling from about 40 °C to 15 °C, and rewarming), and the simultaneous recording of the temperature changes. The mean value (0.18 mm. ± 0.04) obtained from a great number of measurements, is in good accordance with histological findings.

1184. Hensel, H., and Y. Zotterman. Response of mechanoreceptors to thermal stimulation. *J. Physiol., Lond., v. 115, Sept. 28, 1951: 16–24.*

The tongue of the cat or dog was cooled as in earlier experiments and the action potentials of the lingual nerve were observed. Usually only the smaller cold spikes, but occasionally a large spike, were recorded. The large spikes appeared only when cooled strongly and disappeared within a few seconds at a constant low temperature, whereas small cold spikes appeared with slight cooling and persisted at constant temperatures for long periods. The large spikes could be produced by cooling only in preparations containing mechanoreceptors. The experiments showed that the mechanoreceptors could be stimulated by cooling and that this could not be due to secondary mechanical stimulation of the pressure receptors by local vasoconstriction, nor to stimulation of the nerve trunk by cooling. It was not possible to stimulate the receptors of the largest pressure fibers by cooling.

1185. Horvath, S. M., and A. Freedman. The influence of cold upon the efficiency of man. *J. Aviat. M., v. 18, Apr. 1947: 158–164.*

Reaction time of subjects to visual stimuli was not altered during exposure to low environmental temperatures (−10° to −14°F; and −20°F) for periods of 8 to 14 days. Strength in the hands of finger dexterity of subjects, was greatly diminished by even short times of exposure to the low environments.

1186. Jenkins, W. L. A new basis for cutaneous temperature sensitivity. *In: American Institute of Physics. Temperature, its measurement and control in science and industry, p. 502–508. New York, Reinhold, 1941.*

This paper describes an attempt to arrive at a more exact method of mapping warm and cold spots on the skin. Based on his results with serial mapping, the author proposes the Concentration Theory, as a new basis for explaining cutaneous sensitivity to warmth and cold, which assumes that variations in sensitivity are caused primarily by the concentration of many tiny sensory receptors in one area.

1187. Kellgren, J. H., A. J. McGowan, and E. S. R. Hughes. On deep hyperalgesia and cold pain. *Clin. Sc., Lond., v. 7, 1948: 13–27.*

Clinical and experimental study of spontaneous pain was experienced when an injured part was chilled and was relieved by warmth. Phenomenon known as "cold pain" was seen in patients with a variety of traumatic injuries such as fractures, gunshot wounds of peripheral nerves, etc. Cold pain was found to be deep and diffuse in distribution with a quality similar to pain found in muscles and joints. The authors also discuss the relation of cold pain to causalgia and vascular disorders.

1188. Kleitman, N., S. Titelbaum, and P. Feiveson. The effect of body temperature on reaction time. *Am. J. Physiol., v. 121, Feb. 1938: 495–501.*

Performance of sensory-motor and sensory-mental-motor tests was found to follow the diurnal body temperature curve, being best in the afternoon when the body temperature is highest and less good in either the morning or late at night when the body temperature is lower. Either a spontaneous or induced lowering of the body temperature brought about a slowing of the reaction time. This was more marked in complex than in simple processes and performance.

1189. Kunkle, E. C. Phasic pains induced by cold. *J. Appl. Physiol.*, v. 1, *June 1949: 811–824.*

Two types of pain are described as occurring in a finger cooled in a water bath. The first or principal type termed "cold" pain is associated with vasoconstriction, not itself the cause of the pain. This is apparently due to the direct effect of cold on the tissues and nerves. The second pain is noted only during the recovery phase from the marked vasoconstriction and ischemia induced by the intense cooling.

1190. Leusen, I., and J. Demeester. Effect of temperature on vasomotor centers [In French]. *Arch. internat. physiol.*, Liége, v. 59, *May 1951: 40–48.*

A cooled physiological solution was introduced by needle into the lateral ventricles of the brain of dogs, under anesthesia, and the fluid drained out by needle at the sub-occipital level. Such direct cooling of the brain brought about a lowering of the arterial pressure and a depression of the vasomotor reflexes of the carotid sinus. The hypotension observed was more evident as the temperature was lowered. At the close of the experiment all functions returned to the normal level.

1191. Macht, M. B., and R. A. Kuhn. Response to thermal stimuli mediated through isolated spinal cord. *Arch. Neur. Psychiat.*, Chic., v. 59, *June 1948: 754–788.*

Withdrawal response evoked in 41 "spinal cats" by immersion in "cold" water was produced by stimulation of Krause's end bulbs and the sensory modality involved was cold. Similar response by immersion in "hot" water was found to be independent of skin or blood temperature, and apparently was produced by stimulation of free nerve endings; sensory modality involved was probably pain.

Twenty of twenty-four "spinal men" who had suffered complete transections of the thoracic spinal cord (3rd to 12th segment) through war injuries, exhibited similar responses to thermal stimulation. The level of transection was not found to be related to strength, type, or threshold of response. The threshold of "cold" stimulus varied from 18° to 32°C; for water above body temperature, from 47.5° to 54°C. Examinations above threshold were not performed because of fear of injury. Four who did not respond had exhibited no spinal reflexes of any kind since the initial injury.

1192. Marshall, W. H., C. F. Essig, and S. J. Dubroff. Relation of temperature of cerebral cortex to spreading depression of Leão. *J. Neurophysiol.*, v. 14, *Mar. 1951: 153–166.*

By means of surgical procedures, under anesthesia, a very shallow (1 cm) pool of oil was maintained on the surface of the cortex of the brain of rabbits or monkeys. Cooling of the cortex by the circulation of cooled oil through this pool produced various changes including reduction of the amplitude of the brain wave and reduction of the specific sensory response amplitudes. The cooling of the surface of the cortex of monkeys in this manner, to approximately 10° to 15°C below normal body temperature, decisively favored the spreading cortical depression described by Leão.

1193. Menzio, P. Investigation of the relation between the temperature of auditory conduction and the threshold temperature using heat tests [Abstract, in Italian]. *Minerva med.*, Tor., anno 39 (v. 1), *June 2, 1948: 554–555.*

Experimental studies were made of the relation of auditory conduction and the temperature of water introduced into the external ear. When the temperature of water used was cooler than the rectal temperature, the vestibular response was less prompt and less prolonged than that of the controls. This is thought to be due to a vasomotor reaction.

1194. Moffie, D. Congenital universal indifference to pain and temperature. [In English, summaries in English, German, and French]. *Confinia neur.*, Basel, *v. 11 (4), 1951: 219–226.*

The author describes a patient with congenital universal indifference to pain and temperature who in later life developed the picture of acquired cerebellar atrophy.

1195. Pecciarini, A. M. Investigations on guinea pigs concerning the reception for warmth and cold [In Italian]. *Arch. fisiol.*, Fir., v. 41 (2), 1941: 141–156.

Using as the test mechanism the reflex dorsal flexion of the head of the guinea pig when water (water bath, 12° to 45°C) stimulated the cutaneous thermal receptors at the edge of the external nares, various substances (including Stovaine, chloroform, menthol, and phenol) were tested for their modification of the response of the receptors.

1196. Pollock, L. J. Reflexes evoked by cold stimuli in injuries of spinal cord. *Arch. Neur. Psychiat.*, Chic., v. 65, May 1951: 622–627.

Forty-three patients with lesions of the cervical portion of the spinal cord, 69 with lesions of the thoracic level, and 40 with lesions of the lumbar level were observed for their reflex responses to cold stimuli. Cold stimuli were applied to various areas of the body by use of a wisp of cotton saturated with ether; a dry wisp of cotton produced no effect. As was expected, the stimulus of cold, as in the case of other exteroceptive stimuli, produced reflex activity from the distal end of an injured spinal cord. The responses occurred from stimulation of similar reflexogenous zones. The greatest number of muscle groups participating in the reflexes occurred with injury of the cervical portion of the spinal cord; next, with injury of the thoracic portion; and least, with injury of the lumbar portion. The greatest number of cases in which no response followed stimulation was that of injuries to the lumbar portion of the spinal cord; next, that of injuries to the thoracic portion; and least, that of injuries of the cervical portion. Additional information was also obtained including some on other reflex activities and on crossed reflexes. It would appear that with partial lesions radiation occurs upward as well as downward in the spinal cord.

1197. Pshonik, A. T. Analysis of cutaneous thermal reception. I. The instability of the temperature of the thermal skin apparatus [In Russian, summary in English]. *Ber. ges. Physiol.*, v. 112, 1939: 452–453.

The functional activity of the peripheral thermal skin receptors was analysed, using vascular responses (recorded by a plethysmograph) as the basic physiological index for the evaluation of the changes in thermal reception and for verification of the subjective indications of this reception. It is concluded that there are no specific points on the skin for specialized cold or heat reception since the same spot responds to both or any intermediate sensation, and varies in response even within a few minutes. The sensation, whether cold or hot, is the result of functional action of the whole complex of receptor apparatus which are caught by radiating impulses from the stimulated region. The radiating stimulation does not always cover the same receptor field. The functional activity of the thermoreceptors is highly dependent on the general condition of the body and of its organs. Experimental data demonstrated clearly that the condition of the whole body creates such connections and relationships for skin reception which excludes the possibility of an isolated study of any skin receptor. The tests indicated the importance of the cortical connection, linking skin reception with the body as a whole.

1198. Pshonik, A. T. Analysis of cutaneous thermal reception. II. The relationship of the thermal reception of the skin to the cerebral cortex [In Russian, summary in English]. *Ber. ges. Physiol.*, v. 112, 1939: 453.

Investigation was made into the relationship between the role of the cerebral cortex and the thermal reception in the skin, and of the interrelations between cold and heat reception. A stable conditioned vascular reflex was established in two subjects in response to a bell or to light and the words "cold" or "warm"; the plethysmographic method was used. All the experiments produced clear evidence of the very important role played by the cerebral cortex in cutaneous thermal reception. The cortex acts in organizing and controlling thermal reception, and may elicit peripheral sensations without direct thermal stimulation. The subject experiences thermal sensations which are sometimes more vivid than those elicited by the unconditioned stimulation, and responds by corresponding vascular and circulatory changes. It was found that the cortical connections of cold reception are much stronger than those of heat reception.

1199. Sahlgren, E. Referred cold sensation [In Swedish, summary in English]. *Nord med., v. 28, Nov. 23, 1945: 2468–2470.*

In a study of the subjective epigastric localization of cold, it was proven that the sensation of cold experienced in that area following the intubation of 20 cc of ice water into the stomach was one of referred sensation and not due to conduction through the abdominal wall to the skin. When the epigastric skin area was anesthetized with Novocain, or the sensation paralyzed by spraying the area with ethyl chloride, the sensation of cold in the area disappeared when the cold water was consumed.

1200. Sinclair, D. C., and J. R. Hinshaw. Sensory changes in nerve blocks induced by cooling. *Brain, Lond., v. 74, Sept. 1951: 318–335.*

Studies were made of the sensory paralysis induced by cooling (by immersion of the elbow in a trough of chopped ice and brine, at 0° to −2°C) the ulnar and lateral popliteal nerve trunks. Some individual variation existed but the order of sensory loss appeared to be more stable in a given nerve territory in blocks induced by cooling than in procaine or compression blocks on the same subjects. Although it is not known how cooling a nerve trunk produces sensory dissociation in its cutaneous territory, it is clear that the mechanism differs from that operating in the other two methods of blocking.

1201. Spealman, C. R., E. W. Bixby, J. L. Wiley, and M. Newton. Influence of hemorrhage, albumin infusion, bed rest, and exposure to cold on performance in the heat. *J. Appl. Physiol., v. 1, Sept. 1948: 242–253.*

The ability of 4 young men to perform certain simple physical tasks in the heat (33°C) was tested following 24-hour periods of bed rest, withdrawal of 500 cc of blood by venesection, and exposure to cold (20°C). In similar experiments the effects of infusing serum albumin and of hemorrhage on performance ability in the heat was studied. Exposure to cold resulted in poor performance and an increase in hemoglobin concentration.

1202. Tisdall, F. F. The national nutrition problem. *Tr. Am. Ass. Cereal Chemists, v. 4, Aug. 1946: 75–83.*

Studies in the Arctic in connection with strong sunlight and glare revealed cases of vascular invasion of the cornea of the eye identical with symptoms produced by riboflavin deficiency. Another condition often observed was a thickening of the conjunctiva. It is known that exposure to extreme cold and a great deal of light increases the susceptibility to these diseases of the eye and it is suspected that modification of the diet would afford some protection against them.

1203. Tsuji, S. Experimental study of abnormal temperature conditions. II. Influence of clothing upon mental work in low temperature environment [In Japanese, English summary]. *Kosei Kagaku, v. 2, Sept. 1941: 288–301.*

Subjects were exposed to −30°C while performing mental tests. Efficiency increased with amount and protective value of clothing but this result was not always consistent.

1204. Voll, M. M. Restitution of temperature sensitivity and of skin temperature after repeated local applications of cold and heat [In Russian, with English summary]. *Fiziol. zh. SSSR, v. 28 (2–3), 1940: 235–244.*

Threshold determinations of heat and cold sensitivity were made on both arms of 5 subjects, after immersion of the right arm only in water of 10° or 45°C for 10 minutes. The effect of repeated application of cold was evidenced in the first phase by a decrease of sensitivity to cold, an increase of the sensitivity to heat, and a fall of skin temperature. In the second and third phases, there was an increase of rate of restitution of temperature sensitivity and of skin temperature. After repeated application of heat, following repeated application of cold, restitution of temperature sensitivity and of skin temperature was not accelerated but rather tended to be retarded. The similarity of the course of restitution of temperature sensitivity and of skin temperature, after repeated thermal stimulation, suggests that the processes are mutually linked.

1205.   Wells, H. S. Temperature equalization for relief of pain; an experimental study of the relation of thermal gradients to pain. *Arch. Phys. M., v. 28, Mar. 1947: 135–139.*

The effect on experimental pain (intensity, duration, threshold stimulus) of temperature alteration, is studied in one human and in other subjects. Within temperature ranges not injurious to tissue, thermal gradients, or differences in temperature between superficial and deep tissues, are effective stimuli for pain nerve fibers. Pain depends on steepness of gradient not its direction; it adds to that of tissue injury so that pain of injury is aggravated when neither condition of itself causes pain. Heating or cooling which abolishes these temperature gradients can be very effective in relief of pain.

1206.   Winter, ... Illness from chilling [In German]. *Hippokrates, Stuttg., v. 10, Nov. 23, 1939: 1214–1217.*

Capillary disturbances in the mucous membrane of the nose after exposure to cold are attributed to the effect of cold on the nerve ends rather than to bacterial infection. The author recommends prophylactic treatment by "hardening" to cold.

1207.   Wolf, S., and J. D. Hardy. Studies on pain; observations on pain due to local cooling and on factors involved in the "cold pressor" effect. *J. Clin. Invest., v. 20, Sept. 1941: 521–533.*

When the hand of a subject was immersed in cold water, a deep aching pain was felt which reached its maximum after 60 seconds. The pain then subsided to give way to a "pins and needles" effect. The various factors which cause pain are discussed.

See also items: 59, 152, 336, 337, 340, 346, 549, 554, 561, 569, 582, 607, 644, 715, 873, 1111, 1118, 1140, 1183, 1214, 1217, 1218, 1229, 1284, 1317, 1415, 1425, 1460, 1494, 1498, 1515, 1550, 1639, 1682, 2070.

E. Circulatory System, General
(includes also lymph, and fluid shifts)

1208.   Alam, M., and F. H. Smirk. Blood pressure-raising reflexes in health, essential hypertension and renal hypertension. *Clin. Sc., Lond., v. 3, Aug. 15, 1938: 259–266.*

The blood pressure-raising effects of immersion of the hand and lower forearm in cold water, were studied in healthy subjects and in patients with renal and essential hypertension.

1209.   Ayman, D., and A. D. Goldshine. Cold as a standard stimulus of blood pressure. *N. England J. M., v. 219, Oct. 27, 1938: 650–655.*

Using a method devised by Hines and Brown (1932), it was found that cold (immersion of a hand in water of 4°C) caused some rise in blood pressure in 98% of the 136 subjects tested.

The test caused a rise in blood pressure two to four times greater in hypertensive patients than it did in normal persons.

1210. Bader, M. E., and J. Mead. The effect of local cooling and heating of the finger and wrist during exposure to high ambient temperature [Abstract]. *Fed. Proc., Balt., v. 8, Mar. 1949: 6–7.*

When the finger and wrist were cooled at 0°C until the finger skin temperature fell to 70°C, blood flow through the cooled finger was not affected. Stimuli (from pain, startle, or deep respiration) produced a sudden decrease in blood flow. Local cooling of the wrist at 0°C brought about a decrease in blood flow.

1211. Bader, M. E., J. Mead, and M. E. Pillion. Effect of local cooling on finger blood flow in individuals exposed to warm ambient temperature. *J. Appl. Physiol., v. 3, Feb. 1951: 508–512.*

Local cooling of the end of a finger (either water bath temperature to −6°C, or air temperature to 0°C) while the subject was kept in an environmental temperature of 32°C, did not produce a measurable alteration of blood flow in the finger. General vasoconstrictive stimuli (deep respiration; being suddenly startled) did produce a more marked and prolonged vasoconstriction in the cooled than in a normal finger.

1212. Barbour, H. G. Reflex intracellular water increase in cold environments [Abstract]. *Am. J. Physiol., v. 129, May 1940: 304–305.*

The intracellular water content in cats exposed to cold was found to have increased over that of cats exposed to normal temperatures.

1213. Barcroft, H., and O. G. Edholm. The effect of temperature on blood flow and deep temperature in the human forearm. *J. Physiol., Lond., v. 102, June 30, 1943: 5–20.*

Blood flow and deep muscle temperature were measured in the human forearm for 2 hours after immersion in water at temperatures from 13° to 45°C. The following observations were recorded: at 13°–35°C, slight decrease in flow; 37°–42.5°C, flow increases to a maximum in about 1 hour, then decreases; 45°C, flow increases to a maximum in 30–45 minutes, then remains constant. Deep muscle temperature ranged from 18°C after 2-hour immersion at 13°C to 39°C after 30-minute immersion at 42.5°–45°C.

1214. Barmack, J. E. Studies on the psychophysiology of boredom. II. The effect of a lowered room temperature and an added incentive on blood pressure, report of boredom, and other factors. *J. Exp. Psychol. v. 25, Dec. 1939: 634–642.*

Heart rate and blood pressure were recorded for each of 10 subjects, in room temperatures of 24.7°C and of 15.6°C, before and while operating a Poffenberger pursuit meter for eight 15-minute periods. At the colder room temperature a slight increase in systolic pressure and a slight decrease in heart rate was recorded. Although there were reports, from the subjective rating sheets of the tested individuals, of increased alertness (an antihypnotic effect), there was an insignificant effect on the attitude toward the pursuit work. This latter finding which is in opposition to the expected finding was also reported when an initial room temperature of 24.7°C was lowered to 15.6°C. Several explanations are suggested including the possibilities that the antihypnotic quality of a lowered temperature is a transient quality, and that continued exposure to cold is a source of discomfort.

1215. Bazett, H. C., F. W. Sunderman, J. Doupe, and J. C. Scott. Climatic effects on the volume and composition of the blood in man. *Am. J. Physiol., v. 129, Apr. 1940: 69–83.*

Exposure of an individual to environmental cold results in a decrease in blood volume. There is simultaneously a decrease in total circulating hemoglobin and in total plasma protein.

1216. Belding, H. S., J. Mead, and M. E. Bader. Digital skin temperature and blood flow relationship following change in environmental temperature. *Fed. Proc., Balt., v. 8, Mar. 1949: 9–10.*

Digital skin temperatures and blood flow were recorded for the terminal phalanx of the fingers of men exposed to environmental cold for three hours. Temperature of the finger was varied with an initial drop from 32° to as low as 13°C followed by a return to 32°C. On initial exposure to cold the skin temperature decreased less rapidly than did the blood flow rate; on return to a higher environmental temperature both the blood flow rate and the digital skin temperature increased.

1217. Berdan, W. Influence of temperature changes on capillary permeability. *Med. Arts & Sc., v. 3 (4), 1949: 77–91.*

The eye of a rabbit was heated or cooled (by diathermy or application of ice to a saline-soaked eye pad) and the capillary permeability was studied, taking as an indicator the time of appearance of injected fluorescein in the aqueous humor. There appeared to be an absence of any change with a moderate increase (2.5°C) in temperature, but a possible increase in permeability on cooling of 4.0°C.

1218. Berris, B., and G. N. Aagaard. Effect of piperidinomethyl benzodioxane on the cold pressor response. *Proc. Soc. Exp. Biol., N. Y., v. 73, Feb. 1950: 287–289.*

Experimental findings by earlier workers had shown that the rise in systolic blood pressure, caused by intravenous injection of epinephrine, could be abolished by administration of piperidinomethyl benzodioxane. In the current experimental work, it was found that the comparable increase in blood pressure, following immersion of a hand of a subject in cold water (4°C) for one minute, was not abolished by use of the benzodioxane. The authors suggest that the cold pressor response is not due to release of epinephrine. The fact that cold stimulation causes a rise in both systolic and diastolic blood pressure indicates that this response is on a neurogenic rather than an epinephrine-induced basis.

1219. Bierman, W. Temperature changes in the muscles of the human leg. *In: American Institute of Physis. Temperature, its measurement and control in science and industry, p. 553–556. New York, Reinhold, 1941.*

Temperature changes occurring simultaneously in the skin and muscles of the lower extremities following various procedures—including the injection of alcohol, sodium chloride solution, and typhoid vaccine and the application of ice bags—were measured by thermocouple. The author believes that the temperature changes observed correspond to changes in blood supply to the extremities and may have application to the treatment of peripheral vascular disease.

1220. Brown, E., C. S. Wise, and E. O. Wheeler. The effect of local cooling on the filtration and absorption of fluid in the human forearm. *J. Clin. Invest., v. 26, Sept. 1947: 1031–1042.*

The effects of local cooling on the volume of tissue fluid under resting conditions in 4 normal human subjects were studied with the pressure plethysmograph. Measurements were made of the rate of filtration of fluid per unit increase of venous pressure and the rate of reabsorption of excess tissue fluid after release of venous congestion. Exposure to cold (water at 4.5°C) results in increased permeability of the capillary wall to protein. In the exposed forearm the effective colloid osmotic pressure of the blood was reduced by 7–10 cm (of water). The relation of the results to such conditions as immersion foot is discussed.

1221. Burckhardt, W. Relation of peripheral circulation to internal secretion and to metabolism as revealed by the measurement of cutaneous temperature [In German]. *Arch. Derm. Syph., Berl., v. 191, 1950: 137–141.*

Studies were made of the spontaneous rewarming of the skin after a cold (12° to 15°C) hand bath, in both normal persons and in those suffering from various circulatory diseases and in various hormonal states. A close relationship was found to exist between the peripheral circulation of the skin, the hormonal secretion, and the metabolic level, all of which must be taken into consideration in treatment of circulatory disturbances.

1222.   Byer, E., L. A. Toth, and R. Ashman. Electrocardiographic changes induced by cooling or warming the inner surface of the dog's ventricle. *Am. J. Physiol., v. 149, Apr. 1, 1947: 264–276.*

Introduction of cool (1° to 3°C) Ringer's solution, by arterial catheterization, into the apex of the left ventricle of a dog's heart, changed and widened the QRS complex of the electrocardiogram and also caused conspicuous increase in the heighth and width of the T waves. Warming had opposite but less striking effects on the T wave and changed the form of the QRS complex. Cooling the inner surface of the right ventricle caused similar T wave changes but reversed the effects on the form of the QRS complex. By similarly cooling the basal left endocardial surface, the T wave was inverted and, usually, widened. The author concludes that, if the electrical effects were brought about by a change in rate of repolarization of the endocardial surface, then changes in the electrical state of the subendocardial muscle surface play a part in the genesis of the electrocardiogram.

1223.   Christensen, E. H., and M. Nielsen. Measurement of blood flow in skin at rest and at varied external temperatures [In English]. *Acta physiol. scand., v. 4, Aug. 1942: 171–174.*

Considerable differences in blood flow were found at comparatively slight variations in external temperature, when studies were made of blood flow of the skin of a finger of a human at rest and during work at external temperatures of 15° and 21°C. No relation was found between the subjective sensations of temperature and the absolute values of blood flow but an incipient increase in the flow was attended by sensations of warmth, and conversely, an incipient decrease was accompanied by sensations of cold.

1224.   Conley, C. L., and J. L. Nickerson. Effects of temperature change on the water balance in man. *Am. J. Physiol., v. 143, Mar. 1945: 373–384.*

Studies were made on the changes in fluid balance in normal human subjects exposed alternately to cold and warm environmental temperatures. Extrarenal water loss was constant during any period of exposure to constant high or low temperature. When the temperature was changed, extrarenal water loss and skin temperature quickly changed levels. No evidence of acclimatization was noted. Plasma volume was lowered during exposure to cold, returning to normal in a few days.

1225.   Essen, K. W., and K. Janzik. On blood pressure fluctuations after temperature stimulation in the presence of vegetative nervous disturbances [In German]. *Zschr. klin. Med., v. 136, 1939: 407–415.*

Fluctuations in blood pressure after varied thermal stimulations were studied in 17 healthy subjects and in 19 patients suffering from autonomous nervous disturbances (giddiness, pressure in the head, heart palpitations, erratic perspiration, etc.). The right arm was stimulated by hot (45°C) or cold (8°C) baths, lasting usually 4 minutes, and the blood pressure measured before, during, and after the immersion. The galvanic skin reflex was also determined. Results showed a general increase in blood pressure after hot or cold stimulation in all healthy subjects as well as in the majority of patients. However, in 63.2% of the patients the blood pressure reaction curve showed great spontaneous fluctuations upward or downward before, and sometimes during, the thermal stimulation; in the healthy subjects such fluctuations occurred in only 17.6% of the cases. In only 3 patients was the increase of the blood pressure and its return to normal slower than in the normal subjects. After the stimulation there was an inversion of the reaction, and the galvanic skin reflex was torpid. In all the other subjects the average figures for the blood pressure after stimulation by heat was 5.1 mm; with cold it was 11.6 mm. The blood pressure and the galvanic skin reflex curves did not necessarily coincide in character.

1226. Friedlander, M., S. Silbert, and W. Bierman. Regulation of circulation in the skin and muscles of the lower extremities. *Am. J. M. Sc., v. 199, May 1940: 657–668.*

Circulation in the skin and muscles of the extremities is independently regulated. The blood flow in the muscles of the extremities is not directly controlled by the sympathetic nervous system.

1227. Gardner, E. Mechanisms of certain forms of sudden death in medico-legal practice. *Med. Leg. Crim. Rev., Lond., v. 10, July 1942: 131.*

The author recounts the experiences of a colleague who attributed the deaths of several babies, who had been placed out of doors to sleep in severely cold weather, to the action of the cold on the carotid sinus. In these cases the area near the carotid sinus had been unprotected by either the head covering or the blankets.

1228. Glaser, E. M., F. R. Berridge, and K. M. Prior. Effects of heat and cold on the distribution of blood within the human body; radiological investigations of the liver, lungs, and heart. *Clin. Sc., Lond., v. 9, May 30, 1950: 181–187.*

Radiographs of the chests and abdomens of healthy young men, recumbent and dressed only in bathing trunks, during exposure to cold (by use of cold wet towels and a fan) and to heat showed the contour of the liver to be larger and the shadows of pulmonary vessels to be wider and more numerous when the skin was cooled than when it was warmed. These findings suggest that the lungs and liver contain more blood when the skin is exposed to a cool environment. The transverse diameter of the heart remained unchanged in the recumbent men during the temperature changes.

1229. Greenfield, A. D. M., and J. T. Shepherd. A quantitative study of the response to cold of the circulation through the fingers of normal subjects. *Clin. Sc., Lond., v. 9, Aug. 31, 1950: 323–348.*

At a comfortable environmental temperature, immersion of a finger in a water bath between 0° and 6°C brought about an initial almost complete cessation of blood flow, followed after 5–10 minutes by a rapid increase. Behavior during continued immersion for 1 hour followed individual patterns, with most persons experiencing a general decline. Immersion in a water bath between 6° and 12°C brought about similar but smaller changes following the initial constriction. Pain was felt when the temperature was low and the temperature gradient between the inside and skin of the finger was small; pain was not felt when the internal temperature was high and the gradient steep.

*1230. Grigorova, O. P. The blood picture as related to living conditions and to avitaminosis of the Russian and Samoyed population of Novaya Zemlya [In Russian]. *Antrop. zh., no. 1–2, 1933: 163–177.*

"*Contains* a report of a study made in 1928 on 118 individuals (67.5% of the population). An account is given of the people, their food, vital statistics, social and occupational conditions and previous studies of the problems. Environmental conditions were found to exert a stimulating effect on the hematopoietic organs augmenting their regenerative processes. Reduction of the percentage of hemoglobin, increase in number of erythrocytes and decrease of their diameter, hypochromia and polychromatophilia of the red blood cells, lymphocytosis and eosinophilia, were found in the permanent residents. The blood pictures in scurvy in age, sex and racial groups are also discussed. Bibliography (7 items)."—Arctic Bibl., v. 4, 1954: 359.

1231. Halperin, M. H., C. K. Friedland, and R. W. Wilkins. The effect of local compression upon blood flow in the extremities of man. *Am. Heart J., v. 35, Feb. 1948: 221–237.*

* Original not seen.

The effect of pressures of 10 to 50 mm Hg locally applied to the extremities was investigated by thermometric, blood gasometric, and plethysmographic methods. At 20 mm Hg pressure, arteriovenous oxygen difference rose 25% and plethysmographic tracings showed a corresponding decrease in blood flow. At 10 mm Hg, blood flow decreased 10%. Results are believed to be applicable to study of the effects of constricting clothing, shoes, and gloves on the circulation, especially under cold conditions.

1232.　Happ, W. P., Jr., W. W. Tuttle, and M. Wilson. The physiologic effect of abdominal cold packs. *Res. Q. Am. Ass. Health, v. 20, May 1949: 153–169.*

Data were collected relative to the effect of abdominal ice packs on recovery from fatigue and on some of the physiological responses involved, such as blood pressure and pulse rate changes. Application of abdominal ice packs facilitated recovery from fatigue resulting from strenuous exercise.

1233.　Haupt, L. E. The effect of cold on tissues. *MD, Chic., v. 2, July 1947: 9–12.*

Cooling of tissues has been found to bring about a moderate loss of water from the blood to the tissues, the migration being attributed to the vascular changes following the spasmodic constriction of the cutaneous arterioles and the local slowing of the blood flow. By reflex action, the spasms occur in the arterioles of the limb opposite to that which is cooled and in the deep collateral circulation of the same limb. To overcome this action, continuous caudal anesthesia, local anesthetic block of lumbar sympathetic ganglia, or use of papaverine are recommended. Nerve conduction has been found to be arrested between 25° and 30°C, and skin to freeze in the neighborhood of −1° to −3°C. The author discusses also the various uses of cold therapy and the technique of local refrigeration.

1234.　Helmholtz, H. F., Jr. Response of blood pressure and pulse rate of the newborn rat to changes in body temperature [Abstract]. *Fed. Proc., Balt., v. 5, Feb. 1946: 44.*

By cannulation of the carotid arteries of a group of newborn rats, the mean blood pressure and the pulse rate were recorded using a damped glass spoon manometer. Rectal temperatures were recorded by differential thermocouple; body temperature was varied by means of water circulating below the metal platform on which the animals were placed. From the starting blood pressure and pulse rates at body temperature of 37°C, lowering the body temperature caused a parallel fall of both rate and pressure. Reheating from as low as 20°C caused a parallel fall of both rate and pressure. Reheating from as low as 20°C essentially restored the levels. Raising the body temperature above 37°C caused at first a parallel rise of blood pressure and pulse rate; above a certain level, which was quite variable, it caused a drop in pressure but a still further increase in pulse rate. Cooling to 37°C from temperatures as high as 43°C, after exposure at this high level for up to ½ hour, returned values essentially to the original levels.

1235.　Henry, J. P., and O. H. Gauer. The influence of temperature upon venous pressure in the foot. *J. Clin. Invest., v. 29, July 1950: 855–861.*

Venous pressure in the foot—when the subject is in an erect position— is the result of the relative rates at which blood flows from the arteries through the capillary system and back into the veins. Muscular activity aids blood flow. During the vasodilatation induced by heat, even vigorous walking does not reduce the mean venous pressure below 70 mm Hg. At moderate temperatures, far less activity is necessary to reduce the pressure to this level. At cool temperatures, even slight involuntary changes reduce the pressure to 50 mm Hg. The latter level is approximately that of the counter-balancing osmotic and tissue pressures.

1236.　Hicks, C. S., and W. J. O'Connor. The effect of changes of environmental temperature on the skin circulation of the naked Australian aboriginal as measured by the Sahli-Jaquet volume bolograph. *Austral. J. Exp. Biol., v. 16, Mar. 1938: 19–28.*

Studies of the effects of extreme temperatures were made on the radial pulse of Australian aborigines, using a Sahli volume bolograph. The pulse amplitide decreased during exposure to cold and increased with exposure to heat.

1237.   Hines, E. A. Jr., and W. F. Kvale. Circulation: effect of heat and cold, exercise and posture. *In: Medical physics, p. 194–206.* Ed. by O. GLASSER. *Chicago, Year Book Publ., 1944.*

This is a review of the physiology and clinico-pathologic aspects of the peripheral circulation. Included are discussions on the effects of cold on circulation time and on diseases produced by the effects of cold on the vascular system. 76 refs.

1238.   Hoff, H. E., and L. H. Nahum. The factors determining the direction of the T wave: the effect of heat and cold upon the dextro- and levo-cardiogram. *Am. J. Physiol., v. 131, Jan. 1, 1941: 700–709.*

The T wave of the electrocardiogram is thought to be caused by the interference of the electric impulses from the right (dextrocardiogram) and left (levocardiogram) ventricles. The author applied heat (55 °C) or cold (5 °C) to either ventricle of the heart of dogs in order to study the effects on the electrocardiograms. The following conclusions were reached: heat locally applied shortens the electrogram of either ventricle; cold lengthens it. Prolongation of the dextrocardiogram or shortening of the levocardiogram produces an upright T wave; shortening of the dextrocardiogram or lengthening of the levocardiogram causes an inverted T wave.

1239.   Hoff, H. E., and L. H. Nahum. Comparison of the electrocardiographic changes produced by heating and cooling epicardial and endocardial surfaces of the dog ventricle. *Am. J. Physiol., v. 153, Apr. 1, 1948: 176–182.*

The effects on the electrocardiogram of warming and cooling of restricted areas of the endocardium and epicardium of both the right and left ventricles were studied in dogs. For a given region, the results were the same whether the thermal change was applied to the endocardium or epicardium. Cooling of the zone underneath the chest electrode produced an inverted T wave; cooling of some areas (anterior surface of right ventricle, some septal and basal areas) increased the T wave; and cooling of the posterior surface and apex of the left ventricle inverted the T wave. Warming of these regions produced the opposite effects.

1240.   Hoff, H. E., and H. Stansfield. Ventricular fibrillation induced by cold. *Am. Heart J., v. 38, Aug. 1949: 193–204.*

The lateral wall of the left ventricle of dog's heart was cooled locally (to 10 °C) by insertion between the pericardium and the heart of a small flat thermode through which water was circulated. Electrical stimulation of the right ventricle, which would normally create only ventricular extrasystoles, induced ventricular fibrillation. Fibrillation developed as a terminal event after a short period of ventricular tachycardia caused by a series of separate impulses arising from pacemaker activity in the cooled area. These responses develop in the cooled area because cooling has produced a potential difference between the cooled and the adjacent areas and is maintained because the cooled tissue does not accommodate itself to the currents as normal tissue would do.

1241.   Horvath, S. M., and S. Y. Botelho. Orthostatic hypotension following hot or cold baths. *J. Appl. Physiol., v. 1, Feb. 1949: 586–596.*

Passive alteration of position of the subject from the supine to the erect on a tilting ballistocardiograph was accompanied by an elevated heart rate and a reduced stroke volume. Approximately one-half of the subjects developed orthostatic hypotension following a hot bath for 20 minutes; following immersion for 20 minutes in a cold bath (18 °C), the erect posture was maintained with greater ease and with reduced cardiovascular demands.

1242. Ishikawa, T., S. Matuoka, and K. Tatai. Studies on the effect of cold upon human bodily functions. I. On the effect of cold upon pulse rate and body temperature [Abstract, in English]. *Jap. J. M. Sc., v. 8, Mar. 1943: 12*.*

Study of the physiological effects of low atmospheric temperature (down to −40°C) on human beings during work or while sitting still, and in varied wearing apparel, were made to show any changes of pulse rate and of temperature of several superficial parts. No results are stated.

1243. Jochim, K. E., and A. B. Hertzman. The effects of cold on the blood vessels of the skin of the forearm. *Fed. Proc., Balt., v. 3, Mar. 1944: 22.*

Studies were made on the arterial blood supply and the number of arteriovenous anastomoses in the skin of the forearm and in the finger. The differences found correlate with significant changes in vascular reactions. The direct effects of cold on the skin vessels appear to be dominant, vasomotor reflexes being of minor importance. The relation of the findings to the "immersion foot" syndrome is indicated.

1244. Jung, W. Influence of "sauna" bath on cutaneous vascular reactions to cold [In German]. *Schweiz. med. Wschr., v. 76, Oct. 12, 1946: 1058–1062.*

The reaction of the skin to cold was investigated before and after sauna baths. There was found to be an increase in arterial circulation and an increased tonus of the small arteries of the skin when the baths were used to rewarm after cold exposure.

1245. Kanno, H. Influence of application of cold and heat upon the blood pressure and heart beat of non-fastened, non-anaesthetized rabbits [Abstract, in English]. *Jap. J. M. Sc., Biophysics, v. 6, 1940: 123*–124*.*

About 150–200 cc of water of 1°–2°C was introduced into a previously prepared stomach fistula of rabbits, to cause heat debts of about 3,000 cal/kg. Experiments were done on normal rabbits, on rabbits with denervated hearts, and on those with demedullated suprarenals; about half the animals were fastened to a board and half were not. Blood pressure of the animals rose quickly, reaching a maximum of 10–40 mm Hg above normal within 5–10 minutes; pulse rate fell in most cases, the minimum of about 10–30 beats/minute occurring after 5–10 minutes; body temperature decreased by about 1°–3°C in about 20–40 minutes. Recovery to normal, of all conditions, occurred within 1–2 hours. Loss of suprarenal medulla brought about an excessive and prolonged fall of body temperature but there were no noticeable changes in pulse rate or blood pressure between the normal or any of the other animals.

1246. Karády, S., H. Selye, and J. S. L. Browne. Changes in the chloride distribution between red blood cells and plasma during the course of the general adaptation syndrome. *J. Biol. Chem., v. 131, Dec. 1939: 717–731.*

When rats were exposed to cold or given subcutaneous injections of formaldehyde during a 24-hour period, there was noted a decrease in the concentration of chlorides in the red blood cells immediately after exposure or treatment was stopped. Hemoconcentration was also observed. When animals became adapted by treatment for 12 days, however, the blood chlorides and concentration increased. This reversed response may reflect an increased resistance to the stimuli.

1247. Kisch, B., and F. M. Groedel. Changes in the electrocardiogram due to local cooling of the chest wall [In English, summaries in English, German, French, and Italian]. *Cardiologia, Basel, v. 4 (3–4), 1940: 206–213.*

Localized cooling, for 10–15 minutes with an ice bag, of certain areas of the chest wall, brought about typical changes in the electrocardiogram. Cooling of the area above the left ventricle led mainly to a change from the C R 5 lead; cooling over the right ventricle to a change from the C R 2 lead.

1248. Kisch, B., L. H. Nahum, and H. E. Hoff. The predominance of surface over deep cardiac injury in producing changes in the electrocardiogram. *Am. Heart J., v. 20, Aug. 1940: 174–185.*

Studies of the effect of various injurious agents were made on the hearts of dogs, cats, and rabbits. The effects of cold were observed by placing test tubes of cold water in contact with the heart. It was noted that the S and T interval of the electrocardiogram was elevated and the T wave was inverted.

1249. Koĭranskiĭ, B. B. Seasonal influence on the vascular reaction in the skin under low temperatures [In Russian]. *Klin. med., Moskva, v. 24, 1946: 15–22.*

The influence of seasonal changes on the circulatory system was studied in 7 healthy individuals, 25 to 35 years of age. At a room temperature of $21°–23°C$, the gloved hand of the subject was immersed in a water-bath at $5°$ or $15°C$ for 30 minutes or 2 hours, with the skin temperature of the index finger measured each minute. In the summer, the skin temperature of the finger was found to remain at a higher (by $1°–3.7°C$) level than in the winter, but was more labile, showing waves of rise and fall of greater amplitude. In the winter these fluctuations (at $15°C$) were either absent, or few and of lesser amplitude. The fall temperature curves occupied a middle position between those of the summer and of the winter. It is concluded that the contraction of the blood vessels in the skin was less in the summer than in the winter and the vessel tonus was more labile. At a water temperature of $5°C$ the seasonal variations were more pronounced than at $15°C$. Further tests over an environmental temperature range of $-31°C$ to $31°C$ showed no relationship between the temperature of the air on the day of testing and the decrease of the skin temperature in water at $5°C$. It is therefore to be assumed that the lesser reaction to cold during the summer is the result of prolonged action of the environmental temperature on the thermoregulatory centers, in which an altered reactivity is created in the course of the season possibly due to inhibition.

1250. Kvale, W. F., and E. V. Allen. The rate of the circulation in the arteries and veins of man. III. The influence of temperature of the skin, digestion, posture, and exercise. *Am. Heart J., v. 18, July 1939: 546–556.*

Cooling of the skin by removing the subject to a room which was $5°$ to $7°C$ colder than the control room, decreased the velocity of blood flow; warming increased it.

1251. Landsteiner, E. K., and M. Hayes. The effect of temperature of the blood on the heart rate. *Am. J. Physiol., v. 140, Nov. 1943: 256–259.*

In the cat and rabbit, the injection of cool ($22°–36°C$) physiological salt solution into the external jugular vein resulted in a slowing of the heart rate.

1252. Lange, K. The effect of cold on capillary permeability. *Bull. N. York M. Coll., v. 5, Dec. 1942: 154–162.*

A decrease in capillary permeability as tested by the injection of fluorescein was claimed to have been shown in the skin of man, dogs, and rabbits when exposed to an environmental temperature of $10°C$ for 10 minutes.

1253. Lee, W. Y. Physiological reactions to a changing environment. II. Changes in skin temperature, blood pressure and pulse rate [In English]. *Chin. M. J., v. 66, Nov. 1948: 597–601.*

The significant relationships of different elements of the circulation—pulse rate, blood pressure—to skin temperature during changes of environmental temperature ($67°F$ to $104°F$) are discussed.

1254. Maasik, E. On the effect of cold on the peripheral blood picture of infants; experimental investigation [In German]. *Acta paediat., Upps., v. 35, suppl. 7, 1948: 1–107.*

The effect of cold stimuli on the peripheral blood picture was studied in 109 infants and 30 guinea pigs. In the animals, exposure to atmospheric cold of 6.6°C for 9 minutes resulted in decreases of the erythrocyte, leucocyte, and hemoglobin values. Infants subjected to cold baths, cold foot-baths, or the feeding of cold milk and cold barium mash, showed a decrease in the erythrocyte, hemoglobin, and leucocyte counts in all cases except the cold bath, where there was a sharp increase in the leucocyte count. 112 refs.

1255. McCarrell, J. D. The effect of warm and of cold nasopharyngeal irrigation on the cervical lymph flow. *Am. J. Physiol., v. 128, Jan. 1, 1940: 349–354.*

Lymph was collected from anesthetized dogs by cannulation of the right and left cervical lymph vessels during passive movement of the head of the animal. Quantity of lymph flow was calculated in mg/min; protein concentration in the lymph was determined refractometrically. The effect of heat and cold was determined by irrigation of the nasal pharynx with isotonic saline at temperatures ranging from 5° to 55°C for periods of 20–30 minutes at each temperature. At the termination of the experiment, sections of the nasopharyngeal mucosa were removed for histological examination. Irrigation with isotonic solution above 5°C and below 45°C had no marked effect on either the lymph flow or its protein concentration. Reducing the temperature of the solution below 37°C caused no marked changes until a temperature of 5°C was reached. After a latent period of 10–15 minutes at this low temperature, the flow became definitely greater. By histological examination it was demonstrated that whether this increase was temporary or more prolonged depended upon the absence or presence of capillary damage.

1256. Mayer, W. The blood picture of horses in a polar winter climate, 1943 [Abstract in German]. *Wien. tierärztl. Mschr., v. 34, Jan. 1947: 42.*

Hematological studies were made on a group of 6 Norwegian geldings, and on 14 mares and geldings brought to Narvik in July 1940 by German cavalrymen. The temperature at Narvik which, because of the Gulf Stream, is an ice-free port in Northern Norway, ranges from +6° to −30°C. The studies were begun in January and continued through May. In the German horses, the erythrocyte count rose sharply for a short period and then dropped again. In the white blood elements the ratio between the myelocytes and lymphocytes was in favor of the lymphocytes with many young and developing forms. The blood picture for the Norwegian horses was similar but not as pronounced. It is concluded that the polar climate is a factor influencing the blood picture of all the horses but that it could not be determined whether the variations in the findings could be traced back to any breed differences or to some acclimatization of the native Norwegian horses.

1257. Miller, H. R., J. Marrus, and B. C. Smith. The reaction of the peripheral circulation to cold in scleroderma, Raynaud's disease and thrombo-angiitis obliterans [Abstract]. *Bull. N. York Acad. M., v. 21, Aug. 1945: 441.*

On the basis of results in acclimatization carried out on normal subjects at Fort Monmouth, experiments were undertaken to determine the reaction of the circulation to intense cold in patients with scleroderma, Raynaud's disease and thromboangiitis obliterans. Extremities of patients exposed to intense cold showed two types of reaction, a spontaneous warming, i.e., a phasic rise and fall in skin temperature and then a progressive raise lasting for several hours. During this latter phase increased tolerance to cold, decrease of pain, and signs of clinical improvement in some cases were noted. It has been found possible to induce a marked and sustained increase in digital skin temperature; this response may have therapeutic value.

1258. Miller, J. H., and M. Bruger. The cold-pressor reaction in normal subjects and in patients with primary (essential) and secondary (renal) hypertension. *Am. Heart J., v. 18, July 1939: 329–333.*

Changes in blood pressure were studied in normal and hypertensive subjects in response to immersion of a hand for about 1 minute in cold water (4° to 5°C). About 39% of the normals and 76% of those with essential hypertension responded to cold by a decided rise in blood pressure. Patients with renal hypertension showed a percentage response similar to that of the normals.

1259. Miller, M. R., and A. J. Miller. Physiological effects of brief periods of exposure to low temperatures. *J. Aviat. M., v. 20, June 1949: 179–185.*

Sixteen subjects lightly clothed were exposed to low temperatures of from +34° to −15°C for 20-minute periods. The immediate reaction was a rise in systolic and diastolic blood pressures. The pulse rate fell early, and in 75% of the cases hemoconcentration was noted. Adequate food and sleep before exposure increased resistance to cold.

1260. Okuda, A. Experiment on freezing (first report). [Abstract, in English]. *Jap. J. M. Sc., Part 3, v. 8, 1943: 150*–151*.*

Observations were made of skin temperature, blood flow, and finger volume on an index finger enclosed in a water-jacketed plethysmograph through which water at temperatures of −1° to −2°C, was flowing. During the first 5 minutes the finger volume and skin temperature decreased; in 6–7 minutes the volume increased while the skin temperature fell and the blood flow decreased; in 8–16 minutes finger volume increased, skin temperature rose, and pulsations were noted; later, finger volume tended to decrease and skin temperature to fall.

1261. Paranskiĭ, A. G. Meteorological factors of the polar regions, and blood pressure [In Russian]. *Gig. & san., Moskva, v. 14, Aug. 1949: 7–12.*

The blood pressure was studied in 230 healthy subjects during one year in the polar region; variations of pressure were correlated with the daily meteorological conditions. Measurements were made before dinner and 30 minutes after nonstrenous work. The fact that the results obtained in several different groups of men corresponded, indicates the existence of a certain correlation between the meteorological conditions and the blood pressure as follows: (1) A sharp increase in atmospheric pressure was accompanied by an increase in blood pressure; sharp decrease, by a decrease in blood pressure. The latter effect was more pronounced than the former. (2) A considerable increase in the temperature of the air was accompanied by a tendency of the blood pressure to decrease; a sharp decrease in the temperature induced an increase in blood pressure. (3) If the temperature dropped and the atmospheric pressure increased simultaneously, the blood pressure increased in the majority of cases; if the temperature increased and the atmospheric pressure dropped, the blood pressure decreased in the majority of cases. (4) The influences of relative humidity and wind direction were not studied.

1262. Petersen, H. Investigation on the evaluation of the effects of baths on the circulation [In German]. *Balneologe, v. 8, Mar. 15, 1941: 65–71.*

A cold (12°C) footbath was shown, by the use of a finger plethysmograph, to result in vasoconstriction with a decrease of the volume of the finger, diminution of the pulse volume, and considerable increase of blood pressure. The pulse frequency showed no essential change. After a considerable period of cooling a reactive hyperemia took place bringing about an increase in finger volume over the normal, and a greater pulse volume.

1263. Petersen, W. F. Coronary death. *In: Conference papers of the Clin. Conf. Chicago M. Soc., Mar. 5–8, 1946, p. 101–103.*

The author cites several coronary deaths—which had occurred after a period of sudden and relatively severe cold followed by a period of relatively marked increase in temperatures—as resulting from the undue environmental demands on circulatory adjustments to temperature.

1264. Piaggio Blanco, R. A., J. Dighiero, and E. J. Canabal. Electrocardiographic changes provoked by precardial application of ice [In Spanish, English summary]. *An. Fac. med., Montev., v. 34 (10, 11, 12), 1949: 1153–1174.*

Before and after ice bags were applied to the chest wall for 60–90 minutes, an electrocardiogram was made to study any modifications which cooling the precardial region would produce. In 6 subjects without signs or symptoms of disease, there was a definite lowering of voltage of the T wave; in patients with cardiovascular or respiratory diseases, the changes were very varied. The authors assume that cooling of the cardiac muscle was produced by the cooling in the precardial region and that this gave rise to a reflex coronary vasospasm. They do not believe that the modifications were caused by a local change in tissue conductivity or by pure coronary reflex.

1265. Proskauer, G. G., C. Neumann, and I. Graef. The measurement of the blood pressure in rats with special reference to the effect of change in temperature. *Am. J. Physiol.,* v. 143, Feb. 1945: 290–296.

The relation between blood pressure, cardiac rate, and the temperature of the rat was studied. Blood pressure was measured by either the indirect (plethysmographic) or direct (Hamilton's optical manometer) method. With no change in the cutaneous or rectal temperature and at a room temperature of 24°–28°C the blood pressure of normal, unanesthetized rats was found to be 65–95 mm Hg. Raising the cutaneous and rectal temperatures of anesthetized or unanesthetized rats was followed by a progressive rise in blood pressure. Depressing cutaneous and rectal temperature below normal by exposure to a draft of cool air did not lower the blood pressure of normal unanesthetized rats. However, in anesthetized animals exposure to a draft of cool air brought about a fall in body temperature below normal which was accompanied by a progressive fall in blood pressure to below normal. In spite of continued depression of body temperature, a secondary rise in blood pressure occurred. In one group of animals, with one exception, this secondary rise exceeded the pre-anesthetic level. In tracings made with the direct method, heart rate decreased and increased parallel to the fall and subsequent rise of blood pressure.

1266. Raab, W. The pathogenic significance of adrenaline and related substances in heart muscle. *Exp. M. & S.,* v. 1, May 1943: 188–225.

Experimental, pathological, and clinical evidence suggests that adrenaline and adrenaline-like substances, including neurogenic sympathin originating in the heart itself, play a fundamental role in the processes determining physiological and pathological heart action and myocardial metabolism and structure. Both excess amounts and low concentrations of these substances may cause myocardial changes, heart failure, or cardiac death. Racial, nutritional, age, and seasonal factors are discussed briefly. Seasonal differences in myocardial concentrations of adrenaline or adrenaline-like substances which were previously reported for rats were not noted in humans, but such information makes some hormonal factors in the greater incidence of cardiac disturbances which have been reported in man during cold seasons, appear possible.

1267. Roberts, B. The study of man's reaction to a polar climate. *Polar Record,* v. 4, July 1943: 63–69.

Adjustment to low environmental temperatures is chiefly through constriction of the peripheral vascular systems of the upper and lower extremities, especially the fingers and toes, but also the ears, nose, and chin. Blood flow is reduced, heat loss is diminished, the total volume of circulating blood is reduced, and the blood becomes more concentrated. This constriction limits the amount of cooled blood returning to the body and guards against an excessive fall of body temperature but at the same time brings about an even greater cooling of the limbs. Blood flow in the peripheral tissues may be varied through a hundred-fold range by the control of the sympathetic nervous system acting on the walls of the blood vessels. The most obvious change in the body on exposure to cold conditions is a fall of skin temperature with wide variations occurring in different areas of the body, the trunk surface varying least and the extremities most. Local stimulation of one area may cause enormous changes in other areas. Continuing physiological studies of the elimination of heat from the body are needed so that clothing may be properly chosen, in relation to activity, in order to maintain an average skin temperature approaching the optimum in spite of exposure to severe cold.

1268. Schwiegk, H., and W. H. A. Schöttler. Circulatory changes after anemia produced by an Esmarch bandage [In German]. *Klin. Wschr.,* v. 22 (30–31), 1943: 477–481.

Each of a group of dogs had an Esmarch bandage applied to a lower extremity to deprive it of circulation; in some of the dogs the leg was then packed in ice for periods up to 10 hours.

Contrary to the results obtained in the group of dogs with uncooled extremities, only small drops in blood pressure and for short periods of time were observed after the bandage was removed. No circulatory collapse occurred in any of the cooled animals and two of them were running about two days after their legs were removed from the ice. Histological examination of tissues from the legs of both groups of dogs showed that tissues suffering lack of oxygen were less damaged when the temperature was lowered by use of the ice. The damage to capillaries was decidedly less. Restoration of blood flow should be accomplished before rewarming since the increased tissue metabolism can do considerable damage if circulation is not adequate. The author suggests this same procedure in cases of local cold injury; in cases of hypothermia, quick rewarming by hot baths is advised.

1269. Scott, J. C., H. C. Bazett, and G. C. Mackie. Climatic effects on cardiac output and the circulation in man. *Am. J. Physiol.*, *v. 129, Apr. 1940: 102–122.*

Human subjects were exposed, in an air-conditioned room, to temperatures ranging from 21.1° to 32.6°C, simulating the seasons. It was found that the effect of mild changes in environmental temperature on the blood pressure is an initial rise and a later fall in the warm environment and an initial fall and later rise in the cold. In subjects lying down in a warm atmosphere, cardiac output increased and then returned to normal; in cold atmosphere, cardiac output fell to subnormal levels and then returned to normal. Maximal finger constriction was attained after several days of exposure to cold.

1270. Smith, D. E., W. C. Randall, and A. B. Hertzman. Some cutaneous responses to "reflex cooling" [Abstract]. *Fed. Proc., Balt.*, *v. 7, Mar. 1948: 116.*

Blood flow and skin temperatures were estimated in the finger, forearm, and cheek of men whose legs and lower trunk were immersed in cold water. In the finger, blood flow decreased rapidly and then changed little; skin temperature fell markedly and continued to fall. In the forearm, blood flow decreased immediately and either remained low or rose to normal; skin temperature fell gradually. In the cheek, blood flow and skin temperature showed parallel increase or decrease.

1271. Spealman, C. R. Temperature and blood flow in extremities immersed in water. *Proc. Soc. Exp. Biol., N. Y.*, *v. 56, May 1944: 38–40.*

The temperature and blood flow of the hand of subjects were measured at different room temperatures (16°, 24°, or 32°C) while one hand of each subject was immersed in water of varied temperatures (5°, 10°, 15°, 20° and 25°C). The difference between skin and water temperatures was minimal when the hand was immersed in moderately cold water (15° to 20°C). With the higher or lower water temperatures this difference was increased. The effect of increasing the temperature of the ambient air was usually to increase the difference except that with very cold water the air temperature had less effect. The results are discussed in terms of blood flow through the hand and assuming that this is minimized as the hand temperature is progressively lowered. Plethysmographic studies of blood flow verified this assumption.

1272. Spealman, C. R. Effect of ambient air temperature and of hand temperature on blood flow in the hands. *Am. J. Physiol.*, *v. 145, Dec. 1945: 218–222.* Abstract in: *Fed. Proc., Balt.*, *v. 4, Mar. 1945: 67.*

Blood flow was measured in the hands of young men who were sitting in rooms of varying temperature (uncomfortably warm, comfortable, and uncomfortably cold). The hands were immersed in water of 5°, 15°, or 35°C. It was found that, in the comfortable environment, blood flow was less in moderately cold hands than in very cold hands or in warm hands. At any given temperature blood flow was greater as the body was warmer.

1273. Spealman, C. R., M. Newton, and R. L. Post. Influence of environmental temperature and posture on volume and composition of blood. *Am. J. Physiol.*, *v. 150, Oct. 1947: 628–639.*

Human subjects were exposed for 4–6 days each to an uncomfortably warm (91 °F), then to an uncomfortably cold (69 °F), and again to the warm environment, while they were either standing of lying down. Other subjects were similarly exposed to cold, then warm, and again to cold. Studies indicated that changes in both volume and composition of the blood occurred. In general, the concentrations of plasma protein and hemoglobin decreased on exposure to heat and increased on exposure to cold. Plasma protein increased in amount when the upright position was maintained and decreased progressively in the recumbent position; detectable changes in amount of circulating hemoglobin did not occur.

1274. Spealman, C. R., W. Yamamato, E. W. Bixby, and M. Newton. Observations on energy metabolism and water balance of men subjected to warm and cold environments. *Am. J. Physiol.,* v. *152,* Feb. *1948: 233–241.*

Energy metabolism and water balance were studied in two human subjects in a controlled-temperature room. In one experiment subjects were exposed for four days to warmth, six days to cold, and then four days of heat again. Another test included two days of cold, seven of heat, and then a brief re-exposure to cold. Little effect was produced on energy metabolism. It was found, however, that, on changing from a cold to a warm environment, water was stored; on going from warmth to cold, water loss occurred.

1275. Stabilini, G., and G. Cerabolini. Reduction of spleen due to cold with special regard to doctrine of spleen; reduction and pathogenesis of Banti's congestive splenomegaly [In Italian]. *Arch. pat., Bologna,* v. *26, 1948: 114–138.*

Ten cases are presented of reduction of spleen size, 5, 15 and 30 minutes after application of experimental cold by use of a spray of ethyl chloride on the skin at each of 4 small areas of the back, including one just over the spleen. The authors conclude that the experimental results confirm the opinion that reduction of spleen size is essentially a vasomotor phenomenon, caused by a reflex and dependent on the vasoconstriction of intra-splenic arterioles.

1276. Staemmler, H. J. The development of stasis in the terminal circulation following the application of cold stimuli [In German]. *Virchows Arch.,* v. *312,* Apr. *25, 1944: 437–463.*

Laparotomies were performed on rabbits or rats exposing the mesentery which was then cooled by spraying the area with cold salt solution or placing small pieces of frozen dilute salt solution directly on the tissue. The body of the test animal tended to cool, especially since the animal was under narcosis; this was avoided by use of heat lamps. By microscopic examination the order of sensitivity to cold of the blood vessels in the mesentery was found to be first the capillaries, then the arterioles, arteries, and veins. Weak stimulation from cold resulted in a slowing-down of the flow in the peripheral circulation of the area, in the capillaries and pre-capillaries. Strong stimulation led mostly to dilatation in the capillaries, contraction occurring in the arteries. Stronger stimulation resulted in a stagnation in the peripheral vessels. Disturbances in the composition of the blood then occur in the capillaries and pre-capillaries leading to the circulation of plasma only or to the balling-together of erythrocytes. These disturbances of the blood and slowing of the circulation led to the formation of red and of white thrombi and eventually to complete stasis which in a later stage of cold effects dominate the picture. Whether or not the extravasation of the blood serum from the vessels is caused by injury to the vessel wall, in addition to the conditions of stasis, would need to be investigated following autopsy.

1277. Sturm, A., and G. Troschke. The effect of cold in relation to regional differences in dermatographic reaction [In German]. *Zschr. klin. Med.,* v. *141,* Sept. *29, 1942: 434–442.*

Comparison was made of capillary reaction to a 3-minute application of a piece of ice on the skin of the leg and of the breast in three groups of subjects (34 healthy, young soldiers, 53 hospital patients, and 25 children aged 3 to 14 years). Response in the skin of the leg showed a longer period of latency than that in other areas. This explains the frequency of frostbite of the lower extremities in World War I, which occurred in a ratio of 5:2 as compared with frostbite of the fingers. The need for adequate boots for the infantry to afford protection from irreparable vasoconstrictive cold injury is strongly urged.

1278. Suzuki, S. The effects of the climatic conditions of Manchuria on the human body [Abstract, in English]. *Jap. J. M. Sc., Biophysics, v. 9, 1944: 106**.

Experiments in outdoor temperatures of −20° or −30°C in Northern Manchuria showed the following changes in the electrocardiogram of the experimental subjects: pulse rate increased; R and T wave rose, especially the former, except in subjects who were acclimatized. Fibrillation of the muscles of the heart was probably responsible for the increased fibrillation of the heart action current in the intense cold.

1279. Tanner, J. M. The relationship between the frequency of the heart, oral temperature, and rectal temperature in man at rest. *J. Physiol., Lond., v. 115, Dec. 28, 1951: 391–409.*

Two sets of measurements, approximately 8 days apart, were made on 46 healthy young men. The mean values for resting heart rate were 62.8 ± 1.39 beats/minute on the first test and 61.6 ± 1.15 beats/minute on the second test. The mean rectal and oral temperatures, pooling the two tests for each individual, were $98.80° \pm 0.062°F$ and $98.09° \pm 0.061°F$. From these and reports of other experiments at both high and low temperatures, it was evident that significant differences exist between different individuals, and that these presumably arise from differences in the reactivity of their sino-atrial nodes to changes in temperature or in the changes in nervous tone or blood composition caused by temperature changes. Arguments are presented favoring the hypothesis that there is no general reaction to temperature change common to all individuals tending to modify heart rate upon heating or cooling; also that among mammals there may exist two systems in the pacemaker of the heart, one sensitive to temperature change and of about the same character in most mammals, and one relatively insensitive to temperature change and of an activity appropriate to the animal's size.

1280. Taquani, A. C., and T. A. Capris. Pressure responses to cold and to Ephetonin before and after sympathectomy [In Spanish, summaries in Spanish and English]. *Medicina, B. Air., v. 11, Dec. 1951: 366–373.*

Blood pressure responses following cold-pressor tests, or the administration of Ephetonin [racemic ephedrine], have been studied in 10 hypertensive patients before and after being subjected to thoraco-lumbar sympathectomy. The modifications in the magnitude of the responses after the operation were of no great significance.

1281. Taylor, C. B., C. B. Davis, Jr., G. F. Vawter, and G. M. Hass. Controlled myocardial injury produced by a hypothermal method. *Circulation, N.Y., v. 3, Feb. 1951: 239–253.*

Following surgical exposure of the dog's heart while under anesthesia, an experimental injury to the heart was brought about by the use of a hypothermal instrument on which the small endplate was cooled by a flow of carbon dioxide. Transmural lesions were produced in any cardiac chamber, including the right atrium, without danger of rupture, aneurysmal dilatation, or intracardiac thrombosis. Estimates of myocardial damage were quite accurate as shown by later post mortem examination. Necrosis of muscle cells was complete throughout the lesions produced.

1282. Ulrich, S. Post-traumatic arterial spasm; an object demonstration of circulatory disturbances and impaired strength reflexly caused by cold [In Danish]. *Ugeskr. laeger, v. 100, Nov. 17, 1938: 1295–1300.*

Effects of cold exposure are noted in the differences in measurements of muscle strength, electrical resistance of the skin, skin temperature, and blood pressure.

1283. Wilkins, R. W., J. S. Hunt, and C. K. Friedland. The effects of sudden changes in peripheral circulation upon cardiac output [Abstract]. *J. Clin. Invest.*, v. 21, Sept. 1942: 625–626.

It is reported that cardiac output was changed very slightly by a decrease in peripheral blood flow produced by the occlusion of circulation in the limbs or by peripheral vasodilatation or vasoconstriction produced by warming or cooling the body.

1284. Wolff, H. H. The mechanism and significance of the cold pressor response. *Q. J. Med., Oxf.*, v. 20, July 1951: 261–273.

Cold pressor tests were carried out by immersing either a hand (four fingers only) or a foot of the subject in an ice-water bath (0°C) for at least 3 minutes, and observing the rise in blood pressure. Tests were done on normal subjects and on several with peripheral nerve lesions or suffering from hysterical anesthesia. It is concluded that the vasoconstriction underlying the cold pressor response is not the result of a reflex but that it occurs only in response to the pain experienced during the cold immersion. The cold pressor test provides a measure of sensitivity to a standard painful stimulus rather than of vascular reactivity.

See also items: 4, 105, 107, 111, 228, 254, 262, 263, 264, 337, 339, 340, 346, 551, 560, 623, 666, 669, 671, 697, 711, 722, 737, 1044, 1072, 1389, 1402, 1408, 1417, 1424, 1434, 1439, 1459, 1471, 1479, 1519, 1530, 1533, 1535, 1544, 1575, 1589, 1591, 1592, 1701, 1758, 1783, 2079.

F. Circulatory System, Vasomotor Effects

1285. Aschoff, J. Communication on the spontaneous and reflex vasomotor mechanism of the skin [In German]. *Pflügers Arch.*, v. 248 (1–3), 1944: 171–177.

Blood pressure measurements were made of the fingers and hand as well as the nasal membrane of test subjects to study the effect of cooling in ice water, of the extremities, on the vasomotor mechanism.

1286. Aschoff, J. The vasodilatation of an extremity by local cold effect [In German]. *Pflügers Arch.*, v. 248 (1–3), 1944: 178–182.

In the immersion of a hand in water at 10° to 13°C, the local effect on the blood vessels is one of vasoconstriction with a decrease in heat dissipation. When the temperature of the water is kept at 8° to 10°C for 30 minutes, however, a marked dilatation takes place and the heat production rate rises. This reaction is of great importance in the heat economy of the body and the regulation of peripheral circulation.

1287. Aschoff, J. Regulation of circulation by cold vasodilatation following localized cooling of an extremity [In German]. *Pflügers Arch.*, v. 248 (4–6), 1944: 436–442.

By extreme chilling of the hand by immersion in water at 8°C, a sudden localized increase in blood flow was noted in the extremity followed by a rapid fall of the skin temperature of the face.

1288. Aschoff, J. A few general controlling factors of physical temperature regulation [In German]. *Pflügers Arch.*, v. 249 (1), 1947: 125–136.

Either one or both hands of the test subject were immersed in water baths of 8°–10°C or 25°C. By use of a flow calorimeter it was found that the temperature of the cold-water bath rose sharply after immersion of the hands. After the hand had cooled and this heat had been expended to the water, a vasoconstriction began in the hand. This vasoconstriction lasted about 7–10 minutes and led to a curtailment of the heat loss. When the hands were immersed in the bath of 25 °C, there was an oscillation between dilatory and constricting regulation with both hands behaving in a fairly similar manner; the fluctuations of heat loss were reflected in changes in the temperature of the water. This physiological oscillation of temperature regulation should not be confused with blood pressure waves which follow in a much quicker rhythm. It is also different from the spontaneous dilatation arising from severe cooling, the latter being peripherally resolved and influenced by the total tonus of the vascular system at that time purely in an assisting or hindering manner. Following experiments with the immersion of a knee and a hand of the subject in a water bath at 32 °C, a genuine 24-hour rhythmic pattern of physical temperature regulation, similar to rectal temperature variations, has been demonstrated. The lowest point of heat loss occurred in the late afternoon with decreasing temperatures until midnight. During sleep there was a decrease in skin blood flow of the lower as well as the upper extremities.

1289. Bader, M. E., M. B. Macht, and E. L. Pillion. Peripheral vascular effects produced by localized warming of various skin areas [Abstract]. *Fed. Proc., Balt., v. 7, Mar. 1948: 4–5.*

Results show that warming certain skin areas is more effective than warming others in overcoming the vasoconstriction of the extremities produced by cold.

1290. Brecht, K., and K. Pulfrich. Vasomotor reactions in normal and frost-bitten skin of the toes [In German]. *Pflügers Arch., v. 250, Apr. 29, 1948: 109–124.*

Blood flow in the skin of the toe was recorded photoelectrically by means of an infrared cell, vasoconstriction and vasodilatation being indicated by the volume curve. Vasomotor reactions of the normal and frostbitten terminal phalanges of the toe (skin area, but not muscle) were investigated photoelectrically, skin temperature by thermoelectric measurement, and the variations in the dorsalis pedis artery by the pulse curve. The vasomotor reflexes were found to correspond to the temperature rise in the normal toe; vasoconstriction in cold, vasodilatation in heat. In the frostbitten toe, however, vasomotor reflexes appear to run counter to the temperature rise. It was concluded that the blood vessels of the frostbitten toe differ from the normal toe in their reactions, not only in degree, but also in kind.

1291. Calabresi, C. Behavior of temperature of the oral mucosa after skin stimulation [In Italian]. *Arch. ital. otol., v. 51, Nov. 1939: 563–570.*

Immersion of one foot of a subject in water of 10 °C for either 20 minutes or 5 minutes, at a room temperature of 18 °C, brought about a lowering of the temperature of the nasal mucosa. The temperature was lowest in the first 5 minutes and then rose so that at 15 minutes it had often reached the starting level. If immersion was continuous, there was generally a new lowering of temperature at 20 minutes. On cessation of cold stimulus, the temperature of the nasal mucosa rose quite rapidly to normal.

1292. Dail, C. W., and F. B. Moor. Effects of heat, cold, and other stimuli upon human circulation. *Arch. Phys. Ther., v. 19, Mar. 1938: 135–141.*

In tests with medical students, application of cold water or ice to any part of the body caused peripheral vasoconstriction as shown by a decrease in the volume of the arm. The drinking, or introduction by stomach tube, of either hot (42°–55 °C) or cold (9°–12 °C) water also caused constriction. Water of approximately body temperature (36°–37.5 °C) also caused some constriction when drunk but did not when introduced by stomach tube. Psychic stimulation, such as anticipation of the application of ice to the body, was a potent means of producing peripheral constriction. Cold applied to the body surface appeared to cause an increase in the size of the heart and in the density of the lung fields.

1293. Dalla Torre, L. On the reaction of digital arteries to temperature and to vasodilators [In French]. *Schweiz. med. Wschr., v. 73, Oct. 16, 1943: 1274–1277.*

Arteries of the finger, exposed to water at 8°C for 1 minute, showed an increase in amplitude of the sphygmographic wave. An injection of 0.2 mg of acetylcholine or Priscol at a room temperature of 18°C produced an increase of amplitude, but no change was shown at a temperature of 14°C. The conclusion is that the vasodilators are limited in action by the state of the vessel, which depends directly on the ambient temperature.

1294.   Fabbi, F., and T. Posteli. Nasal vasomotor reactions due to thermal stimulation of extremities [In Italian, summaries in Italian and English]. *Riv. otoneuroft.*, v. 24, May–June 1949: 287–296.

Vasoconstriction in the mucosa of the nasal septum was observed, by photo-plethysmographic methods, following immersion of the hands or feet in water of 4°C. The vasoconstriction was found to be more marked when the lower extremities were immersed.

1295.   Grayson, J. Responses of the colonic circulation in man to cooling of the body [Abstract]. *J. Physiol., Lond.,* v. 110, Dec. 31, 1949: 13P.

General body heating produced a vasoconstriction in the human bowel followed by a vasodilatation. Immersion of an arm in ice-cold water brought about a variable and transient colonic vasodilatation at first, always followed by a pronounced vasoconstriction and a fall in body temperature. With the circulation to the arm occluded, immersing it in ice-cold water always produced a marked vasodilatation. Releasing the occluding pressure with the arm still in the water, brought about a rapid fall in body temperature and a pronounced vasoconstriction in the bowel. Vasoconstriction was never observed in response to cooling while the circulation in the arm was occluded. The vasodilator effect of cold on the bowel circulation is, therefore, not the result of direct cooling of the blood. The effect of circulating cooled blood appears, in fact, to be vasoconstrictor in the bowel.

1296.   Grayson, J. Cold and warmth vasoconstrictor responses in the skin of man. *Brit. Heart J.,* v. 13 (2), 1951: 167–176.

Experimental subjects were placed in a controlled-heating cabinet, or wrapped in blankets, with the head and right arm outside, and a study was made of the changes in peripheral blood flow with changes in temperature. From 28°–36°C, the peripheral blood flow increased; above 36°C, it decreased; and at 40°C, it increased again and so, often, did the rectal temperature. Below 28°C, the peripheral blood flow decreased. In 5 apparently healthy subjects there was no vasodilatation on raising the temperature from 20° to 40°C; in 2 of these a definite, and in 1 other a questionable, history of chilblains was established.

1297.   Greenfield, A. D. M., J. T. Shepherd, and R. F. Whelan. The part played by the nervous system in the response to cold of the circulation through the finger tip. *Clin. Sc., Lond.,* v. 10, Aug. 1951: 347–360. Abstract in: *J. Physiol., Lond.,* v. 115, Sept. 1951: 10P–11P.

Several patients with peripheral nerve injury, all of whom had complete anesthesia of at least one finger, were studied for the vasodilator response of the finger following immersion in cold water. After a sufficient interval for the degeneration of the somatic nerve fibers (between the 30th and 201st days after nerve injury), the response was 20% to 50% of the normal size after preliminary immersion in water at 29°C for 20 minutes and before insertion into the cold calorimeter. If the preliminary immersion of the anesthetic finger was at 42°C, a vasodilator response of 50% to 90% of the normal size was obtained. After preliminary immersion at 15°C the response was almost absent. It is concluded that it was unnecessary to postulate a local axon reflex as the basic mechanism of cold vasodilatation, but that the response was considerably improved if the somatic nerves were intact.

1298.   Greenfield, A. D. M., J. T. Shepherd, and R. F. Whelan. Cold vasoconstriction and vasodilatation. *Irish J. M. Sc., Sept. 1951: 415–419.*

The sudden changes in blood flow that occur during immersion of a finger tip in cold water is said to suggest that there is a simultaneous opening and closing of all or nearly all of the arteriovenous anastomosis, or else a sudden dilatation or constriction of the digital arteries. Coordination of this kind is most often brought about by a nervous mechanism. The initial vasoconstriction which follows immersion of a finger tip in cold water (0° to 6°C) is usually sudden in onset and complete in degree; the subsequent vasoconstrictions are also occasionally sudden in onset. The episodes of vasodilatation start abruptly but it was not possible to say whether their onset was ever as sudden as that of cold vasoconstriction.

1299. Guthrie, T. C. Studies on skin temperature. *Tr. Am. Neur. Ass., 1951: 242–243.*

Intravenous injection of cold (65°–48°F) or hot (103°–109°F) saline into the arm of the subject caused a transient decrease or increase, respectively, of the skin temperature of the opposite arm and leg. On the basis of these findings there would seem to be some thermo-regulatory mechanism in the body sensitive to small changes in the temperature of the blood and capable of causing reflex vasodilatation or vasoconstriction. Normal subjects, as well as patients with paraplegia or multiple sclerosis had one extremity immersed in cold water. An elevation of blood pressure occurred immediately and lasted about 6 minutes in the normal subject and in those patients whose pain perception in the extremity was not impaired. At the end of the pressure rise or up to 39 minutes later, a reflex vasoconstriction occurred caus-ing a decrease in skin temperature of the opposite arm and leg. Cold water immersion some-times caused extensor and flexor leg spasms in the paraplegic or the multiple sclerotic; these were associated with generalized vasoconstriction. The findings would seem to indicate that blood pressure elevation and reflex vasoconstriction are unrelated responses.

1300. Hemingway, A. The standardization of temperature regulatory responses of dogs to cold. *Am. J. Physiol., v. 128, Mar. 1940: 736–746.*

Threshold values for vasoconstriction, vasodilatation, and shivering as reflected in skin and rectal temperatures were determined on unanesthetized dogs cooled to a point of vaso-constriction and shivering, and then rewarmed by diathermy applied at a heating rate equal-ing the basal metabolic rate.

1301. Hermann, H., G. Morin, and J. Cier. Local vascular reactions following chilling of the paw of the dog with transected spinal cord [In French]. *C. rend. Soc. biol., Par., v. 127, Dec. 20, 1938: 312–315.*

Dogs with spinal cords transected at the sciatic level were found to be aided, in rewarming following chilling, by the dilatation of blood vessels innervated by spinal ganglia below the level of transection.

1302. Hertzman, A. B., L. W. Roth, and J. B. Dillon. Vascular reactions of the finger to cold [Abstract]. *Am. J. Physiol., v. 133, June 1, 1941: P325–P326.*

Vascular reactions of the finger to cold were examined by photoelectric plethysmograph. It was found that vasoconstriction occurred in the exposed finger and in the control fingers as well. This constriction occurred at once and was independent of the presence or absence of pain. This reaction emphasizes the importance of vasomotor changes to cold brought on by thermosensory or other stimuli. It neither affirms nor denies the participation of arterio-venous anastomoses.

1303. Hertzman, A. B. The relative responses of the dorsal metacarpal, digital and terminal skin arteries of the hand in vasoconstrictor reflexes. *Am. J. Physiol., v. 134, Aug. 1941: 59–64.*

The intermediate arteries of the hand, the dorsal metacarpal arteries, and the digital ar-teries do not participate in the vasoconstrictor reflexes elicited by immersion in ice water or by application of cold to the finger.

1304. Hertzman, A. B., and L. W. Roth. The vasomotor components in the vascular reactions in the finger to cold. *Am. J. Physiol., v. 136, June 1942: 669–679.*

Vascular reactions in the finger to chilling were examined by the photoelectric plethysmograph. The immediate constriction on application of cold is due to vasoconstrictor reflexes on which is superimposed the direct constrictor action of cold.

1305. Hertzman, A. B., and L. W. Roth. The reactions of the digital artery and minute pad arteries to local cold. *Am. J. Physiol., v. 136, June 1942: 680–691.*

Continuous application of cold to a digit results in a delayed constriction of the digital artery. The arterial pulse of the finger was changed only slightly.

1306. Hertzman, A. B., and L. W. Roth. The absence of vasoconstrictor reflexes in the forehead circulation; effects of cold. *Am. J. Physiol., v. 136, June 1942: 692–697.*

In the forehead there are no spontaneous rhythmic constrictions of vasomotor origin such as occur in the finger; nor are there any vasoconstrictor reflexes comparable to those elicited by the immersion of the hand in ice water.

1307. Homans, J. Circulatory disease of the extremities. *New York, Macmillan, 1939. 330 p.*

In Chapter 4, Spasm of the arteries and arterial embolism (p. 111–167), the author discusses recurrent arterial constrictions of the extremities, some of which are caused by cold. He recommends protective clothing and avoidance of exposure to cold, and discusses the use of sympathectomy for which he gives great detail on surgical procedures.

1308. Iida, T. Studies on temperature reaction of blood vessels of human skin to cold. II. [Abstract, in English]. *Jap. J. M. Sc., Biophysics, v. 9, 1944: 7*–8*.*

In an earlier work (item 1309), it had been found that when a finger was immersed in ice water and the temperature of the finger had fallen to a certain level, the skin circulation increased reflexly and the temperature rose. When the testing room temperature rose above 15°C, the reaction of the blood vessels to temperature was accelerated. Seasonal differences in effect were primarily due to changes in environmental temperature. From simultaneous records of changes of temperature and volume of the finger immersed in ice water, it is concluded that the arteriovenous anastomoses play the important, but possibly not the entire, role in this temperature reaction. Following an investigation of about 50 factors involved in resistance to frostbite, it is concluded that the temperature reaction is the most important. A method of estimating frostbite resistance, based on this reaction, was devised and called the "point test of frostbite-proof."

1309. Iida, T. Studies on the temperature reaction of blood vessels of human skin to cold. I. [Abstract, in English]. *Jap. J. M. Sc., Biophysics, v. 9, 1944: 73*–74*.*

When a finger was exposed to cold by immersion in ice water, and its temperature had fallen to a certain degree, the skin circulation increased reflexly and the temperature rose. The following aspects of these reactions are shown: marked individual differences, but a fairly constant reaction for each individual; "first finger" most reactive and "fifth finger" the least so; adults of 25 to 29 years of age show the most pronounced reaction; reaction more pronounced in summer than in other seasons; more vigorous after exercise, hot baths, or hearty eating, and less after cold baths, hunger, or lack of sleep.

1310. Koĭranskiĭ, B. B. Reaction of the blood vessels in the skin of the foot in response to local cooling. (On etiopathogenesis of colds) [In Russian]. (Trudy nauchnoĭ sessii posv. 30-letiiu vel. oktiabr. sotsial. revoliutsii) *In: Trudy Voenno-morskoĭ Med. Akad. (Leningrad), 1947, p. 359–368.*

The skin temperature of the right big toe was measured, by means of electric thermocouples, in 4 healthy subjects, 20–30 years of age, while the foot was immersed for 30 or 20 minutes in water of 10°C or 5°C respectively. In contrast to the reaction of the hands to the same temperatures, in which there is a rhythmic vascular contraction followed by dilatation, the vascular contraction continued during cold stimulation but with unequal intensity. The temperature was greatest (60–70%) during the first 5 minutes, then slowed down; the stronger the stimulation, the greater the temperature decrease. Vascular constriction continued during the 20 minutes of immersion, at which time an adaptation occurred resulting in decreased local sensitivity. At 5°C no adaptation developed but vasoconstriction was more intense than at 10°C and elicited pain. The cooling of the foot at 5°C resulted in a running nose and a slight rise in body temperature which disappeared after the 5th–8th time of immersion, although the vasodilatory reaction in the nose persisted. The temperature of the exhaled air decreased from 36.2°C to 35.3°C, which can be explained by the vasoconstriction of the mucosa of the respiratory passages. Thus, because of the absence of reactive hyperemia in the foot during hypothermia, the protective reaction to cold is incomplete and the resistance of the hypothermic tissue is lowered.

1311. Koĭranskiĭ, B. B. The role of subnormal temperature in the etiology of "chills" [In Russian]. *Gig. & san., v. 13, May 1948: 18–24.*

Warm clothing does not constitute a sufficient protection for workers at subnormal temperatures of 10° to −10°C. Oxygen consumption is increased even at 2°C with warm clothing. The skin temperature of the 3rd phalanx of the index finger was measured in 4 young subjects at environmental temperatures of 21°–23°C and during the cooling of the gloved hand in water at 15° or 5°C. After 8 minutes the skin temperature had dropped from normal (30°C) to 7°C, then increased to 16°C, and dropped again. This zig-zag curve of reflex hyperemia (alternating vasodilatation and vasoconstriction) was repeated many times. In water at 15°C, the skin temperature decreased and after 10 minutes reached a level at which it remained the same for 1½ hours. The chronaxy increased during the first 10 minutes, decreased somewhat until the 15th, then remained constant. In the mucosa of the nose, the vascular reaction is strongest during the cooling of the feet. The less accustomed a part of the body is with regard to low temperatures, the stronger the reflex reaction from this part to other organs, in particular to the nasal mucosa. The reaction of the mucosa may in turn contribute to the weakening of its preventive function and thus aid in the development of an infection. It is known that the vessels in the kidneys react to thermal stimulation in a manner similar to that of the skin. The above data show that the "cold" (infection) results not so much from a strong, as from a weak cold stimulus (subnormal temperature). Cold-induced, prolonged anemia in the kidneys leads to ischemia and nephritis, as was shown by Afanas'ev in 1877.

1312. Koĭranskiĭ, B. B. The etiology and pathogenesis of the common cold. Influence of local refrigeration on the reaction of skin vessels of the foot [In Russian]. *Klin. med., Moskva, v. 26, Oct. 1948: 76–82.*

Thr right foot and right hand of four young healthy adults were immersed in cold water 10°C for 30 minutes and at 5°C for 20 minutes. After 20 minutes of exposure at either temperature, the temperature of the foot or hand had decreased from 35° to 15°C. The greatest temperature fall occurred in the hand within 5 minutes; in the foot the fall was slower and adaptation—brought about by a reactive dilatation of the vessels from time to time—set in after about 8 minutes. In the foot a slow adaptation occurred after refrigeration at 10°C for 20 minutes, whereas there was no adaptation after exposure at 5°C. During the first 8 sessions the subjects developed colds but thereafter did not show signs of cold. From these and animal experiments it was thought that local refrigeration of the lower limbs may lead to an alteration in vascular tone in the upper respiratory tract, producing a loss of protective power against infection.

1313. Kramer, K., and W. Schulze. Local cooling [In German]. *Klin. Wschr., v. 23, June 1944: 201–204.*

A finger or a hand was immersed in an ice bath, or a piece of ice was held in the hand or against the forehead of the test subject. Various observations were made on the finger, including the skin temperature, the degree of oxygen saturation of the blood, and the blood volume in relation to conditions of vasoconstriction or vasodilatation. Parallel studies were made both during and after administration of Novocain and without medication. The more severe and continued was the pain following cold exposure, the longer in general was the duration of vasodilatation. The over-all effect of Novocain on the defense mechanisms against cold—in reducing the range of reaction of the vascular system in the course of both vasoconstriction and vasodilatation—was an unfavorable one. At temperatures of 0°C in the tissues some circulation was possible but at −5°C or below the vasoconstriction was so severe (10% of maximal blood content) that even with very severe pain blood could no longer be forced through the blood vessels of the area. It is only after the vascular system has exhausted itself in its defense against cold injury, that injury by ice formation occurs.

1314. Kramer, K., and W. Schulze. Dilatation of the skin blood vessels by cold. I. Continuous measurement of oxygen content, blood volume, and blood flow of the skin of the fingers [In German]. *Pflügers Arch.*, v. 250, July 20, 1948: 141–170.

Studies were made of the physiological mechanisms underlying responses of the blood vessels in the skin to varying degrees of cold (15°C to −5°C, occasionally −18°C). Measurements were made of blood volume, blood flow, and oxygen saturation of the blood of the finger, and of the skin temperature of the finger of human subjects.

1315. Leriche, R. Paradoxic condition of vasoconstriction of face characterized by active vasodilatation under influence of cold; inversion of reactions to cold [In French]. *Presse méd.*, v. 55, June 7, 1947: 389.

A detailed discussion is given of a young man who, on exposure to a cold atmosphere with some wind, experienced an active hyperemia of the face. This is an inversion of the usual reaction to cold.

1316. Pellegrini, A., and G. Riva. Behavior of the temperature of the nasal mucosa in relation to cutaneous thermal stimulation [In Italian]. *Arch. fisiol.*, Fir., v. 48, 1949: 320–328.

Alternate thermal stimulation of the skin of the feet by use of water baths of 40°C and of 10°C brought about a reflex vasomotor response, changing the temperature of the nasal mucosa. In general, stimulation with cold water brought a lowering in temperature of the nasal mucosa by about 1.5°C; immersion in 40°C baths, a rise of temperature of 0.5°–1.0°C.

1317. Perkins, J. F., Jr., and M. C. Li. A sudden fall of the skin temperature of denervated or sympathectomized paws exposed to cold. *Fed. Proc.*, Balt., v. 6, Mar. 1947: 178–179.

In one unanesthetized dog and 31 lightly-anesthetized cats a sudden continued fall in the skin temperature of denervated or sympathectomized paws was found to occur in a cold environment. After ruling out other factors, the authors suggest that the sudden vasoconstriction is due to increased sensitivity of the blood vessels themselves or of residual nerve fibers in close relation to the arteriovenous anastomoses.

1318. Perkins, J. F., Jr., M. C. Li, F. Hoffman, and E. Hoffman. Sudden vasoconstriction in denervated or sympathectomized paws exposed to cold. *Am. J. Physiol.*, v. 155, Nov. 1948: 165–178.

A sudden, late fall of skin temperature was observed when denervated or sympathectomized paws were exposed to cold for prolonged periods, and a corresponding rise was seen when the chilled extremities were again exposed to warm air. The vasoconstriction was marked enough to reduce blood flow to 1/10 its previous value. The vasoconstriction appeared when the skin reached critical temperature, which was experimentally determined. This effect of prolonged cooling appears to be due chiefly to locally increased sensitivity of the denervated blood vessels to cold.

1319. Ralston, H. J., and W. J. Kerr. Vascular responses of the nasal mucosa to thermal stimuli with some observations on skin temperature. *Am. J. Physiol.*, *v. 144, July 1945: 305–310.*

Nasal temperature and volume changes in response to cutaneous chilling and warming were studied in humans. There was a parallel between nasal and finger temperature. Local cooling resulted in a drop of nasal temperature with return to normal in a few minutes.

1320. Rapaport, S. I., E. S. Fetcher, and J. F. Hall. Physiological protection of the extremities from severe cold [Abstract]. *Fed. Proc., Balt., v. 7, Mar. 1948: 99.*

By the use of forced internal ventilation of clothing of the body (and excluding the hands and feet which were warmed only by the circulating blood supply) the thermal state of the body was controlled through regulation of a hot air supply. Normal hand and foot temperatures were maintained in 3 subjects when approximately 180 Cal/hour were supplied at 0°F, or 280 Cal/hour at −30°F; under these conditions the body did not need to conserve heat. The temperature of even the bare hands could be kept within a comfortable range under these conditions. When the heat supplied to the body was reduced, insulation could not prevent hand and foot temperature from falling. At −30°F the extremities of 2 of the 3 subjects rewarmed after the body was rewarmed. A slight heat deficit caused a fall of foot temperature but not of hand temperature despite the greater insulation of the foot. It is concluded that hand and foot temperatures in the cold can be made primarily dependent upon the state of thermal balance of the body and nearly independent of ambient temperature and insulation.

1321. Razgha, A. von, and L. Zselyonka. Temperature measurements in reference to the study of cold susceptibility [Abstract, in German]. *Ber. ges. Physiol.*, *v. 121, 1940: 658.*

The skin temperature of 12 young men was studied after footbaths at 14°–18°C. Three of the men were subject to frequent "colds"; cold baths elicited in them a warming of the hands, similar to that which would occur normally after warm baths. The subjects who were non-sensitive to cold reacted by a regular cooling of the body surface. Such a sharp difference in the reaction of cold-sensitive and non-sensitive subjects suggests that this paradoxical reaction of the cold-sensitives is related to the tendency to catch "colds". Apparently it is an external manifestation of an abnormal vascular reactivity, which, if appearing in other regions, such as the mucosa of the nasal passages, could create favorable conditions for the occurrence of "colds".

1322. Reis, G. von, and F. Sjöstrand. On the influence of local physical and chemical skin stimuli on the peripheral blood distribution [In German]. *Acta physiol. scand., v. 1, 1940: 183–202.*

The amount of peripheral blood in the liver and adrenal cortex during the application of heat and cold to the skin of the abdomen was studied in guinea pigs under Pernocton narcosis. Heat produced by ultraviolet radiation and oil of mustard had no effect on blood distribution in liver and adrenal cortex; but with the application of local cold (water at 5°–10°C, applied by means of a rubber hose), peripheral blood in the adrenal cortex and in the liver showed a marked increase. These effects were lacking when the cold irritation was applied to denervated skin areas.

1323. Rosen, S. R. Vasomotor response in hysteria. *J. Mount Sinai Hosp., N. York, Sept–Oct. 1951: 179–190.*

The use of the cold pressor test (immersion of a hand in ice water for 2 minutes) in evaluating vasomotor responses in various mental disorders yielded the accidental finding of a paradoxical response in cases of conversion hysteria. Tests done on a conversion hysteria group showed consistently low responses including several minus responses. In 3 cases differential diagnosis between organic conditions and conversion hysteria supported the suggested significance of the test. The possible role of vasomotor mechanism is discussed with reference to its universal application in the understanding of the physiology of conversion symptom formation.

1324. Sarnoff, S. J., and F. A. Simeone. Vasodilator fibers in the human skin. *J. Clin. Invest.*, v. 26, May 1947: 453–459.

Studies were made on reflex vasodilatation of a leg, while an arm was immersed in water of 43°–44°C, or vice versa, at the time the subjects were being kept in a cold room. It was found that at the height of elevation of skin temperature due to reflex vasodilatation, block of the nerve supply to that area did not cause a fall in skin temperature but usually caused a rise in the normal as well as in other groups of subjects. It is concluded that if active vaso-dilator fibers exist in the skin of the digits their functional significance is very limited; the indirect vasodilatation on heating is probably due to the central inhibition of vasoconstrictor impulses.

1325. Schulze, W. On the influence of alcohol on peripheral circulation during local cooling [In German]. *Klin. Wschr.*, v. 24–25, Aug. 1, 1947: 646–654.

Research on the vasomotor reaction in exposure to local cold of −2° and −16°C is re-ported. Alcohol was found to produce vasodilatation in skin areas exposed to cold; accord-ingly it can serve as protection against cold injury. The effective dosage was found to be relatively high. A difference was found in the response of the upper and lower extremities, blood vessels of the hand reacting more strongly than those of the foot. As to whether alcohol can be recommended as prophylaxis against local cold injury, further research under condi-tions of actual winter cold will be necessary. In therapy for local freezing, alcohol, used as a means of vasodilatation, is superior in effectiveness to ordinary medication.

1326. Sheard, C., G. M. Roth, and B. T. Horton. Normal vasoconstriction, vasospasm and environmental temperature. *In: American Institute of Physics. Tem-perature, its measurement and control in science and industry, p. 571–575. New York, Reinhold, 1941.*

Vasoconstriction and vasomotor regulation during changes in environmental temperature are discussed as they occur in the normal individual, in those patients with peripheral vascular diseases of various kinds, or in patients following sympathectomy. An instance is cited of a normal individual exposed to gradually changing environmental temperatures from 27° to 23°C (decreasing by 2°C every two or more hours), where the vasoconstriction occurred first in the toes (a decrease of about 10°C), and finally in the fingers (a decrease of about 2°–3°C) with only a degree or two of change in the temperature of the forehead.

1327. Takahashi, S. Changes in the circulatory reaction of the human skin to cold by training [Abstract, in English]. *Jap. J. M. Sc., Biophysics, v. 6, 1940: 122*–123*.

Changes in the reaction of skin temperature to repeated exposure to cold were tested by immersing one hand or one foot in water of −2° to −5°C for about 1½ hours once or twice a day. Changes in reaction were observed, and the opposite hand or foot was compared. After 10 applications, an increase in the reaction was noted, the magnitude of increase reach-ing 10°C at times. Cold sensation was less marked in feet which had been so adapted, even after 1 year.

1328. Timofeev, N. V., and N. IA. Sinitsyna. Effect of peripheral cooling on the vasomotor reactions of the nasal mucosa in man [In Russian]. *Vest. otorinolar., 1940 (4–5): 26–31.*

When the foot was experimentally cooled at 15°C for 15 minutes, vasoconstriction, vaso-dilatation, and then again vasoconstriction were noted in the nasal mucosa.

1329. Weber, H. Investigations on the sensory portion of the trigeminal nerve as the site of origin of circulatory reflexes. *Pflügers Arch., v. 248 (1–3), 1944: 143–148.*

The volume of the ear of the subject was decreased, then increased, and returned to normal following stimulation by cold when ice was applied to the side of the face. When the arm on the opposite side was immersed in ice water (11°–12°C for 15 minutes) similar but slower reactions occurred. More significant reactions between the two areas of stimulation were found when heat was used. Changes in the ear volume were determined by plethysmographic studies of the blood flow. It is concluded that the trigeminal nerve plays an important role in temperature regulation.

1330. Wolff, H. H., and E. E. Pochin. Quantitative observations on vascular reactions in human digits in response to local cooling. *Clin. Sc., Lond., v. 8 (3), 1949: 145–154.*

Fingers subjected to experimental cooling showed vasodilatation which increased if the chilling was prolonged or the temperature lowered. Stopping blood supply during or after exposure to cold did not prevent subsequent vasodilatation.

See also items: 352, 375, 644, 1137, 1172, 1190, 1193, 1405, 1413, 1415, 1433, 1470, 1695, 2106.

G. Endocrine System

1331. Anon. Feeling the cold. *Brit. M. J., 1943 (v. 2): 501.*

"Feeling the cold" depends on at least 3 factors, psychological, vascular, and endocrine. Much work has been done on the vascular response to cold but very little on the individual reactions. The most important endocrine glands involved are the adrenal medulla and the thyroid. The first reaction to chilling is a discharge of adrenaline and consequent peripheral vasoconstriction, whereas the thyroid gland exerts a constant control by regulating the degree of intracellular oxidation and hence of heat production. The author mentions the giving of thyroid hormone as a therapeutic measure in persons suffering from sensations of continuing cold.

1332. Bacchus, H. Cytological distribution of cholesterol and ascorbic acid in adrenal cortex of rat exposed to cold. *Anat. Rec., v. 110, Aug. 1951: 495–503.*

Eight rats were sacrificed after 1 hour, and 6 rats after 48 hours, of exposure in a cold room at 0°–4°C. The mean adrenal weight of the animals under stress for 48 hours was significantly higher than that of normal control animals while that of animals under stress only 1 hour was higher but not significantly so statistically. A marked depletion of cholesterol from the cells of the zona fasciculata and the zona reticularis was observed in the adrenals of animals exposed to cold for 1 hour. There was also a profound depletion of ascorbic acid from these cells and the adjacent sinusoids, with the ascorbic acid present in the cells being at the periphery of the cytoplasm. There was a marked re-accumulation of both these substances in the cells of the fasciculata and reticularis of animals exposed to the stress of cold for 48 hours. Ascorbic acid was present in large amounts in the sinusoids but cells adjacent were devoid of the vitamin. The observations of the lack of ascorbic acid during the alarm reaction stage and its re-accumulation during the "resistance phase" of the "general adaptation syndrome" is said to suggest that ascorbic acid is in some manner associated with cholesterol in the production of cortical hormones.

1333. Bader, R. A., H. J. Stein, J. W. Eliot, and D. E. Bass. Hormonal alterations in men exposed to heat and cold stress [Abstract]. *Am. J. Physiol., v. 155, Dec. 1, 1948: 425.*

Hormonal alterations were studied in 3 men subjected to heat and cold stress. Cold of −20°F was not sufficient to deplete the adrenal cortical reserve as measured by response to ACTH. A combination of cold and exercise reduced the number of circulating eosinophils.

1334. Baillif, R. N. Microscopic changes in the hypophysis of the albino rat following exposure to cold, and their relationship to the physiology of secretion. *Am. J. Anat., v. 62, May 1938: 475–495.*

The pituitary glands of rats exposed to cold showed microscopic changes indicative of increased secretory activity. The gland itself was hypertrophied and the blood vessels dilated. Severe or long-continued cold was followed by extensive degeneration of tissue components and the formation of colloid.

1335. Barrnett, R. J., and R. O. Greep. Regulation of secretion of adrenotrophic and thyrotropic hormones after stalk section. *Am. J. Physiol., v. 167, Dec. 1951: 569–575.*

Following section of the pituitary stalk, the hypophyseal-portal blood vessels did not regenerate. There was histological evidence of the hypofunction of the pituitary gland and the adrenals and thyroid had become atrophic, indicating a deficiency in release of adrenotrophic and thyrotropic hormones. On exposure to cold (3°C for 7 days) there was an increase in the output of both these hormones, indicating that the pituitary gland responded to the stress of cold despite the absence of direct neural or neurovascular connections between the central nervous system and the anterior pituitary. The data suggest that the titer of cortical and thyroid hormones in the blood appears to play the major role in the regulation of pituitary adrenotropic and thyrotrophic activity.

1336. Bernstein, J. G. The effect of thermal environment on the morphology of the thyroid and adrenal cortical glands in the albino rat [Abridgement of Ph.D. thesis, New York University]. *Endocrinology, v. 28, June 1941: 985–998.*

Following the examination of tissues from young albino rats, the author reports a seasonal variation in epithelial cell heights in the thyroid gland (high in winter, low in summer) and in the distribution of adrenal cortical sudanophilic substance (low in winter, high in summer). No correlation with seasonal environmental temperature was found. However, under experimental conditions of heat and cold (53°F for 10 days, 23.5°F for 2 days, or 32°F for 5 days), thyroid epithelial heights were found to be inversely related, adrenal cortical sudanophilic substance directly related to temperature.

1337. Blaizot, S., and J. Blaizot. Creatinuria due to cold in the white rat; influence of the thyroid and vitamin B_1 [In French]. *C. rend. Acad. sc., Par., v. 226, May 31, 1948: 1838–1840.*

Upon exposure to cold, thyroidectomized rats showed less creatinuria than normal controls. Similarly rats subcutaneously injected with vitamin B_1 showed less creatinuria than normal controls when both groups were exposed to cold.

1338. Booker, W. M., F. M. Dent, W. M. Jones, M. L. Hudson, and R. L. Hayes. Factors influencing survival time of adrenalectomized mice in cold stress [Abstract]. *Am. J. Physiol., v. 164, Dec. 1951: 769–770.*

Using adrenalectomized and normal mice, a study was made of the relation of the adrenal gland to ascorbic acid metabolism under the stress of cold room temperatures (42°F).

1339. Brolin, S. E. A study of the structural and hormonal reactions of the pituitary body of rats exposed to cold, illustrating the regulatory influence of the anterior lobe on the thyroid gland [In English]. *Acta anat., Basel, 1946 (suppl. 3): 1–169.*

An elaborate and detailed study was made of the role of the pituitary, thyroid, and adrenal glands in white rats as they react to a degree of cold not severe enough to cause structural damage. 232 refs.

1340. Brolin, S. E. Influence of temperature on endocrine glands [In Swedish, English summary]. *Nord. Med.*, v. 30, June 28, 1946: 1401–1406.

The role of the thyroid gland and the adrenal medulla in the increased metabolic rate at low temperatures, is discussed. Hormonal analyses indicate that an increase of the secretion of thyrotropic hormone occurs in the pituitary gland at low temperatures, and that this activity occurs in the basophilic cells of the anterior pituitary.

1341. Cahane, M., and T. Cahane. On the existence of infundibular nerve centers regulating the function of the thyroid gland [In French]. *Acta med. scand.*, v. 94 (3), 1938: 320–327.

Rats which had injuries of the infundibulum of the pituitary gland—which regulates thyroid stimulation—were found to have abnormalities of thyroid functioning. Histological examination of tissues of this area of the pituitary of 4 rabbits, after exposure to cold, showed evidence of hyperfunctioning in the increase in heighth of the acinar epithelium and in the decrease in colloids present. The authors postulate that cold acts not directly on the thyroid gland but indirectly through the pituitary gland.

The urine of subjects exposed to cold (−15°C, for 3–4 hours) was found to contain a thyroid stimulant when it was injected into guinea pigs. The thyroid glands were increased in size and showed definite histological evidence of hyperfunctioning; the pituitary glands showed slight increases in size only. Guinea pigs kept in a hot room showed histological evidence of hypofunctioning of both the thyroid and pituitary glands.

1342. deGrandarias, F. M. Ascorbic acid in adrenal glands of animals submitted to the action of physical and traumatic agents [In Spanish, summaries in Spanish and English]. *Rev. españ. fisiol.*, v. 7, Dec. 1951: 215–220.

The effect of exposure to cold (1° to 4°C) and of violent injury (multiple fractures of the extremities) on the level of vitamin C in the adrenal glands was studied in guinea pigs. Some of the animals before the injury were injected with Doca [desoxycorticosterone acetate]. In animals not treated in any way, an increase in vitamin C was found following exposure to low temperatures. A slight rise in vitamin C was likewise observed when animals were injected, previous to injury, with Doca. But in those injured and not given the injection, the quantity of vitamin C was considerably lowered.

1343. Dempsey, E. W., and E. B. Astwood. Determination of the rate of thyroid hormone secretion at various environmental temperatures. *Endocrinology*, v. 32, June 1943: 509–518.

The maintenance or restoration of normal thyroid weight by the administration of thyroxin to rats simultaneously treated with the anti-thyroid drug, thiouracil, was used as the basis of an assay procedure for thyroid hormone. In rats exposed to a cold environment (1°C or 5°C) it was found that the rate of thyroid enlargement after thiouracil administration was high. At 1°C the thyroxin requirement was 9.5 micrograms; at 35°C, it was 1.7 microgram; at a normal room temperature of 25°C, 5.2 micrograms.

1344. Dorfman, R. I., B. N. Horwitt, and W. R. Fish. The presence of a cortin-like substance (cold-protecting material) in the urine of normal men. *Science*, v. 96, Nov. 27, 1942: 496–497.

A cortin-like substance was obtained from the urines of three normal men. When this substance was administered by stomach tube to adrenalectomized rats which were exposed to an environmental temperature of 5°C, the survival time for the rats was increased by 37% to 51% over that of the control animals which did not receive the medication.

1345. Dugal, L. P., and M. Thérien. The influence of ascorbic acid on the adrenal weight during exposure to cold. *Endocrinology, v. 44, May 1949: 420–426.*

The typical enlargement of the adrenals which occurs under a condition of stress such as cold (exposure to temperature of 1 °C for 72 hours, then 4 °C for 244 days) is completely prevented in rats and guinea pigs by large doses of ascorbic acid. Normal hypertrophy is prevented while resistance to cold is simultaneously increased.

1346. Dugal, L. P., and J. Leblanc. Influence of ascorbic acid on the variations of adrenal cholesterol in animals exposed to cold [Abstract, in French]. *Rev. canad. biol., v. 8, Nov. 1949: 440.*

Ascorbic acid prevents hypertrophy of the adrenals on exposure to cold and the question arose if it might also inhibit the activity of the gland. The results of experiments would indicate that, on the contrary, ascorbic acid furthers the activity, with the lowering of the cholesterol content being a true indication of this activity.

1347. Ekström, T., N. Lundgren, and C. G. Schmiterlöw. On the effect of local stimulation by cold on the adrenaline secretion [In English]. *Acta physiol. scand., v. 6 (1), 1943: 52–61.*

In rabbits with intact innervation of the skin the adrenaline secretion showed an increase during cold-stimulation (by application of a salt-and-ice bag to the stomach area) even if the body temperature was kept relatively constant. The effect of the cold-stimulation was shown to be reflex in nature. A considerable fall in general body temperature would not of itself provoke any detectable reflex liberation of adrenaline.

1348. Ershoff, B. H. Failure of growth hormone to promote a weight increment in immature rats under conditions of low environmental temperature. *Endocrinology, v. 48, Jan. 1951: 111–113.*

Massive doses of a growth-promoting fraction of anterior pituitary failed to counteract the growth-retarding action of a low environmental temperature (2 °C) on immature rats. The average gain in body weight (original weight of 57.0 ± g) over an 18 day period, while on "growth hormone" treatment, was 32.9 g for rats kept at environmental temperatures of 2 °C in contrast to 85.0 g for those kept at 23 °C.

1349. Fortier, C., and H. Selye. Adrenocorticotrophic effect of stress after severance of the hypothalamo-hypophyseal pathways. *Am. J. Physiol., v. 159, Dec. 1, 1949: 433–439.*

The hypothalamo-hypophyseal pathways were altered in rats through partial hypophysectomy, total hypophysectomy, or by homotransplantation of the anterior lobe of the pituitary to the anterior chamber of the eye. All animals, including control groups of untreated rats, were then submitted to unilateral (left) adrenalectomy. Following exposure to cold (0 °C) for one hour, the animals were killed by bleeding. Concentration of ascorbic acid in the adrenals was considered as a quantitative index of corticotrophic stimulation. A comparison of ascorbic acid concentration of the right adrenal with that of the left adrenal, previously removed, showed that a significant decrease—in all except totally hypophysectomized animals—of adrenal ascorbic acid had resulted from the stress of the surgical intervention of adrenalectomy and exposure to cold. The author concludes that this release of corticotrophin by cold and surgical trauma is not necessarily mediated through nervous pathways.

1350. Freeman, W., G. Pincus, and E. D. Glover. The excretion of neutral urinary steroids in stress [Abstract]. *Endocrinology, v. 35, Sept. 1944: 215.*

Normal male subjects and mental patients were subjected to the stresses of exposure to cold, pursuit-meter operation, and psychological tests. Normal subjects showed an increased excretion of 17-ketosteroids in the urine during stress and a sharp decline afterwards; reactions of patients were varied but they generally failed to show this increase.

1351. Gallone, L., and W. Galluzzi. Effect of sex hormones on response of thyroid to cold [In Italian]. *Arch. fisiol., Fir., v. 51, Aug. 27, 1951: 18–22.*

The administration of estrogens (testosterone and gonadotrophin) induced in mature male guinea pigs a depression of the activity of the thyroid which resulted in the partial or total inhibition of the animals' defenses against cold. Animals were kept at 16°–18°C, or were exposed for short periods at −2°C over 4 consecutive days, with and without hormone treatment. Exposure to cold alone brought about an increase to 6.38 microns in the height of the epithelial tissue layer of the thyroid while exposure to cold combined with treatment with hormones gave values (4.87, 4.98, or 3.86 microns) similar to or less than those of untreated controls (4.20 microns) kept at 16°–18°C. Administration of estrogens acts to decrease the activity of the hypophysis so that there is a limited production by it of both gonadotrophin and thyrotropin.

1352. Hemphill, R. E., and M. Reiss. Regulation of endogenous cortin production. *Endocrinology, v. 41, July 1947: 17–20.*

The content of cortin in the blood of rats kept in the cold (5°–6°C) increased by over 300%; the increase after 70 hours of exposure of the cortin content of the adrenals was much greater in the males than in the females. It was noted that the average adrenal weight and adrenal cortin content of the female control group of rats (kept at normal room temperature) was higher than similar findings of the male control group, but that the blood cortin content was lower.

1353. Hermann, H., J. Chatonnet, and J. Vial. Influence of cold on the adrenaline content of the adrenals of the rat [In French]. *C. rend. Soc. biol., Par., v. 143, Feb. 1949: 273–275.*

Placing rats in a cold room (2°C) for periods of 15 minutes to 2 hours caused a marked decrease in the content of adrenaline in the adrenal glands of the rat. It had been expected that the increase in the production of adrenaline upon stimulation by cold would result in an increase in the gland content. On the contrary, emission of adrenaline from the gland was increased more than the production of adrenaline is increased so that a veritable drainage of adrenaline from the gland results. This utilization of the reserve of adrenaline within the gland, and the suddenness with which the action begins, are some of the aspects of adrenaline secretion which constitute its "emergency function."

1354. Hoffman, E. Observations on the effect of environmental temperature on body temperature, growth, and weight of spleen, comb and endocrine glands of chickens (typewritten copy of thesis). *College Park, Md., University of Maryland, 1949. 73 p.*

Part I (p. 1–33). The effect of a 3-week exposure to a warm or cool environment on the weight and function of the thyroid of 7-week-old New Hampshire cockerels, was studied. Cold exposure (45°F) of cockerels resulted in a heavier thyroid and higher oxygen consumption and, in addition, in a higher thyroxin secretion rate than in the warm-exposed birds. De-pluming the birds resulted in an increase in oxygen consumption but no change in thyroid weight. A low incubation temperature for eggs (96.8°F) resulted in enlarged thyroids in the chicks after hatching. Part II (p. 34–73). Exposure of the cockerels to 45°F for 3 weeks resulted in an increase in adrenal weight (not statistically significant) but no increase in body, pituitary, or spleen weights. Exposure to 80°F for 3 weeks resulted in an increase in weight of the testes and comb. Testes weight was not always proportional to comb weight.

1355. Ickert, · · · , and · · · Kütter. The blood sugar during chilling and warming [In German]. *Deut. med. Wschr., v. 70, June 23, 1944: 365–366.*

When human subjects kept their arms in ice water for 15 minutes, an increase in the secretion of adrenaline, and a rise of the blood-sugar level was noted. On rewarming, the blood-sugar level declined, and the authors regard this as the result of stimulation of the parasympathetic system with an increase in the secretion of insulin.

1356.   Jailer, J. W. The pituitary-adrenal relationship in the infant rat. *Proc. Soc. Exp. Biol., N. Y., v. 72, Dec. 1949: 638–639.*

Exposure of newborn rats to refrigeration (5 °C) for 2½ hours did not cause a decline in ascorbic acid content of the adrenals until the 16th day of life. Experiments indicate that the infant rat does not respond to stress in the same manner as the adult animal.

1357.   Kendall, E. C. The function of the adrenal cortex. *Proc. Mayo Clin., v. 15, May 8, 1940: 297–304.*

Corticosterone, compound E, and the amorphous fraction of the extract from the adrenal cortex, have been shown to be about equal in their protective action against cold when given to adrenalectomized, and normal, rats.

1358.   Kojima, S. A note on the calorigenic effect of cold in cats deprived of the suprarenal medulla [In English]. *Tohoku J. Exper. M., v. 40, 1941: 353–370.*

The gaseous metabolic rate was studied in cats in whom a heat debt of 1.3–2.0 Cal/kg had been obtained by introduction of ice water into a previously prepared stomach fistula, both before and after removal of the suprarenal medulla. This heat debt raised the metabolic rate about 40% both before and after demedullation; the rate was not altered by demedulation alone. Any intensification of shivering due to such cooling was difficult to determine.

1359.   Leblond, C. P., T. Nguyen-van, and G. Segal. Fatty infiltration of the liver by the action of noxious agents [In French]. *C. rend. Soc. biol., Par., v. 130, Apr. 29, 1939: 1557–1559.*

Response of the rat to various noxious agents—including exposure to cold—is shown by a group of non-specific symptoms constituting what is called the "alarm reaction". Indications of the "alarm reaction" are shown by the fatty infiltration of the liver and the involution of the thymus. These conditions do not occur in animals which are incapable of responding because of adrenalectomy.

1360.   Leblond, C. P. Non-specific syndrome (Alarm reaction of Selye) [In French]. *Ann. endocr., Par., v. 1, May 1939: 179–196.*

Rats and mice were exposed to various toxic materials and physical agents, such as cold (rats at 2 °C; mice at 6 °C) for 48 hours. The animals were then sacrificed and the spleen, thymus, and adrenal glands were examined, weighed, and compared with normals. Evidence of alarm reaction was shown by hyperplasia of adrenals, atrophy of thymus and other lymphatic organs. The symptoms were found to be greatly aggravated by cold and by fasting.

1361.   Leblond, C. P., and J. Gross. Factors modifying the response of thyroidectomized rats to low temperature [Abstract]. *Anat. Rec., v. 84, 1942: 489.*

Thyroparathyroidectomized adult rats on whom surgery was performed over 5 days previous to exposure to cold (0 °C), died within a few days. Parathyroidectomized and thyroxine-treated thyroidectomized rats exposed in a similar manner survived for several weeks. If the thyroid was removed only 12 hours before exposure to cold, the survival time was greatly lengthened—over 10 days in female rats. Traces of thyroid hormone known to remain in the body for several days, probably helped in adaptation to cold. Thyroidectomized rats kept at 32 °C and then exposed to cold, died over night; kept at 22 °C, average survival was 6 days. The thyroidectomized rats surviving the cold, with a rise of food consumption to 180% of normal, showing that a marked adaptation to cold was possible in the absence of the thyroid.

1362.   Leblond, C. P., and J. Gross. Effect of thyroidectomy on resistance to low environmental temperature. *Endocrinology, v. 33, Sept. 1943: 155–160.*

Adult rats thyroparathyroidectomized two weeks previously died within a week when exposed to temperatures of 0° to 2 °C. Parathyroidectomized and thyroxine-treated thyroidectomized rats survived for several weeks at the same temperature.

1363. Leblond, C. P., J. Gross, W. Peacock, and R. D. Evans. Metabolism of radioiodine in the thyroids of rats exposed to high or low temperatures. *Am. J. Physiol., v. 140, Feb. 1944: 671–676.*

The effect of exposure to cold on thyroid activity was studied by following the metabolism of radioactive iodine injected into rats kept at low environmental temperatures (0° to 2°C) for varying periods of time. It was found that in rats exposed to cold, an increased thyroid activity was definite after 7 days, maximal at 26 days (rising to 2.7 times the normal level), but absent after exposure for 40 days.

1364. Lesser, A. J., R. J. Winzler, and J. B. Michelson. Effect of iodide on thyroid glands of rats kept at low temperature. *Proc. Soc. Exp. Biol., N. Y., v. 70, Apr. 1949: 571–573.*

Hyperplasia of the thyroid epithelium was produced in rats by exposure to a cold room temperature (4°C) for 3 weeks. Increasing the iodide level of the diet prevented this hyperplasia.

1365. Levin, L. The effects of several varieties of stress on the cholesterol content of the adrenal glands and of the serum of rats. *Endocrinology, v. 37, July 1945: 34–43.*

The adrenal cholesterol of adult male rats decreased slightly when the animals were exposed to environmental temperatures of 0° to 5°C for 16 to 22 hours. In those exposed for 72 hours, however, the cholesterol content of the adrenals was normal.

1366. Long, C. N. H. The relation of cholesterol and ascorbic acid to the secretion of the adrenal cortex. *Recent Progr. Hormone Res., N. Y., v. 1 (Sect. II), 1497: 99–122.*

When normal, fasted, rats were exposed to temperatures of 0°–4°C for periods of 1 to 24 hours, the body temperatures remained approximately normal. The adrenal ascorbic acid fell after one hour of exposure but rose to about normal levels after the sixth hour; adrenal cholesterol levels fell later than did the ascorbic acid and remained low throughout the exposure. Hypophysectomized rats could be similarly exposed for approximately four hours, but after this period the mortality rate was very high. Such an exposure caused a fall in body temperature to around 94°F. The rats showed no changes in adrenal ascorbic acid and cholesterol even though they were rendered moribund in the cold. In guinea pigs, exposure to cold produced a rapid and sustained fall in adrenal ascorbic acid; adrenal cholesterol was also markedly and persistently lowered.

1367. Macbeth, R. A., and R. L. Noble. The metabolic response to thyroid depressant drugs in animals maintained in a cold environment. *J. Endocr., Oxf., v. 6, Apr. 1949: 28–40.*

Both surgically thyroidectomized and normal rats were exposed to lowered environmental temperatures by decreasing the temperatures 5°C each day until after 10 days the temperature reached, and was maintained at, 2°–0°C. Both groups of animals had a decided increase in oxygen consumption but that of the thyroidectomized animals was considerably greater. However, the surgically treated animals were unable to adapt to the cold and died within a day or two, having sustained a drastic weight loss. Normal rats which were given thiouracil before cold exposure did not experience this increase in oxygen consumption on exposure.

1368. Morin, G., J. Vial, and J. Guyotat. Effect of cold on epinephrine secretion in dogs [In French]. *C. rend. Soc. biol., Par., v. 136, Mar. 16, 1942: 593–595.*

Dogs exposed to environmental temperatures of from −6° to 9°C show a greatly increased secretion of adrenaline together with hyperglycemia.

1369. Morin, G. External temperature and the calorigenic action of Adrenalin [In French]. *C. rend. Soc. biol., Par., v. 137, Mar. 22, 1943: 488–490.*

Dogs injected with Adrenalin while in an environmental temperature of 7°C produced more heat than when in an environment of 20°C.

1370. Morin, G. Adrenaline, hormone of defense against the cold [In French]. *Biol. méd., Par., v. 37, Sept–Oct. 1948: 196–230.*

The lowering of exterior temperature brings about, by reflex action, an augmentation of adrenaline. Adrenaline has a calorigenic action, preferentially on the combustion of lipids, in acting as a catalyst in tissue metabolism. Suppression of adrenaline secretion, and elimination of neuro-endocrine regulation, does not hinder the efficacy against the cold of other hormone factors. Suprarenalectomized animals had been found by earlier workers to have a decreased resistance to cold and a reduced power of chemical thermoregulation. 140 refs.

1371. Onti, T. Effect of inactivating the suprarenal medulla upon shivering after application of cold [In English]. *Tohoku J. Exp. M., v. 40, Sept. 25, 1941: 506–510.*

Cats were cooled by introduction of cold water into a previously prepared stomach fistula, to obtain a heat debt of 1.3–2.0 Cal/kg. Shivering occurred with similar intensity and duration in the cats both before and after the inactivation of the suprarenal medulla. One suprarenal capsule was denervated; the other removed. Experiments on dogs, prepared in a similar manner and with a heat debt of 1.0–2.2 Cal/kg, gave similar results.

1372. Ring, G. C. Thyroid stimulation by cold. *Proc. Postcoll. Clin. Assemb. Coll. M., Ohio State Univ., v. 6, 1939: 137.*

Rats which had lived in a cold environment (0°–5°C) for 3 or 4 weeks, showed histological and chemical changes in their thyroid glands which indicated increased activity of the gland. Basal metabolic rates had increased in the cold and decreased on return to normal temperature. Completely thyroidectomized animals did not survive in the cold environment for more than a week. The mechanism responsible for thyroid stimulation on exposure to cold is not known; removal of the basal cervical ganglia did not materially alter the degree of metabolic increase.

1373. Ring, G. C. Thyroid activity after iodine ingestion. *Am. J. Physiol., v. 134, Oct. 1941: 631–635.*

When rats, kept in a refrigerator for 3 weeks, were given sodium iodide their basal metabolic rate was increased. It was also found that administration of thyrotropic principle alone would increase the basal metabolic rate more than when combined with sodium iodide.

1374. Ring, G. C. The importance of the thyroid in maintaining an adequate production of heat during exposure to cold. *Am. J. Physiol., v. 137, Oct. 1942: 582–588.*

Prolonged exposure to cold stimulates the thyroid gland and produces a small increase in basal metabolism. It was also found that the maximal metabolic response to cold as well as response to epinephrine was potentiated by thyroxin.

1375. Robinson, F. B., and J. M. Yoffey. Histochemical changes produced by cold and Adrenalin in suprarenal cortex of adult male rat. *J. Anat., Lond., v. 84, Jan. 1950: 32–37.*

White rats, after exposure to 0°C for 5 minutes, or 10 minutes after an intraperitoneal injection of Adrenalin, could be shown histochemically to have a depletion of cholesterol from areas of the adrenal cortex. The glands returned to normal within 3 days after a 3-hour exposure to cold or after a single injection of Adrenalin.

1376. Roos, A. Assay of adrenal cortical extracts in adrenalectomized rats exposed to cold. *Endocrinology, v. 33, Nov. 1943: 276–281.*

An assay method for adrenal cortical extracts is described based upon the action of the extract in maintaining the body temperatures of adrenalectomized young rats exposed to an environmental temperature of 1°C.

1377. Sayers, G., and M. A. Sayers. Regulation of pituitary adrenocorticotrophic activity during the response of the rat to acute stress. *Endocrinology, v. 40, Apr. 1947: 265–273.* Advance abstract, similar title, in: *Proc. Soc. Exp. Biol., N. Y., v. 60, Oct. 1945: 162–163.*

The increase in the rate of elaboration of adrenocorticotrophic hormone by the pituitary during exposure of the rat to stress (including cold of 4°C for one hour) was found to be proportional to the decrease in the concentration of adrenal ascorbic acid. Administration of adrenal cortical hormone before the stress, suppressed this enhanced elaboration of adrenocorticotrophic hormone.

1378. Schmidt, L. H., and I. G. Schmidt. The relation of environmental temperature to the action of thyroxin. *Endocrinology, v. 23, Nov. 1938: 553–558.*

Thyroxin was found to be much more toxic for guinea pigs kept at a high environmental temperature (32°C) and high humidity than for those kept at a lower temperature (20°C). It has been suggested that this increase in thyroxin toxicity might be due to adrenal exhaustion which also led to formation of gastric ulcers.

1379. Schricker, J. A., R. Hertz, and W. W. Tullner. B vitamin content of rat adrenals with respect to exposure to cold. *Proc. Soc. Exp. Biol., N. Y., v. 78, Nov. 1951: 522–524.*

After surgical removal of their left adrenals and recovery from anesthesia, rats were confined in a plastic cage and kept in a cold room at 5°C for 1 hour. The animals were then immediately killed with ether and the right adrenal glands removed; the ascorbic acid content of the glands was found to be extensively depleted, in accordance with findings of earlier workers. However, the content of biotin, folic acid, niacin, and riboflavin of the adrenals was found not to be materially altered by exposure to the cold.

1380. Sealander, J. A. Effect of environmental temperature and starvation on adrenal glands of the white-footed mouse. *Am. J. Physiol., v. 163, Oct. 1, 1950: 92–95.*

There was marked hyperemia of the adrenal glands in white-footed mice which were starved and held at temperatures of 40° and 50°C; noticeable amounts of hyperemia at the extremely low temperatures of −20° to −33°C; and little or no evidence of it at temperatures in between. Increases in adrenal weight, which ranged from 13 to 49%, were least at intermediate and moderately high temperatures. Starvation seemed to be the most probable cause for adrenal weight increase at intermediate temperatures. Low temperature further stimulated the adrenals to bring about an increase in size. There was no apparent correlation between the increase in adrenal weight and the survival time. From this and other work, the author concludes that the hypertrophic changes may involve either the medulla or cortex of the adrenal glands.

1381. Sellers, E. A., and S. S. You. Role of the thyroid in metabolic responses to a cold environment. *Am. J. Physiol., v. 163, Oct. 1, 1950: 81–91.*

The oxygen consumption of rats increased when the animals were placed in a cold room (1.5°C). Sodium pentobarbital anesthesia reduced the metabolic activity during cold exposure suggesting that a large part of the increase was due to muscular activity. Studies on "athyroid" rats to whom thyroxin was given, and on normal rats given NaI, indicated that the elevation of metabolic rate in cold is not dependent on increased activity of the thyroid. The author postulates that the increase in metabolic rate in animals after exposure to cold does not depend on a hyperthyroid state but does depend on the presence of thyroid hormone and that this increase in metabolic rate is associated with the ability of the animal to survive.

1382.　Selye, H., and V. Schenker. A rapid and sensitive method for bioassay of the adrenal cortical hormone. *Proc. Soc. Exp. Biol., N. Y., v. 39, Dec. 1938: 518–522.*

A method for the bioassay of adreno-cortical hormone is described, based upon its ability to maintain life in adrenalectomized rats exposed to temperatures of 2° to 5°C.

1383.　Skoog, T. von. Alterations of the quantitative histological relations of the thyroid gland by extreme temperature [In German]. *Anat. Anz., v. 88, July 27, 1939: 289–320.*

Changes of environmental temperature (−3°, 38°, and 43°C) were studied for their effect on the size and histological structure of the thyroid gland. Animals kept at a low temperature were found to have a thyroid gland increased in size over those kept at room temperature; the epithelial layer of the gland was three times as thick; the colloid amount was decreased; the gland was rich in capillaries; and there was an increase in the number and size of the granules. When the animals were kept in a hot environment, the size of the thyroid gland was decreased; the parenchymal cells were smaller; and the granules were very insignificant.

1384.　Starr, P., and R. Roskelley. A comparison of the effects of cold and thyrotropic hormone on the thyroid gland. *Am. J. Physiol., v. 130, Sept. 1940: 549–556.*

In rats exposed to cold (12° to 17°C) over periods of time ranging from 3–14 days, hypertrophy of the thyroid resulted. Iodine in small amounts tended to limit the hypertrophy. Cell height measurements are cited as the basis of comparison between the hypertrophic effects of refrigeration and the hypertrophic effects of thyrotropic hormone administered in gradually increased dosages.

1385.　Stein, H. J., R. A. Bader, J. W. Eliot, and D. E. Bass. Hormonal alterations in men exposed to heat and cold stress. *J. Clin. Endocr. Metab., v. 9, June 1949: 529–547.*

In attempts to evaluate adrenal cortical responses to stress, 3 healthy males were—after a preliminary period of physical conditioning—exposed repeatedly to heat (107°F dry bulb, 89°F wet bulb), then to cold (−20°F), then re-exposed to heat, and then—following a period without environmental stress—a further re-exposure to heat. There were no significant differences found in the excretion of 17-ketosteroids; neither daily urinary acid-creatinine ratios nor absolute lymphocyte counts could be used in evaluation due to the marked daily variations. No significant differences in basal metabolic rates were observed in any of the periods of exposure.

1386.　Swingle, W. W., and J. W. Remington. The role of the adrenal cortex in physiological processes. *Physiol. Rev., v. 24, Jan. 1944: 89–127.*

This general review of the literature of the role of the adrenal cortex in physiological processes has a section (p.108–109) on the relation of the adrenal cortex to cold. 531 refs.

1387.　Takács, L., and A. Fekete. The effect of feeding methylthiouracil on the hormonal body temperature regulation in cold environment [In Hungarian, with English summary]. *Orv. hetil., v. 89, Apr. 4, 1948: 59–61.*

Confirmation of the existence of a "heating hormone" is presented. Results indicate that the primary effect of cold is stimulation of thyroid secretion. One function of thyroxin appears to be stimulation of production of "heating hormone" by the hypophysis.

1388. Thérien, M., and L. P. Dugal. Content of ascorbic acid in the tissues of the rat partially exposed to intense cold [In French]. *Rev. canad. biol., v. 8, Nov. 1949: 440–443.*

Rats were sacrificed 2½ to 24 hours after exposure of their tails to intense cold (about −15°C). Ascorbic acid content of the liver and kidney showed an increase of 41.9% and 45.7% respectively after 2½ hours of exposure, decreasing to 19% and 2.9% after 24 hours, compared to the control animals which had been kept at room temperature. The content of ascorbic acid in the adrenals of the cold-treated rats seemed to be fairly normal with an increase of only 4.6% after 2½ hours, but increased to 18.2% after 24 hours.

1389. Tournade, A., M. Chevillot, and G. Chardon. Adrenaline secretion in dogs under the influence of cold [In French]. *C. rend. Soc. biol., Par., v. 128, June 18, 1938: 563–565.*

Under the influence of cold, adrenaline secretion and blood pressure in dogs were shown to be increased.

1390. Uotila, U. U. The role of the cervical sympathetics in the regulation of thyroid and thyrotropic function. *Endocrinology, v. 25, July 1939: 63–70.*

The anterior pituitary is the principal activator of the thyroid. Hypophysectomy in rats was followed by thyroid atrophy which could not be compensated for by a sympathetic nervous stimuli such as that caused by cold exposure. The reaction to cold of the thyroid is mediated through the anterior pituitary.

1391. Vigdorovich, B. G. Results of the effect of thermal factors on the function of the thyroid gland [In Russian]. *Sborn. rabot Minskogo med. inst., 1949 (2): 14–16.*

The author subjected the thyroid region of dogs and rabbits to local cooling (ethyl chloride spray, 10–15 minutes). The functional morphological changes in the gland itself, the changes in blood composition, body weight, metabolism, and general conditions of the animals, served as indicators of the response to cold. Results showed that after such cooling the number of lymphocytes, but not noticeably any other leukocytes, were increased. The body temperature remained unchanged; there was a loss of weight; a sharp vascular spasm in the ears and dilatation of the pupil of the eye, appeared during the tests. On the other hand, warming of the thyroid area by diathermy produced inconclusive results.

1392. Voïtkevich, A. A. The influence of temperature on the thyrotropic action of the pituitary gland [In Russian]. *Doklady Akad. nauk SSSR, v. 69 (6), 1949: 873–876.*

Study was made of the thyrotropic activity of the pituitary gland in guinea pigs and white rats. The animals were administered thiouracil or sulfadine [sulfapyridine] for 12–15 days, and kept at a low (4°–5°C) or a high (22°C) environmental temperature. The degree of activity of the thyroid and pituitary glands was then tested biologically on tadpoles. In guinea pigs, at low temperature the thyrotropin in the pituitary gland decreased to half its normal amount; administration of thiouracil altered this result very little. In rats, sulfadine at low temperature induced first a decrease, then an increase in pituitary thyrotropic secretion even above normal. In both rats and guinea pigs the thyroid gland increased over twice its normal weight. In both species the effects of low temperature were identical. However, the effect was greater in guinea pigs whose pituitary gland has a lower thyrotropic activity.

1393. Voïtkevich, A. A., and S. A. Temkina. The reaction of the thyroid gland of the guinea pig to thiouracil at various temperatures [In Russian]. *Doklady Akad. nauk SSSR, v. 70 (1), 1950: 161–163.*

Young guinea pigs of average weight were kept at environmental temperatures of 4°–5°C and at 22°–25°C for 12 or 20 days. To half of each group of animals, thiouracil (100 mg) was administered daily. At low temperatures, thiouracil induced an increase of the thyroid to double its weight with severe hyperplasia (increased glandular epithelium) and loss of the colloidal reserve (vacuolated follicles), while the biological activity was almost completely lacking. At a normal room temperature, conditions were similar, but much less pronounced. Administration of thyroiodine after the thiouracil treatment almost completely eliminated the morphological changes; however, the tissue remained either nearly or completely inactive. Thus, the phase of functional exhaustion of the thyroid gland, induced by thiouracil at low temperatures, is followed by a phase of exuberant colloid formation in the glandular follicles, while the thyrotropic function of the pituitary gland is excluded. The newly-formed colloid is not very active even after thyroid administration. These results were similar to those obtained in rats treated with thiouracil or a sulfonamide, showing an altered thyroid-pituitary complex in both animal species.

1394. Williams, R. H., H. Jaffe, and C. Kemp. Effect of severe stress upon thyroid function. *Am. J. Physiol.*, v. *159*, *Nov. 1, 1949: 291–297.*

The concentration of radioiodine by the thyroid of rats, and its distribution in the serum were found to be influenced by adrenaline, trauma, and typhoid vaccine. Fasting, or exposure to heat (38°C) or to cold (5°C) for three-day-periods, was associated with a subnormal concentration of radioiodine in the thyroid.

1395. Zummo, C., and F. Infantellina. On the behaviour of the hepatic lipids in adrenalectomized rats exposed to low temperature [In Italian, summary in English]. *Biochem. ter. sper.*, v. *27, 1940: 118–127.*

In normal rats exposed for two hours to low temperatures, there was an increase in the fat phosphatidic acids in the liver; in adrenalectomized rats there was a decrease in fatty acids (non-phosphatidic) of 43.1%. When cortical extract was given to the adrenalectomized animals exposed to low temperatures, there was an increase of 9.6% in the fat phosphatidic hepatic acids, but the non-phosphatidic acids showed no variation.

See also items: 412, 421, 424, 556, 562, 563, 636, 649, 651, 652, 687, 1221, 1275, 1403, 1422, 1446, 1449, 1455, 1467, 1492, 1514, 1518, 1520, 1521, 1530, 1536, 1547.

H. Digestive System

1396. Allen, F. M. Ligation and refrigeration of intestine. *Surgery*, v. *3, June 1938: 893–898.*

Experimental animals survived ligation and refrigeration of short loops of intestine for as long as 16 hours and of half of the small intestine for 4 hours, but a condition of anemia and of cachexia proved fatal in all experiments involving the entire intestine.

1397. Bisgard, J. D., and D. Nye. The influence of hot and cold application upon gastric and intestinal motility [Abstract, in German]. *Ber. ges. Physiol.*, v. *123, Mar. 26, 1941: 456.*

Ice packs on the abdomen and the lumbar region of the back brought about, after a short period of suppression, a heightened gastric and intestinal motility, especially the latter. Gastric acidity was increased. Drinking ice water quickly brought about an inhibition of motility for 10 to 30 minutes, then a return to normal, followed by a slight rise in peristaltic action of the stomach and small intestine but it was without effect on the large intestine. The acidity, through dilution, was lessened. Ice packs on the upper thighs increased the acidity and motility of the stomach; the small intestine and large intestine showed no distinct changes.

1398. Chevillard, L., A. Gasnier, and A. Mayer. The standards of ingestion of rabbits who eat spontaneously [In French]. *Ann. physiol., Par., v. 15 (2), 1939: 271–281.*

Studied over 24-hour periods, rabbits showed great daily and individual variation in their manner of eating, regardless of the environmental temperature in which they were living. In general, with a surplus of food available, the animals ate in the middle of the night rather than in the day time and ate little or nothing between six and nine o'clock in the morning, but this was subject to considerable variation. The animals may have been conditioned somewhat by the fact that fresh food was added, to the food already available, each morning at approximately nine o'clock. The animals living at the colder temperature (0° to −3°C) seemed to eat in the same general pattern but over a somewhat longer period of time.

1399. Chevillard, L., and A. Mayer. Variation of the mass and the composition of the liver when the animal is fasted [In French]. *Ann. physiol., Par., v. 15 (2), 1939: 282–293.*

In rabbits living in an environment of 18°–20°C, the mass and composition of the liver was diminished during the first 3 hours following the last meal, the diminution showing not only in the carbohydrates, but also in the water content, lipids, and proteins. Between 6 and 12 hours of fasting the additional diminution in weight of the liver was relatively little. The results are quite different if, however, the animal had been fasted 24 hours previous to the final meal, or if he had lived in a cold environment. In animals kept at an environmental temperature of 0° to −3°C there was no dimunition of the mass or composition of the liver after 6 hours of fasting.

1400. Chevillard, L., and A. Mayer. The mass of the liver of rabbits and the reaction when the intensity of metabolism is varied. Influence on the prolonging of life in conditions of varied heat depletion [In French]. *Ann. physiol., Par., v. 15 (2), 1939: 294–304.*

When kept in an environment of 18°–20°C, it was difficult to see any differences in the weight of the liver of individual rabbits of the same sex and body weight, but there was some variation between racial groups. Rabbits of either of two racial groups, living at low environmental temperatures (18° to 20°C, and 0° to −3°C) increased their ingestion of food and their metabolism as the temperature lowered, and the mass of the liver was also increased. Most of the animals of another racial group, when subjected to similar low environmental temperatures, did not increase their ingestion of food or their metabolism; they grew thin and the mass of the liver was not increased. When some of the individuals of this group did increase their ingestion of food with the decrease in temperature, the mass of the liver was but little increased.

1401. Chevillard, L., and A. Mayer. Variations of the mass and of the composition of the liver of rabbits. Influences prolonging life in varied conditions of lowered temperature [In French]. *Ann. physiol., Par., v. 15 (2), 1939: 305–337.*

On analysis following autopsy, the livers of three racially different groups of rabbits, living at environmental temperatures of 28°–30°C, showed considerable differences in composition individually but no significant differences racially. However, they varied considerably racially when they lived at low temperatures (0° to −3°C). One racial group which increased the ingestion of food as the temperature lowered, had larger livers in the lower temperatures and the constituents of the liver (water, protein, and lipids) changed considerably. A second group which did not augment their food intake at lower temperatures, had no increase in liver size. If kept in continuing but not too severe cold, the rabbits of the first group responded by an augmentation of glycogen in the liver; the second group by a diminution.

1402. Chevillard, L., and A. Mayer. Hypertrophy of certain essential organs during the increase in metabolism which accompanies acclimatization to cold;

consequences relative to the plasticity and regeneration of these organs [In French]. *Ann. physiol.*, *Par.*, v. 15 (3), 1939: 411-431.

In rabbits of one racial background and in white mice, which acclimatized to cold (20° to 18°C, and 0° to −3°C) by an increase in metabolism, not only the livers but also the hearts, lungs, and kidneys were hypertrophied. This hypertrophy was due to an increase in mass of the basic cellular constituents (water, inorganic substances, proteins, lipids, carbohydrates), but the relative concentrations within the organs were little changed. The author concludes that certain organs, previously thought to be stable, may be subject to considerable change.

1403. Cordier, D., and Y. Piéry. Influence of cold on the speed of gastric transit and intestinal absorption of glucose solutions in the rat [In French]. *C. rend. Soc. biol.*, *Par.*, v. 144, Nov. 1950: 1521-1523.

After rats had been given 2 cc of isotonic glucose solution (warmed to 38°C) by stomach tube, placing them in a cold chamber (−5°C, for 1 hour) slightly accelerated the passage through the stomach and significantly increased the rate of intestinal absorption. Adrenaline secretion did not serve to explain the observed phenomenon; subsequent research would indicate it to be due to increased secretion of the thyroid.

1404. Hersh, A., F. T. Woodbury, and W. Bierman. Influence of heat and cold on the temperature of mouth tissues. *Arch. Phys. Ther.*, v. 24, Apr. 1943: 219-228.

A difference in temperature of over 3°F was found to exist, in 5 healthy persons, between the coolest area (hard palate, 95°F) and the warmest area (sublingual, 98.27°F) of the mouth. Application of cold (50-55°F) to the surface of the cheek brought about a rapid decrease in the temperature of the buccal mucosa within the first 10 minutes and then a slower drop by a maximum of 11.7°F in 40.9 minutes. After removal of the cold, the temperature returned to a normal level rapidly, with a slight momentary rise above normal. This application of cold did not change the alveolar temperature. However, the application of ice directly to the gingiva caused a lowering of the alveolar temperature of 6.2°F in 4.2 minutes.

1405. Kershaw, G. R. Acute non-specific diarrhea and dysentery; local chilling of the abdomen as a causative factor. *Brit. M. J.*, 1947 (v. 1), May 24: 717-719.

Three outbreaks of acute enteritis of unknown etiology are discussed in which the chilling of the anterior wall of the abdomen appeared to be a causative agent. No evidence could be found of the disease being borne by infected water, food, insects, or droplets. Some clinical observations are noted by the author indicating that chilling of the abdomen or its anterior wall, can cause acute enteritis. Despite the overwhelming opinion in favor of infection being the primary cause of such outbreaks, the author believes that where no bacterial etiology could be found, it is not without reason to suspect them of being sequelae of the stimulation by cold of vascular reflexes in the abdominal area.

1406. Lazard-Kolodny, S. New researches on the variations of the inorganic constituents of the liver of the rabbit. I. Variations of the total inorganic constituents [In French]. *Ann. physiol.*, *Par.*, v. 15 (3), 1939: 392-402.

Rabbits of the same racial background living in the same environment and with similar feeding, were found to have individually varying quantities of total inorganic constituents present in the liver, but the percentage concentration of the inorganic ash, when compared with the total wet weight of the liver, was constant. This constancy was not altered by changes in nutrition, lowering of environmental temperature (20° to 18°C, or 0° to −3°C), or by giving injections of saline, glucose, oxalic acid, citric acid, Adrenalin, or acetylcholine. The concentration of inorganic constituents in the liver varied very little during the first 24 hours of fasting but they increased somewhat on prolonged fasting.

1407. Lazard-Kolodny, S. New researches on the variations of inorganic constituents of the liver of the rabbit. II. Variations of potassium, of sodium, and of calcium [In French]. *Ann. physiol.*, *Par.*, v. 15 (3), 1939: 403-410.

The author found previously that the total inorganic constituents of the livers of rabbits varied individually but that the percentage concentration of the inorganic constituents did not, and that this constancy was not altered by different environmental temperatures. In the livers of rabbits which had lived at environmental temperatures of 30 °C, 20° to 18 °C, and 0° to −3 °C, the amount of sodium, potassium, and calcium—especially the former two—was found to vary also, following quite closely the pattern of the total inorganic constituents. The percentage concentration of sodium and potassium in liver tissue varied very little.

1408.   Naftalin, J. M., and J. W. Howie. Hepatic changes in young pigs reared in a cold and damp environment. *J. Path. Bact., Lond., v. 61, July 1949: 319–328.*

The pathological finding following the death of young pigs reared in a cold and damp environment, was found to be that of a nutmeg liver and its sequelae. Experimentally the condition could be produced by rearing young pigs in a similar environment and could be prevented by providing them with additional warmth. The liver changes would appear to be explainable on the basis of a derangement of the hepatic circulation such as might be expected to occur after prolonged exposure to excessive cooling.

1409.   Naftalin, J. M. Interaction between environment and diet in the production of acute liver necrosis in the rat. *J. Path. Bact., Lond., v. 63, Oct. 1951: 649–666.*

The incidence of acute liver necrosis in young male albino rats was studied under different environmental conditions, with either restricted or unlimited amounts of a special diet. The diet was low in protein, high in sucrose, and deficient in vitamin E. With restricted quantities, the casein consumed was 320–480 mg/rat/day. The highest incidence of liver necrosis occurred when environmental temperatures were 70°–74 °F. At 60°–65 °F, the rats given unlimited food showed a lower incidence of necrosis and survived longer. In two experiments done during the spring, at a temperature range of 35°–50 °F (extremes of 20°–68 °F) there were no deaths from liver necrosis. Three of 10 rats died when kept in an unheated shed (about 50 °F) during a winter experiment. Also in the unheated environment food restriction resulted in the deaths without liver necrosis of 7 of 19 rats. Liver necrosis was prevented by food restriction at an environment of 60°–65 °F but not at 70°–74 °F.

1410.   Ono, T. Seasonal observations of urobilinogen urine in a severely cold place [Abstract, in English]. *Jap. J. Gastroenter., v. 14, Dec. 1942: 213.*

The author had been observing seasonal changes in liver function in a "training station for prevention of tuberculosis" in North Manchuria where the temperature was often lower than −40 °F. He found that the urobilinogen reaction of urine tended to be positive in winter.

1411.   Papierkowski, J. Influence of temperature on movements of the large intestine [In French]. *Arch. mal. app. digest., Par., v. 30, July–Oct. 1941: 380–387.*

Loops of the colon and duodenum of rabbits were suspended in Tyrode's solution (0° to 55 °C). Below 38 °C there was an elevation of muscle tonus, then a slackening off, the reaction being strongest when the temperature was lowest. Elevation of the temperature above 38 °C brought about an immediate relaxing of tonus. The time of appearance of this reaction was strongest between 41° and 43 °C. Enemas of an opaque substance (0° to 45 °C) were administered to subjects. It was found that such enemas exercise an important influence on the motility and sensitivity of the colon and caecum, and that enemas in the 0 °C range caused physiological stress in the area; that a wide range of temperature changes are well tolerated; that enemas do not appear to influence in an appreciable manner the rhythm of the colon; and that enemas can be given at temperatures between 15° and 40 °C without undue discomfort.

1412.   Roth, G. M., and M. A. Gabrielson. Variation in the concentration of acids of the gastric content in normal subjects before and following immersion of hand and entire body in water at various temperatures. *Am. J. Physiol., v. 131, Nov. 1940: 195–199.*

When the hands of normal subjects were immersed in water at 10°C there was only a slight increase in gastric acidity while the hands were in the water and for 15 minutes afterwards. When the subjects were immersed to the neck in water from 18.3° to 29.4°C, there was a definite rise in gastric acidity, which could be inhibited by the administration of histaminase.

1413. Tidow, R. Cold injury of the gastrointestinal tract, with special reference to general chilling [In German]. *Münch. med. Wschr., v. 90, Oct. 22, 1941: 597–600.*

The importance of cold injury as a source of gastrointestinal disturbances, is discussed on the basis of war experience. These injuries are classified as follows: (1) Local necrosis as the direct effect of cold; (2) changes in mucous membrane due to chilling of the entire organism; and (3) functional disorders of other areas of the body, reflected in the gastrointestinal tract. The reciprocal interaction between infection and chilling in causing disease, is emphasized. Tissue changes in the mucous membranes resulting from cold are shown to be a predisposing cause of ulcers.

1414. Tidow, R., and O. Nekarda. Observations on gastric illnesses in war [In German]. *Deut. med. Wschr., v. 69, Feb. 26, 1943: 171–176.*

Among the gastric illnesses occuring during a war period which are discussed by the author, are the case histories of two sailors who, because of shipwreck, had swallowed cold sea water and some marine oil. One sailor had a resultant erosive gastritis in which the cold was thought to be a predisposing factor; the other, appeared to have no injury to the gastric mucosa.

1415. Voll, M. M. Effect of thermal stimulation of the gastrointestinal tract on the temperature of the stomach, intestine, and skin [In Russian, summary in English]. *Arkh. biol. nauk, v. 55 (3), 1939: 29–36.*

The effect of thermal stimulation of the gastric and intestinal mucosa upon the vascular reaction of the skin and of the gastrointestinal tract was studied in 8 dogs having gastric and intestinal fistulae. Stimulation was done through water at 6°, 8°, 10° or 16.5°C. The temperature of the skin, stomach, and intestine served as an indicator of the vascular reaction. Injection of cold water into the intestine induced first a sharp decrease in temperature, followed in the first 10–15 minutes by a rapid then a slow return to normal. In more remote areas (skin, colon, etc.) 3 phases of temperature changes were noted: immediately after cold water stimulation of the stomach, the temperature of the skin and of the colon rose 0.1° to 0.2°C in 1–3 minutes; then the skin temperature began to decrease gradually (to maximum of 1°C) during 20–30 minutes; 30–40 minutes after stimulation it had been slowly restored to its initial level. The rise in skin temperature in the first phase of reaction points to a vasomotor effect, conditioned by the impulses proceeding from the thermoreceptors of the stomach and intestine, showing the thermosensitivity of the gastro-intestinal tract. The temperature changes in the stimulated stomach, and in the non-stimulated skin, colon, and other intestinal locations, after administration of cold water into the stomach, produces similar but more pronounced results than those obtained earlier with local cooling of various skin portions.

1416. Weitz, W. Dependence of digestibility of foods on their temperature (with a remark on the effect of drinking mineral water) [In German]. *Deut. med. Wschr., v. 76, Mar. 23, 1951: 361–363.*

A study was made of the effect of internal and external temperature on the contractility of the digestive system of test subjects. A balloon-manometer was used to record changes in pressure in the stomach resulting from the drinking of fluids of various temperatures. Ingestion of warm water resulted in a rapid decrease in the intragastric pressure; cool liquids, including water, when ingested raised the intragastric pressure. The contractions after the ingestion of cold liquid were more sustained but not more frequent than before ingestion. Alcoholic liquids such as beer and whiskey increased intragastric pressure. Exposing the upper trunk of the subject to room temperature resulted in a decline in intragastric pressure. Preliminary experiments on the effect of mineral water on gastric pressure are underway. Mineral water stimulates the gastric mucosa and in that way stimulates gastric contraction.

See also items: 108, 648, 1228, 1359, 1465, 1597.

I. Respiratory System

1417. Altschule, M. D., H. Linenthal, and N. Zamchek. Lung volume and pulmonary dynamics in Raynaud's disease. Effect of exposure to cold. *Proc. Soc. Exp. Biol., N. Y., v. 48, Nov. 1941: 503–505.*

No changes in pulmonary volume and related measurements were found regardless of the original values when the legs and at least one hand of each of 3 patients were exposed to water cooled with ice. All of the patients were suffering from Raynaud's disease. Two of the patients showed no physiological evidence of impaired respiratory function; the third patient suffered from cough and dyspnea and there was definite evidence of fibrosis of the lungs. The fact that these values did not change on exposure to cold is thought to indicate that the blood vessels of the lungs do not react in the manner similar to those of the hands and feet. This view is further supported by the finding that exposure to cold did not bring about a change in the circulation time through the lungs.

1418. Khaleťskaĭa, F. M. On the influence of general cooling on the development of purulent infection in the lungs of the rabbit [In Russian]. *Arkh. biol. nauk, v. 60 (3), 1940: 3–14.*

Thirty male rabbits were given intratracheal inoculations of a 24-hour-old culture of staphylococcus. Eight of the rabbits were placed in a room at 15° to 17°C, while 22 were placed outdoors at temperatures ranging from −4° to −20°C. Only the latter group developed pneumonic foci in the lungs.

1419. Navarre, P. Harmfulness of cold [In French]. *Médecine, Par., v. 23, Mar. 1942: 16–20.*

The author states that the manifestations of the harmful action of cold take many forms. He discusses the role of cold in pleurisy following exposure; in urticaria and allergy citing an incident of sudden death of a young child in a cold bath; in susceptibility to infection; and in rheumatic ailments.

1420. Watrous, R. M. Health hazards of the pharmaceutical industry. *Brit. J. Indust. M., v. 4, 1947: 111–125.*

The passing of workmen from the refrigerated rooms (40°F and 0°F) to other working areas (70°–80°F) was thought to cause more frequent coughs and colds than among other personnel, but no increase in incidence of respiratory infections could be demonstrated objectively.

1421. Webb, P. Air temperatures in respiratory tracts of resting subjects in cold. *J. Physiol., v. 4, Nov. 1951: 378–382.*

Using a thermocouple which could measure true air temperature with satisfactory speed, the temperature of inspired and expired air was measured from the front, middle, and back of the nasal airway in 18 subjects in warm (23° to 28°C), cool (5° to 8°C), and cold (−21° to −31°C) ambient air temperatures. The data indicated that air which was cold when inspired was rapidly warmed in the nose. The temperature of expired air was below 37°C; expired air was found to give up heat as it approached the outside.

See also items: 222, 1228, 1311, 1402.

J. Urinogenital System

1422. Bader, R. A., J. W. Eliot, and D. E. Bass. Renal and hormonal mechanisms of cold diuresis [Abstract]. *Fed. Proc., Balt., v. 8, Mar. 1949: 7.*

Experiments were done on man (exposed almost nude at 15 °C, and covered with blankets at 24°–27°C) to study the mechanism of cold diuresis. The evidence seemed to indicate that diuresis from cold is controlled by the posterior lobe of the pituitary gland.

1423. Birnie, J. H., and W. J. Eversole. The effect of physiological stress on water diuresis. *Anat. Rec., v. 105, Nov. 1949: 563.*

Rats subjected to cold and tested one hour after exposure showed a marked antidiuretic response.

1424. Eliot, J. W., R. A. Bader, and D. E. Bass. Blood changes associated with cold diuresis [Abstract]. *Fed. Proc., Balt., v. 8, Mar. 1949: 41.*

Men were exposed for 2½-hour periods to temperatures of 27 °C or 15 °C, with the exposures alternated between men and in each man from day to day. During exposure to cold, the plasma proteins, the hematocrit, and the corrected erythrocyte sedimentation rate all rose. In experiments where a warm exposure followed the cold, these values fell. Average urine output in the cold over output in the warm was 287 cc which corresponded to an accompanying average plasma loss of 277 cc. Despite the fact that in one experimental group cold diuresis was largely abolished by Pitressin, plasma proteins and the hematocrit rose during cold exposure only slightly less than without the drug, indicating that there is no direct connection between changes in urine output and plasma volume in the cold. Plasma chloride levels showed no significant change during cold diuresis despite the fact that in other experiments the total chloride output was high in the cold and low in the warm environment.

1425. Engel, A. Bladder disturbances from cold (Dysuria e frigore) [In Swedish]. *Sven. läk. tidn., v. 38, May 1941: 1190–1193.*

Report is made of 23 cases of bladder disturbances caused by exposure to severe cold among troops in Sweden. The symptoms ceased after short periods of hospitalization without any special therapy. These cases point to disturbances of the reflex mechanism controlling the bladder with the patients showing such symptoms as frequency, incontinence, or retention of urine, and often with some pain, burning, or tenderness on urination. The author states that he found mention in the literature of the condition among German infantry regiments during World War I, but no references concerning the Finnish-Russian war of 1939–1940. Previously the condition was diagnosed as cold cystitis; the preferred term now is "dysuria e frigore."

1426. Graham, S. A., and E. C. O'Roke. How to take care of yourself in wild country; a manual for field and service men. *Minneapolis, Univ. of Minnesota Press, 1943: 150 p.*

In a section dealing with meeting the physical extreme of low temperatures (p. 7–9) there is a warning to maintain water intake even though not thirsty. There is a tendency to go on a reduced intake which results in a disturbance in waste elimination. Under cold conditions the kidneys must take over elimination of wastes which would normally be lost through perspiration in a warmer climate. Until he becomes acclimated, and metabolism is established at a slightly higher level than normal, the person new to a cold climate will need warmer clothing than he will later need. Clothing should be porous to allow evaporation of perspiration, should be kept dry, and be loose enough not to interfere with circulation. A wind-proof parka or overgarment will help reduce the quantity of clothing worn but will not make it possible to omit a heavy jacket and a wool or fur cap. Protection of the nose and cheeks may be provided by a hankerchief folded in a triangle and tied across the face with the loose end hanging free over the mouth and chin. Frequent light rubbing of the face will aid circulation ahd help prevent frostbite. If frostbite occurs, the area should be thawed slowly. Warming a frozen ear or nose with the bare hand is to be preferred over rubbing with snow since in the latter method there is danger of further tissue injury and infection if skin is broken. In more severe injury the patient should be immobilized and the frozen area kept cool while the patient is kept warm.

1427. Leblond, C. P., and L. P. Dugal. Pathologic manifestations produced by cold in kidneys and extremities [In French]. *Rev. canad. biol., v. 2, Dec. 1943: 542–545.*

Animals exposed to intense environmental cold ($-2\,^{\circ}C$), showed renal lesions (nephrosis) in less than 2 months. Skin lesions were also observed.

1428. Nedzel, A. J. Sulfathiazole and exposure to cold. *Urol. Cut. Rev., v. 49, Apr. 1945: 235–237.*

Groups of dogs were given sulfathiazole after surgical denervation of the left kidney. One group of 4 dogs was in addition subjected to daily cold-water showers for 5–10 minutes. All animals were exsanguinated and autopsied 56 days after beginning of the experiment and the remaining kidney of each was examined microscopically. It had previously been demonstrated that the blood vessels of the normal kidney respond to chilling whereas the vessels in the denervated kidney do not. Acidification was attained, in one other group of animals, by the giving of ammonium chloride; cold showers brought about some acidification also. There was approximately the same incidence of damage to glomeruli of the denervated kidney in dogs which were acidified, but the group of dogs subjected to cold showers lost 13% of its total weight. The group given ammonium chloride lost 3%, while the control group, despite some pathological changes in the kidneys, gained 21%. Since the gross and microscopic studies of the kidneys did not furnish evidence of sufficient tubular obstruction to explain all of the pathological changes found in the kidneys, it appeared probable that sulfathiazole was toxic to the cells themselves. Since the drug is eliminated in the urine, injuries might well occur in the kidneys. Repeated exposure to cold could well bring about further toxic effects from sulfathiazole.

1429. Odell, L. D., J. F. Aragon, and R. C. Smitter. Renal response to thermal stimulus. *Am. J. Obst., v. 56, Nov. 1948: 835–845.*

In a group of women—pregnant with toxemia, normally pregnant, and non-pregnant—the immersion for 15 minutes of a hand or a foot in an ice water bath ($1\,^{\circ}C$), brought about a decrease in the urine excretion. This phenomenon was associated with an increase in specific gravity of the urine and in some cases, a change in protein excretion per minute. Evidence suggests that the stimulation produces an antidiuretic hormone, and that the site of liberation is not within the immersed limb or within the kidney but is above the level of cervical 4 (posterior pituitary gland?). The phenomenon was apparently not abolished by inhalation anesthesia.

1430. Stutinsky, F. S. Action of temperature on the diuresis provoked in the normal and hypophysectomized rat [In French]. *C. rend. Soc. biol., Par., v. 143, Feb. 1949: 195–198.*

When diuresis was provoked in the normal rat by the administration of large quantities of water, the elimination of urine was found to be influenced by the environmental temperature. In a cold environment the excretion began sooner, was of shorter duration, and was of greater volume than at a neutral thermal temperature. At a warm temperature ($35\,^{\circ}C$) the animal eliminated about $2/3$ of the quantity at thermal neutrality; at temperatures of $15\,^{\circ}$ or $5\,^{\circ}C$ elimination was 2 and 3 times as much respectively. In the hypophysectomized rat, regardless of the environmental temperature, diuresis was very greatly delayed. Meanwhile extrarenal elimination kept the value near to normal.

1431. Talso, P. J., A. P. Crosley, and R. W. Clarke. Effects of the cold pressor test on glomerular filtration and effective renal plasma flow. *J. Laborat. Clin. M., v. 33 (4), 1948: 430–434.*

In six out of seven subjects, glomerular filtration (as measured by mannitol clearance) and effective renal plasma flow (as measured by sodium para-aminohippurate clearance) were decreased either during or within 30 minutes after the immersion of one foot in ice water at $1\,^{\circ}C$ for fifteen minutes. The average decreases in filtration rate and plasma flow, from that of control values, were 14% and 21% respectively.

1432. White, H. L., and D. Rolf. Effects of exercise and of some other influences on the renal circulation in man. *Am. J. Physiol., v. 152, Mar. 1, 1948: 505–516.*

Immersion of a hand in painfully cold ice water (0°C) resulted in a slight fall in PAH [para-aminohypurate] and inulin clearance rates with a slight rise in mean blood pressure; in the one subject studied, there were no such effects when the hand was immersed in water which was cold (14°–15°C) but not painfully so.

1433.   Wolf, G. A. Pain. In: The effect of pain on renal function. *Proc. Ass. Res. Nerv. Ment. Dis., 1943. Res. Publ., v. 23, 1943: 358–364.*

It is concluded that pain may cause a diminution in renal function (as measured by inulin and Diodrast clearance tests). Because the renal plasma flow is decreased, it is strongly suggested that this alteration is on the basis of vasoconstriction. The results on the effects of cold pain, caused by the subject immersing a hand in water of 5° to 10°C, were, however, not as conclusive as they were with the other test methods of producing pain.

See also items: 128, 772, 1311, 1402.

K. Metabolic Aspects

1434.   Amano, M. Metabolism during low temperature. I. The relation between low temperature and serum cephalin [In German]. *J. Biochem., Tokyo, v. 35, 1942: 219–223.*

Experiments were made on rabbits to determine the relation of severe cold (−10° to −30°C) to nitrogen metabolism. Data obtained indicated that the amount of cephalin in blood plasma decreases as temperature decreases; that non-protein nitrogen constituents of the blood are highest at −10°C; and that temperature has no important effect on over-all nitrogen content.

1435.   Bomskov, C. H., and K. N. Kaulla. Contribution to the subject of fluctuations in the glycogen values of the liver, heart, and muscles in healthy animals as seen in the literature, together with a note on the chemical determination of glycogen [In German]. *Zschr. ges. exp. Med., v. 110 (6), 1942: 603–616.*

The glycogen content, and fluctuations of the content, of the liver, heart, and muscle were determined in rats and guinea pigs under the influence of feeding, old age, and lowered body temperature. For the glycogen determination in the heart, as well as in the liver, the temperature at which the animal was kept preceding the experiment was of greatest importance. At an average temperature of 15°C (in the winter) the glycogen content of the liver was found to vary between 1.7 and 2.7% or more. At 23°C this value increased up to 7% in 14–21 days (average, 6.1%). At a temperature of 9°C the values of both the liver and heart glycogen decreased; the heart glycogen occasionally reached very low values. It is concluded that the heart glycogen is most easily influenced by even slight temperature variations. The glycogen of the skeletal muscles varied very little.

1436.   Chanutin, A., and E. C. Gjessing. Electrophoretic analyses of sera of injured dogs. *Journ. Biol. Chem., v. 165 (2), 1946: 421–426.*

The serum protein of dogs injured experimentally by various methods including cold (by the application of dry ice to inner areas of the back legs and front legs) showed a decrease in albumin concentration and an increase in the γ-globulin fraction.

1437.   Clement, G. Mobilization of reserve glycerides in the rat. I. Demonstration of a difference in the mobilization caused by fasting and by thermoregulation [In French]. *Arch. sc. physiol., Par., v. 4 (1), 1950: 5–11.*

The iodine values of fat of different areas of the animal body were essentially the same in each individual though there was great variation from animal to animal within the same species even though engaged in the same activity. A method was established to present a qualitative evaluation of the mobilization of fatty acids and the storing of reserve fatty acids under various physiological conditions. Rats had perirenal adipose tissue removed surgically from the left side, and then, after exposure to a cold (10°C) environment for 3 days, the animal was killed and comparable tissue was removed immediately from the right side. A fundamental difference in the choice of fatty acids to mobilize was shown to be caused by the cold exposure; following the exposure the iodine value of the fat was increased (by 1.7-5.5%), was only slightly increased by starvation alone, but was decidedly increased (by 3.2-7.6%) by a combination of exposure and starvation.

1438. **Coover, M. O., L. J. Feinberg, and J. H. Roe.** Effect of cold, adrenocorticotrophic and thyroid hormones on urinary excretion of pentose in the rat. *Proc. Soc. Exp. Biol., N. Y., v. 74, May 1950: 146-147.*

Rats exposed to cold (−1°C) showed a significant increase in urinary excretion of pentose. Administration of adrenocorticotrophic hormone prevented the increased pentosuria produced by cold.

1439. **Crile, G. W., and D. P. Quiring.** Indian and Eskimo metabolisms. *J. Nutrit., v. 18, Oct. 1939: 361-368.*

Basal metabolic rates, blood pressure, and pulse rates were studied in groups of Eskimos and of Chippewa Indians living in the Canadian subarctic regions of Chesterfield Inlet and Churchill Bay, respectively. Basal metabolic rate for Eskimo males was +14.5% and for females was +21.12%. Blood pressure for both males and females was lower than that of white persons of corresponding age; the pulse rate corresponded rather closely to white persons. Basal metabolic rate for Indian males was +18.0% and for females was +18.5%. Pulse rate and blood pressure both appear to be lower than for the American white population, the Eskimo groups, or the Mayan Indians of Central America.

1440. **Dontcheff, L., and G. Schaeffer.** Evolution of the extra heat of the specific dynamic action of proteins in the rabbit at neutral and at a low temperature [In French]. *C. rend. Soc. biol., Par., v. 127, Mar. 11, 1938: 1290-1293.*

Rabbits which were fed only a Witte peptone solution and kept in a cold room for 6-8 hours, did not shiver. Although their metabolic rate increased greatly in the cold, when the rabbits were returned to a normal room temperature the rate quickly dropped to the much less accelerated rate of the animals kept continuously at a normal room temperature. The duration of the increased metabolism, attributable to the proteins ingested, was approximately the same for the two groups.

1441. **Engel, F. L.** Observations on the interrelationship between insulin, the adrenal cortex, and non-specific stress (cold) in adipose tissue glycogen synthesis in the rat. *Endocrinology, v. 49, July 1951: 127-135.*

Exposure of normal, fasted, rats to 4°C for 48 hours had no influence on the level of glycogen of the interscapular adipose tissue, on liver glycogen, or on blood sugar after administration of glucose. However, insulin stimulated a striking increase in the interscapular adipose tissue glycogen concentration of rats exposed to cold when compared with those at room temperature. Blood sugar levels were lower in rats exposed to cold after insulin. Exposure of cortisone-maintained adrenalectomized rats to 4°C for 24 hours did not modify the concentration of interscapular adipose tissue glycogen after insulin and glucose compared to similar animals kept at room temperature; liver glycogen and blood sugar levels were significantly lower.

1442. **Gasnier, A., and A. Mayer.** Research on the regulation of nutrition. III. Regulatory mechanisms of the nutrition and the intensity of the metabolism [In French]. *Ann. physiol., Par., v. 15 (1), 1939: 186-194.*

Studies were made of groups of rabbits in their adaptation to environmental temperatures of 28° to 30°C, 18° to 20°C, and 0° to −3°C; two additional groups of animals were kept at the lower two temperature ranges after their coats of fur had been sheared. All of the animals of this racial stock increased both their metabolic rate and their food intake as the temperature became more severe. Measurement of energy being produced against energy being used showed an increasing reserve as the temperature lowered. Movement of water within the body was greater as the metabolism was augmented, but the regulatory mechanisms of this were less definite and less pronounced than for other constituents.

1443. Gasnier, A., and A. Mayer. Research on the regulation of nutrition. IV. Differences between two races of domestic rabbits [In French]. *Ann. physiol., Par., v. 15 (1), 1939: 195–209.*

Studies were made of groups of rabbits from two different racial stocks in their adaptation to environmental temperature of 28° to 30°C, 18° to 20°C, and −3° to 0°C. Under similar conditions the two racially different groups differed greatly in the intensity of their metabolism, and in the amount of energy kept in reserve as the metabolic rate increased. Their differences were accentuated when the environmental conditions differed greatly from their usual ones.

1444. Gasnier, A., and A. Mayer. Research on the regulation of the nutrition. V. Individual character [In French]. *Ann. physiol., Par., v. 15 (1), 1939: 210–214.*

Studies were made of rabbits from two different racial stocks in their adaptation, as individuals, to environmental temperatures of 0° to −3°C. It was found that animals of the same race, age, and weight living under identical conditions do not react similarly in the intensity of their increase of metabolic rate or in the amount of energy which they put in reserve.

1445. Gray, E. L., F. C. Consolazio, and R. M. Kark. Nutritional requirements for men at work in cold, temperate, and hot environments. *J. Appl. Physiol., v. 4, 1951: 270–275.*

Various physiological functions, including caloric output, of healthy young men were measured at arctic (−15°F), temperate (60°F) and desert (90°F) temperatures with the subjects wearing various outfits of clothing each of which was the standard wearing apparel for one of the three climatic conditions. The caloric output for a given amount of external work performed at a constant temperature increased about 5% when clothing was changed from desert to temperate, and increased about 5% more when clothing was changed from temperate to arctic. For each outfit of clothing, the caloric output of the subject at work decreased about 2% as the temperature was raised from −15° to +60°F, and decreased another 2% as the temperature was raised from 60°F to 90°F.

1446. Hardy, J. D., E. Shorr, and E. P. DuBois. Hormonal influence on basal metabolism of women in cold and warm environments [Abstract]. *Fed. Proc., Balt., v. 6, Mar. 1947: 122–123.*

In calorimetric studies of young women having a normal menstrual cycle, a lower basal metabolism was found at a temperature of 32°C than at 26°C. From these and other findings, it is assumed that these changes in basal metabolism in normal women are dependent upon estrogenic activity.

1447. Hart, J. S. Interrelations of daily metabolic cycle, activity and environmental temperature of mice. *Canad. J. Res., v. 28, sect. D, Dec. 1950: 293–307.*

The daily metabolic cycle of fully-fed, adult, white mice at temperatures from −8° to 37°C, averaged 48 ml O$_2$/mouse/hour. The value was significantly greater at higher temperatures. A given amount of work was found to produce the same increase in oxygen consumption at all temperatures when the work level, in terms of running speed, was below about one-half the maximum rate. At the maximum running speeds, however, the metabolism produced by the work decreased with decreasing temperature, with some gain in efficiency.

1448. Hemingway, A., and S. R. Hathaway. An investigation of chemical temperature regulation. *Am. J. Physiol., v. 134, Oct. 1941: 596–602.*

Oxygen consumption rates and carbon dioxide production rates of three dogs were measured while the animals were being cooled. The onset of shivering was recorded electrically, mechanically, and visually. It was noted that the increase of the metabolic rate without shivering had little effect on resistance to dry cold.

1449. Henriques, S. B., O. B. Henriques, and H. Selye. Influence of cold on blood fibrinogen concentration. *Proc. Soc. Exp. Biol., N. Y., v. 71, May 1949: 82–84.*

Rats fasted for 24 hours and then kept in a cold room (2°–5°C) showed a fall in their plasma fibrinogen concentration which was maximal at the end of the first 24 hours. The level then rose but remained slightly subnormal for as long as 21 days. Weight of adrenal glands increased during this same period while the weight of the thymus decreased.

1450. Henriques, O. B., S. B. Henriques, and H. Selye. Influence of cold, fasting and adrenalectomy on the blood-fibrinogen response to trauma. *Proc. Soc. Exp. Biol., N. Y., v. 73, Apr. 1950: 611–613.*

Simultaneous exposure of rats to fasting and cold (24 hours at 1° to 5°C) markedly decreased the blood-fibrinogen content. Cold and fasting also significantly reduced the fibrinogen response (rise) induced by the trauma caused by a unilateral nephrectomy.

1451. Høygaard, A. Studies on the nutrition and physio-pathology of Eskimos [In English]. *Skrifter Norske Videnskaps-Akad. i Oslo. I. Mat.-Naturv. Klasse, No. 9, 1940: 1–176.*

The author did not find that the metabolic rate of Eskimos was essentially different from that of other peoples, but that the differences noted had been due primarily to the fact that Eskimos live on a diet almost exclusively of meat. 195 refs.

1452. Johnson, R. E., C. G. Bly, R. M. Kark, and C. F. Consolazio. Metabolic changes in heat acclimatized men during abrupt exposure to a very cold climate [Abstract]. *J. Clin. Invest., v. 28, July 1949: 792.*

Thirty-two men acclimatized to hot weather were suddenly transferred to a very cold region (−26°C). Physiological effects observed included transient hypothermia, diuresis, hemoconcentration, eosinophilopenia, lymphopenia, neutrophilic leukocytosis, hyperphosphatemia, hyperuricemia, and hyperkalemia. The observed changes have many similarities to those resulting from the injection of adrenocorticotropic hormone and the "general adaptation syndrome" of animals during stress.

1453. Lathe, G. H., and R. A. Peters. Some observations on the comparative effects of cold and burns on protein metabolism in rats. *Q. J. Exp. Physiol., Lond., v. 35, 1949: 55–64.*

Rats were fed a constant calorie and protein diet, high in fat, administered by stomach tube, and were experimentally burned or exposed to cold (15° to 20°C). They were found to have an increase in nitrogen excretion within 24 to 48 hours following either cold or burning. These increases were not always additive when both burning and cold were done. A methionine supplement did not reduce the excess nitrogen excretion due to cold or to burning in the cold.

1454. Lee, R. C. Heat production of the rabbit at 28°C as affected by previous adaptation to temperatures between 10° and 31°C. *J. Nutrit., v. 23, Jan. 10, 1942: 83–90.*

Level of metabolism of rabbits kept at 28°C for 24 hours was dependent on the temperature they had lived at prior to that time (at 17° and 31°C, and 10° and 29°C). It was found that metabolism varied inversely with the change in previous temperature.

1455. Lemonde, P., and P. S. Timiras. Behavior of the interscapular brown fat of rats receiving various toxic agents; effect of ablation of this tissue [In French]. *Ann. Ass. canad. fr. advanc. sc., v. 17, 1951: 99–102.*

Groups of rats were either exposed to cold, subjected to vigorous exercise, or kept at rest at a normal room temperature. All the rats were sacrificed at about 18 days. At autopsy the interscapular gland (hibernating gland) appeared to be hypertrophied and was pale yellow in color. In other groups of rats, including one exposed to cold and partial fasting, which were sacrificed after reaching a state of exhaustion, the hibernating gland was found to be atrophied, deep red in color, and completely devoid of lipids. From these and other experiments parallelism was noted as existing between the interscapular tissue and the adrenal cortex in the change of lipid content and in coloration of the tissue. The adrenals are also red and divested of lipids during the alarm reaction, pale and heavy with lipids during the resistance phase, and dark red and emptied of lipid contents in the exhausted state. It is concluded that in rats, and probably in hamsters, the hibernating gland is not indispensable either for normal living or for resistance to adverse conditions such as cold.

1456. Levine, V. E., and C. G. Wilber. Fat metabolism in Alaskan Eskimos [Abstract]. *Fed. Proc., Balt., v. 8, Mar. 1949: 95.*

The examination of blood sera of Eskimos (adults and children of both sexes) at Point Barrow, Alaska, showed the various lipid components to be high when compared with normal values for white persons. At the time of the tests, the Eskimos were eating a normal, fat-rich, diet of walrus and seal. The authors state that the lower lipid content found by another investigator may reflect a low-fat intake or even a diet close to a starvation level.

1457. Levine, V. E. Studies in physiological anthropology. I. The basal metabolic rate of the Eskimo [Abstract]. *Am. J. Phys. Anthrop., v. 7, n. s., June 1949: 278.*

The basal metabolic rates in a group of 23 Eskimos were found to be normal. The author believes that the higher rates (+19 to +23) for Eskimos reported in the literature and attributed to various factors, including cold climate and race, point to either pathological states or to lack of basal conditions for the test.

1458. Lundholm, L. The effect of adrenaline, on the oxygen consumption of resting animals [In English]. *Acta physiol. scand., v. 19, Suppl. 67, 1949: 1–139.*

Chapter VIII, p. 123–124, is titled The Effect on the lactic acid content of the blood of exposing rabbits to cold. Rabbits kept at a room temperature of 20°C were put in a cool room (7°C) for 60 minutes, then a colder room (0°C) for another 60 minutes. Blood samples did not show any increase in lactic acid content after exposure to cold of either temperature. The calorigenic effect of adrenaline, increasing metabolic rate and therefore increasing the amount of lactic acid, did not appear to be produced by cold. Various investigators and their postulations of the role of adrenaline in thermal regulation, are mentioned. One is that the adrenaline-like substance which is discharged following sensory stimulation of the skin by cold, has the physiological function of contracting the cutaneous blood vessels so less heat is given off. 202 refs.

1459. Matuoka, S., H. Sakabe, T. Suzuki, K. Tatai, and T. Sato. Urine, heart rate, and blood pressure; studies on some physical functions as indicators of the effect of coldness [Abstract, in English]. *Jap. J. M. Sc., Biophysics, v. 9, 1944: 43*.*

Four male subjects remained for 50 minutes in a room with temperature of 20°C, then entered a cold room (−30°C) and remained there for one hour performing light repetitive tasks, and then returned to the original room for one hour. During the hour in the cold room and the following one, measurements were made of various physiological functions as indicators of response to cold. Intake of oxygen and production of carbon dioxide began to increase after 40 minutes, and 5 minutes later reached a steady high level. The increase was found to be dependent on severity of cold as governed by weight of clothing worn. In the cold the pH and the quantity of urine increased but its volume decreased only when the subject was too cold. Excretion in urine of potassium, calcium, and chlorine increased in the cold and decreased in various ways upon return to normal conditions. Heart rate and blood pressure tended to increase as the severity of cold increased.

1460. Milch, L. J., H. F. Midkiff, P. Matthews, and H. I. Chinn. Changes in acetylcholine content of the brain during exposure to cold. *Proc. Soc. Exp. Biol., N. Y., v. 77, Aug. 1951: 659–661.*

Rats exposed to environmental cold (− 12 °C) for 2 hours showed a significant increase in the free and total acetylcholine content of the brain.

1461. Milhorat, A. T., J. D. Hardy, W. E. Bartels, and V. Toscani. Effect of shivering, iodoacetate, and epinephrine on vitamin C and creatine excretion in fasting dogs. *Proc. Soc. Exp. Biol., N. Y., v. 45, Oct. 1940: 397–399.*

Shivering in dogs, under nembutal anesthesia, produced considerable increase in the excretion of vitamin C and creatine, an increase in urinary nitrogen and urea and a decrease in creatinine. Muscular paralysis—which followed long periods of shivering—was accompanied by a large output of urinary creatine and vitamin C. Slight shivering, under anesthesia, induced a definite increase in urinary nitrogen but only a slight increase in vitamin C excretion and was without effect on the creatine. The data suggest that the metabolism of vitamin C is related significantly to that of glycogen. Both shivering and epinephrine are known to remove glycogen from the muscles.

1462. Müller, E. A. The influence of local cold stimuli on the metabolism [In German]. *Pflügers Arch., v. 248, Nov. 22, 1944: 521–526.*

An increase in metabolism is reported following cooling of the forehead with ice water, dipping the arm in cold water, or cooling of the face.

1463. Nekhorocheff, J. Utilization of ketone bodies in the rat under basal metabolic conditions and during the thermogenesis provoked by chilling [In French]. *C. rend. Soc. biol., Par., v. 143, June 1949: 797–800.*

At an environmental temperature of 8° or 29 °C, or following the subcutaneous injection of 1 mg/kg of Adrenalin, there was no significant difference in the utilization of ketone bodies, even though exposure to low temperatures is known to speed up the metabolism of many other compounds. Although there was considerable individual variation, after injection of Adrenalin the passage of ketone bodies in the urine tended to increase. The method of evaluation of destruction of ketone bodies in the animal body by use of a tissue brei of the rat and its excreta 1 hour after injection of one of the ketone bodies (β hydroxybutyric acid), is given by the author in an earlier paper in the same journal volume.

1464. Ohta, K. The effect of muscular work and cold on vitamin C excretion in the urine [In German]. *Arb. med. Fak. Okayama, v. 6, Oct. 1938: 87–92.*

The ascorbic acid content of the urine of a normal man appears to be unaffected by the amount of the urine excreted. Muscular work increases ascorbic acid excretion in man. Exposure to cold causes increased excretion of ascorbic acid in the urine of the rabbit.

1465. Onti, T. Influence upon the blood sugar of application of cold to the cat's body [In English]. *Tohoku J. Exp. M., v. 40, May 15, 1941: 78–85.*

After the introduction of ice water into the stomachs of cats, it was found that their temperatures dropped an average of 1.5 °C in 30 minutes, and that there was an increase in blood sugar concentration.

1466. Pagé, E., and L. M. Babineau. The effects of high fat diets and cold environment on the ascorbic acid content of the brown adipose tissue. *Canad. J. Res., Sect. E, v. 28, Oct. 1951: 196–201.*

In rats adapted to a cold environment (about 8°C, and then 0° to −3°C), there occurred a considerable hypertrophy of the brown adipose tissue, and a rise in its ascorbic acid content of from 4 to 8 times that at room temperature, with little change in body weight. At room temperature the ascorbic acid content of the brown adipose tissue was doubled on a high-fat ration. The authors conclude that cold stimulates fat metabolism and that both ascorbic acid and the brown adipose tissue are involved in the process.

1467. Ring, G. C. Thyroid stimulation by cold including the effect of changes in body temperature upon basal metabolism. *Am. J. Physiol., v. 125, Feb. 1939: 244–250.*

The elevation of the basal metabolism of rats exposed to brief periods of cold was accompanied by a slight rise in body temperature. When living for 3 or more weeks at temperatures of from 0° to 5°C an average increase of 21% in metabolism was noted, brought about mainly through the stimulation of the thyroid gland.

1468. Rinne, H. J. Variations in basal metabolic rate and adaptation to experimental conditions. An interferometric study with white rats as experimental animals [In English]. *Ann. med. int. fenn., v. 40, 1951: 251–257.*

Using an interferometer to determine the oxygen consumed and the carbon dioxide produced, a study was made with white rats of the effect of temperature, adaptation time, and Evipan sodium anesthesia on metabolic rate. At an environmental temperature of 25°C the values were lower and more uniform and movements of the animal were less than when kept at a temperature of 18°C. Placing the animal in the test chamber for 1 hour instead of 10 minutes before making the determinations gave a smaller variation in the values irrespective of any adaptation of the animal to the conditions of preceding days. The 1-hour period was considered insufficient if the animals had not been in the test chamber previously.

1469. Robinson, W. B. The effect of environmental temperature on the thiamine requirement of the growing albino rat [Abstract]. (Thesis for Ph.D. at University of Illinois.) *Urbana, Illinois, [University of Illinois], 1943. 8 p.*

Lowering of environmental temperatures from the region of the body temperature (about 35°C) to 15°C decreased the thiamine requirement of growing rats; at 4°C, where physical regulation of body temperature comes into play, the requirement rose (to 1.6 micrograms). The maximum, which was also at the highest temperature, was between 2.0 and 2.4 micrograms per gram of food. At 15°C, when no shivering occurred, the minimum requirement appeared to be less than 0.7 micrograms per gram as measured by the food utilization method. Exercise did not increase the percentage of thiamine required in the ration. The human requirement for thiamine, based upon interpretations of the rat's requirement, is no more than 1.2 milligrams per 2500 Calories.

1470. Roth, G. M., and C. Sheard. Relation of basal metabolic rate to vasodilatation and vasoconstriction of the extremities of normal subjects as measured by skin temperatures. *Circulation, N. Y., v. 1, May 1950: 1142–1147.* Abstract in: *Fed. Proc., Balt., v. 7, Mar. 1948: 105.*

Subjects kept at 25.5°C for one hour were exposed successively to temperatures of 21°C for one hour and then to 30°–31°C for one hour. Vasoconstriction took place more rapidly in subjects with low basal metabolic rates while vasodilatation was more rapid in those with high basal metabolic rates.

1471. Roth, J. L. A., and J. A. Frantz. Metabolic balances in the cold environment. I. Nitrogen and water exchanges [Abstract]. *Fed. Proc., Balt., v. 7, Mar. 1948: 105.*

Studies were made of the influence of a USAF emergency ration and a restricted water intake on the nitrogen, water, and energy exchanges in human subjects living for 9 days in a cold environment ($-32\,°C$). No evidence of azotemia, dehydration, or hemoconcentration was observed. Loss of body water by fasting subjects was greater than with the ration. Water requirements during the first 3 days of a fast were less than with the ration; during the subsequent 3 days it was greater.

1472. Sarzana, G., and F. Fazio. On the energy-producing material utilized by phloridzinated rats as a defense against lowering of their temperatures. [In Italian, summaries in Italian, French, English, and German]. *Biochim. ter. sper.*, v. 26, 1939: 297–303.

Studies on albino rats at an environmental temperature of $3\,°$–$4\,°C$ before and after phloridzination, showed that, contrary to earlier opinions, thermogenesis was not greatly altered even when in the treated animals very little glucose was available as energy-producing material for metabolism.

1473. Schwabe, E. L., F. E. Emery, and F. P. Griffith. The effect of prolonged exposure to low temperature on the basal metabolism of the rat. *J. Nutrit.*, v. 15, Feb. 10, 1958: 199–210.

Exposure of rats to low temperatures ($7\,°$–$12\,°C$) for the major portion of each day for periods of 15, 30, or 60 days, was found to increase the basal metabolic rate 11% to 16%, to increase body temperature, and to retard gain in weight, but not to affect the respiratory quotient.

1474. Suzuki, S., T. Hukuyawa, T. Suzuki, and T. Sato. Studies on the effect of cold upon human bodily functions. II. On the effect of cold upon gas exchange and upon urine and its secretion [In English]. *Jap. J. M. Sc.*, Biophysics, v. 8, Mar. 1943: 12*.

Studies were made of the effect of low atmospheric temperature on clothed human beings while working or sitting still. Samples of expired gas and urine were measured and analyzed chemically; no results are given.

1475. Suzuki, S., and M. Murokawa. The effect exerted on the human body by the climatic conditions of Manchuria. III. The effects of cold on energy metabolism and body temperature [Abstract, in English]. *Jap. J. M. Sc.*, Biophysics, v. 9, 1944: 71*–72*.

After 30 minutes of bed rest in a room kept at $10\,°C$ the subject, in his bed and covered by only one blanket, was placed outdoors in temperatures of $-20\,°C$ or colder. After about one hour of exposure the subject was returned indoors. This procedure was repeated several times. Oxygen intake rate increased outdoors, and after a lapse of time reached the peak of increase, then began to decrease. This peak came later as experiments continued, changing from 15 minutes in the first experiment to more than an hour in about the 5th experiment, indicating a pronounced change in respiration with acclimatization. If the subject was taken indoors at the time of this peak, the decrease was more clearly perceptible and at times became less than one-half of the indoor basal metabolism. Maximum expiration varied markedly, from 7 to 22 liters per minute, whereas the maximum oxygen intake volume showed less of a difference, ranging from 220 to 509 cc/min. When the peak of oxygen intake came later, as noted above, the oxygen intake amount became greater.

1476. Suzuki, S., G. Nishi, T. Ogo, and S. Yamazoe. The effects of the climatic conditions of Manchuria on the human body [Abstract, in English]. *Jap. J. M. Sc.*, Biophysics, v. 9, 1944: 72*–73*.

A subject was placed on diets of all protein, all sugar, or all fat in succession for one day each; these diets were repeated two more times with the protein intake remaining the same but with the sugar decreasing and the fat increasing on each succeeding time. The diets were arranged to give a daily nitrogen intake of 14.02 grams and a Calorie count of from 2100 to 2300 per three-day period. Tests to show any changes in energy metabolism were made while the subject was out of doors in −20°C, either at rest lying on a bed covered by a single blanket or taking a walk clothed only in a summer shirt. In the cold environment, the N intake in general equalled N excretion. It was clear that fats as well as sugars were utilized as fuel; the RQ of basal metabolism during sugar diets was 0.9 or above and 0.8 or below on fat diets.

1477. Suzuki, S., and G. Nishi. The effect of the climatic conditions of Manchuria on the human body [Abstract, in English]. *Jap. J. M. Sc., Biophysics, v. 9, 1944: 105*–106*.*

Energy metabolism was measured by the Douglas bag method at −20° or −30°C outdoors in Northern Manchuria. The oxygen intake of the subject, walking out of doors in a summer shirt and trousers, reached its maximum after 10 minutes, then declined and entered a steady state. The intake was then 200 cc/min greater than in a similar experiment during the summer. By changing the amount of clothing worn, the optimum of clothing was found which required the minimum oxygen intake.

1478. Thérien, M., and L. P. Dugal. Excretion of urinary ascorbic acid in the rat and the guinea pig exposed to cold [Abstract, in French]. *Ann. Ass. canad. fr. advanc. sc., v. 19, 1949: 77–78.*

In rats exposed to cold for a long-time period (60 days), there was a considerable increase in the excretion of ascorbic acid in the urine when compared with that of the control animals kept at normal room temperature. It was greatly increased in the rats which lost weight in the cold, but was always more even in rats whose weight remained the same during exposure. The rate of increase was also accelerated. In guinea pigs, on the contrary, there was marked diminution of urinary ascorbic acid in the cold. This occurred whether or not the animals acclimatized to cold, and did not return to a normal level. This decrease, which coincided with an increase of ascorbic acid in the tissues, was a little less marked in groups which received less vitamin C. These results would indicate that cold does not act only during the first hours of exposure (period of transition) but continues to produce effects during relatively long periods.

1479. Thérien, M. and L. P. Dugal. Urinary excretion of ascorbic acid in rats and guinea pigs exposed to cold [In French, summaries in French and English]. *Rev. canad. biol., v. 8, Sept. 1949: 248–256.*

Exposure of rats to cold (5° to 7°C) for periods of 3 or more months brought about a decided increase during the entire period in the ascorbic acid excreted in the urine; in guinea pigs there was a clear-cut decrease throughout the entire period.

1480. Treichler, R., and H. H. Mitchell. The influence of plane of nutrition and of environmental temperature on the relationship between basal metabolism and endogenous nitrogen metabolism subsequently determined. *J. Nutrit., v. 22, Oct. 10, 1941: 333–343.*

A prior low environmental temperature (4°C) was found to elevate the endogenous level of nitrogen excretion (2.0 mg of endogenous urinary nitrogen per calorie of basal heat, average for adult rats) whether or not the plane of nutrition was simultaneously raised. However, such a lowering of temperature elevated the basal metabolic rate only when accompanied by an elevation in the plane of nutrition (caloric intake) and then only to an extent no greater than could be produced by the raised plane of nutrition itself. Hence the ratio of endogenous nitrogen to the basal heat could be unaffected in the albino rat by a lowering of the environmental temperature if the plane of nutrition was increased in proportion to the increase in energy requirements. If the plane of nutrition was raised with no parallel lowering of the environmental temperature, it would be depressed in the same animal. In animal species whose basal metabolic rate is not so sensitive to changes in nutrition, the results would probably not be the same.

1481. Truka, J. Blood lactic acid and external temperature [In Hungarian]. *Magy. orv. arch., v. 41 (2), 1940: 139–144* and [German summary] *p. 168* and [English summary] *p. 172.*

The average value of the lactic acid level of the blood was found to vary according to the environmental temperature, being elevated at higher temperatures and depressed at lower temperatures.

1482. Vinokurov, S. I. The effect of temperature factors on the ascorbic acid and dehydroascorbic acid content in the tissues [In Ukranian, with English summary]. *Biokhem. zh., v. 11 (1), 1938: 89–102.*

Overheating (at 45°–50°C) or cooling (at 4°–5°C) of mice for periods of 1½–2½ hours led to a sharp decline in the ascorbic acid content of the liver, kidneys, and brain. The greatest decrease was observed in the liver; the least, in the brain. With the diminution of ascorbic acid content, the content of the reversely-oxidized form (dehydroascorbic acid) was increased, and the ratio dehydroascorbic acid/ascorbic acid increased also. This fact is one of the arguments in favor of regarding dehydroascorbic acid as a transition product in the ascorbic acid metabolism of the animal body.

1483.   Vinokurov, S. I., and M. L. Butom. Formation of dehydroascorbic acid during the decomposition of ascorbic acid in the animal body [In Russian]. *Biull. eksp. biol. med., v. 7 (1), 1939: 98–100.*

Studies were continued on the changes in the dehydroascorbic and ascorbic acid content of the animal body during thermal stimulation. It was established that the decrease in ascorbic acid was not due to a change in its distribution in the body; the total content in the mice had diminished (from 11.2 mg% to 7.5 mg%) during a period of 6–10 hours at an environmental temperature ranging from −2° to 4°C. Determination of the ascorbic and dehydroascorbic acid content in the liver, showed, simultaneously with the decrease of ascorbic acid, an absolute and relative increase in dehydroascorbic acid. These results indicate that the dehydroascorbic acid is an intermediary product of ascorbic acid metabolism in the animal organism.

1484.   Westphal, A. On the influence of the climate on the serum composition of man [In German]. *Zschr. Tropenmed., v. 1, Aug. 1944: 153–162.*

In a study of the effect of climate on the protein content of the serum, blood samples were collected from persons residing in three different areas: Skopje (Yugoslavia), 291 meters above sea level in a mountain area, with a temperature at the time of the tests of 20°–30°C; Salonica (Macedonia, Greece), on a gulf off the Aegean Sea, with a temperature in August of about 40°C; and Ströbing, near Rosenheim (Bavaria, Germany), on the edge of the Alps at a height of 580 meters, with a temperature of −10° to −15°C. In one type of protein-precipitation reaction, a similar fairly high average value was noted for the blood samples from Skopje and Salonica and a lower value in that from Ströbing. Malaria present in Skopje may account for the higher value at Skopje. In another type of test the results for Skopje and Ströbing were high and for Salonica low. The pathological condition of mysedema in Ströbing may account for the high values noted there. In Ströbing, experiments with dogs artificially raising the temperature of the dog's environment to that prevailing at Skopje did not produce the same diagnostic levels in the blood serum as had been previously demonstrated in the serum from Skopje. It is concluded that the climatic factors causing these alterations are still unknown, and that the serological changes are thought to be vegetatively conditioned changes in the protein structure.

1485.   Wildführ, G. On the influence of cold stimuli on the specific antitoxic diphtheria immunity [In German]. *Zschr. Immunforsch., v. 107, Aug. 1, 1950: 512–517.*

Experiments were made with 71 young subjects to determine the influence of cold stimulation on the level of diphtheria antitoxin in their blood serum. Cold stimulation was induced by inhalation of cold air (8°C) with open mouth (group A); by ice packs around the neck (group B); or by cooling of the feet with cold air (group C), for one half to one hour. The antitoxin titer was determined by the intradermal technique of Roemer before the cooling, and then immediately, one-half hour, and 24 hours afterwards. The cold application induced a body temperature decrease in group A, and especially in group B. In group C the temperature of the feet dropped in some cases by 3°–10°C (to 22.4°C), mostly in the subjects hypersensitive to cold, or in those with some vasomotor incapacity, returning rapidly to normal after the stimulation in 40% of them. In the majority of cases, however, the temperature changes in the feet were slight, especially in the cold-resistant subjects. In neither group did exposure to cold air appear to induce noticeable fluctuations in the antitoxin titer of the blood. In 83% of the cases there was no change; in 17% (12 cases) the fluctuations ceased after approximately 24 hours. These changes were found mostly among the cold-sensitive subjects (9 cases out of the 12). It is concluded that there is no marked change of the specific diphtheria antitoxin immunity after a limited cold stimulation.

1486. Yosida, N. Study of various influences on alterations of albumins and phosphatides of blood plasma especially on their mutual relationship [In German]. *J. Biochem., Tokyo, v. 31 (2), 1940: 243.*

The amount of cephalins in rabbit blood in the fall was found to be less than in summer and was considerably less in winter being decreased then to only about ⅓ of the summer amount. Total proteins in the blood were diminished in winter. This was caused chiefly by the decrease in the albumins while the globulins, especially the euglobulins, increased. Non-protein nitrogen increased in winter to double that of the summer.

1487. You, S. S., R. W. You, and E. A. Sellers. Effect of thyroidectomy, adrenalectomy, and burning on urinary nitrogen excretion of the rat maintained in cold environment. *Endocrinology, v. 47, Sept. 1950: 156–161.*

Rats excreted 77% more nitrogen in their urine when kept in a cold environment (1.5°C) than when kept at room temperature (25°C). Doubling the food intake in the cold increased the urinary nitrogen to 2.3 times its original value. Growth, as measured by increase in body weight, was slowed by the cold. The effect of a mild burn and exposure to cold on urinary nitrogen excretion appeared to be cumulative, the sum being greater than the total of each stimulus acting independently.

1488. Ziemke, H. Blood histamine content in localized cold injury [In German]. *Arch. exp. Path., Berl., v. 206 (2–3), 1949: 288–291.*

The presence of histamine or histamine-like substances immediately before, during, and after cold injury was investigated in rabbits' ears frozen experimentally [carbon dioxide snow, 15 minutes). The blood was taken from the vein of the non-frozen ear, analyzed for histaminic substances, and tested on the ileum of the guinea-pig. Tabulated results showed in 4 animals out of 6 a pronounced increase (about 50%) in blood histaminics, and an insignificant decrease in 2 animals, immediately after the cold injury. It is suggested that the amines which act on the vascular system are liberated in the injured part even during the period of cold injury, and that all circulation has not ceased in this part, for otherwise the increase in histaminics in the body could not be explained. The author concludes that the increase in blood histaminics and the acceleration of blood coagulation are to be considered as a general manifestation of serous inflammation.

See also items: 216, 484, 652, 653, 662, 670, 686, 689, 691, 1051, 1112, 1135, 1141, 1174, 1215, 1224, 1230, 1246, 1268, 1274, 1332, 1334, 1336, 1337, 1338, 1340, 1341, 1342, 1346, 1350, 1352, 1353, 1354, 1355, 1356, 1358, 1365, 1366, 1367, 1368, 1370, 1372, 1373, 1374, 1375, 1385, 1388, 1395, 1399, 1400, 1401, 1402, 1406, 1407, 1410, 1412, 1424, 1426, 1429, 1500, 1507, 1523, 1546, 1547, 1563.

L. Growth and Development

1489. Allee, W. C., and C. Z. Lutherman. An experimental study of certain effects of temperature on differential growth of pullets. *Ecology, Brooklyn, v. 21, Jan. 1950: 29–33.*

Pullets, housed in a pen at a room temperature of 6°C, during their 3rd through 6th month of age, had a shorter body length, greater body weight, shorter tarsus bones and tails, and larger hearts than the control animals kept at 21° to 24.5°C.

1490. Bullough, W. S. Effects of high and low temperatures on epidermal mitotic activity of adult male mouse, Mus musculus L. *J. Exp. Biol., Lond., v. 26, May 1949: 76–82.*

Bits of tissue were taken by ear clip at 2-hour intervals, from the ears of mice kept at environmental temperatures of 20°C both awake and asleep, and at lowered temperatures of 10° and 0°C. Histological examination of the tissue showed that a reduction in mitotic activity occurred in mice kept at the lower temperatures. The artificial prevention of a drop in body temperature of a sleeping mouse did not interfere with the normal rise in mitotic activity which takes place during sleep; artificial reduction of body temperature of a waking mouse to a level similar to that of sleep was not followed by a rise in mitotic activity.

1491. Chang, M. C. Normal development of fertilized rabbit ova stored at low temperature for several days. *Nature, Lond., v. 159, May 3, 1947: 602–603.*

Rabbit ova in the first cleavage stage were kept at temperatures of 0° to 25°C for varying lengths of time and then cultured at 37°C to determine effects on cleavage. Rapid cooling was harmful; slow cooling was less so. The optimum temperature for survival was 10°C. When the cultured ova were transplanted into the Fallopian tubes of doe rabbits, litters of normal healthy young were produced. After storage at 5° or 10°C for long periods of time (120–144 hours), however, failure of pregnancy or birth of an abnormally small animal occurred.

1492. Emery, F. E., L. M. Emery, and E. L. Schwabe. The effects of prolonged exposure to low temperature on the body growth and on the weights of organs in the albino rat. *Growth, Phila., v. 4, May 1940: 17–32.*

In the rat exposed to a cold room temperature of 1.6°C, the carcass, tail, spleen, ovaries, uterus, testes, epididymides, pituitary, and thymus were smaller, while kidneys, thyroid glands, adrenal glands, heart, lungs, intestinal tract, and liver were larger. No gain in weight was found for individual organs, but the mean weight of the intestinal tract was found to have increased. The amount of gonad-stimulating hormone secreted by the pituitary remained unchanged. Estrous cycles were inhibited.

1493. Ershoff, B. H., J. N. Pagones, and H. J. Deuel, Jr. Comparative nutritive value of butter and vegetable fats under conditions of low environmental temperature. *Proc. Soc. Exp. Biol., N. Y., v. 70, Feb. 1949: 287–290.*

Immature female rats were raised to maturity under cold room (2°C) and ordinary (21°C) temperature conditions on purified rations differing only in the nature of the 20% of fat they contained. Gain in body weight was significantly reduced in all of the rats kept in the cold; the nature of the fat (cottonseed oil, corn oil, margarine fat, butter fat) in the diet had no influence in either the groups in the cold room or those kept at ordinary temperature.

1494. Fuller, R. H,. E. Brown, and C. A. Mills. Environmental temperatures and spontaneous tumors in mice. *Cancer Res., v. 1, Feb. 1941: 130–133.*

In virgin female mice the time from discovery of a spontaneous tumor until death was 28 days in animals kept at 65°F, 47 days at 70°–75°F, and 60 days at 90°–91°F. The tumor incidence was also highest at 65°F and lowest at 90°–91°F. Studies by earlier investigators, of human cancer death rates by age groups, had indicated that cancer incidence was higher in northern states under stimulating, cooler, climatic conditions than in southern states.

1495. Hellmer, L. A. The effect of temperature on the behavior of the white rat. *Am. J. Psychol., v. 56, July 1943: 408–421.*

Rats were raised at room temperatures of 55° (cold), 75° (control), and 90°F (hot) and studied through two generations. In the cold room, rats grew most rapidly, matured earlier, and gave birth to litters of larger, healthier young. In the hot room, growth and maturity were much delayed. The rats were also smaller in adult-size and had an average length of tail at least one centimeter longer than those in the cold. Significant morphological differences appeared in the two groups. Adaptation to climatic conditions appeared to be continuous and cumulative from one generation to another. Rats raised in the cold room were from two to three times more efficient in maze learning than those from the hot room, and also superior to the control animals. There appeared to be no significant differences in retention of learning although the hot room rats required several times as many trials to relearn the maze.

1496. Herrington, L. P., and J. H. Nelbach. Relation of gland weights to growth and aging processes in rats exposed to certain environmental conditions. *Endocrinology, v. 30, Mar. 1942: 375–385.*

The tensile resistance of the rat's thoracic aorta is affected by continuing exposure of the animal to low (65°C) or high (95°C) temperatures, to thyroid feeding, or to continued sensory stimulation. In the rats kept at 65°F the aorta showed values associated with younger animals (or higher tensile resistance). Histologically no change in the aorta was obvious but a dystrophy in endocrine development, as measured by organ and gland weights, was associated with the changes in the aorta.

1497. Hume, J. T. The tensility of the rat's aorta as influenced by age, environmental temperature, and certain toxic substances. *Am. J. Hyg., Sect. A, v. 29, Jan. 1939: 11–23.*

The tensile resistance of the aorta of groups of rats, after the animals had been kept in environmental temperatures of 65°, 82° and 90°F for 180 days or more—as measured *in vitro* with a tensometer—was normal or slightly increased for those kept at 65°F and markedly decreased for those kept at 82° and 90°F when compared with the rats kept at a normal room temperature. Growth was retarded, metabolism was increased, and the prostate glands were heavier in the animals kept in the cold.

1498. Moore, K. The effect of controlled temperature changes on the behavior of the white rat. *J. Exp. Psychol., v. 34, Feb. 1944: 70–79.*

Rats kept in a cold room (55°F) grew more rapidly, were shorter, more stocky, and had shorter tails than those kept in control (75°F) or hot (90°F) rooms. Rats living and learning the maze in the cold room were superior to those of the hot room; those of the control group were about midway between. In re-learning, the number of trials increased when animals were moved to a room of higher temperature. Rats from the hot room re-learned in fewer trials when they were changed to the control room, and in still fewer in the cold room.

1499. Nelbach, J. H., and L. P. Herrington. The significance of the tensility of the aorta as an index of the aging process in the animal body. *Am. Heart J., v. 22, Nov. 1941: 661–682.*

Tensility of the aorta of rats normally decreases with aging. When the rats had been exposed to environmental temperatures of 65°F for 120 or 210 days, the tensility of the aorta was increased over that of animals exposed to environmental temperature of 83°F. When animals which were kept at temperatures of 83° or 95°F were given thyroid extract to increase their metabolism to the level of that of animals kept in the cold, the tensility did not increase but decreased below that of untreated animals kept at 83°F.

1500. Sellers, E. A., and R. W. You. Prevention of dietary fatty livers by exposure to cold environment. *Science, v. 110, Dec. 30, 1949: 713.*

Fatty livers ahd hemorrhagic kidneys are more easily produced experimentally in rats when the food intake is high and growth is rapid. Groups of rats were given a diet deficient in choline and its precursors and were kept at temperatures of either 2.5°C or 25°C. Rats kept in the cold room ate more than the control group; their increase in body weight was less; and, when sacrificed at the end of two weeks, the fat content of their livers was found to be much less than that of the controls. It is postulated that some intermediary pathways in the action of choline may be affected by exposure to a cold environment.

1501. Smith, L. W. Effect of temperature on the development of the chick embryo [Abstract]. *Arch. Path., Chic., v. 28, Sept. 1939: 422.*

Temperature changes had a profound effect on the development of the chick (over 700 instances). The temperature range between 90°–95°F (normal body temperature of chick, 102°–103°F) was critical, causing not only a delay in development but also failure of cell growth, differentiation, and organization. The first 48 to 96 hours of development were the most important. Temperatures below this critical range resulted in delayed maturation; above 105° or 106°F caused rapid disintegration of the embryo.

1502. Sturkie, P. D. Suppression of polydactyly in the domestic fowl by low temperature. *J. Exp. Zool., v. 93, Aug. 1943: 325–346.*

Chick embryos which were genetically homozygous or heterozygous for polydactyly were subjected to varying periods of time and degrees of lowered environmental temperature from the 12th hour to the 5th day of development. The degree of suppression of polydactyly was directly proportional to the intensity and duration of the lowered temperature, with duration of the time of exposure being the more important factor. A high degree of suppression was achieved when exposure was in the 2nd to 3rd day of embryonic development, the 3rd day being the most sensitive, decreasing greatly in 4th and 5th days and being quite insensitive in the later stages of development.

1503. Tannenbaum, A., and H. Silverstone. Effects of sodium fluoride, dinitrophenol, and low environmental temperature on the formation of spontaneous mammary carcinoma in mice [Abstract]. *Cancer Res., v. 6, Sept. 1946: 499.*

In groups of DBA female mice, kept at cold room temperatures (41° and 55°F), 10% developed spontaneous mammary carcinoma. In groups kept at an environmental temperature of 80°F, 74% without further treatment, 42% treated with sodium fluoride, and 2% treated with dinitrophenol, developed spontaneous mammary carcinoma.

1504. Tannenbaum, A., H. Silverstone. Effects of low environmental temperature, dinitrophenol, or sodium fluoride on the formation of tumors in mice. *Cancer Res., v. 9, July 1949: 403–410.*

Keeping a group of DBA female mice at an environmental temperature of 45° to 55°F, or feeding them either sodium 2,4 dinitrophenol or sodium fluoride, significantly inhibited the formation of spontaneous mammary carcinomas. Effects of the chemicals are reported on other types of tumors. These and other experiments indicate that neither the food consumption (caloric intake) nor the amount or rate of metabolic turnover are consistently related to tumor formation. However, some of the results would imply that the inhibition of tumor formation brought about by food restriction is associated with the low weight of the animals.

1505. Wallace, E. W., H. M. Wallace, and C. A. Mills. Effect of climatic environment upon the genesis of subcutaneous tumors induced by methylcholanthrene and upon the growth of transplantable sarcoma in C3H mice. *J. Nat. Cancer Inst., v. 3, Aug. 1942: 99–110.*

When the methylcholanthrene-induced transplantable sarcoma was injected subcutaneously into strain C3H mice, the sarcoma grew rapidly in the animals kept in the hot room (92°F, 50% humidity) but grew only slowly or actually regressed when the animals were kept in the cold room (65°F, variable humidity). When the injection was intramuscular, the sarcoma grew equally well in both the hot and the cold room.

See also items: 442, 1091, 1092, 1094, 1348, 1354, 1487, 1507, 1579, 1583.

M. Effects of Cold Combined with Other Agents
(including acceleration, barometric pressure, asphyxia, infection, and drugs)

1506. Arkhangel'skaĩa, N. A. The influence of low and high environmenta. temperatures on the resistance of the organism to hypoxic hypoxia [In Russian], In: Opyt izucheniĩa reguliãtsiĩ fiziologicheskikh funktsiĩ, Moscow-Leningrad, 1949, p. 107–122.

Both adult and young rats were subjected to temperatures of 6°–8°C or 26°–28°C, under atmospheric pressures from sea level to 5500 meters of simulated altitude, during a period lasting up to 70 days. Results showed an increased oxygen consumption and a somewhat lower ceiling of resistance to high altitudes in the animals kept at low temperature than in the controls; increased respiratory frequency indicated a greater sensitivity of the nervous system to hypoxic hypoxia in the cooled animals. The erythrocyte and hemoglobin content of the blood of the rats kept at low temperature changed only slightly, but decreased in the controls as it would be expected to do.

1507. Babineau, L. M., and E. Pagé. Effect of diet and temperature on distribution of fats in rat [In French]. Ann. Ass. canad. fr. advanc. sc., v. 17, 1951: 102–107.

One group of rats was sacrificed immediately to act as controls; 2 groups were kept at normal room temperature, with one group fed a diet rich in fat (39%) and the other a diet poor (5%) in fat; 2 groups were kept at an environmental temperature of 0° to 3°C, and fed the diets as above. After three months the animals were sacrificed and various studies made of wet weight and lipid content of tissues. From the point of view of growth a diet rich in lipids is superior at either a normal or cold temperature. A diet rich in lipids favors the accumulation of lipid reserves in the rat exposed to normal temperatures, while only a slight nonsignificant increase of the total lipids occurred on exposure to cold. Of the two groups exposed to normal temperature, the greater amount of visceral fat was found in those on the higher fat diet. Of this fat the carcass fat was slightly different, the subcutaneous was identical. Of the animals exposed to cold the total fat content did not vary significantly. There was a slight increase in subcutaneous fat in those on the high fat diet but the proportion of visceral fat was the same. On exposure to cold the hibernating gland, or brown fat, was found to be hypertrophied with a considerable elevation of the total content of ascorbic acid.

1508. Blood, F. R., R. M. Glover, J. B. Henderson, and F. E. D'Amour. Relationship between hypoxia, oxygen consumption, and body temperature. Am. J. Physiol., v. 156, Jan. 1949: 62–66.

The effect of environmental temperature (18°–20°, 26°–28°, 35°–37°C) and altitude levels 5,280 to 40,000 feet) upon the oxygen consumption and body temperature of normal and thyroxin- and thiouracil-treated rats, was investigated. In normal rats oxygen consumption was found to be limited by oxygen availability only at altitudes approaching 40,000 feet; at lower altitudes consumption was found to be affected by availability only in rats subjected to cold or treated with thyroxin. In general a lowering of body temperature was found to be accompanied by a lowered oxygen consumption; in some instances, however, no correlation was noted.

1509.   Bon Signore, A., and C. Lombroso. Sensitivity to the action of Adrenalin in animals exposed to cold [In Italian]. *Biochim. ter. sper., v. 25, 1938: 101–106.*

Narcotized cats exposed to dry cold showed an increased sensitivity to the action of Adrenalin as indicated by isotonic contractions of the nictitating membrane.

1510.   Brooks, B., and G. W. Duncan. The effects of temperature on the survival of anemic tissue. *Ann. Surg., v. 112, 1940: 130–137.*

Experiments were carried out to determine the minimum time for applying a pressure of 130 mm Hg to a rat's tail, when maintained at a given environmental temperature, in order to occlude the circulation and lead to the subsequent development of an experimental gangrene. Observations were made at temperatures of −5°, 1°, 5°, 15°, 30°, 35°, or 40°C. Results indicated a range of 96 hours for the duration of the anemic condition to produce a subsequent gangrene at 1° or at 5°C, to 3–4 hours when the temperature was 40°C.

1511.   Bunge, J. Experimental animal contributions on the problem of "Altitude cramps and air temperature." [In German]. *Luftfahrtmedizin, v. 6, Apr. 5, 1942: 127–131.*

White mice were placed in a decompression chamber and their tolerance to altitude hypoxia was determined at various environmental temperatures. The appearance of spasms served as an indicator of the tolerance limit. The highest tolerance was found to be at −10°C at a simulated altitude of 12,900 meters, decreasing at temperatures both above and below −10°C. At 10°C the tolerance limit was at 11,000 meters; at 20°C, at 10,000 meters. The author assumes that at higher environmental temperatures the oxygen absorption in the pulmonary capillaries is decreased while at lower temperatures the severe hypothermic state limits the tolerance.

1512.   Burkhardt, W. L., R. E. Hedblom, A. W. Hetherington, and H. F. Adler. Extent of pathological damage to animals explosively decompressed in a cold environment. *J. Aviat. M., v. 21, Aug. 1950: 304–308.*

Experimental rapid decompression—simulating aircraft situations—of guinea pigs produced no pathological differences whether it occurred in a warm (20°C) or cold (−10°C) environment. Similarly in dogs, either slowly or rapidly decompressed, a warm (20°C) or cold (−10°, −50°C) environment brought about no augmentation of the pulmonary damage from the additional stress of chilling.

1513.   Cameron, G. R. Some recent work on barbiturates. *Proc. R. Soc. M., Lond., v. 32, Feb. 1939: 309–314.*

From time to time toxic effects have been observed after the administration of quite small amounts of barbiturates. Experiments were done on laboratory animals to study the effects of Nembutal (which is believed to be detoxicated in the liver) under various conditions. In studying the effect of cold, small blocks of ice were applied to the upper abdomen of rabbits as soon as they were asleep after being given Nembutal intravenously. Two of the group of 12 animals died after 60 and 70 minutes and the duration of the period of sleep for the others was increased considerably (99–250 minutes) over that for animals not treated with ice (60–160 minutes; average 109 minutes). Of a group of 13 rats kept in a cold draught while under the influence of Nembutal, 3 died; litter mates kept warm and with similar dosages of the anesthetic, all recovered in the usual period of time.

1514.   Campbell, J. A. Effects of oxygen pressure as influenced by external temperature, hormones, and drugs. *J. Physiol., Lond., v. 92, 1938: 29P–31P.*

Rats died when exposed to high oxygen pressure (6 atmospheres for 30 minutes) at 33°C, but survived if the temperature was about 24°C. Thyroidectomy had a protective effect against oxygen poisoning with the external temperature at 33°C. Rats exposed to low oxygen pressure (barometric pressure lowered to 240 mm Hg for 32 minutes, with oxygen in the air about 7%) survived at 20°–25°C but died if the external temperature was kept at 33°C.

1515.   Case, E. M., and J. B. S. Haldane. Human physiology under high pressure. I. Effects of nitrogen, carbon dioxide, and cold. *J. Hyg., Lond., v. 41, Nov. 1941: 225–249.*

In experiments with human subjects, breathing air at 8.6 atmospheres of pressure after about 3 minutes brought about little reduction of manual dexterity but considerable reduction in effect on performance of arithmetic and on practical activities. At 10 atmospheres these effects were somewhat increased. Breathing 3%–4% or 6% carbon dioxide at atmospheric pressure caused little deterioration in the subject, but when air containing 0.4% carbon dioxide (partial pressure of about 4%) was breathed at 10 atmospheres, there was a marked deterioration of manual dexterity and a good deal of confusion. While breathing carbon dioxide at partial pressures of 6.6%–9.7% at 10 atmospheres, several subjects lost consciousness in 1–5 minutes; some subjects could tolerate partial pressure of 8% for 5 minutes or more. Immersion of the test subjects in a water bath (below 40°F) did not increase the effects of breathing air at high pressure, or of carbon dioxide at atmospheric pressure, but somewhat increased the effects of combined high pressure and carbon dioxide. It was realized that the degree of cold involved was rather extreme and it is, therefore, considered doubtful whether exposure to moderate cold under the conditions would produce as much of an effect.

1516.   Cleghorn, R. A. The effect of different environmental temperatures on the survival of dogs after severe bleeding. *Canad. M. Ass. J., v. 49, Dec. 1943: 363–367.*

The mortality rate of dogs which had been bled to a critical level was lowest when they were kept at an environmental temperature of 72°F. At environmental temperatures of either mild cold (52°F) or mild warmth (85°F), the mortality was twice that at 72°F. A more extreme degree of warming (95°F) led to a mortality of about 100%.

1517.   Code, C. F., E. J. Baldes, E. H. Wood, and E. H. Lambert. The effect of environmental temperature upon man's G tolerance [Abstract]. *Fed. Proc., Balt., v. 5, Mar. 1946: 18.*

Tests performed on 15 normal men revealed that they had a greater G tolerance (capacity to withstand increased positive accelerative forces) in a cool environment (average 63°F, 72% relative humidity) than in a warm environment (average 89°F, 77% humidity).

1518.   Dugal, L. P., and M. Thérien. Effects of ascorbic acid on the hypertrophy of the adrenal during exposure to cold: repercussion on the thymus and the thyroid [Abstract, in French]. *Rev. canad. biol., v. 8, Oct. 1949: 309.*

Earlier experiments had shown that ascorbic acid in large doses had prevented the hypertrophy of the adrenals during exposure to cold. Current studies, under the same conditions, confirmed this finding but also indicated that the acid partially inhibited the atrophy of the thymus and favored an increase in the weight of the thyroid during the first day of exposure to cold.

1519.   Dugal, L. P., and O. Héroux. Is ascorbic acid a regulator of arterial pressure in a cold climate [Abstract, in French]. *Rev. canad. biol., v. 8, Oct. 1949: 310.*

Preliminary experiments with rats indicate that ascorbic acid seems to prevent the characteristic hypotension of shock caused by sudden exposure to cold of −2° to 0°C. Also, the acid lowers the hypertension provoked by a prolonged exposure to the cold.

1520.   Dugal, L. P., and M. Thérien. Influence of ascorbic acid on the activity of the adrenals against cold [Abstract, in French]. *Rev. canad. biol., v. 8, Oct. 1949: 315–316.*

In conditions of stress there is a hypertrophy of the adrenals, a condition which is easily demonstrated in the increase in weight of the organs. Several authors have stated that this hypertrophy corresponds to the increased activity of the adrenal cortex in resisting the stress.

The authors earlier had shown a direct relation between the amount of ascorbic acid in the adrenals and resistance to cold and had assumed that the hypertrophy of the adrenals which would normally be seen on exposure to cold would be augmented or not depending on whether the amount of ascorbic acid present in the glands was sufficient to resist the cold satisfactorily. But, contrary to this hypothesis, the following results were obtained. On exposure to a short period of severe cold (72 hours at $-3°C$), ascorbic acid prevented the hypertrophy of the adrenals of the rat even though the hypertrophy was produced normally in the controls. The same phenomenon occurred on exposure to cold for a long period (8 months). The survival of the rats given ascorbic acid was superior to that of the controls. The initial weight of the adrenal was regained a month earlier in animals receiving ascorbic acid over those which did not. In the animals exposed for a long period the increase in weight of the glands was less marked in the groups which received more of the acid and which adapted better to cold. The presence of edema of the penis was more frequent (6:1) in the groups receiving more ascorbic acid.

1521. Dugal, L. P. Effect of cold, ascorbic acid, and age on "formaldehyde-induced" arthritis in the white rat [In English, summaries in French and English]. *Canad. J. M. Sc., v. 29, Apr. 1950: 35–47.*

Formaldehyde-induced inflammatory processes, which increased the volume of the leg into which the injection was made, were considerably greater in either the young or adult rats who were also exposed to cold ($1°C$). Edema of the penis which appeared after long exposure to cold, appeared sooner and was much more intense in the formaldehyde-treated animals. Ascorbic acid greatly diminished the increase in volume of the leg of adult rats but not of young rats. The possible action of ascorbic acid on the hypophysis-adrenal function is not clear.

1522. Fuhrman, G. J., F. W. Weymouth, and J. Field. The effect of environmental temperature on the toxicity of 2,4-dinitrophenol in mice. *J. Pharm. Exp. Ther., v. 79, Oct. 1943: 176–178.*

Toxicity of 2,4-dinitrophenol (DNP) for albino mice, at environmental temperatures between $6°$ and $40°C$, was found to be lowered by decreases in temperature. Calculated values of LD_{50} for DNP were 35.7 mg/kg at $6°C$ and 30.0 mg/kg at $25°C$. The LD_{50} at $40°C$ was not determined but was significantly lower than that at $25°C$.

1523. Fuhrman, G. J., and F. W. Weymouth. The effect of dinitrophenol on the oxygen consumption of albino mice at graded levels of environmental temperature. *Am. J. Physiol., v. 147, Nov. 1946: 527–530.*

Mice kept at environmental temperatures of $10°$, $15°$, $20°$, $25°$, or $30°C$, were injected with dinitrophenol in doses of 15 mg/kg body weight and the oxygen consumption was measured manometrically. At environmental temperatures of $30°C$, the basic metabolic rate was augmented but not significantly above that of the controls at other temperatures studied. At the lower temperatures, both control and treated mice had a metabolic rate higher than that of control animals at $30°C$. After 70 minutes at each of the experimental temperatures, the rectal temperature of both control and treated mice did not differ more than $1°C$.

1524. Gaylord, C., and H. C. Hodge. Duration of sleep produced by pentobarbital sodium in normal and castrated female rats. *Proc. Soc. Exp. Biol., N. Y., v. 55, Jan. 1944: 46–48.*

Normal and castrated female rats were given pentobarbital subcutaneously (30 mg/kg). The normal rats slept significantly longer than did the castrate rats. Groups of both normal and castrated rats were exposed to environmental temperatures of $13°$, $23°$, and $37°C$. In general, the duration of sleep decreased with the increase of environmental temperature. For the normal animals these average times were 247 and 292 minutes at $13°C$, 251 and 276 at $23°C$, and 173 and 186 at $37°C$; for the castrate animals, 168 and 161 minutes at $13°C$, 118 and 166 at $23°C$, and 109 and 88 at $37°C$.

1525. Giaja, J. Protective role of hypothermia in asphyxia [In French]. *C. rend. Acad. sc., Par., v. 225, Sept. 8, 1947: 436–437.*

At an environmental temperature of 20°C the resistance of rats to asphyxia, repeated bleedings, or to carbon monoxide poisoning was greater than at a temperature of 32°C. The latter temperature is considered to be the neutral thermal level for the rat.

1526. Goebel, A., H. K. Fukas, W. Klante, and H. Imdahl. Oxygen consumption and body temperature of rats during oxygen insufficiency [In German]. *Zschr. ges. exp. Med., v. 117 (4), 1951: 384–392.*

Oxygen consumption during hypoxia was studied in rats in relation to body temperature. The animals were exposed about 20 hours to inhalation of a mixture of 7% oxygen in nitrogen. The oxygen consumption decreased soon after the onset of hypoxia, reaching 50% of its normal value after 20 hours. The body temperature dropped immediately after hypoxia began, reaching an average decrease of 13°C toward the end of the experiment. This decrease is interpreted as a passive, thermal, diminution in metabolism enabling the animal to tolerate the lack of oxygen during the 20 hours. After resumption of normal respiration, the temperature rose rapidly reaching its normal level simultaneously with the oxygen consumption after 6 hours. The augmented oxygen consumption which followed the hypoxic test was shown arithmetically to have been applied to the warming of the body.

1527. Griffin, D. R., S. Robinson, H. S. Belding, R. C. Darling, and E. S. Turrell. The effects of cold and rate of ascent on aero-embolism. *J. Aviat. M., v. 17, Feb. 1946: 56–66.*

During simulated ascents in a controlled-temperature (+32° to −50°F; 80° to 85°F) chamber, men kept comfortably warm by either the environmental temperature or by loose, warm clothing, suffered significantly less from joint "bends" than did those who were definitely cold. The time of onset was also later in the warm group, and twice as many were able to remain at 35,000 feet without symptoms.

1528. Ipsen, J., Jr. The effect of environmental temperature on the reaction of mice to tetanus toxin. *J. Immun., v. 66, June 1951: 687–694.*

Survival time was longer in groups of mice given more than one minimal lethal dose of tetanus toxin and kept at a temperature of 10°C than it was in those kept at 25°C, and still longer than in those kept at 35°C. Sublethal doses of toxin gave more severe reactions at 10°C than at 25°C, in that more mice died.

1529. Jötten, K. W. Influence of cold on action of carbon monoxide [In German, summaries in English, French, and German]. *Arch. Hyg., Münch., v. 132 (1), 1950: 3–10.*

Chronic illnesses (headaches, dizziness, cramps, head sweating and heart palpitation) were reported in personnel working in and out of a cold room (−35°C) where motors were being tested for starting in the cold. Tests of the air of the room indicated that carbon monoxide and some carbon dioxide, were being released into the room. In experiments with mice all animals died within 30 minutes when kept in a cold room at −8°C with a carbon monoxide concentration of 0.06–0.08 volumes %. Control animals kept at normal room temperatures with the same concentration of gas, or in the cold room at −8°C with no carbon monoxide present, showed no ill effects. The author recommends aeration of such a room to eliminate also the carbon dioxide since its action on respiratory centers contributes to the ill effects, and the wearing of gas masks or the transfer from the area of personnel particularly susceptible to the gases.

1530. Kadykov, B. I. On the action of low temperatures on the animal body [In Russian]. *In: Trudy iubileĭnoĭ nauchnoĭ sessii Instituta Gigieny Truda i Profesional'nykh Zabolevanii (Leningrad, iiunia 15–19, 1939), p. 148–157. Leningrad, 1940.*

The following studies were made by the author and colleagues: influence of (1) local cooling on the animal body, (2) of local and general cooling on the body sensitivity to chemical factors, (3) of general cooling on normal and albumin-sensitized animals, (4) of low temperature on the adrenal glands, and (5) of cold on anaphylaxis. V. M. PANKOV, established that local cooling of short duration induces a slight increase in arterial blood pressure and in increase in the frequency and amplitude of respiration; these factors returned to normal after rapid re-warming. Experiments by KADYKOV and N. E. LEVIN have shown that camphor injection induced a brisk vasodilatation in the cooled foot, increasing the volume of the foot. In cases of general cooling, the camphor injections induced a drop in arterial pressure (apparently due to vasodilatation in the peripheral parts which were contracted by cold), particularly in hypothermia, causing death. These facts indicate an abrupt alteration of body sensitivity toward chemical factors under the effect of cold, increasing or even changing the effect of the chemical action. Study of the influence of the adrenal glands during cold stimulation was made in rabbits kept at $-8°$ and $-18°C$ for 4½-5 months. These glands showed a great increase in weight and a hypertrophy of the cortical tissue. The anapylactic shock induced after subsequent sensitization at room temperature was much stronger than in the controls. Further experimentation revealed that augmented cortical secretion sensitizes the animal to the anaphylactic shock by altering the body reaction to chemical and physical factors. In K. D. LAVROVA's experiments with temperature inducing a disturbance of thermoregulation in normal and albumin-sensitized rabbits, death occurred in 50% of the animals, including all of the sensitized animals, through hemorrhages in the lungs and small-foci pneumonia. N. F. MARGOLINA's experiments showed the same sensitizing action of the foreign serum to cold, as well as a greater increase in lactic acid and a greater decrease of glycogen in the blood, muscles, and in the organs, under the effect of cold, than in the non-sensitized animals. It is assumed that these two latter studies indicate a parallergic reaction of the body to cold.

1531. Levkovich, L. I. The action of chemicals on the organism at various temperatures [In German]. *Usp. sovrem. biol., v. 26 (3), 1948: 801–818.*

Some of the factors discussed regarding the nature of the changes in pharmaco-dynamic reactions under the influence of temperature are: the changes in the sensitivity of the organism toward the given substance; the influence of the surrounding temperature on the substance through the body medium; the influence of the temperature upon the medication against bacterial or parasitic agents in the body in regard to medication; and the influence of temperature on the action of hormones. The changes induced in the organism by variations in environmental temperature depend on a series of conditions such as degree, duration, and rapidity of temperature change; the influence of the body covering (skin, hair, or clothing); the surrounding medium (air, water); meteorological factors (humidity, wind velocity); and the season of the year.

1532. Levkovich, L. I. The influence of external temperatures, diet, and motion on the pharmaceutical action of thallium [In English]. *Bull. biol. méd. exp. URSS, v. 5 (3), 1938: 271–273.*

The variations in the body's reaction to sublethal doses of thallium acetate or aluminate was studied in rabbits or sheep under conditions of high or low environmental temperature. Results in the first series of experiments, done chiefly with rabbits, showed that the keeping of the animals at various temperatures, or the local warming or cooling of separate parts of the skin, did not affect the process of experimental shedding of the hair induced by the action of thallium but that the resistance of the animals to this poison depended on the temperature. At a low temperature $(-3°C)$ death was observed less often, diarrhea did not occur, and the toxic process developed much more slowly and was less severe. The loss of weight, however, was greater than at 11° or 24°C. Following further experimentation, it was observed that the depilatory and toxic action of thallium were dissociated at various temperatures; the best correlation of both effects was obtained at low temperature.

1533. Macht, M. B., and M. E. Bader. Iontophoresis with acetyl-beta-methyl-choline and blood flow through the hand at low environmental temperatures. *J. Appl. Physiol., v. 1, Sept. 1948: 205–214.*

Using a specially constructed variable temperature plethysmograph, blood flow through the hand was studied before and after iontophoresis of acetyl-B-methylcholine chloride (Mecholyl, or ABMC). Blood flow through the hand which was curtailed by exposure to cold (10°C), was increased by iontophoresis of ABMC.

* **1534. Mirskiĭ, M. ÎA.** Temperature as a factor in the occurrence of caisson disease [In Russian]. *Gig. & san., Moskva, v. 12 (4), 1947: 35‒41.*

"*Contains* findings from work of the author and others: a too low temperature, as well as a high one, of the compressed air increases the possibility of occurrence of caisson disease ("the bends"). A relation between a definite pressure and a corresponding optimal temperature is established by the author, viz: up to 2 atm., 16°‒21°C.; 2.1‒2.5 atm., 17°‒22°C.; over 2.5 atm., 18°‒26°C. Conditions around foregoing temperature are also discussed."—Arctic Bibl., v. 4, 1954: 693.

1535. Mookerjee, G. C., and B. K. Ghose. Hematological response of Indian troops to moderate anoxia in extreme cold environment. *Indian J. M. Res., v. 39, Oct. 1951: 543‒552.*

The hematological response was studied of a group of Indian troops subjected to the cold and snow of a moderately high (6,800 and 12,000 feet above sea level) environment. The expected rise in the number of red blood cells was observed on the 10th day of acclimatization although the response was not well marked. The packed cell volume (P.C.V.) and the mean corpuscular volume (M.C.V.) showed higher values than are found in similar troops living on the plains. The rise in hemoglobin level was not significant until the 50th day of acclimatization. Due to unavoidable irregularity of supply, the animal-protein content of the diet was found to be below the optimum and the daily content varied considerably. Local civilians, living on the plains and acting as a control group, who ate a low-protein and high-carbohydrate diet did not show adequate response of the red cells and hemoglobin; their P.C.V. and M.C.V. values were also higher.

1536. More, R. H., and S. B. Kobernick. Observations on the role of the adrenal gland and on the pathogenesis of cardiac valvulitis, necrotizing arteritis, and glomerulonephritis produced in rabbits by foreign proteins: effect of ACTH, cortisone, and cold on the tissues [Abstract]. *Am. J. Path., v. 27, Apr. 1951: 708‒709.*

Rabbits, with their backs shaven and exposed continuously to temperatures of 0° to 20°C, were sensitized to foreign proteins by massive intravenuous injections of horse serum. Typical cardiac valvulitis, necrotizing arteritis, and glomerulonephritis occurred in both the group of rabbits kept in the cold room and in those kept at room temperature. At autopsy the adrenal glands were shown to be slightly increased in weight in the animals exposed to cold or given ACTH, and slightly decreased in those given cortisone.

1537. Nedzel, A. J. Toxicity of morphine sulfate in white mice under the influence of cold. *J. Aviat. M., v. 22, June 1951: 244‒247.*

Administration of morphine sulfate to mice at the peak of repeated exposures to cold (70°‒75°F reduced to 30°‒35°F over 3‒4 hour period; returned to 70°‒75°F over 6‒8 hour period) increased the toxicity of the morphine. However, exposure to the cold after subcutaneous injection of morphine sulfate delayed its action.

1538. Nielsen, M., W. H. Forbes, J. W. Wilson, and D. B. Dill. The effects upon dogs of low oxygen tensions combined with low temperatures. *In: Am. Institute of Physics. Temperature, its measurement and control in science and industry, p. 453‒461. New York, Reinhold, 1941.*

Dogs exposed to 6 per cent oxygen in a cold room showed inhibition of shivering and decrease in body temperature. When the animals were permitted to breath atmospheric air in the cold room, shivering began almost at once and body temperature rose. The ability of the dog to withstand low oxygen seems to depend on his tolerance of alkalosis, his accumulation of lactic acid, and the resistance of the brain to oxygen deprivation.

---

* Original not seen.

1539.   Phillips, N. E., P. A. Saxon, and F. H. Quimby. Humidity and tolerance to low barometric pressure. *Science, v. 106, July 18, 1947: 67.*

Young male mice (20–30 grams) were placed in a low-pressure chamber and submitted to various combinations of humidity and temperature (22°, 10°, 0°, −10°, or −20°C). At all temperatures used, air of 100 per cent humidity increased, in comparison to dry air, the tolerance of the mice to reduction of pressure. This effect was most noticeable at −10°C, at which temperature mice in dry air died at an average pressure of 418 mm Hg (15,500 ft simulated altitude). In air at 100 per cent humidity, at this temperature, death did not occur until the pressure was 180 mm Hg (35,000 ft).

1540.   Poppen, J. R. The effects of cold and high speed on the flyer. *Internat. Clin., v. 1, n.s. 5, 1942: 60–67.*

Aside from the dangers of frostbite and freezing which could be encountered at the very low temperatures prevailing at high altitudes, two complications not found at sea-level were noted in flying personnel. The lowered oxygen tension produced alterations in metabolism and heat control, and the lowered barometric pressure influenced heat loss. In cold dry air at sea level, 15% to 25% of the total heat production was dissipated through the lungs and respiratory passages; at high altitude the rapid respiration increased the heat loss, and the potential heat gain by oxygen consumption was decreased. Because of the lowered molecular concentrations at high altitudes, convection and conduction were decreased while radiation was increased. Insulation alone can in general preserve comfort in a resting state at temperatures no lower than 20°C; at lower temperatures additional heat must be supplied to the air surrounding the pilot in the cockpit or by heating the insulated clothing.

1541.   Pulewka, P., and D. Berkan. Influence of the environmental temperature on resorptive effects of Novocain and Tutocaine in mice [In Turkish, summaries in Turkish and German]. *Türk Ijien Tecrube Biol. Dergisi, v. 11 (2), 1951: 202–208.* Abstract, in English, in: *Biol. Abstr., v. 26, June 1952: ✳1106; Chem. Abstr., v. 47, 1953: ✳1853.*

The degree of mydriasis produced in mice following the injection of Novocain showed little change at environmental temperatures of 13°–22°C but was markedly decreased with rising environmental temperatures from 22° to 30°C. However, the maximum resorptive mydriatic effect was found to be independent of temperature. Variations in these findings from those of the earlier work of Sievers and McIntyre [J. Pharm., v. 59, 1937: 90] on variations of toxic doses of Novocain with changes in temperature, are discussed.

1542.   Raventós, J. The influence of room temperature on the action of barbiturates. *J. Pharm. Exp. Ther., v. 64, Dec. 1938: 355–363.*

Mice were half immersed in water baths of either 20° or 30°C for 2 or 3 hours before, and a considerable period of time after, being given intraperitoneal injections of either the short-acting barbiturate sodium Evipan, or the longer-acting barbiturate sodium, phenobarbitone [phenobarbital]. The duration of action of sodium Evipan was not greatly changed by a reduction of temperature to 30°C, but reduction to 20°C increased the duration 2½-fold. In the case of sodium Evipan the lethal action was the same at 30°C as at 20°C; for sodium phenobarbitone the LD_{50} at 20°C was only 69% of that at 30°C.

1543.   Robillard, E. Effect of temperature on survival time and O_2 consumption of the white rat submitted to low barometric pressure [Abstract, in French]. *Ann. Ass. canad. fr. advanc. sc., v. 15, 1949: 79.*

The resistance of the white rats to acute anoxia was found to be maximum at a temperature around 4°C, and the consumption of oxygen was diminished (hence producing more anoxia) as the environmental temperature was lowered. These effects are attributed to a sudden drop of the internal temperature of the animal.

1544. Schulze, W. Influence of smoking on peripheral circulation during local cooling [Abstract in German]. *Klin. Wschr., v. 24–25, Sept. 15, 1947: 738–742.*

The effect of tobacco smoking on peripheral blood pressure and on the peripheral temperature was studied. The temperature of a hand kept in a water bath maintained at room temperature showed a decline in temperature from 36° to 21 °C when tobacco smoke was inhaled by the subject. The temperature of a hand kept in the cold (−4°C) fell as much as 28 degrees after inhalation. Peripheral blood pressure increased at the same time from 40 to 80 mm Hg. Individual responses, however, varied considerably; five of twelve subjects tested showed no change in hand temperature following inhalation. Extreme cold and alcohol were shown to mask the vasconstrictor properties of nicotine.

1545. Streicher, E. Toxicity of colchicine, di-isopropyl fluorophosphate, Intocostrin, and potassium cyanide in mice at 4°C. *Proc. Soc. exp. Biol., N. Y., v. 76, Mar. 1951: 536–538.*

Toxicity of colchicine, di-isopropyl fluorophosphate, Intocostrin, and potassium cyanide injected subcutaneously in mice was found to be increased 33, 45, 76, and 110% respectively when the mice were kept in the cold (4°C) as compared to those kept at normal room temperature (23°–25°C). However, when mice were first acclimatized to the cold, there was no significant increase in toxicity in the mice kept in the cold room after injection of di-isopropyl fluorophosphate.

1546. Thérien, M. Influence of ascorbic acid on the variations in the amount of histamine in the tissues of guinea pigs exposed to cold [Abstract, in French]. *Rev. canad. biol., v. 8, Oct. 1949: 309.*

Two groups of guinea pigs were given, respectively, 2 or 25 milligrams of ascorbic acid per day while being exposed for three days to an environmental temperature of −1.5°C; two other groups were kept at normal room temperature. It was clearly indicated that the acid had lowered the concentration of histamine in the tissues of the adrenals and the kidneys of the guinea pigs exposed to cold, an effect opposite to that at normal room temperatures.

1547. Thérien, M., J. Le Blanc, O. Héroux, and L. P. Dugal. Effects of ascorbic acid on several biological variables normally affected by cold [Abstract, in French]. *Rev. canad. biol., v. 9, Apr. 1950: 96–97.*

It is stated that ascorbic acid given in large doses to rats or guinea pigs exposed to a cold environment: (1) partially inhibited the atrophy of the thymus which was very marked in the controls; (2) hastened the appearance of hypertrophy of the thyroid which showed in the controls at the time of the atrophy which was encountered habitually in the first stage of exposure to cold; (3) caused an increase in the weight of the spleen contrary to the findings in the control group; (4) decreased the concentration of histamine in the adrenals and the kidneys; (5) caused a very rapid decrease of cholesterol in the adrenals; (6) and diminished in a very significant manner the hypertension characteristic of the first hours or first days (depending on the conditions of the experiment) of exposure to cold.

1548. Tripi, H. B., G. M. Gardner, and W. C. Kuzell. Effects of temperature and ultraviolet light on experimental polyarthritis of rats. *Proc. Soc. Exp. Biol., N. Y., v. 70, Jan. 1949: 45–47.*

Experimental polyarthritis was produced in rats by the L₄ strain of pleuropneumonia-like organisms. It was found that exposure to cold in an out-of-door shelter (at a temperature ranging between 30°–84°F) or exposure to increased ultraviolet light caused increased mortality but resulted in a smaller incidence and severity (females only) of arthritis. Increased heat caused little deviation in mortality and arthritic involvement from the inoculated controls.

1549. Trumper, M., and G. J. Thompson. Prolonging the effects of penicillin by chilling. *J. Am. M. Ass., v. 130, Mar. 9, 1946: 627–630.*

Chilling of the deltoid muscle before and after injection of penicillin (ice bag around upper shoulder area 2 hours previous to injection and 12 hours after) resulted in prolonging the effective action of this drug so that the amount of penicillin required to successfully treat uncomplicated gonorrhea was drastically reduced.

1550. Tyler, D. B. Effect of body temperature and of pentobarbital on brain damage produced by insulin shock. *Proc. Soc. Exp. Biol., N. Y., v. 45, Oct. 1940: 117–119.*

At normal body temperature the brain damage during insulin shock was greater than when animals were cooled. When, during insulin shock, the body temperature of cats was not allowed to drop, either by use of a hot pad or by working at a room temperature of about 30 °C, there was a greater incidence and a greater degree of brain damage.

See also items: *487, 496, 544, 657, 1110, 1261, 1293, 1342, 1409, 1428, 2070, 2146, 2261.*

N. Clinical Use of Local Cold, General
(includes also basic studies on animals)

1551. Allen, F. M. Effects of ligations on nerves of the extremities. *Ann. Surg., v. 108, Dec. 1938: 1088–1093.*

In this article of the effect on nerves of the extremities of the ligation of those extremities, the author states that the experiments were all carried out at a comfortable room temperature. However, in earlier experiments he had found that the effects of asphyxia, including nerve degeneration, following ligation were progressively retarded by local cooling to a minimum close to 0 °C.

1552. Allen, F. M. Mechanical treatment of venomous bites and wounds. *South. M. J., v. 31, Dec. 1938: 1248–1253.*

Local refrigeration was found, experimentally, to extend the time of absorption of snake venom far beyond anything possible at ordinary temperature, up to a day or two if necessary. It also drastically inhibited the action of the proteolytic enzyme of the tissues.

1553. Allen, F. M. Experiments concerning ligation and refrigeration in relation to local intoxication and infection. *Surg. Gyn. Obst., v. 68, June 1939: 1047–1051.*

A solution of the poison, strychnine, many times the normal lethal dose could be injected into rabbits without harm if a tourniquet was immediately placed on the leg above the level of injection and the leg was immersed in ice water. Similar slowing down of the metabolic rate, with the resulting reduction of toxic absorption from injury or bacterial infection, occurs in the limb of a person which is cooled before a surgical operation.

1554. Allen, F. M. Reduced temperatures in surgery. III. Experiments on pelvic and abdominal refrigeration with especial reference to traumatic and military surgery. *Am. J. Surg., v. 55, Mar. 1942: 451–466.*

The lower part of the body of dogs was refrigerated in various manners with chipped ice and iced saline solutions in order to study the effect of refrigeration when added to an abdominal tourniquet. Refrigeration added considerably to the period of time the tourniquet could be used and gave excellent preservation of tissue vitality. The addition of low temperature greatly reduced shock, paraplegia, and enteritis, and helped to check infection and toxic absorption.

1555. Allen, F. M., and L. W. Crossman. Tourniquet and refrigeration in war injuries [Abstract]. *Bull. Am. Coll. Surgeons, v. 28, Feb. 1943: 53.*

A narrow rubber tourniquet was found experimentally to be well tolerated for 12 to 15 hours, and for 7 to 8 hours with clinical safety. The danger from temporary inflammation or paralysis is decreased by cooling to any degree short of freezing. Refrigeration without a tourniquet can check pain, infection, and necrosis for days or weeks in such conditions as embolism or gangrene. The authors recommend military trials of the use of this method for treatment of casualties at the front or in the nearest field hospitals.

1556.   Allen, F. M. Therapeutic uses of low temperature. *Heating Piping,* v. 17, Dec. 1945: 633–636.

It is said that while intense heat always kills, intense cold may either destroy or preserve life. Effects of cold are discussed briefly in relation to the whole organism, local parts, and isolated tissues. Because local temperatures can be far lower than those which can be applied safely to the body as a whole, greater beneficial effects can be obtained. Therapeutic use of local cold is discussed under the headings of surgical anesthesia, infection and intoxication, brief preservation after wounds, prolonged preservation after wounds, saving a limb, embolism, shock, injuries due to cold, burns, and in military surgery.

1557.   Allen, F. M. Therapeutic uses of low temperature. *Tr. Am. Soc. Heat. Ventil. Engin.,* v. 52, 1946: 123–130.

The therapeutic effects of cold on the whole organism, on local parts, and upon isolated tissues are discussed. The use of cold in the treatment of immersion foot is also discussed.

1558.   Allen, F. M. Uses of cold in medicine and surgery. *Clinics, v. 4, Apr. 1946:* 1642–1674.

Section A, Effects of cold upon the entire organism, discusses time factors of survival. Section B, Effects of cold on local tissues, considers the physiology of tissue death from freezing, and the vasomotor effects of low temperatures. Section C, Effects of cold on isolated parts, notes that somewhat isolated parts are freer from the overtaxed defense reactions of the general organism and thus exhibit some greater capacity for resistance to cold. Also discussed are the therapeutic uses of cold such as refrigeration anesthesia combined with tourniquet. Other uses of refrigeration include refrigeration anesthesia without tourniquet; arrest of necrosis and infection; prevention of thrombosis and embolism; relief of trauma; treatment of injuries due to cold or burns; treatment of shock; and military and miscellaneous uses of refrigeration.

1559.   Allen, F. M., and F. K. Safford, Jr. Experiments on local hypothermia for treatment of burns and frostbite. *Arch. Surg., v. 61, Sept. 1950: 515–523.*

The physiological action of cold with reference to its effects on pain, shock, bacterial activity, tissue devitalization, and absorption of toxic substances, is discussed. The value of local hypothermia in frostbite therapy was tested on rats, and on dogs and cats, and found to be uniformly injurious.

1560.   Allen, F. M. Thermal and fluid therapy of atomic bombing injuries [In English, summaries in English, French, Italian, and German]. *J. Internat. Coll. Surgeons, v. 15, Feb. 1951: 201–211.*

Evidence is reviewed for the important uses of treatment by reduced temperature in radiation, and in mechanical and thermal injuries due to an atomic explosion. Outside the central zone of annihilation, a populated area should have some remaining sources of refrigeration, stocks of ice or cold water, or snow if the blast occurs during the winter. Cold is unique in inhibiting simultaneously pain, exudation, thrombosis, shock, infection, toxic absorption, and tissue devitalization. Local treatment of radiation injury has been stated to consist of routine burn therapy with accessory cooling, and possibly elevation of an extremity. Refrigeration may have a special place in saving life, or the vitality of tissues, until surgical operation is possible.

1561.   [Ar'ev, T. IA.] Arieff, T. J. Reparation of wounds exposed to cold air; experimental study [In French]. *Lyon chir., v. 35, Mar.-Apr. 1938: 154–177.*

Observations of chilled wounds showed that regenerative capacity was weakened under cold conditions. Necrosis was noted in wounds at temperatures of $-40\,°C$ and below, and edema of tissues surrounding the wound was remarked when the temperature was lowered to $0\,°C$. Wounds rendered inactive by cold were found to afford favorable conditions for the development of infections, especially since most pathogenic microorganisms are not sensitive to cold.

1562. Austin, D. W. Applications of cold therapy in dermatological and traumatized areas. *J. Nat. Ass. Chiropod.*, v. 33 (9), 1943: 13–16.

The author discusses the therapeutic use of cold on three levels of cooling: freezing, or reducing temperature to 15–$20\,°F$; chilling, down to $40\,°F$; and cooling, down to $59\,°F$. Contrary to the use of radiant heat—where the increased circulation helps dissipate the heat—the longer the cold is applied to the area, the deeper the penetration of cold becomes. The author discusses the various methods for use of cold to control infection; reduce edema; allay pain or soreness; and to provide anesthesia, especially of a local area.

1563. Badaro, H. Applications and technic of refrigeration anaesthesia [In French]. *Rev. méd. Moyen Orient*, v. 5, Jan.-Mar. 1948: 74–80.

The use of cold is discussed in therapy or in prevention of traumatic shock; as a method of anesthesia; to reduce toxic absorption in an infection; as a temporizing measure to obtain time necessary for better pre-operative preparation of the patient; in treatment of burns or cold injuries; in treatment of venomous bites or stings; in the conservation of tissue grafts; and in treatment of malignant growths. These uses of cold are based on the physiological response of tissues to cold which brings about a reduced metabolism of the area treated, lessening the demand for nutrient material and oxygen, slowing the local capillary circulation, and decreasing the absorption of toxic materials.

1564. Baxter, H., and R. H. More. The effect of the local reduction of temperature on scald burns in the rat. *Am. Surg.*, v. 125, Feb. 1947: 177–193.

Experiments on the effect of locally applied cold on scald burns of the tails of rats indicated that hypothermic therapy was definitely harmful. The authors believe that disturbances in the circulation and interference with vasomotor controls are important elements in the deleterious effects of cold.

1565. Blalock, A. Effects of lowering temperature of an injured extremity to which a tourniquet has been applied. *Arch. Surg.*, v. 46, Feb. 1943: 167–170.

Previous experiments had shown that when a tourniquet was applied for 5 hours to an experimentally injured extremity, the period of survival of the dogs was drastically shorter (14 hours) than in similarly injured animals in which no tourniquet was used. With the use of the tourniquet the majority of the dogs recovered and all periods of survival were of much greater duration (4 and 12 days). In the current experiments it was found that the harmful effects of the tourniquet in such a situation were lessened (resulting in survival of 5 of the 10 animals), if the temperature of the part distal to the constriction was lowered by surrounding the area of the extremity with ice for an 11-hour period. However, the authors advise that the use of the tourniquet in such injuries be avoided whenever possible.

1566. Bowers, W. F. Refrigeration therapy in vascular trauma. *Mil. Surgeon*, v. 93, 1943: 289–294.

The use of refrigeration, rather than the earlier practice of using heat, in the treatment of peripheral trauma and impending gangrene is discussed and case histories of four military personnel are cited. Refrigeration decreases metabolic needs so that a damaged circulation may be adequate. In cases of vascular impairment, elevation of an injured lower extremity should be employed with caution. Refrigeration aids bacteriostasis during a period of evacuation or while getting the patient in suitable condition for operation; it can also give sufficient anesthesia to permit of debridement or amputation.

1567. Brooks, B., and G. W. Duncan. The influence of temperature on wounds. *Ann. Surg.*, v. 114, Dec. 1941: 1069–1075.

Experiments to determine the influence of temperature on the reaction of living tissues to injury, are reported. Observations were made on the effects of hot and cold applications on aseptic necrotic wounds and on wounds infected with *Staphylococcus aureus* in experimental dogs. The experiments demonstrated that the temperature does exert an influence on the development of inflammation and on the post mortem changes in necrotic tissue. Changes in temperature also had a marked effect on infected lesions. The authors suggest that it may be doubtful wisdom to inhibit an inflammatory reaction by the application of cold or to apply heat in cases of surgical shock.

1568. Brown, H. R., and V. DeLalla. The use of a cold room in treatment of hyperexia and burns. *Arch. Phys. M., v. 30, Feb. 1949: 98–102.*

A patient with 50% of his body area burned and with pressure bandages over 85% of his total surface area, during a period of summer heat above 90°F, developed an extreme elevation of body temperature (up to 106°F). The patient was placed in a cold room (68°F) and within 90 minutes his temperature and pulse returned to normal. Body temperature was maintained below 101°F during the 3½ days the patient remained in the cold room.

1569. Bruneau, J., and P. Heinbecker. Effects of cooling on experimentally infected tissues. *Am. Surg., v. 120, Nov. 1944: 716–726.*

Effects of local cooling on infected subcutaneous tissues in mongrel dogs were studied. *Streptococcus hemolyticus* was the infecting organism. Results suggest that prolonged refrigeration may prove harmful to tissues.

1570. Crossman, L. W. Refrigeration for the preservation of traumatized tissues. *Canad. Hosp., v. 21, Aug. 1944: 30–32.*

The author reviews some of his own experiences, and those of others, with the use of cold to preserve damaged tissues. Badly mutilated tissues and those injured by burns and frostbite are among the injuries suggested for treatment by refrigeration. The author mentions the debridement, under refrigerated conditions, of a badly infected and neglected burned area.

1571. Crossman, L. W. Refrigeration for crushed finger. *J. Am. M. Ass., v. 130, Mar. 9, 1946: 667.*

The author cites two cases in which digits of the hand, which had been almost completely severed, were saved by chilling before and following suturing. He points out that cold preserves tissues by reducing metabolism and by greatly minimizing the circulatory needs of the area.

1572. Crossman, L. W. The uses of refrigeration in surgery [In English, summaries in English, French, German, Italian, and Spanish]. *J. Internat. Coll. Surgeons, v. 15, Jan. 1951: 76–84.*

The use of refrigeration of localized areas is discussed in such situations as amputations; orthopedic and reconstructive operations on extremities; fractures; delayed surgical operation; fulminating limb infections; shock; and in frostbite, trench foot, and burns. Such cooling of tissues is valuable because of its unique power to control simultaneously pain, shock, exudation, infection, tissue devitalization, and retardation of toxic adsorption. New applications of refrigeration are in the field of the treatment of burns, and for certain new developments in surgery.

1573. Devine, J. Temperature in shock. I. Local effects. *Med. J. Australia, v. 30, Dec. 11, 1943: 476–479.*

One hind leg of each of a group of anesthetized dogs was severely injured by crushing blows from a mallet below the level of a tourniquet, and the leg kept for 20 minutes in a water bath at 50°C. This procedure is known to produce shock when the tourniquet is released. After release of the tourniquet some of the injured legs were kept in a 50°C water bath while others were kept at 8°C. When the average temperature of the water bath was 52°C, the increase of the limb volume was 17% and two of the dogs died within 100 minutes. When the bath was 8°C, the average limb volume increase was 5%, and no dog died within the 100-minute period.

1574. Doane, J. C., and H. D. Stein. Refrigeration in medicine and surgery [In English, summaries in English, French, German, Spanish, Italian, and Portuguese]. *J. Internat. Coll. Surgeons., v. 16, Sept. 1951: 346–349.*

Local use of cold, by application of ice packs or use of a specially designed blanket, is discussed in cases of hyperexia and/or severe pain following hemorrhages, head injuries, surgical operations, in pneumonia or typhoid crisis, in acute pleurisy, or for severe migraine headaches. Some of the uses of cold as an anesthetic, other than in amputation of extremities, are during incision and drainage of infections, debridement of ulcers, reduction of fractures, treatment of burned areas, and after a severe strain or sprain. Limited experience has been obtained recently by the author on the use of refrigeration associated with sympathetic block in treatment of certain peripheral vascular conditions.

1575. Ebin, J. The solid carbon dioxide-ferric chloride technic for hemostasis. *Arch. Surg., v. 46, Mar. 1943: 386.*

Blocks of solid carbon dioxide applied with moderate pressure to a severely bleeding area of the brain, viscera, or superior saggital sinus, were effective experimentally in stopping the blood flow temporarily while a chemical coagulant (ferric chloride) was applied. The damage done by the procedure was negligible. The author discusses its possible use on human beings, especially in war surgery.

1576. Elman, R., W. M. Cox, Jr., C. Lischer, and A. J. Mueller. Mortality in severe experimental burns as affected by environmental temperature. *Proc. Soc. Exp. Biol., N. Y., v. 51, Dec. 1942: 350–351.*

Rats were experimentally burned and then kept at environmental temperatures of 32°, 55°, 75°, and 99°F. Mortality, within the first 24 hours, was lowest (32%) at 75°F and was increased at the higher temperature (100%) or the lower two temperatures (82% to 100%).

1577. Eltorm, H. Experimental studies on the susceptibility of certain mouse tumors to lowered temperature in vivo compared with the susceptibility of normal mouse tissue [In English]. *Copenhagen, E. Munksgaard, 1946. 149 p.*

In experiments to determine the effectiveness of treating tumors in mice with low temperatures, both generalized and localized cold was used. Data on the effects of cold upon normal tissues are also included. 111 refs.

1578. Entin, M. A., H. Baxter, and R. H. More. Experimental and clinical studies of reduced temperatures in injury and repair in man. II. Effect of moderate cold and referigeration on wound healing and regeneration of human skin. *Plastic & Reconstr. Surg., v. 3, Jan. 1948: 11–33.*

Areas from which a uniform layer of skin had been removed were studied in experiments designed to investigate the effects of cold on wound healing. At 65° to 53°F, epithelialization was found to be delayed in proportion to the degree of cold and the duration of exposure. Fibrous tissue formation appeared to be increased, at least for the first few weeks after cooling. Optimum temperature for healing was found to be between 70° and 80°F.

1579. Fay, T. Human refrigeration. *Q. Rev. N. Y. City Cancer Com., v. 4, Jan. 1940: 68–73.*

Although normal body temperature is thought of in terms of oral temperature, which is usually 98.6°F, skin temperature below the elbows and knees was found to be as much as 10° to 22°F lower than the mouth temperature and the skin temperature of the breast area 0.5° to 3.0°F higher than adjacent skin temperatures. Deep internal temperatures ranged around 100°F. Local application of cold was found to bring prompt and dramatic relief of pain; general refrigeration usually brought relief after 24 hours. In more than 100 cases studied, continuous local application of cold selectively destroyed or arrested the growth of cancer cells without injury to normal cells, even for periods as long as 5 months at temperatures of 40° to 50°F. Following studies of general refrigeration—in some cases of which the whole body was cooled to a rectal temperature of 90°F—it would appear that the limit to which the whole body could be reduced in temperature, and the person rewarmed without injury, would lie in the zone of 70° to 75°F.

1580. Fralick, E. H. Hypothermia in military practice. *Med. Clin. N. America,* *v. 27, July 1943: 1166–1177.*

Hypothermia is defined by the author as the "local or systemic application of cold." The therapeutic uses of cold applied locally, with special reference to use in military injuries, are discussed. Treatment of immersion foot, trench foot, and frostbite with local cold is noted. In military casualties refrigeration, if it were to be made available, might well render invaluable service in the treatment of a mangled extremity when the patient might need to wait hours, or be transported miles, for treatment. Some of the disadvantages of its use in military situations are that ice or some cooling mechanism is not apt to be available in a military emergency; many, not just occasional, casualties arise; the need for nursing care is increased; and the slower rate of healing would prolong the period of hospitalization.

1581. Freeman, N. E. Influence of temperature on the development of gangrene in peripheral vascular disease. *Arch. Surg., v. 40, Feb. 1940: 326–333.*

Gangrene results from a discrepancy between the nutritional needs of the tissues and the ability of the circulation to supply those needs. Investigations on the effect of temperature on the blood flow through sympathectomized extremities have shown that the circulation is conditioned by the metabolic needs of the tissues, and that tissue metabolism is increased with temperature. In view of these findings it is suggested that the air temperature about the foot of a patient, with an impaired circulation in the foot, should be kept no higher than 30°C (86°F). If a gangrenous situation exists, or is impending, the temperature should be lowered.

1582. G., V. Therapeutic applications of refrigeration [In French]. *Progr. méd.,* *Par., v. 76, Feb. 24, 1948: 87.*

Considerable review is given of experimental work with cold, and of the good results obtained by earlier workers using either local or general cooling of the patient. Cold was found to prevent shock, to decrease or prevent pain, prevent or limit the development of gangrene, and limit the spread of an infection.

1583. Goldfeder, A. *Cancer Res., v. 1, Mar. 1941: 220–226.*

Mice bearing tumors (Crocker mouse sarcoma 180) 8 to 10 days after inoculation were exposed to environmental temperatures of 5° to 7°C either intermittently or continuously for 8, 24, or occasionally 48 hours. Of the 95 mice in the group, tumors disappeared in 5; in other mice a small decrease or transitory arrest in growth occurred. Tumors of larger size (16–18 days following inoculation) did not change in size or they ulcerated during refrigeration. Studies of respiration and aerobic glycolysis of excised tumor or of kidney tissue showed no appreciable effect of low environmental temperatures. It is concluded that on the basis of the high mortality rate of the mice from the cold, the comparatively few successful results, and the unaffected viability of tumor cells, the inadequacy of the use of refrigeration in the treatment of malignant growths is indicated.

1584. Hansen, O. E., and L. Kreyberg. The effect of ice water upon the development of skin lesions due to mustard gas in rabbits [In English]. *Acta. path.* *microb. scand., v. 29 (3), 1951: 468–472.*

Cooling caused a reduction of the damage to the skin of rabbits after local application of a 2% solution of mustard gas. The reduction was most pronounced when the exposed area was in direct contact with the ice water.

1585. Herrmann, J. B. Low temperature therapy of malignancy. *Connecticut* *M. J., v. 5, Oct. 1941: 721–726.*

The low-temperature therapy of malignancy, with special reference to physiological effects of cold, is discussed.

1586. Hildenbrand, E. J. C. Refrigeration in surgery [In English, summaries in English, French, Italian, Spanish, and Russian]. *J. Internat. Coll. Surgeons, v. 10, July–Aug. 1947: 385–389, 393.*

Both experimental and clinical uses of cold, for anesthesia and for therapy, are reviewed. Immediate application of cold in contusions and sprains relieves pain and, by vasconstriction, helps prevent hemorrhage and edema by limiting extravasation of blood and lymph to the tissues. Cold should only be used in an early state of acute inflammation and congestion, before much exudation has taken place, to help prevent that condition by constricting the blood vessels of the hyperemic area. If cold is too intense or is kept on too long or used too late in an inflammation, it may do harm by decreasing the nutritive activity of the cells, constricting lymph channels and spaces, and increasing existing stasis, thus increasing the possibilities of devitalization of tissues and development of gangrene. Use of cold in control of pain is noted, as in cold in treatment of damage due to cold. 93 refs.

1587. Kanaar, A. G. Refrigeration in the treatment of trauma, with review of crymotherapy. *Current Res. Anesth., v. 25, Sept–Oct. 1946; Nov–Dec. 1946: 177–190; 228–241.*

The author gives a summary of the literature on the use of cold as a therapeutic agent. He also gives a detailed case history of the return to nearly normal functioning of the almost-completely-severed thumb of a sailor by reducing the metabolism of the thumb to a minimum—by refrigeration with ice water—pending the development of a collateral circulation. 77 refs.

1588. Kross, I. Low temperature therapy for preservation of limbs. *J. Am. M. Ass., v. 128, May 5, 1945: 19–20.*

A case history is reported in detail in which the severely infected leg of a patient was exposed to refrigeration therapy continuously for 89 days. With this treatment there was recovery of the patient and successful preservation of the limb which under ordinary circumstances would have been amputated. The case is cited by the author both because of the lengthy period of treatment with cold and also to show the need of continuation of treatment until the infection is fully and completely overcome.

1589. Krusen, F. H. Local and general application of cold. *In: Oxford Medicine, v. 1, part II, Chapt. XXI, p. 785–792. Ed. by H. A.* CHRISTIAN. *New York, Oxford University Press, 1940.*

In this section of Chapter XXI, Physical medicine, it is said that while studies in a few cases have indicated that prolonged general application of cold affects apparent modifications in cancer cells, the number of cases is meager and this use of cold has not been established as yet as a rational therapeutic procedure. Cooling of the surface of the body without compensation produces many systemic changes: constriction of peripheral vessels with associated peripheral stasis and anoxemia; lowered leukocytic responses; impairment of fixed phagocytic cells; delay in processes of immunity; decrease of local blood volume and of local metabolic activity. Application of cold to the abdomen tends to cause a temporary increase in peristalsis, then a decrease. Hypersensitivity to cold, manifested both locally and systemically, suggests that a substance with histamine-like reaction is produced following exposure to cold. Peripheral vasoconstriction caused by local application of cold is balanced by opposite changes in the remaining vessels, particularly the splanchnic or other deep vessels. Vasodilatation caused by extreme cold was shown to occur only when the temperature of the skin was less than 64.4 °F (18 °C); the reflex producing such dilatation is probably akin to a mild inflammatory reaction, and may protect the peripheral region from injury. Experiments with animals and observations on people under cold "hibernation" indicated a decided increase in circulation time. Circulation, in the latter group, increased approximately 5% for each 1 °F that the rectal temperature decreased. Chief among the indications for local application of cold, are traumatic lesions, inflammations, and congestions. In general, local cold produces vasoconstriction and relief of pain. Local application to the abdomen produces little, if any, change in the temperature of the underlying viscera.

1590. Krusen, F. H. Physical medicine; the employment of physical agents for diagnosis and therapy. *Philadelphia, Saunders, 1941. 846 p.*

Included in Chapter 4, Local and general applications of cold (p. 166–175), are sections on the physics of cold; physiological effects of cold; desensitization of patients hypersensitive to cold; use of cold pressor tests; and indications or contraindications for the use of cold therapy.

1591. Langohr, J. L., L. Rosenfeld, C. R. Owen, and O. Cope. Effect of therapeutic cold on the circulation of blood and lymph in thermal burns. *Arch. Surg., v. 59, Nov. 1949: 1031–1044.*

Immersion of the experimentally-burned foot of a dog in a cold water (10°C) bath did not alter the pattern of arterial blood flow in that foot until its removal from the cold bath. The pattern of lymph flow, however, was strikingly altered only during the period of immersion. After removal of the foot from the bath, the blood flow in the injured foot rose immediately, but no striking or consistent change occurred in the uninjured one, indicating that the rise in blood flow in the injured foot was the result of a reflex locally governed. No consistent changes in blood pressure were noted throughout the procedures. The limitations of the use of cold in the therapy of burns are analyzed and discussed.

1592. Langohr, J. L. Some observations on the effect of therapeutic heat and cold in experimental thermal injuries. *Bull. Alexander Blain Hosp., v. 9, Mar. 4, 1950: 66–67.*

Although the application of cold to a burn wound diminishes the rate of edema formation and therefore the rate of loss of plasma volume, it is not necessarily true that cold is a treatment of choice for the burned patient. Cold may retard development of infection and diminish damage due to impaired circulation, but it also may reduce the rate of the healing processes and may of itself cause tissue damage. The disorders of arterial and lymphatic circulation induced by experimental frostbite are noted as being strikingly similar to those found following a hot water burn. It is felt that the use of cold for the temporary alleviation of the pain of burns of small extent might be extremely useful but that it would be wise to so limit the use of cold until more is known of the critical temperature and period of exposure.

1593. Large, A., and P. Heinbecker. The effect of cooling on wound healing. *Am. Surg., v. 120, Nov. 1944: 727–741.*

The nature of the healing process in clean incised wounds of the chilled forelegs of dogs was studied. No effects appeared during the cooling period, but a definite delay in healing was observed after removal of the cold. In a second group of dogs, chilled for 24–48 hours and then subjected to secondary suture, there was a greater incidence of infection. Relative ischemia of the cooled part is held to be a basic cause.

1594. McCravey, A. The treatment of tumors of the bladder by refrigeration. *N. York State J. M., v. 40, Oct. 1, 1940: 1435–1440.*

Control of severe pain was adequately maintained by local refrigeration (circulation of cold water of 40°F through an applicator) through a surgical opening in the lower abdominal wall, for a period of 43–133 days, in 3 patients with terminal states of carcinoma of the bladder and in a similarly afflicted fourth patient by use of a combination of local and general refrigeration (body temperature of 90°F). Death occurred in two patients following ascending infection resulting in pyelonephrosis but in the other two patients there was no gross or microscopic evidence of tumor inside the bladder as shown by biopsy material.

1595. McElvenny, R. T. The effect of cooling traumatized and potentially infected limbs. *Surg. Gyn. Obst., v. 73, Aug. 1941: 263–264.*

The author cites his own experience in saving the life of a 50-year-old man, both of whose legs had been traumatically amputated in a train accident, by enclosing the leg stumps in ice and giving him various sulfa drugs until his condition warranted a surgical amputation. The cooling appeared to stop the local pain, to aid in combatting shock, and to stop all odors emanating from the stumps. The author suggests the similar use of ice in holding infections in abeyance—in hopelessly traumatized limbs or parts—in those civil or military cases in which surgical aid is not immediately possible either because of the poor condition of the patient or the remoteness of the locale.

1596. Mignard, O. C. Indications for the use of refrigeration in surgery [In French]. (*University of Lyon, Faculty of Medicine and Pharmacy. Thesis No. 55, 1949.*) *Lyon, Bosc Frères, 1949. 72 p.*

Refrigeration provides excellent pre-operative treatment, as well as anesthesia during the surgery, in amputation of limbs especially of patients with arteritis and gangrene of the extremity who are in poor physical condition. Use of local cold becomes an important adjuvant in the immediate treatment of a frozen hand or foot. It is also useful in treatment of burns, of certain chronic suppurative conditions, of severe trauma of an extremity, and in skin grafting and certain orthopedic surgery procedures. Cold acts to suppress pain, limit infection, decrease toxic absorption, and—by reducing the tissue metabolism—to aid in the development of collateral circulation.

1597. Seifert, E. Caution!: Beware of the thoughtless and purposeless application of the ice bag [In German]. *Münch. med. Wschr., v. 93, May 4, 1951: 925–930.*

The author warns of the indiscriminate use of the ice bag, fully realizing that many standard treatment procedures call for the application of cold. Use of the ice bag may interfere with the making of the correct diagnosis, and should not be considered until the diagnosis is definite. In inflammation and in bleeding of the abdomen or stomach, the ice bag may cause further harm by retarding pyloric or peristaltic action, or by slowing down circulation in the area and giving a false sense of security while a slow, but severe, hemorrhage is actually taking place.

1598. Sellers, E. A., and J. W. Willard. The effect of plaster bandages and local cooling on haemoconcentration and mortality rate in burns. *Canad. M. Ass. J., v. 49, Dec. 1943: 461–464.*

When the experimentally-burned extremities of dogs were immediately suspended in double-walled sleevings through which cold water (8°C) was circulated for 48 hours, the combined cooling, elevation, and slight pressure from the water appreciably reduced the hemoconcentration and also reduced the mortality rate. The immediate application of plaster bandages to similar burns also resulted in a decided decrease in mortality.

1599. Sequeira, J. H., J. T. Ingram, and R. Brain. Diseases of the skin. 5th edit. *London, Churchill, 1947. 782 p.*

In a section entitled Dermatoses due to cold (p. 301–305), there is a short discussion of the local use of intense cold in the treatment of naevi and warts; information on frostbite; trench foot, immersion foot, shelter foot; either acute (erythematous) or chronic (acrocyanosis and erythrocyanosis crurum) chilblains; livedo reticularis and livedo annularis; and dermatitis hiemalis. In trench foot, immersion foot, or shelter foot the patient is to be removed to the hospital bed, the feet are elevated and kept cool by ventilation in the air or use of cold compresses. Dusting with salicylic acid or boric powders or painting with a 1% gentian violet solution is recommended. It is said that no best treatment for chilblains exists since erythema pernio is the outward sign of the inability of the skin, including its small blood vessels, to adapt itself to low temperatures.

1600. Solente, G. Advantages of cryotherapy; its present role in skin therapy [In French]. *Gaz. méd. France, v. 58, Nov. 1951: 1255–1258.*

Therapeutic use is made of brief and localized freezing of small areas of cutaneous or mucous tissue. The use of cryotherapy is discussed in treatment of small tuberous angiomas and lymphangiomas, or stellar naevi; various facial erythroses; cheloids, cicatrices, and sclerodermas; some skin cancers and precancerous growths; some piliary and pigmentation disorders; various erythematous conditions; and in the obliteration of small superficial blood vessels. Results from cryotherapy compare very favorably with those from other procedures which are much more complicated, more difficult to use, and more dangerous. Cryotherapy, therefore, merits a role of greater importance than is generally attributed to it.

See also items: 115, 120, 800, 1055, 1072, 1082, 1089, 1091, 1094, 1097, 1107, 1109, 1200, 1205, 1233, 1268, 1396, 1671, 1675, 1790, 2011, 2256, 2731.

O. Clinical Use of Local Cold, for Anesthesia, Analgesia, and Surgery

1601. Anon. *In: The 1943 Yearbook of General Surgery, p. 30–33.* Ed. by E. A. GRAHAM. *Chicago, Year Book Publishers, 1943.*

Anesthesia by use of refrigeration methods is said to abolish nerve impulses in the area refrigerated and to greatly reduce metabolic activity; shock in the patient is usually non-existent; pain is practically eliminated; edema is effectively checked; thrombosis and embolism are avoided; and infection is controlled or avoided.

1602. Anon. Refrigeration (crymo-) anesthesia. *J. Am. M. Ass., v. 122, May 1, 1943: 40–41.*

The maintenance of life processes at a reduced rate by lowering of the body temperature, is discussed. Oxygen consumption of the tissues can be reduced about 13% for each degree Centigrade of reduction of body temperature. Packing of an extremity in chipped ice, together with the use of a tourniquet, brings about a reduction of the oxygen demands sufficiently to prevent any necrosis of the extremity for several hours. The skin temperature of the area will fall to 2°–4°C and a state of anesthesia sufficient for surgical purposes, will be complete in about 2 hours.

1603. Alberto, F. Cold anesthesia with ice in amputation of extremities; 6 cases [In Italian]. *Chir. ital., v. 3, Mar.–June 1949: 153–161.*

Amputation of extremities using ice anesthesia is discussed with 6 typical cases being cited. The continuing low metabolism of the tissues of the area after the amputation helps to slow down the absorption of any toxic substances from tissue injuries.

1604. Allen, F. M. Reduced temperatures in surgery. I. Surgery of limbs. *Am. J. Surg., v. 52, n.s., May 1941: 225–237.*

In earlier experimental studies made on tissues deprived of all blood supply by the use of a tourniquet, it had been shown that the modification of metabolism by temperature was such that survival time was lengthened from a few hours at high temperatures to 54 hours at reduced temperatures. No blood clots and no tissue damage resulted, and nerve injuries were reduced. Clinical methods in the application of ice refrigeration for surgical anesthesia are discussed in some detail. Because healing is somewhat delayed by the cold, an early but gradual raising of the temperature of the amputated stump is advised. Thrombosis and after-shock following surgery are greatly reduced by using ice refrigeration. The uses of refrigeration in war wounds is discussed.

1605. Allen, F. M., L. W. Crossman, V. Hurley, E. C. Warden, and W. F. Ruggiero. Refrigeration anesthesia [In English, summaries in English, French, and Spanish]. *J. Internat. Coll. Surgeons, v. 5, Mar.–Apr. 1942: 125–131.*

A series of amputations for gangrene, using refrigeration anesthesia and a tourniquet, are discussed. The operation can be performed in a blood-less field and the patient is without shock, experiences no pain, and has little likelihood of infection.

1606. Allen, F. M. Refrigeration anesthesia for limb operations. *Anesthesiology,* v. 4, Jan. 1945: 12–16.

Refrigeration anesthesia differs fundamentally from other anesthesia in greatly lowering all the activities of the protoplasm rather than abolishing just the functioning of the nerves. Its role in prevention of shock and its usefulness in control or prevention of pain, edema, thrombosis, infection, and loss of tissue vitality, are discussed.

1607. Allen, F. M. Refrigeration in general surgery of limbs. *Am. J. Surg.,* v. 68, n.s., May 1945: 170–184.

The principal surgical uses of refrigeration anesthesia are reviewed. Included is material on the general physiological effects of lowered body temperature with respect to infection, pain, shock, and vasomotor effects. One section deals with "Cold in treatment of lesions due to cold," including frostbite and immersion foot.

1608. Amorth, G. The use of cold in surgery of the joints [In Italian]. *Minerva chir., Tor.,* v. 4, Jan. 15, 1949: 45–47.

The author discusses the use of cold for anesthesia in joint surgery and for therapy in severe joint injuries. He mentions also the role of cold in control of infection; reduction of tissue asphyxia and, therefore, reduction of loss of tissue; suppression of pain; arrest of shock; and reduction of toxic absorption.

1609. Bancroft, F. W., A. G. Fuller, and W. F. Ruggiero. Improved methods in extremity amputations for diabetic gangrene. *Ann. Surg.,* v. 115, April 1942: 621–627.

The authors discuss in detail the procedures and techniques involved in a series of leg amputations in an aged and poor-risk group of patients, using refrigeration anesthesia. These patients had an absence of post-operative shock and there was no formation of thrombi. The cold seemed to have an inhibitory effect upon growth of bacteria in the tissues. In patients with severe diabetes, the diabetic status was not made worse.

1610. Batalha, E. Refrigeration in orthopedic and traumatic surgery [In Portugese, summaries in Portugese and English]. *Rev. Hosp. clin., S. Paulo,* v. 1, 1946: 48–74. Abstract, in English, in: *Internat. Abstr. Surg.,* v. 83, 1946: 499.

The author states that refrigeration anesthesia is especially valuable for use with patients who are in shock or who present grave organic conditions because, in addition to not aggravating the symptoms, the reduced metabolic state allows a delay in the operation until the patient's condition is improved.

1611. Baumann, J. Amputation of the thigh under refrigeration anesthesia (Allen's method) [In French]. *Mém. Acad. chir., Par.,* v. 73, June 25–July 9, 1947: 490–495.

The use of refrigeration anesthesia in an operation for amputation of a thigh is discussed. Anesthesia from cold by acting directly on the nervous tissue and by general lowering of metabolic activity, eliminates the need of the body to combat a foreign and somewhat toxic substance. Use of refrigeration is said to produce an anesthesia without either toxic effect or development of shock.

1612. Baumann, J. Local refrigeration anesthesia with delayed action (Allen method) [In French]. *Rev. Med. fr.,* v. 29, Jan. 1948: 8–14.

The use of local area refrigeration according to the method of Allen, is discussed both as a method of anesthesia and as a method of temporization to allow a period of waiting while a severe intoxication or infection is controlled and the patient's general state is built up. The latter situation applies especially to the elderly cardiac or diabetic patient in poor physical condition who is confronted with the need for amputation of a limb. Various instances of these uses of local cold are quoted from the literature.

1613.   Bickel, M. G. Utilization of cold as therapy [In French]. *Rev. méd. Suisse rom., v. 67, 1947: 266.*

After a short discussion of the response of various organisms to cold—in which he states that human tolerance to cold appears to be in the range of 20° to 23 °C body temperature— the author discusses the use of ice for anesthesia especially in the amputation of limbs of persons who are otherwise poor surgical risks.

1614.   Bird, H. M. James Arnott, M.D. (Aberdeen), *1797–1883*; a pioneer in refrigeration analgesia. *Anesthesiology, v. 4, 1943: 10–17.*

Information is given on the writings, and the unsuccessful attempts, of Dr. James Arnott to win recognition of his pioneering work on use of benumbing cold for anesthesia and analgesia.

1615.   Carter, R., and F. B. Moor. Refrigeration anesthesia. A review. *Arch. Phys. M., v. 28, Nov. 1947: 712–722.*

The literature on refrigeration anesthesia is reviewed. In addition to the use of cold as a pre-operative anesthetic and its use in gangrene conditions and in tumor therapy, the author discusses its use in the treatment of immersion foot and frostbite.

1616.   Cayford, E. H., and H. G. Pretty. Refrigeration anesthesia and evaluation of amputation sites by arteriogram. *Ann. Surg., v. 121, Feb. 1945: 157–163.* Abstract in: *Internat. Abstr. Surg., v. 121, 1945: 157.*

Use of refrigeration anesthesia (skin temperature about 5 °C) brings about a general local depression of tissue activity rather than a selective action on the nerve tissue alone; a mild analgesia over the local area; no disturbance of digestive functions; no symptoms of shock; and when the tourniquet is dispensed with, no interference with early healing of the amputation stump. Arteriograms are of great aid by visualizing the state of the blood vessels, in determining the amputation site.

1617.   Cook, B. A. Experiences with refrigeration anaesthesia in general practice. *Med. J. Australia, 1950 (v. 1), Apr. 8: 467–468.*

Refrigeration anesthesia is discussed not so much for the anesthetic effect *per se* but because of the generally lowered metabolism and lack of absorption of toxins which allow for better preparation of the patient before surgical repair of severe traumatic damage. The author presents 6 case histories as illustrations of these points.

1618.   Crossman, L. W. [Refrigeration anesthesia]. *War Med., Chic., v. 1. Nov. 1941: 795–798.*

In the discussion of a paper by A. L. TYNES, W. W. NICHOLS, and S. C. WIGGIN on anesthesia for military needs, the author states that in accordance with the techniques developed by DR. FREDERICK M. ALLEN of New York City Hospital, the method of anesthesia used at that hospital for amputations of lower extremities in diabetic and arteriosclerotic gangrene cases, is refrigeration anesthesia. The author outlines its use, stating that there is no pain and no postoperative shock, and recommends its use by the Army and Navy for war surgery.

1619.   Crossman, L. W., F. M. Allen, V. Hurley, and W. F. Ruggiero. Reduced temperatures in surgery. II. Amputation for peripheral vascular disease. *Arch. Surg., v. 44, Jan. 1942: 139–156.*

Forty-five cases of amputation for peripheral vascular disease using refrigeration anesthesia, are discussed. Refrigeration gave definite relief of pain, brought about a limitation of necrosis and infection, and totally eliminated thrombosis or embolism. Some deaths in the group may have been due to delayed shock.

1620. Crossman, L. W., F. M. Allen, V. Hurley, and W. F. Ruggiero. Refrigeration anesthesia. *Current Res. Anesth., v. 21, Sept.–Oct. 1942: 241–254.*

Clinical information is presented on 58 patients, all poor surgery risks because of diabetic or arteriosclerotic conditions, who had undergone amputations using refrigeration anesthesia. Anesthesia by refrigeration, in contrast to other methods, is an anesthesia of all protoplasm rather than of nerve tissue only. The non-reactivity and lack of formation of chemical toxins in tissue thus anesthetized was largely responsible for mitigation of local damage, preservation of local vitality, lack of systemic shock, and, probably, the avoidance of post-operative gastrointestinal disturbances. Uses of refrigeration anesthesia as a pre-operative or palliative measure for relief of pain, retardation of infection, and reduction of tissue necrosis, are also discussed.

1621. Crossman, L. W., and F. M. Allen. Surgical refrigeration and preservation of tissue. *J. Am. M. Ass., v. 133, Feb. 8, 1947: 377–382.*

On the basis of studies by other investigators, and after an analysis of their own findings, the authors confirm the safety and benefit of refrigeration anesthesia. Anesthesia by brief chilling (packing the limb in ice for a period of several hours) offers advantages for both orthopedic and reconstructive surgery. By keeping cellular metabolism at a minimum, chilling permits a delay in surgery until the patient's general condition has improved. Successful healing has occurred in limbs which have been refrigerated for a number of days or weeks. Hypothermic treatment is recommended in some operations involving shock (not in abdominal operations), and therapeutically for burns.

1622. Crossman, L. W. Refrigeration—uses in surgery. *Med. Rec., Houston, v. 44, May 1950: 131–139.*

Uses of refrigeration anesthesia are discussed as well as its unique ability to control simultaneously pain, shock, exudation, infection, and tissue devitalization. Its use for retarding toxic absorption and to gain time for other treatments, is often the one means of saving the extremity or the life of the patient.

1623. Crossman, L. W., and H. D. Stein. Additional uses for refrigeration in surgery. *Am. J. Surg., v. 79, n.s., June 1950: 837–840.*

Several therapeutic and anesthetic uses of refrigeration—both by local application of cold or by packing of part or all of an extremity in chipped ice—for minor surgical procedures as well as in certain peripheral vascular states, are discussed. Use of cold refrigeration brings relief of pain, decrease of edema, and often decrease of tissue damage, but the reduced metabolism involved may contribute to a slowed healing time.

1624. Davis, W. J. Refrigeration anesthesia. *J. Am. Osteopath. Ass., v. 46, Mar. 1947: 408–409.*

Anesthesia was obtained by refrigeration of a limb, using ice or iced water until the tissue temperature was approximately 5°C. The resulting lowering of tissue metabolism and the blocking of nerve conduction (at tissue temperatures of 25°–30°C or below) aided greatly in preventing regress of toxic material and production of shock. Pulse and blood pressure usually showed practically no variation during surgery; edema was prevented; wound healing was occasionally slightly delayed.

1625. Doane, J. C. Proof of the practicability of refrigeration anesthesia (in theory). *Mod. Hosp., v. 60, May 1943: 64–65.*

Limbs, completely deprived of blood, were found to survive from 12–15 hours at ordinary room temperature, whereas tissues at a temperature just above freezing would live for days or even months. In using refrigeration anesthesia, and a tourniquet, for amputation of limbs, the temperature of the skin was found not to fall below 40°F, no sloughing of tissue occurred from the cold, and healing was not retarded. There was no pre- or post-operative pain, the anesthesia being of the protoplasm instead of the nerves alone. There was little circulation of chemical toxins from the tissues and little or no shock experienced by the patient.

1626. Donati, G. S. Action of cold in amputations [In Italian]. *Atti Accad. fisiocr. Siena, sez. med. fis., v. 18, July 1950: 117–128.*

The author reviews the effects, advantages and indications for the use of refrigeration anesthesia in some cases of amputation, and presents two case histories. The local and general effects of refrigeration of tissues consisted of nearly total inhibition of metabolism; notable anti-shock action; control of pain without additional anesthesia; effective control of grave infections; lack of effect on rate of pulse, respiration and blood pressure; and retardation of coagulation, effective against the arising of thrombi.

1627. Dziob, J., and R. K. Brown. Reduced temperature anesthesia. *Indust. M. & S., v. 12, Feb. 1943: 79–80.*

Presentation is made of a case of surgical amputation using refrigeration anesthesia following an accident causing spontaneous amputation of a foot at the ankle. Following refrigeration anesthesia there was prompt relief of pain, rapid improvement of the shock state, complete anesthesia, and absence of unfavorable post-operative reactions.

1628. Ebin, J. The carbon dioxide snow-electrocautery technique for occlusion of large veins; suggested application to venous angioma of the brain. *Sur. Gyn. Obst., v. 76, Jan. 1943: 43–50.*

An experimental method, used successfully on the inferior vena cava of cats is described, which involves the use of carbon dioxide snow or dry ice and electrocautery in the emptying and occluding of large veins. A small block of dry ice applied to the segment of the blood vessel with moderate pressure for one minute was found to bring about an emptying and freezing of the segment. The electrocautery must be done immediately as the section remains frozen only about one minute after removal of the dry ice. Tearing does not usually occur but if it does the vessel can be re-frozen and the area about the tear coagulated. The method is suggested for use especially in cases of venous angioma of the brain.

1629. Ebin, J. The carbon dioxide snow-electrocautery technique for occlusion of arteries; suggested application to arteriovenous angioma of the brain. *Surg. Gyn. Obst., v. 76, Apr. 1943: 456–459.*

The method described earlier for the occlusion of large veins has been used successfully to occlude the femoral artery of dogs in six instances. Application of this method to the treatment of arteriovenous angioma of the brain is suggested. The procedure is such as to do little damage to adjacent brain tissue.

1630. Ferguson, L. K. Anesthesia aboard a hospital ship in combat areas. *U. S. Nav. M. Bull., v. 43, Oct. 1944: 697–706.*

The author discusses the types of open wounds, and the anesthesia of choice in surgical procedures in each type, in approximately 3000 battle casualties received aboard a hospital ship in World War II. He comments on the use of refrigeration anesthesia and presents a typical case in which this anesthesia was used for amputation necessitated by a very severe gas gangrene infection.

1631. Friederwitzer, H. H. Ice as a local anesthetic. *Med. Rec., Houston, v. 157, Jan. 1944: 42–43.*

Application of ice is discussed for use as a safe, simple, and practical local anesthesia. The author discusses its use for such conditions as infected toenails; carbuncles or boils; dislocations of wrist, finger or elbow; abscesses or simple growths on the skin. Such anesthesia does not spread an infection; it temporarily paralyzes nerve endings in the area so that pain is not felt.

1632. Haley, E. R. Arteriosclerotic gangrene: a report on refrigeration prior to amputation. *Arch. Surg., v. 46, Apr. 1943: 518–524.*

The author discusses the use of ice for anesthesia, together with one or two tourniquets, in amputation of gangrenous limbs of bady debilitated patients. He presents in detail 4 case histories, and states that preoperative and postoperative sedation was practically eliminated and that the healing of the amputation stump was perfectly satisfactory.

1633. Hartl, H. "Physiological amputation" by refrigeration [In German]. *Wien. med. Wschr., v. 99, June 25, 1949: 282–283.*

Eight amputations were performed after physiological anesthesia had been induced by packing the extremity in ice for 3 to 6 hours until the tissue temperature was reduced to about 4°C. All patients were in poor physical condition, suffering from diabetes, arteriosclerosis, thromboangiitic gangrene, or last-stage cancer. Pain, which had often been intense, was relieved.

1634. Helliwell, P. J. Refrigeration analgesia. *Anesthesia, Lond., v. 5, April 1950: 58–66.*

Analgesia by refrigeration is based on the fact that the conductivity of nerve trunks fails between 25–30°C and, therefore, no sensory impulses are able to pass to the central nervous system. It has been shown that below 10°C hemoglobin does not release oxygen but at the low level of metabolism of this temperature the tissues can obtain the oxygen needed from that dissolved in the plasma. Human tissue has been found to be reduced to a temperature of −4°C and survive, but to freeze and not survive at −5°C. Between −4° and 10°C tissue lived between 15 and 17 days; between 10° and 27°C, less than 15 days with the worst period being about 15°C when survival time was reduced to 4 days; above 27°C, survival time was rapidly increased. At 10°C both anabolic and catabolic processes ceased, anabolism stopping before catabolism did; at 10°C there were less catabolites to draw fluids to the site. The author suggests that when cold is used for analgesia, the area be rewarmed gradually, high elevation be employed, and vasoconstrictors be used to reduce vascular transudation.

1635. Hewer, C. L. Refrigeration anesthesia. *Brit. M. J., 1947 (v. 1), June 21: 901.*

The author disagrees with the procedure of Hughes (item 1638) and states that the use of a tourniquet is an essential part of the technique in refrigeration anesthesia. He believes that in an aged or toxic patient the anesthesia time would be longer without the use of the tourniquet and that there would be a much more pronounced fall in the general body temperature tend-to bring on heart failure, anuria, or low-grade bronchopneumonia. However, in therapeutic limb-cooling in defective circulatory conditions, to lower the tissue metabolism to where the limited blood supply is adequate, a tourniquet is not to be used. These latter patients are usually younger, more physically fit, patients than the amputation group and the necessary temperature reduction is also not as great.

1636. Hinchey, P. R. Refrigeration in surgery of the extremities. *N. England J. M., v. 230, Feb. 24, 1944: 63–69.*

Refrigeration provides a quick and satisfactory anesthesia within a few hours with minimal disruption for the patient from the operative procedures. Such refrigeration brings about freedom from pain, hemorrhage, shock and infection.

1637. Horner, H. O. Refrigeration anesthesia. *Am. J. Surg., v. 70, Nov. 1945: 201–212.*

Refrigeration anesthesia is based on the fact that the lowering of tissue temperature to a level slightly above freezing produces anesthesia by stopping cellular metabolic processes and that in this inactive state the cells do not respond to stimuli. The author discusses his series of 12 cases and states that the advantages of refrigeration anesthesia—especially for patients in a poor physical state—are relief of pain, prevention of shock, marked inhibition of infection and edema, as well as allowing a long deferment of operation without harm. The author mentions similar therapeutic cooling of hyperemic, painful, feet in immersion-foot injury.

1638. Hughes, E. S. R. Refrigeration anesthesia. *Brit. M. J., 1947 (v. 1), May 31: 761–764.*

Report is made of 25 consecutive cases of limb amputation, in seriously arteriosclerotic and diabetic patients, under refrigeration anesthesia by use of ice bags. Excellent results were obtained in control of infection and control of all primary, and lessening of any secondary, shock. The use of a tourniquet is not an essential requirement at any stage of the procedure and may be dispensed with altogether. The post-operative use of ice is counteracted by the negative effect on the patient of having a wet bed. The temperature used for anesthesia was never lower than 0°C on the basis of work by Lewis (item 1772, pages 869–871) who found that the skin, by virtue of its capacity for supercooling, did not freeze unless the temperature was below −2.2°C.

1639. Ingraham, F. D., D. D. Matson, and R. P. Woods. Inhibition of cutaneous pain responses by the local application of cold; a simple method of reducing the pain of hypodermic injections. *N. England J. M.*, v. 237, Nov. 20, 1947: 773–776.

When the skin temperature is reduced to 11°–13°C by external application of cold to a small area, pain response to cutaneous stimuli in that area is inhibited. Based on this information, a technique for inserting a hypodermic needle into the skin without pain to the patient, is discussed.

1640. Johnson, M. D. Proof of the practicability of refrigeration anesthesia (in practice). Experience in St. Louis. *Mod. Hosp.*, v. 60, May 1943: 65.

The author describes his experiences using refrigeration anesthesia in 11 cases of amputation. In cases of suspected infection of the amputation stump, ice bags were left around it to retard the agglutination of the wound edges and permit drainage of the stump. Healing was then somewhat retarded. Patients seldom required sedation postoperatively; meals were not missed; and shock was not produced in otherwise poor operative risk cases.

1641. Johnston, C. G. Refrigeration in surgery. *Am. J. M. Sc.*, v. 209, Feb. 1945: 253–257.

A review is made of the literature concerning the use of refrigeration anesthesia in surgery, the therapeutic use of cold, and the physiological responses of tissues to cold. 53 refs.

1642. Kirz, E. Gas gangrene after amputation under refrigeration anesthesia; a warning. *Brit. M. J.*, 1944 (v. 2), Nov. 18: 662.

The author warns of the danger of using contaminated ice, especially with spore-forming bacteria, following the death of a patient from gas gangrene of the stump of the right leg following an amputation using refrigeration anesthesia. *Clostridium welchii* was isolated from the infected area during the life of the patient, and from the center of two other cakes of ice from the same source of supply.

1643. Kopp, J. G. Refrigeration anaesthesia [Abstract, in Dutch]. *Ned. tschr. geneesk.*, v. 93, July 30, 1949: 2666–2670.

In this report and the discussion (by VERMEULEN, LEGIUT, and the author) which followed, it is brought out that anesthesia by the use of cold was especially successful when older or debilitated patients were concerned; that shock was usually avoided; and that the cold seemed to produce a bacteriostatic action.

1644. Koskoff, Y. D., V. Markson, and N. M. Wall. A method for removal of areas of brain following freezing *in situ*. *Am. J. Surg.*, v. 50, Nov. 1940: 271–273.

Areas of the brain of a cat were removed experimentally by the use of an instrument which is described. The instrument consists of 2 metal cylinders, the inner cylinder being 10 cm long with a funnel top. The outer cylinder is equipped with a handle and spring lever. The depth of the segment to be removed is determined by the adjustable collar of the inner cylinder. After the cortex of the brain is exposed surgically, the instrument is inserted to the depth of the previously determined projection of the inner cylinder beyond the outer. Liquid nitrogen is then poured into the funnel top of the inner cylinder and the segment of the brain is frozen in a few seconds. Hemorrhage resulting from insertion of the instrument and after its removal is promptly controlled by refrigeration. It is suggested that such refrigeration may be a useful procedure in neurologic surgery.

1645. Krieg, E. G. Control of postoperative pain; application of cold to the operative site. *Am. J. Surg., v. 62, 1943: 114–116.*

Application of ice caps directly to the postoperative site, over a moisture-proof dressing, brought about a local temperature decrease of about 6°C and the control of pain with the use of only a slight amount of codeine.

1646. Krieg, E. G. Cold to the postoperative wound for controlling pain and other complications. *Harper Hosp. Bull., Detr., v. 8, Jan.–Feb. 1950: 6–9.*

The author presents two series of surgery cases where the postoperative use of local cold materially decreased the amount of narcotic necessary to control pain, which in turn markedly decreased the incidence of lowered vital capacity, atelectasis, and urinary retention.

1647. Laird, G. J. Crymotherapy in surgery of the extremities. *Air Surgeon Bull. v. 2, July 1945: 220.*

A short survey of the present status of crymotherapy in surgery is given with the stated intention that it serves as a ready reference for indications and technics in use of refrigeration therapy. Refrigeration anesthesia has been suggested for surgical amputations of the extremity especially in conditions of arteriosclerosis with circulatory insufficiency, uncontrolled infection in the extremity, and in severe limb injury with impaired circulation. Chilling of the area with ice bags for ten to fifteen minutes relieved the pain involved in application of the tourniquet. The extremity below the tourniquet was immersed in ice-water (about 5°C) for several hours. Pain, which was usually moderate, was relieved by morphine. Surgery can be done in a relatively bloodless field, the tourniquet released, and blood vessels ligated. The amputation stump was allowed to return to room temperature gradually. With ice anesthesia the amputation may be done distal to the tourniquet within the first six hours; after that, it must be at the level of the tourniquet.

1648. Lam, C. R. Refrigeration anesthesia in lower limb amputation. *Bull. Am. Ass. Nurse Anesth., v. 12, Feb. 1944: 17–19.*

Six cases of amputation of lower limbs, with the use of refrigeration anesthesia and a tourniquet, are discussed. In such operations the anesthetist's chart shows no change in pulse or in blood pressure, and makes no mention of cyanosis, vomiting, struggling, or shock.

1649. Lam, C. R. Refrigeration anesthesia. *Arch. Phys. M., v. 26, Jan. 1945: 20–22.*

A partial review of earlier work with refrigeration anesthesia is given, with discussion of 2 case histories presented by the author. He states that following refrigeration anesthesia, with the use of a tourniquet on the limb, the tissues adjacent to the injury were in good condition, and that during the operation there was no complaint of pain, no change in pulse rate or blood pressure, and no nerve sensation. The only disadvantage of the method would appear to be the slight retardation of wound healing in some instances.

1650. Large, A., and P. Heinbecker. Refrigeration in clinical surgery. *Ann. Surg. v. 120, Nov. 1944: 707–715.*

Six case histories are presented in which refrigeration anesthesia, combined with the use of a tight tourniquet, was used in the successful surgical amputation of an extremity under general or spinal anesthesia. Because the patient's general condition could be improved so greatly under the combined use of cold, the tourniquet, and ordinary restorative measures, it was found unnecessary to avoid the use of inhalation or spinal anesthesia.

1651. Lesser, A., and S. T. Glasser. Refrigeration anesthesia in amputation—with a report of cases. *Bull. Am. Coll. Surgeons, v. 28, Feb. 1943: 53.*

The authors report on the successful use of refrigeration anesthesia in a series of cases of amputation of a lower extremity in which the patients were in poor physical condition and varied in age from 56 to 88 years. All the cases were characterized by little or no postoperative pain. Although many of the amputation stumps healed readily, about half of them did not and it is the opinion of the authors that the refrigeration technique apparently contributed to a slower healing rate.

1652. Lobachev, S. V. Refrigeration anesthesia in surgery of the extremities. *Current Res. Anesth., v. 25, Jan.–Feb. 1946: 22–30.* Also, in English, in: *Am. Rev. Soviet M., v. 2, Apr. 1945: 323–331.*

The author presents many case histories in discussing in detail the use of refrigeration anesthesia in surgery of the extremities of 100 patients. No other type of anesthesia was used. The local reduction of temperature counteracted traumatic shock by numbing the tissues, especially the nerves. The application of the tourniquet and the cooling of the limb retarded the formation and absorption of toxins. A bacteriological examination of material from the skin, and muscle of the wounded area, and of the wound secretions showed a very great reduction in number of bacteria after the cooling period.

1653. Lund, P. C. The physiology of refrigeration anesthesia. *Manitoba M. Ass. Rev., v. 27, Mar. 1947: 141–142.*

Definitions are given of the medical use of the terms crymotherapy, refrigeration, cooling, and freezing. Supercooling is a property of protoplasm which permits of chilling to several degrees below the true freezing point without ice formation. The author discusses many of the physiological effects of cold, and lists several of the benefits and advantages from the use of refrigeration.

1654. McElvenny, R. T. The present status of cooling limbs in preparation for surgical procedures. *Am. J. Surg., v. 58, Oct. 1942: 110–112.*

The author discusses the use and advantages of refrigeration anesthesia for amputation of limbs, and cites several cases in which the cooling prevented the advance of bacterial infection, stopped local pain, prevented the absorption of toxin, materially aided the patient in combatting shock, and stopped all odors emanating from the limb stumps. In one instance, the damaged limb without a tourniquet was kept in shaved ice for 28 days without damage to the small area of normal skin, just above the injury, which was enclosed in the ice.

1655. Marin, L. A., and L. delFabro. Ice anesthesia in surgery of extremities [In Italian]. *Gior. ital. anest., v. 16, Oct.–Dec. 1950: 571–579.*

Seven cases are presented in which ice refrigeration of the extremity provided the anesthesia for amputation. The ease of application and lack of harmful effects on the patient recommend its use especially for patients with bad heart conditions.

1656. Massie, F. M. Amputation with refrigeration anesthesia. *South. M. J., v. 37, Jan. 1944: 1–5.*

Fourteen cases of amputation using refrigeration anesthesia are presented in which there was a complicating cardiac, diabetic, or other condition. Anesthesia, produced by a combination of tourniquet and low temperature, was found to be complete; the tourniquet could safely be left on for many hours. Shock was absent during and following amputation; infection was completely controlled in the post-amputation stumps by further cold packs. There is some experimental evidence that tissues so treated may be more susceptible to infection after the temperature is restored to normal. Heat should at no time be applied to a tissue with a reduced or inelastic blood supply.

1657. Massie, F. M. Refrigeration anesthesia for amputation. *Tr. South. Surg. Ass., v. 57, 1946: 472–482.*

Experimental and clinical work has shown that tissues remain viable for many hours when a tourniquet is used and the tissue temperature is kept between 33° and 40°F. Cooling of tissue in this manner stops pain, controls the spread of an infection, does not produce shock, and gives excellent anesthesia entirely satisfactory for cases of amputation. It is also an excellent procedure in treatment of burns of the extremities, of snake and insect bites, and for preserving areas of tissue.

1658. Massie, F. M. Refrigeration anesthesia for amputation. *Ann. Surg., v. 123, May 1946: 937–947.*

The author discusses the cooling, but not freezing, of the tissues of a limb to an inactive state without a tourniquet or with one for only a short time; the long-time use of a tourniquet under the above conditions when an eventual amputation is contemplated; and the "physiological amputation" by freezing solid of the tissues of the limb and use of a tourniquet until the patient is in a better physical state for later amputation. Cooling of tissue, with or without a tourniquet, was found to stop pain and to control or prevent the spread of infection.

1659. Melick, D. W. Refrigeration anesthesia. *Am. J. Surg., v. 70, Dec. 1945: 364–368.*

The author discusses both the experimental and clinical use of cold for anesthesia, and the varied results obtained. He found the mortality rate to be the same in a series of amputations of the lower extremity in elderly, poor-risk patients—23 cases under refrigeration anesthesia and 70 cases under anesthesia other than refrigeration. Refrigeration for purposes of detoxication of infected, gangrenous extremities, he states, has a limited field of usefulness as a preliminary to amputation.

1660. Miller, H. I., and P. R. Miller. Refrigeration in surgery. *Am. J. Surg., v. 72, Nov. 1946: 694–699.*

In the early work of Allen local cold was postulated to do four things: to produce anesthesia; to increase survival time of anemic tissue; to control infection; and to prevent and control shock. Of these only the first has been proven, chiefly because of a lack of well-controlled clinical studies. Evidence tends to show that survival time of anemic tissue is prolonged. The experimental evidence is discussed under the headings of general effect of refrigeration on tissues; survival of tissues; control of infection; control of shock; effect of cooling on wound healing. Some clinical evidence, and the technics involved, are also discussed.

1661. Miyakawa, G. Refrigeration anesthesia with special reference to treatment of severely damaged extremity complicated by visceral injury. *Am. J. Surg., v. 66, Dec. 1944: 384–386.*

The author discusses the types of clinical cases in which the producing of a state of suspended animation of the tissues of the area, by use of refrigeration anesthesia, allows time for the development of collateral circulation, or for the physician to carry out therapeutic or preoperative treatment. Another undoubted value of this type of anesthesia is the control of traumatic shock.

1662. Mock, C. J. Refrigeration in surgery. *J. Michigan M. Soc., v. 45, Oct. 1946: 1344–1348.*

This is a general discussion of the use of cold in surgery including some case histories. It is pointed out that the effect of refrigeration on an extremity reduces cellular metabolism, produces lack of response to stimuli, decreases need for blood and oxygen supply, prolongs survival time of tissues with inadequate circulation and limits the formation of histotoxins. Use of refrigeration as a therapeutic measure in immersion foot is recommended.

1663. Mock, H. E., and H. E. Mock, Jr. Refrigeration anesthesia in amputation. *J. Am. M. Ass., v. 123, Sept. 4, 1943: 13–17.*

The authors discuss their experiences with 17 cases of amputation using refrigeration anesthesia. In such anesthesia the tissues are cooled, by use of cracked ice, to about 0.5° to 5.0°C above freezing, producing an anesthesia of protoplasm rather than just of nerve tissues. Cellular metabolic processes are almost stopped by the cooling, and such inactive cells do not respond to stimuli. Use of refrigeration anesthesia eliminated operative and postoperative pain; controlled or reduced infection; greatly reduced the absorption of toxins; prevented shock; allowed time for the giving of blood or plasma, or for carrying out other pre-operative procedures.

1664. Mock, H. E., Jr. Refrigeration anesthesia in skin grafting. *J. Am. M. Ass.,* *v. 122, June 26, 1943: 597–598.*

Single or multiple small split-thickness skin grafts were very successfully done under refrigeration anesthesia. The anesthesia was achieved by application, for about two hours before operation, of one or more uncovered ice bags directly to the skin of the area to be removed. No sensation was felt by any of the patients except two—in these instances the period of application of the ice was not a full two hours. The refrigeration did not noticeably affect the growth of the graft or the repair of the donor site.

1665. Mock, H. E., Jr. Refrigeration in surgery [Abstract]. *Indust. M. & S.,* *v. 16, May 1947: 248–250.*

The author gives a historical sketch of the use of refrigeration anesthesia, and the indications for its application. The advantages of its use are stated to be: inhibition of pain; preservation of tissues; limitation of infection; prevention of shock from toxic absorption; lowering of incidence of postoperative infection; and ready availability of the method.

1666. Montagne, A. Refrigeration anesthesia in amputation; author's experience [In Spanish]. *Cir. ap. locomotor, Madr., v. 5, July 1948: 326–329.*

The author discusses the successful use of refrigeration anesthesia in six cases of amputation, stating that mortality was greatly decreased; danger of shock was eliminated; incidence of infection was decreased; and the possibility of embolism or thrombosis was decreased.

1667. Mukherjee, M. Advantages of regional anaesthesia in poor surgical risk cases with special reference to refrigeration method (a report of 16 poor risk cases) [In English]. *Ind. M. J., v. 42, Sept. 1948: 219–224.*

Use of refrigeration anesthesia is discussed in a series of poor risk cases, and the following advantages of its use are enumerated: relief of pain of the affected part; limiting of activity and spread of infection; prevention of absorption and spread of toxins from bacteria and traumatized tissue; suspension of disease process in severely ill patient to allow time for other restorative treatment; preventing and combating of surgical shock; and protecting anemic tissues by preserving them in a lowered physiological state until a collateral blood supply develops.

1668. Neller, J. M., and E. R. Schmidt. Refrigeration amputation. *Wisconsin M. J., v. 43, Sept. 1944: 936–941.*

Surgical amputation of limbs of poor risk patients, using refrigeration anesthesia, is discussed from the theoretical, experimental, and clinical points of view. Refrigeration anesthesia brought about elimination or relief of pain, reduced metabolic activity, and eliminated shock.

1669. Newman, M. K. Present status of therapeutic hypothermy. *Arch. Phys. Ther., v. 24, July 1943: 389–395.*

Observations are made on the physiological principles and the clinical manifestations inherent in the application of cold. The use of local cold is discussed for preoperative anesthesia, peripheral vascular disease, immersion foot and frostbite, skin grafting, and shock or burn conditions.

1670. Nixon, E. A. Amputation anesthesia by freezing. *Northwest M., v. 42, May 1943: 131–133.*

Use of refrigeration anesthesia in several patients who were very poor surgical risks, is discussed. Such anesthesia reduces the liability to edema, infection, and necrosis of the amputation stump. Postoperative pulmonary complications are markedly decreased and gastrointestinal disturbances are eliminated.

1671.   Noble, E. A. Refrigeration anesthesia. *Canad. M. Ass. J., v. 58, Jan. 1948: 5–9.*

The author reviews the use of refrigeration not only for surgical anesthesia but also for control of an otherwise overwhelming infection; treatment of an extensive third degree burn of the legs; and for preservation of tissues in cases of severe crushing and mutilating injuries.

1672.   O'Neil, E. E. The use of refrigeration in amputations and peripheral vascular disease. *N. England J. M., v. 230, Feb. 24, 1944: 209–216.*

Two series of patients who were poor surgical risks for limb amputations showed decreased mortality rates when refrigeration anesthesia and a tourniquet were used, than did similar groups in which other anesthesia was used. Refrigeration anesthesia brought about an inhibition of shock, relief of pain, and retardation of infection and of thrombosis.

1673.   Ottsen, M., and E. Thyssen. Refrigeration anesthesia [In Danish, with English summary]. *Nord. med., v. 36, Oct. 1947: 2183–2185.*

Report is made of 7 cases of amputation of gangrenous lower extremities using refrigeration (0°–5°C) anesthesia. The authors discuss the good effects of low temperature on oxygen-deprived tissue—such as control of infection and relief of pain—and warn against any use of heat in treatment of gangrenous limbs.

1674.   Parodi, L., M. Miglietta, and L. Cabaleri. Refrigeration in the treatment of ischemic gangrene of the extremities [In Italian, summaries in Italian, French, English, German, and Spanish]. *Riv. chir. med., Parma, v. 2, Aug. 1950: 438–369.*

Case histories are presented in detail for 4 patients with ischemic gangrene of the lower extremities on whom amputation of the limb was done under refrigeration anesthesia. The good results obtained especially postoperatively, some of the physiology involved, and some details of the technic are discussed.

1675.   Perlow, S. Refrigeration anesthesia in leg amputation. *U. S. Nav. M. Bull., v. 42, Feb. 1944: 433–437.*

Refrigeration (reduction of local temperature to about 5°C by packing an extremity of a seriously debilitated patient in chipped ice) was used successfully as a method of anesthesia in surgery of the extremities. The author also notes the use of such cooling for relief of pain and prevention of toxemia.

1676.   Perruchio, P. Refrigeration anesthesia in minor surgery of extremities [In French]. *Presse méd., v. 59, May 12, 1951: 646.*

Refrigeration for minor surgical procedures—such as those for partial amputation of fingers or toes, treatment of ingrown nails or felons is recommended by the author. The affected finger or toe when placed in a container of ice water (0°C) was well anesthetized in 15 to 20 minutes. The results were excellent with no postoperative difficulties encountered.

1677.   Pétriat, . . . , and . . . Doutre. Gangrene due to arteritis treated by amputation following ice refrigeration; 2 cases [In French]. *Bordeaux chir., (4), Oct. 1947: 174–176.*

Two cases are presented in which amputation was performed following anesthesia by ice refrigeration in which there was abolishment of pain, an arresting of the infection, and reduction in the absorption of toxic products because of the lowering of the metabolic activities of the area.

1678.   Pickett, W. J. Refrigeration in surgery of extremities. *Illinois M. J., v. 91, Feb. 1947: 74–75.*

Refrigeration anesthesia was found to be an effective and advantageous procedure in management of gangrene of the extremities. It is commended by the author as being a simple procedure which does not require any unusual equipment; one that controls the activity of the saprophytic bacteria and does away with foul odors and the frequent messy dressings; and one that allows time for thorough preparation of the patient, and for the development of collateral circulation near the area of trauma, before the surgery is undertaken.

1679.   Piulachs, P. Refrigeration anesthesia. *Med. clin., Barcel., v. 8, June 1947: 369–373.*

Some of the experimental and clinical effects of cooling and of refrigeration anesthesia, are discussed. The author states that the advantages of refrigeration anesthesia are: the avoidance of shock; the chance to hold the patient at a low metabolic level during a treatment phase; prevention or inhibition of infection; diminution of postoperative hemorrhage; avoidance of thrombosis and of pulmonary embolism; and the lack of any interfence with the patient's normal eating habits.

1680.   Pratt, G. H. Surgical management of traumatic lesions of the arteries. *Surg. Clin. N. America, v. 23, Apr. 1943: 358–376.*

Refrigeration anesthesia is suggested for the treatment of frostbite, immersion foot, and related conditions.

1681.   Restarski, J. S. Dental anesthesia induced by local refrigeration. Preliminary report. *J. Am. Dent. Ass., v. 31, May 1, 1944: 599–604.*

No pathological cellular changes were seen on histological examination of the jaw of a dog which had been subjected to continuous local refrigeration ($1°–2°C$) for as long as two hours. Local refrigeration by use of a metal applicator (through which a refrigerant solution was circulated) placed in the gingival root area of the tooth of a patient gave complete anesthesia during the filling of 15 cavities and reduced the pain to a mild degree during the filling of 7 other cavities.

1682.   Restarski, J. S. Anesthesia induced by local refrigeration of the jaws. *J. Dent. Res., v. 25, Dec. 1946: 433–440.*

Local refrigeration, by use of gingival applicators through which a refrigerant at $0°$ to $1°C$ was circulated, gave complete anesthesia in 63% of the instances during filling of 52 tooth cavities of human patients. Studies were also made of the temperature differences in different areas of the mandible of a dog subjected to similar local refrigeration for 2-hour periods; histological examination did not disclose any evidence of injury to either the inferior alveolar nerves, or to nerves of the mucous membrane and periosteum.

1683.   Richards, V. Refrigeration anesthesia in surgery. *Ann. Surg., v. 119, Feb. 1944: 178–200.*

A detailed report is given of two cases of refrigeration anesthesia, with a considerable review of the literature. There are also sections of discussion and literature review on the survival of tissue from cold, and on the control of infection and of shock, by lowered temperatures.

1684.   Safford, F. K., Jr., and M. B. Nathanson. Clinical observations on tissue temperatures; pathologic and therapeutic effects. *Arch. Surg., v. 49, July 1944: 12–22.*

Studies were made on the optimum temperature required for satisfactory refrigeration anesthesia, the maximum duration of refrigeration, and temperatures which may cause tissue damage. It was found that tissue temperatures below 50 °F for more than 12 hours may damage tissues when other factors such as circulatory disturbances, slight pressure, and subsequent warming are present.

1685. Schaubel, H. J. The local use of ice after orthopedic procedures. *Am. J. Surg., v. 72, Nov. 1946: 711–714.*

Studies were made of the postoperative use of ice bags at the site of orthopedic procedures in the case of 345 patients. Cooling with ice bags brought about a lowering of temperature, pulse, and respiratory rate; white blood counts were nearer normal; the amount of narcotic given per patient was drastically reduced; postoperative complications were greatly reduced; and, subjectively, such patients appeared better in all respects than similar patients on whom no ice was used in the postoperative period.

1686. Schiebel, H. M. The use and evaluation of anesthesia by "freezing" for surgery of the extremities in diabetic patients. *North Carolina M. J., v. 3, May 1942: 227–229.*

The author discusses the successful use of refrigeration anesthesia for amputation and other operative procedures and states that this method of anesthesia diminishes infection; eliminates anesthesia shock; and decreases postoperative pulmonary complications. The popular term of "freezing" is a misnomer since no actual freezing of the tissues occurs.

1687. Segerbery, L. H. Methods of mortality reduction in amputations for arteriosclerotic gangrene. *Rocky Mountain M. J., v. 90, 1943: 663–665.*

The author reports good results using refrigeration anesthesia in a series of 12 cases of thigh amputation. There was little postoperative pain; eating habits remained normal—which is especially important in the difficultly-controlled diabetic—; no shock was experienced; little blood was lost; and healing occurred within the normal time and was uncomplicated.

1688. Shaar, C. M., D. T. Jones, and T. R. Lehan. Refrigeration anesthesia. *Surg. Clin. N. America, v. 24, 1944: 1326–1336.*

The use of refrigeration anesthesia is discussed in amputations on nine desperately ill patients, all but two of whom recovered. Refrigeration is credited with reducing metabolism greatly, reducing shock, slowing or preventing infection, producing anesthesia by reducing cellular metabolism, causing no change in pulse or blood pressure during operation, and minimizing postoperative discomforts. Since healing is usually slower, sutures can not be removed as quickly as in other types of operative procedure.

1689. Sprengell, H. Cold anesthesia and delay of treatment through the application of cold [In German]. *Beitr. klin. Chir., v. 181, 1950: 389–394.*

Several case histories, including those of patients with gangrene and circulatory disturbances, are described to illustrate two possible applications of therapeutic or anesthetic cold in injuries of the extremities. The extremity was placed in an open box and covered with ice for 1 to 3 hours, the water being allowed to flow off. This therapy by localized cooling removed the pain, delayed blood clotting, and considerably improved the general condition of the patient without damaging the healthy tissue. This delaying method of handling allows time for the surgeon to wait for further developments before deciding on surgery. Used as anesthesia this method enables the amputation to be performed almost painlessly without the use of narcotics. After the amputation, 3 ice packs were left around the wound and were removed one at a time at 24-hour intervals. When a weak heart or weak vasomotor function is known to exist the use of cold anesthesia may not be possible because of the danger of severe circulatory collapse. When a large area is involved, the exact skin temperature should be measured to avoid an excessive degree of cold.

1690. Stokes, R. J. Refrigeration anesthesia. *Bol. As. méd., Puerto Rico, v. 41, May 1949: 174–178.*

The author reviews the literature and discusses the use of refrigeration anesthesia not only in amputation of the limbs of patients in poor physical condition but also in controlling the harmful effects of absorption from damaged tissue. This method of anesthesia involves chilling but not freezing of the tissues.

1691. Thoizon, M. The several applications of cryotherapy in medical practice [In French]. *Clinique, Par.,* v. 45, July–Aug. 1950: 15–18.

The author discusses several instances of the use of local application of cold for the removal of small growths, such as small angiomas of the face or neck, small cutaneous epitheliomas, warts, or wart-like growths, and the keratotic growth from lupus erythematous and senile keratosis. The treatment is said to be quite painless—because of the anesthetizing of the tissue by the cold—and to leave practically no scar tissue.

1692. Toakley, J. G. Refrigeration anesthesia, with report of case. *Med. J. Australia,* 1947 (v. 1), June 14: 729–730.

The author discusses refrigeration anesthesia, reporting the case history of a typical patient. He mentions the following advantages of refrigeration anesthesia, over other anesthesia, for amputations: primary and secondary shock inhibited; anesthesia complete with absence of pain; incidence of infection and of mortality lowered; postoperative convalescence less stormy; temperature, pulse, and respiration unaltered during an operation; and delay of operation time permitted to allow improvement of patient's condition.

1693. Tovena, A. Anesthesia with ice in amputation of extremities; 6 cases [In Italian]. *Chir. ital.,* v. 3, Mar.–June 1949: 153–161.

The author discusses the indications for the use of refrigeration anesthesia in leg amputations, the results obtained, and the advantages. Among the latter he notes the absence of shock by the inhibition of the histamine-like substance causing it; the constant level of the blood pressure; the lessening of absorption of toxic substances; and the continuation of normal eating habits. He considers it the method of choice for the old and debilitated patient.

1694. VanBlarcom, C. Nursing care in ice anesthesia. *Am. J. Nurs.,* v. 43, Sept. 1943: 799–800.

Postoperative nursing care following amputation of an extremity of the severely debilitated, older, patient is greatly simplified with refrigeration anesthesia from that following the use of other anesthesia. The danger of postoperative complications is almost negligible since shock or severe hemorrhage seldom occurs. Lack of nausea enables the patient to continue with a normal diet.

1695. Wertheimer, P., L. Mansuy, and P. Girard-Madoux. Refrigeration anesthesia in vascular surgery [In French]. *Lyon chir.,* v. 45, Apr. 1950: 327–329.

The authors discuss the use of refrigeration anesthesia (at tissue temperature of 4°C) not only for amputation of limbs but also for relief of vascular spasm—induced originally by cold exposure—and for treatment of arteritis, of gangrene of the extremities, and of phlebitis. They explain the apparent contradiction of the relief of such vascular spasm by refrigeration by stating that refrigeration acts as an antispasmodic agent by anesthetizing the nerve supply of the musculature of the arteriole.

1696. Wilson, J. L. Amputation under refrigeration anesthesia. *Harlem Hosp. Bull., N. Y.,* v. 2, Sept. 1949: 58–75.

The author discusses the successful use of refrigeration anesthesia in a series of 44 amputations in a group of older, toxic, and debilitated patients. He mentions that refrigeration anesthesia, with the use of a tourniquet, is of great value in the preoperative control of serious infections in the area.

1697. Yudin, S. S. Refrigeration anesthesia for amputation. *Current Res. Anesth.,* v. 24, Sept.–Oct. 1945; Nov.–Dec. 1945: 216–219; 252–255. Also in English, in: *Am. Rev. Soviet M.,* v. 2, Oct. 1944: 4–13.

The author discusses his experiences with refrigeration anesthesia for amputations stating that it did not diminish the viability of tissues at the amputation level nor did it delay healing, and that the conditions of lowered cellular metabolism apparently inhibited the growth and reproduction of pathogenic microorganisms. Fatalities from postoperative shock were greatly reduced. The author recommends this method of anesthesia for use in military hospitals behind the front line where late amputations of seriously infected extremities are fairly common, because of the better chance of survival and because no complicated equipment is needed.

See also items: 1566, 2000.

V. PATHOLOGICAL EFFECTS OF COLD

A. COLD INJURIES, NON-SPECIFIC

1. General

1698. Albrecht, O. On gelosis [In German]. *Wien. klin. Wschr., v. 56, Jan. 29, 1943: 61–66.*

A condition known as "gelosis" is described in which the tissue colloids change from a sol to a gel state due to the exposure of a person to an environmental temperature of $-12°C$. These tissue changes are chronic and painful.

1699. Bénitte, A. C. War and the cold; study on the behavior of man at low temperatures [In French]. *Mâcon, France, Perrous et Fils, 1949. 53 p. (Reprint from Bulletin d'information technique et scientifique, No. 21/G and No. 22/G, July and Oct. 1948).*

The importance of understanding some of the physiology, prophylaxis, and therapy of cold exposure especially in the time of a major war, is discussed in a short foreword. Experimental findings and other information on cold exposure are discussed under the subject headings of physical factors of heat loss; climate; homeotherms, and poikilotherms; temperature of homeotherms; limit of resistance to cold; metabolic factors; various ways of temperature regulation (physical, chemical, endocrine, and nervous); physiopathology and pathological anatomy; death from cold; treatment; and prophylaxis.

1700. Birken, S. Accidents due to cold in the armies with special reference to the last world war [In Turkish]. *Askeri sihhiye mecmuasi, v. 69 (30), 1940: 28–48.*

In this discussion of accidents due to cold in the armies, the experiences described are those of the war of 1914–1918.

1701. Bordet, F., M. Brongniart, and J. Volckringer. The possible role of ergot substances in the vascular disturbances of the extremities due to cold. *Bull. Acad. nat. méd., 3d ser., v. 125, Dec. 16, 1941: 377–379.*

The authors consider the possible role played by ergotism (from contaminated flour made into bread) in the abnormal susceptibility to cold injury and the higher incidence of vascular disturbances of the extremities, during the winters of 1940 and 1941.

1702. Champy, C., and R. Coujard. Localization and acceleration of the neuritis of vitamin B_1 deficiency by cold [In French]. *C. rend. Acad. sc., Par., v. 210, Jan. 22, 1940: 150–152.*

The observation that alcoholics suffering from freezing injuries had a tendency to neuritis presumably due to vitamin B_1 deficiency was tested in experiments on chickens and pigeons. Birds with B_1 deficiency developed earlier neural lesions when chilled than did normal controls.

1703. Gerecht, K. Early and late circulatory injuries during prolonged exposure to hunger and cold [In German]. *Zschr. Kreislaufforsch.*, *v. 38, Apr. 1949: 238–243.*

The clinical symptoms, and the therapies used in treatment, of a group of 300 cases of acute, or early, injury and 200 patients with late injuries from a combination of cold and hunger, are discussed. Intense hunger, either from a shortage or a complete lack of food, when combined with severe cooling, brought about, more than any other, injuries to the circulatory system, especially the peripheral. If the trauma were not as intense and of longer duration there was also a peripheral circulatory crisis with edema as a sign of disturbed cellular circulation. In the acute cases discussed, sympathetic block was used successfully in relieving the circulatory condition. In all cases the injury from the combined action of hunger and cold appeared to be caused less by the problems of nutrition and metabolism than to the direct injury of the circulation.

1704. Geriola, F. Clinical observations on the role of constitutional factors in the pathogenesis of injuries due to cold [In Italian]. *Minerva med., Tor., anno 31 (v. 2), Dec. 15, 1940: 589–590.*

The correlation of activity of the endocrine glands with susceptibility to cold, is discussed. Thyroid instability with a tendency to hypoglycemia, results from cold exposure. Other factors in cold susceptibility are neuro-muscular hyperexcitability, tendency to myo-edema, and fibrillar contractions of muscle.

1705. Grandpierre, R. Elements of aviation medicine [In French]. *Paris, Expansion scientifique française, 1948. 502 p.*

Part 2, Chapter 4, The physiopathological effects of low temperature, wind, light, noise, and vibrations (p. 165–186), includes sections on: The effects of low temperature; the physiopathological effects due to high-altitude cold; and the accidents due to high-altitude cold (including frostbite). Part 3, Chapter 3, The protection of the individual during flight against physical factors, includes sections on protection against the effects of variations of temperature (p. 292–293) and protection against cold (p. 293–295). Part 3, Chapter 8, The treatment of the principal affections incidental to flying (p. 401–421) includes sections on cold injury therapy and local frostbite therapy.

1706. Hillenbrand, H. J., and N. Wolf. Endangiitis following cold injury [In German]. *Mschr. Unfallh., v. 53, Nov. 1950: 335–344.*

A case history is given of a 49-year-old man whose left foot was amputated following injury from exposure to severe cold. Endangiitis obliterans developed which was thought to be caused by the cold injury.

1707. Killian, H. Cold injury [In German]. *Forsch. & Fortsch., v. 19, Nov. 20–Dec. 1, 1943: 345–347.*

Brief summary is made of the knowledge of cold injuries following exposure to severe cold from the standpoint of pathological anatomy and physiology, based upon the experience of the winter of 1941–1942 on the Russian front.

1708. Lickint, F. Tobacco and cold injury [In German]. *Med. Mschr., v. 3, Nov. 1949: 801–804.*

On the basis of fairly detailed statistics on the use of tobacco by a large group of soldiers exposed to cold while on the fighting front, and from the previous literature, it is concluded that the smoking of tobacco plays a considerable role as a predisposing factor in cold injury. Persons with a cold injury should, therefore, abstain for some time from the use of tobacco.

1709. Nassau, E. Cold injury in sub-tropical climate [In German, summaries in German, English, and French]. *Ann. paediat., Basel, v. 171, Sept. 1948: 167–176.*

Illnesses in children due to the effects of cold were observed during the winter season in Palestine. With the beginning of the first rainfall, about the end of October or beginning of November, the temperature becomes cold with occasional drops to freezing in the higher areas. Morning temperatures are in the range of 3° to 10°C, with a mid-day temperature of 20°C, and with a relatively high humidity. Heating of the houses is not very adequate. Among the injuries observed were swelling and discoloration in exposed skin, subnormal temperature, and a tendency to lung complications. Some deaths occurred following severe pulmonary edema. Therapy included careful rewarming, use of heart stimulants, oxygen, and plasma transfusions.

1710. Osborne, J. W., and J. Cowen. Psychiatric factors in peripheral vaso-neuropathy after chilling. *Lancet, Lond, v. 249, Aug. 18, 1945: 204–206.*

Twenty-four soldiers suffering from peripheral vasoneuropathy after exposure to severe cold were given a brief psychiatric examination. It was found that men of unstable personality were most liable to suffer injury from cold. Such men often gave a history of sweaty hands and feet and showed a tendency to neurosis.

1711. Patterson, R. H., and F. M. Anderson. War casualties from prolonged exposure to wet and cold. *Surg. Gyn. Obst., v. 80, Jan. 1945: 1–11.*

Experiences with injuries of the feet caused by prolonged exposure to wet and cold acquired during the Battle of Attu in May 1943, are reported. Clinical findings, therapy, and certain complications such as gas infections and circulatory disturbances are described. The authors also discuss x-ray findings, surgical intervention—especially amputations—and morbid anatomy. Most of the patients seen, even those with 2nd degree injury, developed foot deformities.

1712. Sabatini, G. Cryopathology or pathology of cold lesions [In Italian]. *Rass. clin. sc., v. 18, May 15, 1940: 163–165.*

This is a general discussion of cryopathology, or the pathological effects on human beings of exposure to low temperatures. The author includes some remarks on temperature regulation.

1713. Safford, F. K., Jr., J. R. Lisa, and F. M. Allen. Local and systemic effect of heat and cold in rats. *Arch. Surg., v. 61, Sept. 1950: 499–514.*

Experimental studies were made on white rats concerning the injurious and therapeutic effects of temperature. Thermal effects were established as being the result of both the degree of temperature and the length of time. This applies to both heat and cold as etiological factors.

1714. Schmitz, R. Late sequelae of cold injuries of the skin in their relation to blood circulation [In German]. *Derm. Wschr., v. 122 (49), 1950: 1167–1174.*

The various skin injuries, which appeared as late sequelae of injuries from cold, are discussed as seen at the Skin Clinic of Tübingen during 1949 and 1950. Their relationship to circulatory disturbances which occurred before or after the cold injury is considered. Cold injuries were found to be much more severe when there had been a previous disorder of the peripheral circulation such as that of endangiitis obliterans or that caused by an earlier bone fracture or by a chronic weakness. Previous workers had found a great histological similarity between x-ray injuries and cold injuries. The author has found that x-rays applied at the time of cold injury can produce a combined greater degree of peripheral circulatory-nerve damage which then appears as late sequelae.

1715. Starlinger, F., and O. Frisch. Freezing as localized cold injury and the generalized chilling in war [In German]. *Dresden u. Leipzig, T. Steinkopff, 1944. 151 p.*

This comprehensive monograph, well-illustrated, on local and generalized cold injury, is based mainly on experience with casualties during the winter campaigns on the Russo-German front during World War II. The authors cover etiology, pathological anatomy and physiology, clinical aspects, management, and prognosis in considerable detail, both in the combat area and in the field hospitals.

1716. Stein, I. D. Physical medicine and cold injury of the limbs. *Arch. Phys. M.*, *v. 28, June 1947: 348–351.*

Various types of injury, pathological physiology, and treatment are considered by the author in this general paper on cold injuries of the limbs.

1717. Towner, A. A. Physiologic effects of high altitude flying. *U. S. Armed Forces M. J., v. 1, Mar. 1950: 317–320.*

One of the several important physical problems involved in stratospheric flights at supersonic speed is that of the extreme cold experienced at high altitudes. Exposure of body surfaces to windblast and temperatures as low as 50 degrees below zero, can cause severe physical damage in a matter of seconds.

1718. Veith, G. Cold injury [In German]. *In: FIAT review of German science, 1939–1946. Pt. II, General pathology, p. 78–97. Wiesbaden, Office of Military Government for Germany (Field Information Agencies Technical), 1948.*

This is a general review of German research on cold injury, especially of the pathological aspects. Both localized injuries and generalized cooling are considered. 66 refs.

See also items: 734, 756, 1110, 1773.

2. Effects on Body Systems and Functions

1719. Abbate, V. A case of paralysis of left levator palpebrae superioris of eyelid and of external rectus superior due to cold; therapy by means of injections of irradiated maternal blood [In Italian]. *Ann. ottalm., v. 74, May 1948: 369–374.*

The case history is given of a girl of 9 who suffered a paralysis, from cold exposure, of the left levator palpebrae superioris and of the external rectus superior. Recovery followed injections of irradiated maternal blood.

1720. Ambrosi, F. The test of Aldrich and McClure in persons injured by cold [In Italian]. *Clinica, Bologna, v. 7, Sept. 1941: 484–492.*

Report is made of a study, using the technique of Aldrich and McClure, of local and general absorption of edema in injuries from cold.

1721. Applerath, ... Bone injuries from cold and their observation by radiogram [In German]. *Röntgenpraxis, v. 15, July 1943: 241–249.*

The author discussed Röntgen, or X-ray, picturization of bone injuries following cold exposure. Cartilage is particularly sensitive to cold injury. Such x-rays are of particular value in the surgical handling of cases, and this is a method which can be used by military groups.

1722. Baxter, H., and M. A. Entin. Experimental and clinical studies of reduced temperatures in injury and repair in man. I. Structure and potentialities of human skin in temperature control and in defense against thermal trauma. *Plastic & Reconstr. Surg., v. 2, Nov. 1947: 569–584.*

This is a short review of the pathogenesis of cold injury. The authors describe the physiology of the protective function of the skin and the role of the skin in temperature regulation. An outline is given of the scope of the investigation to be reported in subsequent articles.

1723. Bean, W. B., and C. A. Mills. Coronary occlusion, heart failure, and environmental temperatures. *Am. Heart J., v. 16, Dec. 1938: 701–713.*

From a study of the medical records of all patients with non-infectious cardiac failure who were admitted to the Cincinnati General Hospital from 1920 through 1937, it was concluded that coronary occlusion attacks were definitely more frequent in winter than in summer. Heart failure was likewise more frequent during winter cold among arteriosclerotic and rheumatic patients, with a marked reduction in deaths shown during the warmer and less stormy years. Syphilitic heart failure from aortic insufficiency failed to show any significant seasonal relationship. Greater frequency of infections and heightened general body metabolism probably act together to increase the winter hazards of existence for cardiac patients.

1724. Chwalla, R. Urologic diseases due to cold [In German]. *Chirurg., v. 17–18, Aug. 1947: 513–520.*

Urogenital disorders induced by cold, based on the author's clinical experiences, are discussed. Constitutionally-cold feet are the most common exogenic symptom of all urogenital diseases which are generally of nervous origin, with the exception only of typical nervous pollakisuria cases. Response to cold appears to be transmitted by nervous reflexes which create a constant irritation of the bladder. Such urogenic disorders are those of endogenic cold-pollakiuria (not due to external cold influence), polyuria, and varied complaints such as pain, burning, or sensations of pressure. There are also mixed forms of nervous and cold-induced diseases. The total of these bladder disorders is called cold-feet, or refrigerator, dysuria. Of the two types of cold feet, the inborn and the acquired, the first type is urologically more significant. A local defect in blood circulation in the feet or toes, a chronic disturbance in vasomotor function, or an infectious cystitis to which cold is added will sensitize the bladder to further cold and recurrences and results in a chronic bladder disease with continued diuria which will persist even with warm feet. In cases of extreme sensitivity, actual cooling of the body is unnecessary; cold water on the hands or a slight air current on any area of the skin can elicit bladder irritation. In subjects with chronic cold feet, a severe cold will finally induce a cystitis or an aseptic purpura of the bladder mucosa; hyperemia of the bladder has also been observed. Diuresis may become excessive, as in diabetis. A cold chill alone can induce a prostate neurosis, or angiospasms in the kidneys, which simulates regular kidney colic. Such attacks of pain can be elicited by cold drinks, as well as emotional upsets. If a prostate hypertrophy occurs in cold-footed subjects, it is always more severe. It is assumed that chronic cold feet in old age, and in postclimacteric women, are due to a lack of sex hormones, as this condition is eliminated by hormone administration. The direct cause is seen in a local spastic condition of the vessels, in the deeper layers as well as in the periphery. Moreover, a central nervous connection is possible, since in cases of vasolability (hypersensitivity to cold) a general regulatory disturbance in the thermal and vasomotor centers is probable. Some of the therapies for such bladder disturbances induced by cold feet, include walking barefoot, wearing ventilated footwear, taking alternating hot and cold baths or of hot-water or hot-air foot baths, applying friction with a cold, damp cloth, or washing with alcohol and salicylic acid. In severe dysuria from cold, therapy with hormones of the opposite sex have produced excellent results. However, all these remedies have only a temporary effect; a permanent cure is still to be found.

1725. Faggionato, A. L. Cold in industrial accidents [In Spanish, with French summary]. *Arch. med. leg., B. Air., v. 14, 1944: 460–467.*

The author discusses the case of a laborer whose work necessitated his going into and out of a cold room, who died of a severe suppurative tonsillar inflammation. The death was ruled to be accidental, entitled to compensation, with the cold being named as part of the trauma contributing to his death.

1726. Georgievskaĩa, L. M., and M. Z. Kotik. Lung chill [In Russian]. *Klin. med., Moskva, v. 22 (1–2), 1944: 36–42.* Also, translation in: E. HOPE. *Frostbite. Translations from the Russian of a collection of sixteen papers published between 1939 and 1944, p. 85–93. Ottawa, Defence Research Board, Canada, 1950.*

The authors found that on exposure of the respiratory passages to cold, there resulted pharyno-laryngo-tracheal bronchitis, bronchiolitis, small foci of bronchopneumonia, and acutely-developing emphysema of the lungs.

1727. Gerstenberg, H. W. Acute glomerulonephritis in Russian winter military campaigning [In German]. *Deut. med. Wschr., v. 68, Sept. 1942: 929–934.*

Seventy cases of acute glomerulonephritis treated at a field hospital on the Russian front, are discussed as to symptomatology, treatment, and etiology. The long and continuous exposure to cold, in winter campaigning, was considered to be a primary causative factor of the nephritis.

1728. Goldstein, L. S. Cold weather as a factor in the epidemiology of grippe and common cold. *Arch. Pediat., N. Y., v. 68, Dec. 1951: 577–584.*

Acute illnesses, localized in the respiratory and/or gastrointestinal tract, of a large group of children in New York during February and March 1951, were analyzed with special reference to their frequency and time of occurrence in relation to isolated days (5) of subzero weather. Evidence is presented indicating that extreme cold is a potent stress factor which brings about acute illness in the form of the common cold, cold-equivalent, or grippe 8 to 12 days following initial exposure with possible secondary infection 3 to 5 days later. The secondary rise in acute illness 3 to 5 days after the initial onset may be explained on the basis of the variable and intermittent activity of the body's defense mechanisms.

1729. Herbig, H. Is nicotine a blood vessel poison? A contribution on the pharmacology of nicotine under special considerations of the complementary action of nicotine and adrenal gland function in blood vessel physiology [In German]. *Deut. Zschr. Chir., v. 256 (9–12), 1942: 467–487.*

Vasoconstriction following an injection of nicotine, shown by arteriographs using Thorotrast, was studied experimentally in dogs. Constriction did not occur when the animals were adrenalectomized nor when the adrenal gland was denervated, leading to the conclusion that this action of nicotine is mediated through the adrenal gland. The author warns that persons whose blood supply to the tissues may already be impaired—including persons injured by cold—, refrain from smoking.

1730. Killian, H. The significance of the adrenal gland in cold injury [In German]. *Zbl. Chir., v. 70, Jan. 9, 1943: 50–54.*

Three phases of cold injury are described: changes in circulation; oxygen deficiencies in various tissues, leading to asphyxiation and the formation of vasoactive amines; and injurious processes which may affect the adrenal cortex. The author indicates that the administration of a preparation derived from the adrenal cortex enables subjects to better withstand the effects of cold exposure and of the toxic products resulting from generalized cooling; such a therapy has also been used in cases of heat injury.

1731. Kreyberg, L. The development of acute tissue damage due to cold [In English]. *Avhandl. Norske Vitenskaps-Akad. Oslo. I Mat. Naturv. Klasse, no. 5, 1948. Oslo, Dybwad, 1948. 23 p.*

The experimental findings on the damage to the tissues by cold, distinguishing between the damages which are immediately lethal to cells and the damage caused by subsequent events in the tissues, are reviewed. The early clumping in vascular stasis following cold injury is not a process related to thrombosis. The term "conglutination" is suggested for this clumping of the red blood cells which is without the presence of sticky substances on the cell surfaces, in contrast to the "sludging" of Dr. M. Knisely and others. Following the immersion of a limb of a subject in ice water, the author observed a hindrance to fluid entry and an even greater hindrance to fluid drainage as much as 24 hours later, in the area of stagnant blood in surface vessels following vascular spasm.

1732. Large, A., and P. Heinbecker. Nerve degeneration following prolonged cooling of an extremity. *Ann. Surg., v. 120, Nov. 1944: 742–749.*

Immersion of a dog's limb in water at 6°C for 96 hours resulted in edema and depression of sensory and motor functioning of the leg. Nerves in the cooled area degenerated by varying degrees.

1733. Learmonth, J. R. Peripheral vascular disorders. *Brit. M. Bull.*, v. 2 (7), *1944: 136–138.*

The general problem of ischemia is briefly discussed. The author presents a clinical classification as (a) resulting from injury, (b) occurring in organic vascular disease, and (c) from local effects of cold. The author discusses the clinical and pathological features common to all and stresses that rational treatment depends upon control of hemorrhage when present and maintenance of tissue nutrition.

1734. Lindemann, H. Arterial diseases due to cold [In German]. *Deut. med. Wschr.*, v. 69, Feb. 19, 1943: 154–156.

Clinical experiences of an epidemic-like occurrence on the German Eastern Front, are reported. The condition was characterized by very severe pain in the skin; presence of fever; increased blood sedimentation rate; and, concurrently, presence of symptoms indicative of renal disorders. The latter included the presence of blood cells (both red and white) in the urine; of albuminuria; and of high blood pressure. The author believes that prolonged and repeated exposure to severe cold had caused arterial spasm and injuries to the sympathetic nerves of the legs and kidneys.

1735. Moritz, A. R., and J. R. Weisiger. Effects of cold air on the air passages and lungs: an experimental investigation. *Arch. Int. M.*, v. 75, Apr. 1945: 233–240.

Dogs which were made to inspire air at temperatures ranging from −50°C to 28°C developed a localized sub-laryngeal tracheitis. There was no evidence of primary injury to the lower trachea, bronchi, or lungs.

1736. Navarre, P. Epidemic of facial neuralgia due to cold [In French]. *Ann. hyg., Par.*, v. 25, n.s., Nov.–Dec. 1947: 274–277.

Clinical manifestations are given of an "epidemic"—in the Paris area and in some other regions of France—of severe facial neuralgia due to exposure to cold, especially in the presence of a cold wind, during the severe winter of 1946–1947. Treatment by steam inhalation, and the use of analgesics and of Vitamin B_1, were effective.

1737. Ribadeau-Dumas, L., . . . Chabrun, and . . . Walther. Clinical note on the action of cold on infants [In French]. *Bull. Acad. med., Par.*, v. 123, Dec. 1940: 992–996.

A high incidence of serious illnesses and deaths, especially from pulmonary complications, of tiny infants as the result of cold, occurred during the excessively cold winter of 1939–1940. The reaction of infants to cold, its emergency treatment and prophylaxis are discussed in detail as well as the influence of such factors as food, infections, and family surroundings.

1738. Schneider, H. Illnesses caused by cold [In German]. *Militärsanität. Zür.*, v. 28, Nov. 1946: 86–89.

The author discusses illnesses caused directly by exposure to cold (bronchopneumonia and lesser respiratory inflammations), or secondarily because of a current infection (grippe, measles, whooping cough, cystitis), or because the person for some reason has a lowered resistance. Cold exposure is known to cause a desire to urinate and so is an added strain in urinary infections or disturbances, whereas it would probably not be sufficient to cause urinary inflammation by itself. In addition to protection from wind and the wearing of warm, loose, clothing, the taking of vitamin C and eating of fresh fruits and vegetables is suggested.

See also items: 718, 1161, 1702, 1704, 2608.

3. Prophylaxis and Therapy

1739. Adams-Ray, J. Treatment of acute cold injury [In Swedish]. *Nord. med.*, v. 13, Mar. 1942: 915–916.

The following general procedures are suggested in therapy of cold injury: That no further cooling methods, such as rubbing the skin with snow or ice, be used; that vasospasm be released by such methods as sympathectomy or periarterial block with Etocain, or that vasodilator drugs such as Eupaverin, Doryl, or Prostigmin, be administered; that warmth not be applied above normal body temperature; that warm drinks be given; that radiant, dry, heat be used in preference to moist warm packs; and that pain-controlling drugs be given. Zinc ointment or paste is suggested for use in treatment of skin lesions; blisters should be opened aseptically and covered with sterile zinc-treated bandages.

1740. Allendorf, J., and H. Sarre. Evaluation of Priscol and Eupaverin in circulatory disturbances with the aid of skin temperature measurements [In German]. *Zschr. Kreislaufforsch., v. 35, Oct. 1943: 562–570.*

An attempt was made to evaluate the efficacy of Priscol and Eupaverin in elevating skin temperature in cases of peripheral vascular disorders resulting from exposure to cold.

1741. B., R. B. Care of injured personnel under conditions of extreme cold. *Bumed News Lett., Wash., v. 2, Sept. 17, 1943: 11–12.*

The author discusses the need for provision of adequate warmth for injured persons who cannot exercise to promote circulation. He advises wrapping of an injured leg with the opposite one and bandaging of the arms close to the body to help prevent heat loss.

1742. Bader, M. E., and M. B. Macht. Indirect peripheral vasodilatation produced by the warming of various body areas. *J. Appl. Physiol., v. 1, Sept. 1948: 215–226.*

It was found that by warming the face with infrared rays, there was an increase in the temperature of the left hand together with an increased blood flow through that hand. The results suggest that maintaining a high skin temperature of the face may be of value in the prevention of pathologic changes in the extremities caused by cold-induced ischemia.

1743. Byrd, R. E. With Byrd cloth at the South Pole: my experience with cotton fabrics for protective clothing. *Textile Colorist, v. 70, July 1948: 28–29.*

Byrd cloth is a lightweight, tightly-woven cotton fabric which has been proven, by actual wear at the South Pole, to be wind-resistant, and water-repellent, but still to be sufficiently porous to allow for some air penetration and circulation. This latter feature eliminates much of the difficulty of the accumulation and eventually cooling or freezing of perspiration in the clothing. The use of loose-fitting, comfortable, woolen garments worn in layers under a garment of tightly-woven cotton provides excellent insulation for the body when in an extremely cold environment.

1744. Fohn-Hansen, L. Proper clothing for improper weather. *Alaska Health, v. 5, May 1947: 2–4.*

A practical guide to selection of proper clothing for wear in Alaska, recommends loose clothing in good repair and that it be kept dry; states that feet should be kept dry and warm; undue exposure to cold should be avoided; and that a healthy, well-nourished, vitamin-saturated person stands cold much better than one who is not in good physical condition.

1745. Goldhahn, R. Cold injury and its management [In German]. *Ther. Gegenwart, v. 84, Feb. 1943: 50–56.*

Progress in the treatment of cold injuries is reviewed briefly. 24 refs.

1746. Harcourt Got, J. d', A. Folch Pi, and J. Bofill. Contribution to the study of trophic disturbances of the limbs due to cooling [In Italian, with French and English summaries]. *Rev. san. guerra, v. 2, Mar.–Apr. 1938: 113–137.*

Frostbite injuries of soldiers during the Tereul offensive (1938) are discussed. The etiology, pathology, and therapy of cold injury are considered, and the importance of vascular disturbances in the affected parts is emphasized. Blocking of the sympathetic nervous system is recommended.

1747. Hyndman, O. R., and J. Wolkin. The sympathetic nervous system; influence on sensibility to heat and cold and to certain types of pain. *Arch. Neur. Psychiat., Chic., v. 46, Dec. 1941: 1006–1016.*

It was found that sympathectomy diminishes and almost abolishes the aching and stinging pain in the hand and foot which results from exposure to severe cold.

* 1748. Krotkov, F. G. On the prevention of cold injury [In Russian]. *Voen. san. delo, 1943 (1): 65–71.*

"*Contains* a discussion of: proper clothing, footwear, and hygiene of feet in the army; supply of (hot) food; proper construction and heating of tents, huts, dugouts, etc.; pocket heaters and their use."—Arctic Bibl., v. 4, 1954: 555.

1749. Medvei, V. C. Thyroid and cold sensitivity [Letter to Editor]. *Lancet, Lond., 1947 (v. 1), Mar. 15: 347.*

The author comments on the suggestion of Simpson (item 430) that thyroid preparation might be given to increase resistance to cold, and warns against the possibility of the moderate thyroid addiction which has occurred in patients under such treatment for other conditions.

1750. Pazzagli, C. The injection of novocaine into the femoral canal in the treatment of late frostbite [In Italian]. *Sperimentale, v. 45, Dec. 31, 1941: 802–806.*

A brief survey of the literature is given, together with some discussion of the successful treatment by the author of 19 cases of various types of cold injury using Novocain injection into the femoral canal.

1751. Popkin, R. J. Effect of climate on evaluation of sympathectomy for peripheral vascular disease. *Ann. West. M. & S., v. 1, Aug. 1947: 255–257.*

Cold injury produces constriction of the surface vessels. Release of the constriction by sympathectomy in peripheral vascular conditions has been reported, being used most frequently in the colder areas of northern and eastern United States and in England.

1752. Rein, H. Physiological basis for the understanding of heat and cold injury in human organisms [In German]. *Arch. Derm. Syph., Berl., v. 184, Jan. 15, 1943: 23–33.*

The author stresses the importance of preventing cold injury by protecting the blood circulation. He advises temperature defense training to acclimate personnel to severe cold. The moist-skin individual is more susceptible to cold injury than the type who has dry or oily skin. The production of a systematic inversion in carbohydrate metabolism due to extreme cold shows that sympatheticomimetic treatment is highly dangerous.

1753. Starlinger, F. Errors and dangers in combating heat and cold injuries. *In: Fehler und Gefahren der Feldchirurgie, p. 27–39 [In German]. 2nd ed. Berlin und Wien, Urban und Schwarzenberg, 1943.*

This is a critical discussion of the prevention and treatment of cold injury based on observations and practices in the German armies on the Eastern front.

1754. Starlinger, F. Prevention of cold injuries in the field [In German]. *Zbl. Chir., v. 70, Oct. 30, 1943: 1570–1573.*

Prophylactic measures against cold injuries are of utmost importance. Protective clothing should consist of several layers of clothing to increase the insulating air-volume underneath;

---

* Original not seen.

any tightness of clothing should be avoided. Marches and guard duties are to be shortened as much as possible. Physical exercise should be repeated at regular intervals. The diet should be calorie-rich, abundant in fats, and not lacking in any vitamin; food should be warm. Alcohol may be added in small quantities to hot drinks, but other alcoholic consumption should be banned. Smoking should be reduced to the barest minimum or, even better, be completely avoided. Asthenic types of soldiers, or those who have recently recovered from disease or accident, are more inclined to frostbite since there is a hypertonicity of the muscle fibers of the small blood vessels which tends to cause constriction and impairment of blood flow. Such soldiers should be assigned to duty only in warm climates. Fatigue is one of the most serious predisposing factors to cold injuries; if it cannot be avoided, all the other preventive measures greatly increase in importance. Acclimatization can be achieved by cold baths, rubbing of the feet with snow or running barefoot on snow, or by massage and physical exercises. For perspiring feet, special foot-baths with oak-bark, tannin, or alum earth, together with a powdering with Formalin-talcum, are suggested. The question of administration of electrolytes, vitamins, hormones, and various types of stimulants for increased resistance to cold, should be studied.

1755. Telford, E. D. Sympathectomy in treatment of the cryopathies. *Brit. M. J., 1943 (v. 2), Sept. 18: 360.*

Late results of injury from cold were treated by preganglionic sympathectomy. Pain was relieved and ulcers healed quickly.

See also items: 1019, 1144, 1174, 1202, 1736, 1738, 1783, 2723.

B. COLD INJURIES, MIXED

(if more than two specific conditions are considered.)

1. General

1756. Anon. Trench foot. *Bull. U. S. Army M. Dep., No. 74, Mar. 1944: 46–48.*

Trench foot, immersion foot, and frostbite, which are related conditions resulting from exposure to wet and cold, can have a disastrous effect on military operations in time of war. In the American forces during World War II, these kinds of cold injury have been a grave menace in only certain quarters. In the Eighth Air Force, high altitude frostbite was the second most frequent cause of battle injuries; in the Kiska campaign, immersion foot and trench foot comprised about 10% of total injuries and diseases; in the Attu campaign, 93 cases of immersion foot or trench foot required hospital admission. Contributing factors to trench foot, in addition to prolonged exposure to wet and cold, are tight foot gear, immobility, and dependency, all of which reduce peripheral circulation. Since treatment is not very satisfactory and recovery is slow, prevention is especially important. Prevention consists of providing proper equipment for operation in areas of wet and cold, careful instruction of personnel, and exercise of proper discipline by unit commanders to see that instructions are followed. Provision of loose-fitting waterproof boots with replaceable thick felt innersoles and woolen socks provide good insulation as well as ventilation. Feet, the innersoles, and the socks should be kept dry and as clean as possible. Cramped positions, dependency of extremities, and constriction by tight clothing, shoes, etc., should be avoided. Treatment consists essentially of rest, avoidance of further trauma or infection, and elevation of feet to promote drainage of edema fluid and reduction of metabolism in the affected parts. No external heat should be applied to the feet, and local cooling may reduce pain; pressure from bed clothing should be eliminated by use of a cradle; massage or rubbing of the area should not be done; tetanus injection and sulfa drugs by mouth may be given; and areas of necrosis and ulceration should be treated conservatively unless surgical intervention becomes necessary.

1757. Anon. Field Surgery Pocket Book (Revised); Memoranda mainly based on experience in the 1939–1945 war. (Prepared under the direction of the

Director General of Army Medical Services [Gt. Brit.]). *London, His Majesty's Stationery Office, 1950. 187 p.*

Section XXIV (p. 156–163) is entitled Lesions Caused by Exposure to Cold. The subject is discussed under the headings of general effects; local effects (frostbite, trench foot, immersion foot, shelter foot, seaboot foot, chilblains); pathology; prevention (against general effects and local effects); treatment of frostbite; and management of the wounded in sub-arctic regions. In peacetime serious injury or death from a general fall in body temperature is from two main causes: drunkeness and injury or exhaustion while in mountainous country. A feeling of weakness, loss of normal urge to struggle for life, and a dangerous overwhelming sleepiness are the outstanding symptoms. In injury from local cold the predisposing factors are a general fall of body temperature, interference with the circulation usually because of inability to change position for a long period, and compression of the limbs by clothing. Trench foot, immersion foot, shelter foot, and sea-boot foot are similar as to clinical features and pathology; the conditions may be grouped under the term "peripheral vasoneuropathy after chilling." The treatment involves keeping the patient warm and in bed while keeping the feet cool. The feet should be kept clean by a gentle soap and water wash and kept loosely wrapped in a sterile towel. Anti-tetanus injections and a prophylactic course of penicillin or a sulpha drug, are advised. Sympathectomy should not be considered during the earlier stages but only to relieve pain, swelling, and cold sensitivity if they persist.

1758. Abramson, D. I. Vascular responses in the extremities of man in health and disease. *Chicago, Univ. Chicago Press, 1944. 412 p.*

This study of peripheral circulation includes chapters on the anatomy and physiology of the circulation in the extremities, nerve control of blood vessels, methods of study, physiological responses of blood vessels in different portions of the extremities, responses of the peripheral blood vessels to pharmacological agents, blood flow in abnormal states and in systemic diseases, peripheral vascular diseases and evaluation of methods used in their treatment. There is a discussion of responses to cold (p. 95–100) and of diseases produced by prolonged exposure to cold, including chilblains, trench foot and immersion foot, and frostbite (p. 316–321). Many references are given (p. 109–111; 328–330).

1759. Blair, J. R. Military significance of cold injury in the Korean theatre of operation. *Mil. M. Notes, U. S. Army M. Serv. Grad. School, v. 2, 1951: 1–7.*

Slightly over 5,000 military casualties with a diagnosis of frostbite, trench foot, or immersion foot were evacuated from Korea as of Mar. 5, 1951. This figure represented 25% of all casualties (including dead, wounded, and missing) suffered by U. S. Armed Forces from Nov. 15, 1950 until Mar. 5, 1951. Clinical diagnosis attributed 85% to frostbite and 15% to trench foot. Prior to Mar. 5, 1951, there were 3,687 cold injury admissions to Osaka Army Hospital in Japan, of which 28% were sent to the zone of the interior for treatment. An additional 1,400 cold injuries were evacuated to other Japanese hospitals or, by hospital ship, directly to the U. S. Of the above cold injuries, 35% had in addition suffered combat wounds which in many cases had led to the cold injury. Interviews of members of enemy troops by the Cold Injury Research Team and observations of prisoners of war, led to the conclusion that their cold weather protective clothing was grossly inferior to that of the American soldier and that approximately one-fourth of the total strength of enemy units had suffered cold injuries. Poor command, carelessness, inadequate clothing, and willful intention did not appear to be causative factors but it was rather the severity of the weather and the difficulty of the terrain. Despite this, the troops in Korea have suffered a lower cold injury rate than did the U. S. Forces in Europe in 1944–1945.

1760. Bowers, W. F., F. T. Merchant, and K. H. Judy. The present story on battle casualties from Korea. *Surg. Gyn. Obst., v. 93, Oct. 1951: 529–542.*

In a section on Cold Injury (p. 539–542) it is stated that during World War II the total number of recorded injuries from cold of ground type in the American Army was 55,331 with an average time away from duty of 55 days. The figures represent the total loss of a 15,000 man division for 6 months. In the Korean conflict the records show that a total of 630 Army evacuees suffering from cold injuries had been received in the United States from the Far East up to

Feb. 21, 1951. Of this group it is estimated that 68.5% would be returned to duty. Of the group, 13.8% underwent surgical amputations. Ultraconservatism has been advocated in the surgical sacrifice of tissue subjected to cold injury. The cold injuries which occurred were not primarily due to carelessness or willful intention, inadequate clothing, or poor command performance, but to the low environmental temperature and the extremely difficult combat conditions and terrain. About 35% of the casualties had received some other injury before frostbite occurred. During the period of Sept. 1950 to Feb. 1951 approximately 85% of the cold injuries were from frostbite and 15% from immersion foot. Graphic representation of statistics shows that the incidence of cold injuries in Korea has been greatest during periods of heavy combat during cold weather.

1761. Critchley, M. Shipwreck-survivors, a medical study. *London, Churchill, 1943. 119 p.*

Chapter 1 (p. 1–23) deals with the effects of cold as seen in survivors of shipwreck. Illustrative case histories are included together with a tabular comparison of immersion foot, trench foot, and frostbite. On pages 100–109 the author discusses the prevention and treatment of immersion foot and the problem of protection against cold.

1762. Dredge, T. E. Physical treatment of disabilities of the foot commonly encountered in military service. *Arch. Phys. M., v. 24, Nov. 1943: 653–659.*

Under a heading of occupational—in a classification of the commoner disabilities of the foot encountered among military personnel—the author lists trench foot, march foot, immersion foot, and frostbite or pernio. The etiology, clinical symptoms, pathology, and some therapy and prophylaxis, are discussed for each condition.

1763. Edwards, J. C. The diagnosis and treatment of conditions of exposure; trench foot, immersion foot, and frostbite. *J. Missouri M. Ass., v. 48, Aug. 1951: 621–626.*

The diagnosis, clinical findings, treatment, and prevention are discussed for trench foot, immersion foot, and frostbite. The author doubts that anticoagulant therapy or prophylaxis is applicable for use by combat soldiers, also that rapid thawing should be considered only within the first few hours after injury and that the period has usually passed by the time the soldier has reached the hospital. Sympathectomy gave only slight relief and would appear to be indicated only in cases where there is demonstrable circulatory insufficiency.

1764. Friedman, N. B. The reactions of tissue to cold; the pathology of frostbite, high altitude frostbite, trench foot, and immersion foot. *Am. J. Clin. Path., v. 16, Oct. 1946: 634–639.*

This study is based upon tissues from more than 100 cases of freezing injury sent to the Army Institute of Pathology in Washington, D. C. The tissues were from extremities representing local injury, rather than general chilling, with fatal termination. The author concludes that the lesions of trench foot and high-altitude frostbite are essentially similar.

1765. Greene, R. Frostbite and kindred ills. *Lancet, Lond., v. 241, Dec. 6, 1941: 689–693.*

Frostbite and kindred conditions of trench foot, shelter foot, and immersion foot are produced by combinations in differing proportions of many causes, the most important being cold and damp. Of secondary, but still great, importance, are excessive warmth during recovery, circulatory stagnation, wind, anoxia, dietetic deficiencies, and trauma, especially during poorly-directed treatment. The author states that trench foot is almost identical with gradual frostbite, and—not having seen a case of immersion foot—he assumes from the literature that clinically immersion foot is almost identical with trench foot and that the etiology is the same. Treatment consists primarily of the avoidance of trauma and infection. Amputation is said to be necessary only seldom and, in the absence of a spreading infection, is never urgent. By bearing in mind the causes, and by proper care of the feet, most cases are preventable.

1766. Greene, R. The prevention and treatment of frostbite. *Practitioner, Lond., v. 148, Jan. 1942: 38–43.*

This is a general discussion of frostbite, trench foot, shelter foot, and immersion foot together with recommended treatment and prevention.

1767. Harkins, H. N. The treatment of burns and freezing. *In: D. D. Lewis. Practice of surgery, v. 1, p. 1–177. Hagerstown, Md., Prior, 1951.*

Under the heading of Freezing (p. 151–167) is included discussion of the physiology and therapy of freezing injuries; frostbite (defined as cold injury of less severity than freezing); immersion foot; immersion hand; and trench foot. An extensive bibliography appears on p. 167–177.

1768. Hart, D. Injuries due to cold. *In: A textbook of surgery, p. 96–98. Ed. by F. CHRISTOPHER. 5th edit. Philadelphia, Saunders, 1949.*

The feet, hands, nose, ears, and cheeks are most readily damaged by cold. This is due in part to tissue anoxia caused by vasoconstriction. Injury may result from freezing (frostbite) or may be the end result of long term exposure to cold (immersion hand or foot). The former is more important in high altitude flying. Chilblains occur often in persons with low resistance and poor circulation. They are characterized by itching and erythema of the exposed part. Ulceration of the skin, and infection, may occur. Treatment varies with the extent of the injury. Over-heating is to be avoided. Gangrenous parts should be kept aseptic and separation of the dead tissues awaited until the extent of the gangrene is ascertained.

1769. Kleinsasser, L. J. Vascular and neurologic lesions which result from the exposure of extremities to moisture and cold. *Rocky Mountain M. J., v. 42, Aug. 1945: 580–586.*

The author regards immersion foot, trench foot, shelter foot, and frostbite as different degrees of reaction to varying severity of exposure to moisture and cold. A classification based on degree of injury is presented. A series of 20 cases is analyzed.

1770. Kreyberg, L. Tissue damage due to cold. *Lancet, Lond., v. 250, Mar. 9, 1946: 338–340.* Also, in Norwegian with English summary, in: *Nord. med., v. 30, May 3, 1946: 973–976.*

The changes occurring in tissue after exposure to cold and during subsequent rewarming are discussed for three different types: (1) short exposure to moderate cold; (2) after freezing to ice and return to normal; and (3) after prolonged exposure to moderate cold not involving freezing, as in trench foot or immersion foot. Initial changes were found to be due to physiological adjustment to cold, but prolonged exposure produced pathological changes, which are described. The cause of pathological reaction to cold is ascribed to acute aseptic inflammation.

1771. Lesser, M. A. Frostbite. *Drug & Cosmet. Indust., v. 61, July 1947: 41–43; 125–132.*

The author mentions the serious incapacitation of troops during World War II from high-altitude cold injury, trench foot, immersion foot, and shelter foot. He discusses the physiology of cooling and, in rewarming, states that no warmth greater than body temperature be used and that no vigorous rubbing be employed. Vitamin therapy is discussed, as well as use of anticoagulant drugs, protective greases and ointments, short-wave therapy, and anesthetic infiltration of the sympathetic nervous system.

1772. Lewis, T. Observations on some normal and injurious effects of cold upon the skin and underlying tissues. I. Reactions to cold and injury of normal skin. II. Chilblains and allied conditions. III. Frostbite. *Brit. M. J., 1941 (v. 2), Dec. 6; Dec. 13; Dec. 20: 795–797; 837–839; and 869–871.*

These three Holme lectures delivered at the University College Hospital, London, are a discussion of work done by the author and his colleagues on the injurious effects of cold. Distinction is made between the effects of cooling and of freezing on the normal skin. It was noted that the skin, by virtue of its capacity for supercooling, does not freeze until its temperature is below 0°C sometimes not until −2° to −5°C. The author also discusses chilblains and trench foot and points out that they result from prolonged exposure to cold. The final lecture takes up the pathogenesis of frostbite with remarks on prevention and treatment.

1773.   Lucke, H. Sicknesses from external physical causes. I. Cold, heat, roentgen and radium radiation, electric energy, noise, concussion, passive movement (seasickness and similar states), compressed air [In German]. *In: Handbuch der Inneren Medizin, v. 6 (part 1), Berlin, Springer-Verlag, 1941. 798–841; 948–965.*

In section A (p. 798–841), on Injuries from Cold, review is made of the literature with a discussion of injuries from local cold (cold erythema, pernio, gangrenous frostbite of 2nd and 3rd degree cold injuries) and from generalized cold. Symptomatology, physiological manifestations, diagnosis, prognosis, prophylaxis, and treatment of cold injuries are discussed. There is included also information on cold hypersensitivity; on chilling and illnesses caused by chilling; various theories of the mechanisms of injury; and various body systems or organs susceptible to injury by cold. The bibliography, of 102 references, for section A is on pages 948–965.

1774.   Park, R. G. Disorders due to cold. *New Zealand M. J., v. 44, Aug. 1945: 159–164.*

The effects of cold on the skin and underlying tissues are discussed. The etiology, prevention, clinical picture, and treatment of trench foot, immersion foot, and frostbite are detailed.

1775.   Richards, R. L. Injury from exposure to low temperature: clinical features, prevention, treatment. *Brit. M. Bull., v. 2 (7), 1944: 141–142.*

This brief note on cold injury points out the distinguishing features of frostbite, immersion foot, trench foot, etc., from the standpoint of etiology, prevention, and treatment.

1776.   Schumacker, H. B., Jr. Injuries due to cold, with particular reference to frostbite and trench foot. *Wisconsin M. J., v. 46, Mar. 1947: 317–324.*

This general discussion of the etiology, clinical picture, pathology, management, and prophylaxis of frostbite, trenchfoot, and immersion foot, is based largely on the author's experience with military casualties studied at the Vascular Center of Mayo General Hospital, Galesburg, Illinois, and with civilian injuries seen at the Johns Hopkins Hospital in Baltimore. 39 refs.

1777.   Strandell, G. Injuries due to cold [In Swedish, German summary]. *Nord. Med., v. 10, Apr. 5, 1941: 1077–1089.*

This is a discussion of the etiology, clinical aspects, pathology, prophylaxis, and treatment of local cold injuries which are classified as: (1) injuries due to short exposure to intense cold, including frostbite; and (2) injuries due to prolonged exposure, generally combined with moisture, including trench foot. The effect of cold on colloidal composition (sol or gel) of the cells, is discussed. Normally these changes are reversible but after cold injury they are not, with a resulting cellular necrosis. Cooling of the cellular plasma can lead to either organic functional circulatory alterations bringing about a vasoconstriction, or to the building up of thrombi in the circulation. This, in turn, leads to a lack of nourishment of the tissues and to further cooling and injury. X-ray examination of injured bone has indicated the damages to be located at the epiphyseal line at the edge of the cartilage. Some methods of therapy are discussed including Novocain infiltration of the lumbar sympathetic or of the stellate ganglion.

1778.   Whayne, T. F. Cold injury in World War II; a study in the epidemiology of trauma. (*typewritten copy of Doctoral dissertation, Harvard School of Public Health.*) [*Cambridge, Mass.*], 1950. 306 p.

This epidemiological study (agent factors, host factors, and environmental factors) of cold injuries is based primarily on records and communications having to do with the United States Army during World War II. Injuries are discussed in ground forces only and are designated as "cold injury-ground type". This term covers frostbite, trench foot, and immersion foot; high altitude frostbite is excluded from the study. It is stated that "throughout all theaters during World War II the total recorded number of injuries due to cold-ground type, based on provisional wartime data, was 55,331." On the basis of some earlier studies where the figure was higher, and on some incomplete data, a conservative figure of 50 days lost from combat, support, or service duty for each case of cold injury is used to interpret the seriousness of such losses in man-hours and divisional effectiveness when the cost of cold injuries (p. 216–231) is discussed in Chapter V. Consideration also has to be given to the fact that cold injury is a malady of the front line infantryman when the true cost in military effectiveness is considered. There are several tabulations of information on the number of cases, days lost, and average duration of days, for immersion foot and trench foot, for frostbite, and for over-all cold injuries in the various theaters. Evacuation of cold-injury casualties is often made more difficult because of the fact that many are not ambulatory. In addition to a bibliography of 121 items, mostly on published literature, there are 15 appendices containing texts of certain Army orders and reports on trench foot.

1779. Wright, I. S., and E. V. Allen. Frostbite, immersion foot, and allied conditions. *Bull. U. S. Army M. Dep., no. 65, Jan. 1943: 136–150.*

This is a general account of the various types of cold injury and their military significance. Frostbite and immersion foot are specifically discussed, with sections on etiology, mechanism, aggravating factors, clinical classification, and treatment.

See also items: 629, 1113.

2. Effects on Body Systems and Functions

1780. Allen, E. V., N. W. Barker, and E. A. Hines, Jr. Diseases which primarily are effects of environmental temperature on the vascular system. *In: Peripheral vascular diseases, p. 243–271. Philadelphia, Saunders, 1946.*

This general account of diseases which primarily are effects of environmental temperature on the vascular system, has sections discussing sensitivity to cold and heat; on the pernio syndrome; trench foot and immersion foot; and frostbite.

1781. Denny-Brown, D., R. D. Adams, C. Bremer, and M. M. Doherty. The pathology of injury to nerve induced by cold. *J. Neuropath., v. 4, Oct. 1945: 305–323.*

Studies were made on the pathological effects of cold on the sciatic nerves of cats. Sections of nerve in the intact animal were subjected to varying degrees of cold injury. The myelin and axis cylinders of the peripheral nerves were selectively damaged. Necrosis of whole nerve bundles only occurred on freezing, and regeneration was rapid and complete in all grades of injury short of complete necrosis. The findings are discussed in relation to the pathogenesis of trench foot, and frostbite.

1782. Kossman, C. E. Responses of the body to cold. *Air Surgeon Bull., v. 1, Mar. 1944: 1–4.*

The responses of the body to cold are discussed from the standpoint of the peripheral circulation. Factors controlling local circulation of the skin, are reviewed including the role of vasomotor nerves and the metabolism of the part especially the assembling of catabolites or "H substances." Subcutaneous and chronic inflammatory responses of skin to cold, in such conditions as chilblains (pernio), erythrocyanosis, trench foot, immersion foot, and frostbite, are given. Slow thawing is suggested in the treatment of frostbite with the use of peripheral vasodilatation after demarcation has begun. Warning is given against too early amputation since the appearance of the skin indicates little about the viability of the deeper tissues. The effectiveness of pavex (passive vascular exercise), and paravertebral block, are discussed.

1783. Monro, R. S. The peripheral effects of cold. *Middlesex Hosp. J., Lond., v. 44, Sept. 1944: 38–42.*

The physiological, especially peripheral vascular, changes due to chilling or to freezing are discussed in general and under the headings of chilblains, trench foot, immersion foot, and frostbite. Tissue, either frozen or chilled, should be rewarmed by very gentle heat; rubbing of any sort is harmful; and if feet are involved, walking is to be avoided.

1784. Natvig, H. Prevention and treatment of frostbite [In Norwegian]. *Nord. med., v. 8, 1940: 2560–2562.*

The vasomotor aspects of frostbite and other cold injuries, and the physical and chemical means used in treating them, are discussed in this paper presented at the Norske Medicinske Selskab. Included is information about both gangrene and trench foot.

1785. Redisch, W. Differential diagnosis of peripheral vascular diseases. *J. M. Soc. N. Jersey, v. 46, May 1949: 238–243.*

The author states that the differentiation between chilblains (pernio) and frostbite, or trench foot is not simply a matter of degree of injury but of the segment of the vascular tree affected. He discusses the vascular changes involved in the various conditions.

1786. Wright, I. S. Vascular diseases in clinical practice. *Chicago, Year Book Publishers, 1948. 514 p.*

Chapter 13, which is entitled Syndromes produced by temperature changes (excluding Raynaud's syndrome), includes sections on the vascular aspects of frostbite (p. 313–321), trench foot (p. 321–326), immersion foot (p. 326–328), the pernio syndrome (p. 329), acute pernio or acute chilblains (p. 329–330), and chronic pernio or chronic chilblains (p. 330–338). References to the literature are found on p. 338–341.

3. Prophylaxis and Therapy

1787. Greene, R. Cold in the treatment of damage due to cold. *Lancet, Lond., v. 243, Dec. 12, 1942: 695–697.*

Description is given of a cabinet to provide therapeutic cold for use in the treatment of cold injuries such as frostbite, trench foot, and immersion foot. The physiological and clinical basis for this therapeutic device is also presented. The author states that in true frostbite most of the affected tissue is doomed and no treatment can save it. But some of the tissue is merely chilled and in the same condition as is the whole affected tissue in immersion foot and trench foot. The treatment should therefore be identical.

1788. Harness, W. N. Injuries to cold. *Seminar papers, Dept. Surg., Univ. Iowa, 1945–1946: 181–193.*

Frostbite, trench foot, and immersion foot are considered as to symptomatology, physiology, pathology, treatment (including use of sympathetic block and sympathectomy, short-wave therapy, and pavex (passive vascular exercise), and late treatment. In summary the author states that he has found no essential differences in symptomatology, physiology, or pathology of trench foot, frostbite, and immersion foot. Although they are caused by great differences in temperature and different environments, it is felt they should be treated largely in the same manner. A conservative treatment is suggested as outlined in the paper including the use of sympathetic block (if seen within the first 24 hours), the paves boot, or preferably, with Dicumarol or heparin.

1789. Hauser, E. D. W. Diseases of the foot. 2nd ed. *Philadelphia and London, Saunders, 1950. 407 p. (Also 1st ed., 1939).*

Chapter 12 on Circulatory Disturbances has short sections on Chilblain (Pernio or Frostbite), p. 187–189; on Trench Foot, p. 189; and on Immersion Foot, p. 189–190. The symptomatology and treatment of the three conditions are discussed briefly as well as the etiology of chilblains. Wearing of warm clothes and the avoidance of over-exposure to extreme cold, are stressed in the prophylaxis of chilblains. Circulation can be improved by the use of pavex apparatus, or some other form of intermittent venous occlusion, or by massage. The giving of various vitamins and hormones and of calcium are suggested against the constitutional deficiencies often encountered in chilblains. Use of the Unna's paste boot (in the same manner as a compression bandage), administration of roentgen rays, and local application of ethyl chloride are treatments suggested for chilblains especially for the relief of pain. Bilateral sympathectomy may be resorted to in an old case if painful patches of erythrocyanosis are also present. The patient with either chilblains or trench foot should be placed in bed with the feet elevated, and aspirin and codeine used to control the pain of trench foot. As circulation is re-established, mild heat and gentle massage may be applied. The treatment of immersion foot is the same as that for trench foot.

1790. Pratt, G. H. Surgical management of acute arterial occlusion. *J. Am. M. Ass., v. 130, Mar. 30, 1946: 827–830.*

This is a general discussion of the surgical handling of acute arterial occlusion based upon the author's experience. Among the various conditions where arterial occlusion is a factor are listed frostbite, immersion foot, and trench foot. These are briefly described, and treatment is discussed. Refrigeration therapy, combined with the use of anticoagulants such as heparin and Dicoumarol, are regarded as most promising.

1791. Pratt, G. H. Surgical management of vascular diseases. *Philadelphia, Lea and Febiger, 1949. 496 p.*

A large part of this volume is applicable to frostbite surgery: Frost Bite, Trench Foot, Immersion Foot, p. 104–110 (refs 26–39), p. 128–129); Pernio (Chilblains), p. 110–112 (refs 40–41, p. 129); Interruption of the Sympathetic System, p. 260–284 (60 refs).

1792. Sacksteder, M. E. Physical therapy in the early cure of cold injuries. *Phys. Ther. Rev., v. 31, 1951: 518–522.*

At the Cold Injury Section of the Osaka, Japan, Army Hospital, 4,216 patients were treated for cold injuries in the period of Dec. 1, 1950 to Apr. 1, 1951. Of this group, 4,131 were treated for frostbite and the remaining 85 for trench foot, immersion foot, or for hyperhidrosis. Analysis of 1,878 clinical summaries of frostbite cases indicated that 26% had suffered 1st degree injuries, 27%, 2nd; 35%, 3rd; and 12%, 4th. An early physical-therapy treatment was instituted as an individual program at the bedside simultaneously with other treatment. As in other injuries of the extremities, the early motion of the involved segments was considered essential in the maintenance of joint motion, prevention of deformities, minimizing the degree of muscle atrophy, as a stimulating factor to circulation, and for the early functional restoration and over-all recovery of the individual.

1793. Shumacker, H. B., Jr. Sympathetic interruption in cases of trauma and in posttraumatic states. *Surg. Gyn. Obst., v. 84, Apr. 15, 1947: 739–749.*

Experiences during World War II of the results of temporary and permanent interruption of the sympathetic nerves in cases of injury involving the peripheral circulation, are reviewed. A section on the use of sympathectomy in cold injuries (frostbite, trench foot, and immersion foot or hand) is included.

See also items: 1015, 1017, 1054, 1580, 1599, 1762, 1766, 1784.

C. CHILBLAINS, PERNIO, AND RELATED SKIN CONDITIONS

1. General

1794. Anon. Chilblains. *Pharm. Advance, no. 170, Mar. 1946: 16–17.*

Chilblains are mentioned as one of the diseases caused by seasonal disturbances of the skin affecting peripheral circulation. Acute, recent cases with some ulceration are usually aided by bathing of the area with alternating hot and cold water and—after being blotted dry from the last hot water—by the application of Iodex with methyl salicylate. In chronic cases an alteration of endocrine functioning should be suspected. An article in Lancet is mentioned which recognized two types of chilblains: one occurring in fat subjects, especially young females; and a second in the thin type of individual, of either sex. As therapy for the first type, thyroid gland extract and iodine, were recommended; for the latter, parathyroid gland extract and calcium lactate.

1795. Anon. *Brit. M. J., 1947 (Pemmican issue; ⚹ 4495), Mar. 1: 1.*

A woman doctor states that she had relief from chilblains during a recent pregnancy and suggests that the disease may have a hormonal etiology.

1796. Arnold, P. Pruritis hiemalis; review of literature and case report with new observations. *Brit. J. Derm., v. 61, Feb. 1949: 58–66.*

Pruritis hiemalis is a clinical entity, distinct from other skin disorders of winter; the strictly seasonal incidence suggests that cold or some other agent met in winter is a necessary factor in its production. Possibly some combination of cold with another agent is required. A case of pruritis hiemalis is discussed in detail. The 21-year-old patient complained of severe itching of the skin which had begun with the onset of cold weather in the autumn. The attacks had recurred each year since the age of 13. Severe local chilling with ice application did not bring on the attack but return to a warm atmosphere following general chilling of the body (immersion in a cold bath) did. Exposure to cold did not produce urticaria, collapse, or hemoglobinuria nor was there any evidence of chilblains or any relevant family history. Absence of symptoms while at sea in cold weather and after bathing in summer, suggest that another agent was involved in addition to cold.

1797. Burckhardt, W., and M. Schröder. Determination of rewarming time of the skin afflicted with chilblains [In French, summaries in French, English, and German]. *Dermatologica, Basel, v. 89, 1944: 180–184.*

In normal persons the return to normal temperature—measured by thermoelement held between thumb and first finger—after a cold water arm-bath (10°C) for 10 minutes, was rapid and almost up to the original temperature level. In patients with chilblains the return to warmth was slow and incomplete; in severe cases, the impairment remained even after recovery from the chilblains. Two to 15 minutes after an injection of Priscoline there was a rise in skin temperature of about 7°C. An injection before the cold bath did not influence the return to warmth; after the bath, such an injection accelerated the return to warmth in 5 out of 10 cases.

1798. Curschmann, H. On perniosis and other dermatoses [In German]. *Zschr. Haut & Geschlkr., v. 9 (8), 1950: 328–331.*

The author's own case of perniosis of the middle phalanx of the right middle finger is discussed. It is hinted that this finger which was used extensively in his medical practice, had received a slight mechanical injury which had predisposed it to the later cold injury. Moreover, an increase in incidence of cold injuries, as well as in cases of dermatosis and infectious dermatitis, had been observed to occur during the years of privation which followed the second World War.

1799. Downing, J. G., and J. M. Edelstein. Poikiloderma vasculare atrophicans [In English]. *Arch. Derm. Syph., Chic., v. 62, Aug. 1950: 206–213.*

Excessive contact with ice which occurred in the course of the patient's duties delivering ice over a period of 28 years, determined the site of the lesion on the left shoulder in a case of poikiloderma vasculare atrophicans.

1800. Favre, ..., G. Chanial, and J. Kohler. Multiple lenticular maculo-papulous chilblains of the hands [Abstract, in French]. *Bull. Soc. fr. derm. syph., v. 48, May 9, 1941: 771.*

A case of "froidures" as described by Gougerot (item 1803), such as had been observed more or less frequently in the last few months, is presented, together with a discussion of the etiology of similar cases of atypical chilblains.

1801. Flandin, C., and H. Rabeau. Cyanotic skin of the hands with hyperkeratosis and ulcerations occurring during the cold season [In French]. *Bull. Soc. fr. derm. syph., v. 48, Nov. 13, 1941: 687–689.*

The clinical picture and case histories are given of patients whose hands were exposed to cold during the winter season. Cyanosis, ulcerations, and hyperkeratosis were observed on the skin of the hands.

1802. Gadrat, J. Ungual lesions and chilblains [In French]. *Bull. Soc. fr. derm. syph., v. 48, Nov. 13, 1941: 692.*

The relative frequency of lesions of the matrix of the finger nails in patients afflicted with chilblains, during the cold winter of 1940, is reported together with a discussion of their possible relationship to chilblains.

1803. Gougerot, H., and R. Degos. Miliary papular and lenticular injuries from severe cold, a type of polymorphic erythema with and without freezing; discussions of diagnoses and etiology [In French]. *Bull. Soc. fr. derm. syph., v. 47, Dec. 12, 1940; 398–402.*

The author discusses the many manifestations of cold injury, and the various problems involved in terminology and classification. The group causing difficulties, also of etiology and pathogenesis, are the atypical erythematous lesions resembling lupus erythematosus.

1804. Harris, H. A genetic factor in perniosis. *Ann. Eugen., Lond., v. 14 (Part I), Oct. 1947: 32–34.*

An unselected series of airmen (107) and airwomen (49), ages 18–24, living in a Royal Air Force camp in southern England, in February and March 1947, were examined for perniosis after the finding of a case of chilblains of the hands, with severe acrocyanosis, in which the family history showed 9 individuals so affected over 4 generations. An incidence of 3% in the group appeared higher than would be expected to occur by mere chance as judged by occurrence in an unselected group. This tendency to severe perniosis appeared to be inherited as an irregular Mendelian dominant.

1805 Haxthausen, H. Adiponecrosis e frigore; peculiar areas of necrosis and infiltration in the facial subcutaneous fatty tissue in children, following exposure to cold [In Danish, English summary]. *Nord. med., v. 7, July 1940: 1174–1176.* Also, in English, in: Adiponecrosis e frigore. *Brit. J. Derm. Syph., v. 53, Mar. 1941: 83–89.*

Description is given of a hard well-defined infiltration of the subcutaneous adipose tissue in 4 very young (6 months to 3 years) children following exposure to intense cold. These lesions, and a similar one described in a young woman who was suffering also from frostbite and perniosis, were clinically and histologically quite similar to the infiltrations of adiponecrosis neonatorum. The lesions each took a benign course and subsided spontaneously within a few weeks.

1806. Johnson, R. E. Chilblains [Letter to Editor]. *Lancet, Lond., 1947 (v. 1) Jan. 25: 160.*

Comments are made on the article by Winner and Cooper-Willis on chilblains among the members of the Auxiliary Territorial Service (item 1824). The author relates the changes in incidence of chilblains of himself and his immediate family in relation to their changes in living environment. He expresses the opinion that chilblains should be classified as disorders related to environmental stress and not to familial or degenerative factors.

1807. Loos, H. O. Perniosis [In German]. *Med. Klin., Berl., v. 37, Jan. 17, 1941: 54-55.*

Many aspects of the clinical picture of perniosis are still unclear, especially that of etiology. Great individual susceptibility is seen to the condition. Various areas of the body such as the side of the little finger or little toe and the back of the hands, are especially prone to be affected while areas like the palms of the hands or feet are seldom involved. Chronic alcoholism and various disease conditions, especially those which interfere in some way with the peripheral circulation, appear to contribute to the incidence.

1808. Menard, E. Concerning keratotic chilblains [In French]. *Bull. Soc. fr. derm. syph., v. 48, Oct. 9, 1941: 642-643.*

The author's observation of patients with chilblains would indicate that, in opposition to the findings of Sézary and Rabut (item 1818), the keratotic type occurred after exposure to more severe cold than that which caused the common type of chilblain. The author gives in detail the history of a typical case in point.

1809. Mercadel Peyri, J., and J. Piñol Aguade. Papulo-keratogenous cornifying toxi-tuberculous perniosis [In Spanish]. *Actas derm. sif., Madr., v. 37, Dec. 1945: 383-390.*

A group of varied skin lesions similar to those of a keratic pernio erythema or lupus erythematosis—but not of lupus vulgaris—and from which tubercle bacilli could be cultured, are discussed together with some of the difficulties involved clinically in assigning a correct primary etiology and therapy. The author suggests for this group the term "perniosis papuloqueratosica, cornificante, toxicituberculosa" [papulo-keratogenous cornifying toxi-tuberculous perniosis].

1810. Mitchell-Heggs, G. B. Chilblains [In English, French summary]. *Arch. belg. derm. syph., v. 4, Mar. 1948: 120-127.*

Chilblain lesions are produced by damp cold, not by frost, whereas a cold but not damp location is more likely to have a low incidence of chilblains and a high incidence of frostbite. Chilblains and frostbite are different clinical and pathological entities. Lesions occur on lower extremities in about 70% of cases, as against 28% on upper extremities, and 2% on other, unusual, sites. A higher incidence appears to occur among a tubercular population than among a normal population group. Incidence is, of course, high in limbs affected by neurological complaints or by diseases of peripheral circulation. Large doses of calcium by mouth or parenterally, appeared to be helpful; also B complex vitamins by mouth following injections of vitamin B_1. Ingredients are given of an ointment found helpful in treatment of chilblains among women of the British Army's Auxiliary Territorial Service during World War II.

1811. Mouriquand, G., J. Gaté, and P. Cuilbret. Preliminary note on chilblain cases observed in the region of Lyon during the winter of 1940-41; their frequency; the abnormal forms; etiological problems; avitaminosis? [In French]. *Lyon méd., v. 166, Sept. 14, 1941: 753-757.*

The authors discuss the abnormally large number of cases of erythema pernio seen in the region around Lyons during the winter of 1940-41, commenting on its prevalence among women and on the large number of atypical forms of the erythema which were encountered. They discuss the etiology and raise the question of the role of vitamin deficiency.

1812. Myhrman, G. An erythema nodosum-like cold injury [In Swedish]. *Sven. läk. tidn., v. 37 (11), 1940: 491–492.*

Description is given of a protruding, localized, blue-red area of infiltration, slightly painful, occurring on the inside of the leg at about the knee level, as seen in 5 women patients in a medical clinic. All lesions had occurred during a very cold period and in most cases there was a history of the knees having been frostbitten. Difficulties of diagnosis led to its being confused with erythema nodosum, and with erythema multiforme exudativum. Later studies especially with the use of fluorescent methods, showed the lesions to be different from those of erythema nodosum.

1813. Polano, M. K. Lichen ruber mucosae oris et labii [Abstract, in Dutch]. *Ned. tschr. geneesk., v. 92, Oct. 16, 1948: 3367.*

The author discusses this red papulous skin eruption of the oral mucosa and lips, known as lichen ruber mucosae oris et labii. The histological changes of a typical afflicted area are discussed. Improvement of the condition follows medication with calciferol. Other eruptive conditions are mentioned including chilblain lupus which also is manifested as a purplish infiltration commonly found at the inter-phalangeal junctures. In answer to a question regarding the possible confusion in the clinical picture of chilblain lupus, lupus vulgaris, perniosis, lupus pernio, and lupus erythematosus, the author mentions the distinguishing features of several of the conditions.

1814. Schaefer, C. L., and C. E. Sanders. Pernio (chilblains). *J. Missouri M. Ass., v. 38, May 1941: 159–160.*

The author states that pernio is a definite peripheral vascular disease in patients who are sensitive to sudden changes of temperature and that it is not known whether this condition is solely a vasomotor reaction of allergic origin or is due in part to chronic inflammation. He discusses the clinical picture involved, the therapy, and the possible prophylactic treatment of the disease condition, together with the presentation of a typical case history.

1815. Schneider, W. Etiology and pathogenesis of skin injuries due to cold [In German]. *Arch. Derm. Syph., Berl., v. 186, Aug. 1946: 3–31.*

The European literature on the etiology and pathogenesis of pernio is discussed. The author believes that the condition is a manifestation of a constitutional susceptibility to cold involving the sympathetic nervous system, the endocrines, as well as the metabolism of carbohydrates. Experimental evidence is presented to support this view.

1816. Schneider, W. Cold effect and the whole organism [In German]. *Deut. med. Wschr., v. 71, Nov. 15, 1946: 259–262.*

Perniosis is said to be manifested as two clinically distinct illnesses—chilblains and erythrocyanosis crurum puellaris. In this discussion, the pathogenesis of perniosis is considered to be on a whole-organism basis, being due primarily to a thermoregulatory insufficiency. In patients suffering from perniosis and subjected to a foot bath of $12°–15°C$, the normal reaction of hyperglycemia did not occur. The blood sugar content either did not change or fell slightly. In the normal person, response to Adrenalin injection brings about a high blood sugar level which reached a high point after about 30 minutes and then decreases; in the patient with perniosis the curve rises only slightly, maintains that level for an hour or two, and then decreases. Changes in the K/Ca quotient of the blood were noted probably caused by a potassium shortage. Such changes, together with alterations in the vegetative equilibrium, characterize the constitutionally cold-sensitive perniosis patient.

1817. Schneider, W., and H. Erasmy. Potassium-calcium metabolism in perniosis. *Arch. Derm. Syph., Berl., v. 186, Mar. 25, 1947: 137–143.*

A study of the calcium (Ca), the potassium (K) and the potassium/calcium (K/Ca) values was made of the blood of 23 persons with perniosis who had fairly severe erythrocyanosis. Ca was found to be increased, occurring over a range of 12.83 mg/100 cc to 16.66 mg/100 cc [normal value, about 10 mg/100 cc], and K occurring over a range of 15.05 mg/100 cc to 31.52 mg/100 cc [normal value, from 16 mg/100 cc to 22 mg/100 cc]. The K/Ca ratio was usually less than the 1.6 average of the normal value. From his studies the author concludes that in perniosis the increase in Ca in the blood is parallel with the elevated sympathetic tone found in the spasm state of the arterioles.

1818.   Sézary, A., and R. Rabut. Punctuate and keratotic chilblains [In French]. *Bull. Soc. fr. derm. syph., v. 47, Dec. 12, 1940: 402–405.*

The authors discuss 2 types, keratotic and punctuate, of chilblain lesions from cold seen by them and occurring as 10–20 lesions on the finger and the palms of the hands of each of about 15 women and 1 man patient. The principal etiological factor they believe was cold less intense than that which causes the more common chilblain lesions, and that a predisposing factor might be a fragility of the cutaneous capillary system.

1819.   Simada, T. Freezing injuries [In Japanese]. *Hokkaido Igaku Zasshi (Acta medica hokkaidonensia), v. 21, 1943: 1168–1184.*

Included in the discussion is information on chilblains, on freezing injuries of the 1st, 2nd, and 3rd degree, and on gangrene. Of the 108 references in the bibliography at the end of the paper, 36 are in German.

1820.   Tisserand, M., and R. Suchet. Chilblains among Parisian school children during the winter of 1945–1946 [In French]. *Arch. fr. pédiat., v. 3 (6), 1946: 584–585.*

Incidence of chilblains among 510 girls (6 to 17 years of age) and 231 boys (6 to 15 years), from several schools in Paris, was 21.7% and 13.8% respectively. These figures were compared with those from an earlier investigation of pupils of the same schools in 1942, and of a group at a skin clinic, analyzing such data as location of lesions, effect of retarded puberty, and effect of cutaneous temperature. The authors conclude that immunity to cold is acquired; and that in a non-immune person the effects of cold are closely allied to the individual's level of nutrition.

1821.   Tisserand, M. Chilblains of the school children of three districts during the winter of 1946–1947 [In French] *Arch. fr. pédiat., v. 5 (1), 1948: 46–48.*

A continuing study of the influence of different factors on the incidence of chilblains in a group of 395 school girls and 213 school boys (ages 6 to 17 and 6 to 15 years respectively), which is part of a long term study of the same groups being carried on since 1939. The previous incidence of 39% for girls and 21% for boys had risen, during the especially cold winter, to 60% and 29%; 53% of the boys suffered chilblains for the first time as against 35% of the girls. The boys appeared to have resisted longer during the cold of previous winters, but the percentage of boys having more severe, ulcerative, lesions was 17% as against 14% for the girls. The areas of the body most affected were approximately the same for each group, being about 90% for feet only, 35–40% for hands and feet, and 6–8% for hands only, with 1 case each for ankles and knees. During the war years, lesions of the knees of girls were often seen but these had practically disappeared with the wearing of snow pants. Although the group was too small for accurate statistical analysis, retarded puberty or malnutrition appeared to accompany or augment frostbite.

1822.   Touraine, A., and … Rouzaud. Punctuate keratotic acrodermatitis [In French]. *Bull. Soc. fr. derm. syph., v. 47, Dec. 12, 1940: 405–410.*

The authors discuss numerous and varied erythematous lesions, especially of the fingers, which had been given various diagnoses. After review of the cases, the authors conclude that a diagnosis of erythema pernio, froidures, or engelures, would be fairly compatible with all the facts. For most of the patients, the case history showed that the affection had begun during a period of cold weather.

1823. Wigley, J. E. M. Chilblains. *Practitioner, Lond., v. 157, Nov. 1946: 353–356.*

Damp, rather than dry, cold and poor general nutrition are said to be factors to a considerable degree in the etiology of chilblains. The author quotes from an early worker who has stated that chilblains were frequent between the ages of 5 and 15 years of age, rare after 20, and exceptional after 30. The diagnosis of first and second degree chilblains and their differentiation from other erythematous conditions, is discussed. The prescriptions for several ointments for treatment are included and penicillin paste is recommended for use on ulcerated skin areas.

1824. Winner, A. L., and E. S. Cooper-Willis. *Lancet, Lond., 1946 (v. 2), Nov. 9: 663–667.*

A study was made, on the basis of 3000 questionnaires, of chilblains suffered by members of the Auxiliary Territorial Services during the winter of 1942. The incidence rose from childhood—ages 15 and 16 years being most susceptible to first attack—until about age 40, after which it decreased (in so far as the figures were reliable for the later years). Incidence within the group was about 30%, being greatest in the more sedentary occupations; some familial tendency was noted. Seventy-eight remedies were tried with varying results, probably none being specific. The authors make some review of the literature.

1825. Wit, J. C. de. The incidence and treatment of chilblains [In Dutch]. *Geneesk. gids, v. 27, Oct. 6, 1949: 393–396.*

The author discusses the pathology, etiology, incidence, and therapy of chilblains. His study of 300 men and 300 women showed, in general for both groups, the first manifestation of chilblains to be between the 5th and the 18th year; the affliction occurred in about 40% of the women and about 20% of the men. Therapeutic treatment with vitamin K showed promising results in the 15 cases so treated.

1826. Wright, R. D. Temperature hazard and protection. *Med. J. Australia, 1943 (v. 1), Aug. 14: 122–123.*

In normal environmental conditions there are few instances of chilblains, and frostbite is practically unheard of. In aircraft in the cold of high altitudes, frostbite is still a relatively trifling occurrence despite the inadequacy of the insulation of the extremities and the fact that in the design of aircraft the hands and feet are often in touch with metal. The author discusses the physiology of temperature regulation, and something of the protection of the body from cold.

1827. Zlatić, ... Perniosis; livedo racemosa [Abstract, in Croatian]. *Liječ, vjes., v. 70, Aug. 1948: 323.*

A case of pernio occurring in a young woman is described. A sporadic, maculous, reddish erruption was present. The diagnosis was made as multiple, atrophic dermatitis with surrounding pigmentation.

See also items: 560, 682, 751, 784, 1109, 1296, 1953, 2099.

2. Prophylaxis and Therapy

1828. Anon. Chilblains [Abstract]. *J. Am. M. Ass., v. 118, Apr. 4, 1942: 1264.*

A clinical description of chilblains is given together with that of other erythematous conditions resembling chilblains. Local treatment with camphor liniment or bay rum, and improvement of the circulation by exercise or massage, are recommended. Administration of small doses of arsenic can be considered prophylactically. Acetylcholine and related substances, administered by inotophoresis, should be used cautiously as a newer and not entirely evaluated remedy.

1829. Anon. Chilblains. *Brit. M. J., 1947 (v. 2): 756.*

A man of 60 years asks regarding treatment of chilblains which have afflicted the base of his finger nails. Combined doses of phenobarbital, thyroid, and vitamin K are suggested as being helpful in treatment.

1830. Anon. Chilblain of the nose. *Brit. M. J., 1947 (v. 2): 1017.*

A man of 74 had developed chilblain of the nose within the past 5 or 6 years and reported that he had treated it without success with calcium lactate, vitamins, nicotinic acid, and diathermy. In answer to his request, Lugol's iodine, possibly combined with dried thyroid especially if the patient was overweight, was suggested as a treatment. Bathing the area with hydrogen peroxide and water, rubbing with methylsalicylate ointment, and (as a prophylaxis) exposure to artificial sunlight, were also suggested.

1831. Anagnostidis, N. Chilblains and hypovitaminosis. Contribution to the pathogenesis and the therapy of chilblains [In French]. *Rev. chir., Par., v. 84, Feb. 1947: 113–123.*

From his experiences, and from information on capillary permeability, the author recommends combined dosages of vitamins C and P for treatment of chilblains. Lacking synthetic vitamin C (vitamin P is not yet introduced into Greece), lemons and oranges should be eaten.

1832. Andrews, G. C. Dermatoses due to physical causes. *In: Diseases of the skin, p. 56–75. Philadelphia, Saunders, 1946.*

In short sections on chilblains (p. 59) and frostbite (p. 59–60), and on some other less commonly-occurring skin conditions arising from exposure to cold (p. 61–62), the author gives other names for some of the conditions, discusses the clinical symptoms, and recommends various methods of treatment. In chilblains, he suggests dosages of nicotinamide and calcium gluconate, the use of electric pads for warming, and localized x-ray for open lesions. The therapies suggested for treatment of frostbite are use of short-wave current, sympathetic anesthesia and sympathectomy, plasma transfusion, and administration of nicotinamide and parenteral vitamin B complex.

1833. Anning, S. T. Calciferol in the treatment of chilblains. *Lancet, Lond., 1947 (v. 2), Nov. 29: 794.*

The incidence of chilblains, during the period of September 1946 to March 1947, in persons taking large doses of calciferol was not significantly different from that of persons in the untreated, control, group. Also, there was no significant alteration of the course of the disease after it had developed, in either of the groups.

1834. Banchieri, F. R. Pathogenesis and treatment of perniosis. Notes on a personal method of treatment (anesthetic block) [In Italian]. *Minerva med., Tor., anno 39, (v. 1), Mar. 31, 1948: 331–334.*

The etio-pathogenesis, symptomatology, prophylaxis, and therapy of perniosis are discussed. The author mentions the therapeutic use of injected fluorescein; of vitamins B, B complex, C, and PP; anesthetic block; sympathetic ganglionectomy; and radiotherapy. He describes in detail the techniques he has used successfully, in treatment of perniosis, employing a 1% solution of Tutocaine in repeated anesthetic block of the femoral artery by injections into the popliteal space.

1835. Bernhard, E. On the treatment of cold-sensitivity illnesses [In German]. *Praxis, Bern, v. 34, Dec. 27, 1945: 753–755.*

Illnesses caused by cold sensitivity—acrocyanosis, perniosis, peripheral circulatory disturbances, and inflammatory processes causing joint deformities— are discussed. The author mentions the therapeutic use of sodium fluorescein, both by injection and orally; of periarterial infiltration of Priscoline; and, in joint cases, of the intra-articular injection of a Percaine-Novocain emulsion.

1836. Bonjour, ... A popular, rapid, and inexpensive treatment of chilblains. *Ther. Umschau, Bern, v. 2, Mar. 1946: 269.*

The author suggests quick immersion and withdrawal from very warm water as a therapy for the feet when afflicted with chilblains, even for ulcerated areas. For chilblains of the ear tip, cloths are to be wrung from very warm water and applied to the ear tip.

1837. Boruchin, S. A. New treatment of chilblains [In French]. *Médecin fr., v. 10, Nov. 10, 1950: 302–303.*

The author discusses the successful local use, on 38 patients afflicted with chilblains, of a pomade incorporating the dried leaves of a plant, *Verbascum tapsus.* The mode of action is thought to be vasomotor, acting on the sympathetic innervation of the capillaries to relieve the vascular spasm.

1838. Brack, W. Perniosis and Raynaud's disease and their treatment with benzylimidazoline (Priscoline) [In German]. *Schweiz. med. Wschr., v. 40, 1940: 948–954.*

Perniosis and Raynaud's disease are discussed as angioneuroses, or vasomotor impairments, affecting the thermoregulatory mechanisms. The physiology of blood flow through the skin, its regulation, and its importance in heat regulation are discussed. Case histories are given indicating successful treatment with benzylimidazoline (Priscoline) of patients suffering from insufficient circulation, especially patients with perniosis or Raynaud's disease. After treatment—administration can be oral—the hands and feet became warm again.

1839. Célice, ... , ... Duchesnay, and ... Pélicier. Chilblains—Vitamin B_1 and nicotinic acid [In French]. *Presse méd., v. 50, Oct. 10, 1942: 627–628.*

Satisfactory results in treatment of chilblains were obtained using nicotinic acid (which has a vasodilatory effect) in combination with vitamin B_1 (which aids vasomotility).

1840. Cordero, A. A. Treatment of chilblains with 2249F associated with vitamin K [In Spanish]. *Prensa med. argent., v. 38, May 11, 1951: 1158–1160.*

Treatment with a combination of vitamin K and the parasympathomimetic, 2249F, was successful with 21 of 25 patients suffering from chilblains.

1841. Daïnow, I. Treatment of chilblains with vitamins A and D. [In French, summaries in French, German, and English]. *Dermatologica, Basel, v. 86, 1942: 123–127.*

Intramuscular injections of vitamin A, D, and β-carotene gave good therapeutic results in treatment of chilblains. The author concludes that the primary factor in the production of chilblains is a dietary deficiency, and that cold acts only as the immediate stimulus for their appearance.

1842. Daïnow, I. Treatment of chilblains with synthetic antihistaminics [In French]. *Ther. Umschau, Bern, v. 3, June 1946: 51–55.* Abstract, in German, in: *Dermatologica, Basel, v. 93, 1946: 247.*

Successful treatment of several patients, suffering from chilblains, with the synthetic antihistaminic, Antergan, is discussed. Nicotinamide, known to have vasomotor properties, also acted favorably against chilblains. The author believes that nicotinamide acts through its antihistaminic properties, exercising an indirect vascular action opposite to the vasomotor effects of histamine, the latter being produced following the tissue injury.

1843. Deeds, D. Pernio: an instance of apparent recovery [Abstract]. *Proc. Centr. Soc. Clin. Res., v. 20, 1947: 88.* Similar abstract in: *J. Laborat. & Clin. M., v. 32, Dec. 1947: 1550.*

The author discusses the unsuccessful use of bilateral sympathectomy in the treatment of a case of perniosis which occurred on exposure to cold. Oral administration of dilute hydrochloric

acid, given as medication for gaseous indigestion in hypochlorhydria, seemed to have a beneficial effect on the pernio lesions. Histamine desensitization appeared to have been a successful
therapy since there had been no recurrence of the lesions for some time despite numerous
exposures to cold.

1844. Dowling, G. B. Chilblains and their treatment. *Practitioner, Lond., v. 161,
Dec. 1948: 465–468.*

Etiology, predisposing factors, pathology, and treatment of chilblains are discussed. Calciferol in large doses in treatment of chilblains is said to have gained little support as judged
from the literature; use of vitamin K has gained some support; and nicotinic acid has usually
been effective. However, adequate physical activity to promote peripheral circulation and
protection of warm footwear and gloves are most effective means of combating chilblains.
Local massage with medicated ointments, or preferably, exposure to ultraviolet light, are
effective means of promoting increased circulation.

1845. Farber, E. M. Chilblain and frostbite. *In: Current Therapy, p. 299–300.
Philadelphia, Saunders, 1949.*

In treatment of acute chilblains, further cold, trauma, or excessive heat is to be avoided.
Rubbing with snow is not recommended since it can cause further vasoconstriction and local
trauma. Warm boric acid dressing is to be used for 3 hours, then removed and the area dried,
and the whole procedure repeated. Heparin therapy is effective only if administered in the
first 24–48 hours. The prophylaxis recommended for chronic chilblain or chronic pernio, is to
keep warm, move to a milder climate, or wear elastic stockings or bandages before exposure
to cold. A wet dressing of penicillin or aluminum subacetate may be used if such areas become
infected. As a systemic treatment in cold injuries, to improve arterial and arteriolar circulation,
typhoid vaccine therapy or lumbar ganglionectomy is recommended.

1846. Fischer, G. The season of chilblains returns [In French]. *Concours méd., v.
64, Jan. 25, 1942: 119–120.*

This is a discussion of the incidence of chilblains during a severely cold winter in a war
year when there was a shortage of protective clothing, of good nutrition, and of sufficient
heating ($-2°$ to $4°C$) in living quarters. Despite the other factors, the author considers the
intensity of the cold to be the principal one causing the chilblains. For therapy of frostbite the
author discusses the use of injections of fluorescein, of radiation by ultraviolet, of anesthetic
injection of the sympathetic ganglia, of folliculin, of vitamin P-P, and of various antiseptic
solutions and ointments. Of the latter those containing glycerin are recommended for prophylactic use since glycerin intensifies the cutaneous circulation.

1847. Fracasso, E. Roentgenotherapy [In Italian]. *Ann. radiol. diagn., Bologna,
v. 18 (2), 1946: 190–192.*

Twenty-five patients with chilblains were treated successfully with roentgen therapy. The
techniques involved are discussed.

1848. Furniss, A. Chilblains and their treatment. *Nurs. Mirror, Lond., v. 84,
Dec. 28, 1946: 235–236.*

Chilblains are discussed briefly as to their incidence, predisposition, pathogenesis, prophylaxis, and treatment. As general preventive measures adequate clothing during cold exposure,
active exercise to improve peripheral vascular tone, good diet supplemented by vitamins A
and D, are discussed. As both prophylaxis and early treatment, alternate hot and cold baths
are recommended. Use of calcium, of thyroid and other glandular extracts, and of various
kinds of heat and light rays are discussed in treatment of the condition.

1849. Gourlay, R. J. The problem of chilblains, with a note on their treatment
with nicotinic acid. *Brit. M. J., 1948 (v. 1), Feb. 21: 336–339.*

Discussion with a considerable review of the literature is given, regarding the etiology, pathology, pathogenesis, and treatment of cold injuries. From the author's experiments on immersion

of a hand in water at 45°F (7.2°C) for a few minutes with or without a tourniquet, he concluded that a chilblain will result only when cold causes an arterial spasm, by vasoconstriction, and there is an upset of the balance between vital cellular activity and venous drainage. Because of the observed vasodilator action of nicotinic acid, the author used it, by oral administration, for cold-congested hands and noses of children and for chilblains. (That the action was not enzymatic was shown by the fact that nicotinamide—radical of co-enzyme 1 and 2—was ineffective.) Results were good but relapse usually occurred when administration stopped. 47 refs.

1850. Gruber, C. M. Handbook of treatment and medical formulary. *Philadelphia, Davis, 1948. 107 p.*

A brief description of the clinical symptoms and treatment of chilblains (pernio) is given including the formula for an ointment to be used in therapy.

1851. Hasler, H. P. Adrogel (histamine-acetylcholine) for perniosis [In German]. *Praxis, Bern, v. 36, Nov. 6, 1947: 757–759.*

Treatment, with Adrogel ointment, of perniosis suffered by 24 patients in the Thurgauer Hospital in Davos, is described as producing palliative effects somewhat superior to other, similar, treatments.

1852. Herxheimer, H. Passive hyperaemia for chilblains. *Lancet, Lond., v. 243, Nov. 28, 1942: 640–641.*

Successful treatment of chilblains is reported in 21 of 24 patients, employing passive hyperemia induced by peripheral venous congestion from a constricting bandage (Bier's method).

1853. Hinojosa, G. Peripheral vasodilators in therapy of erythema pernio [In Spanish]. *Medicina, Méx., v. 28, Aug. 10, 1948: 355–356.*

Three patients with erythema pernio treated with nicotinic acid obtained little relief. Intramuscular injection of acetylcholine brought relief to each of 14 similar patients. Treatments with histamine, in 9 cases, also brought relief of the erythema pernio condition.

1854. Holliday, C. B. The feet and the pharmacist; some useful formulas. *Chemist & Druggist, Lond., v. 148, July 5, 1947: 15.*

Formulas for several analgesic ointments, and other lotions for use in treatment of chilblains, are given.

1855. Ingram, J. T. Refresher course for general practitioners; chilblains. *Brit. M. J., 1949 (v. 2), Dec. 3: 1284–1286.*

The author discusses the etiology, diagnosis, complications, prophylaxis, and treatment of chilblains. Except as a general nutritional level may reflect in vascular tone, diet as such does not play a part. The tendency to have chilblains is essentially an individual matter, with, however, a familial tendency. Young persons, especially during puberty, appear to be more susceptible; recurrences are found at menopause and in old age; and disappearance often during pregnancy. In treatment he recommends general stimulation from massage and active movement but that local stimulation not be undertaken because of danger of skin irritation and breakage; calcium to be given by mouth or by injection, and also vitamin D to be given. Thyroid extract sometimes gives drastic relief.

1856. Jausion, ... , ... Somia, and ... Meunier. The treatment of chilblains with vitamin PP [In French]. *Bull. Soc. fr. derm. syph., v. 48, 1941: 219–227.*

A detailed account is given of the successful treatment with vitamin PP of chilblains in 39 women and 8 boys or men. Thirty-three of the patients had a positive tuberculin reaction with 14 of these also showing clinical signs and symptoms of tuberculosis; 10 had a negative tuberculin reaction. Vitamin PP, or nicotinamide, was given in doses of 50 mg both orally and by a combination of oral and intramuscular routes. Other factors which may be pertinent are climatic, endocrine (implied by great frequency of chilblains in women), and dietotoxic (being combated by nicotinic acid) conditions.

1857. Laquerrière, A. [Chilblains] [In French]. *Concours méd., v. 64, Mar. 1, 1942: 299–300.*

Contrary to the opinion of Fischer (item 1846) the author believes that cold alone does not cause chilblains but that other conditions, especially the presence of humidity, are equally responsible. He discusses the use of high-frequency electrical stimulation in treatment of chilblains.

1858. Lefevre, P., and B. Dubarry. The use of fluorescein in the treatment of chilblains [In French]. *Bull. Soc. fr. derm. syph., v. 48, Mar. 13, 1941: 217–219.*

Good results are reported following intravenous injection of isotonic fluorescein solution 2 or 3 times per week in the treatment of chilblains, whether of the erythematous papulous type or complicated by ulceration. The authors quote another worker as believing that the beneficial action of fluorescein in treatment of chilblains is caused by its properties of producing photosensitivity in the tissues being treated.

1859. Lefevre, P., B. Dubarry, and G. Halle. Preliminary results of treatment of chilblains with intravenous injections of fluorescein [In French]. *Ann. derm. syph., Par., v. 2, ser. 8, 1942: 178–181.*

Treatment of 85 chilblain patients (ages 8 to 80) with intravenous injections of fluorescein was reported: 57 with good results, 20 with questionable results, and 8 failures. Fluorescein seems to have a selective action on the peripheral blood vessels.

1860. Legrand, M. A. Comments on a treatment of chilblains [In French]. *Therapie, Par., v. 4 (2), 1949: 60–61.*

In the treatment of non-ulcerous chilblains, the author suggests a bath for 15 minutes each morning and evening using a physiological "solution oxygénée alcaline au ⅕e à pH 7.4". The bath is to be followed by gentle massage with cod or halibut oil or with the oil in a pomade incorporating vitamin PP. Calcium gluconate can be given by suppository. By the physico-chemical method of osmosis the oxygen of the solution combines with the hemoglobin in the capillaries below the skin to form oxyhemoglobin resulting in a gradual change in skin color from bluish to rosy red. In an alkaline medium the oxygen is able to release and replace the CO_2 to form still further oxyhemoglobin. Although cold is the primary cause of chilblains, other predisposing factors are anemia, lymphatism, avitaminosis, hormonal insufficiency, and poor nutrition. These factors should be considered also in any adequate therapy.

1861. Legrand, M. A. Considerations of chilblains and their treatment [In French]. *Bull. Soc. méd. Paris, v. 152, Jan. 1949: 5–6.*

The etiology of chilblains depends on two factors: exposure to cold and the physical state of the subject. Hormonal deficiency, avitaminosis, poor nutrition, anemia, and poor lymphatic or peripheral vascular states, are some of the conditions predisposing to chilblains. For therapy the author recommends the use of hydrogen peroxide, the giving of vitamin PP and of gluconate of calcium, and the use of tepid foot baths.

1862. LeRoy, L. G. Treatment of perniosis [In Dutch]. *Geneesk. gids., v. 20, Feb. 1942: 99–100.*

Three cases of perniosis, or chilblains, were treated successfully with a salve by the name of "Clovine". One patient, after the healing of the original lesion, used the preparation prophylactically before later exposures to cold and was able to avoid further lesions.

1863. Lesser, M. A. Chilblains. *Drug & Cosmet. Indust., v. 63, July 1948: 44–46; 125–128.*

The author states that the signs and symptoms of chilblains are well known although the causes are not; the condition is more prevalent in damp than in dry cold; the personal differences in susceptibility are great. The treatments advocated for relief of chilblains have been legion but their main object has been to improve local circulation of the affected limb. They include: exercise, special massage, electrical stimulation, diathermy, x-ray and other rays. He mentions the protective use of vitamins, and gives the formulas for several ointments for relief from chilblains.

1864. McGovern, T., and I. S. Wright. Pernio: a vascular disease. *Am. Heart J., v. 22, Nov. 1941: 583–606.*

Pernio is defined and distinguished from related conditions described in the literature. Four case histories are given in detail. It is concluded that pernio is a vascular disease affecting the smaller vessels of the skin, causing anoxemia of the tissues, and resulting in necrosis and ulceration. It is associated with exposure to cold, though not necessarily freezing. Acetyl-β-methylcholine chloride administered by iontophoresis, and protection of the legs by proper clothing, are suggested as treatment and prophylaxis.

In the discussion following the paper, DR. N. E. FREEMAN of Philadelphia stated that he had done a paravertebral block, anesthetizing the sympathetic lumbar ganglia, with good results in cases of pernio.

1865. Malherbe, A. Chilblains of the face and the hands. Pathological considerations and physiological treatment [Abstract, in French]. *Ann. derm. syph., Par., v. 1, 1941: 204.*

The author practiced infiltration of the sympathetic ganglion with Novocain, done with the use of the x-ray screen. He also stated that intramuscular acetylcholine gave good results in less severe cases.

1866. Milian, G. Chilblains [In French]. *Paris méd., v. 31, Dec. 30, 1941: 365–368.*

The author discusses the occurrence of chilblains in contrast to other manifestations of cold injury. Cold is often considered as a secondary factor in the etiology of chilblains, with vitamin insufficiency and endocrine disorders being considered to be primary factors. Patients with tuberculosis appear to be particularly susceptible to chilblains. Therapeutic aid has been achieved with the use of vasodilator substances, with fluorescein, or with vitamin PP and nicotinic amide.

1867. Nágera, J. M. Kinesiology and dermatology [In Spanish]. *Rev. argent. derm. sif., v. 31 (2), 1947: 238–248.*

Kinesitherapy is recommended by the author for lesions and scars resulting from cold and from chilblains.

1868. Newman, M. Chilblains; a review of a common winter problem. *Med. Illust., Lond., v. 4, Dec. 1950: 591–597.*

Since there is no specific treatment, either local or general, for chilblains, prevention is of greatest importance. As preventive measures the author suggests a good diet supplemented by cod-liver oil or vitamins A and D; adequate protective clothing when exposed to cold; and exercise, especially for persons doing sedentary work. In generalized therapy, the use of nicotinic acid, vitamin K, thyroid extract, calcium, and ultraviolet light are mentioned; in local therapy, various sedative salves, iodine for ulcerated areas, and possibly low-level exposures to x-ray, are suggested. For severe cases, paravertebral sympathetic block is discussed.

1869. Nomland, R. Cutaneous manifestations of the circulatory disorders of the foot. *J. Am. M. Ass.*, v. *124, Mar. 18, 1944: 747–750.*

In the section on Acrocyanosis, chilblain circulation, pernio, erythrocyanosis crurum puellaris (p. 749), the author discusses something of the pathogenesis of these conditions and also the therapy. He states that there is probably a large element of vasospasm in the causology of each of these conditions, and in the more advanced or complicated forms there is added vascular inflammation with stasis. Exposure to cold, particularly damp cold, should be avoided. Use of potassium permanganate or aluminum chloride may help prevent sweating. In severe cases lumbar sympathectomy may be necessary.

1870. Noordin, R. M. Chilblains. Pathology—prophylaxis—treatment. *S. Barth. Hosp. J. War Bull.*, *Lond.*, v. *1, Mar. 1940: 95–96.*

Chilblains are discussed as a minor ailment which is, however, often very distressing and incapacitating. Chilblains are stated to be, essentially, lesions of the capillary circulation. Cold appears to be the stimulus for the appearance of the condition and the length of the cold exposure determines the production and severity of the lesion. Early arterial constriction of spasm is followed by dilatation and later by an interruption in the venous return by constriction of the venules. As a prophylaxis injections of colloidal calcium and vitamin D, as well as the taking of cod-liver oil, are suggested. In severe cases bed rest should be advised together with injections of colloidal calcium.

1871. Obermer, E. Calciferol in the treatment of chilblains. *Lancet, Lond.*, v. *254, Mar. 20, 1948: 460–461.*

The author discusses the possible role of calcium in the etiology of chilblains and reports successful treatment in cases given one or two doses (10–20 ml each) of colloidal calcium plus calciferol (50,000–100,000 I. U. calciferol + 5–10 ml colloidal calcium).

1872. Pellerat, J. T2249 in chilblains [Abstract, in French]. *Ann. derm. syph.*, *Par.*, ser. *8, v. 5, 1945: 103.*

A new synthetic compound—T2249 (formol de trimethylaurmonium propanediol)— which manifested an interesting peripheral vasodilatating activity, was used in treatment of a group of 16 patients with typical symptoms of chilblains of hands and feet and a second group of 6 patients with less typical symptoms. In the first group, results with 8 patients were excellent; in 6, symptoms were considerably improved; and in 2, no improvement was seen with possibly some worsening of symptoms. In the second group, 1 patient showed improvement; there was no change in the 5 others.

1873. Pérez Guillermo, D. F. Therapy of erythema pernio (chilblains); pharmacology of fluorescein and its therapeutic use [In Spanish]. *Farmacoter. actual*, *Madr.*, v. *3, July 1946: 491–493.*

In the therapy of chilblains, the subjective disturbances were relieved after the first injection of fluorescein. Although scar formation occurred promptly in some cases of ulcerative lesions, in other cases there was little or no change noted. The author suggests the use, as an adjunct to fluorescein therapy, of a medicated ointment at the site of the lesion.

1874. Pérez y Rivera, M. E. Something about chilblains [In Spanish]. *Rev. pract., Valencia*, v. *5, Jan. 1949: 16–18.*

The author discusses chilblains as to general concepts, clinical features (erythematous phase, vesicular phase, and atypical forms), prophylaxis, and treatment. For local therapy he mentions the use of potassium permanganate, or salves with sulfonamide or penicillin base. Radiotherapy and diathermy have given beneficial results. Liver extracts, calcium salts, ergotamine tartrate (for neurovegetative dystonia), and vitamins A and D have also been used.

1875. Petges, G. Treatment of chilblains [In French]. *J. méd. Bordeaux, v. 119, 1942: 82–83.*

The author discusses the increased incidence of chilblains in persons who are immobile while at work in a cold environment; those who have a positive tuberculin reaction; and those who have a deficiency in calcium, phosphorus, or the vitamins A, D, or PP. Treatment by massive doses of vitamins, by diathermy or ultraviolet rays, and by use of various ointments and lotions, is discussed. The author states that the only rapid and certain method for good results is complete bed rest.

1876. Phelan, J. J. Chilbains. *Lancet, Lond., v. 252, Jan. 25, 1947: 160–161.*

Report is made of the use of vitamin D in treatment of 14 cases of chilblain with 8 cases reported cured, 3 improved, and 3 not benefited.

1877. Ranjan, M. P. Chilblain [In English]. *Ind. M. Rec., v. 65, Nov. 1945: 244–246.*

Chilblains are discussed as to definition of the term, pathology, etiology, clinical picture, sequelae, and treatment. Under generalized medical treatment, the author recommends the use of: calcium lactate or gluconate; vitamin D; codliver oil preparations; thyroid extract; ovarian extract; parathyroid or polyglandular tablets; or acetylcholine hydrochloride. Hyperemia may be produced by: Bier's congestion; ultraviolet or x-rays; local counter-irritants such as tincture of iodine or Friar's balsam; or sympathectomy in severe cases.

1878. Raybaud, A. Vitamin therapy of chilblains. Selective action of vitamin PP [In French]. *Marseille méd., v. 79, May 15, 1942: 325–328.*

The increased frequency of chilblains, during the unusually cold winters of 1940–41 and 1941–42, brought about a renewed interest in the pathogenesis, incidence, and treatment of the condition. An anemic state, lymphatism, general debility, a tuberculous condition, and endocrine or vitamin deficiency states have all been considered in the pathogenesis without the exact cause becoming known. The author discusses his experiences in successfully treating chilblains by topical application of vitamins A and D, in a pomade with cod-liver oil, and by vitamin PP given orally.

1879. Ross, C. C. Treatment of painful feet. *Canad. M. Ass. J., v. 43, Dec. 1940: 537–540.*

In a short section on chilblains of the feet the author states that good food and vitamins seem to help control the condition. He mentions the use of lumbar sympathectomy in severe cases.

1880. Ross, J. Chilblains. *Lancet, Lond., v. 252, Feb. 8, 1947: 233.*

The successful use for several years of calciferol in the therapy of chilblains is reported, but the author says that it has less value as a prophylactic.

1881. S., L. Therapy of chilblains and frostbite [In Italian]. *Clin. nuova, Roma., v. 13, Oct. 27, 1951: 527–528.*

In the local treatment of frostbite wet packs of warm (not to exceed 30 °C) boric acid applied to the injured area for 3-hour intervals, with an hour for drying between successive applications, are suggested. If there is itching of the area, application of Schamberg's lotion may be used. The lotion contains menthol, phenol, olive oil, lime water, and zinc oxide powder. In cases of severe injury, the use of intravenous heparin within the first 24–48 hours may be indicated, as well as the prophylactic use of large doses of penicillin. The therapy of chilblains is even less specific. Wet packs for the area using penicillin solution at the same time intervals as described above, are suggested. An eczematous condition may be relieved by the use of a zinc paste twice a day, removing the first application with mineral oil before putting on the next one. In a severe case, unless contraindicated by the patient's condition, the production of a fever by the administration of typhoid vaccine is suggested. In cases unresponsive to other treatment, lumbar ganglionectomy is advised.

1882. **S., S.** Chilblain liniment. *Chemist & Druggist, Lond., v. 148, July 5, 1947: 26.*

The formula is given for a liniment used successfully in treating chilblains.

1883. **Schneider, W.** On Priscoline treatment of perniosis and true freezing injury [In German]. *Med. Klin., Münch., v. 42, Jan. 1947: 15–17.*

Persons with perniosis often have a hypercalcemia and poor sympathetic nervous system tonicity. Variations of the K/Ca (potassium/calcium) quotient of such patients after treatment with Priscoline are discussed in cases of perniosis or of true freezing injuries. Treatment was considered to be successful when the K/Ca quotient became and remained at the normal value.

1884. **Simmons, H. J.** Treatment of chilblains by paravertebral sympathetic block. *Brit. M. J., 1945 (v. 2): 884.*

The successful use of anesthetic paravertebral sympathetic block to relieve vascular spasm of the vessels is reported in 6 of 8 patients where severe chilblain symptoms had been unrelieved by other methods of treatment.

1885. **Simon, C.** Chilblains, 1940 [In French]. *Bull. méd., Par., v. 55, Feb. 1941: 63–66.*

The discussion at a scientific meeting, of a new name for chilblains—pernio—is reported. Some generalized advice on therapy is also given.

1886. **Tecoz, H.** Annual occurrence: chilblains [In French]. *Praxis, Bern, v. 32, Dec. 16, 1943: 878–879.*

The symptomatology, etiology, predisposing factors, possible confusion with tubercular erythematous conditions, and therapy of chilblains are discussed together with some findings of earlier workers. Treatment of the condition is generally based on attempts to stimulate the peripheral circulation by such means as exercise, saline baths, or ultraviolet irradiation. Also used are vasomotor drugs (quinine, ergot, or belladonna) and others to help prevent edema (arsenic, calcium). Use of vitamins B and PP is often beneficial.

1887. **Watson, G. I.** Treatment of chilblains. *Lancet, Lond., v. 240, Mar. 1, 1941: 301–302.*

Six patients suffering from chilblains of hands, feet, or ear tips, were successfully treated by subcutaneous injection of small doses of histamine in or near the lesion. Histamine gave quick relief, often within an hour or so following a period of immediate and intense local irritation; this did not preclude another chilblain developing near the site of the treated one. Bee-toxin ointment was also used locally on four of the patients. The use of ointment, easily applied, gave slower but more prolonged relief, and therefore may be used prophylactically as well as in treatment.

1888. **Wheatley, D.** Chilblains and prothrombin levels. *Lancet, Lond., v. 258, Apr. 15, 1950: 712–714.*

Prothrombin-times of only one of sixteen persons with chilblains showed a slight deviation from normal. Of 26 cases studied, 23 responded completely to Vitamin K therapy, while 3 cases were not relieved by Vitamin K, by Vitamin P, or by vasodilator drugs.

1889. **Wheatley, D.** Vitamin K for the relief of chilblains. *Brit. M. J., 1947 (v. 2): 689–691.*

The successful treatment of 8 cases of chilblains with vitamin K is discussed.

1890. **Wooders, M. A., and D. A. Curtis.** Thermal effects of heat and cold. *In: Emergency Care, p. 96–99. Philadelphia, Davis Co., 1942.*

The etiology, pathology, symptoms, and treatment are outlined briefly for both frostbite and chilblains, and for hypothermia. In frostbite the frozen area should be rewarmed slowly, possibly by gentle rubbing with soft snow, while the patient himself is rapidly rewarmed. Suggested also is immersion of a frostbitten extremity in a water bath (about 50°C) while the patient gradually performs active movements with the foot or hand. Cold compresses, which are gradually warmed, are suggested for other areas such as the face. Aseptic procedures should be used to avoid infections which are apt to become very serious. Gentle exposure to heat or to sunshine for short periods is suggested. In hypothermic states the patient is to be placed in a recumbent position in a cool room; artificial respiration to be given if necessary; external heat to be applied consistently using blankets and the rubbing of the extremity with wet cloths (69°F, increased gradually to 85°F); warm enemas and intravenous solutions to be given as indicated. The patient should be carefully watched as delirium may result from the pain or elevation of body temperature.

1891. Yang, K. L. The use of honey in the treatment of chilblains, non-specific ulcers and small wounds: a preliminary report [In English]. *Chin. M. J., v. 62, 1944: 55–60.* Abstract in: *J. Am. M. Ass., v. 127, Mar 17, 1945: 680.*

Honey ointment was used successfully in more than 50 cases of chilblains, chilblain ulcers, and small wounds, treated at the National Medical College during its war-time location in Chungking in the winter of 1942. Because neither vaseline nor cod-liver oil was available during the war-time conditions, 80% honey and 20% lard were combined as an ointment, the rationale for the use of honey being its bacteriostatic action based on the high sugar content, and its probable high content of vitamin A. The ointment was found to have a hypertonic property to relieve passive congestion and edema. It appeared to stimulate epithelization and granulation tissue formation.

1892. Zarapico Romero, M. Perniosis [In Spanish]. *Medicina, Madr., v. 18, Mar. 1950: 216–224.*

The author discusses the affliction of perniosis with respect to incidence, etiology, complications, diagnosis (especially the atypical forms), therapy, complications, and prophylaxis. Under therapy is mentioned the use of various ointments and salves; pomades with a sulfonamide or penicillin base; radiotherapy; diathermy; and the use of fluorescein.

See also items: 732, 1791, 1794, 1810, 2330, 2368.

D. FROSTBITE

1. General

1893. Anon. Clinical aspects and management of localized freezing. Report of the military surgeon on 26 cases of frostbite encountered while on ski maneuvers. *Ed. by H. Debrunner. Bern, H. Huber, 1941. 128 p.*

Detailed analysis is given of 26 cases of frostbite in military personnel, including accounts of first aid, clinical picture, history, and roentgenologic aspects. The text is generously illustrated with black and white, and a few colored plates.

1894. Anon. Frostbite. *Bull. U. S. Army M. Dep., no. 71, Dec. 1943: 24–27.*

Frostbite injury results from actual freezing of the skin and subcutaneous tissue combined with prolonged peripheral vasoconstriction. The acute inflammatory reaction produced is very similar to that seen in burns. The reactive hyperemia which follows thawing depends on the degree and duration of exposure to cold and the rate at which the temperature of the part is raised. The characteristic "triple response" as found in burns is present; it consists of a local reddening, a wheal and/or a blister, and a flare, and is due to the release of histamine-like substances from the tissue cells probably from the injury by ice crystals. Transudation of fluid and even of blood cells into the tissue spaces occurs during the reactive hyperemia, and is due to the increased permeability of the damaged capillary endothelium. The incidence and severity of frostbite depend on the degree of cold and duration of exposure, and on the presence of wind and moisture. Circulatory stagnation due to inactivity is a contributing factor as are constriction of body areas, general vasoconstriction, trauma, nutritional deficiencies, and anoxia. Prophylactic measures involve avoiding heat loss by proper clothing and a minimum of exposure. Constricting clothing should not be worn; mittens will be warmer than gloves; hot food and non-alcoholic drinks are helpful but smoking should be avoided. In both first aid and treatment of frostbite, thawing should be induced gradually (often by the warmth of the bare hand over small areas of the face); massage or exercise should be avoided; general body warming may be done by wrapping in warm blankets. Treatment for shock or oxygen inhalation, may be necessary. Tetanus shots, and sulfa drugs by mouth, are indicated. Areas of ulceration and necrosis should be treated conservatively.

1895. Anon. Frostbite among air crews. *U. S. Air Force M. Serv. Digest, Nov. 1950: 14–16.*

Frostbite incidence among heavy bomber crews of the 8th Air Force flying from England in World War II, is tabulated with regard to the part of body affected, and the position of the crew member in the plane. Frostbite accounted for 43% of all wounds or injuries received in action by returning combat crew members. However, 59% of cases of frostbite involved the face, neck, and ears where the injury was often quite mild. The greatest single cause of frostbite was windblast (52%), and the second, failure of electrical equipment (22%). The waist gunners were the most frequently affected, and next the tail gunners and ball turret gunners. The problem was met during World War II by more structural improvement of the airplane itself, warmer clothing, and adequate training of crewmen. Since World War II the incidence among crewmen in flight has been practically negligible. The problem currently can become more acute because of the lower temperatures of the higher altitudes if cabin pressurization is lost through enemy action or equipment failure. Current experiments on effect of windblast on personnel exposed to short periods of very rapid chilling occurring during free-fall parachute descent from the stratosphere, have produced few instances of frostbite injury. Some of the improvements in flying clothing and the training of aircrewmen, are noted. Treatment of cold injuries is discussed in detail. Although paravertebral block or sympathectomy may relieve vasoconstriction, the painful sequelae are seldom relieved.

1896. Ar'ev, T. IA. Pathological and clinical considerations on frostbite [In Russian]. *Sovet. vrach. zh., v. 43 (7), 1939: 392–402.*

Some characteristics of the physiological reaction to cold as related to frostbite pathogenesis are noted. (1) Icing does not take place in living structures; (2) tissues possess greater resistance to excessive cold than to excessive heat, owing to the coagulating effect of heat on protein; (3) the retardation of biological processes in cold conditions improves the chances of recovery from cold injury; (4) the full effects of cold injury do not become apparent until after rewarming; (5) tissue processes resulting from freezing are highly reversible. Cold injury is shown to occur in certain regions of the body with greater frequency than in others. Sequelae are listed and analyzed. A section concerned with therapy recommends rapid rewarming, measures to promote circulation, and prevention of infection.

1897. Ar'ev, T. IA. Basic features of the present-day knowledge of frostbite [In Russian]. *Moskva, Medgiz, 1943. 48 p.*

Present-day knowledge of frostbite is discussed under the following chapter headings: pathogenesis and etiology; pathological anatomy; clinical considerations; treatment of trench foot, frostbite of the heel or face, and complications of frostbite; organization of hospital and medical facilities for treatment of frostbite during war time; and prefention of frostbite. In the introduction the author lists the names of several other Russian scientists currently active in the field of cold injury, including some technical specialists, roentgenologists, surgeons, and therapists.

* **1898. Ar'ev, T. I͡A., V. S. Gamov, S. S. Girgolav, and D. G. Rokhlin.** Frost-bite injuries. *In: Opyt sovetskoĭ medit͡siny v Velikoĭ Otechestvennoĭ Voĭne, 1941–1945 v. 1, p. 191–331 [In Russian]. Moskva, Medgiz, 1951.* Also, translation in: E. HOPE. *Frostbite. Translations from the Russian of a collection of sixteen papers published between 1939 and 1944, p. 3–12. Ottawa, Defence Research Board, Canada, 1950.*

"*Contains* an extensive monograph on frostbite written by leading Russian authorities, with the following chapters: 1. Historical data (p. 194–95), dealing with frostbite losses in wars since Napoleonic Russian campaign. 2. Statistical data (p. 196–210) on localization, extent, degree of damage; wound and frost damage combined; freezing to death. 3. Etiology and pathogenesis of frost injury (p. 211–37), dealing with kinds of frost damage; theory of pathogenesis; disseminative necrosis; conditions creating and assisting frostbite: mechanical impediments to circulation, local and general loss of resistance, effect of the tactical position. 4. Some data on tissue changes due to frostbite (p. 238–39). 5. Diagnosis (p. 241–51), presenting general and x-ray diagnosis. 6. Classification and symptomatology of frostbite (p. 252–59), discussing 4 degrees of frostbite, symptoms, x-ray pictures, etc. 7. Complications (p. 260–80), dealing with local complications of soft tissues, joints and bones; general complications; late complications and sequelae. 8. Therapy (p. 281–321), including first aid; conservative therapy; surgical therapy; post-operative treatment; therapy according to the degree of frostbite. 9. Prophylaxis (p. 322–23), collective and general. 10. Results and conclusions (p. 326–31), stressing the value of instructing the soldier about frostbite and its prophylaxis; the importance of proper clothing and shoegear; the great success of therapy by quick rewarming, and the preference for early necrotomy and necrectomy."—Arctic Bibl., v. 4, 1954: 51.

1899. Arnulf, G. Frostbite of limbs and its treatment [In French]. *Presse méd., v. 58, May 31, 1950: 605–606.*

In the etiology of freezing injuries of the fingers and toes exposure to cold (0°C or lower) is the primary factor with moist-cold being more dangerous than dry-cold. Poor circulation, fatigue, or anxiety are contributing factors. Cold injuries have been found to be benefited by cleansing of the area with mercurochrome; giving of vitamins B, PP, C, D; giving of anti-histaminics; use of antibiotics; in some cases, the use of anticoagulants. The therapy employed should take into account the phase of the injury, whether it is early, late, or is a sequelae condition.

1900. Bankert, C. W. Frostbite. *Arch. Phys. Ther., v. 25, Mar. 1944: 144–149.*

In this brief and general account of frostbite, the author discusses the etiology, clinical and pathological findings, prevention, and treatment.

1901. Baumann, E. Cold injuries in war [In German]. *Allg. schweiz. Militärztg., v. 90, Jan. 1944: 67–92.*

A general account is given of frostbite as seen among military casualties. Local and generalized freezing injuries are described in detail, including the clinical picture, pathology, prophylaxis, and treatment. The various stages of gangrene following frostbite are illustrated in color.

1902. Beek, C. H. On a peculiar predilection for frostbite [In German]. *Dermatologica, Basel, v. 82, 1940: 21–25.*

Ten cases of frostbite are described with the lesions on the inner side of the knee. This region is said to be unusually sensitive to cold injury.

1903. Beltramini, A. Clinical aspects and therapy of wartime frostbite [In Italian]. *Settimana med., v. 36, Aug. 31, 1948: 308–321.*

---

* Original not seen.

This general discussion of frostbite covers the etiology, pathogenesis, clinical aspects, and symptomatology of 1st, 2nd, and 3rd degree frostbite. The use of oscillometry and radiography, and of therapy by physical, medicinal, and surgical measures, are reviewed.

1904. Bering, F. On frostbite [In German]. *Münch. med. Wschr. v. 88, Jan. 31, 1941: 123–125.*

This is a general account of the clinical picture, pathology, and prophylaxis of frostbite.

1905. Block, W. The significance of the autonomic nervous system in the etiology of localized freezing [In German]. *Arch. klin. Chir., v. 204, Dec. 30, 1942: 64–83.*

A study was made of 100 cases of frostbite among German soldiers on the Eastern Front. Special attention was paid to signs of autonomic imbalance, which the author regards as a very important factor in the pathogenesis of frostbite. Psychological factors such as fear and mental stress (with its accompanying adrenaline production) were also regarded as important.

1906. Böttcher, H. Experimental investigations on localized freezing by prolonged exposure to mild cold [In German]. *Virchows Arch., v. 312, Apr. 25, 1944: 464–485.*

Groups of white rats had their tails packed in a mixture of ice and salt (temperature of 0° to −4°C) for various periods of time. In one group, the tails were cooled for 10 hours at a time on each of 4 days, and the process was repeated after a recovery period of 2 to 3 days, until visible changes appeared. Other groups had their tails cooled continuously until the animals died or were killed after the appearance of a visible effect. By these methods of local cooling damage to all tissues, up to the appearance of genuine gangrene, was produced. The extent of damage and the time of appearance depended on the duration of the cold exposure, on the interval of repetition, and on the individual animal's sensitivity to cold. Tissue damage is said to be caused by derangements of metabolic functions because of the state of vessel contraction.

1907. Borgoraz, N. A. Plastic surgery [In Russian]. 2nd edit., volume 1. *Moskva, Medgiz, 1949. 378 p.*

Brief statistical data on frostbite injuries are given (p. 51–52). In peacetime, at the Leningrad Medical Institute, 71 frostbite cases were seen in 5 years (as against 419 cases of burns). According to Girgolav's report at the 24th Session of Surgeons (1938), 30,000 frostbite casualties occurred in the French Army in one year of war, 37,000 in the Italian Army, and 2,500 in the Republican Spanish Army (in a mountain range, near Ternela). In the Tomsk region, where the winter lasts 8 months and the temperature drops to −45°C, frostbite injuries were 2% of all the hospital cases during 5 years. In Rostov on the River Don, frostbite injuries represented 0.16% of all 1912–1936 hospital cases.

1908. Breitner, B. On frostbite [In German]. *Deut. Zschr. Chir., v. 259, Sept. 27, 1944: 273–295.*

A review is made of German literature on frostbite up to 1944 in World War II. No conclusion seems to emerge from a study of the problem of why certain individuals are more sensitive to frostbite than others. Pathogenesis, clinical picture, sequelae, and methods and results of treatment are exhaustively and critically discussed. 47 refs.

1909. Brownrigg, G. M. Frostbite in shipwrecked mariners. *Am. J. Surg., v. 59, Feb. 1943: 232–247.*

Account of the author's experience with cold injuries among shipwrecked mariners treated by himself and his colleagues in hospitals at St. John's, Newfoundland. Etiology, clinical aspects, pathology, and treatment are discussed. The author points out the similarities between his cases and those described as immersion foot. He prefers the term frostbite since he regards cold as the common and decisive etiological factor.

1910. Castellaneta, V. Cold accidents in the armies with special regard to the last great war [In Italian]. *Gior. med. mil., v. 87, Aug. 1939: 815–837.*

The information given deals with frostbite and trench foot suffered in the first World War, 1914–1918.

1911. Cavina, G. Some pathological considerations on frozen feet in wartime [In Italian]. *Minerva med. Tor., anno 33 (v. 1), Jan. 27, 1942: 121–125.*

This is a brief note on the pathological findings in various degrees of frostbite of the feet.

1912. Craig, H. K. Frostbite and the effects on the human body. *J. Nerv. Ment. Dis., v. 101, Mar. 1945: 272–276.*

This is a brief general statement on the etiology and pathogenesis of frostbite. Mention is made of recent Russian writings on this subject.

1913. Curry, W. A., and R. W. Begg. Experiences with frostbite and allied conditions among torpedoed merchant seamen. *Nova Scotia M. Bull. v. 21, Dec. 1942: 313–317.*

Groups of torpedoed merchant seamen who, during the winter of 1941–42, had been exposed to the cold of the North Atlantic for one to eighteen days, were treated at the Halifax Infirmary. The crews represented all the United Nations. The mortality rate in the boats had been high, but it was noted that the rate had been particularly high amongst the Chinese and South Americans who were prone to give up hope of being rescued and to make no effort to stimulate their failing circulation. Of 50 cases admitted to the hospital, 2 died, 2 developed an acute mania, 12 required amputation, and 5 other primary guillotine amputations were performed for uncontrolled infection. During 1942 all exposure cases were transferred to Camp Hill Hospital where the group of about 250 cases were treated very successfully with dry cold. Immersion of feet in sea water, not necessarily cold water, for relatively long periods of time brings about the intensely painful condition known as immersion foot in which the foot looks quite similar to one recovering from frostbite.

1914. Davis, L., J. E. Scarff, N. Rogers, and M. Dickinson. High altitude frostbite: preliminary report. *Surg. Gyn. Obst., v. 77, Dec. 1943: 561–575.*

This is a very detailed and well illustrated study of high altitude frostbite. The authors take the view that this is a separate clinical entity and that the anoxia and very low temperatures encountered at high altitude are important contributory factors. Detailed observations on the pathological physiology and treatment of this condition are also recorded.

1915. E., J. Frostbite in horses. *J. R. Army Vet. Corps, v. 15, Feb. 1944: 32.*

This brief note is based on German accounts of frostbite in horses observed on the Russian front. It was noted that horses exposed to cold adapt to it by growing long-haired coats. When over-exerted and under-fed they sometimes developed a hypothermic state. Local frostbite was rare and most commonly affected the penis and ears although the extremities were sometimes also injured. Clinically, it resembled human frostbite with erythema, edema, and necrosis. Treatment included the gradual thawing of exposed members, rubbing with snow, and applying of ointments.

1916. Erickson, D. J. A histopathological study of the effects of hypothermic applications on the trunk of experimental animals. (Thesis, M.S. in Physical Medicine.) *Minneapolis, University of Minnesota, 1948. 43 p.*

Cold injuries were produced experimentally on the anterior and lateral abdominal walls of rabbits and dogs by the direct application to the shaved surface of solid carbon dioxide for periods from 30 seconds to 2 hours. Tissues were removed for histopathological examination over periods of time from 1 minute to 2 months after exposure. Gross and microscopic changes were outlined during the thawing period, the early-through-late reactive periods, and during early and late healing. It is concluded that damage by frostbite is due to the direct action of cold as well as to the effect on circulation secondary to the damage to blood vessels.

1917. Fièvez, J. Severe frostbite of the feet: tri-colored foot; some pathogenic, prophylactic, and therapeutic considerations [In French]. *Progr. med., Par., v. 67, Dec. 9, 1939: 1326–1333.*

The etiology, clinical aspects, pathology, prophylaxis, and treatment of severe frostbite, are discussed. Included are sections on rewarming and on surgery.

1918. Franz, C. A. O. War surgery [In German]. *In: Lehrbuch der Kriegschirurgie, p. 349–350. Berlin, Springer-Verlag, 1942.*

In this section of Chapter XIX on Frostbite and Burns it is stated that, during the course of a war, cold injuries of the feet become a major problem. Susceptibility to frostbite would appear to be related to constitutional type and to be more prevalent in persons addicted to the use of alcohol. Novocain infiltration of the stellate ganglion is discussed as an aid to recovery and in the prevention of amputation. Anti-tetanus injections are advised.

1919. Frey, S. Local freezing in war [In German]. *Med. Klin., Berl., v. 38, Oct. 23; Oct. 30; Nov. 6, 1942: 1009–1012; 1036–1038; 1067–1069.*

A study was made of 900 cases of cold injury seen by the author on the Eastern Front. The pathogenesis, clinical manifestations, and treatments of freezing injuries are discussed. Three clinical forms are described: erythematous, bullous, and gangrenous. Novocain block and lumbar sympathectomy are recommended treatments.

1920. Frias, G. G. L. Problems on parachute jumps over the Andes. *J. Aviat. M., v. 21, Aug. 1950: 343–346.*

One of the several problems enumerated and discussed in connection with emergency parachute jumps over the Andes, at altitudes of 15,000 feet or above, is that of frostbite injury.

1921. Friedman, N. B., and K. Lange. The pathology of experimental frostbite [Abstract]. *Fed. Proc., Balt., v. 5, Mar. 1946: 220–221.*

Exposure of the legs of heparinized rabbits to cold resulted in a few small vesiculating and necrotizing lesions of the skin, but gangrene did not occur.

1922. Friedman, N. B., and R. A. Kritzler. The pathology of high altitude frostbite, *Am. J. Path., v. 23, Mar. 1947: 173–187.*

Studies on the morbid anatomy of high-altitude frostbite were made on amputated tissues (mostly fingers) sent to the Army Institute of Pathology in Washington, D. C. The injuries occurred on high-altitude bombing missions, and fingers were most commonly affected on account of the removal of gloves. Agglutinative thrombosis and vascular lesions were the most prominent microscopic findings, and gangrene was thought to result from ischemia rather than from freezing. Lesions resembled those of trench foot.

1923. Fuhrman, F. A., and J. M. Crismon. Studies on gangrene following cold injury. I. A method for producing gangrene by means of controlled injury by cold. *J. Clin. Invest., v. 26, Mar. 1947: 229–235.*

This is the first of a series of papers on experimental frostbite. A method is described for inducing gangrene in the ears and feet of rabbits by immersion in a water-ethylene-glycol mixture at a temperature of −55°C.

1924. Fuhrman, F. A., and J. M. Crismon. Studies on gangrene following cold injury. II. General course of events in rabbit feet and ears following untreated cold injury. *J. Clin. Invest., v. 26, Mar. 1947: 236–244.*

The pathogenesis of experimental frostbite and gangrene in the ears and feet of rabbits is described. Injury was produced by immersing the extremities in a water-ethylene-glycol-alcohol mixture at −55°C.

1925. Gamov, V. S. Clinical handling and operative treatment of the higher degrees (3rd, 4th) of frostbite [In Russian]. *Leningrad, Medgiz, 1946. 140 p.*

The world literature is reviewed on the nomenclature and classification, pathogenesis, clinical aspects, complications, and surgical treatment of frostbite, covering the period from 1939 to 1946. 200 refs.

1926. Giordanengo, G. General concepts on freezing injuries [In Italian]. *Minerva med., Tor., anno 31 (v. 2), Dec. 15, 1940: 594–596.*

The protoplasm of warm-blooded animals does not freeze at 0°C but often not until the tissue temperature reaches −5°C do these irreversible changes occur. Other factors which condition the extent of freezing are the intensity and duration of cold exposure; whether or not there is also exposure to wind; the physical and nutritional state; and whether it is a dry or wet cold. The major injury is not that directly from the cold but that due indirectly to the vascular changes resulting from the exposure. The author discusses also the pathological manifestations of 1st, 2nd, and 3rd degree injuries, including the complications often found in the latter two groups.

1927. Girgolav, S. S. Frostbite and its treatment [In Russian]. *Trudy 24-go Vsesoiuznogo S"ezda Khirurgov, Kharkov, 1938, p. 188–196. Kharkov, Medgiz, 1939.*

This general discussion of frostbite and its treatment includes the author's theory of the pathogenesis of the injury. Pathological changes are of an inflammatory nature. Disruption of the colloid state within the cells results in the death of the cells and dissemination of necrosis in the tissue. These disseminated necrotic areas are especially manifested near the blood vessels and nerves and induce proliferating, long-lasting, inflammatory processes. This necrosis differs from that of the large necrosed tissue areas observed clinically after frostbite, which are almost exclusively a secondary consequence of the cessation of blood circulation. In the treatment of frostbite the decisive role is played by first aid measures, which determine the reversibility of the processes. Rapid rewarming (up to 37°–38°C) starting from a temperature slightly above that of the chilled body, is recommended. Restoration of the circulation can be aided by long, careful, massage under aseptic conditions. Use of mild antiseptic solutions and of ointments containing cod-liver oil is helpful. Amputations should be done only after appearance of the demarcation line.

1928. Girgolav, S. S. Frostbite [In Russian]. *Leningrad, Medgiz, 1939. 28 p.*

A very general outline of frostbite injuries is presented in popular pamphlet form including the following subject headings: incidence of frostbite and the general circumstances of its appearance, degrees of frostbite, general action of cold, factors contributing to frostbite, most susceptible parts of the body, prophylaxis, first aid, and treatment. The importance of immediate warming of the body (by baths, starting at 22°–25°C and increasing to 36°C) and of the restoration of circulation is stressed. For prophylactic purposes annointing of the exposed parts with a mixture of beef grease and cod-liver oil (with added antiseptic for preservation) is useful. Early mobilization is very important.

* 1929. Girgolav, S. S. Frostbite [In Russian]. *Nov. Khir. arkh., v. 43 (1–2; kn. 170–171), 1939: 148–158.*

"*Contains* text of an address delivered before the 24th All-Soviet assembly of surgeons. Includes information on: causes of frost injuries; some mass occurrences of frostbite in war and peace; pathogenesis and pathology of frostbite; clinical course and degrees of frostbite; comparisons with heat damage and burns; mitigating and complicating factors in frostbite; trench-foot; first-aid in frostbite."—Arctic Bibl., v. 4, 1954: 340–341.

---

* Original not seen.

* **1930. Girgolav, S. S.** Clinical aspects and treatment of frostbite [In Russian]. *Vest. khir. t. 60, kn. 1–2, July–Aug. 1940: 86.*

> *"Contains* an abstract of a paper delivered at the Leningrad Conference of workers of evacuation hospitals and of special departments of hospitals and institutes (May 25–27, 1940). Includes information on the condition of frostbite cases seen in the evacuation hospitals; degrees of frostbite (4); the problems of gangrene and mummification."—Arctic Bibl., v. 4, 1954: 340.

1931. Girgolav, S. S. Modern findings on frostbite [In Russian]. *Klin. med., Moskva, v. 21 (1–2), 1943: 3–6.* Also, in English, in: *Am. Rev. Soviet M., v. 1, June 1944: 437–440.* Translation also in: E. HOPE. *Frostbite. Translations from the Russian of a collection of sixteen papers published between 1939 and 1944, p. 13–17. Ottawa, Defence Research Board, Canada, 1950.*

> The physiology, pathology, therapy, and prophylaxis of frostbite, are considered in this general review of work done by Soviet investigators.

* **1932. Gogin, E. E.** Frostbite [In Russian]. *Med. sestra, Nov. 1951 (11): 21–23.*

> *"Contains* elementary information on the causes and pathology of frostbite; degrees of frostbite; recognition of frostbite; first aid and local therapy."—Arctic Bibl., v. 4, 1954: 345.

1933. Goldhahn, R. Freezing [In German]. *Deut. med. Wschr., v. 66, Jan. 19, 1940: 58–61.*

> The etiology, clinical aspects, and treatment of general and local freezing injuries are discussed. Recommendations for therapy include the use of alternating hot and cold baths. In mild cases of frostbite salves such as $CaCl_2$ with Euresol-eucalyptol were used; in more severe cases lumbar sympathectomy was resorted to.

1934. Goldhahn, R. Freezing injury [In German]. *Med. Welt, v. 15, Nov. 15, 1941: 1173–1176.*

> This article covers the etiology, clinical aspects, and treatment of freezing injury. For severe cases lumbar sympathectomy is used.

1935. Goldstein, N., and M. P. Manning. Frostbite from prolonged exposure to moderate temperatures. *J. Pediat., S. Louis, v. 39, Nov. 1951: 616–617.*

> A case history is given of a Negro girl of 8 who developed typical frostbite of the helix of the right ear after her head had rested within 6 inches of an oxygen outlet (temperature, 65° to 70°F) of an oxygen tent for several days. The child had been suffering from acute rheumatic fever and congestive heart failure. About two months after exposure the entire frostbitten area had sloughed.

1936. Greene, R. Frostbite and trench foot. *Lancet, Lond., v. 238, Feb. 17, 1940: 303–305.*

> This general account of frostbite and trench foot includes sections on etiology, prophylaxis, and treatment. The author also describes certain experiences with high-altitude frostbite observed on an expedition to the Himalayan Mountains and mentions the successful use of oxygen inhalation from a mouthpiece at high altitudes. Supercooling does not harm the skin; prolonged freezing does. The capacity to supercool may be abolished by soaking the skin in water. To help induce supercooling skin should be dried and unwashed for a week or so or be rubbed with olive oil. Frostbite and trench foot are said to be essentially the same condition with the former due primarily to cold exposure alone, and the other from lesser degrees of cold but with added damp and muscular inactivity. In both, the damage is due primarily to cold and secondarily to transudation from the blood vessels. Because of the latter condition it is essential

---

* Original not seen.

not to use warmth in treatment. Emphasis should be given to prophylaxis, use of gentle methods, complete rest, and avoidance of sepsis.

1937. Guénon des Mesnards, G. M. Contribution to the study and treatment of frozen feet [In French]. (Dissertation, Univ. Paris.) *Paris, Univ. Paris, 1941. 64 p.*

This doctoral dissertation deals with the etiology, clinical aspects, pathological anatomy, pathogenesis, prophylaxis, and treatment of frostbite and trench foot.

1938. Hass, G. M., and C. B. Taylor. A quantitative hypothermal method for the production of local injury of tissue. *Arch. Path., Chic., v. 45, May 1948: 563–580.* Abstract in: *J. Laborat. Clin. M., v. 32, Dec. 1947: 1512;* and in: *Proc. Centr. Soc. Clin. Res., v. 20, 1947: 49–50.*

An instrument and method are described by which a flat or circular cooling element produces cylindrical lesions of identical size by the flow of cold liquids through the element. Areas of the brain, heart, or liver of experimental animals were progressively and selectively destroyed by this method. Detailed histological examinations indicated a sharp line of demarcation between the non-viable and viable cells at the periphery of the area treated. Such hemorrhage as occurred was capillary in type and spontaneously controlled. Healing was slow but otherwise uncomplicated; suppuration did not occur.

1939. Hayward, E. On freezing [In German]. *Zschr. Ärtzl. Fortbild., v. 37, Jan. 15, 1940: 44–47.*

This article covers the etiology, clinical aspects, and treatment of frostbite.

1940. Holman, D. V., and M. Pierce. Non-gangrenous frostbite of the feet. *Am. Heart J., v. 34, July 1947: 100–113.*

An analysis is given of 200 cases of frostbite casualties observed during the fall and winter of 1944–1945 in the European Theatre of Operations. Etiology and clinical findings are discussed, and a classification of degree of injury is presented. Marked vasospasm appears to be the chief morbid finding. The results of treatment are indicated. Of the 200 cases only 45 recovered sufficiently to return to duty, 21 to combat and 24 to limited duty.

1941. Hübner, A. Frostbite and its recognition as the result of industrial accident [In German]. *Mschr. Unfallh., v. 48, Mar. 1941: 130–131.*

The severe cold of winter brings with it many injuries due to freezing which present to industrial medical personnel the problem of determining whether or not the injury was the result of occupational accident. Decision must depend upon the time of exposure, i.e., whether the damage took longer to develop than the time spent on the job.

1942. Jausion, . . . , . . . Meunier, . . . Somia. Frostbite and circulatory syndromes of the extremities [In French]. *Bull. Soc. fr. derm. syph., v. 48, 1941: 227–231.*

This is a discussion of frostbite with emphasis on etiology. It is concluded that susceptibility to tuberculous infections may result from the hormonal disturbances and the vascular instability induced by frostbite. It is noted that vitamin PP, or nicotinamide, used successfully in therapy, is a derivative of pyridine and has parasympathicomimetic action.

1943. Jenrich, ... A contribution to the subject of freezing [In German]. *Deut. med. Wschr., v. 68, Nov. 6, 1942: 1092–1093.*

This discussion on frostbite as seen among soldiers is based upon the author's experiences with the German Army. He points out that some soldiers suffer from frostbite only infrequently even in extreme cold while others are affected even at moderately cold temperatures.

The author who saw all grades of severity of frost injury recommends dry treatment, very conservative surgery, and great patience. He obtained generally good results, and such complications as suppuration, edema, and gangrene either were prevented or they rapidly subsided.

1944.   Johnson, C. A. Frostbite—experimental and clinical observations. *Arch. Phys. M., v. 28, June 1947: 351–359.*

Experiments were performed on monkeys in which the hands and feet were exposed to cold for 15 minutes. The pathogenesis of the injury was observed by studying amputated fingers and toes removed at varying intervals. Attempts to evaluate various forms of treatment were inconclusive. However, the beneficial effects of immediate use of the feet during the healing process was noted. A case of a man who suffered frostbitten hands, and lost several fingers by spontaneous amputation, is described. Active physical therapy is recommended in such a case.

1945.   Jordan, J. On the management and complications of acute freezing [In German]. *Sitzber. Phys. med. Soz. Erlangen, v. 73, 1943: 111–120.*

Experiences with frost injury among German soldiers on the Eastern Front are noted. The clinical findings are discussed. Emphasis is placed on early treatment aimed at restoring the circulation as quickly as possible and thus reducing complications.

1946.   Keynes, G. L. Cold—R.A.F.'s other enemy—is beaten. *Mil. Surgeon, v. 95, July 1944: 3–5.*

During the early years of World War II, in 1939 and 1940, frostbite was a real hazard to the efficiency of bomber air-crews. Flights were often for many hours at heights of 15,000 feet and over when the temperature inside the earlier, unheated, bombers was often −20° to −30°C. The body areas most susceptible were the hands when accidentally uncovered, and the ear and nose tips when not covered by ear phones and oxygen mask. The use of protective, light-weight clothing, but particularly the re-designing of the bomber to provide adequate warming without drafts, removed this cause of disability of bomber air-crews.

1947.   Killian, H. On the pathological physiology of frostbite and the foundation of a rational treatment [In German]. *Z. Chir., v. 69, Nov. 7, 1942: 1763–1775.* Abstract, in German, in: *Deut. med. Wschr., v. 69, Mar. 26, 1943: 286.*

An elaborate study of the pathological physiology and morbid anatomy of cold injury, general and localized, is made in order to provide a basis for a theory of treatment.

1948.   Killian, H. Frostbite [In German]. *Deut. Gesundwes., v. 1, Feb. 15, 1946: 33–37.*

This is a report on body changes observed in cold injury during a drop in blood temperature from 37°C to 25°C. In generalized cooling the author distinguishes four phases, ending with cell necrosis or death. In local frostbite 3 degrees are described, ending with irreversible cyanosis.

1949.   Korhonen, A. Frostbite injuries in war [In Finnish, with German summary]. *Duodecim, Helsin., v. 56 (8), 1940: 128–135.* Also, in Swedish, in: *Nord. med., v. 103, Feb. 15, 1941: 516–518.*

The author's experiences with frostbite in the Russo-Finnish War during the winter of 1939–1940, are recounted. Of the 142 cases reported, 60% had one foot frostbitten and 40% had both. Therapeutic measures were designed to keep the necrotic areas dry and to prevent the spread of wet gangrene.

1950.   Krotkov, F. Frostbite and its control in the armed forces [In Russian]. *Voen. san. delo, 1938 (1): 18–24.*

The prevalence of frostbite as a cause of injury during wartime, is reviewed for several major wars. There is discussion of the pathology of both local and generalized cold injuries. The protective value of clothing, especially of footwear and in ski troops, is considered. Since good nutrition is an aid in resistance to cold, special attention should be paid to providing a high-calorie, nutritive diet, of approximately 4,000 Calories including about 100 g of fat per day. At an environmental temperature of −30°C, meals should be eaten indoors and food should be served hot at least twice a day. The prophylactic value of various salves and ointments for use on exposed areas of the body is still debatable. Much depends on the chemical composition of the fats used in the compounds. They should be non-irritating to the skin; contain no water, soap, or acid; have a melting point in the range of 30°–40°C. Goose grease, Vaseline, paraffin, and paraffin oil appear to produce best results. The author's personal observations lead him to prefer the use of mineral oil, and he shares the English point of view that ointments or salves should be well-rubbed into the skin rather than be used merely to cover it.

1951. Kulikov, S. I. Diseases in a motorized unit in war [In Russian]. *Voen. san. delo, 1940 (10): 97.*

In a brief statistical account of casualities (not combat-connected) in a motorized unit in wartime, the percentage of frostbite injuries was 2.6% to 3.3%. The duration of treatment of these injuries, together with other purulent conditions, was the longest of any in the group.

1952. Lacroix, P. Frostbite and trench foot [In French]. *Concours méd., v. 62, Mar. 17, 1940: 409–410.*

The etiology, clinical aspects, pathology, prophylaxis, and treatment of frostbite and trench-foot are reviewed. Recommendations for treatment include the use of camphor-borate solution, warm baths, anti-tetanus serum, passive massage, and in severe cases lumbar sympathectomy.

1953. Lambert, A. Frostbite and chilblain, eczema of nurslings [In French]. *Union méd. Canada, v. 70, 1941: 640–641.*

Although both frostbite and chilblains are the result of injury following cold exposure, they vary greatly in symptomatology, development, and treatment. In frostbite the cold is of primary concern in etiology. In chilblains many factors besides cold may contribute to the etiology: previous infections, especially tubercular; familial predisposition; vascular state; or endocrine state. Chilblains also are a dermatotic state with certain body areas being predisposed to attack.

1954. Landis, E. M., and H. Montgomery. Diseases of the circulatory system; frostbite. *In: Modern medical therapy in general practice, v. 3, p. 2841–2842. Ed. by* D. P. Barr. *Baltimore, Williams & Wilkins, 1940.*

Lesions from frostbite are divided into three degrees according to the severity of the injury. First degree injury is usually followed by spontaneous recovery but second and third degree injuries produce some amount of mutilation. Moisture, wind velocity, and temperature all affect the incidence. Brahdy [J. Amer. M. Ass., v. 104, 1935: 529–532] is quoted as stating that when the temperature falls below 8°F in New York City there will be 5 or more cases of frostbite per 10,000 persons exposed regardless of other conditions; between 8° and 14°F frostbite will occur only if wind velocity is high; above 24°F, occurrence is rare even with a strong wind. Persons suffering from diabetes, myocardial disease, arteriosclerosis, peripheral vascular disease, or asthenia are more likely to be frostbitten. A previous history of frostbite, presumably because of residual organic vascular injury, renders the person more susceptible. In prevention of frostbite, clean, dry clothing without any constricting areas, should be worn; use of alcohol should be moderate; and smoking before or during outside work should be prohibited. Rest periods of a half hour indoors every two to four hours, should be arranged when the weather is very severe. Rewarming of a frostbitten extremity by reflex vasodilatation following the rewarming of the body or an unaffected extremity, is very effective; direct rewarming may cause further injury. Vasodilatory drugs can be used. The prompt use of suction and pressure therapy may prevent gangrene or limit the amount of tissue destruction.

1955. Leditznig, C. Constitution and frostbite [In German]. *In: Wehrmedizin. Kreigserfahrungen, 1939–1943, v. 3, p. 148–153. Ed. by A. ZIMMER. Wien, F. Deuticke, 1944.*

A study of susceptibility to frostbite in relation to constitution indicates that individuals with darkly-pigmented skins appear to be more susceptible to cold injury than those with lighter skins.

* 1956. Levin, O. A., A. A. Zakharova, and O. L. Katsnel'son. Clinical aspects and therapy of frostbite [In Russian]. *Vest. khir., v. 60, Aug. 1940: 86–87.*

"*Contains* an abstract of a report before the Leningrad Conference of Workers of Evacuation Hospitals and Socialist Sections of Hospitals and Institutes (May 25–27, 1940). Authors point out that third-degree frostbite actually encompasses widely differing cases, and suggest a division of this group into three further grades, making altogether five grades; characteristics of the additional grades are given; the variability of the clinical picture of frostbite is stressed and a corresponding therapy demanded; therapeutic methods are summarized."—Arctic Bibl., v. 4, 1954: 603.

1957. Liebesny, P. Physiopathology, treatment, and prevention of frost injuries. (With special reference to frost injuries in warfare.) *N. York State J. M., v. 44, Oct. 1, 1944: 2118–2123.*

This is a general discussion of the physiology, pathology, treatment, and prevention of freezing injuries viewed as a problem in military medicine. Under the problem of prevention the author limits himself to a discussion of protective clothing and predisposition to frostbite in flying personnel. Electrically-heated suits are regarded as best protection but heat must be automatically regulated in proportion to altitude.

1958. Löhe, H. Freezing, with particular reference to observations in the campaign of 1941–1942 [In German]. *Arch. Derm. Syph., Berl., v. 184, 1943: 45–57.*

In this general account of freezing injury as seen in the campaigns of 1941–1942, the author describes general as well as local freezing, including etiology, clinical picture, treatment, and prophylaxis. It was observed that sympathectomy used early prevented 2nd degree injuries from progressing to the 3rd degree type.

1959. Loeser, A. Frostbite and tobacco enjoyment [In German]. *Deut. med. Wschr., v. 70, Jan. 7, 1944: 9–10.*

Tobacco smokers were found to be more prone to frostbite injury than were non-smokers.

1960. Loos, H. O. Histamine as a tissue toxin in frostbite [In German]. *Derm. Ztschr., v. 109, Aug. 26, 1939: 1017–1023.*

The author reports that an H-substance, which he believes to be histamine, is found in increased amounts in patients with frostbite.

1961. Loos, H. O. Recognition and treatment of frostbite [In German]. *Zbl. Chir., v. 68, Mar. 8, 1941: 449–456.*

This is a discussion of the clinical types of frostbite, their diagnosis, and the treatment appropriate for each degree of injury.

1962. Loos, H. O. On the clinical aspects and treatment of local frostbite [In German]. *Münch. med. Wschr., v. 90, Feb. 26, 1943: 155–158.*

The etiology, clinical symptoms, pathology, treatment, and prophylaxis of local frostbite are given.

---

* Original not seen.

1963. Matras, A. On freezing [In German]. *In: Wehrmedizin. Kreigserfahrungen, 1939–1943, v. 3, p. 139–147. Ed. by* A. ZIMMER. *Wien, F. Deuticke, 1944.*

This general account of freezing injury is based on observations on casualties In the German Army on the Eastern front in the winter of 1941–1942. Etiology, clinical picture, prognosis, prevention, and treatment are discussed.

1964. Moser, O. A. Frostbite [Abstract, in German]. *Med. Welt., v. 17, May 22, 1943: 418.*

The pathology and treatment of injuries of 1st, 2nd, and 3rd degree frostbite are discussed on the basis of the author's work with 632 cases. Predisposition of individuals to cold and the location of the site of injury are mentioned. Infection of a 3rd degree injury may change from a dry condition to that of a wet gangrene. When such a condition has developed there are easily noted zones of edema, of granulation, and—past an area of demarcation—a zone of gangrene. By study of x-ray films the line of demarcation was seen about the 14th or 15th day. In injuries of 1st degree a series of alternating cold (15°C) and hot (36°C) baths is suggested as a therapeutic measure, if there is no break in the skin. Participation in sports and gymnastic exercises helps restore circulation. Painting the area with tannic acid may avoid infection of 2nd degree injuries. In 3rd degree injuries, the use of Marfanyl-prontalbin powder is suggested to control infection. Use of cod-liver-oil salve in cases of gangrene may be helpful.

1965. Pikin, K. I. Material on frostbite [In Russian]. *Voen. san. delo, 1941 (2): 26–31.*

The clinical aspects, pathology, and treatment of frostbite are discussed.

* 1966. Plotkin, F. M. Treatment of frostbite [In Russian]. *In:* A. I. NESTEROV, and I. G. RUFANOV. *Osnovy kompleksnogo lecheniĩa v gospitaliãkh, p. 210–217. Moskva, Medgiz, 1946.*

"*Contains* a general article, dealing with: the four degrees of frostbite; their pathological physiology and anatomy; clinical aspects; therapy at different stages of each degree; complications and sequelae."—Arctic Bibl., v. 4, 1954: 809–810.

1967. Poglayen, C. Histological lesions in frozen tissue [In Italian]. *Arch. ital. anat. pat., v. 21 (1–2), 1948: 75–92.*

A microscopic study was made of the morbid anatomy of frostbite lesions based upon amputation materials.

1968. Rachou, C. Contribution to the study of frostbite [In French]. *France med., v. 10, Feb. 1947: 6–8.*

A group of 125 cases of frostbite among soldiers in the French army, treated by the author, are reviewed. Pathogenesis, clinical picture, treatment, and prophylaxis are discussed.

1969. Raposomontero, L. Frostbite and its treatment [In Spanish]. *Medicina, Madr., v. 12, Mar. 1944: 211–226.*

This general account of frostbite is based on the author's experience at the Surgical Clinic of the University of Heidelberg. Included is information on etiology, pathogenesis, clinical aspects, prophylaxis, and treatment.

* 1970. Riabinkin, A. N. Frostbite and its treatment [In Russian]. *Pediatriĩa, Moskva, 1942 (6): 68–71.*

"*Contains* discussion of the frequency of frostbite in various body regions; symptoms of frostbite of I–IV degree; first aid and subsequent therapy of the different types."—Arctic Bibl., v. 4, 1954: 868.

---

* Original not seen.

1971. Richards, P., and J. J. Banigan. How to abandon ship. *New York, Cornell Maritime Press, 1943. 196 p.*

This non-technical book summarizes some aspects of marine safety. Various factors dealing with survival after abandoning ship are discussed. These include the positive relationship between cold, exhaustion, and exposure, the treatment and diagnosis of frostbite, and the proper use of clothing in an open boat.

1972. Romberg, H. W. On the pathological effects of cold. *In: Jahrbuch der deutschen Luftfahrtforschung, 1941, Sect. III, p. 95–98. München, Oldenburg, 1941.*

This is a general account of the local and generalized effects of cold, with emphasis on the morbid anatomy, both gross and microscopic.

1973. Ruiz Buitrago, P. Freezing injuries [In Spanish]. *Rev. españ. cirug., Valencia, v. 7, Sept.–Oct. 1947: 128–146.*

The author states that in general the action of cold is influenced by two groups of factors: external (wind, and humidity) and internal (constitutional, and state of peripheral circulation). Frostbite, various skin lesions, and sometimes gangrene, result from cold exposure. The various physiological responses to cold, and both medical and surgical treatment, are discussed.

1974. Sabatini, G. Concepts and directives for the study of freezing injuries and research carried out at the Center of Cryopathology of Genoa [In Italian]. *Minerva med., Tor., anno 31 (v. 2), Dec. 15, 1940: 562–567.* Abstract, of the Symposium, in English, in: *Internat. Abstr. Surg., v. 73, Aug. 1941: 166–167.*

In this paper from a symposium on Injuries Caused by Freezing, are discussed the concepts and directives of the Center at Genoa established for the study of changes in structure and function of living material caused by exposure to cold, under the general term of Cryopathology. The author discusses in detail the etiology, pathogenesis, prophylaxis, and therapy of frostbite.

1975. Sauerbruch, F. Frostbite [In German]. *Deut. Militärarzt, v. 7, Aug. 1942: 477–479.*

Author uses the general term "Erfrierungen" to include both frostbite and trench foot. Clinical and pathological aspects are briefly reviewed. Complete rest and the necessity of keeping the injured area cool until the line of demarcation is formed, are stressed. In cases of dry gangrene, mummified tissue should be permitted to separate of its own accord. A number of sequelae of freezing are mentioned including loss of vasomotor control of the blood vessels.

1976. Schwiegk, H. Pathogenesis and treatment of local cold injury. *In: German aviation medicine, World War II, v. 2, p. 843–857. Washington, D. C., Dept. of the Air Force, [1950].*

German work on local frostbite, based on human and animal data, is reviewed. The etiology, pathogenesis, prophylaxis, and therapy of frostbite are considered, as well as information on physiological acclimatization to cold. 43 refs.

1977. Senske, E. On the pathology of local freezing injury [In German]. *Zbl. Chir., v. 71, Oct. 7, 1944: 1275–1278.*

The clinical aspects and the pathology of localized freezing injury are discussed.

1978. Shenis, V. N. On frostbite [In Russian]. *Feldsher & akush., 1944 (12): 14–20.*

The pathology and treatment of frostbite are discussed.

1979. Siegmund, H. Pathology of general and local cold injuries [In German]. *Jahrkurs. ärztl. Fortbild., v. 34, Jan. 1943: 9–19.*

This review of the physiopathology of hypothermia and of frostbite includes discussion of the physiology of temperature regulation and the sequelae of cold injuries. 13 refs.

1980. Siegmund, H. The pathological-anatomical basis of frostbite [In German]. *Arch. Derm. Syph., Berl., v. 184, July 10, 1943: 34–35.*

This is a general discussion on the pathology of frostbite.

1981. Silverman, J. J. Frostbite: a subjective case history in a German soldier. *Mil. Surgeon, v. 103, Sept. 1948: 216–219.*

This is a personal account of a German soldier who sustained mutilating frostbite injuries while serving on the Eastern Front in 1942. He describes in detail the pathogenesis and clinical course of his injuries with subsequent treatment.

1982. Siple, P. A., and C. F. Passel. Measurements of dry atmospheric cooling in subfreezing temperatures. *Proc. Am. Philos. Soc., v. 89, Apr. 1945: 177–199.*

This is a report of atmospheric cooling measurements made at Little America, Antarctica. The effect of extreme cooling on the human body was studied, and the actual freezing time of various exposed parts at $-32.5\,°C$ was measured.

1983. Smith-Johannsen, R. Some experiments in the freezing of water. *Science, v. 108, Dec. 10, 1948: 652–654.*

From current experiments, and a review of the literature, it is concluded that the super-cooling of water is not at all an unusual phenomenon. The normal temperature at which water freezes, in the absence of any known foreign nucleating materials, is very close to $-20\,°C$ and not, as is commonly believed, at $0\,°C$. Considerable vibration was present during all of the current tests but appeared to have no observable nucleating effect. A number of powdered materials added to the sample did not make the water freeze at $0\,°C$. Some observations on the formation of ice crystals, together with the known effects of such materials as sublimation nuclei for ice, would indicate that the mechanisms of nucleation for "freezing nuclei" and for "sublimation nuclei" are different.

1984. Sorrel, E., and . . . Compagnon. Freezing of the feet and hands in children [In French]. *Bull. Soc. pédiat., Paris, v. 38, Feb. 18, 1941: 91–93.*

The authors state that since the first of the year they have treated 8 children, ages 6 to 12 years, with freezing injuries of the hands and feet which were of 2nd degree level or considerably worse and which in two cases would probably involve loss of toes and a Lisfranc amputation of the foot. The causes are evident in the especially severe winter and in the war-time shortage of heat, clothing, comfortable shoes, and adequate nutrition.

1985. Sostegni, A., and T. Augenti. Considerations on one hundred cases of freezing injuries of the limbs [In Italian]. *In: Atti Congresso Nazionale di Chirurgia di Guerra, May 24–26, 1942, p. 228–229. Roma, 1943.*

A group of 100 cases of 2nd and 3rd degree frostbite injury, from the Greek-Albanian front, are discussed. In all cases, the lesions were allowed to proceed to the point of demarcation. Treatment used was periarterial sympathectomy, and excellent results were produced. One case developed tetanus and another gas gangrene before arriving at the hospital.

1986. Spaccialbello, R., and A. Castagni. Contribution to the study and the therapy of frostbite [In Italian]. *Policlinico, sez. prat., v. 49, Apr. 27, 1942: 597–603.*

Statistical analysis is made of 397 cases of frostbite classified by degree of injury, and including clinical histories and methods of treatment.

1987. Spitzmüller, W. Freezing injuries [In German]. *In: Wehrmedizin. Kreigser-fahrungen, 1939–1943, v. 1, p. 238–254. Ed. by* A. ZIMMER. *Wien, F. Deuticke, 1944.*

Generalized and localized freezing injuries are discussed, especially those sustained in military operations. Included is information on clinical aspects, pathology, physiology, prophylaxis, and treatment.

1988. Staemmler, M. Freezing; investigation on the pathological anatomy and pathogenesis [In German]. *Leipzig, G. Thieme, 1944. 115 p.*

Special emphasis is placed on localized freezing in this comprehensive monograph. The author discusses localized freezing and circulation; sequelae in experimental animals; metabolic effects; and changes in blood vessels, the nervous system, muscles, skin, and joints. The subject of generalized chilling is discussed in the last chapter. Bibliography, p. 108–115.

1989. Tabanelli, M. Frostbite of war [In Italian]. *Bologna, Cappelli, 1946. 92 p.*

A general account of frostbite, especially as seen in the Italian theater during World War II, is given. Etiology, clinical aspects, pathology, and treatment are discussed. Included are 100 illustrations, many of which are of cases involving amputations.

1990. Teneff, S. The lesions of cold in war. *In:* O. UFFREDUZZI *and* S. TENEFF. *War surgery, p. 538–545. Torino, Unione Tipografico-Editrice Torinese, 1940.*

The effects of low temperature are discussed, especially with reference to frostbite. Among the subjects treated are: susceptibility to cold injury; the characteristics of the three degrees of frostbite injury; and gangrene. Treatment is outlined for the various types and degrees of frostbite injury; prophylaxis is discussed. The bibliography on pages 547–548 includes a number of pertinent references.

1991. Theis, F. V. Frostbite of extremities; clinical and pathologic considerations in its diagnosis and treatment. *Arch. Phys. Ther., v. 21, Nov. 1940: 663–670.*

The physiology, pathophysiology, differential diagnosis, clinical picture, and treatment of frostbite are reviewed briefly. The author points out the importance of considering contributing factors before establishing the diagnosis of frostbite and beginning the treatment. Such factors include arteriosclerosis and thromboangiitis obliterans.

1992. Ullrich, H. Biological effects of frost and resistance to frost of plasma (with special consideration of plants) [Abstract, in German]. *Klin. Wschr., v. 22, May 1, 1943: 351–352.*

In this abstract of a paper given before the Biological Society of Leipzig, Nov. 24, 1942, the effect of freezing on the structure and function of various organisms is discussed. Some homeotherms, because of their complex organization, are best able to ward off the effects of cold and maintain a uniform body temperature. Some poikilothermic animals whose body temperatures fall in the cold, are hibernators. The resistance of plants to cold is related to their inter- and intra-cellular structure. The cellulose wall affords some protection. Cold injury in plants is related to plasmolysis and the building up of internal pressures within the cell. The destruction is mechanical and physiochemical in extreme freezing. The ability of plants to withstand severe dehydration affords them an advantage over that of animals.

1993. Vaglianos, M. New knowledge on frostbite in soldiers in Greece during the war of 1941–1942 [In Italian]. *Policlinico, sez. prat., v. 50, Mar. 22, 1943: 365–367. Similar material in: Frostbite in Greek troops during the campaign of 1941–1942 [In German]. Münch. med. Wschr., v. 90, Nov. 19, 1943: 649–650.*

This is a general discussion of military experiences with freezing injuries sustained by Greek soldiers during the war of 1941–1942. Of 28,000 cases enumerated, 4,000 required surgical treatment.

1994. Višnar, F. Frostbitten hands as an occupational injury [In Serbo-Croatian]. *Liječ. vjes.*, v. 62, *July 1940: 360–361.*

The etiology, clinical aspects, and pathology of an industrial case of frostbite are discussed.

1995. Wachsmuth, W. Frostbite [In German]. *In: Wehrhygiene, p. 215–220. Ed. by S. HANDLOSER. Berlin, Springer, 1944.*

This general account of frostbite included information on the etiology, clinical picture, pathology, prevention, first aid, and treatment.

1996. Webster, A. P. High altitude-high velocity flying with special reference to human factors. I. Outline of human problems. *J. Aviat. M.*, v. 21, *Apr. 1950: 82–84; 89.*

In his outline of some of the factors which need study in the realm of high-altitude high-velocity flying, with special reference to the human ones, the author mentions the physiological limits and tolerance to cold. One of the several causes of accident or death in escape from such aircraft, is that of frostbite at high altitudes.

1997. Webster, A. P., and H. A. Smedal. High altitude-high velocity flying with special reference to the human factors. III. Bare skin hazard from frostbite in escape from aircraft. *J. Aviat. M.*, v. 22, *Apr. 1951: 89–99.*

One of the serious physiological hazards in escape from aircraft flying at high altitudes is stated to be that of frostbite. Equations, tables, and charts are presented for estimating safe regions of escape to avoid this hazard.

1998. Zanotti, M. Some data on the individual predisposition to freezing injuries of soldiers [In Italian]. *Boll. Soc. med. chir., Modena,* v. 42, *1941: p. XIII.*

From a morphological study of 250 soldiers with freezing injuries, the author noted a prevalence of individuals of the long, thin, body type. In the discussion which followed the paper, the author stated that there were bilateral injuries in 94% of the cases; amputations, however, were most often of the right leg.

1999. Zanotti, M. Results of the Rotter intracutaneous reaction in military frostbite patients [In Italian]. *Gior. med. mil.*, v. 94, *Nov.–Dec. 1947: 442–453.*

Vitamin C deficiency was noted when cases of severe frostbite among soldiers were tested with the Rotter intracutaneous reaction (decoloration of dichlorophenol-indophenol by Vitamin C). The reaction did not appear when synthetic vitamin C was administered.

See also items: 212, 394, 681, 834, 862, 864, 1029, 1109, 1115, 1116, 1277, 1558, 1634, 1819, 1826, 1948, 2641, 2648, 2649, 2650, 2651, 2693, 2707, 2724.

2. Effects on Body Systems and Functions, General

2000. Ar'ev, T. I͡A. Frostbite [In Russian]. 2nd ed. *Leningrad, Medgiz, 1940. 221 p.*

This book on frostbite contains the following chapters: (1) Pathological anatomy; method of experimental frostbite, effect of frostbite on tissues, cultures and transplants, organs, skin and subcutaneous tissue, blood vessels, peripheral nerves, muscles and tendons, bones, joints, and cartilage. (2) Pathological physiology of frostbite; action of cold on the living organism, on the heart, blood vessels, blood, central nervous system and peripheral nerves, muscles, respiration and respiratory organs. (3) Pathogenesis of freezing. (4) Clinical considerations of frostbite; nomenclature and classification, statistics of frostbite during war years and in peacetime,

localization of frostbite, symptomatology and differential diagnosis, complications after frostbite, prognosis, factors contributing to the occurrence of frostbite. (5) Treatment. There is
also a supplement on the use of cold as a curative factor.

2001. Cerbone, R. Experimental research on the action of severe freezing injury on the testicles [In Italian]. *Gazz. osp., v. 56, May 3–10, 1942: 290–296.*

Two groups of young male guinea pigs were subjected to experimental freezing injuries of
the scrotal area for 5 minutes or 10 minutes. Injury to the testicles resulted in circulatory disturbances and edema. Histological examination indicated that permanent changes had been
produced in the seminal cells.

2002. Galli, T. Influence of the thyroid function on the predisposition to cold
lesions [In Italian]. *Mnerva med., Tor., anno 31 (v. 2), Dec. 15, 1940: 590–592.*

A study of a group of 100 soldiers at a clinic being treated for frostbite of first or second degree, showed that 32 of the soldiers had an increase in size of their thyroid gland and displayed clinical evidence of hypothyroidism. Basal metabolic tests showed considerable variation
from the normal in these as well as in the total group of patients. It is concluded that dysfunction of the thyroid gland is one of the causes predisposing to cold injury.

* 2003. Gerasimenko, N. I. A rare case of frostbite [In Russian]. *Khirurgiĩa,
Moskva, v. 19, Feb. 1949: 76–77.*

"*Contains* a report of a rare case of third-degree freezing of the scrotum and penis. The case
occurred in an accident at the cold pole, the condition having been noticed too late to prevent
serious involvement. The further cause of the disease and the therapy are outlined."—Arctic
Bibl., v. 4, 1954: 333.

2004. Hoelscher, B. Morphological changes of adrenal cortex in frostbitten
rabbits with and without heparin treatment. *Arch. Path., Chic., v. 52, Oct. 1951,
378–383.*

Groups of rabbits had one hind leg frozen by immersion to the knee joint in an alcohol-dry
ice bath, or were less severely injured by exposure to cold (−15° or −30°C) for 30 minutes.
Some of the animals were heparin-treated by intravenous injection of 3 cc of heparin sodium
solution every 6 hours for 6 days. Animals were later killed by the guillotine method and the
adrenal glands examined microscopically. The increase found in the weight of the adrenal
glands, in a study of 199 glands, was in direct relation to the degree of cold injury and was accompanied by a decrease in body weight. In animals receiving heparin but not exposed to cold,
the adrenal was only slightly augmented. In severe cold injury, degenerative changes of the
adrenal cortex were seen which were increased in severity by heparin treatment.

2005. Kaplan, A. V. [The treatment of frostbite and its sequelae] [In Russian].
*In: Trudy 2-go plenuma Gospital'nogo Soveta Narkomzdrava SSSR, Dec. 20–25, 1942,
p. 269–271. Moskva, Medgiz, 1943.*

Secondary pathological symptoms observed in frostbite injuries (115 cases of 3rd degree,
and 35 of 2nd degree) are described. These symptoms, as well as the complications which
arose later, were related to vascular and peripheral nervous, particularly to autonomous, disorders. There was frequent hypertrophy of the epidermis and peeling; increased hair growth
above the site of injury; augmented perspiration; venous hyperemia; lowered skin temperature at the site of injury (rarely the contrary); weakened or even complete absence of arterial
pulsation at the site of injury, especially in the dorsal artery of the foot; frequent complete
atrophy of the subcutaneous fat layer and sometimes its swelling; and atrophy of the muscles.
Osteoporosis persisted even after the healing, especially in the epiphyses and articulations
of the metacarpal and metatarsal bones and the phalanges of the hand. Disturbance of the

---

* Original not seen.

sensations of pain and touch were noted in 41.5% of the cases. Energetic application of Sollux rays from the first day of hospitalization reduced the duration of hospital treatment 9%, and gave good results in cases of sluggish healing of trophic ulcers when combined with paraffin therapy.

2006. Korányi, A. War nephritis caused by injury due to cold [In Hungarian]. *Orv. Lapja, Budapest, v. 3, 1947: 1217–1219.*

War nephritis is ascribed to the effect of cold. The author believes that in cases of frostbite the symptoms are masked by the "alarm reaction" called forth by local cooling.

2007. Kreyberg, L. Development of acute tissue damage due to cold. *Physiol. Rev., v. 29, Apr. 1949: 156–167.*

The literature on the effects of local damage due to cold is reviewed. The author analyzes some of the reactions to cold and distinguishes between damage which is lethal to the cells and damage caused by subsequent events in the tissues. Late and secondary complications are not considered. Discussion is under the three headings: preliminary and transient responses to lowered temperature, prolonged exposure to low temperature above freezing, and damage caused by the freezing of the tissues to ice. 45 refs.

2008. Lewis, R. B., and R. M. Thompson. Nephrosis following experimental local cold injury. *Mil. Surgeon., v. 109, Oct. 1951: 518–830.*

Rabbits were exposed to cold by having one hind leg immersed for 30 minutes in an alcohol bath at temperatures of 5°C to −25°C. After periods of less than a week to longer than a week following immersion, both gross and microscopic examinations were made of the kidneys of 423 of the rabbits. The degree of renal pathological changes showed no direct correlation with the degree of frostbite injury or with the survival time after injury. Severe kidney lesions were found after minor degrees of cold injury, less than that required to produce muscle necrosis. The degenerative changes were not necessarily confined to the lower portion of the nephron.

2009. Loos, H. [O.] Diagnosis and therapy of frostbite [In German]. *Münch. med. Wschr., v. 88, May 1941: 538.*

Freezing injuries suffered during sport activities are discussed. Death from hypothermia is not so much to be feared as injury to the vegetative nerve centers. Such injury can be followed by cold gangrene or cold neuritis. The most common complication is wet gangrene. Next to the disturbance of the water content of the affected tissues, the formation of so-called vasoactive substances is important. These, with their vasodilatory effect, lead to an increased blood flow and an inflammatory erythema. In severe cases these materials exercise a poisoning effect and become tissue toxins. In prophylaxis, excessive sweating of the feet is to be avoided. Fat salves applied especially to the nose, cheeks, and chin, may be helpful. But the best protection of all is the accurate evaluation by the individual of his susceptibility to cold.

2010. Luyet, B. J., and P. M. Gehenio. The physical states of protoplasm at low temperatures; review and critical study [In English]. *Biodynamica, Normandy, Mo., v. 2 (48), June 1939: 1–128.*

In the order of decreasing temperature, matter exists in 4 physical states: as a gas, a liquid, a crystal, and as a glass. Crystallization is possible only within a limited range of temperature; below this temperature range matter is too inert to crystallize. The vitreous state is reached by cooling very rapidly so that liquid traverses the zone of crystallization temperature before it has time to crystallize. The author states that such super-cooling resulting in a good vitrification, is not injurious to protoplasm, while an incomplete vitrification, or devitrification which would allow crystallization, is injurious to the extent that it disrupts the living structure. Frog muscle fibers responded to electric stimuli after their vitrification followed by vitrofusion (passing directly from a vitreous to a liquid state without any crystallization) was achieved by rapid rewarming. 127 refs.

2011. McDonald, J. H., C. B. Taylor, and N. J. Heckel. Rapid freezing of the bladder: an experimental and clinical study. *J. Urol., Balt., v. 64, Aug. 1950: 326–337.*

Rapid, controlled, freezing (−49°C) of the wall of the bladder of a dog was found to kill the normal cells in that area but not to interrupt the continuity of the interstitial structure. The technique is stated to be applicable and safe for use in humans but its value in treatment of tumors of the bladder has not been fully determined.

2012. Massons Esplugas, J. M. Etiologic factors in freezing injuries [In Spanish]. *Acta méd. hisp., v. 6, Apr.–May 1948: 253–272.*

A review is made of literature on the etiologic factors in freezing injuries. The discussion covers the role of environmental temperature, wind, and humidity in cold injury; types of cold injury; predisposing physiological factors, such as nutrition, metabolism, endocrine activity, and the use of alcohol and tobacco; and the protective role of clothing.

2013. Massons Esplugas, J. M. Pathological anatomy and pathogenesis of freezing injuries [In Spanish]. *Acta méd. hisp., v. 6, June–July 1948: 347–364.*

This is a general review of literature on pathologic anatomy and pathogenesis of freezing injuries, including effects of cold on skin, muscles, blood vessels, bones, cells, and nervous system. 90 footnote refs.

2014. Matthes, K., and C. Korth. Cold injury [In German]. *In: FIAT review of German science, 1939–1946. Pt. I, Internal medicine. Chapt. III, Diseases of the circulatory system, p. 255–260. Wiesbaden, Office of Military Government for Germany (Field Information Agencies Technical), 1948.*

In this short review of German writings on cold injury during World War II, both local injury or frostbite and over-all chilling or hypothermia are discussed. Some investigations are noted on the direct effect of cold on the cell—on the cellular proteins and colloidal structures; on the increased cellular permeability; blood flow changes; and on changes in blood composition and in muscular glycogen following the freezing of the left hind leg of dogs while the right leg remained at a normal room temperature. There is a bibliography of 30 references (p. 275–276).

2015. Müller, W. On the pathological anatomy of local cold injury [Abstract, in German]. *Deut. med. Wschr., v. 70, Mar. 3, 1944: 141.*

Clinical observations made over a period of 9 days to 1 year—on previously frostbitten areas of epithelium, muscle, and bone—demonstrated a re-building of tissue accompanied, in bone, by re-canalization. Infections in 3rd degree frostbite were encountered when subcutaneous tissues were affected. Metastatic infection could occur anywhere in the body. Frostbite frequently resulted in degeneration of the liver and impairment of glycogen synthesis.

2016. Pichotka, J., R. B. Lewis, and E. Freytag. Sequence of increasing local cold injury. *Texas Rep. Biol. M., v. 9, Fall 1951: 613–630.*

One hind leg of each of a group of rabbits was exposed for 30 minutes in water baths with temperatures from +5° to −40°C (at 5°C intervals). Three levels of injury were noted depending on the severity of the exposure. With exposure at +5°, 0°, or −5°C functional changes occurred but were temporary. These functional changes were loss of muscular power in leg and foot, absence of response or hyperactive reaction to pinprick, loss of spreading reflex of the toes and in some cases hyperextension of the ankle joint. In the more severe cases some muscle atrophy occurred representing extension into the second category of increasing injury. Exposure to −10° to −12°C brought about atrophy and isolated necrosis of muscle in addition to the functional changes. Exposure to temperatures below −12°C brought, in addition to the above, a necrosis of the skin.

2017. Platareanu, V. M., I. Gadescu, and S. Dimitru. Physiological pathology of freezing [In German]. *Zbl. Chir., v. 70, Sept. 11, 1943: 1340–1345.*

Pathological physiology and morbid anatomy are reported in two representative cases of freezing injury. In one case the soldier had suffered a frozen lower extremity which had been amputated; the other soldier had been severely chilled and had died of a bulbar embolism. Studies were made on the circulatory and nervous systems; on the connective, bone, and muscle tissue; and on the blood.

2018. Poglayen, C. The behavior of reticular tissue in third degree freezing injuries [In Italian, with summaries in Italian, French, and German]. *Arch. ital. anat. pat., v. 23 (3), 1950: 214–224.*

A histological study of reticular tissue changes in the areas of third degree freezing injuries, was made using the same material from amputation cases reported in 1948 (item 1967). There was complete absence of reticular stroma in the necrotized portion; fragments of fibrils increased in number out from the center of the injury until, in the area nearest to the living tissue, the fibrils were quite frequent and well-preserved. At the line of demarcation between the normal and injured tissue, the fibrils were present in normal quantity but showed a considerable hypertrophy and hyperplasia to give a rise in height of the tissue at that line.

2019. Pytel', A. IA. [The treatment of frostbite and its sequelae] [In Russian]. *In: Trudy 2-go plenuma Gospital'nogo Soveta Narkomzdrava SSSR, Dec. 20–25, 1942, p. 282–285. Moskva, Medgiz, 1943.*

The detoxicating function of the liver was studied (measuring the synthesis of hippuric acid) in 108 frostbite cases with 2nd, 3rd, and 4th degree injuries. The detoxicating function was found considerably diminished in 84% of the cases, which received only local treatment, 10–16 days after hospital admission. It began to increase slowly 3–4 weeks later with clinical and general improvement up to its lower normal rate. The glycogenic function was equally diminished. Changes in the detoxicating function depended on the course of the disease and on the method of treatment. In the majority of febrile patients, especially in cases of humid gangrene, the rates of hippuric acid synthesis were very low. A definite relationship was found to exist between the functional activity of the liver and the healing of the frostbite wounds: the higher the detoxicating function in the first stages of the disease, the speedier and the better the processes of healing. In order to improve the antitoxic hepatic function (by raising the glycogenetic, and the basal metabolism) injections of 40% glucose and 8–10 units of insulin were made daily for 5–7 days, with 80–100 cc of 10% salt solution every other day. This combined therapy, especially the glucose and NaCl, produced exceptionally good results, as the detoxicating hepatic function rose to the upper normal limit in 4–6 days, the falling off of the necrotic tissue was accelerated, and the wounds healed rapidly. This method of combined therapy, together with physiotherapy and local surgery, is believed to be the answer to the search for the most rapid and most effective measures in frostbite treatment. In patients with humid gangrene, phlegmon, and sepsis, whose synthesis and isolation rate of hippuric acid was 16–0% of the normal rate 2–3 days before death, glucose and NaCl injections produced no improvement. It is believed that a synthesis and isolation rate of hippuric acid below 20% of the normal constitutes a very unfavorable prognosis.

2020. Pytel', A. IA. Detoxicating element of liver: function in frostbite [In Russian]. *Hosp. delo, 1943 (1): 50–54.*

Impairment by frostbite of the detoxicating function of the liver was determined, in 182 patients with frostbite of the extremities, by the decrease in the percentage of hippuric acid excreted. Disturbance of the detoxicating function was accompanied in almost every case by a decrease In glycogen formation by the liver. Injections of glucose and insulin (together with sodium chloride to counterbalance a deficiency observed in the blood) were administered, with the result that the detoxicating activity of the liver was improved, necrosed tissues showed more rapid demarcation, and healing of ulcers was accelerated.

2021. **Shtern, L. S., ĪA. Rosin, M. M. Gromakovskaĩa, and L. E. Kaplan.** Contribution to the treatment of shock; traumatic shock complicated by frostbite [In Russian]. *Biull. eksp. biol. med., v. 15 (6), 1943: 3–6.*

Study was made of the influence of frostbite on the appearance and development of traumatic shock and the possibility of treatment by injection of potassium phosphate into the spinal cord or cerebral ventricles or, suboccipitally, into the subcerebellar cistern. The four feet of dogs were placed in a mixture of snow and salt at −20° to −25 °C for 1–3 hours. After the feet had been removed from the bath and measurement had been made of blood pressure, respiration, and body temperature, trauma was experimentally produced by a 30% to 35% loss of total blood volume. Results showed that limited, though prolonged and severe, frostbite did not induce any symptoms of shock in the dog, except some sleepiness, but that it increased the animal's sensitivity to trauma and blood loss, shock appearing and developing quicker than in the normal animal. Injection of potassium phosphate, rapidly and completely removed the shock condition in the frostbitten, as well as in the normal, traumatized animal. Surgical amputation was then possible but the frostbitten animal perished within the first 24 hours unless forced diuresis was undertaken. This suggests that toxic substances are released from the necrotic tissues into the blood and are spread as the body is warmed and circulation is restored.

2022. **Siegmund, H.** Pathological anatomy and histology of local cold injury. *In: German aviation medicine, World War II, v. 2, p. 858–875. Washington, D. C., Dept. of the Air Force, [1950].*

A review of German work on the clinical aspects and pathology of frostbite, is made with emphasis on the vascular, neural, muscular, bone, and skin changes involved. Progressive changes are illustrated by a series of 30 plates. Also included in the discussion are the complications and causes of death from local freezing. 67 refs.

2023. **Smith, S.** Frostbite of lungs. *Air Surgeon Bull., v. 1, June 1944: 17.*

Frostbite of the lungs is a condition which occurs in man after mouthbreathing in an environment at temperatures of −40 °F or colder for a few minutes. Sharp chest pains usually begin about 30 minutes after exposure, followed by a painful cough and hemoptysis. Body temperature may reach 106 °F. Alveolar damage and actual freezing of small areas of lung tissue are thought to occur but they have not been demonstrated. Treatment consists in administration of drugs to act on the central nervous system; recovery usually occurs in 10–14 days. Preventive measures include decreased physical exertion during exposure to severe cold, and breathing through a porous material with the tip of the tongue placed against the roof of the mouth in order to warm the inspired air.

2024. **Staemmler, M.** On anatomical effects of localized freezing [In German]. *Virchows Arch., v. 312, 1944: 501–533.*

Histological examinations were made of tissues from the amputated extremities of frostbitten patients whose injuries had occurred 2 to 12 weeks before the amputation date. Endarteritis obliterans was occasionally found occurring far outside the area of demarcation or developing interruptedly in the higher arteries of the calf or thigh. Nerve tissue was frequently seriously damaged, with extensive deterioration of the medullary sheath and axis cylinder which may have resulted from inflammatory changes in the perineurium. Atrophy of muscle tissue, independent of inflammation, was found with damage occurring in either single groups of muscle fibers or in extensive bundles of fibers. Hyperkeratosis of the skin frequently occurred, occasionally with an atrophy of the elastic fibers of the cutis. An occasional instance of atrophy of bone was observed. The changes would appear to be caused by a serious disturbance of the circulation at the time of the injury and for several weeks after it. In order to estimate the reversibility of the tissue damage it would be necessary to make observations after a much longer lapse of time.

2025. **Stoss, ...** Cold injuries in the horse [In German]. *Deut. tierärztl. Wschr., v. 50, Oct. 24, 1942: 444–446.*

Frostbite injuries of the penis, the lips, and the legs of horses are described. Suggestions on treatment and prophylaxis are given.

2026. Tangari, C. Freezing of adrenals and its effect on their ascorbic acid and adrenaline content [In Italian, summaries in Italian, French, English, and German]. *Arch. ital. med. sper., v. 7, 1940: 415–426.*

Adrenal glands of rabbits were subjected to freezing by direct application for 5 minutes of a carbon dioxide spray after the area had been exposed surgically. The animals were sacrificed at periods of 6 hours, 10 days, and 30 days after freezing. The content of ascorbic acid and of adrenaline in the adrenal glands was found to be markedly, and probably permanently, decreased. This decrease was greater as the time following injury was lengthened.

2027. Vagliano, M. Frostbite; clinical studies, treatment, physiology, pathological anatomy [In French]. *Paris, Masson, 1948. 255 p.*

Frostbite is discussed under the main headings of Early Period, of Later Period, and of Physiology and Pathological Anatomy. The early period and the later period in frostbite injury are considered as to symptomatology, degrees and development of injury, and treatment. Infection, both generalized and local, is considered in the earlier period. Physiology and pathological anatomy are discussed as to thermogenesis, temperature regulation, conditions of the appearance of cold injuries, direct effect of cold on cells, and vasomotor, vascular, and nervous system disturbances from cold.

2028. Zenow, Z. I. On the changes in the endocrine system after experimental localized freezing [In German]. *Virchows Arch., v. 312, 1944: 486–500.*

Groups of rats had their tails immersed in an ice-water bath for various periods of time. The techniques, periods of time, and some of the animals were the same as those used by Böttcher (item 1906). In an additional series of animals, the tails were kept continuously in the ice bath for 3 days except for about 2 hours a day while they were being fed; the surviving animals were killed at the end of the third day. The thyroid and adrenal glands of these and other animals were examined microscopically. A lipid atrophy was found in the cortex of the adrenals and histological changes in the zona fasciculata indicated a heightened functioning of the cortex. With the longer periods of continuous cooling an increased storage of lipids above the normal level was found and regarded as an indication of adaptation. In the medulla of the gland an increased release of adrenaline was indicated with some increase of production. An increased functioning of the thyroid was indicated by the heightening of the epithelial layer.

See also items: 836, 2015, 2149, 2214, 2492, 2703.

3. Integumentary System

2029. Degos, R., S. Kaplan, and B. Hacker. Freezing injuries with hemorrhagic blisters, followed by serous blisters later [In French]. *Bull. Soc. fr. derm. syph., v. 46, Feb. 9, 1939: 97–99.*

The authors discuss two unusual types of hemorrhagic blisters which they have seen in freezing injuries: a blackened, dry and gangrenous-appearing lesion which was really a hemorrhagic blister with a hyperkeratotic epidermal surface; and the formation of a second, serous, blister in the same area of skin where the primary blister had appeared and been opened about a month previously.

2030. Kreyberg, L., and O. E. Hanssen. Necrosis of whole skin and survival of transplanted epithelium after freezing to −78°C and −190°C [In English]. *Scand. J. Clin. Lab. Invest., v. 2 (2), 1950: 168–170.*

Tips of the ears of rabbits were frozen for 5 seconds with solid carbon dioxide. Immediately, 3 hours, and 6 hours after thawing *in situ* autotransplantation of a very thin tissue slice from the ear was made to a pocket on the flank of the animal, between the whole skin and the muscular fascia. Freezing of the ear, without transplantation of the tissue, invariably led to stasis and necrosis. If the transplantation was immediate the number of "takes" was approximately the same (about ⅔ of the group) as for the control group using normal ear tissue. If transplantation was not done until later, only about ¼ were successful "takes". The decrease in vitality of the tissues remaining longer at the site of injury, might be explained as resulting from either (1) local development of injurious metabolites directly resulting from freezing or (2) stasis and necrosis following vascular obstruction; the author favors the latter view. When the tips of the ears of mice were frozen by the use of liquid air at a temperature of approximately −190°C, and transplanted as above, there was little or no growth.

2031.   Lewis, T. Effects of supercooling skin. *Clin. Sc., Lond., v. 5, Aug. 1944: 9–15.*

A distinction is made between freezing and supercooling of skin. Supercooling at −15°C for 10 minutes did not give wheals, but freezing at this temperature for 20–30 seconds always did. Freezing coming right after supercooling checked the full development of the wheal.

2032.   Plassa, T. Research on the skin temperature in frostbite [In Italian]. *Forze san., Roma, v. 10, Apr. 15, 1941: 60.* Also, in Italian, in: *Policlinico, sez. prat., v. 48, Aug. 4, 1941: 1364.*

Measurements were made of the skin temperature of the legs of frostbitten soldiers. Temperatures of the injured areas were found to be lower than the skin temperatures above the lesion.

2033.   Taylor, A. C. Survival of rat skin and changes in hair pigmentation following freezing. *J. Exp. Zool., v. 110, Feb. 1949: 77–111.*

When the skin on black rats was frozen by contact for 5 seconds with solid carbon dioxide or more slowly to −10°C, no subsequent effects were noted. However, hair growing from such areas was unpigmented. Microscopic studies made on skins which survived freezing showed that melanophores were selectively killed.

See also items: 2064, 2079, 2106, 2191, 2217.

4. Muscular and Skeletal Systems

2034.   Annovazzi, G., and L. Belloni. Histological study of the skeletal lesions in the inferior acromelic segments of third degree frostbite [In Italian]. *Atti Accad. med. lombarda, v. 31, Jan. 17, 1941: 38–41.*

The authors studied the histology of 23 lower skeletal segments of 3rd degree frostbite. Changes in the bony substance, marrow, and cartilage were followed through to the elimination of the necrotic part.

2035.   Belloni, L. Pathological appearances of the adipose tissue of bone marrow in bone necrosis caused by cold or trauma. Foam cells, atrophy with proliferation, oil cysts [In Italian]. *Arch. Ortop., Milano, v. 59 (4), 1947: 366–380.*

Microscopic studies were made of the bone marrow of portions of fingers which had been amputated from patients following cold gangrene resulting from third degree freezing injuries during the winter of 1940–1941 on the Greek-Albanian front. Necrotic appearance of the fatty marrow, including the appearance of foam cells and oily cystic formations—evidently a reaction to the necrobiotic processes in the adipose tissue caused by the vascular lesions due to cold—is discussed in detail.

2036.   Breitner, B., and E. Ruckensteiner. Examinations of old cold injuries [In German]. *Zbl. Chir., v. 71 (4–6), 1944: 140–144.*

X-ray examinations were made of more than a hundred cases of old, benign, cold injuries in order to study any alterations of bone structure which may have been caused by the cold. Various pathological bone conditions, such as osteolysis and Sudeck's atrophy, were seen. Although it could not be said specifically that cold was the cause of these changes, in view of the high incidence, and the selection of the cases, the findings were significant.

2037. Cengiarotti, G. B. On the consequence of the action of cold on the epiphysis of growing animals [In Italian]. *Ann. ital. chir.*, *v. 19, Jan.–Feb. 1940: 607–619.*

Studies were made of the effect of cold (localized exposure to a jet of ethyl chloride) on the epiphysis of the lower end of the right femur of actively-growing laboratory animals. The legs were x-rayed periodically, and the animals sacrificed 1 to 9 days after treatment. Structural modifications of form and a drastic and permanent change of cellular morphology were noted after freezing. When superficial lesions were produced by cold, the slight burning necrosis which followed was thought to be caused by the alteration of the circulation by the very low temperature.

2038. Cirenei, A. Local cold lesions and their sequelae [In Italian]. *Gior. med. mil., Suppl., v. 95, Jan.–Feb. 1948: 1–103.*

A review is made of the literature on the physiological reactions to cold and on the etiology, clinical aspects, pathology, and treatment of local lesions due to cold. Included is a series of case histories demonstrating the late sequelae, especially the involvement of the bones. Of special interest are cases of frostbite incurred during World War I where the bone lesions were still observable up to 25 years later. Bioliography appears on p. 89–103.

2039. Davanzano, G. On traumatic flat foot caused by freezing injury [In Italian]. *In: Atti Congresso Nazionale di Chirurgia di Guerra, May 24–26, 1942, p. 249–251. Roma, 1943.*

The author has studied 200 cases of freezing injury which show osteoporosis (bony atrophy) caused by a decalcification resulting from 2nd and 3rd degree freezing injury. The decalcification was due to a circulatory disturbance. Some cases were found where traumatic flat foot was due to decalcification, but they were rare with only 3 cases occurring in the group of 200.

2040. Dondero, A. P. Guiding principles of the therapy of freezing injuries [In Italian]. *Minerva méd., Tor., anno 33 (v. 1), Feb. 24, 1942: 250–251.*

The author discusses freezing injuries particularly as they involve injury to bone, stating that the epiphysis at the proximal end of the metatarsal bone of the little toe has a predilection to such injury. He mentions the use of sulfanilamides to control infection and help avoid gangrene; use of vitamin C; infiltration, to relieve vasospasm, at the colpita region; sympathectomy; use of Marconi therapy; and early ambulation of the patient to improve circulation.

2041. Falk, W. A contribution to the pathogenesis and clinical features of acute inflammatory bone diseases in children [In German, summaries in German, French, and English]. *Ann. paediat., Basel, v. 173 (1), 1949: 23–33.*

Report is made of a 10-month-old child in whom severe bony changes occurred following cold injuries of 3rd degree on the hands and feet. Radiologically these changes were seen as a severe osteoporosis of the distal parts of both ulnae and as dactylitic processes with periosteal thickening in several areas of the fingers and toes. With only symptomatic treatment, the bony changes rapidly regressed and complete healing occurred.

2042. Heybroek, N. I. Frostbite presenting the appearance of spina ventosa [In Dutch]. *Mschr. kindergeneesk., v. 9, Aug. 1940: 453–456.*

A case is described of a baby showing a swelling of the left foot with necrosis of the fifth metatarsal. The injury is interpreted as having been the result of frostbite.

2043. Lewis, R. B. Pathogenesis of muscle necrosis due to experimental local cold injury. *Am. J. M. Sc., v. 222, Sept. 1951: 300–307.*

Degenerative changes in muscle tissue were found almost immediately after exposure of the hind legs of albino rabbits in an alcohol bath of −12 °C for 30 minutes. It is concluded that early tissue damage from cold is not secondary to vascular changes—such as vasoconstriction, stasis and plugging of capillaries with red blood cells, edema, or actual thrombosis—but is due to the direct action of cold on the tissue cells.

2044. LoMonaco, G. Radiological aspects of bone lesions in freezing injury [In Italian]. *Nuntius radiol., Siena, v. 13, 1947: 38–44.*

Bony lesions following frostbite injuries are described, and classified as follows: Sudeck's atrophy, trophoneuritic atrophy, osteitis, and osteonecrosis.

2045. Mazzola, P. Early and late changes in bone in frostbite [In Italian]. *Arch. sc. med., Tor., v. 74, Dec. 1942: 459–468.*

A radiological study was made of the early and late changes occurring in various degrees of frostbite injuries, based on 430 cases.

2046. Oehlecker, F. Sudeck's disease, specifically after frostbite [In German]. *Chirurg, v. 14, July 15; Aug. 1, 1942: 422–428; 459–472.*

The author demonstrated by the use of radiograms that severe frostbite had injured the bones as well as the soft tissues. When severely frozen limbs were x-rayed shortly after exposure to severe cold these pictures indicated no pathological changes. X-rays taken 6 to 8 weeks later, however, demonstrated changes above the injured area typical of Sudeck's atrophy.

2047. Radasewsky, G. Alterations of bony tissue after congelation [In German]. *Beit. path. Anat., v. 109, Dec. 15, 1947: 567–588.*

Detailed histological description is given of the changes in bone tissue found in amputation and autopsy material from 12 to 82 days after various freezing injuries.

2048. Rokhlin, D. G. [The treatment of frostbite and its sequelae]. [In Russian]. *In: Trudy 2-go plenuma Gospital'nogo Soveta Narkomzdrava SSSR, Dec. 20–25, 1942, p. 280–282. Moskva, Medgiz, 1943.*

On the basis of clinico-roentgenological examinations of 200 patients with frostbite injuries of the 2nd, 3rd, or 4th degree, the author describes the various alterations occurring in the bones and their probable causes.

2049. Ruckensteiner, E. Considerations on the X-ray picture of local freezing injury [In German]. *Zbl. Chir., v. 72, 1947: 163–171.*

Interpretation is given of roentgenograms of bones from the area of frostbite injuries.

2050. Salsano, P. Roentgen aspect of a frozen limb; pathogenic interpretation [In Italian]. *Gior. med. mil., v. 87, Aug. 1939: 864–867.*

The author discusses a case of frostbite of the foot which he observed. From his observations and on the basis of the radiographs, he has made a diagnosis of atrophy of the bone from decalcification.

2051. Scow, R. O. Retarding effect of brief refrigeration upon skeletal development in the newborn rat [Abstract]. *Anat. Rec., v. 88, Apr. 1944: 457.*

If the feet, or vertebrae of the tail, of newborn rats which had come in contact with the cold surface of a glass beaker (internal temperature of $-5°$ to $-10°C$) for 15 minutes, growth and ossification were either seriously retarded or stopped. The soft tissues did not appear, grossly, to be injured. The author warns that, in refrigeration anesthesia experiments with newborn animals, precautions be taken to prevent contact between animals and surfaces of the refrigeration apparatus.

2052. Scow, R. O. Destruction of cartilage cells in the newborn rat by brief refrigeration, with consequent skeletal deformities. *Am. J. Path., v. 25, Jan. 1949: 143–161.*

The unossified tails of 1-day-old rats were held in contact with the freezing plate of a freezing microtome for 15–20 seconds until the tails became white. Cartilage cells were found to be especially sensitive to cold, lethal effects being caused by direct action upon the nuclear and cytoplasmic proteins of these cells. Marked deformities of the caudal vertebral column resulted from the injury to cartilage cells which would normally be active in lengthening and shaping the skeletal parts through endochondral ossification. Other tissues of the tail in order of their decreasing suceptibility to cold injury were: muscles, subcutaneous tissue, and skin. The cells of the intervertebral disk, perichondrium, future periosteum, and caudal tendons did not appear susceptible to cold. Several plates illustrating these conditions are found on pages 153–161.

2053. Spivak, T. L. Roentgenological data on bone changes in frostbite [In Russian]. *Vrach. delo, v. 23 (2), 1941; 102–109.*

After nearly all degrees of frostbite injury, roentgenological study showed structural bone alterations of the so-called Zudekov type. These osteoporotic alterations were not limited to the hands or forepart of the feet, but spread proximally to the shin and forearm. The exact moment of appearance of osteoporosis could not be determined. In general, the type, degree, and extent of osteoporosis is related to the clinical course of the frostbite. A normal bone structure found, in some severe cases, toward the distal end of the demarcation line, can be explained by the arrest of vital physiological processes in the bone before the alterations could take place.

* 2054. Stoliarenko, D. Contribution to the question of the clinical aspects of frostbite [In Russian]. *Ortop. travmat., Kharkov, v. 14 (5–6), 1940: 101–107. Translation in: E. Hope. Frostbite. Translations from the Russian of a collection of sixteen papers published between 1939 and 1944, p. 53–60. Ottawa, Defence Research Board, Canada, 1950.*

The author distinguishes between the local action of cold, which he calls frostbite, and the general action, which he calls "congelation." This latter action is called the myalgic (muscular) form, and a clinical description of 31 cases is given. No patients were found who exhibited both forms at the same time. It is suggested that the general action be called "pernio communis" or "cryomyalgia" since the old names of "lumbago" or "fibromyositis" have no etiological reference.

2055. Thelander, H. E. Epiphyseal destruction by frostbite. *J. Pediat., S. Louis, v. 36, Jan. 1950: 105–106.*

X-ray examination of the hand—known to have been severely frostbitten 2½ years previously—of a boy showed that the epiphyses of the distal and middle articulations of the second to fifth digit were missing. There was a considerable flaring of the diaphyses and the phalanges were shorter than on the normal, left, hand. The pathology is presumed to be on the basis of prolonged ischemia and possibly of thrombosis of small blood vessels.

* 2056. Verbov, A. F. On osteomyelitis in frostbite [in Russian]. *Khirurgiĩa, Moskva, v. 15 (4), 1945: 40–45.*

"*Contains* a study dealing with lack of specificity in frostbite-osteomyelitis; its etiology and pathology; causes of osteomyelitis not directly connected with frostbite; characteristic features of frostbite-osteomyelitis; prophylaxis."—Arctic Bibl., v. 4, 1954: 1119.

---

* Original not seen.

2057. Via, E. Osteoporosis due to cold [In Italian]. *Gior. med. mil., v. 94, July–Aug. 1947: 268–279.*

The author discusses bone lesions from various causes and compares them with the osteoporosis caused by cold exposure.

See also items: 1777, 2081, 2085, 2303, 2519.

5. Nervous System and Sense Organs

2058. Bariatti, R. Certain cytological modifications of the motor cells of the anterior horn of the spinal cord following freezing of an extremity [In Italian]. *Biol. med., Milano, v. 3 (1), 1950: 112–122.*

One hind leg, depleted of hair, of each of a group of guinea pigs was frozen by exposing it to a spray of carbon dioxide for 20 minutes and then packing the leg in solid carbon dioxide within a metal box (temperature, −2°C) for the duration of the experiment. The animals were sacrificed after 48 or 72 hours, or 6, 10, 11, 20, or 30 days. Cross sections of the spinal cord at the point of emergence of the radices of the sciatic nerves were studied and reports made of histological changes and alterations in content of nucleonic acid. The author reports that, following freezing injury, the increase in nucleonic acid was not as pronounced as had been observed earlier for ribonucleic acid in the motor cells of the anterior horn of the spinal cord.

2059. Bariatti, R. The influence of freezing upon the phosphatase activity of motor cells of the anterior column of the spinal medulla (In Italian). *Biol. med., Milano, v. 3 (1), 1950: 154–163.*

The left front leg of each of a group of guinea pigs was subjected to a jet of carbon dioxide snow for 20 minutes and then kept packed in carbon dioxide within a metal box where the temperature was about −2°C. The animals were sacrificed after 48 or 72 hours, or 6, 10, 20, or 30 days. Histological changes in the motor cells of the anterior horn of the spinal cord, are given in some detail. The phosphatase activity of the cells appeared to be increased. The possible significance of this is discussed.

2060. Block, W. On the extension of frostbite lesions and the changes which they occasion in the ganglia of the lateral sympathetic chain [In German]. *Arch. klin. Chir., v. 205, May 18, 1944: 719–727.*

Studies on the sympathetic fibers of frozen extremities show changes first inflammatory and later degenerative similar to those described by M. Staemmler (item 2122) in motor and sensory fibers. A characteristic lymphocytic infiltration around and between the ganglion cells is clearly demonstrated in lumbar ganglia removed from patients with frostbitten feet. A year after exposure ganglion cells are claimed to show degenerative changes. The author states he has observed the same changes in thromboangiitis obliterans.

2061. Bugliari, G., and G. Canavero. Neuro-arthralgic syndrome in frostbite [In Italian]. *Minerva med., Tor., anno 31 (v. 2), Dec. 15, 1940: 567–571.* Also, in Italian, in: *Gior. med. mil., v. 89, 1941: 505–522.*

This general account of frostbite, with emphasis on the neuro-arthralgic syndrome, is based on experiences in the Italian Army. The etiology, pathogenesis, prognosis, and treatment are discussed. Therapeutic measures include the use of light massage, medicated ointments, diathermy, use of Novocain either locally or by infiltration of the lumbar ganglion, and the use of vasodilator or anti-rheumatic drugs.

2062. Davidenkov, S. N. [The treatment of frostbite and its sequelae]. [In Russian]. *In: Trudy 2-go plenuma Gospital'nogo Soveta Narkomzdrava SSSR, Dec. 20–25, 1942, p. 277–278. Moskva, Medgiz, 1943.*

The neuritis which occurs in 90% of frostbite cases affects chiefly the sensory and autonomous-trophic functions of the nerve trunks. The motor, muscular-trophic, and the reflex functions are little disturbed. Sensory disturbances may pertain to various types of sensations and various degrees of dissociations. However, as a rule, the thermal sensibility suffers most. Topographically, there appear islands of anesthesia, which are not localized on the course of a nerve trunk, and disseminated among islands of hypesthesia. Sometimes, both are distributed in the manner of diffuse areas assuming the zone of influence of a larger nerve trunk. These are chiefly end-neurites. Segmentary repercussions of neuritis are often found in the healthy contralateral extremity. Frostbite neuritis is a persistent symptom, which requires special attention at the time of hospital discharge.

2063. Gaudenzi, C. de. On the neuro-arthralgic syndrome in freezing injury [In Italian]. *Forze san., Roma, v. 10, Nov. 15, 1941: 44–47.*

The neuro-arthralgic syndrome, which occurs in frostbite cases, is described together with its treatment with vitamin B.

2064. Giugni, F., and C. Castelli. Freezing injuries and supercooling. Lesions of the nervous system and bone changes in freezing injuries [In Italian]. *In: Atti Congresso Nazionale di Chirurgia di Guerra, May 24–26, 1942, p. 243–246. Roma, 1943.*

Freezing injury is usually due to freezing of the feet following contact with snow and ice, while supercooling is a local action on tissue casuing nervous system lesions. Cases of 3rd degree freezing injury are cited, as examples of supercooling, where there are painful symptoms and fatty necrosis of the extremity. The nerve lesions were treated with vitamin B preparations with excellent results. Radiographs showed the damage done to bony tissues to be caused by atrophy of the spongy substance and sometimes a true osteomalacia. The early period of treatment consisted of anesthetic block of the femoral canal, and protein therapy; later treatment by Marconi therapy, infrared radiation, and salves.

2065. Grant, W. M. Ocular injury due to sulfur dioxide. II. Experimental study and comparison with ocular effects of freezing. *Arch. Ophth., Chic., v. 38, n. s., Dec. 1947: 762–774.*

Freezing of the anterior portion of the living rabbit eye with the relatively non-toxic refrigerant Freon-12 (dichlorodifluoromethane) for several seconds produced mild and transient disturbances. Freezing for 30 to 90 seconds caused loss of the endothelium with consequent edema of the stroma and epithelium. The changes were unlike those produced with liquid sulfur dioxide.

2066. Hass, G. M., C. B. Taylor, and J. E. Maloney. Quantitative hypothermal production of closed cerebral injury [Abstract]. *Am. J. Path., v. 23, Sept. 1947: 898–899.*

Description of a method for producing a quantitatively controlled destruction of local areas of cerebral cortex of rabbits by use of a freezing device (cooling plate temperature of −50°C) applied to the external surface of the intact skull. Lesions produced resembled strictly localized infarcts or contusions. Survival of animals depended on the volume and depth of the lesions. By use of successive sublethal lesions, 30% of the brain could be progressively destroyed without opening of the skull.

2067. Leger, G., and . . . Jeanjean. Polyradiculoneuritis with cytological albumin dissociation following a freezing injury of the feet [In French]. *Lyon chir., v. 41, May–June 1946: 357–358.*

A history is presented of a patient who following treatment by infiltration of the lumbar ganglion—to relieve the after-effects of severe freezing injuries of the feet—developed a loss of visual accommodation as well as a flaccid paralysis of the legs. The possible role of cold in the etiology of the nervous afflictions is discussed.

2068.   Marshall, C., L. F. Nims, W. E. Stone. Chemical changes in the cerebral cortex following local thermocoagulation and local freezing. *Yale J. Biol., v. 13, Mar. 1941: 485–488.*

Local, superficial, freezing of the cerebral cortex of cats (by use of an ethyl chloride spray) produced increased concentrations of lactic acid and inorganic phosphate, and decreased concentrations of phosphocreatine and hexose phosphates in the injured areas. It is suggested that not all the cells are killed and that the altered electrical patterns of the brain are produced by cells working in an altered chemical state.

2069.   Merwarth, H. Concept of refrigeration as a cause of facial paralysis [Abstract]. *J. Nerv. Ment. Dis., v. 106, Dec. 1947: 696–701.*

The author discusses a series of 500 cases of peripheral facial paralysis in many of which there was indication of the causative effect of cold. It is the belief of the author that the cause of the facial paralysis which is known as Bell's palsy is an infection rather than a direct effect of cold.

2070.   Nims, L. F., C. Marshall, and A. Nielsen. Effect of local freezing on the electrical activity of the cerebral cortex. *Yale J. Biol., v. 13, Mar. 1941: 477–484.*

Freezing of small areas of the cerebral cortex produced convulsive electric waves in dogs, the condition being greatly increased if morphine was given at the time freezing was carried out. These disturbances were caused not only in the frozen area but also in untreated areas. Initially there was complete obliteration or severe depression of electrical activity. Later, partial recovery occurred and still later abnormal patterns appeared. The mechanism of production of these dysrhythmias is thought to be caused by the slowly-developing chemical changes.

2071.   Panchenko, D. I. On the patho-histological changes of sympathetic ganglia in frostbite [In Russian]. *Biull. eksp. biol. med., v. 15 (4–5), 1943: 15–18.*

In twelve patients suffering from frostbite who died of intercurrent infections, histological studies revealed considerable amounts of structural disturbance in the peripheral nerve trunks (ischemic neuritis); retrograde changes were seen in the motor cells of the anterior lobes of the spinal cord and in the nervous cells of the spinal ganglia. A striking similarity of pathomorphological disturbances were found in all the cases: polyblastic infiltrates were accumulated in the connective tissue stroma of the ganglia. In three cases small infiltrates were observed around the vessels, particularly, a polyblastic infiltrate around the veins. In some cells the nuclei were seen to be displaced toward the cell border. Staining by Cajal's method, however, showed no deviation from normal. The author concludes that (1) the changes in the sympathetic ganglia do not correspond in severity to the injuries in peripheral nerves; (2) the histopathological data in frostbite cases are in many respects similar to those found in spontaneous gangrene. The changes in the sympathetic ganglia are a consequence of vasomotor disturbance.

2072.   Panchenko, D. I. The role of histopathological deformations of nerve trunks in the pathogenesis of cold injury [In Russian]. *Biull. eksp. biol. med., v. 16 (10–11), 1943: 60–63.*

Histological examination was made of the peripheral nerves of the frostbitten extremities, at three different levels, in further studies on twelve human casualties who had died of intercurrent infections. Hyperplasia and hypertrophy of the fibroblasts were the most typical and constant forms of reaction of the connective tissue elements of peripheral nerves. There was a striking resemblance to spontaneous gangrene and emboli of the vessels. Also typical was the process of demyelinization of the fibers. The author stressed the fact that in cases of frostbite, if severe, reflex vascular spasms are found on both the injured and non-injured side; the intensity of the pain is in proportion to the intensity of the spasm. The reflex mechanism of this phenomenon is apparently achieved with the participation of the endocrine system (hyperadrenalinemia). These functional changes may lead to structural alterations in the nerves, while the pathomorphological nervous changes contribute in turn to structural disturbances in the vessels. At the same time regeneration of the nerves occurs. The disturbances in the nerves during frostbite may be considered as ischemic neuritis. These changes are of great importance for the outcome of the disease. Gangrene develops not from the direct effect of cold, but from a combination of exocrine and endocrine factors. Sensitivity and tendency to recurrence is an unavoidable, acquired, property of the neuro-vascular apparatus after frostbite.

2073. Panchenko, D. I. Retrograde changes in the spinal cord in frostbite of the extremities [In Russian]. *Nevropat. psikhiat.*, v. 12 (3), 1943: 75–79.

In continuing studies of the effect of cold on the central nervous system as seen in 12 frostbite patients who had died from an intercurrent infection, the microscopic picture of the nerve trunks was that of a typical ischemic neuritis. The structural nervous alterations consisted in intensive fibroblastic hyperplasia and pronounced hypertrophy of the connective tissues; simultaneously with these destructive processes there occurred regeneration of the nerve fibers. The foci of necrosis, which accumulated in a distal direction, were as a rule located in the immediate vicinity of the blood vessels, suggesting that nerve degeneration and tissue necrosis are due to vascular disturbance. Detailed microscopic study of the nerve cells in the anterior horns of the spinal cord and in the intervertebral ganglia, at the levels corresponding to the innervation of the injured lower extremity, revealed a typical chromatolysis of varying degree, and dispersion of the Nissl bodies. These retrograde changes did not occur at other levels of the spinal cord. These pathological changes must be related to the effect of cold on the peripheral portion of the axone (Wallerian degeneration). The length of exposure, the intensity of cold, and the site of the injury determine the extent of the damage in the neurones of the spinal cord and intravertebral ganglia. The structural alterations in the cell, induced by the deterioration of the axone, may influence the regeneration process in the axone when the reaction becomes reversible. For this reason, any therapeutic measure which would augment the damage to the axone or carry it to a higher distal level, is contraindicated. The higher the level of damage to the axone, the stronger the retrograde changes in the cell and the greater the danger of relapse, infection, etc.

2074. Panchenko, D. I. On the significance of neuritis in the pathogenesis of frostbite [In Russian]. *Khirurgiia, Moskva*, v. 16 (1), 1946: 25–30.

A histopathological examination was made of all the main, deeply-situated, and peripheral nerves in the 12 patients with various degrees of frostbite of the extremities who had died from an intercurrent infection. At the amputation line the nerve trunks showed a periaxial degeneration (progressively diminished and altered myelin), alternating with that of Wallerian degeneration, both accumulating distally from the injury. The foci of disseminated necrosis are situated not only near the vascular and nervous trunks but also within the nerve trunks, scattered in vertical and horizontal direction at various levels. The origin of these foci is seen in prolonged vascular spasm. Evidence of reflex vascular spasms can be observed also on the healthy contralateral side of the injury. Hyperplasia and hypertrophy of the fibroblasts is the most constant reaction of the connective tissue membranes of the nervous trunks in response to cold injury. The pathomorphological changes in the peripheral nerves may be considered as an ischemic neuritis. It is concluded that the gangrene of frostbite is caused by a combination of changes induced by the cold injury. In the final gangrenous period the neuritis becomes complicated by toxico-infectious influences. The chief rule of therapeutics should be a regime of careful forbearance. Any measure which would increase pain should be avoided, in order to avoid the remote severe consequences of frostbite.

* 2075. Plesso, G. I. State of peripheral innervation in frostbite [In Russian]. *Nevropat. psikhiat.*, v. 16, Sept.–Oct. 1947: 56.

"*Contains* a note on observations of 50 cases of severe frostbite, mostly of the 4th degree; some reflexes on the most injured sites were heightened or lowered, the tonus of some muscles lowered, suggestions of muscle and skin atrophy were in evidence. Author does not consider all this as symptoms of a simple neuritis but as signs of over-activation of the adreno-sympathetic system caused by the severe exposure to cold; he offers general therapeutic directives."—Arctic Bibl., v. 4, 1954: 809.

---

* Original not seen.

2076. **Shirai, K., T. Iida, and H. Yoshimura.** Frostbite and the function of the autonomic nervous system. I. [Abstract, in English]. *Jap. J. M. Sc., Biophysics,* v. 9, 1944: 74*–75*.

Frostbite patients were, in general, found to be vagotonic regardless of the tone of the autonomic nervous system in their healthy state. More than half of the subjects who were known, by previous experiences, to be resistant to frostbite were vagotonic, while the tone of the sympathetic nerves was increased in those known to be susceptible. The sweat of sympatheticotonic subjects was found to contain more chloride than that of vagotonic ones, as did the sweat of the subjects susceptible to frostbite.

2077. **Tamura, S.** The influence of low temperature on the eyes [In Japanese, with German summary]. *Acta Soc. ophth. jap.,* v. 43 (2), 1939: 1704–1712, and [abstract section] p. 99.

Injuries to the eye of laboratory animals caused by temperatures of −20° and −30°C were, in general, less than those to other parts of the body. The areas first affected were the eyelids, the bulbar conjunctiva, and the cornea in the area of the lid fissure. Of the changes, corneal clouding was the most striking. Eye changes from cold appeared clearly short of death-from-cold, and in the following order in animals: mice, rats, guinea pigs, and rabbits. The changes appear faster the more intense the cold. When all the hairs were snipped from the upper and lower eyelids of one eye, the injuries from cold were more serious to that eye than they were to the other. Also the effect of wind currents at such a low temperature increased the degree of injury. Microscopic changes also were studied.

See also items: 2081, 2180, 2415, 2621, 2624, 2629.

6. Circulatory System

(includes also fluid and electrolyte changes)

2078. **Baldwin, D., C. B. Taylor, and G. M. Hass.** A comparison of arteriosclerotic lesions produced in young and in old rabbits by freezing the aorta. *Arch. Path., Chic.,* v. 50, July 1950: 122–131.

The abdominal aorta of senescent rabbits (varying in age from 150 to 248 weeks) was exposed surgically and frozen *in situ* while the rabbits were under ether anesthesia. The rabbits were allowed to live from 1 to 24 weeks, then killed, and the arteriosclerotic lesions of the aorta which had been produced by the cold, were examined microscopically. In comparison with the lesions produced in a similar manner in young rabbits in an earlier experiment (item 2125), the regeneration of a new aortic wall was quantitatively less than in the young rabbits while qualitatively the reactions were similar. In the senile rabbits the aortic adventitial connective tissue frequently showed the formation of cartilage and bone.

2079. **Baxter, H., and M. A. Entin.** Experimental and clinical studies of reduced temperatures in injury and repair in man. IV. The effect of cold on vascular elements of human skin. *Plastic & Reconstr. Surg.,* v. 5, Mar. 1950: 193–216.

Clinical and histological observations were made of the reaction of normal intact skin, traumatized skin, and skin pedicles to temperatures of 65° to 50°F, 32°F, and −108°F. Prolonged exposure to moderate cold resulted in an increased permeability, which was attributed to damage of the smaller blood vessels. Early administration of heparin was suggested, to assist lymphatic circulation and prevent coagulation. Freezing by contact for 1–15 minutes with solid carbon dioxide (−108°F) involved serious injury to the vascular tree which anticoagulants could not repair. It was concluded that the main problem in the clinical management of frozen tissue is to discover some method of retaining the fluid elements of the blood within the damaged vessels.

2080. **Bigelow, W. G., H. O. Heimbecker, and R. C. Harrison.** Intravascular agglutination (sludged blood), vascular stasis, and the sedimentation rate of the blood in trauma. *Arch. Surg.,* v. 59, Sept. 1949: 667–693.

Both localized and generalized trauma were induced in experimental animals by use of agents such as cold (Ringer's solution at 3°C, or solid carbon dioxide, applied to the local area), heat, and crush injury. Following local trauma there was cessation of blood flow in the smaller vessels of the area leading to the clumping of the red blood cells and the production of the phenomenon known as vascular stasis. Resolution of stasis was observed in which part of the congesting mass broke off into the general circulation as circulating clumps. Animals exposed to trauma consistently showed agglutinated clumps of red blood cells in the general circulation after injury; the clumps often appeared to act as emboli and produced stasis in areas remote from the trauma. Observations were made of the conjunctiva of the eyes of 60 human subjects, some of whom had mild or moderate clinical symptoms including some hospitalized for burns or frostbite, and some apparently healthy. There was a rough correlation between the severity of clinical symptoms and the degree of intravascular agglutination; only 1 of 26 apparently healthy persons showed any degree of agglutination.

2081. Borsani, L. Oscillometry in frostbite [In Italian]. *Atti. Accad. med. lombarda, v. 31, Apr. 17, 1942: 233–235.*

Oscillometric studies of arterial blood pressure were made in 12 cases of frostbite. A neuromuscular reaction is believed to be involved. It was found that the blood pressure decreased in the course of treatment.

2082. Breitner, B. On arteriography in frostbite [In German]. *Chirurg, v. 16, Jan. 1944: 8–10.*

Results are reported of arteriographic studies of frostbite injuries in women.

2083. Chidichimo, G. Contribution to the study and treatment of the ulcerous termination of freezing injuries [In Italian]. *In: Atti Congresso Nazionale di Chirurgia di Guerra, May 24–26, 1942, p. 241–242. Roma, 1943.* Also, in Italian, in: *Policlinico, Sez. chir., v. 51, Sept. 15, 1944: 185–198.*

The author describes what he considers to be a new malady, the neurovascular-spastic syndrome, occurring in 3rd degree freezing injuries. The syndrome is characterized by pain, cramps, exaggerated perspiration, pigmentation of the skin, and paresthesia. The condition responds favorably and quickly to periarterial sympathectomy or arterioectomy.

2084. Costantini, E., and T. Posteli. Clinical observations on frostbite. I. Results of cutaneous thermometry. II. Results of arterial oscillometry [In Italian]. *Bull. sc. med., Bologna, v. 113, Mar.–Apr.; May–June, 1941: 174–182; 226–231.*

Observations on frostbite injuries made in the military hospital in Bologna are reported. For the most part, observations were made 3–4 weeks after the injury, and patients were found to be suffering from circulatory and vasomotor disturbances in the injured extremities. Changes in temperature regulation in injured extremities were shown to be dependent upon vasoregulation. Cold injury of a distant part was found to have vasomotor effects on uninjured extremities. The second half of the paper continues the study of the vasomotor effects and compares oscillometric findings, skin color and temperature, in the injured and the uninjured limbs.

2085. Crismon, J. M., and F. A. Fuhrman. Distribution of sodium and water in muscle following severe cold injury. *Science, v. 104, Nov. 1, 1946: 408–409.*

Studies of the distribution of sodium and water in the muscles of rabbits subjected to experimental frostbite showed that the gain of water by muscle was from 5% to 60%. The increase in sodium was 30% in the case of the smallest increase, and from 237% to 697% in the remaining 5 animals. The pattern of sodium re-distribution appears to be characteristic of severe tissue injury, regardless of cause.

2086. Crismon, J. M., and F. A. Fuhrman. Studies on gangrene following cold injury. IV. The use of fluorescein as an indicator of local blood flow: distribution of fluorescein in body fluids after intravenous injection. *J. Clin. Invest., v. 26, Mar. 1947: 259–267.*

The use of fluorescein to indicate blood flow conditions was studied with special reference to the distribution of injected fluorescein in normal rabbits. Maximum intensity of skin fluorescence was found to be reached at a time when concentration of dye in the blood was falling; thereafter, the disappearance of dye from the blood and decrease in fluorescence occurred at about the same rate. Of the dye added to heparinized whole blood 83% was recovered from the plasma; loss of dye was attributed to adsorption on the surface of red blood cells rather than to cell penetration. Determinations made of the fluorescein content of muscle, the bile, and the intestinal lumen are also reported.

2087.   Crismon, J. M., and F. A. Fuhrman. Studies on gangrene following cold injury. V. The use of fluorescein as indicator of local blood flow: fluorescein tests in experimental frostbite. *J. Clin. Invest.*, v. 26, Mar. 1947: 268–276.

Results of the analyses made of the distribution of intravenously injected fluorescein in normal ears of rabbits and in ears severely injured by frostbite show that the dye's entrance into and exit from injured regions were slower than were the exchanges in uninjured tissues.

2088.   Crismon, J. M., and F. A. Fuhrman. Studies on gangrene following cold injury. VI. Capillary blood flow after cold injury, the effects of rapid warming, and sympathetic block. *J. Clin. Invest.*, v. 26, May 1947: 468–475.

Report is made on a microscopic study of blood flow in the small vessels of ears of rabbits during the first hour after freezing. Similar studies were made on ears of animals rapidly thawed in warm water and on the effects of a procaine block of the stellate ganglion on the injured site. Vasomotor activity was paralyzed in the injured part of the rabbit's ear frozen at −55°C for 1 minute. After thawing at 25°C in air, blood flow was re-established and all vessels were markedly dilated. Procaine block of the stellate ganglion augmented the hyperemia and delayed onset of stasis for 50 to 60 minutes.

2089.   Deliallisi, A. Research on peripheral oscillometry in frostbite [In Italian]. *Forze san.*, Roma, v. 10, Apr. 15, 1941: 59–60.

A study, using the oscillometric method, was made of the arterial flow in cases of frostbite.

2090.   Ducuing, J., J. d'Harcourt [Got], A. Folch [Pi], and J. Bofill. Nutritional disorders of the extremities, caused by wartime pathological dry cold [In French]. *J. chir.*, Par., v. 55, May 1940: 385–402.

An account of experience with frostbite in the Spanish Civil War, is given. Lesions were found to be due to circulatory disturbances, especially arterial lesions, and not to the freezing of the tissues. Blood supply was directly reduced by vasoconstriction, a condition which when long-continued produced gangrene.

2091.   Essex, H. E., and R. Quintanilla. Effects of frostbite on the minute blood vessels of a peripheral vascular bed [Abstract]. *Fed. Proc.*, Balt., v. 5, Feb. 1946: 25–26.

Observations of the effects of freezing on small blood vessels were made through a transparent chamber inserted in the ears of rabbits. Vessels completely frozen in 30 seconds by carbon dioxide snow showed signs of serious injury. Five or 10 minutes after thawing, vessels were widely dilated; permeability of wall was increased; plasma was drained out; and cells were agglomerated in uncoagulated masses. A similar picture was seen in animals previously injected with heparin.

2092.   Friedman, N. B., K. Lange, and D. Weiner. The pathology of experimental frostbite. *Am. J. M. Sc.*, v. 213, Jan. 1947: 61–67.

Studies were made on the pathogenesis of experimental frostbite in rabbits. The basic lesion produced is vascular with agglutinative erythrocytic thrombi resulting in vascular occlusion and ischemic gangrene. Thrombosis and gangrene are both prevented by the injection of heparin.

2093. Fuhrman, F. A., and J. M. Crismon. Studies on gangrene following cold injury. III. Edema following cold injury: its magnitude and the composition and sources of edema fluid. *J. Clin. Invest.*, v. 26, Mar. 1947: 245–258.

Following severe cold injury from immersion of one hind foot of rabbits in liquid at −55°C for 3 minutes, massive local edema occurred. During the period of swelling, tests were performed on the blood for hemoglobin concentration and for venous and arterial oxygen content. The edematous fluid was tested for protein concentration and for toxic substances.

2094. Gelderen, C. van. Local freezing; a new instance of functional pathology [In Dutch, with English summary]. *Ned. tschr. geneesk.*, v. 92, Apr. 17, 1948: 1142–1145.

The author observed that, following local frostbite, vasospasm caused a reduction in blood flow, which, if continued, could cause thrombosis. In early cases, Novocain infiltration of the stellate or lumbar ganglia is used to dilate the blood vessels; in cases of longer duration, lumbar sympathectomy is found to be effective.

2095. Greene, R. The immediate vascular changes in true frostbite. *J. Path. Bact., Lond.*, v. 55, July 1943: 259–267.

Tails of 10 mice were subjected for 1 minute to freezing at −62°C. Development of necrosis was studied by amputation of some of the tails immediately after freezing and of others after 30 minutes, 1 hour, 1 day, and 2 days. Generalized necrosis of the distal centimeter of the tail was discerned in the last group. Loss of fluid from blood vessels was noted, which left the vessels silted up with corpuscles, tending to cut off blood supply to distal tissues.

2096. Hausler, H. The behavior of reactive hyperemia after frostbite [In German]. *Münch. med. Wschr.*, v. 90, May 7, 1943: 301–302.

In 22 out of 29 frostbitten limbs, it was found that the distal limit reached by reactive hyperemia was higher than the proximal level of the lesion. By using reflex vasodilatation, the reactive hyperemia was made to extend more distally.

2097. Judmaier, F. The treatment of peripheral circulatory disturbances with particular regard to old freezing injuries [In German]. *Wien klin. Wschr.*, v. 61, Feb. 11, 1949: 85–90.

The pathology and treatment of freezing injuries, with special reference to circulatory disturbances, are discussed. Such disturbances may be organic injuries to the blood vessels resulting in endarteriitis obliterans, or spastic contraction of the collateral circulation. Medicinal, physico-mechanical, and surgical therapeutic measures are described. Drugs mentioned include Priscoline, Eupaverin, Padutin, Progynon, and acetylcholine. The use of warm baths and irradiation therapy is also described together with the indications for sympathectomy or anesthetic block.

2098. Kovách, A. G. B., and T. Csáky. Quantitative changes in the fluid content of the organs of rats in traumatic shock by freezing [In English]. *Arch. biol. hungar.*, v. 18, ser. II, 1948: 390–397.

Fatal shock was induced in rats by freezing both hind extremities with liquid air. Although there was very little fluid loss in the kidneys and none in the brain or spleen, many of the organs of the body were found to have a decrease in fluid. There was a reduction of 41.3% of the total weight of the lungs and 49.1% of the total fluid content of the lungs of the animals dying in shock. There was also an important decrease in the fluid content of the liver, heart, and intestinal tract. In the lungs and intestinal tract there was a loss only of fluid, while in the liver and heart there was also a significant loss in dry material. There was also a considerable loss from urination and fluid evaporation in the lungs. The increase in weight of the frozen limbs (29.8%) consisted only of edematous fluids. Whether such extensive changes in the fluid content of the different organs can themselves cause death from shock was not decided by the experiments.

2099. Kramer, D. W. Manual of peripheral vascular disorders. *Philadelphia, Blakiston, 1940. 448 p.*

In the chapter on non-inflammatory occlusive disorders, frostbite is said to be attributed to local disturbances of circulation produced by exposure to cold. Vasospasms are produced, circulation becomes sluggish, and thrombosis may occur with the possible development of gangrene. It is also suggested that a disturbance of the trophic nerves may be part of the clinical picture. Temperatures necessary to produce frostbite are 8°–14°F depending on the wind velocity and the length of time of exposure. The symptoms are coldness, numbness, tingling, and loss of sensation of the area. Redness may appear, with the part later becoming purplish-blue in color and with weakness becoming apparent. In more severe cases the area becomes erythematous and large blebs appear, later breaking down and developing into ulcers. Gangrene, usually of the distal part of an affected extremity, may develop which is usually of a dry type. The red areas of chilblains (pernio) are said to be due probably to some permanent changes in the structure of the walls of the peripheral vessels and these areas may be from time to time influenced by temperature changes. When exposed to cold, tingling and burning sensations are produced. Whether this condition is merely vasomotor or due to a mild form of chronic inflammation has as yet not been determined. Individuals who have a tendency to peripheral vascular disturbances should guard against exposure to cold. When frostbite occurs, the individual should be placed in a warm, not hot, room and gentle massage—no snow— applied to the area. Passive vascular exercise, and various methods of physiotherapy, have been found helpful in treatment. Gangrene, if it develops, should be treated conservatively and any surgery should await the line of demarcation. Histological examination of tissue from amputated digits, following gangrene from frostbite (p. 390–391), showed a proliferative endarteritis. It is thought that this may be due to a low grade infection superimposed upon an already existing pathological condition.

2100. Kunlin, J. Investigations on the pathological physiology of frostbite and sub-malleolar erythrocyanosis [In French]. *Progr. méd., Par., v. 73, Nov. 24, 1945: 373–374.*

Studies are reported on the circulatory changes in frostbite with special reference to the effects of Adrenalin and Novocain on the capillaries.

2101. Läwen, A. Studies on the circulation of the foot of frontline soldiers in a healthy and diseased state, particularly in injuries from cold [In German]. *Deut. Militärarzt, v. 7, Aug. 1942: 479–491.*

Studies were made of the functional state of the blood vessels in the feet of a group of healthy soldiers and in the frostbitten feet of another group of 500 frontline soldiers. The quality of the pulse in the *arteria dorsalis pedis* and in the *arteria tibialis posterior* were used as diagnostic indicators of the functional state of the circulation of each foot. In 318 (63.6%) of the 500 healthy soldiers a good strong pulse was palpable in each of the arteries of each foot. In 182 (36.4%) of the soldiers, the pulse was not palpable or very weak in one or more arteries while that in the others remained strong or extra-strong. The author raises the question of whether the lack of pulse in a foot artery is significant and discusses some of the factors which cause variation including the role of smoking. Of a group of 130 men, 101 had had both feet frostbitten and 29 had had only one. Normal pulse beats in all arteries were noted in 93 men (71.6%), while 37 had a slowed or absent pulse in one or more arteries. In the frostbite cases Novocain infiltration of the sympathetic nervous system produced slight rises in the skin temperature of the leg but it also produced some lowering of skin temperature in other cases.

2102. Leriche, R., and J. Kunlin. Physiological pathology of frostbite, a vasomotor disease at first, later thrombotic [In French]. *Mem. Acad. chir., Par., v. 66. Feb. 14–21, 1940: 196–204. Also, in French, in: Progr. méd., Par., v. 68, Mar. 2, 1940: 169–173.*

The authors regard frostbite as primarily a disease of the circulatory system and recommend for treatment the prompt infiltration of the sympathetic nerves with Novocain.

2103. Leriche, R. Vasomotor diseases, produced by cold and by heat. Frost-bite and burns. *In: Physiologie pathologique et traitement chirurgical des maladies artérielles de la vasomotricité, p. 65–89 [In French]. Paris, Masson, 1945.*

Emphasis is placed on the vasomotor effects, in this general account of frostbite. In mild cases sympathetic infiltration is recommended; in more severe cases lumbar sympathectomy is the method chosen.

2104. Levin, A. I., and F. M. Khaletskaĭa. Contribution to the problem of the pathogenesis of frostbite. I. The role of local disturbances of the blood circula-tion [In Russian, with English summary]. *Arkh. biol. nauk, v. 60 (12), 1940: 15–24.*

Studies were made of the role of local circulatory disturbances on the pathogenesis of frost-bite. Experimental frostbite was induced in 32 rabbits under natural out-door winter condi-tions ($-17°$ to $-23°C$). Localized anemia, or stagnant hypertonia, of the ear was induced by pinching the base of one of the ears between two pieces of cork (with or without a groove for the blood vessel), which were removed after the exposure to cold. The changes observed were very different in the ear in which the artery was occluded from those where it was not, or from those of the control animals. The diminished blood supply sharply increased the tissue's sensitivity to cold and accelerated the development of frostbite in the region. Venous hyperemia had a lesser effect. Repeated and prolonged exposure to cold during localized anemia induced frostbite even at temperatures of $-5°C$ or above, due to gradual accumulation of damage to the tissue. Consequently, in the prophylaxis of frostbite special attention has to be directed to avoiding those factors which, directly or indirectly, induce vasoconstriction of the peripheral parts of the body.

2105. Mantscheff, Z. On frostbite [In German]. *Beitr. klin. Chir., v. 174, May 3, 1943: 337–357.*

The author regards tissue damage in frostbite as the result of changes in the circulatory system, especially of loss of fluid from the circulation with resulting congestion and thickening of the blood in the arterioles and capillaries. The author assumes the formation of thrombi, and his theory of treatment is based on this idea.

2106. Mazaev, P. N. Blood circulation in frostbite [In Russian]. *Khirurgiĭa, Moskva, 1942 (7): 26–38.*

Clinico-roentgenological studies of bone structure deformities in frostbite cases are presented. Experimental vasographic studies of the vascular reaction of dogs (by the roentgeno-vaso-kymographic method) during and after intravenous injection of chilled solution, are also dis-cussed. From these two studies the following observations were made: (1) In 1st degree frost-bite injuries a small spastic vascular contraction of the small caliber vessels occurred, mainly in the peripheral vessels. The circulation was rapidly restored to normal. (2) In 2nd degree injuries there was a permanent spastic contraction of medium and small caliber vessels which caused a sharp disruption of circulation. Osteoporosis appeared after $1\frac{1}{2}$ to 2 months (during cold treatment, after 3-4 weeks). (3) In injuries of deep-lying soft tissues, a permanent dis-rupture of circulation occurred in these tissues as well as in the bone, especially in the distal parts of the bone. Osteoporosis appeared in the third week and persisted for a very long time. (4) After removal of the cold agent, the blood circulation was restored in several vessels situated in the depth of the soft tissue, especially in those supplying the bones, and rate of flow and blood volume were increased. (5) Osteoporosis resulted from increased intra-ossal blood supply and stimulation of cellular function in the bone tissue. Prolonged disrupture of blood-supply, however, led to osteosclerosis and stopped bone regeneration. (6) The destruc-tive bone processes resulted either from primary vasotrophic injury or from bone alterations following osteomyelitis. (7) All blood vessels reacted to temperature changes very strongly but the reaction was more pronounced in the peripheral vessels.

2107. Meyer, O. Sequelae of freezing injury: on the etiology of endangiitis obliterans [In German]. *Schweiz. med. Wschr., v. 73, May 1, 1943: 538–540.*

The author states that a freezing injury can act as a predisposing factor in the etiology of endangiitis obliterans.

2108. Muirhead, E. E., C. T. Ashworth, L. A. Kregel, and J. M. Hill. Experimental freezing shock; changes in body fluids and tissues. *Arch. Surg., v. 45, Dec. 1942: 863–889.*

In experimental freezing of the entire hind limbs of dogs, before the onset of shock there was in the first few hours a rapid loss of blood volume—with indications of the passage of water into the body cells—and with pathological changes showing in the frozen and thawed legs and in the adrenal cortex. The zona fasciculata of the adrenal cortex showed a decrease in lipid content and prominent infiltration by polymorphonuclear neutrophilic leukocytes. After the fourth hour, the loss of plasma decreased greatly, but generalized capillariovenous dilatation was marked, with pulmonary edema, capillary hemorrhages, leukocytosis, and cellular changes in parenchymatous organs becoming evident. The stabilization of hemoconcentration in spite of evidences of generalized damage to the capillaries was directly associated with the drop in the peripheral arterial pressure.

2109. Muñoz, J. D. Frostbite and Buerger's disease [In Spanish]. *Rev. med. leg., Rosario, v. 8, Aug.–Dec. 1944: 246–251.*

The evidence of earlier vascular impairment as the result of cold exposure, in cases of Buerger's disease, is discussed. The differences between the gangrene resulting from cold injury and that from Buerger's disease aggravated by a cold injury, is that the former occurs rather soon after the cold exposure whereas in the latter there is an endarteritis, with frequent exacerbations and remissions over an extended period following the original cold injury.

2110. Ognev, B. V. [The treatment of frostbite and its sequelae]. [In Russian]. *In: Trudy 2-go plenuma Gospital'nogo Soveta Narkomzdrava SSSR, Dec. 20–25, 1942, p. 267–269. Moskva, Medgiz, 1943.*

Seventy-two experiments were made for a comparative study of vascular alterations in the rabbit's ear following frostbite injury (ethyl chloride spray, 1–10 minutes), following experimental burns, or injury by a chemical warfare agent. After the freezing and subsequent defreezing, the vessels were injected with contrast masses of India ink, which penetrated easily after short exposure. After 3–5 minutes one third of the capillaries and after 7–10 minutes nearly all the capillaries and even the basic arterial trunks of the ear remained uninjected. In repeated experiments, despite subsequent return of circulation, the frostbitten tissue fell off after 2–3 weeks. Histological examination showed necrosis of the small vessels and capillaries in the zone of gangrene. In the remaining ear stump all the vessels were greatly dilated. To a lesser degree, the dilatation occurred also in the vicinity of the injury, where it probably represented reactive alterations. Therefore, despite occasional complete penetrability of the frostbitten vessels, the latter die in the zone of gangrene. The degree of alterations depends on the duration and intensity of the cold effect.

2111. Posteli, T., and E. Constantini. Clinical observations on freezing injuries [Abstract, in Italian]. *Minerva med., Tor., anno 32 (v. 1), Apr. 27, 1941: 427.*

The authors have studied the circulatory changes in the extremities of a group of 100 soldiers, with freezing injuries of those extremities, by the use of oscillometric methods. Such studies were also found to be of value in appraising the effectiveness of Marconi and other thermal therapies.

2112. Quintanilla, R., F. H. Krusen, and H. E. Essex. Studies on frost-bite with special reference to treatment and the effect on minute blood vessels. *Am. J. Physiol., v. 149, Apr. 1947: 149–161.*

The authors conclude that the treatment of frostbite must depend upon the severity of the injury. In experiments with rabbits, it was found to be impossible to distinguish by inspection between hopeless and less serious freezing injuries. No method of therapy was found which could save the severely frozen feet of the rabbits. Ears of rabbits frozen in a transparent chamber showed vasodilatation, increased permeability, and the formation of conglomerate masses in vessels from which the plasma was drained. It was concluded that these masses were not the result of coagulation, since they appeared also in heparin-treated animals.

2113. Rosenfeld, L., J. L. Langohr, C. R. Owen, and O. Cope. Circulation of the blood and lymph in frostbite and influence of therapeutic cold and warmth: an experimental study. *Arch. Surg., v. 59, Nov. 1949: 1045–1055.*

Frostbite was experimentally induced in dogs by immersing the foot in a mixture of ethyl alcohol and dry ice. Degree of injury was varied with time of exposure and temperature of the mixture. Studies were made of the effect of freezing on the lymphatic and arterial circulation in the injured limb. The effect of treatment by cold (10°C) and warmth (40°C) was examined. No evidence of positive benefit from the use of either cold or warmth was obtained, and the authors suggest that therapy by use of cold may do more harm than good.

2114. Samuelson, A. Cold weather effects on circulation. *Hygeia, v. 24, Dec. 1946: 896–897; 951.*

The influence of cold weather on the circulation is discussed, especially in causing frostbite and urticarial sensitivity to cold. The author discusses also circulatory disturbances following frostbite as tending to lead to Raynaud's disease or Buerger's disease. Among the treatments mentioned for frostbite are the use of heparin, of sympathetic nerve block, and of Radon ointment—the latter a form of radium treatment—for use in cases of ulceration.

2115. Santucci, G., D. Bussa, and P. F. Antognetti. Inquiry into the cardiovascular apparatus of frostbite [In Italian]. *Minerva med., Tor., anno 31 (v. 2), Dec. 15, 1940: 592–594.*

Physiological studies were made on 4 patients suffering from frostbite. Observations of arterial and venous pressures and circulation time were made. Electrocardiograms were also taken and capillarioscopy was performed.

2116. Schmidt, J. Local freezing and circulatory injury [In German]. (*Dissert., Fried. Wilhelm Univ.*). *Breslau, The University, 1944. 37 p.*

After reviewing the literature on the pathogenesis of local frostbite with emphasis on circulatory effects, the author reports some experiments of his own. The tails of albino rats were frozen in a cold solution at a temperature of −15° to −20°C. When tails so frozen were quickly rewarmed necrosis resulted; necrosis was less evident in tails more slowly rewarmed.

2117. Schulze, W. Experimental contribution to the freezing problem [In German]. *Arch. Derm. Syph., Berl., v. 184, Jan. 15, 1943: 61–65.*

Description is given of a technique for studying circulation in the frozen ear of a rabbit in order to evaluate various therapeutic agents.

2118. Schwiegk, H. Shock and collapse; functional pathology and therapy [In German]. *Klin. Wschr., v. 21, Aug. 22 and Aug. 29, 1942: 741–749 and 765–770.*

A general review is given of the literature on shock following war injuries. Shock resulting from exposure to cold (p. 747–748) is also discussed. Circulatory collapse, resulting from fluid loss through increased capillary permeability and severe edematous conditions following cold injury, brings about a state of shock from cold.

2119. Shumacker, H. B., Jr., B. H. White, and E. L. Wrenn. Studies in experimental frostbite. II. Arteriograms. *Yale J. Biol., v. 20, July 1948: 519–531.*

Arteriographic studies were made on the frozen hind limbs of dogs and rabbits. In animals which survived experimental frostbite without gangrene by virtue of successful treatment with anticoagulant therapy it was possible to demonstrate a normal arterial network in the treated extremities. This confirms the impression that to avoid gangrene arterial thrombosis must be prevented.

2120. Siegmund, H. On the pathogenesis and pathology of local cold injuries [In German]. *Münch. med. Wschr.*, v. 89, Sept. 25, 1942: 827–832.

The pathogenesis and pathology of local frostbite are discussed. The author regards local frostbite as a problem of blood flow in an injured tissue area due to asphyxia resulting in an acute thrombotic angiopathy.

2121. Smith, B. C., and E. H. Quimby. Use of radioactive sodium in studies of circulation with peripheral vascular disease. *Surg. Gyn. Obst.*, v. 79, Aug. 1944: 142–147.

The use of radioactive sodium as a diagnostic aid in cases of peripheral vascular disease, is discussed. Results in a case of frostbite are included among histories of various cases of impaired circulation.

2122. Staemmler, M. Local freezing; its pathological anatomy and pathogenesis [In German]. *Zbl. Chir.*, v. 69, Nov. 7, 1942: 1757–1762. Abstract, in German, in: *Deut. med. Wschr.*, v. 69, 1943: 285.

The cardiovascular changes which result from cold injury are discussed, especially the vascular spasms of the arterioles which bring about a tentative or complete stasis with resulting edema or, possibly, gangrene. The direct tissue injury from cold is secondary to the circulatory injury and this should be considered in the treatment of such injuries.

2123. Tantini, E., G. Baggio, and A. Barbieri. Arteriography in frozen limbs. (Preliminary technical note) [In Italian]. *Minerva med.*, *Tor.*, anno 32, (v. 2). Aug. 24, 1941: 213–216.

Arteriographic studies were made of the femoral artery and its branchings in each of a group of 24 patients with frostbite of the feet, the injury having been acquired on the Greek-Albanian front. The details of the technique are given; its use, combined with a series of x-ray pictures, aided in the study of the pathology.

2124. Tantini, E., and G. Baggio. Contributions to the pathogenesis of frostbite (Arteriographic research). [In Italian]. *Clinica, Bologna*, v. 7, Oct. 1941: 549–565.

The pathological changes produced in the arterial system by frostbite, are studied.

2125. Taylor, C. B., D. Baldwin, and G. M. Hass. Localized arteriosclerotic lesions induced in aorta of juvenile rabbit by freezing. *Arch. Path.*, *Chic.*, v. 49, June 1950: 623–649.

The abdominal aorta of young rabbits (3 months of age) was frozen at 6 locations about 0.5 cm apart for periods of 10–60 seconds by use of a cold needle after surgical opening of the chest under anesthesia. Microscopic studies were made of the changes occurring in the segments over a period of 24 weeks. The pattern of the changes was independent of the duration of the freezing. Continuity of the fibrous and elastic structure of the aortic wall was maintained although there was considerable degeneration of musculoelastic tissue of the media, followed by some medial deposition of calcium. Proliferation of the intima brought about a new aortic wall almost indistinguishable in structural content and thickness from that of the original vessel and one which offered almost a perfect functional substitute for it.

2126. Tittel, S. On the mode of reaction of the vascular system in local freezing. I. The course of reaction in the individual regions of the vascular system [In German]. *Zschr. ges. exp. Med.*, v. 113, June 28, 1944: 698–721.

Cooling of small areas of a rabbit's ear caused constriction of all vessels in the cooled area; after rewarming the vessels became dilated but there was capillary stasis. Areas surrounding the cooled area showed great dilatation of blood vessels followed by secondary spasms.

2127.   Vagliano, M., and G. Tsiro. Experimental frostbite in animals; onset and evolution of chronic arteritis obliterans [In French, English summary] *Rev. path. comp.*, Par., v. 49, Oct.–Nov. 1949: 595–604.

Death of a man occurs at a body temperature lower than 24°C; the death of a tissue culture does not occur until the temperature falls below −10°C. Histological examination of tissues from the experimentally frozen limbs, tail, or ear of animals (rat, rabbit, or dog), showed the development of arteritis over a period of time following the injury. The lesions duplicated those in man following severe cold exposure.

2128.   Vagliano, S. Arteritis from freezing injuries [In French]. *Bull. Acad. nat. méd.*, v. 131, ser. 3, July 8, 1947: 503–505.

The results of research done in Greece on the clinical and histological findings in arteritis caused by freezing, are outlined.

2129.   Zaslavskiĭ, L. D., and E. E. Shimakovskaia. Arteriography in congelations in man [In Russian]. *Khirurgiia*, Moskva, 1945 (2): 30–33.

A comparative study was made of the arteriograms from a group of healthy men and those from men suffering from 1st, 2nd, or 3rd degree frostbite injuries.

See also items: 1290, 1916, 1922, 2037, 2043, 2071, 2072, 2080, 2118, 2153, 2154, 2603, 2605, 2611, 2617, 2621.

7. Metabolic Aspects

2130.   Arkhangel'skaia, N. A., A. V. Drobintseva, I. T. Kurtsin, A. T. Pshonik, and V. N. Chernigovskiĭ. The physiology of the status frigidus (Preliminary communication). [In Russian]. *Biull. eksp. biol. med.*, v. 15 (3), 1943: 17–19.

Experiments were performed on chloroformed or decerebrate dogs in which one limb was chilled by immersion in a freezing solution at −20°C. The other limb served as a control. In 80% of the animals a marked elevation was noted in the oxygen content of the venous blood from the cooled limb. The authors believe that this may have been due to a disturbance in the oxygen capacity of the tissue or in blood distribution.

2131.   Cuppini, R. Concentration of proteins and chlorides in the blood in frostbite injuries during wartime [In Italian]. *Gior. med. mil.*, v. 90, Aug. 1942: 585–587.

Morphological and chemical studies were made on three groups of frostbite cases. It was noted that blood proteins and chlorides decreased in direct relation to the severity of the frostbite injury.

2132.   Frommel, E., and J. Piquet. The serum cholinesterase of guinea pigs submitted to experimental freezing; the hypersensitivity of the experimentally chilled mouse to injections of acetylcholine, with reference to the vasomotor disease of Leriche. I. [In French]. *Arch. internat. pharm. dyn.*, Par., v. 72 (3–4), 1946: 312–320.

The upper portions of the hind legs of guinea pigs were submitted to dry cold by use of dry ice and to humid cold by application of crushed ice cubes. Blood samples were obtained by cardiac punctures and analyzed for serum cholinesterase level. Animals treated with cold showed a diminution of the activity of the enzyme. Mice after chilling were found to be very sensitive to injections of acetylcholine, with death occurring on injection of 300 mg/kg as against 450 mg/kg for the normal animals. Animals treated previously with atropine and then chilled, survived after injection with more than 650 mg/kg acetylcholine. The authors conclude that the decrease in the activity of cholinesterase plays a pathogenic role in freezing injuries.

2133. Lang, K., H. W. A. Schöttler, E. Schütte, H. Schwiegk, and U. Westphal. Tissue metabolism in localized freezing. I. [In German]. *Klin. Wschr., v. 22, June 26, 1943: 444–445.*

It was shown that in narcotized dogs, when one leg was intensely cooled or frozen by immersion for periods up to 6–8 hours in an alcohol-ice-carbon dioxide bath, while the other was not (to serve as a control), metabolism was not markedly different. The cooled tissue continued to obtain energy through normal oxidative processes, although at a diminished rate due to the lowering of the tissue temperature.

2134. Lang K., H. W. A. Schöttler, E. Schütte, H. Schwiegk, and U. Westphal. Tissue metabolism in localized freezing. II. [In German]. *Klin. Wschr., v. 22, Oct. 16, 1943: 653.*

This continuing study of the tissue metabolism of dogs with a right hind leg experimentally frozen, is concerned with the changes taking place on rewarming. The leg was cooled to a solid state by immersion in a carbon dioxide-ice-alcohol bath for periods of 2–3 hours, and then rewarmed over a period of 2–4 hours until it regained the original temperature. Even as in the cooling, metabolism was not fundamentally changed; energy requirements were met through oxidative processes. The lactic acid content of the muscle tissue, at the end of the study, was about 20–40% higher than in the normal leg.

2135. Levin, A. I., and T. ÍA. Maizel. On the state of carbohydrate metabolism of patients with frostbite [In Russian, summary in English]. *Arkh. biol. nauk, v. 60 (12), 1940: 25–28.* Also, translation in: E. HOPE. *Frostbite. Translations from the Russian of a collection of sixteen papers published between 1939 and 1944, p. 40–42. Ottawa, Defence Research Board, Canada, 1950.*

The influence of frostbite on the condition of carbohydrate metabolism was studied in a group of patients suffering from 3rd degree injuries who were free of infection. The sugar and lactic acid content of the blood and the sugar content of the urine, were repeatedly determined. No hyperglycemia, lactacidemia, or glycosuria was found; there was some tendency toward hypoglycemia. Since the slight irregularities in carbohydrate metabolism noted did not appear specific for patients suffering from frostbite, it is concluded that a carbohydrate-rich diet need not be avoided.

2136. Schümmelfeder, N. Investigations on cholinesterase in blood following experimental injuries. II. The content of cholinesterase in whole blood and in serum in experimental freezing [In German]. *Arch. exp. Path., v. 204, July 1947: 466–472.*

Slight and irregular variations in the cholinesterase activity of the whole blood were noted after experimental freezing by immersion of one hind limb of each of a group of dogs in an ice-acetone bath. The greatest decrease was found during the freezing, and during thawing, in the venous blood of the injured extremity. Probably these decreases were brought about through variations of blood composition; these variations also mask the changes in cholinesterase in the serum. In 4 or 5 of the dogs an increase in serum cholinesterase was noted after freezing and during thawing. In the venous blood serum of the injured extremity this increase amounted to 16–41%. There was also an increase in the arterial (5–16%) as well as the venous (19–25%) blood serum of the uninjured extremity. In 5 instances of severe hypothermia —with a deathlike blood pressure fall—the increase was maintained with a drastic decrease only just before the death of the animal. Whether the observed increases are to be interpreted as an increased output of the enzyme from the injured tissue or as a stronger activity of the circulating esterase, is discussed.

2137. Schwiegk, H. Circulation and tissue metabolism in local freezing injury [In German]. *Klin. Wschr., v. 23, June 1944: 198–200.*

In the pathogenesis of local freezing, no pathological effects on metabolism were demonstrated during the course of the exposure to cold. Capillary damage first appeared followed by an insufficient supply of oxygen to the tissues.

See also items: 1752, 1906, 2020, 2026, 2058, 2059, 2068, 2085, 2093, 2108.

8. Complications

(includes infections, gangrene, shock, blood loss, and ischemia)

2138. Accardi, V. Articular localization of infection in patients with injuries from freezing [In Italian]. *Settimana med., v. 35, 1947: 365–370.*

This discussion of complications resulting from cold injuries, gives special emphasis to infections in joints and to arthritis.

2139. Ballard, D. O., A. E. Upsher, and D. D. Seely. Infection with Corynebacterium pyogenes in man. *Am. J. Clin. Path., v. 17, Mar. 1947: 209–215.*

A case of infection with *Cornyebacterium pyogenes*, usually pathogenic only to animals, is reported in the feet of a man after the tissues had first been badly damaged by frostbite. The infection, in both an acute and chronic phase, caused further tissue damage and bone necrosis.

2140. Brooks, B., and J. W. Duncan. Effects of temperature on survival of anemic tissue; an experimental study. *Ann. Surg., v. 112, July 1940: 130–137.*

Tails of rats were rendered ischemic by application of pressure (130 mm Hg) at various temperatures (40 °C to −5 °C), and the results studied in relation to the occurrence of gangrene of the tail when the animals were returned to room temperature. The number of hours in which the ischemic tail did not develop gangrene increased proportionately as the temperature decreased—from 3–4 hours at 40° to 96 or more hours at 1 °C. At room temperature, gangrene did not occur at less than 17 hours. Since it was impractical to submit animals to this confinement for more than 96 hours, in two experiments where rats' tails were subjected to −5 °C without pressure, the tails froze and gangrene developed. Similar results occurred when tails of 4 other rats were frozen by immersion in alcohol at −75 °C.

2141. Csáky, T., and G. Magyary-Kossa. Experimental traumatic shock in the white rat [In German]. *Arch. biol. hungar., v. 17, 1947: 235–244.*

Mortality from experimental traumatic shock, caused by freezing the hind legs of rats with liquid air, could be reduced during the first 24 hours from 47.5% to 10.5% by ligating the frozen extremities.

2142. Eichoff, E. On the differential diagnosis of thermal and traumatic gangrene [In German]. *Zbl. Chir., v. 69, Nov. 28, 1942: 1891–1893.*

Gangrene resulting from various causes is discussed, including that resulting from frostbite.

2143. Glagolov, A. P. Tetanus following frostbite and burns [In Russian]. *Trudy 24-go Vsesoiuznogo S"ezda Khirurgov, Kharkov, 1938, p. 205–207. Moskva, Medgiz, 1939.*

Tetantus infections following burns or frostbite of 3rd degree were very virulent with a very high death rate (68.5%). The infections occurred after surgery of the foot, mostly in peasants or children walking barefoot. When injection of anti-tetanus serum was administered soon after injury occurred, no infection developed.

In the discussion which followed this paper given at the 24th All-Union Congress of Surgeons, A. I. Charugin stated that frostbite cases are more often complicated by infections, in particular with tetanus, than are burns. These tetanus cases were usually lethal, the healing of the frostbite injury having been very poor. I. L. Tsimkhes observed that daily intravenous injections of 70-100 cc of a 10% salt solution restored blood circulation in the frostbitten part, alleviated pain, and shortened the hospital stay. A. P. Nadein stressed the absolute urgency of anti-tetanus injections in all cases of burns or frostbite. S. S. Girgolav remarked that edema had to be fought by elevation of the injured extremity and, in some cases, by surgical incisions to allow for drainage.

2144. Jimeno-Vidal, F. Mutilations resulting from freezing injuries [In Italian]. *In: Atti Congresso Nazionale di Chirurgia di Guerra, May 24-26, 1942, p. 193-210. Roma, 1943.*

The clinical and pathological features of 3rd degree frostbite injury are discussed in detail. The pathogenesis of gangrene, especially during the recovery phases, is outlined.

2145. Kalmanovskiĭ, S. M. Indications for amputation in cases of severe frostbite [In Russian]. *Khirurgiia, Moskva, 1942 (7): 39-41.*

Experience obtained from 127 cases of frostbite and following several autopsies (13 cases were fatal), convinced the author that in severe injuries followed by gangrene of the sole or even the lower shin, amputation should not be delayed until the appearance of a clear demarcation line as the danger of severe sepsis is imminent. All the autopsy material indicated a septic condition, showing that the amputation had been done too late. Generalized infection spreads in the first days of frostbite, usually before the appearance of a demarcation line. Therefore amputation should be done early, even before the appearance of severe, purulent infection (as in such cases there are already many abscesses in the lungs and the chances of survival are slight), and as soon as indications of necrosis are seen.

2146. Kirch, E. Pathologic-anatomical remarks on the lectures on freezing [In German]. *Sitzber. Phys. med. Soz. Erlangen, v. 73, 1943: 121-122.*

Brief comments are made of freezing injuries of the cases which came to autopsy. Typhus fever was observed in some, cardiac inflammation in others, and general sepsis in one.

2147. Klages, F. Frostbite as an opening to surgical infections [In German]. *Zbl. Chir., v. 69, July 25, 1942: 1242-1244.*

Experiences at the front-line with frostbite wounds and their management are discussed with special reference to secondary infections.

2148. McCrea, F. Case of frostbite; loss of all toes. *Q. Bull. Indiana Univ. M. Center, v. 9, Jan. 1947: 16-17.*

In a case of frostbite involving loss of all toes by amputation, the stumps became infected. Bilateral lumbar sympathectomy was used successfully in therapy. Following the presentation of this paper there was some discussion by Drs. W. Woods and F. Taylor.

2149. Maiat, V. S. [The treatment of frostbite and its sequelae] [In Russian]. *In: Trudy 2-go plenuma Gospital'nogo Soveta Narkomzdrava SSSR, Dec. 20-25, 1942, p. 271-272. Moskva, Medgiz, 1943.*

It was pointed out that nearly 30% of all the frostbite patients at the evacuation hospital where the speaker was stationed, were suffering from bronchitis or dry pleurisy. Therefore special attention in such casualties should be directed to the lungs. In 2nd degree injuries, the use of Lubo's brilliant green gave very satisfactory results. Omission of early necrotomy and necrectomy greatly delays the healing of 3rd and 4th degree cases.

2150. **Matras, ...** Tetanus in thermic injuries of the skin. 3 cases [In German].
Klin. med., Wien, v. 2, *July 1, 1947: 639–640.*

The author presents 3 cases of thermal injury to the skin which were complicated by the
development of tetanus. In one of the two fatalities which resulted, the original injury to the
foot had been caused by freezing.

2151. **Maurer, G.** Tetanus after burns and freezing [In German]. *Zbl. Chir.*,
v. 65, *Dec. 10, 1938: 2771–2772.*

Cases are cited of infection with tetanus following frostbite. Therapy involved the giving
of tetanus antitoxin and the use of oil-soaked bandages.

2152. **Müller, W.** On the cause of death from local freezing injury [In German].
Deut. Militärarzt., v. 8, *Jan. 1943: 16–17.*

The cause of death in local cold injury may be due in part to infection of the frozen tissue
with subsequent spreading of the infection to the rest of the body. Endocarditis and diphtheria
are mentioned as secondary causes of death.

2153. **Muirhead, E. E., C. T. Ashworth, and J. M. Hill.** The therapy of shock
in experimental animals with plasma protein solutions. I. Concentrated plasma
as a hemodiluting agent. *Surgery*, v. 12, *July 1942: 14–23.*

When concentrated plasma was given intravenously to dogs, to prevent the usually fatal
shock following experimental freezing of the hind limbs or excessive loss of blood, a hemodilution was produced. This hemodilution was caused by a shift of fluids from an extra-
vascular to an intravascular position, and produced a rise in blood pressure. Normal plasma,
unless there was a comparable protein content, merely added the amount of injected fluid
to increase the blood volume but did not bring about a shift of fluids.

2154. **Muirhead, E. E., C. T. Ashworth, L. A. Kregel, and J. M. Hill.** The
therapy of shock in experimental animals with serum protein solutions. II.
Fate in the body of concentrated and dilute serum and saline solutions. *Surgery,*
v. 14, *Aug. 1943: 171–190.*

In attempts to prevent fatal shock following experimental freezing of the hind limbs of
dogs, concentrated serum, diluted (half strength) serum, or 5% glucose solutions were administered intravenously to the animals. The most important factor in the treatment appeared to be the total amount of protein administered. Concentrated serum was found to be
the most effective, producing consistently a shift of fluids from the tissues into the blood stream
to bring about a reversal of several of the abnormal mechanisms occurring in the capillaries.

2155. **Muirhead, E. E., L. A. Kregel, and J. M. Hill.** Therapy of shock in
experimental animals with plasma and serum protein solutions. III. Freezing
shock; concentrated plasma and serum therapy with and without amputation
of the damaged extremity. *Arch. Surg.*, v. 47, *Sept. 1943: 258–282.*

One or both hind legs of dogs were experimentally frozen and the following methods were
used in an attempt to prevent fatal shock: (1) damaged extremity was amputated; (2) injections of concentrated plasma were made to replace estimated plasma volume lost; and
(3) a combination of 1 and 2 was used. In group 1, 8 of 10 dogs died after a few hours in
shock or in a few days in states resembling shock; in groups 2, all 10 dogs died in shock;
and in group 3, all 10 dogs lived and appeared healthy. Because earlier experiments had
shown that advanced visceral damage appeared after the fourth hour following injury, all
treatments were begun around that time; extensive visceral changes which occurred in the
first two groups were completely absent in the third.

2156. Pichotka, J., R. B. Lewis, and U. C. Luft. Influence of general hypoxia on local cold injury. *Texas Rep. Biol. M.*, *v. 9, Fall 1951: 601–612.*

Rabbits were subjected to a standard cold injury by having one hind leg immersed in an alcohol bath (−12°C or −15°C, for 30 minutes). Hypoxia was produced by transferring some of the rabbits to a simulated altitude of 20,000 feet in a low pressure chamber. The extent of necrosis was not influenced by hypoxia if applied only during exposure and in a preparatory period up to 30 minutes. Exposure to hypoxia after cold injury increased the proportion of necrotic muscle tissue in the cooled leg; the increase was in direct relation to the length of the hypoxic period. Possibly either a local oxygen deficiency or the impairment of the peripheral circulation may be the means by which hypoxia induces this effect. A preparatory period of hypoxia up to 1 hour did not significantly alter the amount of injury; 1 to 2 hours of hypoxia greatly increased it; beyond 2 hours, and up to 5 hours, resulted in injury of no more or less than that from cold alone, indicating that some other factor secondary to general hypoxia must be responsible.

2157. Vagliana, M. S. Infection during frostbite [In French]. *Sem. hôp., Paris.*, *v. 24, Nov. 26, 1948: 2861–2863.*

Infections which occurred as a complication in frostbite, especially those caused by *Escherichia coli*, are discussed. Localized treatment with Dakin's solution and sulfonamide were found to be effective. Active immunization to prevent or relieve the infection, was achieved by means of a slow intravenous injection (0.5 cc, broth culture of coli organisms) followed by a 1.0 cc injection 3 hours later. The slight generalized reaction which occurred 3–4 hours later was of no importance.

2158. Wojta, H. Treatment of gangrene due to frostbite [In German]. *Chirurg*, *v. 15, Feb. 1, 1943: 85–97.*

Frostbite lesions which had become infected or gangrenous, were treated successfully with a Marfanyl-protalbin preparation. Conservative treatment, in order to obtain healing with a minimum of mutilation, is stressed.

See also items: 1899, 1901, 1914, 1926, 1943, 1971, 1985, 1991, 2009, 2022, 2092, 2099, 2104, 2119, 2225, 2236, 2285, 2306, 2502, 2538, 2546, 2563.

9. Therapy, General and Mixed

2159. Anon. Prophylaxis and treatment of frostbite [In Russian]. *Sovet. med.*, *1940 (11): 34–35.*

General rules are given for the prophylaxis and therapy of frostbite in front-line soldiers. Frostbite is possible even at 3°–7°C in humid weather; with wet or tight footwear or shin bandages; and in cases of weakness after severe illness, starvation, fatigue, hunger, uncomfortable posture, immobility, or drunkenness. Prophylactic measures include such things as comfortable, well-greased footwear; frequent washing of the feet and rinsing in 5–10% Formalin solution; and a calorie-rich diet. First aid includes local and general rewarming; stimulation of local circulation of the blood by alcohol friction, then massaging of the area; repeated local cleaning with alcohol, dressing with ointment (Vishnevskii's) and a thick layer of cotton; elevation of the injured part; and evacuation of the soldier to the rear lines. In 2nd and 3rd degree injuries anti-tetanus serum should be administered; morphine and vasomotor drugs when needed. In 3rd degree injuries a dehydrating aseptic ointment is applied under a thick absorbent dressing, after the injured area has been washed with alcohol; vesicles are not to be excised; a splint dressing is expedient. Infection must be fought drastically. No amputation should be done before the appearance of a demarcation line.

2160. Anon. U. S. Search and Rescue Agency. The air-sea rescue manual. *Washington, D. C., Government Printing Office, 1945. 124 p.*

On pages 58 and 59 are given brief instructions in first aid for use in cases of rescued persons who are suffering from frostbite or immersion foot.

2161. Anon. Frostbite. *In: Organization and rendering of first aid to the injured [In Russian].* Ed. *by* S. S. GIRGOLAV *and* F. G. MASHANSKIĬ. *Leningrad, Medgiz, 1949. 139 p.*

General rules to be observed in first aid and in the prevention and treatment of frostbite are presented in the chapter entitled Frostbite (p. 77–82). The chapter discusses: (1) Frostbite prophylaxis (protection by adequate footwear and clothing; avoiding restriction of motion; prevention of perspiration; and providing for acclimatization). (2) First aid: (a) before the stage of inflammation (rewarming, bathing of hands or feet, massaging); (b) after inflammation (stimulation of blood circulation, washing with alcohol, specific treatment of the four different stages of frostbite).

2162. Anon. Japan and Korea studies improve methods of treating frostbite. *Med. Bull. U. S. Army Europe, v. 8, Sept. 1951: 432.*

A team of military and civilian experts—whose names are given in the text—spent a month in Japan and Korea studying frostbite cases and, after consultation with the National Research Council's subcommittee on vascular surgery, recommended improved methods of treating frostbite. These methods involve rest in bed and no smoking for all patients; daily use of a mild, nonirritating, cleansing agent; a room temperature of 72°–78°F; use of penicillin during evacuation for treatment, and of other antibiotics in treatment; and delay of surgery until there is no question of the line of demarcation of the affected part. Announcement is also made of a program to coordinate civilian and military research in the field of cold injuries being guided by the Medical Research and Development Board, Office of the Army Surgeon General, and the National Research Council. Studies are to be carried out at the Army Medical Research Laboratory at Fort Knox, Kentucky, on rapid thawing of the frozen part, regional and general dilation of blood vessels, anticoagulants, and abstinence from the use of tobacco. Forty patients suffering from a post-frostbite condition known as "cold foot syndrome" have been transferred from the Far East Command's cold injury treatment center at the Oksaka, Japan, Army Hospital to Fort Knox for study. The syndrome frequently develops from three to six weeks after the initial cold injury and is characterized by cold feet, excessive sweating, and vague sensory disturbances.

2163. Accornero, S. R. The treatment of frostbite with particular regard to fly larvae extract [In Italian]. *Boll. Accad. med. Genova, v. 57, June 1942: 280–295.* Also, in condensed form, in: *Atti Congresso Nazionale di Chirurgia di Guerra, May 24–26, 1942, p. 221–222. Roma, 1943.*

This discussion of the pathology of 1st, 2nd, and 3rd degree freezing injuries, also reviews the methods of treatment. In addition to short-wave and vitamin therapy, mention is made of the use of gauze soaked in the fly larvae extract "Larvasan" and applied to the necrotic areas. All cases of 2nd degree frostbite treated with the extract recovered fully, but in some of the more severe cases of 3rd degree injuries there was some loss of toes.

2164. Adams-Ray, J. On the treatment of acute frostbite [In Swedish]. *Sven. läk. tidn., v. 39, Mar. 27, 1942: 899–901.*

In this general discussion of the problem of treating acute frostbite the author includes methods used by various peoples native to cold climates as well as experiences recorded by Arctic explorers. He concludes with a discussion of modern methods.

2165. Adams-Ray, J. On the treatment of frostbite [In Swedish]. *Tskr. mil. hälsov., v. 68, 1943: 59–69.*

It is mentioned that in the instructions for the treatment of frostbite which were issued to Swedish troops in the Spring of 1942, contrary to earlier practice, massage with snow is warned against and more rapid rewarming (but not above body temperature) is recommended. The outline of the treatment of local cold injury includes rewarming of the patient in a warm room, while he is being given warm drinks with a little alcohol added, and with his body except for the frostbitten area being covered by felt blankets. Etocain without Adrenalin can be used for periarterial or lumbar ganglion injection to provide blocking of the sympathetic nervous system. In injuries of 2nd and 3rd degree, local massage which is dry and does not become too warm, is recommended. To help control infection use can be made of sulfathiazole powder, sterile bandages and covering, and of anti-tetanus serum. In generalized cooling, or hypothermia, rewarming should be done while the patient is warmly covered in a warm room. He should be given intravenous injection of warmed (body temperature or just below) 5% glucose solution, and oxygen by inhalation. Subcutaneous and intravenous injection of nicotinamide or some preparation of the adrenaline-group may aid in relief of peripheral vasoconstriction. Blood transfusion should be given in case of any blood loss or need.

2166. Alipov, G. V. The treatment of frostbite injuries and their consequences in evacuation field hospitals [In Russian]. *In: Trudy 2-go plenuma Gospital'nogo Soveta Narkomzdrava SSSR, Dec. 20–25, 1942, p. 256–259. Moskva, Medgiz, 1943.*

Treatment is described of frostbite injuries in the evacuation field hospitals deep in the rear of combat areas during the war period. Frostbite injuries represented 5.9% of all the wounded and sick; 63% of the cases were of 3rd degree; 15% were of only the hands, 74% of the feet, and 11% of both hands and feet. Most injuries (63%) occurred in December–January, but there were cases of trench foot in September and in May. Evacuation to the rear of the severely frostbitten cases was much too slow; it should proceed directly, by omitting the intermediate stations, since serious complications were a result of this delay. The various types of injuries encountered are briefly enumerated. Repeated incisions into the necrosed tissue were found to be beneficial. Amputations of the toes or fingers should be conservative and done only when necessary. High amputations were performed according to the methods of Gritti, Pirogov, or Bier. The beneficial influence of mud and paraffin treatments were noted.

2167. Ardy, C. Symptomatology of first degree frostbite [In Italian]. *Gazz. osp., v. 61, Nov. 24, 1940: 944–946.*

The author discusses the symptomatology of frostbite (anesthesia, local pain, paresthesias, numbness, cyanosis, local lesions, fever). In treatment he recommends heliotherapy, warm baths, electrotherapy, and the use of vitamin B_1.

2168. Aretz, H. Frostbite of the skin [In German]. *Med. Klin., Berl., v. 36, Jan. 26, 1940: 96–97.*

Treatment of frostbite of the skin in the author's experience includes the use of alternating hot and cold baths, the use of heat rays, and the application of salves such as Ichthyol and Tumenol.

2169. Ar'ev, T. ÎA. Clinical aspects and treatment of frostbite [In Russian]. *Vest. khir., v. 60, Sept. 1940: 228–230.*

Discussion followed a paper (item 2170) on the clinical aspects and treatment of frostbite, indicated that at A. V. Smirnov's clinic carotene had been used experimentally with success; S. A. Grubina had obtained rapid epithelization using the same material. For M. S. IUsevich, experience had shown the efficiency of osteoplastic amputations in frostbite. O. A. Levin recommended treatment by ultraviolet rays as the best means for drying the necrotic tissues, and suggested the formation of a separate grade in the classification of frostbite injuries, involving deep muscle tissue. N. N. Samarin mentioned that the struggle against severe pain in frostbite cases is very difficult; Vishnevskiĭ's Novocain blockade did not produce stable results. Ultrahigh-frequency therapy is extremely effective in the treatment of frostbite according to A. F. Verbov. The quartz lamp gives lesser results. D. N. Fedorov had obtained good results with Vishnevskiĭ's ointment and with the circular Novocain blockage. V. G. Veinshtein has modified the Italian plastic surgery method for the stump of the heel region by adding to the transplant a sheet from the wide hip fascia; in this manner the transplant can successfully withstand traumatic injury. S. S. Girgolav stresses the necessity of early resection of the necrosed tissue to obtain more rapid drying of the area. Rewarming of the body should start at the body temperature of the injured. According to D. G. Gol'dman, the vascular changes in frostbite (functional spasm, paresis, thrombosis) should determine the plan of treatment. ÎU. ÎU. Dzhaneldze stated that local injuries should be treated individually.

* 2170. Ar'ev, T. ÎA. Clinical aspects and treatment of frostbite [In Russian]. *Vest. khir., v. 61, Feb. 1941: 223–236.*

"*Contains* report to the Pirogov Surgical Society on Apr. 8, 1940, on a five-year study of the problem, with sections on the clinical aspects of the four degrees of frostbite and in various regions of the body, first aid, therapy in general and of the various degrees in particular. The discussion following the lecture is published in this journal, v. 60, p. 228–230 [item 2169]."— Arctic Bibl., v. 4, 1954; 50–51.

2171. Ar'ev, T. ÎA. Prophylaxis and treatment of frostbite under conditions of the army frontline zone [In Russian]. *In: Trudy 2-go plenuma Gospital'nogo Soveta Narkomzdrava SSSR, Dec. 20–25, 1942, p. 254–256.*

The sanitary service of the Red Army has developed an effective system of combating frostbite injuries on the front, following a study begun in 1934. The prophylaxis of frostbite requires the use of field tents and sheds and of clothing and diets especially adapted for field conditions. There is no universal or special treatment of frostbite injuries but it varies according to the degree, stage, and area of the injury. The therapy of 1st degree injuries requires gentle heating; 2nd, 3rd, and 4th degree cases require immediate excision of the vesicles and use of aseptic dressings. Third degree cases are treated in specialized hospital bases established for this purpose. The surgical preparation is aimed at accelerating the formation of the scab. Gypsum dressing is recommended and gives good results. Surgical preparation of 4th degree cases is more complicated because only 15–20% of these cases are diagnosed from the start.

2172. Astuni, A. Orientation and direction in the modern therapy of freezing injury [In Italian]. *Gior. med. mil., v. 90, Oct. 1942: 787–789.*

A general review of treatment in freezing injury is given with reference to the use of short-wave therapy, pavex, nicotinic acid, and sympathetic infiltration.

2173. Astuni, A. Orientation and directives for the modern treatment of frostbite [In Italian]. *Minerva med., Tor., anno 33 (v. 2), Dec. 5, 1942: 566–573.*

In this general discussion of the treatment of frostbite there are sections on physical, medical, and surgical methods.

2174. Austoni, M. Considerations on the question of the treatment of wartime frostbite [In Italian]. *Forze san., Roma, v. 11, Jan. 15, 1942: 11–20.*

Methods of treatment for frostbite as used by military surgeons in the Italian Army are reviewed. Treatment includes use of ultra-short-wave therapy, femoral canal anesthetic block, milk injections, infrared rays, vitamins B and C, and passive vascular exercise.

2175. Bahls, G. The treatment of recent frostbite [In German]. *Deut. med. Wschr., v. 69, Nov. 26, 1943: 808–812.*

This is a critical review of the methods for treating frostbite used in the Germany Army. Recommended treatment includes the use of sulfa drugs as a powder dusted on wounds and also given by mouth; injections of tetanus antitoxin; and very conservative surgery with amputation delayed as long as possible. Caution is advocated in the use of sympathetic nerve blocks.

* 2176. Belaîa, N. K., and M. F. Kirik. The question of treatment of frostbite [In Russian]. *Khirurgiîa, Moskva, v. 19, Apr. 1949: 79–80.*

"*Contains* a report based on 426 cases of frostbite observed during 1941–43. The material is analyzed as to degree of freezing, region of the body, therapy (6 types), amputation, etc.

---

* Original not seen.

Active, surgical interference is claimed to be the basic method in frost injuries."—Arctic Bibl., v. 4, 1954: 89.

2177. Bertocchi, A. Emergency measures in the treatment of frostbite [In Italian]. *Minerva med., Tor., anno 33 (v. 1), 1942: 89–102.*

Details of early treatment, and an analysis of results obtained, are given for groups of cases of frostbite injuries from both World Wars I and II.

2178. Block, W. Interference with the sympathetic nervous system in frostbite [In German]. *Arch. klin. Chir., v. 205, Sept. 21, 1943: 56–75.*

From his experiences in a military hospital the author concludes that local cold injury is caused most often by a long-lasting cold damage which interferes with the functioning of the vegetative nervous system. In the therapy of local cold injury, or frostbite, the author mentions the use of gentle massage, ultraviolet or infrared radiation, or short-wave diathermy. Very early in the condition, surgical sympathectomy or sympathetic block with Novacain or alcohol, may be effective.

2179. Bogetti, M. The value of repeated blood transfusions in the anemia of severe frostbite [In Italian]. *Gazz. med. ital., v. 100, Nov. 1941: 357–358.*

This is a brief note describing the author's experiences with the use of multiple blood transfusions in frostbite casualties from the Greek-Albanian campaign.

2180. Bonnin, ... So-called frozen feet, treated by dry warmth [In French]. *J. méd. Bordeaux, v. 118, June 15, 1941: 521–522.*

The author discusses the very high incidence of frostbite of the feet in a group of Negro troops from Africa during the long journey while being transported to France. They were poorly equipped for cold weather conditions, some being without shoes. Feet were later warmed and dried by close exposure to heat. Bacterial infections were practically eliminated when the injured feet were kept dry. In general the affliction had a very painful nerve involvement. Use of vitamin B in treatment was without effect; cocainization by infiltration at the base of the toes, was effective. Gangrenous conditions developed in some instances and amputations were necessary in others.

2181. Calcagni, A. The problem of freezing injury as seen by a military doctor [In Italian]. *Atti. Accad. med. lombarda, v. 31, Apr. 17, 1942: 204–206.*

From his military experiences with frostbite, the author discusses the pathology of this condition together with its treatment. Among therapeutic measures discussed are (1) short-wave therapy; (2) anesthetic block of the femoral canal with Tutocaine; (3) cool dry air, alcohol, and surgery; (4) irradiated fish-liver oil and vitamin salves.

2182. Canavero, G. On freezing injury [In Italian]. *Gior. med. mil., v. 88, Oct. 1940: 864.*

A case history is discussed in which the patient was treated by short-wave therapy to limit the extent of the lesion, and the neuritic pain was controlled by administration of vitamin B.

2183. Caputo, . . . , and . . . Biagio. Frostbite in war [In Italian]. *Med. contemp., Tor., v. 7, Oct. 1941: 428–430.*

This is a report on 3,257 cases of frostbite of various degrees seen during the period December 1940 to February 1941. Methods of treatment are discussed, including Marconi therapy, periarterial sympathectomy, and protein-shock treatment using injections of milk.

2184. Castro Mendonça, ... Freezing injuries and their treatment [In Portugese]. *Rev. med. mil., Rio, v. 34, Oct.–Dec. 1945: 459–461.*

The author discusses both systemic and local reactions to cold exposure; something of the symptomatology of cold injury; complications and sequelae of freezing injuries especially as they relate to an army on the march; and the treatment of cold injuries. Vascular changes following cold injury are usually an early vasoconstriction, followed by vasodilatation causing an edema and often tissue necrosis. Some of the sequelae from cold injury are neuralgia,. arthralgia, hypoesthesia, claudication, and gangrene. Vitamin B₁ can be used prophylactically; Novocain anesthesia, sympathectomy, diathermy, or vasodilator drugs have been successfully used in therapy.

2185. Cavina, G. Concerning freezing injuries of the feet [In Italian]. *In: Atti Congresso Nazionale di Chirurgia di Guerra, May 24–26, 1942, p. 186–188. Roma, 1943.*

Analysis is made of 196 cases of frostbite as treated by the author. Of these 61 were injuries of 3rd degree, in which lumbar infiltration proved effective. In 1st and 2nd degree cases aseptic medicaments were successfully used, but short-wave therapy proved ineffective in the same patients.

2186. Cirenei, A. Clinical-therapeutic note to the treatment of frostbite in the military hospital in Rome [In Italian]. *Gior. med. mil., v. 90, Jan. 1942: 55–66.*

Account is given of the treatment of frostbite cases seen in the military hospital in Rome. Short-wave therapy, local physiohydrotherapy, and periarterial sympathectomy were among the methods used.

2187. Cirenei, A. Therapy of local cold lesions [In Italian]. *Chir. ital., v. 3, Jan.–Feb. 1949: 59–70.*

This is a general discussion of therapeutic measures used in frostbite and immersion foot. The use of heparin, short-save therapy, passive vascular exercise, and sympathectomy are reviewed.

2188. Crismon, J. M. Frostbite and trench foot. *In: Advances in military medicine, p. 176–181. Ed. by E. C. Andrus and others. (v. 1) (Science in World War II). Boston, Little Brown, 1948.*

In Chapter XV, Frostbite and trench foot (p. 176–181), it is stated that the methods of treatment of acute cold injury, accepted by British and American military surgeons up to 1944, were conservative. They involved prompt thawing at moderate temperatures with the maintenance of the injured extremity in a cool, dry environment. In the chronic stages physical therapeutic measures were directed toward improvement of blood flow and restoration of muscle and joint function. Results since 1944, of research projects at Stanford University and at New York Medical College, have brought emphasis to the fact that injury from frostbite is, within limits, reversible. Injury sufficient to produce gangrene does not occur immediately but depends on a progressive reduction of blood flow in the exposed area. Success in preventing gangrene diminishes rapidly with the increasing length of time between exposure and treatment. Therefore, adequate materials and instruction should be provided to put the recommended methods of treatment in use as first-aid measures. Mention is made of the study done at Tulane Medical School in 1945 to obtain quantitative objective means of assessing the state of the disease in chronic trench foot.

2189. Delevskiĭ, P. S. Symptomatology and treatment of frostbite [In Russian]. *Ortop. travmat., Kharkov, v. 15 (2), 1941: 41–45.*

This is an account of frostbite as seen in the Russo-Finnish War. Clinical classification is given, and treatment is discussed. Lohr's salve and physical therapy were found useful.

2190. De Santis, D. Foresighted treatment in frostbite [In Italian]. *Atti Accad. med. lombarda, v. 31, Apr. 17, 1942: 231–233.*

A general account of therapeutic measures used in frostbite, is given. It includes a discussion of the use of sulfonamide compounds, vitamin preparations, and foreign protein injections as well as the use of sympathectomy, various forms of physiotherapy, and of surgery.

2191. Dondero, A. P. Freezing injuries of the lower extremities with case histories from Greek-Albanian Campaign [In Italian]. *Milan, Industrie Grafiche Italiane Stuichi, 1941. 105 p.* Abstract, in German, in: *Klin Wschr., v. 21, Feb. 7, 1942: 138.*

A detailed presentation is given of 74 case histories of freezing injuries occurring on the Greek-Albanian front during the period of December 1940 through February 1941. Some data on the pathogenesis, etiology, and therapy are given as well as considerable detail on the injuries which occurred to the bones of the foot. Therapeutic use is made of lumbar sympathetic intervention by infiltration with Novocain, of perifemoral sympathectomy, or of ganglionectomy of the lumbar sympathetic chain. Various peripheral dilator substances, follicular ovarian hormones, and Marconi therapy were also used. Sixty-five photographs, including 49 x-ray pictures, illustrate the text.

2192. Fedorov, D. N., and A. S. Korovin. Treatment with balsam dressings of gunshot wounds and frostbite in the field at military hospitals [In Russian]. *Arkh. biol. nauk, v. 62, 1941: 28–33.*

Treatment of frostbite with Novocain block and oil balsam dressing proved successful.

2193. Ferraro, D. The treatment of frostbite in the more recent experiences of our war [In Italian]. *Forze san., Roma, v. 11, Jan. 15, 1942: 20–27.*

The prophylaxis and treatment of frostbite is discussed. Information is given on the use of milk injections, short-wave therapy, anesthetic block, periarterial sympathectomy, vitamin B_1 administration, and follicular hormones.

2194. Finneran, J. C., and H. B. Shumacker, Jr. Studies in experimental frostbite [Abstract]. *Bull. Am. Coll. Surgeons, v. 35, Jan. 1950: 73.*

Contrary to earlier views the rapid rewarming, with an ideal temperature slightly higher than normal body temperature, was found to be of great value in minimizing the tissue loss after experimental frostbite in several species of animals. Results from anticoagulant therapy and vasodilatation were variable but appeared generally beneficial when combined with rapid thawing.

2195. Finneran, J. C., and H. B. Shumacker, Jr. Studies in experimental frostbite. V. Further evaluation of early treatment. *Surg. Gyn. Obst., v. 90, Apr. 1950: 430–438.*

Rapid thawing was found to be remarkably effective in the early treatment of experimental frostbite in mice, rats, rabbits, and dogs. Tetraethylammonium chloride, sympathetic denervation, and immediate heparinization seemed to be beneficial, but unequivocal results were not obtained.

2196. Fridland, M. W. The treatment of frostbite [In Russian]. *Feldsher & akush., 1942 (10): 1–4.*

An account is given of the treatment of 1st, 2nd, and 3rd degree frostbite injuries. In 1st degree frostbite, circulation is first reactivated by increasingly warm baths (from 18° to 35°C), use of alcohol followed by dry friction, coating with a salve or ointment, and wrapping warmly. The area is also to be massaged (from periphery to center), and treated by ultrahigh-frequency radiation. In 2nd degree frostbite the "closed" or the "open" method is used. In either method, the vesicles are excised, then treated with antiseptic followed by ointment. In the "closed" method a bandage is applied; in the "open" the injured part is placed in a heated cradle and left uncovered. In 3rd degree frostbite with dry gangrene, the injured part is treated with alcohol and covered with antiseptic ointment as for 2nd degree frostbite; moist gangrene is dried by alcohol, or by powdering with antiseptics. Incisions in the skin are made in cases of severe edema or purulation. A vitamin-rich diet is necessary in all cases.

*2197. **Girgolav, S. S., and T. I͡A. Ar'ev.** Clinical handling and treatment of frostbite [In Russian]. *Vrach. delo, v. 22 (6), 1940: 415–424. Translation in:* E. Hope. *Frostbite. Translations from the Russian of a collection of sixteen papers published between 1939 and 1944, p. 18–25. Ottawa, Defence Research Board, Canada, 1950.*

The authors divide the clinical aspects of frostbite into four degrees. A tabulation is given setting down the specific treatments for each degree of injury.

2198. **Girgolav, S. S.** Modern data on frostbite [In Russian]. *Klin. med., Moskva, v. 21 (1–2), 1943: 3–6.*

A brief discussion is given of some principles of frostbite treatment. The destruction of tissue does not occur directly from the action of cold, but from secondary conditions brought about by cold. The use of ice-cold water as a first aid is senseless; the sooner the whole body is warmed, the more effective the results of treatment will be. Only when the tissue temperature is raised to 20°–25°C, does stimulation of the circulation become effective. From a practical standpoint the classification of frostbite in 4 degrees is adequate, especially in war cases. It is important to remove the vesicles in order to determine the degree of frostbite. Early resection (within 6–10 days) of the necrosed tissue to let the edematous liquid flow out instead of waiting for its drying up, is strongly advocated. This method means a great economy in time for the patient since the extremity is usually ready for amputation in a few days.

2199. **Gol'dman, D. G., and V. K. Lubo.** Clinical picture, treatment, and prophylaxis of frostbite [In Russian]. *Leningrad, Sanitarnyy Otdel Krasnoznamennogo Baltflota, 1938. 192 p.*

This monograph comprises a general discussion of frostbite, including personal experiences, and advice on prophylaxis. An appendix consisting of 3 sets of government instructions concerning these injuries, is included as well as a bibliography by Gol'dman of the literature on frostbite and hypothermia. A very slight frostbite injury should be considered clinically as a general syndrome, and the therapy other than local treatment should be directed toward the improvement of the general condition. Restoration of the blood circulation must be the first concern. Blood transfusions seem to be indicated in severe cases of frostbite or general hypothermia. Lowered skin temperature, and various neuro-vascular disturbances, are some of the sequelae following frostbite injury. Thermoregulation is often not fully restored in the injured part 6 months after recovery. Roentgenological study 1½ months after recovery showed that osteoporosis was in direct proportion to the severity of the injury.

2200. **Gol'dman, D. G., and V. K. Lubo.** Clinical aspects, treatment, and prophylaxis of frostbite [In Russian]. *Trudy 24-go Vsesoi͡uznogo S"ezda Khirurgov, Kharkov, 1938, p. 202–205. Moskva, Medgiz, 1939.*

The author obtained excellent results in the treatment of 97 frostbite casualties by surgical incisions with simultaneous disinfection (with a 2% solution of brilliant green in 70% alcohol) of the injured part, and by covering of the area with compresses moistened with a mixture of equal parts of cod-liver and camphor oils. This mixture alleviated pain, reduced the inflammation, induced the formation of a protective surface, and prevented secondary infection. The importance of depressed morale in predisposition to frostbite injuries was pointed out among other well-known factors (such as dampness, tight shoes, fatigue, hunger, and anemia). Thus, frostbite injuries were much more frequent in war prisoners than in front-line soldiers whose morale was good, even when the clothing of the latter offered less protection. The author believes that rapid rewarming of the frostbite injury is dangerous, and supports the old method of rubbing with clean, soft snow. A classification of frostbite injuries into light, average, and severe cases is proposed, to avoid any comparison with burns.

---

* Original not seen.

2201. Grasso, R. On the use of vascular gymnastics and the suppression of pain in freezing injuries [In Italian]. *In: Atti Congresso Nazionale di Chirurgia di Guerra, May 24–26, 1942, p. 214–216. Roma, 1943.*

The use of passive vascular exercise (pavex) in the treatment of localized freezing injuries is discussed. The alternate pressure and decompression has the effect of increasing the circulation in the affected part and relieving the pain. In addition to the exercise an ointment of cod-liver oil and 5% of resorcinol is to be applied locally to the lesion.

2202. Greene, R. Treatment of frostbite. *Brit. M. J., 1940 (v. 2): 469–470.*

The author expresses his agreement with the warnings given by Dr. Odelberg (item 2236) that massage of frostbitten areas with snow may well cause further tissue damage and be painful for the patient, but he feels that Dr. Odelberg's recommendation of massaging the area toward the periphery with a coarse towel might also cause damage. He recommends in the treatment of frostbite, that the area be washed with an antiseptic such as proflavine and then protected with layers of sterile dressing with the area or extremity being given complete rest. The patient should be given anti-tetanus serum, hot drinks and food, and extra clothing should be provided, but no direct warming of the area should be done.

2203. Grujić, M. Therapy of angiospastic edema of the hand following frostbite, by intra-arterial injection of procaine hydrochloride [In Serbo-Croatian]. *Voj. san. pregl., Beogr., v. 5, June 1948: 247–248.*

It is concluded by the author that Novocain administered intra-arterially, and combined with hot-air therapy and active functional therapy, represent at this time the most successful treatment of cold and cyanotic segmental angiospastic edemas and cold injuries.

2204. Gucci, G. Moist-heat dressing in the treatment of wounds and freezing injuries of war [In Italian]. *In: Atti Congresso Nazionale di Chirurgia di Guerra, May 24–26, 1942, p. 210–213. Roma, 1943.*

The treatment of frostbite injuries in a group of 300 soldiers by the use of moist-heat dressings, is reviewed. The sterile gauze compresses were moistened with physiological saline at a temperature of 50° to 60°C. Complete recovery occurred in 243 patients; 64 of these had had 2nd or 3rd degree injuries. The more severe 3rd degree cases were treated also by anesthetic block of the femoral canal.

2205. Hildman, ... Practical problems of cold [Abstract, in German]. *Klin. Wschr., v. 22, Mar. 13, 1943: 242.*

This is a report on observations made on a battalion of ski troops in Russia during the Winter of 1941–1942. Protection from cold was obtained by a variety of methods including the use of layers of clothing where the entrapped air acted as insulation. Anti-frost ointments were omitted in most instances. For the treatment of local frostbite, a variety of baths were used primarily to restore circulation and normal temperatures to the afflicted areas. The individuals so treated showed thirst and a loss of appetite; recovery during the first 4 days was slow. The soldiers were maintained on a carbohydrate diet; included in the diet were bread, cakes, and biscuits which were said to aid in resistance to cold.

2206. Hoche, O. On frostbite and its treatment [In German]. *Mschr. Unfallh., v. 50, 1943: 299–305.*

This general account of frostbite is concerned also with its prophylaxis and treatment. The importance of warm clothing, of proper shoes, and the use of vitamins and cod-liver oil is stressed. Infection was controlled by the local application of sulfonamides. Circulatory disturbances were treated with such drugs as Cardiazol, Sympatol, Priscol, and Padutin as well as by periarteriolar sympathectomy in more severe cases.

2207. Irwin, J. B., and H. Schultz. Treatment of frostbite of toes. *U. S. Armed Forces M. J., v. 2, Aug. 1951: 1161–1163.*

Successful treatment of frostbite injuries at a hospital in the rear of a battalion of an Infantry Regiment fighting in Korea, without the evacuation of the patients from the front line, is reported. Only when blistering occurred were patients hospitalized. Treatment consisted of thorough cleaning of the area; excision of blistered and necrotic tissue; trimming or complete removal of toe nails—anesthesia was already present because of chilling—; application of zinc ointment; procaine penicillin in some cases; and early and increasing periods of ambulation. The ultimate strength and personnel of the battalion was not altered by this method of handling casualties, and the average time lost from duty (20 days) was about half that of similar groups evacuated to hospitals in Japan.

2208. Jimeno-Vidal, F. On the treatment of frostbite; experiences in the Spanish Civil War [In German]. *Wien. klin. Wschr., v. 55, July 31, 1942: 601–603.*

Avoidance of infection is of prime importance in the treatment of frostbite. The author therefore recommends leaving the injured area open without dressings or bandages. This serves to speed demarcation and keep the healing process dry. Surgery must be conservative and early amputation avoided.

2209. Kaliuta, A. Medical aid in frostbite cases at the battalion and regiment medical aid stations [In Russian]. *Voen. san. delo, 1938 (1): 25.*

Symptoms of general hypothermia and 1st, 2nd, and 3rd degree frostbite cases are described briefly. Since the outcome of the injuries depends on early medical aid, first aid at the battalion and regiment medical stations is of primary importance. In the squads, self-aid and mutual aid play an important role. After aseptic dressing, 1st degree cases are evacuated to the battalion medical station, and from there to the regiment station; 2nd and 3rd degree cases directly to the regiment medical station, and from there to the division hospital. The treatment at the battalion medical aid station includes washing with alcohol, massaging (if not done already by the first aid group), coating with 5% Xeroform; at the regiment station 1st degree cases may be kept to serve in the 2nd order supply train for further observation. Second and 3rd degree cases at the regiment station should receive anti-tetanus injection and aseptic dressings.

2210. Kaz, B. L., and A. F. Lukanov. On the question of medical aid for frostbite in wartime [In Russian]. *Voen. san. delo, 1942 (9): 21–28.*

On the basis of data on frostbite collected during the Finnish War (1939–1940), an account is presented of conditions contributing to frostbite injuries in front-line soldiers. Basic principles underlying the organization of sanitation and prophylaxis in frostbite cases are given, with special emphasis on the importance of medico-sanitary prophylaxis in the front-line army. A sketchy outline of Ar'ev's method of treatment of frostbitten extremities is presented. The following points are stressed. The success of treatment in 2nd, 3rd, and especially in 4th degree injuries is determined by early surgical intervention to remove necrotic tissue and promote drainage of edematous fluids; this accelerates the healing and prevents possible complications. Diagnostic distinction between 3rd and 4th degree and 1st and 2nd degree frostbite is of importance, since the latter cases may be handled by dermatologists. Third and 4th degree frostbite patients should be evacuated to hospitals where there are personnel trained in the fitting of prostheses and a shop nearby to supply them.

* 2211. Khaskelevich, M. G., and V. IĀ. Vasil'kovan. Some new measures in the treatment of frostbite [In Russian]. *Vrach.delo, v. 23 (2), 1941: 95–102. Translation in:* E. Hope. *Frostbite. Translations from the Russian of a collection of sixteen papers published between 1939 and 1944, p. 26–32. Ottawa, Defence Research Board, Canada, 1950.*

The recommended treatment of frostbite consists first of the rapid rewarming of body tissues by various methods including massage, the giving of intravenous injections of 10% calcium

---

* Original not seen.

chloride solution, and the drinking of hot tea. Following the rapid rewarming, consideration should be given to problems of the reparation of circulatory disturbances, necrosis, and infection.

* **2212. Khodkov, V. N.** Frostbite, its prevention and treatment [In Russian]. *Med. sestra, 1944 (1–2): 3–5.*

"*Contains* an account of the causes of frostbite especially in war; kinds of cold injuries; degrees of frostbite; first aid and early therapy (gradual rewarming, hot drinks and food, topical medication, etc.); therapy of different degrees of frostbite; diet."—Arctic Bibl., v. 6, 1956: 432.

2213. Kiiashev, A. P. Clinical aspects and treatment of frostbite [In Russian]. *Klin. med., Moskva, v. 22 (1–2), 1942: 25–31.*

Frostbite injuries were studied in male patients from 20 to 30 years of age. The most frequent area of injury was that of the toes, mostly of the right foot; the second most frequent was the ears and was usually a 2nd degree injury. As therapy, the methods of Ar'ev and Girgolav are recommended with emphasis on the importance of immediate, penetrating, warming of the whole body and continued, deep, warming of the injured part. Temperatures of baths should be raised from 18°C to about 35°C. Thorough cleansing, massaging, washing with alcohol, painting with brilliant green or 5% tannin solution, use of dry dressings, necrotomy and necrectomy of the area, are recommended. Primary amputation is to be rejected. Surgery is usually possible in 2–5 days if there is no inflammation above the demarcation line. In 3rd and 4th degree injuries, physiotherapy, as well as photoelectrotherapy and ultrahigh-frequency radiation, are to be applied from the start. Anti-tetanus injections are necessary in all cases of foot injuries. Results were good (78.1% with complete healing), and the length of hospitalization time was appreciably shortened.

2214. Kimbarovskii, M. A. The treatment of frostbite in the evacuation field hospitals [In Russian]. *In: Trudy 2-go plenuma Gospital'nogo Soveta Narkmozdrava SSSR, Dec. 20–25, 1942, p. 259–264.*

Frostbite injuries are classified as alternating, degenerating, and necrotic injuries, and some mixed types. Frostbite injury of tissues does not occur in horizontal layers but in pointed wedges, and is not alike in all tissues. In blood vessels and nerves, not only the exposed and visibly injured parts but large stretches beyond the region of exposure are destroyed. The ascending neuritis which follows the degeneration of the lower part of the nerve fibers, may become a new source of pathological alterations. Humidity in the shoes (in the winter) is particularly apt to produce frostbite. Emphasis is placed on the danger of ignoring secondary and slight cold injuries of the vertebral or sacral region which had been caused when wounded soldiers had had to lie in the snow. Such injuries can, through neglect during the first evacuation stages, develop into severe trophic disorders. Therapeutic measures in frostbite injury include: rest in bright and warm hospital rooms; use of open-case treatment; ultrahigh-frequency radiations, or Sollux and quartz lamps; slight elevation of the extremity; resection and cleansing of the vesicles; a rich and appetizing diet; and a conservative use of necrotomy and necrectomy, with amputation or exarticulation to be employed only in the most serious cases.

2215. Klitzner-Schierendorff, H. Cold injuries and their treatment [In German]. *Prakt. Arzt., Jan. 15, 1948: 10–13.*

Methods of treatment for 1st, 2nd, and 3rd degree frostbite are presented. The neuritic effect is treated with vitamin B_1. Frostbite lesions of 2nd and 3rd degree are treated with 3,000 units of tetanus serum, hot air, short-wave therapy, and diathermy. Injuries of 1st degree respond well to the rewarming treatment. Gangrenous tissue is treated with a sulfonamide powder.

---

* Original not seen.

2216. Kohler, O. Results of the treatment of frostbite [Abstracts, in German]. *Zbl. Chir., v. 69, Nov. 7, 1942: 1782–1794.* Also in: *Deut. med. Wschr., v. 69, Mar. 26, 1943: 286.*

An analysis is made based on the practical experiences obtained while handling a large number of cases of frostbite. Frostbite of the feet was seen in 82% of the cases, of the hands hands alone in 4%, of the feet and hands in 12%, of the face alone in 1%, and the face and extremities in 1%. The degrees of frostbite are described with the treatment found most appropriate in each. All methods of choice which were employed involved slow rewarming. For large areas affected by cold injury, it is recommended that a vigorous massage using snow be applied for a long time, at least 2 hours. The essential action of the massage is to retard rewarming, suppress or stop the ensuing hyperemia, and aid recovery of circulation. Cases with 2nd or 3rd degree injuries should receive protection doses of tetanus antitoxin.

2217. Kononenko, I. F. The treatment of frostbite and its sequelae [In Russian]. *In: Trudy 2-go plenuma Gospital'nogo Soveta Narkomzdrava SSSR, Dec. 20–25, 1942, p. 264–267. Moskva, Medgiz, 1943.*

Experiences with 241 cases at an evacuation field hospital indicated an incidence for frostbite of 5.4% among all the wounded and sick. The number of complications noted was found to be in direct proportion to the number of stages, and resultant delays, in evacuation from the frontline. Most of the complications were related to the bone, being a peculiar type of osteomyelitis, or were a sluggishly-developing type of necrosis. In all such injuries which were 4–6 months old, radical amputation alone produced results. More recent injuries were treated with various kinds of therapy and only if necessary by radical amputation. To aid in determining the border of the injury, capillaroscopy was found to be very useful since the roentgenological picture did not always indicate the limit of the injury. Surgery was performed in 114 cases. Therapeutic measures involved the use of quartz lamps, infra-red, activated cod-liver oil, nerve block by Vishnevskiĭ's method, Sollux, paraffin, clay, and diathermy, with paraffin therapy giving the best results. Surgical removal of the cartilage at the head of the phalanges or metatarsal bones was deemed absolutely necessary to avoid a sluggish necrosis. Sequestral operation of the end of the phalanges was abandoned as it only protracted the period of recovery. As the result of treatment, 226 men (93.7%) were returned to army duty. with only 15 (6.3%) being disabled. It is believed that the type of osteomyelitis found following frostbite should be classified and treated differently from that following bullet wounds.

2218. Korhonen, A., and others. On the treatment of frostbite injuries [In Swedish]. *Nord med., v. 9, 1941: 239–241.*

A. KORHONEN was leader of a panel discussion on the subject of The Treatment of Cold Injuries, as shown in the Proceedings of the Finnish Surgical Society at the meeting of June 29, 1940. He stated that in the Finnish-Russian war, in 1939–1940, the cold injuries were approximately 8,000 or 12% of the total casualties of 66,000. There were relatively few third degree frostbite injuries; the most common injuries were of the toes. Of the 142 cases seen by himself, 60% had only one foot frozen; 40% had both feet frozen; the mortality was 0.7%. Therapy consisted in keeping the necrotic area dry. Amputation was delayed in cases of dry gangrene to await a clear line of demarcation between healthy and necrotic tissue, but early amputation was done in moist, purulent cases. Other panel members contributed their experiences as follows.

V. TUOMIKOSKI, told of the use of tincture of iodine and of aseptic bandaging, and recommended against the use of salve bandaging as being the cause of increased infection. He stated that the line of demarcation for amputation was usually well defined by the second week.

A. ELLONEN, told of his experiences, in a war hospital, following the admission of 146 soldiers with frostbite received approximately 2 weeks earlier. Twelve percent had injuries of 1st degree, 48% of 2nd; 49% of 3rd. Of the group, only 10% had had dry feet at the time of injury. The usual therapy was with talc, iodine application, or liver ointment. Activity was recommended. Those with 1st degree injury were returned to front line duty in about 10 days; with 2nd degree, 14 to 30 days; 3rd, usually several months.

P. I. TUOVINEN, mentioned the many cases known in which necrotic finger tips were treated behind the front lines and the soldier did not leave the fighting area. He believes that good hospitalization would have returned them to fighting more quickly. He mentioned also the cold injuries of a lesser degree which occurred in frontline fighting in France.

K. SLÄTIS, stated that at a military hospital a great number of all kinds of cold injuries were treated as open lesions with alcohol and the area exposed to quartz lamp rays.

E. WALLASVAARA, spoke of the use of ultra-short-wave and of quartz-light therapy. Fat salves, especially those containing wax, were found to be injurious since they sealed in the toxic exudates.

S. A. BROFELDT, stated that salves should not be used on first and third degree lesions. Compresses should be avoided in the latter cases since they could cause moist gangrene in a necrotic area. However, compresses moistened with Chloramine could be used in some cases of severe infection.

L. J. LINDSTRÖM, mentioned his experiences in the treatment of 400–500 cases of cold injury at a military hospital, where the uniform treatment was largely with quartz-lamp radiation after any blisters present had been opened and the frozen areas covered with picrin or tannin. Bandages were emphatically not used. There were no deaths.

K. RYTKÖNEN, expressed the opinion that 3rd grade cold injuries would always result in the need for amputations and advised that it be done as quickly as possible after the line of demarcation had been established. Alternating warm and cold baths had been found to have a favorable effect in promoting healing.

Y. MIETTINEN, felt that it was important to rub the frozen body parts with snow and that this should be continued for some time. He stated that almost without exception 3rd grade cold injuries were infected.

M. HÄMÄLÄINEN, warned against repeated and strong iodine treatments injuring the tissues further, causing blistering and a greater possibility of infection. Too early amputation, especially of the tarsus area, should be avoided since the infection usually ensuing resulted in the need later for an amputation higher up on the leg.

P. E. ASCHAN, stated that the treatment of frostbite with tincture of iodine was good unless it was overdone, and that zinc gel bandages were good for subsequent use.

HJ. PEDER, had found that most severe cases of frostbite among the Russian prisoners. Limbs, in many cases both of them, had to be amputated in 49 patients. He felt that such operations should be carried out early to avoid further infection.

L. JÄRVINEN, recommended the spreading apart of the fingers, rather than their flexion or extension, since it stimulated circulation of distal parts of the extremities better. Snow, used for massage, should be of about 0°C rather than −30°C.

M. EIRTO, mentioned the good results obtained from the use of lumbar sympathetic block in treatment of frostbite of the extremities.

2219. Korovin, A. S., and D. N. Fedorov. Method of Prof. A. V. Vishnevskiĭ in certain domains of military surgery [In Russian]. *Sovet. med., v. 4 (21), 1940: 23–25.*

Vishnevskiĭ's method was applied to 220 war casualties, 24 of which were 3rd degree frostbite injuries of the feet. After Novocain block in the ship area, the injured surface, including a large portion of the healthy tissue of the skin, was covered with a dressing of Vishnevskiĭ's ointment. The results were cessation of pain, disappearance of lymphangiitis, a drop in temperature, and recession of the general septic condition. The dressing was not changed for 7–8 days until full of pus. At this time a clearly visible demarcation line was already apparent. Epithelization began and was completed much earlier than with other methods. Moist gangrene never appeared, as a second block removed the first symptoms of it and rapid mummification followed. After amputation the wound cicatrized rapidly. The Novocain block promoted the activation of the bacteriophage which had previously been ineffective.

2220. Kukin, N. N. The treatment of frostbite of the limbs by means of Novocain block and of oil-balsam bandage [In Russian]. *Arkh. biol. nauk, v. 62, 1941: 21–27.*

Analysis and evaluation is made of therapeutic results in 80 cases of 2nd and 3rd degree frostbite seen in a Russian military hospital. In cases of severe and extensive injury, local Novocain block was used and repeated 2 or 3 times in 10 days. Blisters and pockets were painted with iodine and then opened. Oil-balsam bandages were applied above the necrotic area. In less severe frostbite only the oil-balsam bandage was applied. In cases so treated, the line of demarcation formed early and healing was rapid. Conservative surgery is advocated and, of the 80 cases described, amputation was necessary in only one instance.

* 2221. Kukin, N. N. Frostbite therapy under conditions of evacuation hospitals [In Russian]. *Vest. khir., v. 61, Feb. 1941: 276.*

"*Contains* summary of a paper read before the Second Conference on Local Anesthesia and Wound Therapy according to Methods of A. V. Vishnevskiĭ (Moscow, Oct. 28–29, 1940). 300 patients were treated during a five-month period and 80 were closely studied; methods of treatment for the more common and for severe cases, are presented."—Arctic Bibl., v. 4, 1954: 559.

2222. Lempke, R. E., and H. B. Shumacker, Jr. Studies in experimental frostbite. III. An evaluation of several methods for early treatment. *Yale J. Biol., v. 21, Mar. 1949: 321–334.*

The effectiveness in preventing gangrene is reported for the following treatments. Rapid thawing and immediate heparinization; sympathetic block with tetraethylammonium ion; prolonged maintenance of vasodilatation by tetraethylammonium after rapid thawing. It is suggested that gangrene following frostbite is the result of the effect of cold on ischemic tissue with subsequent thrombosis.

2223. Levit, V. S. Treatment of frostbite [In Russian]. *Voen. san. delo, 1941 (10): 12–16.*

Prevention and treatment of frostbite injuries during war periods is discussed. The importance of prophylactic sanitary measures for the feet, face, and hands and of a diet rich in proteins, carbohydrates, and fats (with two hot meals a day) are emphasized. Treatment should include warm baths (gradually increasing from 18° to 35°C), washing with soap, and aseptic massaging. After the appearance of reaction, antiseptic and ointment dressings are applied. Erythemic doses of ultraviolet rays, local d'arsonvalization, and ultrahigh-frequency radiations are very helpful. Second and 3rd degree frostbite cases should be treated in evacuation hospitals. Ultraviolet-ray therapy should be applied in very large doses daily, and ultrahigh-frequency radiation therapy on alternate days. Daily applications of an alcoholic solution of 2% brilliant green and bandaging with a mixture of cod-liver and camphor oil is indicated in 2nd degree cases. Primary amputation should never be done in front-line hospitals, but the necrotic tissue must be removed. In severe cases of moist gangrene with complications, when drying-up cannot be achieved, early amputation is necessary before the appearance of a demarcation line.

2224. Macklin, A. H. Polar exploration. Some medical aspects, with special reference to the Antarctic. *Med. Press & Circ., Lond., v. 202, 1939: 401–406.*

Information of a general nature is given for surgeons embarking on polar expeditions, especially sea voyages to the Antarctic. Among the subjects discussed are food—especially locally-obtained fresh meat—and its preparation; proper clothing; the advantages of the polar climate from the point of view of health; the necessary medical equipment; and of both the prevention and treatment of frostbite.

2225. Malice, A. Freezing injuries and their treatment [In Italian]. *In: Atti Congresso Nazionale di Chirurgia di Guerra, May 24–26, 1942; p. 143–160. Roma, 1943.*

The pathogenesis, morbid anatomy, symptomatology, prognosis, complications, and prophylaxis of freezing injuries are discussed. Under methods of therapy the author mentions the use of Marconi therapy, Novocain infiltration, periarterial sympathectomy, and anesthetic block of the femoral canal.

---

* Original not seen.

2226. Margottini, M. The treatment of freezing injuries and their sequelae [In Italian]. *In: Atti Congresso Nazionale di Chirurgia di Guerra, May 24–26, 1942, p. 229–231. Roma, 1943.*

Experiences with 80 cases of frostbite, and with 42 cases with sequelae following such injury, are cited by the author. Injuries of 2nd and 3rd degree were treated locally, using a carbon-filament electric heat lamp and a cod-liver-oil ointment. In those instances where there was an infection, alcohol packs or Dakin's solution was used. In cases of 3rd degree injury with sequelae, the best method of treatment was found to be lumbar sympathetic block or peri-arterial sympathectomy.

2227. Matheis, H. Note on the treatment of frostbite [In German]. *Deut. Militärarzt, v. 7, Feb. 1942: 153–155.*

In severe frostbite of the fingers and toes deep incisions were made to improve the circulation. In mild cases combined treatment using "Thioseptal," baths, and diathermy were found to be effective.

2228. Matheis, H. Frostbite therapy [In German]. *Wien. med. Wschr., v. 101, Mar. 24, 1951: 227–228.*

The author discusses his own clinical experiences in treating frostbite of the hands and feet (both 1st degree and chronic types). He recommends, in cases of no tissue necrosis, the use of a "Thiosept" emulsion or salve, or of diathermy; in all other cases, a "Thiosept" bath combined with diathermy.

2229. Matras, A. Freezing injury [In German]. *Wien. klin. Wschr., v. 55, May 8, 1942: 378.*

This is a general review on the clinical aspects, pathology, and treatment of frostbite injuries. The section on treatment includes a discussion of the use of astringent baths, x-rays, camphor-Peru balsam-Ichthyol salve.

* 2230. Miroshnikov, I. I. The therapy of frostbite [In Russian]. *Khirurgiĩa, Moskva, v. 14 (6), 1944: 28–32.*

"*Contains* a study based on 500 cases nearly all of the third and fourth degree; includes data on localization of damage, length of hospitalization, early and later pathology, schemes for therapy during early and advanced stages, physiotherapy, after-treatment, etc."—Arctic Bibl., v. 4, 1954: 693.

2231. Moriconi, L. Practical hints on the therapy for war frostbite [In Italian]. *Atti Accad. fisiocr. Siena, v. 9, ser. 11, Aug. 1941: 158–160.*

Dietotherapy is recommended for treatment of war frostbite together with various medicaments. In 2nd degree frostbite alcohol packs and lightly-bound sterile bandages were used. In 3rd degree cases oil salves were found to be effective.

2232. Moser, H. On freezing [In German]. *Deut. med. Wschr., v. 68, May 29, 1942: 549–555.*

Analysis is made of 632 cases of frostbite. Treatment included the use of procaine block of the sympathetic nerves to a body area, use of a sulfonamide powder, and of short-wave therapy.

2233. Nahrath, H. The treatment of severe frostbite, especially of moist gangrene [In German]. *Münch. med. Wschr., v. 90, May 7, 1943: 299–301.*

The author reports his results in the treatment of 120 cases of moist gangrene in frostbitten feet. Amputation was required in the most severe cases. In milder cases use was made of an

---

* Original not seen.

unpadded plaster cast with windows cut through to expose gangrenous areas. These areas were dusted with a sulfonamide powder and the foot kept elevated. The importance is stressed of proper positioning of the foot in the case if amputation should become necessary at a later time.

2234. Niederhäusern, A. de. Progress in the therapy of frostbite [In Italian]. *Accad. med., Tor., v. 55, Aug. 1940: 298–311.*

New developments in the treatment of frostbite are reviewed. No formal bibliography is given.

2235. Norrlind, R. Case of freezing injury [In German]. *Acta derm. vener., Stockh., v. 23, Mar. 1943: 588–590.*

A group of 40 cases of frostbite are reported. Three of the patients had frostbitten hands, the rest had frostbitten ears. In treatment, rapid rewarming was emphasized together with the use of salicylic acid and boric acid.

2236. Odelberg, A. Remarks on war surgery [In Swedish, with German summary]. *Nord. med., v. 5, Mar. 1940: 551–554.* Also, in English, in: *Brit. M. J., 1940 (v. 2), July 13: 43–46.*

Surgical and other experiences and impressions of the author while serving with a unit of the Swedish Red Cross in divisional and field hospitals in Finland, are discussed. Frostbite was treated by massage toward the periphery, using a coarse towel, and by alternating cold and hot baths; tannic acid was used in serious injuries; fish-liver oil and fixation were used for those patients suffering also with infections. Warning is given against using snow for massaging.

2237. Odelberg, A. Acute cold injuries [In Swedish]. *Sven. läk. tidn., v. 39, Feb. 13, 1942: 413–416.*

Because of the inexperience of many physicians in the treatment of severe cold injuries, the author comments especially on the early or acute stages. He advises that the patient be put in a warm room if possible, then given gentle deep massage of the frozen limb—in a direction away from the heart—taking special care in the area of a joint. He prefers not to use cold water which he feels softens the skin and causes it to be prone to infection. A gangrenous area should be kept dry to prevent secondary infection and to help keep it from becoming the more serious, moist, form of gangrene. Blisters should not be disturbed; if they become broken, they should be treated with a medicated salve. He quotes the practices of the native Laplanders who do not use snow or ice but gently massage the area with the hairy part of a fur mitten and then exercise care in the movement of the affected limbs.

* 2238. Otstavnosa, E. I. First aid in frostbite and freezing [In Russian]. *Fel'dsher & akush., v. 12, Dec. 1950: 28–31.*

"*Contains* information on the damaging effect of cold on human tissues and organisms; degrees of frostbite (4); new methods of first aid: quick rewarming (as against the old ways of rubbing with snow, keeping the patients in cold rooms, etc.), warm drinks, alcohol in moderate doses; massage, etc."—Arctic Bibl., v. 4, 1954: 774.

2239. Paolucci di Valmaggiore, R. On numbness, frostbite and trench foot [In Italian]. *Ann. med. Nav., Roma, v. 46, Nov.–Dec. 1940: 505–511.*

The various lesions resulting from cold exposure are discussed, as well as their treatment. For the less severe lesions, with unbroken skin, the author suggests light massage possibly with alcohol or with dry wool, and raising the extremity to help prevent edema. In gangrenous conditions, he recommends the giving of polyvalent anti-gangrene sera and swabbing the area with 40% or 50% alcohol.

---

* Original not seen.

2240. Plech, R. Treatment of frostbite [In German]. *Med. Klin., Berl., v. 39, Apr. 30, 1943: 351–352.*

This is a report of experiences in the treatment of frostbitten patients sent to Berlin hospitals from the Russian front. Continuous wet dressings were used until injured areas were clean, then dry treatment with sulfonamides was begun. Suction, local hot air baths, and Padutin or Priscol were also used. Amputation was not recommended until the line of demarcation was established.

2241. Podolsky, E. New methods of treating frostbite. *Trained Nurse, v. 118, Feb. 1947: 107–108.* Also in: *Med. World, Phila., v. 69, Feb. 4, 1949: 745–747.*

Russian experiences in the treatment and prevention of frostbite during World War II are considered. Among the results discussed are the findings that rapid rewarming of frostbite is better than slow rewarming, that frozen parts are not brittle, and that retrograde degeneration of the peripheral nerves takes place following frostbite. A medical commission, after considerable experimentation, had arrived at the conclusion that the kind of base and moisture content determined the actual value of ointments used on frostbite injuries. They recommended one consisting of camphor, bee's wax, and anhydrous petrolatum.

2242. Podzolov, V. V. Treatment of ballistic wounds by the Vishnevskiĭ method [In Russian]. *Nov. khir. arkh., 1941 (2): 285–295.*

Included is the author's recommendation that, in cases of frostbite injuries, oil-balsam salves and regional anesthesia be used.

2243. Puoz, J. de. On frostbite [In German]. *Allg. schweiz. Militärztg., v. 90, Jan. 1944: 93–104.*

The prophylaxis and treatment of local and general frostbite are discussed. The author mentions the use of alcohol and of the two salves—Cyren-A and "Acrotherm"—in cold protection. He warns against the use of nicotine. Periarterial sympathectomy and Novocain block of lumbar ganglion are discussed as methods of treatment following cold injury.

2244. Rabinovich, ĪA. S. Concerning the question of treatment of frostbite in military zones [In Russian]. *Khirurgiĩa, Moskva, 1941 (6): 46–49.*

Treatment of several cases of 2nd or 3rd degree frostbite, at a front-line army hospital, is discussed. Intravenous injections of 10–15 g of 20% alcohol were administered twice daily. The injured feet were placed in a special case, provided with two chemical heaters and attached to the stretcher. A high-calorie diet was prescribed. Usually, the general condition improved considerably after the second day. However, the temperature remained high for a long time, which may be explained by functional "compensatory hyperthermia". Cyanosis and edema disappeared gradually; the feet became warm; pain appeared on the 2nd day and persisted for 2 or 3 days; mummification developed only occasionally. The author believes that this method is practical for any stage of front-line evaluation, and is effective in both prophylaxis and treatment. The heated case makes possible open, localized, treatment wth hot air.

2245. Rahm, N. Instruction in winter hygiene [In Swedish]. *Sven. läk. tidn., v. 37, Apr. 12, 1940: 633–649.*

Good body care and personal hygiene, the use of protective clothing, and care in exposing oneself to cold, are considerations for preventing injury or illness caused by the cold. A frostbitten area is to be gently kneaded or massaged to help improve the circulation. Snow may be used for massaging if it is soft but not if it is crystalline; salves are to be preferred. Care should be taken because of the great danger of infection after cold injury. In cases of more severe injury the patient may be given a warm drink (coffee or tea but no strong liquor) and have the injured arm or leg placed in a cold water bath (10 °C). As the injured extremity becomes red and less rigid, the temperature of the water bath may be slowly raised. Later, pavex (passive vascular exercise) is also recommended to help restore circulation in the limbs. If the body temperature drops below 23 °C, the outlook is not good. A heart stimulant may be given and, possibly, artificial respiration may be necessary.

2246. Ravina, A. The treatment of recent frost injury [In French]. *Presse méd., v. 52, Dec. 30, 1944: 340.*

The pathogenesis and pathology of the various types of cold injuries are described in this discussion of frostbite therapy during wartime. Ichthyol ointment and various sulfonamide powders were used; and later, surgical sympathectomy and sympathetic block by Novocain infiltration. Periarterial sympathectomy was successful in preventing gangrene. Vascular dilatation was obtained by the use of a number of preparations, especially hormone ones. The circulatory hormones of pancreatic origin, and substances such as benzylimidazoline, gave good results. Amputation was found necessary in extreme cases.

2247. Reimers, C. Symptoms and management of local frostbite [In German]. *Zbl. Chir., v. 70, Oct. 30, 1943: 1573–1584.*

The author advises of measures to improve circulation before the temperature of a frostbitten area is permitted to rise. He recommends "cross-section anesthesia" thus inducing vasomotor paralysis. Early amputation is advised only after necrosis is fully established.

2248. Richter, W. Treatment of blue-red discoloration of the hands after freezing injuries [In German]. *Deut. med. Wschr., v. 67, Mar. 14, 1941: 298–299.*

The author's reply to a question on how to treat the blue-red discoloration of the hands after freezing injuries, was to take measures both local and systemic to increase the blood flow through the area. He suggested several therapeutic measures, including alternating hot and cold baths, use of various salves, and use of antihistaminics. To relieve the vascular reaction, he suggested antihistaminic iontophoresis or antihistaminic salve.

2249. Rietz, T. Foundations of war surgery [In Swedish]. *Sven. läk. tidn., v. 37, May 1940: 797–864.*

A section, Frostbite (moisture injury), p. 839–840, emphasizes the role of moisture in causing more severe injuries from cold than would be caused by a similar degree of dry cold. The author mentions the many cases of trench foot of the Balkan War of 1912 and of World War I, and the prophylaxis since adopted, such as dry socks, roomier shoes, etc. Rubbing of the cold injury areas with snow—or vigorous rubbing at any time—is no longer recommended because of the danger of mechanical tissue injury and of infection. He recommends the use of gradually warmer water, up to normal body temperature, including the use of a camphor soap; Ichthyol and bandaging in the later states; lumbar sympathectomy with "etokain" solution, temporarily paralyzing the vasoconstrictor nerves, to increase circulation and speed of reparative processes; and pavex (passive vascular exercise).

2250. Roux, M., and P. Dautry. Severe freezing injury of the foot on an old arteritic area; arteriectomy; conservative amputation; Syme's operation [In French]. *Presse méd., v. 56, Mar. 31, 1948: 233–234.*

The treatment of a severe case of frostbite is described in great detail. Arteriectomy, and Syme's amputation, brought about good results.

* **2251. Rupasov, N. F.** Frostbite therapy in the rear hospital [In Russian]. *Vest. khir., v. 61, Feb. 1941: 277.*

"*Contains* summary of a report read before the Second Conference on Local Anesthesia and Wound Therapy according to Methods of A. V. Vishnevskiĭ (Moscow, Oct. 28–29, 1940). 424 patients already supplied with specific bandaging and treatment in the front-line hospitals, were further studied. The effects of transportation on the bandages and injuries are discussed."—Arctic Bibl., v. 4, 1954: 900.

---

* Original not seen.

2252. Sauerbruch, ... Cold injuries [In Norwegian]. *Tskr. Norges laegeforen., v. 63, Apr. 1943: 151–155.*

Freezing of tissue usually occurs at 0 °F but may not reach a solid state until the temperature is considerably lower since much depends on the salt concentration of the fluids, on the colloidal composition of the tissues, and also on the individual's constitution. The critical limit for the lowering of body temperature would seem to be approximately 20 °F. In freezing, considerable damage is done by formation of crystals which injure the protoplasm. Fast thawing of frozen tissue may bring about further damage in the formation of vacuoles, followed by some cellular fragmentation, and necrosis. As therapy the author recommends slow rewarming and only gentle massage with towels, elevation of an affected extremity to aid circulation, and, in some cases, the use of multiple incisions to relieve the pressure of edematous fluid. The terms first, second, and third degree, as used to classify injuries from burns, are thought to be somewhat misleading since the extent of injury from cold can not be determined as quickly.

2253. Schneider, E. Treatment of severe frostbite and its late phases [In German]. *Med. Klin., Berl., v. 38, Apr. 24, 1942: 389–391.*

Clinical aspects of severe and late phases of frostbite are discussed. Among the therapies suggested are the use of Padutin by injection, and of various powders such as "Dermatol", Airol, Marfanyl, and "Cibazol." Periarterial sympathectomy was also used in treatment.

2254. Shturm, V. A. Frostbite and its treatment [In Russian]. *Raboty Leningr. vrach. za god otechest. voiny, 1942 (2): 29–39.*

Circulatory disturbances play a leading role in all the phases of the acute and chronic stages of frostbite injury as well as in its pathogeny. The tissue cells do not die immediately at the onset of cold; the whole pathogenic process has a dynamic character with a determined sequence of reactions. The falling-off of the necrotic tissue and the development of reparatory processes are characterized by their sluggishness, due to severe circulatory trophic disturbances. The necroses are indirect, circulatory ones. In the treatment of the acute stage of frostbite the main emphasis should be on the restoration of circulation. Rapid rewarming in the pre-reaction phase accelerates this restoration and prevents enlargement of the necrotic area. In 1st degree cases the pain must be reduced; hot baths or Sollux radiation, which increase the pain, are therefore not indicated. In 2nd and 3rd degree cases the emphasis must be on counteracting the infection: removal of blisters, treatment in an open heated case, Sollux radiation, hot-air baths, and reflex-segmentary therapy of the autonomous nervous system by ultrahigh-frequency radiation or diathermy, are recommended.

2255. Shumacker, H. B., Jr., L. R. Radigan, H. H. Ziperman, and R. R. Hughes. Studies in experimental frostbite. VI. Effect of rutin and Benadryl with some notes on plaster casts and the role of edema. *Angiology, v. 2, Apr. 1951: 100–107.*

Rutin and Benadryl were found to be beneficial in reducing the gangrene following frostbite, but less effective than rapid thawing. Plaster casts applied after frostbite in order to reduce the accumulation of tissue fluid were found to have no effect on the subsequent death of the tissues.

2256. Shumacker, H. B., Jr., and R. E. Lempke. Recent advances in frostbite, with particular reference to experimental studies concerning functional pathology and treatment. *Surgery, v. 30, Nov. 1951: 873–904.*

A review is given of recent investigations in the functional pathology and treatment of experimental frostbite. Frostbite is defined as the condition resulting from exposure to cold of such duration and severity as to result in actual freezing to ice of the tissues. It is concluded that therapeutic use of cold and the use of pressure dressings and plaster casts are not beneficial. Anticoagulant therapy, autonomic block, and other therapeutic measures are discussed. Areas where future research is thought to be needed are indicated. 65 refs.

2257. Shumacker, H. B., Jr. The present status of the treatment of frostbite. *Angiology, v. 2, Dec. 1951: 476–483.*

The author attributes frostbite damage to the results of vasoconstriction and, when freezing occurs, the stoppage of circulation. With thawing, capillary stasis appears, and, in severe cases, thrombosis. The author finds that slow thawing, chilling of the frozen part, and the application of plaster casts to control edema are ineffective. He discusses the value of rapid thawing; the use of heparin, rutin, and ACTH; the effectiveness of sympathetic block and sympathectomy; and problems of gangrene therapy.

2258. Smirnov, S. A. Burns, frostbite, electro-trauma and their treatment [In Russian]. *In: Voenno-polevaia khirurgiia, p. 80–94. Moskva, Medgiz, 1942.*

In cases of frostbite, abrupt passage from cold to heat is dangerous. Rewarming of the frostbitten ears of rabbits by immediate application of paraffin at 60°C leads to necrosis, which did not occur when the rewarming was slow. Application of iodine solutions, after drying of the vesicles, was used successfully in 2nd degree injuries. Under the scab healing proceeded by secondary intent without gangrene. Second and 3rd degree injuries may also be treated by tannic acid solutions, until development of granulation, then by ointment dressings (5% naphthalene borate or Vishnevskiĭ's ointment). Trophic ulcers require long treatment for which Vishnevskiĭ's lumbar or short Novocain block is to be recommended. Cod-liver oil compresses, gypsum dressing, or pedicle skin transplant may also be effective therapies. A vitamin-rich diet and diathermy are to be used as supportive measures. Active and passive motions, massage, baths, and physiotherapeutical measures will help combat atrophy of the extremity.

2259. Spampinato, L. The treatment of freezing injuries [In Italian]. *Ann. med. nav., Roma, v. 52, May–Aug. 1947: 187–190.*

The author recommends conservative treatment of freezing injuries and, when amputation appears to be necessary, waiting for a good line of demarcation between living and necrotic tissues. Among the therapeutic measures suggested are use of warm local baths; salt water foot baths; sulfapyridine; oral, parenteral, and local use of various vitamins and fish-liver oil, and "Thioseptal."

2260. Spasokukotskiĭ, S. I. [The treatment of frostbite and its sequelae]. [In Russian]. *In: Trudy 2-go plenuma Gospital'nogo Soveta Narkomzdrava SSSR, Dec. 20–25, 1942, p. 274–277. Moskva, Medgiz, 1943.*

The effectiveness of Girgolav's theory of rapid rewarming after cold injury is questioned, since such rewarming is said to traumatize the tissues inducing a hyperemia, the formation of vesicles, and production of edema. Results of popular treatment by cold (slow rewarming) were seen which left the site unharmed. Repeated alcohol washings prevent redness and swelling in 1st degree injuries. Rapid rewarming contributes to the production of thrombosis, especially since during the cold effect a great amount of thrombokinase is formed in the blood. Therefore warming should proceed slowly as an interior reaction, not from the surface. As recommended by V. A. Bogdanov in 1939, injection of heparin or synthetic antithrombin (which will make the patient a temporary hemophylic) will prevent gangrene. Possibly, high-level amputations could thus be avoided. Dilatation of the blood vessels can be induced either by drinking a large quantity of alcohol, or by a paravertebral injection of Novocain, or by Vishnevskiĭ's nerve block. Prof. Kazanskiĭ obtained a remarkable result by injecting 20 cc of 0.5% Novocain into the artery of the frostbitten foot. Prof. Lorin-Epsteĭn suggested the transfusion of small amounts of blood of a different blood-group from that of the recipient, into the raised foot which was ligated for 15 minutes; the skin temperature rose 2°–3°C, and the foot remained warm for 6 days, without general disturbances.

2261. Stafford-Clark, D. Emergencies due to cold. *In: Emergencies in medical practice, p. 354–357. Ed. by C. A. Birch. Edinburgh, Livingstone, 1948.*

In this section of Chapter XXI, Medical emergencies in the air, emergencies due to cold become a factor since the temperature falls at a rate of approximately 2°C for every 1,000 feet above sea level until the temperature, in the substratosphere, reaches −55°C. The intense cold produces frostbite and generalized effects. Frostbite should be prevented by the wearing of adequate protective clothing including the wearing of gloves; by heating of the cabin; or, for combat aircrews, the wearing of electrically-heated clothing; combined with adequate oxygen supply and administration. While in the air, emergency treatment is limited usually to rest for the affected part and to administration of oxygen and hot drinks. Upon landing, similar procedure should be followed with protection of the area by cotton and by its being kept at a cool room temperature. An alternate method involves immersing the part in cold water which is gradually warmed, and re-cooled if pain increases. No massaging, or rubbing with snow, should be done. Extremely low temperatures predispose to anoxia, while anoxia diminishes resistance to cold. Warning is given that calculations of oxygen needs at high altitude should be sure to take into account the proportionately greater oxygen debt created by cold.

2262.   Strandberg, J. On cold and frost injury of the skin [In Swedish]. *In: Sveriges Läkarförbund. Handledninyi Försvarsmedicin, part 1, p. 242–248. Stockholm, E. C. Fritz, 1940. Also, in Swedish, in: Sven. läk. tidn., v. 36, Dec. 1939: 2365–2371.*

The author describes the clinical and pathologic aspects of frostbite of the skin. Management includes careful rewarming and the use of salves to promote healing of injured tissue. A recommended salve includes vaseline, calcium chloride, camphor, Peru balsam, gallotannic acid, and Ichthyol. Heart stimulants, and drugs to increase blood pressure, have often shown good results.

2263.   T., R. M. Frostbite, its pathogenesis, sequelae, and treatment [In French]. *Praxis, Bern, v. 30, Mar. 27, 1941: 187–190.*

A discussion is given of the etiology, pathogenesis, prophylaxis, and treatment of frostbite. Immediate treatment has been successfully carried out using massage of the area with camphorated pomade, use of tepid baths, application of methylsalicylate, and surgical intervention of the sympathetic nervous system to relieve vascular spasm. Out of recent findings, the author stresses the existence of a previous infectious condition in cold etiology; the remarkably good results obtained with Marconi therapy; and the efficacy of the newer methods used in surgical intervention of the sympathetic nervous system.

2264.   Tabanelli, M. Frostbite in war [In Italian]. *Arch. ital. chir., v. 68, Mar.–Apr. 1946: 111–195.*

This report is based upon observations on 291 cases of frostbite, principally from the Russian front in World War II. The author describes the treatment in great detail, clinical features being briefly mentioned. Three degrees of frostbite are noted depending on severity. Cases of 1st and 2nd degree were treated by either periarterial neural block, lumbar sympathetic block, or local analgesia just proximal to the affected area. In the most severe or 3rd degree cases, the treatment was mostly surgical. Ovbiously necrosed tissue was removed and various amputations were performed when necessary. Great emphasis is placed upon early ambulation often as soon as 7 days after the operation, special walking irons being supplied.

2265.   Tarsitano, F. Therapy of frostbite lesions in war [In Italian]. *Riforma med., v. 57, Jan. 11, 1941: 47.*

Cases of frostbite in soldiers were treated with follicular hormones as well as by short-wave therapy.

2266.   Traube, R. V. Freezing. *In: Kriegschirurgie im Reservelazarett, p. 75–84* [In German]. *Ed. by W. Zillmer. Dresden u. Leipzig, Steinkopff, 1944.*

This is a general account of freezing injuries, with emphasis on surgical treatment. Antiseptic salves and hormone salves are recommended for use in mild cases, periarteriolar sympathectomy and lumbar sympathectomy in more severe cases.

2267. Uffreduzzi, O. The pathology and therapy of freezing injuries [In Italian]. *Minerva med., Tor.,* anno *31* (v. 2), *Dec. 15, 1940: 578–579.*

Differences between the immediate and the late pathological changes and the different therapies involved in freezing injuries, are discussed. Therapy should be directed toward relieving the vascular spasm and improving circulation, preventing infection in an ulcerated area, preventing gangrene, and relieving painful after-effects when they occur. Novocain injection of the lumbar sympathetic chain is discussed as a therapeutic measure.

2268. Valastro, S. A primary cure for freezing injuries [In Italian]. *Gior. med. Marca trevig.,* v. *4, 1942–1943: 27–31.*

The author reviews the therapeutic measures used against freezing injuries discussing especially the perivascular infiltration of a sympathetic ganglion with Novocain, and the injection of foreign protein material. He prophesies much more extensive use of protein-shock therapy.

2269. Vishnevskiǐ, A. V. Local anesthesia and treatment of wounds during war [In Russian]. *Arkh. biol. nauk,* v. *61* (*1*), *1941: 8–32.*

A favorable effect of novocainization on the inflammatory processes of frostbite was observed; local anesthesia applied for therapeutic reasons acts on the general neurotrophic regulation through nervous stimulation. In severe 2nd and 3rd degree frostbite injuries with weak tissue reaction, without clear delineation of the process and with presence of edema and inflammation, lumbar or other Novocain block was applied. If necessary it was repeated 2 or 3 times at intervals of 10 to 15 days. After the block, the necrosed areas were painted with tincture of iodine, covered with oil-balsam far above the place of injury (for the purpose of action on the neuroreceptor system of the skin), and bandaged with gypsum reinforcement and fixation to an upper joint. The balsam was changed every 5 to 10 days. Vesicles were excised and crusts and pockets removed for greater exposure to the balsam. This method resulted in a great stimulation of the regenerative capacity of the tissues, and rapid recovery took place. In less severe cases of frostbite, the balsam alone was used; amputation became necessary in only one case.

2270. Vishnevskiǐ, A. V. Our methods of wound treatment [In Russian]. *Arkh. biol. nauk,* v. *62* (*1*), *1943: 3–11.*

This is a general review of Russian practices in the treatment of war wounds. Oil-balsam treatment and regional anesthesia are recommended for frostbite injuries.

2271. Wolfram, S. Frostbite and its treatment [In German]. *Wien. klin. Wschr.,* v. *58, Feb. 22, 1946: 56–60.*

This is a general discussion of frostbite with emphasis on the management of the various degrees of severity. The use of sulfonamide compounds, Priscol, and Progynon is discussed. In severe cases the author recommends lumbar sympathectomy, physical therapy, and injections of thyroid extract.

2272. Zanotti, M. Neurological and medico-legal remarks and biological tests on the nature and on the effects of frostbite [In Italian]. *Gior. psychiat.,* v. *69* (*3*), *1941: 175–195.*

Pathogenesis, prophylaxis, and treatment of frostbite are discussed. A modification of Marconi therapy is suggested, so that the electrodes are placed at the top of the popliteal space. Oscillometry and protein-shock therapy are also included in the treatments recommended.

See also items: 558, 655, 732, 1040, 1426, 1705, 1771, 1782, 1832, 1881, 1894, 1896, 1903, 1908, 1915, 1917, 1918, 1927, 1928, 1933, 1943, 1949, 1954, 1956, 1964, 2025, 2040, 2061, 2064, 2075, 2088, 2096, 2114, 2117, 2149, 2575, 2599, 2601, 2628, 2668, 2672, 2721, 2727, 2733.

10. Therapy, Physiotherapy

2273.   Anon. Instructions for the application of physiotherapy in frostbite [In Russian]. *Khirurgiia, Moskva, 1940 (12): 145.*

According to the regulations set up by the Medical Council of the Health Commissarist of the USSR, frostbite is to be treated by the use of ultraviolet radiation, d'arsonvalization, diathermy, Sollux lamp, ultrahigh-frequency radiation, reflex-segmentary physiotherapy, or Novocain iontophoresis. These methods of therapy are discussed in detail in relation to the degree of severity of the frostbite injury. In addition, it is suggested that the vesicles should be excised, but treatment with tincture of iodine or use of stains or grease on the injured surface is not recommended. Ultraviolet rays should be at high erythemic level; the healthy skin should also be treated by these rays, but with smaller doses. Third degree frostbite should be treated by an open method.

2274.   Anon. Instructions for the use of physical therapy of frost injuries [In Russian]. *Sovet. med., 1940 (22): 38.*

Instructions are given for the use of ultrahigh-frequency radiation in the treatment of frostbite injuries.

2275.   Anon. The treatment of frostbite. *U. S. Nav. M. Bull., v. 48, Jan.–Feb. 1948: 99–100.*

This is a brief note on the similarities between burns and frostbite, with special emphasis on the treatment of the two conditions. In the initial treatment of frostbite, gradual thawing is recommended.

2276.   Adams-Ray, J., and C. J. Clemedson. On first aid which can be rendered by laymen in cases of injury by cold [In Swedish]. *Acta chir. scand., v. 89, 1944: 527–545.* Abstract, in English, in: *Bull. War. M., Lond., v. 4, Aug. 1944: 703.*

Methods and results of first aid treatment for cold injuries are given. The advantages and disadvantages of rapid rewarming are discussed. Frostbite lesions of 2nd degree were noted in 70.3% of cases treated by rubbing with snow; only about 45.3% of the cases treated by rapid rewarming developed such lesions. Also all of the cases treated with snow evidenced some necrosis.

2277.   Adams-Ray, J., and B. Falconer. Pathologico-anatomical changes following rapid and slow thawing, respectively, in frozen skin in man [In English]. *Acta chir. scand., v. 101 (4), 1951: 269–278.*

Areas on both median and lateral aspects of a human leg were frozen simultaneously—24 hours before amputation for other causes—and then one side was rewarmed rapidly with water of 37°C while the other was allowed to thaw at room temperature. Later pathological examination of 21 such specimens showed no differences in the two areas in 3 cases; 3 showed more extensive changes after rapid rewarming; and 15 showed greater changes, mostly degenerative, after slow thawing.

2278.   Allen, F. M., L. W. Crossman, and F. K. Safford, Jr. Reduced temperature treatment for burns and frostbite. *N. York State J. M., v. 43, May 15, 1943: 951–952.*

A case of severe frostbite of the right hand was treated by placing it uncovered in an electrically-refrigerated unit at 50°F. The patient reported almost immediate relief of pain. There was also subsidence of swelling, control of infection, and avoidance of gangrene. The less-severely frostbitten left hand did not progress as well until the bandages were removed and, in the absence of another refrigerated unit, it was placed directly on an ice bag rotating the palmar and dorsal surfaces in contact with the ice bag.

2279. Ar'ev, T. I͡A. On rapid and slow rewarming of frostbitten extremities [In Russian]. *Trudy 24-go Vsesouznogo S"ezda Khirurgov, Kharkov, 1938, p. 199–202. Moskva-Leningrad, Medgiz, 1939.*

The ears, or hind legs, of each of a group of 12 rabbits were frozen with an ethyl-chloride spray. The right ear or leg was rapidly rewarmed by use of warm (40°–45°C) compresses; the left extremities were allowed to warm up gradually at room temperature. The inflammatory and necrotic symptoms were much more sharply pronounced in the left extremities than in the right; however, the differences in the histological specimens appeared only after approximately one day following rewarming. All experimental data, as well as several clinical observations of men, showed that the frostbitten tissues suffer much less injury from rapid rewarming than when slowly rewarmed. Gangrene did not result following rapid rewarming. Attempting to rewarm hypothermic subjects in snow or cold water only leads to prolonged cooling and a further drop in temperature.

2280. Ar'ev, T. I͡A. On the slow and fast rewarming of frozen limbs [In Russian]. *Vest. Khir., v. 57 (5), 1939: 527–535.*

The ears, or hind legs, of rabbits were frozen by means of an ethyl-chloride spray. Result of physiological studies made on these animals indicated that rapid rewarming was not detrimental.

2281. Astuni, A. Clinical results of Marconi therapy of freezing injuries. (Preliminary note) [In Italian]. *Atti Accad. med. lombarda, v. 30, Aug. 1941: 311–314.*

Treatment of 47 cases of 3rd degree freezing injuries, with Marconi therapy, gave in general a clear-cut and rapid analgesic action. The scar formation seemed to occur more regularly and quickly than in similar lesions not so treated, and the duration of the hospital stay was shortened.

2282. Astuni, A. The treatment of frostbite lesions by Marconi therapy. Technique and results; clinical observations on the pain syndrome in frostbite [In Italian]. *Minerva med., Tor., anno 33 (v. 1) 1942: 112–121.*

Presentation is made of a series of cases of varying degrees of frostbite treated by diathermy with an analysis of results, giving special attention to the relief of pain.

2283. Attili, S. Radiology in the diagnosis and in the treatment of war-time freezing injuries [In Italian]. *In: Atti Congresso Nazionale di Chirurgia di Guerra, May 24–26, 1942, p. 243. Roma, 1943.*

Use of x-rays as a diagnostic aid in cases of osteonecrosis and for examination of amputation stumps following severe freezing injury is described. Roentgenotherapy for the treatment of infections and relief of pain in frostbite injuries is also discussed.

2284. Barbacci, G. Trial of X-ray therapy on the after-effects of frostbite [In Italian]. *Boll. Accad. med. pistoiese, v. 14, Dec. 1941: 179–181.*

The results of x-ray therapy on frostbite injuries were excellent. Lesions healed very quickly.

2285. Barunin, I. Treatment of frostbite with ultrahigh frequency radiation [In Russian]. *Fizioterapia, Moskva, v. 15 (2–3), 1940: 53–55.*

Forty cases of frostbite (mostly 2nd degree; and 3 cases of 3rd degree) were treated by ultrahigh-frequency radiation. Such treatment sharply decreased the pathological process and averted complications, namely purulation and tissue decomposition. Moist gangrene could be changed into a dry type with a pronounced demarcation line. Pain and edema disappeared, the local temperature of the tissue was raised, the skin resumed its normal coloring, vesicles dried up, purulating surface ulcers changed into granulations, and healing was sharply accelerated. The earlier the treatment was applied, the sooner the favorable results appeared.

2286. Bellander, G. The treatment of acute frostbite injuries [In Swedish]. *Sven. läk. tidn., v. 37, Mar. 8, 1940: 487–490.*

The various procedures for early treatment of frostbite are discussed, together with the reasons for abandoning the time-honored method of rubbing a frozen area with snow.

2287. Berté, G. Physio-therapeutic treatment of freezing injury [In Italian]. *In: Atti Congresso Nazionale di Chirurgia di Guerra, May 24–26, 1942, p. 223–224. Roma, 1943.*

The use of physio-therapeutic treatments, including Marconi therapy, diathermy, warm saline baths, water vapor from boiling water, and moist heat packs, resulted in improvement of the topical condition of frostbite lesions. Such treatment brought relief from pain, facilitated demarcation of the wound area, and aided in the salvaging of tissue which would otherwise have been lost.

2288. Borini, L., and G. Matli. Pathology and physical therapy of cold lesions in the Italian-French campaign of 1940 [In Italian]. *Med. contemp., Lisb., v. 6, July 1940: 295–301.*

Notes on the pathology and therapy of cold injuries are given. Frostbite injuries of 2nd and 3rd degree, which had been treated previously in various ways including Novocain infiltration and alcohol packs, were subjected to short-wave radiation. The results indicated complete recovery in the milder cases and improvement of the more serious ones.

2289. Borini, L., and G. Matli. Marconi therapy of freezing injuries occurring during the Italian-French campaign of 1940 [In Italian]. *Minerva med., Tor., anno 31 (v. 2), Dec. 15, 1940: 586–588.*

The necrosis following freezing injuries is primarily that from anemia brought about by the vasoconstriction or vasospasm resulting from the cold. For relief of this spasm phenomenon, the authors discuss their successful use of Marconi therapy in 50 cases of frostbite incurred during the Italian-French campaign of 1940.

2290. Brandstadt, W. G. Frostbite. *Mil. Surgeon., v. 107, Nov. 1950: 386–388.*

This is a review of the report of a symposium on frostbite by Russian investigators published by the Defence Research Board of the Canadian Department of Defence. The concept that actual freezing of the tissues does not occur in the living man can be clarified and amplified by considering various peculiarities of the action of cold on the living organism, several of which are noted. Contrary to the old rule-of-thumb that frostbitten limbs should be warmed slowly and gradually, it was concluded that rapid rewarming—by the combined use of warm baths and massage was effective and brought about less necrotic and degenerative changes in the tissues. To speed up rewarming 5cc of a 10% solution of calcium chloride were administered until 3 injections had been given. In the urgent first aid of hypothermia the solution may be given intravenously with hot drinks being given by mouth. The patient should be placed in warm surroundings and given energetic massage with the open palm after the body has been tightly wrapped in a sterile towel. In 1st degree frostbite the initial treatment may be followed by simple irrigation with a 5% solution of tannic acid or by painting the area with a 2% solution of brilliant green. Exposure for 10–15 minutes to a sunlamp in the first 3–4 days provides a mild analgesic effect and promotes the rapid restoration of circulation. Unlike burns, not 3 but 4 degrees of frostbite are distinguished.

2291. Brownrigg, G. M. Frostbite: classification and treatment. *Am. J. Surg., v. 67, Feb. 1945: 370–381.*

The author proposes a clinical classification of cold injuries depending on the degree of injury; he also discusses treatment. The use of heat as therapy is contra-indicated, but refrigeration may have some value. In cases of dry gangrene one should await spontaneous separation rather than resort to amputation.

2292. **Burlando, E.** On the treatment of war-time freezing injury with actino-therapy and short-wave therapy [In Italian]. *In: Atti Congresso Nazionale di Chirurgia di Guerra, May 24–26, 1942, p. 231–234. Roma, 1943.*

A group of 224 cases of 2nd and 3rd degree frostbite injuries have been treated successfully by the author with ultraviolet-ray therapy and Marconi therapy, or a combination of both. Lesions were localized in the lower limbs and varied in severity, including conditions of paresthesia; sensations of cold and pain; edema; diffuse redness; pustules containing a green serous fluid; and necrosis. In case of necrosis, the demarcation line took place quickly under the influence of these rays.

2293. **Cabizza, A.** Results obtained with physiotherapy on the effects of freezing injury and surgical intervention on frozen limbs [In Italian]. *In: Atti Congresso Nazionale di Chirurgia di Guerra, May 24–26, 1942, p. 246–248. Roma, 1943.*

The use of hydrotherapy in the treatment of local freezing injuries is described. The local area involved is immersed in, or bathed with, a warm hypertonic solution containing citro-silicate at a temperature of 37°C. This is continued for 7 days, ending with a temperature of 41°C. After this, powdered sulfonamide and then a cod-liver-oil salve is used. The results in cases of 1st or 2nd degree frostbite injury were a decrease in pain, in paresthesia, and in edema after the first application. In 3rd degree injury, the loss of tissue was decreased. A moderate and gradual vasodilatation was produced.

2294. **Cajelli, G.** Contribution to a study of Marconi therapy on the lesions from cold [In Italian]. *Gazz. med. ital., v. 100, Dec. 1941: 361–366.*

The author discusses the types of lesions due to cold injuries, some of the methods of therapy in use, and the good results he has achieved following the use of Marconi therapy. The bene-ficial effects may be caused by the direct thermal action, by a momentary vasoconstriction followed by vasodilatation, its analgesic action, or its bactericidal action. The latter action is thought by the author to play a role in the good results obtained on infected second degree lesions following a combination of ultra-violet and Marconi therapy.

2295. **Campellone, P.** On the results of biological treatment in frostbite [In Italian]. *Atti Accad. fisiocr. Siena, v. 9, ser. 11 (4), 1941: 160–164.*

The author treated frostbite on the 3rd degree with warm moist packs steeped in physiologi-cal saline at 50°-60°C. This is the "biological treatment" of Baggio.

2296. **Cignolini, P., and V. Castellaneta.** Clinical report from the Center of Cryopathological Studies [In Italian]. *Gior. med. mil., v. 87, Apr. 1939: 367–382.*

Two cases of freezing injury are described. One case was treated with short waves, the other by x-rays. Results were favorable in both instances.

2297. **Cignolini, P.** Fundamental experiments and clinical results of Marconi therapy on cold lesions [In Italian]. *Minerva med., Tor., anno 31 (v. 2), Dec. 15, 1940: 579–586.*

A report with case histories (illustrated) is given on the efficacy of short-wave therapy in frostbite.

2298. **Cignolini, P.** Possibilities and limits of Marconi therapy in war-time freezing injuries [In Italian]. *In: Atti Congresso Nazionale di Chirurgia di Guerra, May 24–26, 1942, p. 184–186. Roma, 1943.*

This article concerns itself with the use of Marconi therapy in the treatment of freezing injuries. The effectiveness of this type of therapy is dependent on whether both the sympathetic system and the tissue involved are altered by the irradiation.

2299. Cignolini, P. Short-wave therapy of frostbite, of rigidity, and of hypothermic trauma [In German]. *Zbl. Chir., v. 70, 1943: 63–68.*

Some of the uses and techniques of short-wave therapy are discussed. The availability and
careful use of such therapy, in a field hospital in wartime, during the first or second day after
freezing injuries, will aid in the thawing-out of the area and prevention of further injury.
There are two distinct periods when such therapy is especially effective—in the first hours
after the exposure to cold, and in the relief of the circulatory disorders following injury.

2300. Clouston, H. R. First aid in frostbite. *Canad. M. Ass. J., v. 40, Feb. 1939:
166.*

The milder grades of freezing can be withstood by human tissue with comparatively little
damage if the tissue is not further traumatized by rough handling or by application of excessive heat or excessive cold. Tissue so injured and devitalized is particularly susceptible to
infection. Following thawing of the area at a temperature above freezing but not above normal
body temperature, a cool—but not cold—environmental temperature will be advantageous
to the victim.

2301. Crismon, J. M., and F. A. Fuhrman. Studies on gangrene following cold
injury. VIII. The use of casts and pressure dressings in the treatment of severe
frostbite. *J. Clin. Invest., v. 26, May 1947: 486–496.*

In rabbits with experimental frostbite, it was found possible to prevent gangrene and reduce tissue loss in a significant number of cases by the mechanical control of edema with casts
and pressure dressings. Best results were obtained by rapid rewarming followed by casts applied before swelling occurred or pressure dressings applied after maximum swelling.

* 2302. Dolinskaĭa, A. T. Early application of ultrahigh-frequency radiation in
freezing injury under front-line conditions [In Russian]. *Arkh. biol. nauk, v. 60
(2), 1940: 3–6.*

Recommends early treatment of frostbite with ultrahigh-frequency radiation. See Biol
Abst., v. 18, 1944: #8932.

2303. Dondero, A. P. On the outcome and therapeutic orientation of frostbite
[In Italian]. *Atti Accad. med. lombarda, v. 31, Apr. 17, 1942: 227–231.*

In this general account of the treatment of frostbite lesions, x-ray treatment is recommended
in cases where the bones are involved.

2304. Drulev, V. A. Frostbite and its treatment [In Russian]. *Feldsher & akush.,
1943 (10–11): 19–22.*

Treatment of 1st, 2nd, and 3rd degree frostbite injuries in 57 patients (war casualties)
revealed the importance of repeated warm local and general baths for all frostbite cases. The
baths (37°–40°C for 15–25 minutes) rapidly induced the appearance of a clear demarcation
line of pronounced granulation and an area of rapid epithelization, and promoted healing
without complications. In cases of 3rd degree frostbite, passage from dry gangrene to moist
was never observed; moist gangrene dried more rapidly under the effect of warm baths. A
schedule of frostbite treatment at the Zheleznovodsk balneary is given.

* 2305. Dunaevskaĭa, M. B. Treatment of frostbite by ultra-high frequency rays
[In Russian]. *Fizioterapiĭa, Moskva, 1941 (3–4): 14–19.*

"*Contains* a report on therapy of 84 patients with first to third degree frostbite, part of them
irradiated 0.5–10.0 hours after injury without any preceding treatment. Special emphasis is
placed on effects of this radiation on capillary condition and circulation. Representative
cases are presented."—Arctic Bibl., v. 6, 1956: 234.

---

* Original not seen.

2306. Fell, E. H., and R. Hanselman. Prevention of shock and death by immediate application of a pressure dressing to the severely frozen limbs of dogs; an experimental study. *Ann. Surg.*, v. *117*, *May 1943: 686–691.* Abstract in: *Proc. Inst. M. Chicago*, v. *14*, *May 15*, *1943: 446.*

The right hind extremities of ten anesthetized dogs were frozen. Five dogs were not treated further, their legs being allowed to thaw at room temperature; all five dogs went into clinical shock and four died within 13 hours. The other dogs were treated with plaster bandages of the frozen legs; none of the dogs died as an immediate result of freezing but four of the five developed necrotic limbs which later had to be amputated. In the bandaged group the maximum increase in the hematocrit was only about one-half as great as in the untreated group. The authors conclude that pressure bandages quickly applied to limbs less severely frozen than those of the experiment, would result in saving the limb.

2307. Finocchiaro, G. Treatment of injuries from freezing with Marconi therapy applied to the raised area of the frozen part [In Albanian, and in Italian]. *Fletor. mjeks. shqipt.*, v. *1*, *Feb. 1942: 12–17.*

The author discusses the good results obtained after the use of Marconi therapy on patients suffering from lesions caused by cold while serving on the Greco-Albanese front.

2308. Frenkel', G. L. Actual problems of high-frequency therapy and its use in experimentation [In Russian]. *Arkh. biol. nauk*, v. *61 (1)*, *1941: 147–156.*

The treatment of frostbite injuries with ultrahigh-frequency current is discussed.

* 2309. Frenkel', G. L. Some experimental prerequisites for the application of ultra-short radio waves in surgery [In Russian]. *Vest. khir.*, v. *21*, *Apr. 1941: 435–445.*

"*Contains* an analysis of the physiological activity of these waves and the advisability of their use in inflammatory processes, infected wounds, fractures, frostbite, etc. With regard to frostbite, the possibility of using them for rewarming and for the therapy of sequelae, are discussed. Bibliography (over 30 items)."—Arctic Bibl., v. 4, 1954: 310.

2310. Fuhrman, F. A., and J. M. Crismon. Studies on gangrene following cold injury. VII. Treatment of cold injury by means of immediate rapid warming. *J. Clin. Invest.*, v. *26*, *May 1947: 476–485.*

When cold injuries of rabbit's feet and ears were treated by rapid rewarming, the result, in most cases, was complete preservation of the part. It is suggested that rapid rewarming be supplemented by measures designed to control edema.

2311. Gerundini, G. On the use of the plaster dressing in the treatment of freezing injuries [In Italian]. *Atti Accad. med. lombarda*, v. *31*, *Apr. 17*, *1942: 213–217.*

Treatment of frostbite by use of plaster dressing was found to limit the ulcerous zone and to prevent deformities.

2312. Girgolav, S. S. Frostbite and its treatment [In Russian]. *Sovet. med.*, *1939 (5): 10–14.*

A general discussion of frostbite and its treatment is given. The changes induced by cold are two-fold, those due directly to the effect of cold on the whole body, and those due to disrupted blood circulation, in which the frostbite is a secondary phenomenon. An important factor to be observed in frostbite treatment is to start the rewarming of the frostbitten tissue at a higher temperature than that of the tissue itself, and to raise it as soon as possible to

---

* Original not seen.

37°–38°C. Restoration of circulation to normal is of decisive importance; massaging has to be prolonged, but carefully and under aseptic conditions. Only non-irritating antiseptics should be used. Greases should be applied for prophylaxis.

* **2313. Golendberg, A. D., and N. N. Mishchuk.** Frostbite therapy with d'Arsonval currents [In Russian]. *Sovet. vrach. zh., 1940 (12): col. 843–844.*

"*Contains* a discussion of the value of d'Arsonval (high frequency) currents in the therapy of first- and second-degree frostbite, dosage, application, comparison with other methods, etc."— Arctic Bibl. v. 4, 1954: 346–347.

2314. Gonzales, A. Action of secondary radiation on the aftereffects of freezing [In Italian]. *Policlinico, sez. prat., v. 48, Oct. 20, 1941: 1762–1767.*

This is a report on the use of Luxan on freezing injuries. This preparation is said to emit secondary radiations for a long period of time after activation by strong radiation. It appears to act as a bactericidal agent, and the affected parts heal quickly.

2315. Impallomeni, R. Combined X-ray and shortwave therapy in the treatment of frostbite [In Italian]. *Riv. clin. med., v. 42, Sept. 30, 1941: 384–388.*

This is a general discussion of methods and results of treatment of frostbite, especially the use of combined x-ray and shortwave therapy.

2316. Jamin, F. The scientific basis for the treatment of freezing injury with shortwave diathermy. A. Frostbite and heat treatment with special reference to short waves [In German]. *Sitzber. Phys. med. Soz. Erlangen, v. 73, 1943: 77–101; 123–125.*

A review of the physiological and anatomical aspects of the peripheral circulation is made in order to provide a basis for studying the applications of diathermy to the treatment of cold injuries. The physics of short waves is also discussed.

2317. Jamin, F. Treatment of freezing injuries with short-wave diathermy [In German]. *Zbl. Chir., v. 70, Jan. 9, 1943: 54–63.*

In late stages or in difficult cases of frostbite of the arms or legs, application of short-wave diathermy has been used successfully for relief of pain, in limiting the area of necrosis, and for acceleration of healing. New equipment for this therapy—involving a new arrangement of electrodes for a high-frequency electro-magnetic field for the foot and for an electric condenser field for the hand—are pictured and described.

2318. Kanevskii, G. L. [The treatment of frostbite and its sequelae]. [In Russian]. *In: Trudy 2-go plenuma Gospital'nogo Soveta Narkomzdrava SSSR, Dec. 20–25, 1942, p. 285–286. Moskva, Medgiz, 1943.*

A group of 117 cases of 3rd and 4th degree frostbite (68 of which had 2 to 4 injuries; one third had in addition bullet wounds) were treated by ultraviolet and infrared rays at an evacuation hospital. Infrared rays were applied 2–3 times daily for 30–60 minutes, heliotherapy on sunny days 2 hours a day, ultraviolet rays (40–60–100 biodoses) 2–3 times a week, with reflexsegmentary therapy (10–15–20 biodoses) for the treatment of trophic symptoms. The open-case method was used. As soon as the body temperature dropped to 37.5°C, physiotherapeutical exercises were given. As a rule, after several days, the bad odor disappeared, the passage of humid gangrene into dry was accelerated, pain subsided, the general tonus increased, epithelial regeneration was accelerated, granulation improved, and the narcotic drugs were discontinued. After the appearance of a demarcation line, a conservative amputation was performed. As a result, 65% of the patients were returned to regular army duties. There were no cases of

---

* Original not seen.

impaired motion, contractures, or ankylosis of articulations. It is concluded that the surgeon should be well acquainted with physiotherapeutic methods, since at one period in treatment of the injury these become the primary treatment.

2319. Karlberg, E. On the treatment of frostbite [In Swedish]. *Sven. läk. tidn.,* *v. 39, Mar. 13, 1942: 718–721.*

The author quotes in full his earlier publication (Note on cold injury and its treatment. Hyg. rev., Lund, v. 27, Jan. 1938: 7–8), and says that he has little new to add. In case of severe cold injury, he recommends placing the patient in a warm room and putting the injured extremity in cold water, a few degrees above zero, then gradually warming the water as the feeling returns to the area. Light massage is optional. When sensitivity has completely returned, the injured area is to be wiped dry and covered loosely with stockings or bandages. Warm milk or coffee can be given. Elevation is recommended and in case of an extremity this should always be done. If it is not possible to place the person indoors, the author would recommend the use of ice water out of doors in preference to rubbing the area with snow which might cause further tissue damage.

2320. Komarov, L. V. Attempt to revivify the ears of rabbits frozen in liquid oxygen [In Russian]. *Doklady Akad. nauk SSSR, v. 64 n.s., (5), 1949: 747–749.*

Rabbits' ears were frozen in liquid oxygen (at about $-183\,°C$) for 20 seconds to 5.5 minutes without narcosis, then either (1) immersed in a water bath at $45\,°C$, (2) wrapped in cotton, or (3) wrapped in cotton until their temperature had risen to $-30\,°C$, then immersed in a $45\,°C$ bath. The average temperature drop in the ear (measured by the introduction of a thermocouple) was $30\,°$–$60\,°C/sec$; the average temperature increase during rewarming was $4\,°$–$6.5\,°C/sec$. Regardless of the rapidity of rewarming, the vitality of the tissue cells of the ear returned, and blood circulation resumed immediately after the period of freezing. The hyperemia of the ear varied in intensity. After the tests with slow rewarming, thrombosis of the posterior auricular vein occurred on the 2nd to 9th day, ending in gangrene; the mummified tissue fell off on the 20th to 30th day. In all the tests with rapid rewarming, thrombosis did not occur; the pathological symptoms disappeared on the 35th to 40th day, and hyperemia on the 40th to 45th; the ear returned to normal and full sensitivity. The hair started to grow on the 30th to 35th day.

2321. Koshovets, P. D. On the question of the treatment of frostbite [In Russian]. *Hosp. delo, 1944 (1–2): 49–51.*

Several hospital cases of neglected 3rd degree frostbite demonstrated the important curative influence of passive hyperemia. This method (earlier highly recommended by N. N. Burdenko) was then used in other cases, including 4th degree frostbite. Traction applied at the base of the toes for 2–3 days, together with the use of ointments and aseptic bandages, and followed in the subsequent days by warm baths, Sollux radiation and blue light (no ultrahigh-frequency radiations were available) gave very favorable results. The author concludes that, though passive hyperemia may be harmful in the pre-reaction stage, it is very effective in the period of reactive inflammation and regeneration, accelerating the healing of tissue defects.

2322. Lempke, R. E., and H. B. Shumacker, Jr. Studies in experimental frostbite. VII. An inquiry into the mode of action of rapid thawing in immediate treatment. *Angiology, v. 2, Aug. 1951: 270–281.*

Studies are reported on the mode of action of rapid thawing applied in frostbite therapy. It is concluded that the incidence and extent of gangrene resulting from freezing is not directly related to the duration of actual freezing; and that the efficacy of rapid thawing, although due in part to shortening the period of freezing, is in addition the result of other factors, among which are suggested the effects of rapid transition to optimal temperatures upon cell restitution, and the effects of prompt vasodilatation.

* **2323. Levin, M. I.** On the question of treating frostbite with the condenser field of ultra-high frequencies and with other physiotherapeutic agents [In Russian]. *Vest. khir., v. 61, Mar. 1941: 410–411.*

"*Contains* an abstract of a report to the Conference of Military Hospitals of the Leningrad Military District (July 30–Aug. 1, 1940) based on treatment of 136 patients, with first-, second-, and third-degree frostbite. Dosage, extent of therapy, and results are briefly cited."— Arctic Bibl., v. 4, 1954: 603.

2324. Lewis, R. B. Microwave diathermy treatment of frostbite. *Proc. Soc. Exp. Biol., N. Y., v. 78, Oct. 1951: 163–165.*

Groups of rabbits had one hind leg exposed to an alcohol bath at either $-12\,°C$ or $-15\,°C$ for 30 minutes. Approximately half of the number of rabbits in the two treatment groups had their injured legs rewarmed rapidly by the use of short-wave diathermy; legs of the others were allowed to thaw at room temperature. Rapid rewarming resulted in a decrease in the extent of muscle and skin necrosis from that of the animals which were warmed more slowly.

2325. Liubina, N. I., and V. V. Mitlin. Experiences in physiotherapy of frostbite under field hospital conditions [In Russian]. *Kazan. med. J., v. 36 (6), 1940: 18–22.*

Good results were obtained in the treatment of frostbite injuries by employing segmented irradiation with erythemic doses from Bach's quartz-mercury lamp (at 6 cm distance, for 7–8 min) combined with local irradiation from a Sollux lamp with a red filter (at 50–60 cm, for 15–20 min) on alternate days. In addition, the injured area was washed with an alcoholic solution of brilliant green and subsequently with hot water. This therapeutic method diminished or eliminated pain, often after two or three treatments. In 2nd degree injuries, it greatly shortened the period of treatment; the earlier it was applied, the sooner the edema disappeared and blood circulation was restored. In 3rd degree injuries, it contributed to the transformation of moist gangrene into dry. The general condition of the patient improved rapidly. After amputation, the stump was treated with Vishnevskiĭ's ointment.

* **2326. Magazanik, G. L.** Physical therapy of frostbite [In Russian]. *Sovet. vrach. zh., 1940 (12): 839–844.*

"*Contains* an account of the aims of physical therapy in frostbite; on massage, hydro- and aero-therapy, electrotherapy and irradiation, and their value in frostbite of first to third degree. Their use in sequelae is also dealt with." —Arctic Bibl., v. 4, 1954: 649.

2327. Maggiora, B. della. Indications for the use of passive vascular exercise in the treatment of frostbite [In Italian]. *Gazz. internaz. med. chir., v. 51, Nov. 15, 1942: 251–253.*

The indications for and limitations of passive vascular exercise in the treatment of frostbite are discussed on the basis of experimental and theoretical considerations.

2328. May, E. Treatment of acrocyanosis and of chilblains with fluorescein [In French]. *Bull. Soc. méd. hôp. Paris, v. 57, ser. 3, Mar. 7, 1941: 259–261.*

The successful treatment of acrocyanosis and freezing injuries by the injection of fluorescein is explained on the basis of the photosensitivity which it imparts to the injured tissues. On exposure to light the area of the injury is benefited by the resulting radiation. The author mentions also that the porphyrins are considered to be the physiological photosensitizers, and also that persons having difficulties with porphyrin metabolism are greatly affected by the cold.

---

* Original not seen.

2329. Militsyn, V. A., and P. F. Liūdvinskaiā. Experiences in the treatment of frostbite with ultrahigh-frequency radiation [In Russian]. *Fizioterapia, Moskva, v. 15 (2–3), 1940: 42–52.*

A detailed account of ultrahigh-frequency radiation therapy in 20 cases of frostbite injury is presented. The therapy was applied (for 10 minutes) not only to the injured parts, but also to the corresponding autonomous ganglia (solar plexus, or cervical ganglia) either simultaneously or alternately, first daily then every other day. The author insists on the fact that favorable results can be obtained only by use of the oligothermic technique (very small doses), which elicits no sensation of warmth. At such doses the therapy is able to restore the peripheral and deeper circulation, especially if applied early. The pain is alleviated; the edema disappears very rapidly; in gangrenous conditions the line of demarcation appears much earlier (in about 5 to 15 days), and moist gangrene changes into dry; healing of the wound is rapid and of good quality. Amputations were never higher than metacarpal or metatarsal level. No complications were observed, and the hospital stay was shortened. A much greater number of case histories is necessary in order to draw definite conclusions.

2330. Mogazinik, G. L. Physical therapy of frostbite [In Russian]. *Sovet. vrach. zh., v. 44 (12), 1940: 839–844.*

In the physiotherapy of frostbite injuries, massaging is dangerous and to be rejected in cases of inflammation. The method of rhythmical alternating pressures (within a glass cylinder) improves the blood circulation in the extremity; this therapy, using the "Rhythmohyperem" apparatus, is highly recommended. Warm hydrotherapy is acceptable only in 1st degree injuries; dry-air baths, which induce drying of the tissues and hyperemia, must be used in 2nd and 3rd degree cases. Light-radiation therapy is more effective still if ultra-violet rays are added. Diathermy is incomparable for inducing deep-tissue hyperemia. Ultrahigh-frequency radiations were not tested long enough for definite conclusions, but produced a very favorable impression. In 1st degree cases, the use of daily d'arsonvalization (by close contact) is recommended as early as possible; for pain alleviation the use of the Sollux lamp, warm baths, and massaging, are to be considered. In 2nd and 3rd degree injuries the blisters are to be opened, the part treated in a heated open case (1 or 2 lamps only). Ultra-violet radiations and diathermy (above the injury) are applied from the first day. In more severe 3rd degree cases, Novocain by electrophoresis is applied above the injury. Frostbite complications are best treated by mineral water- and mud-baths. Acclimatization should be employed to prevent chilblains; if injury occurs, treatment should be palliative and local.

2331. Pätzold, J. On the technique of applying short waves to frozen extremities [In German]. *Sitzber. Phys. med. Soz. Erlangen, v. 73, 1943: 102–110.*

The technique for using diathermy in the treatment of frostbite injuries is described in general. Various special procedures are illustrated.

2332. Pichotka, J., and R. B. Lewis. Effect of rapid and prolonged rewarming on local cold injury. *U. S. Armed Forces M. J., v. 2, Sept. 1951: 1293–1310.*

Legs of male albino rabbits were experimentally frozen by immersion in an alcohol bath at $-12\,°C$ or $-15\,°C$ for 30 minutes. Rapid thawing of the leg in water at $42\,°C$ for 5 to 8 minutes almost completely prevented any cutaneous necrosis; spontaneous rewarming in air at room temperature resulted in superficial necrosis of 20% of the legs injured at $-12\,°C$ and of 90% of those at $-15\,°C$. The extent of muscular necrosis was definitely decreased by rapid rewarming but the results were not as striking as were the cutaneous effects. Animals which were rapidly rewarmed exhibited a better general appearance and retained better functioning of the injured leg.

2333. Piontkovskiĭ, I. A. Physiotherapy of frostbite [In Russian]. *Feldsher & akush., 1943 (3): 6–10. Also in: Sovet. med., v. 7 (1), 1943: 9–11.*

In 1st degree frostbite the task of the physiotherapist consists in raising the tonus of the vascular walls, in restoration of the local circulation, acceleration of exudate dispersion, and alleviation of pain. Daily local d'arsonvalization is recommended; application of ultrahigh-frequency produces even more rapid improvement. For pain alleviation and exudate dispersion large hypererythemal doses of ultraviolet rays, local light baths, and Sollux lamp radiation are used. Warm baths, massage, and physical exercise are often helpful. In 2nd degree injuries the vesicles are excised, and the open case method of treatment is applied. In the early phases daily radiations from the Sollux lamp (10–30 minutes) and hypererythemal doses of ultra-violet are used; in the phase of regeneration the doses should be of erythemal or suberythemal level. In 3rd and 4th degree frostbite the best treatment is provided by ultrahigh-frequency radiation applied for 5–10 minutes 2–4 times daily. Hypererythemal doses of ultraviolet rays are helpful after cessation of the ultrahigh-frequency treatment. Anti-tetanus injections are indispensable.

2334. Piontkovskiĭ, I. A., and R. K. IAnoshevskaĩa. Physical methods in the treatment of frostbite [In Russian]. *Moscow, Medgiz, 1944. 19 p.*

This monograph is divided into three main chapters dealing with physical methods in the treatment of frostbite during (1) the pre-reactive stage, (2) the period of reactive inflammation, and (3) the sequelae. In the pre-reactive stage rewarming (local warm baths, dry heat in case of open wounds, ultrahigh-frequency, infrared rays, Sollux lamp, or paraffin therapy) should be combined as soon as possible with massage and exercises for the stimulation of blood circulation. During the reactive stages, in first degree injury, similar therapies are to be used including daily local d'arsonvalization by contact to increase the tonus of the tissues and to alleviate pain. But the method of choice will depend primarily on the predominant clinical symptoms. In 2nd degree injuries, therapy consists of daily Sollux lamp radiations; erythemal doses of ultraviolet radiation applied locally and widely beyond the injury and alternated with irradiation of the reflex segmentary zones (lumbar, or dorso-cervical); similar use of ultrahigh-frequency radiation; ionogalvanization by Novocain or Dionin; and diathermy. In 3rd and 4th degree injuries the use of ultrahigh-frequency radiation helps to alleviate pain, dehydrate the tissues, and accelerate the line of demarcation. Massive doses of ultraviolet rays accelerate the falling off of necrotic tissue, and either type of radiation may help promote epithelization. In the treatment of sequelae, d'arsonvalization, ultraviolet therapy, mud baths, alternating cold (18°–20°C) and hot (38°–42°C) baths are recommended, with individual adjustments being necessary in each case depending on the clinical picture and the progress of the disease.

2335. Ponzio, M. Therapy of wartime freezing injuries [In Italian]. *Minerva med., Tor., anno 31 (v. 2), Dec. 15, 1940: 588–589.*

The efficacy of Marconi therapy used on freezing injuries sustained during Alpine fighting, is stressed.

* 2336. Postnov, A. D., and R. M. Ryskin. Frostbite therapy at health resorts [In Russian]. *Sovet. med., v. 5 (9), 1941: 25–26.*

"*Contains* a report based on 167 cases suffering from trophic ulcerations as result of frostbite. Data are offered on condition of patients before and after cure; types of treatment (mud-baths, electro-mud, quartz-light, etc.), methods of treatment, etc."—Arctic Bibl., v. 4, 1954: 831.

2337. Rivoir, J. Frostbite; frost gangrene and its treatment [In German]. *Mschr. Unfallh., v. 49, Oct. 1942: 295–300.*

Some experiences with frostbitten lower extremities resulting during the Albanian Campaign are discussed. A small portable apparatus is described and pictured which was used for short periods several times a day, in therapy of freezing injuries and frostbite gangrene, to stimulate the circulation of the leg. The apparatus enclosed the injured leg and applied a fluctuating slightly negative and slightly positive pressure, while a bank of light bulbs supplied warmth.

---

* Original not seen.

2338. Röden, S. The treatment of cold injury; experimental studies on the extremities of rabbits. II. The effect of prolonged thawing and warming [In English]. *Acta chir. scand., v. 100 (5), 1950: 515–521.*

The feet of rabbits, experimentally frozen and then allowed to thaw, showed marked edema after reaching about 23 °C in the rewarming. This edema could be checked by cooling below 20 °C, but began again as soon as the feet were rewarmed. Whether rewarming was rapid or slow, from the minimum temperature up to 23 °C, appeared not to have any decisive effect on the starting rate of edema or the final magnitude. However, consequences of cold injury were more severe when rewarming was slow; bloody edema, indicating injuries to capillaries, was found in 80% of the cases.

2339. Rogachevskiĭ, S. L. New apparatus for the treatment of frostbite and burns [In Russian]. *Klin. med., Moskva, v. 20 (7), 1942: 91–92.*

An apparatus for open treatment of frostbite injuries and burns was devised, comprising 18 bispiral heat-lamps with 12% light and 78% heat production. The patients kept the injured part constantly in the treatment chamber; pain disappeared after a few hours and edema after 1–3 days.

2340. Rufanov, I. G. Ultrahigh-frequency current in frostbite [In Russian]. *Feldsher & akush., 1942 (4): 59.*

This medical discussion of the treatment of frostbite is presented in the form of questions and answers. Ultrahigh-frequency currents were used for rapid rewarming of the frostbitten tissue, in order to decrease the possibility of spreading of the edema, to prevent further stasis, and to avoid thrombophlebitis. Furthermore, the therapy has a drying action on the tissue and thus contributes to changing the moist gangrene into dry, limiting the infection. It alleviates severe pain, and favorably influences the metabolism both locally and generally.

2341. Salotti, A. Combined x-ray and short-wave therapy in freezing injury [In Italian]. *Atti Accad. fisiocr. Siena, sez. med. fis., ser. 11, v. 9, Aug. 1941: 166–168.*

It was found that the combined therapy of x-ray and short waves was effective in the treatment of frostbite injuries.

2342. Schiassi, B. Against indecision in the treatment of freezing injuries [In Italian]. *In: Atti Congresso Nazionale di Chirurgia di Guerra, May 24–26, 1942, p. 192. Roma, 1943.*

The author recommends local warm baths in the treatment of freezing injuries. The anatomical elements of the affected region are directly and reflexly stimulated by intensification of the respiration and nutrition, through application of heat.

2343. Shirai, K. Studies on methods of immediate treatment of frostbite. I. [Abstract, in English]. *Jap. J. M. Sc., Biophysics, v. 9, 1944: 7.*

The ears of rabbits were frozen by immersion in a freezing mixture of −10° to −15 °C for 30 to 60 minutes. The most effective treatment for these frostbite injuries of the 3rd degree, was found to be immersion in tepid water. Satisfactory results were also obtained when this treatment was applied to frostbite patients.

2344. Shramchenko, V. V. The use of ultraviolet-ray therapy in surgical cases [In Russian]. *Sovet. med., 1950 (15): 21–23.*

Ultrahigh-frequency radiation therapy has given good results in 13 surgical cases including 3 cases of frostbite. In 2nd degree frostbite this therapy contributed to decreasing the pain, drying up the edema, and diminishing the inflammation. In a number of other surgical cases the radiation therapy was either harmful or without any result. This therapy cannot replace surgical intervention, but only acts as an aid. It must be applied with great care, taking the patient's general condition into consideration.

* 2345.   **Smirnov, I. I., and ... Orlov.** The treatment of congelation cases in evacuation hospitals [In Russian]. *Voen. san. delo, v. 10, 1940: 57–59.* Translation in: E. HOPE. *Frostbite. Translation from the Russian of a collection of sixteen papers published between 1939 and 1944, p. 69–71. Ottawa, Defence Research Board, Canada, 1950.*

A review is given of the treatment, especially that with light-therapy (mercury-quartz lamps and Sollux), of frostbite cases during the Finnish War (1939–1940). Frostbite was of military importance since the percentage of cases which were unfit for further military service as the result of frostbite injuries was three times that for all war casualties.

2346.   **Spadea, ...** Treatment of frostbite [In Italian]. *Clin. nuova, Roma, v. 2, Jan.–Mar. 1946: 123–125.*

This general account of frostbite places emphasis on treatment. The method of rapid rewarming is especially recommended. A clinical classification of the various grades of frostbite is also included.

2347.   **Stefanutti, P.** Variations in technique in the short-wave therapy treatment of frostbite [In Italian]. *Policlinico, sez. prat., v. 48, Apr. 7, 1941: 626–627.* Abstract, in Italian, in: *Minerva med., Tor., anno 32 (v. 1), May 11, 1941: 473.*

In cases of frostbite treated by Marconi therapy, application of the electrodes to the proximal, instead of the distal, end of limbs resulted in quicker relief from pain.

2348.   **Sterzi, G.** X-ray radiation in frostbite of the lower extremities [In Italian]. *Gior. ital. derm. sif., v. 83, 1942: 243–274.*

Indirect x-ray radiation was effective in the treatment of frostbite injuries of 29 soldiers. Clinical history, pathogenesis, and treatment of the cases are reviewed.

2349.   **Stucke, K.** Rapid or slow rewarming for local damage due to cold? [In German]. *Arch. klin. Chir., v. 261 (3–4), 1948: 416–434.*

The fore and hind legs of guinea pigs were frozen solid with ethyl chloride spray; the animals then warmed in the following manners: quickly, by an air current of 60°C; slowly, by being left in a room temperature of 20°C; or by gently massaging of the leg with either fine- or coarse-grained snow. In the first group the mortality was high (40%) and there were cases of deep ulceration; at a room temperature of 20°C, there was necrosis to some extent in 95% of the group and a considerable loss of all or part of the legs but none of the animals died; massage with fine-grained snow gave the best results since no animals died and 43% of the group recovered without loss of tissue.

2350.   **Todoroff, T.** Note on the treatment of freezing injury (frostbite) of the first, second, and third degree with hot dry air [In Italian]. *Policlinico, sez. prat., v. 48, Dec. 22, 1941: 2121–2131.*

The treatment of various grades of frostbite with hot dry air is described. The author found that exposing the injured area to warm dry air at 90°C on the first day of treatment, 110°C on the second, and 130°C on the third day resulted in more rapid formation of granulation tissue.

2351.   **Varshaver, G. S.** [The treatment of frostbite and its sequelae] [In Russian]. *In: Trudy 2-go plenuma Gospital'nogo Soveta Narkomzdrava SSSR, Dec. 20–25, 1942, p. 278–280. Moskva, Medgiz, 1943.*

For proper results through physiotherapy a strict differentiation of the therapeutical measures is necessary. For action on the mesenchyme the electrical ultrahigh-frequency field and

* Original not seen.

long-wave-radiation energy is best; for the stimulation of epithelization ultraviolet rays are indispensable. In the pre-reaction period, ultrahigh-frequency electrical treatment at weak thermal doses induces deep tissue warming and accelerates blood circulation. In 1st degree injuries, ultraviolet rays should be applied in doses increasing at each session (5–10–15 average biodoses); d'arsonvalization stimulates the tonus of the peripheral vessels and local circulation. In 2nd degree injuries, after surgery, ultrahigh-frequency electrical therapy at oligothermal doses will alleviate pain and reduce the edema. For best results this therapy should be applied both locally and segmentally (at the lumbar or the dorsal neck region). In 3rd and 4th degree injuries, ultrahigh-frequency electrical therapy at oligothermal doses should be applied as early as possible after surgery. This accelerates the formation of dry necrosis and of the demarcation zone, and promotes mummification and granulation. In this last stage, ultraviolet ray therapy at the site of injury at large doses and with 2–3 day intervals is indicated. With the beginning of epithelization, application of erythemal doses to the distal healthy skin as well as to the site of injury, is very important. Mud-turf and paraffin treatments are widely applied, especially in protracted and sluggishly-healing cases. Simple exercises of hands or feet will stimulate blood circulation. Circulatory impairment persisting even after clinical healing will necessitate continued physical exercises for body hardening to avoid further oversusceptibility to cold injuries.

* **2352. Verbov, A. F.** Physiotherapy in frostbite. *Vest. khir., v. 60, Aug. 1940: 86.*

"*Contains* a brief abstract of a report to the Leningrad Conference of Workers of Evacuation Hospitals and Specialist Sections of Hospitals and Institutes (May 25–27, 1940). Author used alternately ultra-frequent electric fields and ultra-violet rays in frostbite. The fact is stressed that physiotherapeutic methods applied to frostbite are neither specific nor universal."— Arctic Bibl., v. 4, 1954: 1119.

2353. Volodinskiĭ, I. A. [The treatment of frostbite and its sequelae] [In Russian]. *In: Trudy 2-go plenuma Gospital'nogo Soveta Narkomzdrava SSSR, Dec. 20–25, 1942, p. 271. Moskva, Medgiz, 1943.*

At a hospital in Sverdlovsk good healing results (up to 95%) were obtained by the application of mud therapy, using the mud of lake Karachi, which is rich in hydrogen sulfide, and by mineral baths (radio-active carbonic acid and calcium). The baths are said to aid in accelerating the disappearance of pain, edema, and the formation of a demarcation zone. They stimulate circulation, normalize the nervous tonus, and influence metabolism (by stimulating the appearance of organic metabolites). Active surgical intervention, together with active physiotherapy and balneotherapy, gave the best results in complicated frostbite cases.

2354. Zal'kindson, E. T. Physiotherapy in frostbite [In Russian]. *In: Fizio-terapiia povrezhdenii voennogo vremeni, p. 61–76. Leningrad, Narkomzdrav SSSR, 1943.*

According to Kuprianov, frostbite casualties during the Finnish War (1939–1940) were 8.13% of all the medical casualties, of which, according to Tragarzha, frostbite of the feet occurred in 67%, hands 20%, hands and feet 12%. The pathological aspects of frostbite are described. The following physiotherapeutical measures are recommended: In 1st degree frostbite, arsonvalization by spark for 5–6 minutes daily was indicated as giving best results, and as quickly alleviating pain. Light-baths and Sollux rays were of no avail, since the damage was of neurovascular nature. In 2nd degree injuries the basic method consisted of ultraviolet irradiation, daily or on alternate days; the radiation was applied also above the injury to the lower third of the skin or forearm. Vesicles were excised, the injured part treated with antiseptic, and then covered with Vishnevskiĭs, ointment. After 1 or 2 days the dressing was removed and the open treatment was used. Special attention has to be directed to careful cleansing in warm water baths. This double treatment gave rapid results. In 3rd degree injuries ultraviolet rays and ultrahigh-frequency radiation therapies were applied, in combination with the open method of treatment and use of warm water baths. In cases of considerable edema, Vishnevskiĭ's circular Novocain block was indicated, and surgical incisions were necessary.

---

* Original not seen.

2355. Zherdin, I. V. Ultrahigh-frequency radiation in treatment of frostbite [In Russian]. *Fizioterapia, Moskva, 1941 (1): 41–45.*

Clinical data were collected from 84 patients on the influence of ultrahigh-frequency radiation of frostbite. Results from irradiation (over a 15 minute period) were favorable in a very large majority of cases, consisting in alleviation of pain, decrease of edema, rapid diminution of purulation, and improvement in the mobility of the extremity. In 3rd degree frostbite, ultrahigh-frequency radiation therapy contributes to the development of dry necrosis and of rapid granulation. This therapy gives no guarantee against permanent residual effects such as cyanosis, melanosis, trophic disturbances, and limited mobility. It may be recommended as one of the helpful auxillary methods of treatment in frostbite.

See also items: 545, 577, 580, 585, 1016, 1559, 1570, 1572, 1607, 1615, 1669, 1680, 1890, 1944, 2005, 2010, 2099, 2111, 2113, 2116, 2622, 2729.

11. Therapy, Chemotherapy

2356. Ambrose, A. M., D. J. Robbins, and F. Deeds. Effect of rutin and related compounds on experimental frostbite in rabbits [Abstract]. *Fed. Proc., Balt., v. 9, Mar. 1950: 254.*

Experiments with rutin showed it to be effective in treatment of experimental frostbite as had been shown by Fuhrman and Crismon (item 2378). Treatment with other flavins (quercitrin, quercetin, methyl hesperidin chalcone, 2-3-dihydroqeurcetin, and an extract of muscat raisin seeds) seemed to offer some benefits when compared with the untreated controls. With this treatment, injury to the frozen foot was confined chiefly to the toes with partial to complete loss of phalanges and, in a few cases, to scarring of the dorsum.

2357. Andrews, M. C. Frostbite. *Brit. M. J., 1941 (v. 1), May 17: 763–764.*

The author stresses the importance of avoiding infection in frostbite. He recommends that blisters be left intact and painted with a 1:1000 solution of acriflavine, dusted with antiseptic powder, and covered with cotton.

2358. Becker, J. Remarks on freezing injury and its treatment [In German]. *Med. Klin., Berl., v. 39, Oct. 1, 1943: 679–680.*

The surgical and medicinal treatment of severe freezing injuries is described. Wet gangrene is treated with zinc, vaseline, or borate salve, and dry gangrene with sulfonamide preparations. The amputation process is described.

2359. Bologna, R. Folliculin therapy of freezing injuries [In Italian; summaries in Italian, German, French, and English]. *Ormoni, v. 4, Apr. 1942: 125–128.*

Favorable therapeutic results were obtained in 30 cases of freezing injuries of 1st and 2nd degree by the local application of folliculin pomade to the skin of the injured area. Absorption of the pomade by the skin brought about a vasodilatory action.

2360. Brack, W. On the treatment of frostbite with Priscol [In German]. *Schweiz. med. Wschr., v. 71, Dec. 13, 1941: 1559–1560.*

This is a note on the technique of administering Priscol (benzylimidazoline hydrochloride) in cases of frostbite.

2361. Brambel, C. E., and F. F. Loker. Application of dicoumarin (3,3'-methylene-bis-[4-hydroxycoumarin]) in trauma and gangrene. *Arch. Surg., v. 48, Jan. 1944: 1–16.*

A clinical study on the value of dicoumarin in the treatment of various types of gangrene and trauma. In addition to cases of crush injury, and diabetic and arteriosclerotic gangrene, a case of frostbite was treated. The extension of gangrene in this case was checked and amputation was not required.

2362. Brauner, H. Frostbite medications [Abstract, in German]. *Wien. med. Wschr.*, v. 96, Nov. 1, 1946: 439.

A number of prescriptions for ointments and tinctures to be applied to areas of frostbite injury are presented with special reference to the availability of the substances at the moment of writing [post-World War II]. If the injured part presents no open wound, a skin-stimulating tincture can be used, followed by ointment application. If the wound is open, tinctures of Peruvian balsam, Ichthyol, collodium elasticum, tannin, etc., are to be applied. It is recommended that more ointments than tinctures be used.

2363. Brover, B. I. Early treatment of frostbite with astringents in combination with an exposed method [In Russian]. *Vrach. delo*, v. 23 (2), 1941: 101–102.

A series of frostbite cases was successfully treated during the Finnish war by a modified method of tanning in combination with the open-case treatment. After washing with alcohol and careful excision of the epidermis around the vesicles, the injured area was sprayed 3–4 times with a 5% solution of potassium permanganate, and 5 minutes later it was sprayed twice with a 10% silver nitrate solution. The surface was soon covered with a black scab. The sprayings were repeated 4–5 times daily for several days, then 2–3 times daily, until a new epidermis appeared underneath the sloughing off scab. For control purposes, in several cases of bilateral injury, the tanning method was used on one extremity, and an ointment dressing (2% Rivanol, 5% boric acid) on the other, after excision of the vesicles. In every case the tanning method proved superior, both by its therapeutical efficacy and because of the shorter duration of the healing process. In the presence of gangrene, the tanning has to be continued until appearance of a clearly defined demarcation zone. This demarcation is accelerated, and humid gangrene is changed into dry. Infection is avoided (if the vesicles are excised). A triple anti-tetanus injection and, eventually, anti-gangrenous injections are nevertheless indispensable.

2364. Buckreuss, F. On the treatment of peripheral circulatory disturbances [In German]. *Med. Welt*, v. 15, July 19, 1941: 736–739.

The use of Priscol (a benzylimidazoline derivative) by this author gave excellent results in cases of 3rd degree frostbite.

2365. Bucur, A. I. Frostbite treatment with injections of hypertonic sodium chloride solutions [In Rumanian]. *România med.*, v. 16, Jan. 15, 1938: 18–19.

The author notes the prevalence of freezing injuries in wartime. He discusses the therapy of frostbite injuries, especially by injections of hypertonic sodium chloride solution, with reference to military problems.

2366. Bumm, E. On the question of methods of accelerating the blood flow [In German]. *Deut. med. Wschr.*, v. 75, Dec. 1, 1950: 1627–1629.

Injections of the vasodilator drug, "Dilatol," are recommended in cases of frostbite of the lower extremities. The drug abolishes the circulatory stasis and may prevent gangrene.

2367. Chiurco, G. A. Rules for biological vitamin treatment in the recovery from war injuries and frostbite [In Italian]. *Atti Accad. fisiocr. Siena, sez. med. fis.*, v. 9, ser. 11, Aug. 1941: 170–192.

The use of vitamins applied locally to wounds is reviewed. In frostbite, vitamins A and D derived from fish-liver oils were incorporated into a salve and applied to the lesions. In 1–2 weeks the wound began to granulate and healed rapidly.

2368. Choi, C., and D. Pak. Effect of nicotinic acid on dermatitis congelationis. *Urol. Cutan. Rev.*, v. 52, Aug. 1948: 483–487.

Administration of nicotinic acid or nicotinic acid amide was used successfully in the treatment of injuries from cold, including second degree frostbite injuries, chronic frostbite, and recurrent pernio. This treatment was especially effective in relieving the subjective symptoms of burning, pain, and itching. It is assumed that it acts to improve capillary tonus.

2369. Degos, R., P. Grenet, and P. Bouygues. Delayed hemorrhagic frostbite blister; cutaneous lesions and neuritic pain, rapidly ameliorated by vitamin B_1 [In French]. *Bull. Soc. fr. derm. syp.*, v. 48, Feb. 13, 1941: 124–126.

The authors found that large doses of vitamin B_1 would successfully relieve neuritic pain in frostbite and hasten the healing of cutaneous lesions. A detailed report is made of a case history of a patient where severe hemorrhagic blisters of the feet arose 10 days after cold exposure and were successfully treated by administration of vitamin B_1.

2370. Ekholm, E. On the treatment of burns and freezing injuries [In Swedish]. *Sven. läk. tidn.*, v. 39, May 15, 1942: 1311–1313.

Burns and frostbite lesions were treated in the same manner, by the application of 0.5% Chloramine solution to the lesions by means of a compress which was kept wet with the solution. Serous exudation of any quantity occurred only for a day or two, and in 5–7 days good scar formation had occurred.

2371. Eyssautier, ..., and H. M. Gattefossé. Physico-chemical modifications of skin following frostbite [In French]. *J. med. Lyon*, v. 21, Apr. 5, 1940: 122–123.

Physico-chemical studies of the skin at the site of frostbite lesions of the foot indicated that there is a direct relationship between hydrogen-ion concentration, oxidation-reduction potential, and rate of healing in the lesions. Frostbite lesions treated with an acid cream of pH 6.5 showed a return to normal pH with an improved circulation.

2372. Feltström, E. On the treatment of acute frostbite [In Swedish]. *Sven. läk. tidn.*, v. 40, Jan. 8, 1943: 26–29.

In frozen fingers and toes, vascular spasm is removed by spraying with a 1% Novocain solution, not containing Adrenalin. A few minutes after the spraying, the limb became red and warm again, and free of pain.

2373. Ferrari, S. Results and considerations concerning the therapy of freezing injuries by means of injections of milk protein [In Italian]. *Boll. Soc. med. chir. Modena*, v. 42, 1941: 443–454.

A comparison is made of the treatment of a group of about 200 patients—with various degrees of freezing injuries of the lower limbs—with Marconi therapy or with milk protein-shock therapy. Good results were reported for both methods but the results with protein-shock therapy were better and much more rapidly obtained. In addition the treatment had the advantage of ease of administration and of being applicable to front-line use.

2374. Ferraro, D. Treatment of severe frostbite with air therapy and pulverized Thioseptal [In Italian]. *Forze san.*, Roma, v. 10, Nov. 30, 1941: 22–23.

Treatment of cases of severe frostbite are reported. The author recommends exposing the injured areas to cool air, dusting the area with "Thioseptal" powder, and administering vitamin B_1 to the patient by injection.

2375. Fishman, J. Treatment of frostbite. Report of a case. *U. S. Armed Forces M. J.*, v. 2, June 1951: 957.

A patient's severe, ulcerative, condition of the legs, of several years duration following frostbite, responded immediately to Priscoline (benzazoline hydrochloride) therapy. Six months after discontinuing the treatment, the patient was still symptom-free.

2376. Frommel, E., and J. Piquet. Therapy of freezing injuries, can it give us the key to pathogenesis? Treatment with belladonna (antiacetylcholinic), with the chlorhydrate of dimethylaminoethylbenzylaniline (antihistaminic), with the chlorhydrate of histidine (antiacetylcholinic and antihistaminic), and with a combination of atropine and chlorhydrate of dimethylaminoethylbenzylaniline. II. [In French]. *Arch. internat. pharm dyn., Par., v. 73 (1-2), 1946: 96-105.*

The upper portions of the hind legs of guinea pigs were frozen with dry ice and later the animals were given various antihistaminic and antiacetylcholinic drugs by subcutaneous injection. The injections were continued for 18 days and the progress of healing of the lesions from freezing, was observed. The authors conclude that dimethylaminoethylbenzylaniline is without doubt the medication of choice, with histidine judged to be next best. These results obtained with antihistaminic drugs, they feel, argue in favor of the pathogenic role of histamine.

2377. Fuhrman, F. A. The effect of rutin in experimental frostbite [Abstract]. *Fed. Proc., Balt., v. 7, Mar. 1948: 38.*

Rabbits subjected to experimental frostbite (exposure of clipped hind feet for 3 minutes to −55°C) were treated with rutin. Several rabbits received the drug before freezing. Time for the appearance of wet gangrene was significantly greater than in untreated controls. Tissue loss was much less in rutin-treated rabbits than in controls. The effect of rutin may be the result of an altered pattern of local blood flow.

2378. Fuhrman, F. A., and J. M. Crismon. Studies on gangrene following cold injury. IX. The effect of rutin and other chemical agents on the course of experimental frostbite in rabbits. *J. Clin. Invest., v. 27, May 1948: 364-371.*

The effectiveness of chemical agents in preventing gangrene after severe cold injury, was studied. Rutin was effective in restricting the loss of tissue from gangrene following frostbite.

* 2379. Genkin, R. L., and IA. F. Levin. Clinical consideration, classification, and treatment of frostbite [In Russian]. *Sovet. med., 1943 (11-12): 12-15.* Translation in: E. HOPE. *Frostbite. Translations from the Russian of a collection of sixteen papers published between 1939 and 1944, p. 33-39.* Ottawa, Defence Research Board, Canada, 1950.

Frostbite lesions are divided into four grades on the basis of clinical findings and pathological anatomy. The conditions of each degree are detailed and the treatment recommended includes the use of a 5% tannic alcohol solution or a 5% methylene blue solution.

2380. Gerlach, ... On the treatment of local frostbite [In German]. *Zbl. Chir., v. 70, Sept. 11, 1943: 1337-1340.*

Report is made of the treatment of cases of frostbite in the German Army on the Eastern front during the winter campaigns of 1941-42 and 1942-43. Injections of fever-producing substances, or pyrifers, as well as Euphylline and Eupaverin were used with success on a majority of the mild cases.

2381. Giordanengo, G. The treatment of late pain in frostbite [In Italian]. *Gazz. med. ital., v. 100, Dec. 1941: 379-383.*

This is a discussion of the problem of late pain in various grades of frostbite injury and their treatment by injections of histamine.

2382. Giugni, F. Some notes on the therapy of frostbite [In Italian]. *Policlinico, sez. prat., v. 48, June 16, 1941: 1074-1082.*

The hypodermic injection of milk (protein therapy) in 1st and 2nd degree frostbite was found to give good therapeutic results.

---

* Original not seen.

2383. Giugni, F. Frostbite and hypothermia [In Italian]. *In: Atti Congresso Nazionale di Chirurgia di Guerra, May 24–26, 1942, p. 188–189. Roma, 1943.*

Frostbite injuries of 1st and 2nd degree were treated by injections of milk as a foreign protein. This produced a fever, diminished pain, and caused numbness in the feet and the disappearance of edema and cyanosis.

2384. Goecke, C. A. On the treatment of frostbite with a sulfonamide [In German]. *Münch. med. Wschr., v. 89, June 12, 1942: 542–543.*

The effectiveness of local sulfonamide treatment (Marfanyl-prontalbin powder) was compared with cod-liver-oil ointment and with open treatment without dressings in a large series of 2nd and 3rd degree frostbite. The sulfa drug was found to promote more rapid healing, reduce offensive odor, eliminate danger of secondary infection, and shorten convalescence. No amputations were required and no side effects were noted.

2385. Golimari, E. Contribution to emergency treatment of freezing injuries [In Italian]. *In: Atti Congresso Nazionale di Chirurgia di Guerra, May 24–26, 1942, p. 240–241. Roma, 1943.*

The author recommends for treatment of 3rd degree freezing injury, a salve consisting of picric acid, camphor, histamine, cod-liver oil, and lanoline or vaseline. Camphor is a vasodilator, picric acid an antiseptic, cod-liver oil a vitamin A and D material, and vaseline a base. Histamine is a capillary dilator. The results obtained showed that the necrotic lesions healed very quickly under the influence of this salve.

* 2386. Gol'shmid, K. L., and M. F. Merezhinskiĭ. Topical treatment of frostbite with vitamins [In Russian]. *Sovet. med., 1940 (13–14): 16–18.* Translation in: E. Hope. *Frostbite. Translations from the Russian of a collection of sixteen papers publisted between 1939 and 1944, p. 74–78. Ottawa, Defence Research Board, Canada, 1950.*

A vitamin ointment containing 35–45% lanolin, 10–15% wax, 30–35% fish oil, and the remaining % of Vaseline, was found to be effective in speeding up the regenerative processes in cases of frostbite.

2387. Grätz, H. On the treatment of freezing injuries and poorly-healing wounds [In German]. *Wien med. Wschr., v. 92, Mar. 21, 1942: 215.*

In 12 cases of freezing injuries where there was slow healing of the lesions, a salve known as "Detoxin" (a high molecular ketarin hydrolysate) was used successfully. Severe itching ceased, and the bluish-red coloration of the wound disappeared.

2388. Grosse-Brockhoff, F. Pathological physiology and therapy of severe supercooling [In German]. *Med. Welt, v. 17, Apr. 24, 1943: 360–361.*

The author summarizes the work done by himself and a co-worker, on the pathology of experimental freezing injuries of dogs. Lobeline and Coramine were used in treatment.

* 2389. Grubina, S. A. On treating frostbite with carotene. *Vest. khir., v. 60 (1–2), Aug. 1940: 87.*

"*Contains* an abstract of a report presented before the Leningrad Conference of Workers of Evacuation Hospitals and Specialist Sections of Hospitals and Institutes (May 25–27, 1940). Author had good results with third- and especially second-degree frostbite when carotene (dissolved in oil) was applied to the injured areas; it appears to stimulate epithelization and in some cases has an analgesic effect; it can be applied on any stage of evacuation. Bibliography."—Arctic Bibl., v. 4, 1954: 362.

---

* Original not seen.

2390. Heyse, W. Treatment of freezing injury with Cyrene salve [In German]. *Fortsch. Ther.*, v. 17, July 1941: 230–232. Abstract, in German, in: *Praxis, Bern*, v. 31, Apr. 23, 1942: 302.

The application of Cyren salve in cases of 1st degree frostbite caused a reduction of swelling and redness and full recovery of sensibility in 1 to 1½ days; in 2nd degree cases, necrotic parts were found to heal in half the time (6 days instead of 12).

2391. Holmes, T. W., Jr. Modern concepts in the treatment of frostbite, with the presentation of a case successfully treated with tetraethylammonium. *Bull. Alexander Blain Hosp.*, v. 7, Feb. 1948: 12–18.

Report of a case of frostbite successfully treated with tetraethylammonium chloride. Healing was rapid, painless, and complete. Blood vessels were fully dilated during treatment. A review of the literature on the use of anticoagulants and sympathectomy precedes the case history.

2392. Hurley, L. A., J. E. Roberts, A. R. Buchanan, and G. Tillquist. Preliminary investigation of the value of the dihydrogenated alkaloids of ergot in the treatment of experimental frostbite. *Surg. Gyn. Obst.*, v. 92, Mar. 1951: 303–308.

Report is made of experiments on the effects of injections of a mixture of 3 dihydrogenated alkaloids of ergot administered to a total of 60 rats whose tails had been subjected to freezing. A group of 10 animals received no therapy and 10 received injections of heparin in addition to the dihydrogenated alkaloids. Loss of tails was less in the treated groups, owing to release of vasconstriction, and it was concluded that the dihydrogenated alkaloids of ergot might prove valuable in frostbite therapy, especially in high-altitude frostbite. The improvement in the group receiving both heparin and the dihydrogenated alkaloids was thought to be the effect of the vasodilator and not of the anticoagulant.

2393. J., F. Action of the follicular hormone on freezing injury and its after effects [Abstract, In Italian]. *Policlinico, sez. prat.*, v. 49, Sept. 14, 1942: 1300–1301.

Local use of progynon in balsam, alternated with intramuscular injection of progynon every 3 or 4 days, gave good results in the treatment of 12 soldiers affected with various types of freezing injuries. There was a notable diminution of pain; considerable less edematous formation; the line of demarcation between living and necrotic tissue evolved more quickly; and the necrotic areas sloughed and tissue repair began more quickly than with other treatments.

2394. Jannarone, G. On the subject of therapy in lesions of freezing (efficiency of vitamin C) [In Italian]. *Forze san., Roma*, v. 10, Nov. 30, 1941: 20–21.

Vitamin C, either injected or applied locally in a salve, proved valuable in the treatment of frostbite injuries.

2395. Jean, S. Autohemotherapy in the treatment of sequelae of cold injury; various considerations and personal remarks [In Italian]. *Gazz. med. ital.*, v. 100, Dec. 1941: 366–379.

An account is given of the author's experience in the treatment of late-stage frostbite injury and its sequelae. A method of treatment is described, known as "blood grafting", which uses the patient's own blood.

2396. Kal'chenko, I. I. [The treatment of frostbite and its sequelae] [In Russian]. *In: Trudy 2-go plenuma Gospital'nogo Soveta Narkomzdrava SSSR, Dec. 20–25, 1942, p. 272–273. Moskva, Medgiz, 1943.*

Experiences gathered in the North and during an arctic expedition have shown that frostbite injuries necessitate various methods of treatment in order to preserve the extremity from amputation and to alleviate severe pain. In the treatment of spontaneous gangrene, intra-venous injections of 60–80 cc of 10% sodium chloride induced an increase of 2°–3°C in the skin temperature of the injured part and created a burning sensation in the previously in-sensitive extremity. Warm baths (first at 37°–38°C for 20–30 minutes, then increasing in warmth each day) were given daily in all degrees of frostbite injuries. The NaCl injections were given after the baths. On the first 2 days 30–40 cc were given with the amount increased gradually to 120 cc, with an interval without treatment every third day, over a period of 1½ to 2 months. The diet was rich in carbohydrates and brewer's yeast. Pain was soon alleviated, or disappeared completely. In 28 cases with severe 3rd degree injuries not one amputation became necessary.

In experiments with rabbits half of the group were given an injection with a 5% sodium chloride solution after which all the rabbits had one ear frozen experimentally. The animals given the saline solution either sustained no permanent frostbite injury or only a dry necrosis of the ear tips while all the control animals sustained injuries. However, a preliminary injection with alcohol or being put into a narcotic state, brought about injuries greater than those to the controls and usually resulted in the deaths of the animals.

2397. Kappert, A. Treatment with intra-arterial injections [In German; sum-maries in German, French, Italian, and English]. *Helvet. med. acta, Series A, v. 15 (1), 1948: 25–41.*

The author discusses the indications for intra-arterial injection of various substances— such as Novocain, Priscol, acetylcholine, embran, dihydroergotamine (DHE45), and a combination of nicotinic acid and nicotinic acid amide—especially for the relief of arterial spasms including those resulting from cold injury. He also has successfully used calcium in this manner and presents several case histories.

* 2398. Kevork'ĩan, A. A. On the treatment of frostbite; preliminary report [In Russian]. *Voen. san. delo, 1941 (11): 57–88.* Translation in: E. HOPE. *Frostbite. Translations from the Russian of a collection of sixteen papers published between 1939 and 1944, p. 72–73. Ottawa, Defence Research Board, Canada, 1950.*

The author recommends the use of a 3%–5% alcoholic solution of menthol in the treat-ment of 2nd and 3rd degree frostbite. This results in the elimination of pain, reduction of edema, improvement in skin color, reduction in amount of discharge, and acceleration of the wound-healing process.

2399. Killian, H., H. Voight, R. Hemmer, and E. Koch. Fever therapy of frost injury, along with a contribution on the circulatory effect of artificial fever [In German, with English summary]. *Deut. Gesundhwes., v. 1, Mar. 31; Apr. 15; Apr. 30, 1946: 129–132; 176–183; 206–209.*

This detailed study is based on clinical and experimental data on the use of fever-inducing substances such as "Pyrifer" (a sterile suspension of *Bacterium coli*), in the treatment of cold injuries. The authors report encouraging results.

2400. Konosevich, M. A. Concerning the treatment of frostbite injuries and burns [In Russian]. *Feldsher & akush., 1945 (1): 55–56.*

For treatment of frostbite and burns the author suggests that the permanganate solution be replaced with a 15% solution of tincture of iodine. In cases of 1st degree frostbite or burns the area is to be painted with iodine 2–3 times a day. Vesicles should be excised and dried before-hand. In very extensive injuries only one-third of the surface should be treated at a time. In cases of gangrene, while waiting for the appearance of the demarcation line, application of 40% Ichthyol ointment on top of the iodine is very useful; quite often the gangrene recedes after such a treatment. Streptocide or "Sulfidin" taken internally is helpful. In 1st and 2nd

---

* Original not seen.

degree frostbite and burns a combined treatment including artificial sunlight is useful. In 3rd degree cases the Ichthyol has to be covered by a dressing of cotton. The author opposes early amputation. During one winter there were no deaths because of gangrene, among those treated at the hospital mentioned by the author, after this type of treatment.

2401. Kovanov, V. V. Treatment of burns and frostbite with "ammargen" [In Russian]. *Sovet. med., 1940 (3): 21–22.*

Treatment in 12 cases of burns and 4 cases of frostbite consisted essentially in daily washing of the injury with "ammargen" (ammonium solution of silver salts) and "ammargen" compresses (1:40,000 solution). The compresses were covered with black paper and bandaged. Before its removal, the old bandage was moistened with the warmed solution to make the procedure painless. In two cases of 2nd degree and one case of 3rd degree injury (with involvement of the tendons and bone in the latter instance) the breaking down of the necrotic tissues was greatly accelerated and new granulation tissue appeared rapidly; epithelization, in 3rd degree frostbite, appeared on the 8th day. Pain and itching were diminished. The results were superior to those obtained after using potassium permanganate.

2402. Läwen, A. Clinical remarks on frostbite gangrene of the feet [In German]. *Deut. med. Wschr., v. 70, Mar. 3, 1944: 141.*

Gangrenous conditions of the feet following frostbite were treated using Padutin, Priscol, Eupaverin, and papaverin. Also a Novocain block of the sympathetic nervous system was used.

2403. Landini, U. On the treatment of frostbite with Adisole salve [In Italian]. *Boll. Accad. med. pistoiese, v. 14, Dec. 1941: 171–176.*

The author reports that 72 cases of 2nd or 3rd degree frostbite healed quickly when treated with Adisole (tunny-liver-oil salve).

2404. Lange, K., and L. J. Boyd. The functional pathology of experimental frostbite and the prevention of subsequent gangrene. *Surg. Gyn. Obst., v. 80, Apr. 1945: 346–350.*

The pathological physiology of frostbite was studied in rabbits, using the fluorescein technique. The circulation in a frozen area is completely stopped but is restored within 6 to 16 hours after exposure. This is the most favorable period for therapeutic measures, especially the administration of anticoagulants such as heparin. In 14 cases of human frostbite it was possible to predict the extent of tissue damage to be expected by means of the fluorescein test. Heparin was not used in these cases. It is suggested, however, that results comparable to those in experimental animals should be obtainable in human frostbite injuries.

2405. Lange, K., and L. J. Boyd. The functional pathology of experimental frostbite and the prevention of subsequent gangrene. *Bull. N. York Acad. M., v. 21, Aug. 1945: 441.*

Studies were made of tissue alteration following experimental frostbite in rabbits and in human volunteers. Heparin injected into 16 rabbits during the period of circulatory restoration after freezing, prevented gangrene. Similar results were obtained with human volunteers.

2406. Lange, K., L. J. Boyd, and L. Loewe. The functional pathology of frostbite and the prevention of gangrene in experimental animals and humans. *Science, v. 102, Aug. 10, 1945: 151–152.*

This is a preliminary note on the pathogenesis of experimental frostbite in rabbits and human volunteers. The fluorescein test and the use of heparinization for the prevention of gangrene is discussed. The successful clinical use of heparin therapy in a case of frostbite is also described.

2407. Lange, K., and L. Loewe. Subcutaneous heparin in the Pitkin menstruum for the treatment of experimental human frostbite. *Surg. Gyn. Obst., v. 82, Mar. 1946: 256–260.*

Eight human volunteers subjected to localized experimental frostbite were treated with heparin in Pitkin's menstruum. No loss of tissue resulted, although control lesions, untreated, showed central necrosis.

2408. Lange, K., D. Weiner, and L. J. Boyd. Frostbite; physiology, pathology and therapy. *N. England J. M., v. 237, Sept. 11, 1947: 383–389.*

The physiology and pathology of experimental and clinical frostbite are described as a basis for a more rational approach to therapy. Evidence is shown that the gangrene after frostbite is due to capillary occlusion by red-blood-cell sludge. It was found that heparinization prevented such occlusion in frostbitten rabbits. Two human cases of frostbite severe enough to have produced gangrene were treated with heparin. No loss of tissue resulted.

2409. Lange, K., L. J. Boyd, and D. Weiner. Prerequisites of successful heparinization to prevent gangrene after frostbite. *Proc. Soc. Exp. Biol., N. Y., v. 74, 1950, 1–4.*

Conditions essential to success in heparin therapy are discussed. It is noted that prevention of gangrene requires continuous uninterrupted prolongation of the coagulation time by the administration of heparin for at least 5 days.

2410. Larrizza, P. The local use of follicular ointment in the treatment of first and second degree frostbite [In Italian]. *Minerva med., Tor., anno 32, (v. 2), Sept. 21, 1941: 309–311.*

A follicular hormone salve was successfully used in the treatment of mild frostbite.

2411. Lee, W. Y. Chemotherapy in frostbite; case report. *Am. J. Surg., v. 68, Apr. 1945: 113–115.*

In a case of severe frostbite, infection was successfully controlled by the use of allantoin-sulfanilamide ointment in a non-greasy water-miscible base. The frostbitten hand was saved.

2412. Lempke, R. E., and H. B. Shumacker, Jr. Studies in experimental frostbite. VIII. Treatment with ACTH. *Angiology, v. 2, Oct. 1951: 340–344.*

Experiments indicated that treatment with ACTH did not reduce the incidence or extent of gangrene following freezing of the feet in mice and rats. It was concluded that its use in frostbite would not reduce tissue loss.

2413. Lewis, R. B., and E. Freytag. Use of cortisone in treatment of experimental frostbite. *Proc. Soc. Exp. Biol., N. Y., v. 77, Aug. 1951: 816–817.*

Cortisone was not effective in reducing the extent of muscle or skin necrosis of the legs of rabbits which had been immersed in a cold bath at temperatures of −12°C or −15°C for a period of 30 minutes.

2414. Linberg, B. E. Anti-reticular cytotoxic serotherapy of frostbite and war wounds [In Russian]. *Sovet. med., 1943 (1): 4–5.* Also, in English, in: *Am. Rev. Soviet M., v. 1, Dec. 1943: 124–129.*

Good results were obtained from the treatment of frostbite with anti-reticular cytotoxic serum. The treatment was applied to cases undergoing ultraviolet radiotherapy although some cases received serum alone. Cases treated with serum showed more improvement than cases not so treated.

2415. Livraga, P. Neuro-arthralgic syndrome of freezing injury in combatants treated with vitamin B₁ [In Italian]. *In: Atti Congresso Nazionale di Chirurgia di Guerra, May 24–26, 1942, p. 224. Roma, 1943.*

Vitamin B₁ used parenterally in large doses (amount not stated) alleviates the painful suffering of patients having the neuro-arthralgic syndrome as a result of freezing injuries.

2416. Loewe, L., K. Lange, and P. Rosenblatt. Heparin in the treatment of experimental human frostbite. *Bull. N. York Acad., M., v. 21, Aug. 1945: 442.*

The effect of early heparinization was tested on human volunteers subjected to experimental frostbite. The controls showed necrosis of the injured area, while only superficial damage was sustained by the heparinized subjects.

2417. Loewe, L., L. Berger, and R. Lasser. The prevention of thromboembolism. *Angiology, v. 2, Feb. 1951: 26–45.*

Treatment with repository heparin of thromboangiitis obliterans, diabetic atherosclerosis, endarteritis obliterans and frostbite, is suggested.

2418. Lombardo, C. On the treatment of frostbite lesions with tunny-liver oil [In Italian]. *Rinasc. med., v. 19, Feb. 15, 1942: 67–68.*

Adisole (tunny-liver oil) combined with an anesthetic or a sulfonamide preparation was found to be specific in the treatment of frostbite necrosis.

2419. Luetkens, U. The conservative treatment of frostbite [In German]. *Deut. Zschr. Chir., v. 258, Sept. 3, 1943: 293–300.*

The author emphasizes the necessity for conservative treatment of the more severe forms of frostbite especially where damage is still reversible. Bathing of the injured areas with copper sulfate is recommended since, with this method, surprising amounts of tissue have been recovered.

2420. Luetkens, U. On frostbite [In German]. *Münch. med. Wschr., v. 91, Feb. 25, 1944: 87–88.*

Report is made on cases of frostbite treated with copper sulfate and sulfonamide powder.

2421. Manganotti, G. Observations and studies on the process of epithelization of skin wounds through injury and freezing [In Italian]. *Atti Accad. Fisiocr. Siena, v. 9, ser. 11, Aug. 1941: 192–204.*

The physiological processes of epithelization are discussed. The author recommends the antiseptic protection of the epithelium and the stimulation of the healing process by administration of vitamins and hormones.

2422. Maragliano, O. The therapeutic action of fly larvae extract on chronic osteomyelitis and early ulcerative processes [In Italian]. *Accad. med., Genova, v. 56, Jan. 1941: 6–11.*

"Larvasan" (extract of fly larvae) was found to be effective in stopping ulcerative processes in cases of 2nd and 3rd degree frostbite.

2423. Markowski, B. Contribution to the clinical aspects and treatment of frost-gangrene [In German]. *Schweiz. med. Wschr., v. 76, July 27, 1946: 684–686.*

A series of case histories of frostbite with gangrene are presented. Open treatment in an apparatus especially designed to hold the injured member, is described. Tannin, "Dermatol", Xeroform, iodoform, and silver foil were applied to the lesion.

2424. Marotta, G. Therapy of severe freezing injury by means of open wound treatment and Thioseptal powder [In Italian]. *Atti Accad. Fisiocr. Siena, v. 9, ser. 11, Aug. 1941: 205–212.*

Cases of freezing injury showing necrosis were treated with "Thioseptal" powder with a consequently increased rate of healing.

2425. Mel, E. The treatment of freezing injuries with fly larvae extract [In Italian]. *In: Atti Congresso Nazionale di Chirurgia di Guerra, May 24–26, 1942, p. 238–239. Roma, 1943.*

The author recommends the use of fly-larvae extract for treatment of 3rd degree freezing injuries. The extract was well tolerated, gave no local or generalized reactions, facilitated elimination of necrotic tissue, and stimulated formation of granulation tissue. The zone of demarcation of necrotic tissue was quickly established, and fever and pain were reduced. Sulfa drugs and vitamin and hormone preparations were also used in conjunction with the larvae extract.

2426. Mestiri, A. On the treatment of frostbite [In French]. *Presse méd., v. 49, Feb. 19–22, 1941: 200.*

A tincture of arnica was used in the treatment of frostbite lesions, with good results.

2427. Mettenheim, H. von. The treatment of mild frostbite [In German]. *Med. Welt, v. 16, Mar. 28, 1942: 314–315.*

Ethylene chloride as a spray was used on mild frostbite lesions. Often one application was adequate. "Glaciol"—containing iodine, fat, and tannin dissolved in ethylene chloride—may be used in the same way.

2428. Mire, A. Frostbitten feet [In French]. *Progr. méd., Par., v. 73, Jan. 24, 1945: 38–40.*

In the treatment of necrotic lesions in frostbite of the feet, the author used a picric acid and copper sulfate solution, and a camphor-eucalyptol solution. Sulfonamide preparations were also used to control infection.

2429. Molinari, P. Frostbite of the feet and the importance of vitamin B_1 deficiency [In Italian]. *Riv. ital. terapia, v. 14, June 30, 1940: 198–199.*

This is a brief note on the therapeutic value of vitamin B_1 in frostbite.

2430. Musini, N. Therapeutic treatment of freezing injury with special regard to those of the third degree [In Italian]. *Atti Accad. med. lombarda, v. 31, Apr. 17, 1942: 206–208.*

The author recommends the use of local medication in the treatment of 3rd degree frostbite lesions. A salve containing cod-liver oil and tincture of balsam was used successfully, also one containing a sulfonamide. Use of these preparations changed a wet gangrene to a dry one and brought about a faster line of demarcation of the necrotic from the healthy tissue.

2431. Novak, C. Contribution to the treatment of the lesions from cold [Abstract, in German]. *Zentr. Org. ges. Chir., v. 107, 1943: 293.*

The treatment by injection of milk is described for 50 cases of frostbite all but three of which involved bilateral injuries. Injuries were of 1st and 2nd (34 cases) or of 3rd (10 cases) degree. Four to 10 cc of fresh milk, boiled for 10 minutes, were injected daily. There were no complications. In 35 cases the fever reaction proceeded regularly. In 15 of the 50 cases the results were excellent (disappearance of pain and erythema, drying out of the vesicles, cicatrization of the open wounds, rapid demarcation of the necrotic area). In 32 cases there was marked improvement, including one-third of the 2nd and half of the 3rd degree cases; 3 cases showed no improvement. The development of general symptoms was arrested. It is suggested that the protein content of milk exerts a stimulating action on the general body defenses.

2432. Orsós, J. I. Treatment of freezing injury with nicotinic acid [In German]. *Derm. Wschr., v. 117, Oct. 30, 1943: 613–614.*

Nicotinic acid tablets given for several weeks, were used in the treatment of frostbite lesions. During this time the affected area regained its capillary tonus.

2433. Osipovskiĭ, V. M. The treatment of infected wounds with oil-balsam dressings by the method of Vishnevskiĭ [In Russian, with English summary]. *Arkh. biol. nauk, v. 62, 1941: 39–45.*

A variety of infected war wounds, including those from frostbite, were treated successfully with an oil-balsam emulsion. The emulsion was used on all cases of frostbite and the results were generally good; 90–95% of all wounds healed successfully and 52% of the soldiers were returned to front-line duty.

2434. Panizzi, E. The treatment of frostbite in the military hospital of Arliano [In Italian]. *Atti Accad. fisiocr. Siena, sez. med. fis., v. 9, ser. 11, Aug. 1941: 151–158.*

Several methods were used in the treatment of frostbite in a military hospital. A biological method, after Baggio, gave best results. In this treatment a warmed physiological solution of sodium chloride was used. Wounds were cleansed very readily and healed quickly.

2435. Papkov, N. I. The treatment of frostbite with Formalin-carbol solution [In Russian]. *Khirurgiĭa, Moskva, 1942 (8): 51–54.*

In a front-line army hospital, the author used a Formalin-carbolic acid solution in the treatment of 89 cases of frostbite of 2nd, 3rd, and 4th degrees. The injured part was washed with the solution, all vesicles were excised, and the part was covered with a compress of the same solution and then by a thick layer of cotton. Pain was intense for 30 minutes, then decreased. In 3rd and 4th degree injuries all pain disappeared and epithelization began after the 5th or 6th day. The demarcation line appeared on the 6th-8th day, and inflammation subsided on the 7th or 8th day. No harmful effect was seen following this treatment. The author concludes that the Formalin-carbolic acid solution contributes to rapid epithelization and prevents secondary infection.

2436. Pennock, L. L., and A. M. Minno. Vitamin E in treatment of leg ulcers. *Angiology, v. 1, Aug. 1950: 337–350.*

None of the 15 patients with peripheral vascular disease—one case of which was of frostbite origin—was benefitted by treatment with vitamin E in addition to other accepted therapeutic measures.

2437. Pfister, W. On the chemotherapy of infected wounds and those liable to infection [In German]. *Münch. med. Wschr., v. 90, June 4, 1943: 345–347.*

The efficacy of various chemotherapeutic preparations in the treatment of infected war wounds or injuries liable to become infected, is reviewed. In the case of frostbite the author states that dusting the lesions with sulfapyridine-urea powder gave good results.

2438. Piana, C. Action of follicular hormone on frostbite and its after effects [In Italian]. *Attual. med., Roma, v. 7, Jan.–Mar. 1942: 14–20.*

Progynon, both as a salve and for intramuscular injection, was used in cases of severe frostbite. Lesions from frostbite responded quickly and favorably to the treatment.

2439.   Pichotka, J., and R. B. Lewis. Prevention of secondary infection due to Pseudomonas aeruginosa in frostbitten tissue. *Proc. Soc. Exp. Biol., N. Y., v. 72, Oct. 1949: 127–130.*

Experimental frostbite was produced in rabbits by immersion of a leg in an alcohol bath at temperatures of −10°C to −25°C. Of 78 animals treated in this manner, 30 developed severe infection with *Pseudomonas aeruginosa (B. pyocyaneus)*, although penicillin ointment was applied to the injured area. In another group of 212 animals similarly treated, application of 3% Sulfamylon ointment (p-aminoethylbenzenesulfonamide) with daily changes of dressings, prevented occurrence of infection in 180 animals.

2440.   Pichotka, J., and R. B. Lewis. Use of heparin in treatment of experimental frostbite. *Proc. Soc. Exp. Biol., N. Y., v. 72, Oct. 1949: 130–136.*

Legs of 153 rabbits were exposed to temperatures of −25°C or −15°C for 30 minutes and subsequently treated with heparin, administered intravenously for a period of 6 days. A group of 80 animals exposed to the same conditions of temperature but untreated with heparin, were used as controls. Results indicated that necrosis was not significantly less in the heparin-treated animals. It is concluded that the results reported by Lange and his coworkers in heparin therapy were not reproducible under the conditions of this experiment.

2441.   Plester, D. Interpretation of the mode of action of Novocain (Impletol) in circulatory disorders [Abstract, in German]. *Klin. Wschr., v. 29, May 15, 1951: 391.*

There is an ever-widening clinical use of Novocain in the handling of circulatory disorders; its application, either locally or subcutaneously, following experimental freezing (with dry ice) of the ears of rabbits, the webs of the feet of frogs, or the Vella-Thiry fistula of dogs, is discussed. The essential conclusion from the studies is that the occurrence of a definite intensification of circulatory motility after Novocain use is expressed as a distinct tendency to vasoconstriction. In contrast to the usual view which regards vasospastic phenomena of Novocain as unwelcome, the author believes that the heightened reactivity of the blood vessels is a distinct aid in a blood vessel injury. In agreement with the findings of other workers, caffeine was found to intensify the circulatory effect of Novocain. Clinical use of Novocain in preventing the appearance or in cutting short the duration of a state of pre-stasis—or red stasis—is discussed briefly.

2442.   Polievktov, I. A. Treatment of frostbite [In Russian]. *Khirurgiĭa, Moskva, 1940 (6): 130.*

Experiences in the treatment of frostbite are reported. The author used the so-called open treatment, painting the wounds with 60–70% alcohol solution and exposing them to warm, dry, air. Edema subsided rapidly and a granular crust formed over the lesion.

* 2443.   Prokopchuk, D. T. Comparative evaluation of various methods of medicinal therapy of frostbite [In Russian]. *Sovet. med., v. 8 (12), 1944: 10–11.*

"*Contains* a study on specific causes, degrees and therapy of 250 cases of frostbite. None of the medicinal methods applied in second- and third-degree frostbite proved specific, but alcoholic solutions of dyes (Brilliant-Green) and Vishnevskiĭ's balsam ointment gave good results in combating infection and hastening epithelization; such preparations as iodine, silver nitrate, etc., had opposite effects. The essential requirement for any method is its stimulating effect on epithelization which is the essence of wound-healing."—Arctic Bibl. v. 4, 1954: 836–837.

2444.   Pumpĭanskiĭ, R. G. On the treatment of frostbite [In Russian]. *Khirurgiĭa, Moskva, 1942 (1–2): 58.*

A great number of frostbite cases of all degrees were treated by coating the injured area with Lugol's solution and covering it with a dry dressing. The best results were obtained after the use of a mixture of Lugol's solution and glycerin. In 2nd degree cases in which the vesicles were

---

* Original not seen.

excised, the healing process was much more rapid with this than with other types of treatment. In 3rd degree injuries necrosis was limited to small areas which were dry; there was a clear demarcation line and no purulation occurred. If the treatment was started late, purulation disappeared changing into a dry necrosis.

* **2445. Rapoport, D. M.** Treatment of burns and frostbite with methyl violet [In Russian]. *Sovet. vrach. zh.*, *1940 (12): 843–846.*

"*Contains* a note on excellent results obtained in burns and frostbite with an alcohol solution of methyl violet, followed with a 1% methyl-violet ointment. Best results were observed when applied within 24 hours after injury."—Arctic Bibl., v. 4, 1954: 847.

2446. Rübsamen, W., and G. Glass. Local treatment, with Cibazol, of infected wounds and cold injuries [In German]. *Med. Welt, v. 17, Feb. 6, 1943: 122–124.*

The use of sulfathiazole (Cibazol) in the treatment of localized frostbite is reported. Good results were obtained.

* **2447. Sakharov, M. I., and V. D. ÎAnkovskiĭ.** On the possibility of using antithrombin (heparin) in radical treatment of frostbite sequelae [In Russian]. *Khirurgiĭa, Moskva, v. 16 (7), 1946: 18–21.*

"*Contains* an account of earlier work of V. A. Bogdanov with antithrombins in frostbite of rabbits, followed by a detailed account of four cases of severe frostbite; two of them, treated subcutaneously with antithrombin, showed dubious effects; two others, with second and third degree frostbite, given antithrombin intravenously about 24 hours after the accident showed improvement in circulation of the damaged area; subjective improvement and hastening of recovery. In all four cases no adverse effects followed the administration of relatively large amounts of antithrombin."—Arctic Bibl., v. 4, 1954: 910.

2448. Saltner, L. On the therapy of cold injury of the skin under military circumstances [In German]. *Deut. Militärarzt., v. 5, Mar. 1940: 123–127.*

The author discusses the etiology, clinical picture, and treatment of frostbite as observed on a military front. Treatment was apparently limited to the use of salves, quicksilver, and ammonium ichthyosulfonate.

2449. Sartory, A., and J. Meyer. The influence of vitamin C on human pathologic phenomena due to intense cold [In French]. *C. rend. Acad. sc., v. 210, Feb. 26, 1940: 349–351.* Abstract, in French, in: *Gaz. hôp., v. 113, 1940: 230.*

An emulsion of vitamin C was applied to frostbite lesions. Good results were obtained within a period of 10 days.

2450. Scotti, G. Considerations on the immediate treatment of severe cold injuries in wartime [In Italian]. *Policlinico, sez. prat., v. 50, Aug. 16, 1943: 1085–1088.*

Treatment of frostbite injuries consisted of a combination of vitamin A and a sulfonamide preparation.

2451. Seliger, H. On treatment with follicular hormone salve [In German]. *Deut. Gesundhwes., v. 5, Dec. 14, 1950: 1581–1583.*

Among the patients treated with a salve, "Farmacyrolsalbe", containing dienestrol-diacetate, were 54 with cold injuries. Thirty-four of these had complete healing of lesions; 16 about 80% healing; 3 about 50%; and in only 1 case was there no improvement in the condition.

---

* Original not seen.

2452. Severi, L., and F. Luciani. The phenomena of Spagnol in frostbite [In Italian]. *Lav. Ist. anat. istol. pat. Univ. Perugia, v. 3, 1944: 13–23.*

Third-degree frostbite was induced in rabbits which were then treated by injection, into the striated muscle tissue, of tricalcium phosphate hydrosol. The fixation of the salt, called Spagnol's phenomenon, is reported to have given remarkable curative results.

2453. Sheppard, J. V. Frostbite—facts and fictions. *Hygeia, Chic., v. 25, Jan. 1947: 38–39; 77.*

The author mentions, among others, the following earlier beliefs which have been disproven: that frostbitten areas should be vigorously rubbed with snow; that frozen tissue is very brittle; and that cold injury occurs only at freezing temperatures and below. Concerning the latter he mentions the injuries from only moderately cold temperatures which, when combined with moisture, cause immersion foot. There is also some discussion of circulatory changes from cold exposure and the use of heparin in treatment following frostbite.

2454. Shumacker, H. B., Jr., B. H. White, E. L. Wrenn, Jr., A. R. Cordell, and T. F. Sanford. Studies in experimental frostbite. I. The effect of heparin in preventing gangrene. *Surgery, v. 22, Dec. 1947: 900–909.*

The authors report that, in their laboratory, heparin was not uniformly successful in preventing gangrene following experimental frostbite in rabbits. Heparinization was more often successful in mild than in severe frostbite. Earlier treatment was more effective than delayed therapy.

2455. Simonetti, A. Copper in the treatment of wounds of frostbite, second and third degrees [In Italian]. *Rass. clin. ter., v. 40, July–Aug. 1941: 164–169.*

Frostbite lesions of the 2nd and 3rd degree were treated with a copper preparation, and also with cholesterol and vitamins A and D. Serous seepage was stopped and pain relieved.

2456. Stucke, K. Cold injuries and frostbite on active service [In German]. *Beitr. klin. Chir., v. 174, Nov. 30, 1942: 1–10.*

For best results in healing, frostbitten parts should be kept dry. In therapy the author uses powdered charcoal and "Dermatol", and emphasizes the immobilization and the elevation of injured limbs.

2457. Stuckey, W. and K. Vainio. Heparin treatment of frostbite [In Finnish, with English summary]. *Duodecim, Helsin., v. 65 (3), 1949: 212–217.*

Two cases of frostbite are reported as having been treated successfully with heparin given intravenously.

2458. Theis, F. V., W. R. O'Connor, and F. J. Wahl. Anticoagulants in acute frostbite. *J. Am. M. Ass., v. 146, July 14, 1951: 992–995.*

Fourteen of 30 patients with acute frostbite responded very favorably to treatment with two anticoagulants, heparin sodium and bishydroxycoumarin (Dicumarol). Thawing of affected areas was done at room temperature only. Sterile pressure dressings, either dry or petrolatum-coated, were used. Only one patient required minor amputation; the duration of hospitalization was shortened appreciably for the entire group.

2459. Uspenskiĭ, A. A. Treatment of burns and frostbite with Vitaderm [In Russian]. *Ortop. travmat., Kharkov, 1940 (2): 12–23.*

Treatment with "Vitaderm" of burns and frostbite (in 25 patients, including some with 3rd degree injuries) is discussed, as recommended by Balakhovskiĭ. The drug consists of 50 g carotene; 850 g white, easily-melted, paraffin; 150 g linseed oil; 5 g beta-naphthol; and 15 g eucalyptus oil (the last two substances are to be left out if irritation is caused). The main active ingredient is carotene, whose action is to promote analgesia, stimulate epithelization, and decrease inflammation. The injured surface was washed with warm physiological saline solution or warm Rivanol (1:1000) in case of purulation, carefully dried, and the melted "Vitaderm" was sprayed over it daily, the area then being covered with a thick layer of cotton. Pain was alleviated, the microflora diminished with each consecutive dressing, the inflammation decreased, the falling off of the necrosed tissue and subsequent granulation and epithelization were considerably accelerated, and there were fewer scars and contractures than with other treatments. The author recommends this method because of its excellent results, simple technique, and easy availability, as the method of choice in thermal tissue injuries.

2460.   **Vaglianos, M., A. Zanthopulides, S. Halda, and A. Sarijanis.** The effect of immunity to Coli bacteria on the pathogenesis of frostbite. [In French, with Greek summary]. *Prakt. Akad. athen., v. 16, June 12, 1941: 101–108.*

The giving of *Bacillus coli* antisera—together with tetanus antisera—is recommended in the case of frostbite patients, even before there is any indication of an infection.

2461.   **Wadsworth, R. C., and B. V. Whitney.** The pathology and therapy of frostbite. *J. Maine M. Ass., v. 39, Dec. 1948: 345–350.*

The treatment of frostbite injuries, and the literature on recent experimental work on frostbite, are discussed. Five case histories are presented, one treated by anticoagulant therapy and the others illustrating the effects of delayed treatment.

2462.   **Walther, H.** Contribution to the treatment of cold injuries of the skin [In German]. *Zbl. Haut Geschlkr., v. 3, July 15, 1947: 77–79.*

Forapin ointment is recommended for the treatment of frostbite.

2463.   **Weiner, D., and K. Lange.** Pitfalls in the treatment of frostbite with heparin [Abstract]. *Fed. Proc., Balt., v. 9, Mar. 1950: 324.*

Reports of investigators, who have failed in preventing gangrene by heparinization following experimental frostbite, indicated that the failure was due to inadequate heparinization either in degree or duration. Results of experiments on a group of rabbits with one experimentally frozen hind leg emphasize the importance of maintaining the coagulation time above 30 minutes throughout the treatment period which should be at least 5 or 6 days. The dosage necessary to maintain this level is said to vary widely in individual animals and in different strains so that frequent determinations need to be made.

2464.   **Wobker, W.** The treatment of frostbite with follicular hormone salve [In German]. *Deut. med. Wschr., v. 66, Nov. 15, 1940: 1265–1267.*

The treatment of frostbite, of 1st and 2nd degree, with follicular hormone salve, is reported.

2465.   **Yeager, G. H., J. H. Walker, and W. T. Raby.** Clinical evaluation of tetra-ethyl-ammonium. *South. M. J., v. 41, Feb. 1948: 129–133.*

Tetraethylammonium (TEA), both as chloride and bromide, appeared to be of value in the study and treatment of peripheral vascular disorders. The authors discuss the pharmacology of the drug together with clinical observations in Raynaud's disease, organic obstructive vascular disease, thrombophlebitis, and frostbite. Of 5 cases of frostbite treated with intravenous injections of TEA, all recovered rapidly.

2466.   **Zanotti, M.** A new method of cure in cases of freezing injuries [In Italian]. *Boll. Soc. med. chir. Modena, v. 41 (3–4), 1941: 151–153.*

Successful treatment with protein-shock therapy, using boiled milk, is reported for a group of 200 patients with various degrees of freezing injuries.

2467.   Zanotti, M. Direct protein therapy in the treatment of freezing injuries from the war [In Italian]. *Gior. med. Marca trevig., v. 3 (3–6), 1941: 152–156.*

The author refers to the excellent, simple, and rapid results obtained in treatment of freezing injuries by protein-shock (subcutaneous injection of milk) therapy. He discusses also the role of vitamin C in prevention and therapy of these lesions.

2468.   Zanotti, M. The injection of milk in a case of frostbite [In Italian]. *Policlinico, sez. prat., v. 48, June 16, 1941: 1071–1072.*

Report is made of the successful treatment of several cases of frostbite (1st, 2nd, and 3rd degree) using injections of boiled milk.

2469.   Zanotti, M. On the treatment of freezing injuries: protein shock, its importance and results [In Italian]. *In: Atti Congresso Nazionale di Chirurgia di Guerra, May 24–26, 1942, p. 190–192. Roma, 1943.*

This is a review of the literature on the use of foreign protein injections for the treatment of freezing injuries. The author recommends the use of intramuscular injections of sterile milk at intervals of 2 or 3 days. This method has been found especially effective in first and second degree injuries, pain being quickly relieved and a sense of warmth appearing.

2470.   Zetler, G. Interrelation of local cold injury, blood coagulation, and histamine; the effect of antihistaminics [In German]. *Klin. Wschr., v. 29, Apr. 1, 1951: 255–257.*

Investigation was made of the action of histaminic drugs on blood coagulation and of the influence of antihistaminics upon the effect of histamine and cold exposure. Following experimentation with histamine and subsequent antihistaminic (Antistine or Neo-antergan) injections, shaved portions of rabbits' ears were frozen with carbon dioxide snow for $2\frac{1}{2}$ minutes. The blood coagulation time was found to decrease, reaching its maximum of 63% of the normal rate after 15 minutes. After 94 minutes this effect had diminished by half; after 135 minutes the normal rate was restored. A 10-minute freezing period shortened the blood coagulation time about 73%; the effect was only half removed after 215 minutes. Intramuscular injection of 0.033 g/kg Antistine after the period of cold shortened the coagulation time only 27% (instead of 63%); after 1 hour this time decrease had ceased, and was replaced by a prolongation of coagulation time (up to 38%) lasting in all about 3 hours. A 0.05 g/kg dose of Antistine completely neutralized the effect of cold on blood coagulation and induced a prolongation of the blood clotting time of 40% within 30 minutes, disappearing after 2 hours. Moreover, Antistine lessened the clinical symptoms of frostbite in the ear, accelerated the healing, and prevented gangrene. It would seem possible, therefore, to counteract frostbite injuries in animals by administration of antihistaminics.

2471.   Zhdanova, A. P. Treatment of burns, frostbite, and suppurative wounds with cod-liver oil [In Russian]. *Sovet. med., 1940 (21): 23.*

Burns and frostbite injuries with retarded healing were treated successfully with cod-liver oil at the Surgical Clinic of the Rostov Medical Institute, during the course of a year. At the author's hospital, ordinary cod-liver oil was applied to sluggishly granulating frostbite injuries (40 cases). Pain and fever gradually subsided after 3–4 days; the general condition improved; healing of the injured toes was achieved after 30–60 days. The gypsum dressing was changed twice. Good results were obtained also in cases of osteomyelitis and burns. The author concludes that cod-liver oil accelerates the growth of granulation tissue and epithelization in all purulent wounds. This treatment reduces the number of dressings and accelerates the cure. The remaining scars are more elastic and mobile than after the usual methods of treatment.

See also items: 1325, 1899, 1942, 2004, 2019, 2063, 2079, 2100, 2119, 2143.

12. Therapy, Sympathetic Nerve Block

2472. Adams-Ray, J. Novocain block of the stellate ganglion; a therapeutic aid in sensory disturbances caused by cold [In English, summaries in English, French and German]. *Acta chir. scand., v. 85 (1–3), 1941: 1–6.*

The author treated persistent disturbances of sensation after injuries of the 1st and 2nd degree caused by cold, by the use of Novocain to block the sympathetic ganglia. He believes that the good results he obtained speak in favor of the theory that these disturbances of sensation are, for the most part, to be ascribed to a local relative ischemia occasioned by vasospasm. Vasospasm plays a major role in the injuries caused by cold, and the author recommends an extended and earlier use of blocking of the sympathetic ganglia in treatment of cold injuries.

2473. Altenkamp, T. Contribution to the treatment of frostbite through sympathetic anesthesia [In German]. *Münch. med. Wschr., v. 90, Feb. 19, 1943: 139–142.*

Various methods of interrupting the sympathetic nervous system (peripheral regional anesthesia, lumbar anesthesia, lumbar sympathectomy, ganglionectomy) are discussed in view of the results obtained in the treatment of circulatory dysfunction following cold injury. Sympathetic anesthesia as soon as possible after cold injury is advised to guard against necrosis. Use of short-waves and diathermy can also be advantageous in therapy. Treatment of cold injury must begin with methods designed to relieve vasoconstriction; temporary sympathetic interruption has been found to be particularly useful.

2474. Antongiovanni, G. B. Freezing injuries and sympathetic infiltration (with special regard to infiltration of the femoral canal). [In Italian]. *Minerva med., Tor., anno 33 (v. 1), Jan. 27, 1942: 103–112.*

The author reviews the findings of earlier workers with the use of sympathetic infiltration in the therapy of freezing injuries, discussing the importance of such injuries to the Army, their etiology, incidence, and pathology. He discusses, too, the successful application of anesthetic block of the femoral canal in 10 of his own patients with similar injuries.

2475. Antonioli, G. Perivascular anesthetic block in the treatment of freezing injuries and of some trophic lesions of the limbs [In Italian]. *In: Atti Congresso Nazionale di Chirurgia di Guerra, May 24–26, 1942, p. 234–237. Roma, 1943.*

In the treatment of lesions of freezing injuries of the limbs and of their sequelae, and of some trophic lesions of the limbs, the use of perivascular anesthetic block proved to be very satisfactory. Injections were made into the axillary pit, the fold of the elbow, and in the femoral canal.

2476. Arena, J. A., Jr., F. S. Gerbasi, and A. Blain, III. Experimental frostbite; an inquiry into the effect of sympathetic block using tetraethyl ammonium chloride in the acute stage. *Angiology, v. 1, Dec. 1950: 492–502.*

Frostbite injuries of 3rd degree were produced in 30 rabbits; 15 of the animals were given tetraethyl ammonium chloride (TEAC) intramuscularly as a sympathetic nervous system block, and the 15 other animals were left untreated. Gangrene appeared in the untreated group 40-47 hours after exposure and in the treated group 48–57 hours after exposure. Although the appearance of the gangrenous condition was delayed, the amount of tissue loss was not found to be reduced by the administration of TEAC.

2477. Arena, J. A., Jr., F. S. Gerbasi, and A. Blain, III. Experimental frostbite; an inquiry into the effect of sympathetic block using tetraethyl ammonium chloride in the acute stage. *Bull. Alexander Blain Hosp., v. 10, Feb. 1951: 8–17.*

The right hind legs of a group of rabbits were experimentally frozen by immersion for thirty minutes in a solid carbon dioxide and water bath kept at a temperature of −10°C. Sympathetic block using tetraethyl ammonium chloride (TEAC) in large doses did not reduce tissue loss when compared to the untreated, frozen, control animals. Because no evidence of pain could be detected in the control animals, this aspect could not be evaluated. Release of vasospasm by TEAC caused increased edema and a transient wet type of gangrene to replace the dry gangrene which developed in the control animals.

2478. Arezzi, G. Anesthetic block of the femoral canal, after Bertocchi, in the treatment of frostbite [In Italian]. *Boll. Soc. med. chir.*, Catania, *v. 9, 1941: 551–563.*

In cases of 1st and 2nd degree frostbite, anesthetic block of the femoral canal was found to result in healing after 2 or 3 weeks.

2479. Arnulf, G., H. Boquet, and ... De Tayrac. Sympathetic therapy in the treatment of frostbite of the hands and the feet [In French]. *Mem. Acad. chir.*, Par., *v. 75, Oct. 12, 1949: 665–666.* Also, in French, in: *Rev. chir.*, Par., *v. 7, May–June 1949: 152–164.*

Observations of the authors on the pathology and treatment of 3,000 cases of frostbite seen during the winter of 1944–45, are given. Many of the cases were seen within a few hours after injury and were those in which sympathetic therapy was used to advantage. Novocain infiltration of the lumbar sympathetic ganglion, and also intra-arterial injection, was used very successfully. Sympathectomies—always unilateral—were most successful when the surgical intervention occurred between the third and sixth day.

2480. Bertocchi, A. Anesthetic block of the femoral canal in the treatment of cold injuries [In Italian]. *Med. contemp.*, Tor., *v. 6, Aug. 1940: 343–349.* Similar article, in Italian, in: *Minerva med.*, Tor., *anno 31 (v. 2), Dec. 15, 1940: 571–577.*

Research in anesthetic blocking of the femoral canal is reported. An anesthetic solution of 10–22 cc of 1% Tutocaine was introduced into the femoral canal and infiltrated into the tissues. The effects noted were vasodilatation in the lower extremities, increased systolic pressure, a higher oscillometric index, and higher skin temperature. When it is difficult to apply the block in cases of recent frostbite, the author suggests that the novocainization of the lumbar chain of sympathetic ganglia would be helpful.

2481. Bertocchi, A. Anesthetic block of articular pits in the treatment of freezing injuries [In Italian]. *In: Atti Congresso Nazionale di Chirurgia di Guerra, May 24–26, 1942, p. 182–183. Roma, 1943.*

A brief discussion is given of the anatomical basis for sympathetic block as used in the treatment of freezing injuries.

2482. Bianchi, G. Periarterial sympathetic block in the early treatment of frostbite [In Italian]. *Sperimentale, v. 96, Oct. 31, 1942: 530–538.*

Treatment of 1st, 2nd, and 3rd degree frostbite injuries by means of periarterial sympathetic block, gave excellent results in the healing of frostbite lesions.

2483. Bicci, R. On the periarterial and periganglionic infiltration in the treatment of frostbite lesions of the lower limbs [In Italian]. *Sperimentale, v. 95, Dec. 31, 1941: 797–802.*

The technique for lumbar and periarterial infiltration, together with a series of case histories, is discussed. Infiltration with Novocain gave a release of the vasoconstriction, producing hyperemia. The hyperemia produced by infiltration of the periganglion, was less pronounced in intensity and was of shorter duration than that following periarterial infiltration.

2484. Block, W. Blocking and extirpation of the sympathetic ganglionated cord in freezing injuries [In German]. *Zbl. Chir., v. 70, Nov. 20, 1943: 1691–1692.*

Local frostbite was treated by Novocain blockade or extirpation of the ganglionated cord of the sympathetic system. Alcohol blockade was found to last longer and was used in cases of 3rd degree frostbite.

2485. Bøggild, D. H. Two cases of affection of the vascular system treated by bilateral suprarenal medullectomy [In English]. *Acta chir. scand., v. 96 (4), 1948: 317–322.*

Bilateral suprarenal medullectomy is reported in two cases, one of which suffered severe frostbite. In both cases previous sympathetic ganglionectomy had given only temporary relief.

2486. Breitner, B. On frostbite [In German]. *Klin. Wschr., v. 22, 1943: 220.*

The author discusses two methods for the treatment of frostbite injuries: periarteriolar sympathectomy, and spontaneous amputation. He believes that the former method makes for a strong demarcation of the necrosis.

2487. Bück, F. Novocain infiltration of the sympathetic nervous system as early treatment for frozen limbs [In German]. *Chirurg, v. 15, June 15, 1943: 347–352.*

The author follows the hypothesis of Leriche that the pathological sequence in frostbite is vasoconstriction followed by thrombosis. He therefore recommends infiltration of the stellate ganglion and the lumbar preganglionic fibers with Novocain. Good results are reported.

2488. Burdenko, N. N. The effect of frostbite on the sympathetic nervous system [In Russian]. *Khirurgiĩa, Moskva, 1942 (5–6): 3–10.* Also, in English, in: *Am. Rev. Soviet M., v. 1, Oct. 1943: 15–22.*

Blocking of the sympathetic nervous system at the beginning of the injurious influences of low temperature is discussed with respect to: (1) blocking the efferent nerve fibers close to the arterial vessels in the extremities; (2) blocking the lumbar region by the Vishnevskiĩ method of perfusing the spinal ganglia and aortic plexus; and (3) blocking the efferent nerve fibers by paravertebral and parasacral anesthesia.

2489. Chidichimo, G. Contribution to the study and treatment of the effects of freezing injury [In Italian]. *Policlinico, sez. prat., v. 51, Oct. 15, 1944: 185–198.*

The action of periarterial and low perineural sympathectomy and of arteriectomy in 9 cases of 3rd degree frostbite was studied. Pain was relieved in 80% of the cases so treated and scabs formed on the lesions.

2490. Chinaglia, A. Early results of treatment of freezing injuries of the war with anesthetic block of the lumbar sympathetic nerve [In Italian]. *Atti Soc. med. chir. Padova, v. 19, Mar.–Apr. 1941: 93–102.*

Seventy-eight cases of freezing injuries from the Greco-Albanese front during the winter of 1941, are reported. Of this group 32 were treated with the usual medication and 46 were treated very successfully with anesthetic (Novocain) block of the sympathetic nerve. Detailed case histories from the latter group are given of 10 patients with 1st and 2nd degree injuries and 1 patient with 3rd degree injury.

2491. Chinaglia, A. Anesthetic block of the lumbar sympathetic in the treatment of frostbite injuries in wartime [In Italian]. *Gazz. med. ital., v. 100, Nov. 1941: 329–349.*

Report is made of 56 cases of the use of anesthetic block of the lumbar sympathetic ganglia in treatment of freezing injuries resulting from exposure during the Greco-Albanese war. The author recommends it as the treatment of choice for the rapid cure of 1st and 2nd degree frostbite and as being of the greatest assistance in 3rd degree injuries.

* 2492. Chulkov, I. P. Some data on the role of the nervous system in the pathogenesis and therapy of frostbite [In Russian]. *Khirurgiïa, Moskva, v. 19, May 1949: 62–67.*

"*Contains* a study on the effects of novocaine blockade on frozen extremities of cats during the pre-reactive and during the reactive period. An evaluation of the 'zonal' and 'envelope' methods of blockade is presented as well as information on the histological changes taking place in the kidney, adrenal gland and nervous system as a result of local freezing."—Arctic Bibl., v. 4, 1954: 197.

2493. D'Agostino, F. Freezing injuries [In Italian]. *In: Atti Congresso Nazionale di Chirurgia di Guerra, Roma, May 24–26, 1942, p. 188. Roma, 1943.*

The author recommends the use of an anesthetic block of the femoral canal, because of its ease and effectiveness, in the treatment of freezing injuries.

2494. Damperov, ... Experiences in frostbite treatment [In Russian]. *Hosp. delo, 1944 (1–2): 49.*

In 42 cases of 4th degree frostbite of the feet, 15–20 days after injury (most of whom had had a primary operation; others were mummified), a Novocain block of the autonomic system was done in the lumbar region. On the 3rd to 10th day after the blocking radical surgical operation was performed, consisting usually of amputation of the distal third or fourth of the metatarsal bones, ending with the use of tight sutures and the application of an ointment bandage applied for 4–5 days. The sutures could be removed on the 10th day in 31 cases. The wound was narrow, well granulated, and epithelized; in 8 cases healing proceeded by first intention. There were no complications. Nearly all the patients started walking after the removal of sutures. If the granulation did not proceed satisfactorily, a second Novocain block was applied after 15–20 days; this induced improved granulation and a renewal of the arrested epithelization.

2495. Forster, E., and I. Wiederkehr. Stellate ganglion infiltrations in freezing of the hand [In French]. *Mém. Acad. chir., Par., v. 66, Apr. 3, 1940: 367–368.*

A rare case of freezing injury in the hands is described. Right stellar infiltration by the Leriche method led to cessation of pain and improved mobility of the fingers.

2496. Girardier, J. Results obtained by sympathetic therapy in the treatment of frostbite lesions [In French]. *Presse méd., v. 49, Jan. 15–18, 1941: 44–47.*

The author reports his experience with sympathectomy in cases of frostbite lesions with massive gangrene. His results lead him to the conclusion that sympathectomy represents a marked therapeutic advance.

2497. Giuntini, L. At the clinic on frostbite in war [In Italian]. *Atti Accad. fisiocr. Siena, v. 11, ser. 9, Aug. 1941: 168–170.*

The author has used periarterial sympathectomy in cases of severe frostbite. Report is given here of 12 cases of frostbite in 6 of which periarterial sympathectomy was used.

2498. Gobin, ..., ... Bolot, and ... Challiol. Post-phlebitic sequelae of frostbitten feet; phlebographic exploration; results after lumbar sympathectomy [In French]. *Maroc méd., v. 27, June 1948: 255–257.*

Report is made of an unusual phlebitic condition, of the internal saphenous vein of the left leg, which came about 5 years after acute frostbite of the feet during a military campaign. The thrombotic and edematous conditions were immediately relieved by lumbar sympathectomy.

---

* Original not seen.

2499. Greco, T. Sympathetic infiltration in the treatment of frostbite [In Italian]. *Policlinico, sez. prat., v. 48, Sept. 22, 1941: 1603–1605.*

Cases of freezing injury were treated by infiltration of the lumbar sympathetic with Novo-cain or Scurocaine. Excellent results were obtained in 35 out of 38 cases.

2500. Hämäläinen, M. On the treatment following frostbite by surgery of the sympathetic nervous system [In Swedish]. *Nord. med., v. 18, Apr. 3, 1943: 547–549.*

During the winter of 1939–1940 the weather in Finland was especially severe with an average temperature in Helsingfors of −15.8°F in February 1940 instead of the usual −7.5°F. This resulted in a high incidence of serious frostbite cases. For relief of such conditions as vasospasm and cyanosis, the use of various types of surgical interruption of the sympathetic nervous system (including ganglionectomy, lumbar sympathectomy, and periarterial sympathectomy), are discussed. From clinical experiences it would seem that with cases well adapted to such inter-vention, the operation should be performed as early as possible. Results from such operations have the disadvantage of being short-lived.

2501. Harcourt Got, J. d', and A. Folch Pi. Vasomotor lability as the essential factor in frostbite; its value in clinical practice [In Spanish]. *Arch. lat. amer. card., Méx., v. 12, May–June 1942: 100–109.*

This is an account of frostbite cases seen among military casualties in Spain during the winter of 1937–1938. Among 120,000 men, 600 were afflicted with freezing injuries. The clinical aspects, pathogenesis, pathological anatomy, and treatment are described. Methods for re-storing the functions of the peripheral circulation are emphasized. These include Novocain block, lumbar ganglionectomy, and periarterial sympathectomy.

2502. Igna, N. Conservative treatment in severe frostbite of war; of third degree with lesions [In Rumanian]. *Ardeal. med., v. 8 (3), 1948: 154–156.*

The treatment discussed for third degree frostbite lesions in wartime, includes sympathetic block. Amputation is also discussed. Incidence of infection and of gangrene are also noted.

2503. Jung, A., and H. Fell. Arteriography, sympathetic infiltration and sym-pathectomy in frostbite [In German]. *Deut. Zschr. Chir., v. 255, Feb. 19, 1942: 249–275.*

Seven cases of severe frostbite affecting hands and feet are described. Treatment was begun from 4 to 60 days after exposure. A spastic condition of the arteries, revealed by arteriography, persisted for a long time after freezing and did not respond to rewarming and cooling of the limbs. Novocain infiltration or surgical interruption of the sympathetic nerves, however, pro-duced dramatic results with greatly increased circulation and rapid healing.

2504. Kern, P. Experiences from the Eastern Campaign [In German]. *Münch. med. Wschr., v. 89, Nov. 27, 1942: 1005–1007.*

Injuries to German troops in Russia in 1941, together with methods of treatment, are de-scribed. In a section on cold injuries various types of treatment are mentioned. Periarterial sympathectomy produced good results in promoting a faster demarcation line and in the re-generation of affected tissues in frostbite cases.

2505. Kreyberg, L. Influence of sympathectomy on the necrosis developing in rabbits' ears after the skin has been frozen with solid carbon dioxide. *Arch. Path., Chic., v. 45, June 1948: 707–716.*

The vascular reactions in the frozen ears of rabbits subjected to unilateral sympathectomy were studied. Tissue reactions were more violent and edema was more marked in the sym-pathectomized ear than in the control ear. However, terminal damage was not altered.

2506. Lauro, A., and E. Malan. Periarterial anesthetic block in the treatment of frostbite [In Italian]. *Gazz. med. ital., v. 100, Nov. 1941: 349–357.*

Analysis is made of a series of cases of frostbite treated by periarterial anesthetic blockade.

2507. Leger, L. Recent data on the physio-pathology and treatment of freezing injury [In French]. *Bull. méd., Par., v. 55, Feb. 15, 1941: 73–76.* Abstract, in French, in: *Ann. derm. syph., Par., v. 1, ser. 8, 1941: 204.*

The pathological physiology of freezing injuries and their treatment by lumbar sympathectomy are discussed.

2508. Lempke, R. E., and H. B. Shumaker, Jr. Studies in experimental frostbite. IV. The response of the sympathetically denervated extremity to freezing. *Yale J. Biol., v. 21, May 1949: 401–414.*

The authors discuss the role of the sympathetic nervous system in reactions to cold and report the effects of sympathectomy on dogs having severely frozen extremities. As a preventive measure, sympathectomy does not appear to increase susceptibility to frostbite or influence its end results. It may have some protective value. No data were obtained on the use of sympathetic therapy, but it was concluded that it would have no injurious effects.

2509. Leriche, R. Remarks on frostbite, and its immediate treatment by lumbar infiltration [In French]. *Presse méd., v. 48, Jan. 17–20, 1940: 75.*

Treatment of frostbite by stellate or lumbar sympathectomy was found to relieve pain and circulatory trouble.

2510. Malan, R. Anesthetic block of the femoral canal in the treatment of third degree frostbite [In Italian]. *Gior. med. mil., v. 89, Oct. 1941: 780–789.*

Frostbite injuries are compared in two groups of soldiers, from the Western and from the Greek-Albanian fronts. A 15 cc injection of the anesthetic Tutocaine into the femoral canal caused hyperemia, reduced pain, accelerated granulation, and reduced recovery time.

2511. Paunesco-Podeanu, A., and I. Tzurai. The ideal treatment of frostbite: periarterial Novocain injection [In French]. *Schweiz. med. Wschr., v. 78, Aug. 14, 1948: 795–796.*

The author reports good results in the treatment of frostbite by the use of periarterial Novocain block.

2512. Philipowicz, J. Sympathectomy for frostbites; preliminary report [In German]. *Zbl. Chir., v. 69, Aug. 22, 1942: 1369–1372.*

Experiences with sympathectomy in various degrees of frostbite are reported.

2513. Pieri, G. The treatment of freezing injury from the point of view of the physiological pathology of the sympathetic nervous system [In Italian]. *In: Atti Congresso Nazionale di Chirurgia di Guerra, May 24–26, 1942, p. 161–181. Roma, 1943.*

Some of the Italian and French literature on the treatment of frostbite injuries of 1st, 2nd, and 3rd degree by means of a blockade of the sympathetic nervous system, is reviewed. The pathology of these injuries is also discussed.

2514. Pieri, G. Ganglionic sympathectomy for the effects of frostbite [In Spanish]. *Friuli med., v. 1, Jan.–Feb. 1946: 79.*

In a case of 3rd degree frostbite, bilateral resection of the last lumbar ganglion and the first and second sacral ganglia produced immediate and favorable results.

2515. Pratt, G. H. Recent advances in surgery for obliterative arterial disease. *Angiology, v. 2, 1951: 517–530.*

The use of temporary sympathetic interruption, surgical sympathectomy, and other practices applicable to frostbite treatment are described. One section (p. 526–529) deals with the wartime importance of frostbite and discusses its management.

2516. Rödén, S. The treatment of cold injury. Experimental studies on the extremities of rabbits. I. The effect of periarterial sympathectomy [In English]. *Acta chir. scand., v. 98, 1949: 260–269.*

Denervating the frozen hind foot of a rabbit 1 hour after freezing increased edema and often caused permanent loss of tissue as compared with the non-denervated foot. No apparent effect on freezing injury was noted if sympathectomy was done 2 hours later.

2517. Rosenauer, F. Value of sympathectomy in trophic lesions excluding the true circulatory deficiencies [In German]. *Wien. klin. Wschr., v. 62, Sept. 1, 1950: 696–699.*

The value of sympathectomy is discussed in several trophic conditions, including that of frostbite (p. 697–698). One instance is cited of the successful treatment of 7 men by lumbar sympathectomy soon after frostbite of 3rd degree had been sustained. Sympathectomy was usually not found to be of much use when there was considerable tissue loss and a line of demarcation had been established. Even in cases where part of an extremity had to be lost following 3rd degree frostbite, the sympathectomy brought about a good tissue state in the area above the line of demarcation or in the amputation stump. Endangiitis, or arteriosclerosis, seldom occurred or was of short duration. Novocain infiltration of the cervical and lumbar sympathetic ganglion and intra-arterial injection of acetylcholine have also proven effective in treatment. It is suggested as a treatment in which Army doctors should become proficient and which they should be capable of performing in the field ambulances during the winter.

2518. Roux-Berger, M. Infiltration of stellate ganglion for freezing injuries of the hand [Abstract, in French]. *Gaz. hôp., v. 113 (33–34), 1940: 345.*

The author reports the very successful treatment of the hands of a motorcyclist, which were seriously injured by cold exposure, by infiltration of the stellate ganglion.

2519. Scheiderbauer, M. Observations on frostbitten extremities [In German]. *Wien. klin. Wschr., v. 59, July 18, 1947: 464–469.*

A group of 25 patients with 3rd degree frostbite injuries were observed over a period of 4 to 13 months. Periarterial sympathectomy and Novocain block were used to improve circulation in the milder cases; amputation was necessary in severe cases. X-ray examination indicated the presence of Sudeck's bone atrophy in 7 of the patients.

2520. Schisano, A. On a surgical cure for advanced frostbite [In Italian]. *Gior. med. mil., v. 90, Jan. 1942: 187–196.*

Anesthetic block of the femoral canal followed by peri-arterial sympathectomy (Leriche) was used as therapy in advanced frostbite conditions.

2521. Schürer, F. von. Periarterial sympathectomy in severe frostbite [In German]. *Zbl. Chir., v. 69, Mar. 21, 1942: 486–490.*

A report is given on 22 cases of frostbite among soldiers from the German Army on the Eastern front, treated by periarterial sympathectomy.

2522. Schürer, F. von. Periarterial sympathectomy in severe frostbite [In German]. *Zbl. Chir., v. 69, Nov. 7, 1942: 1797–1801.*

A case of severe frostbite of the hands of a German soldier is noted as having been successfully treated by periarterial sympathectomy.

2523. Senderovich, I. L. Novocain block as a stimulating factor in slow-healing wounds [In Russian]. *In: Sbornik nauchnykh rabot evalogospitaleĭ Narkomzdrava Tadzhikskoĭ SSR, p. 100–113. Stalinabad, Narkomzdrava Tadzhikskoĭ SSR, 1945.*

Over 100 clinical cases including 46 of 3rd and 4th degree frostbite, were treated by Visnevskiĭ's method of Novocain block, mainly of the circular type. A tourniquet was applied above the block area, 0.25% of Novocain in physiological solution (without Adrenalin) was injected intradermally in a circular manner to obtain an uninterrupted chain of small tumefactions, then the tourniquet was removed. In most cases the result was striking, the wounds healed completely with a perfect, movable, scar after 3 days or, at most, one week. In 18 cases, however, where wounds would not heal, a second or a third block was necessary before final healing occurred. To obtain a strong and resistant scar, the area was moistened with solutions such as Formalin, tannin, or brilliant green.

2524. Shumacker, H. B., Jr. Sympathectomy in the treatment of frostbite. *Surg. Gyn. Obst., v. 93, Dec. 1951: 727–734.*

Although there is great need for further study of the effectiveness of sympathectomy in the treatment of human frostbite, available observations indicate that it has been of value in the early treatment of certain cases. Sympathectomy resulted in the disappearance of pain, sensitivity, edema, and in the healing of ulcers.

2525. Simon, R., and H. Filhouland. Frostbite of feet treated with success by the infiltration of lumbar anesthetic and by sympathectomies [In French]. *Mém. Acad. chir., Par., v. 66, Apr. 3, 1940: 359–362.*

In 4 cases of frostbitten feet with necrotic lesions, further necrosis was halted by infiltration of the lumbar sympathetic ganglion.

2526. Sorgo, W., and M. Tomann. Spinal anesthesia in therapy of frostbite in the lower extremities [In German]. *Deut. Zschr. Nervenh., v. 166, June 18, 1951: 81–90.*

Cold interferes with sympathetic control of blood vessels, causing vasoconstriction so that disturbances of metabolism play a major role in cold injury. Lumbar anesthesia was found to give considerable relief from these complications, even in cases of injury which were not too recent.

2527. Southworth, J. L. The role of sympathectomy in treatment of immersion foot and frostbite. *N. England J. M., v. 233, Dec. 6, 1945: 673–681.*

The author, after reviewing the literature, describes 16 cases of immersion foot and 7 cases of frostbite which he treated. He concludes that sympathetic denervation may produce beneficial effects on certain late symptoms but partial disability cannot always be prevented.

2528. Tantini, E., and G. Baggio. Results of treatment of frozen limbs with periganglionic and periarterial infiltration [In Italian]. *Ann. ital. chir., v. 20, Nov.–Dec. 1941: 613–648.*

Results are given in 36 cases of freezing injury treated with Novocain infiltration of lumbar sympathetic ganglion and the periarterial area of the femoral artery. With the lumbar method, 91.3% of cases achieved clinical recovery; with the femoral method, only 7.6% recovered clinically while another 19.6% had amelioration of symptoms. Lumbar infiltration was found also to allow earlier ambulation.

2529. Tosatti, E. Sympathetic infiltration in the treatment of frostbite of the hands and feet [In Italian]. *In: Atti Congresso Nazionale di Chirurgia di Guerra, May 24–26, 1942, p. 252–253. Roma, 1943.*

Report is made on the treatment, by infiltration of the sympathetic nervous system, of a large group of casualties from frostbite during the winter of 1941–1942.

2530. Tosonotti, T. Perifemoral infiltration with Novocain according to the method of Bertocchi in freezing injury of the lower limbs [In Italian]. *In: Atti Congresso Nazionale di Chirurgia di Guerra, May 24–26, 1942, p. 237. Roma, 1943.*

The author found that periarterial sympathetic infiltration of the femoral artery resulted in the prevention of the pain attending freezing injuries of the lower limbs. The treatment has the added advantage of being a relatively simple technique.

See also items: 1895, 1919, 1958, 1985, 2083, 2101, 2102, 2103, 2565.

13. Therapy, Surgery
(for autonomic nerve surgery, see preceding chapter.)

2531. Anon. Leading instructions on amputations [In Russian]. *Voen. san. delo, 1942 (7): 82–87.*

Instructions are contained on amputations which have been necessitated as the result of frostbite injuries.

2532. Arndt, G. On plastic skin covering of freezing injury and amputation stumps with particular regard to the value of short amputation stumps [In German]. *Zschr. Orthop., v. 77, 1947: 40–78 and 121–144.*

Plastic skin covering of freezing injury and amputation stumps is discussed with particular regard to the value of short amputation stumps. These articles deal primarily with the amputation of frostbitten feet and the surgical treatment of the stumps.

2533. Bardon, ..., ... Gaussen, and ... Cornet. Dermatome skin grafting of scar area from cold injury and from a burn [In French]. *J. méd. Bordeaux, v. 126, Mar. 1949: 131.*

A case history is presented of the successful skin grafting, by use of a dermatome, immediately after removal of the scar from a fairly large area of the foot about 1½ months after a cold injury.

2534. Büttner, G. The management and repair of frostbite stumps [In German]. *Arch. klin. Chir., v. 206, Nov. 7, 1944: 512–527.*

In this general discussion of the surgical handling of frostbitten extremities, the author recommends conservative operations in the final treatment of frozen feet.

2535. Cade, S. War surgery in the Royal Air Force. *Brit. J. Surg., v. 32, July 1944: 12–24.*

This is a general account of the surgical handling of injuries in the Royal Air Force. Among the injuries discussed is frostbite (p. 19–21), which for the period October 1942 to March 1943 was almost eliminated from the British Bomber Command. This great decrease in incidence resulted from adequate preventive measures including education, heated planes and flying clothes, and improved oxygen equipment. Treatment of frostbite is briefly discussed. Immersion injuries (p. 21) are accompanied by swelling, loss of sensation, with vasoconstriction followed later by vasodilatation. Treatment used was similar to that for frostbite.

2536. Calati, A., and L. Longli. Anatomical and functional outcome of the mutilation of feet by freezing injuries of third degree with special regard to the outcome of Lisfranc and Chopart operations [In Italian]. *Atti Accad. med. lombarda, v. 31, Apr. 17, 1942: 221–226.*

This is a discussion of 98 cases of amputation of the foot following 3rd degree cold injuries on the Greco-Albanese front during the winter of 1940–1941. These are grouped according to the level of amputation. The criteria for the different levels of operation and the advantages and disadvantages of each, are discussed. Bilateral lesions at the same location had occurred in 88% of the cases.

2537. Chiarolanza, R. On the surgical treatment of frostbitten feet [In Italian]. *In: Atti Congresso Nazionale di Chirurgia di Guerra, May 24–26, 1942, p. 224–227. Roma, 1943.*

The conservation of injured tissue following severe frostbite of the feet, is discussed. In order to obtain a good stump following amputation, there must be sufficient skin to make a closure over the anterior part of the foot. Details of this operation are given, together with the diagrammatic sketches.

2538. Colombini, G. Criteria of relative advantages in surgical treatment of residual limb stumps, in cases of gangrene from freezing injury, in order to obtain them orthopedically suitable [In Italian]. *In: Atti Congresso Nazionale di Chirurgia di Guerra, May 24–26, 1942, p. 778–780. Roma, 1943.*

On the basis of his experiences with gangrene following freezing injuries of the legs, the author believes that in moist, septic, gangrene it will often be necessary to use surgical intervention and he suggests the use of spinal or epidural anesthesia. In dry, aseptic, gangrene it will often be possible to wait for spontaneous amputation but a better stump with less scar tissue will be obtained by earlier surgical intervention. The use of packs moistened with 95% alcohol will give excellent results in the cure or arrest of gangrenous conditions of either type.

2539. Corsi, G. Indications and results of the Lisfranc amputation in the treatment of frostbite of the feet [In German]. *Deut. Militärarzt, v. 7, Aug. 1942: 496–499.*

Amputation by the Lisfranc method is indicated in cases where necrosis is advanced.

2540. Corsi, G. Partial amputation of the foot as the result of freezing injury [In Italian]. *In: Atti Congresso Nazionale di Chirurgia di Guerra, May 24–26, 1942, p. 770–772. Roma, 1943.* Also, in Italian, in: *Arch. ortop., Milano, v. 57, 1942: 341–378.*

Criteria for and different levels of amputation of the forefoot following freezing injuries, are discussed. All but one of 345 such cases treated at the Amputation Center, were necessitated by freezing injuries.

2541. Dainelli, M. Consideration of 67 cases of resection of the metatarsals following frostbite of the feet [In Italian]. *Policlinico, sez. chir., v. 51, Oct. 15, 1944: 206–224.*

Clinical studies were made on 67 cases of metatarsal amputations following frostbite. Details of pre- and post-operative treatment are also given.

2542. Diagostino, F. Particulars of the technique of surgical treatment in frostbite [In Italian]. *Gior. med. mil., v. 90, Feb. 1942: 147.*

Details are given of amputations following frostbite injuries.

2543. Franco, F. Clinical and statistical considerations on amputation and re-amputations of the lower limbs in the Centro Mutilati in Rome [In Italian]. *Gior. med. mil., v. 95 (3), 1948: 233–240.*

A clinical and statistical study of amputation and re-amputation cases in the Centro Mutilati in Rome, up to September 1943, showed that freezing injury was the cause of the largest group (67.2%) of amputations. Of the total of amputated cases, 43.5% underwent amputation of the lower limbs.

2544. Gamov, V. S. Operative treatment of frostbite [In Russian]. *Nov. khir. arkh.*, *1941 (2): 304–310.*

Results obtained from clinical experience demonstrate that early surgical manipulation by Ar'ev's method contributes to a more rapid healing of 3rd degree frostbite and facilitates earlier amputation in 4th degree injuries. Early surgery using a considerable number of sutures results in healing by first intention and makes earlier use of prostheses possible. No septic complications were observed after early surgery. In 4th degree frostbite injuries, good cicatrization was obtained after chiseling off the necrosed bone tissue of the heel area. The author advises early surgical treatment since conservative treatment may favor the spreading of degenerative and inflammatory processes, delaying the healing for many months.

* 2545. Gamov, V. S. On surgical treatment of severe frostbite in evacuation hospitals of Leningrad [In Russian]. *Khirurgiia, Moskva, v. 14 (12), 1944: 35–41.*

"*Contains* a description of primary stumps due to frostbite and an outline of their defects; clinical aspects of 'trench foot' as compared with 'dry' frostbite; early surgical treatment of frost damage and its advantages."—Arctic Bibl., v. 4, 1954: 324.

2546. Gerasimenko, N. I. Treatment of frostbite [In Russian]. *Khirurgiia, Moskva, 1945 (2): 33–41.*

In the Chai-Ur'insk valley of the far north, where the average yearly temperature is −13.4°C (in winter as low as −58°C), the majority of frostbite cases occurred at the beginning of the winter season, about October. The number of casualties diminished through the winter, even though the temperature dropped lower, probably because the individuals become acclimatized. The majority of 3rd and 4th degree frostbite cases were complicated by secondary infection. Four years of experience have convinced the author that in 3rd and 4th degree frostbite injuries, after the inflammation had subsided, surgery was inevitable. The treatment applied at the Neksikan Hospital (Khabarovsk territory) is also described. The author suggests an expanded classification of the four degrees of frostbite injury intended to correspond more closely to the clinical findings.

2547. Getkin, F. L. Plastic methods for amputation defects of the foot after frostbite [In Russian]. *Khirurgiia, Moskva, v. 14 (4), 1944: 23–27.* Abstract, in English, in: *Bull. War. Med., v. 5, Apr. 1945: 502–503.*

Plastic surgery techniques have been perfected by which the raw surface of a guillotine-type amputation stump can be covered by a bridged flap of skin and subcutaneous fascia from the dorsum of the other foot. The operation has been successfully employed on several occasions to provide a skin cover, highly resistant to trauma, for the foot stump after extensive loss of tissue following frostbite injury.

2548. Giugni, F. Some notes on the therapy of freezing injuries. Amputations, re-amputations, and prosthesis [In Italian]. *Policlinico, sez. prat., v. 49, July 6, 1942: 961–967.*

The author discusses a series of 810 cases of severe freezing injuries of the feet and legs treated in a military hospital from December 1940 to April 1941. Many of the patients underwent amputations of parts or all of one or both legs. Something of the criteria involved in deciding the amputation level are discussed.

2549. Iusevich, M. S. Amputation of the anterior part of the foot after frostbite with reference to the prosthesis [In Russian]. *Raboty Leningr. vrach. za god otechest. voiny, 1942 (2): 100–111.*

To prevent the exudate and pus from the damaged front of the frostbitten foot from flowing into the heel, as well as the development of various deformities, it is stressed that patients should be kept lying on the stomach with the ankle supported by a pillow to hold the whole

---

* Original not seen.

foot in suspension. This positioning improves the circulation and diminishes muscular atrophy. Amputation must be made immediately following the appearance of the demarcation line, bearing in mind that the border of necrosis in the deeper soft tissue is usually higher than in the peripheral parts. The value of various surgical methods of amputation are discussed.

2550. Klapp, R. On the treatment of local freezing [In German]. *Zbl. Chir., v. 69, 1942: 1794–1797.*

In advanced cases of frostbite, the use of skin incisions which resulted in improved capillary circulation, were found to be helpful.

2551. Krasovitov, V. K. On the question of the second plastic sole and restoration of the soft tissue cover of the heel [In Russian]. *Vest. khir., v. 60, Dec. 1940: 593–598.*

Information is given concerning plastic surgery in restoration of the sole of the foot and of the soft tissue of the heel, following injury from frostbite.

* 2552. Kupriĩanov, P. A. Surgical aid during battle activities in Finland [In Russian]. *Vest. khir., v. 61, Feb. 1941: 113–170.*

"*Contains* a comprehensive study on the Russian surgical work during the Finnish campaign of 1939–40; outlines of its organization and of surgical aid at various levels of the military organization (Battalion Medical Aid Points to Divisional Hospitals); statistics on kinds, regions and degrees of wounds and kinds of surgical aid; evacuation and moving of hospitals; blood transfusion; wound treatment; burns; etc. Data on frostbite are also included."—Arctic Bibl., v. 4, 1954: 562–563.

2553. Läwen, A. On the operative treatment of freezing injuries of the feet [In German]. *Zbl. Chir., v. 69, Aug. 1, 1942: 1253–1262.*

Description is given of a surgical procedure in severe freezing injuries of the feet. Where amputation is necessary the author uses a 2-stage operation. The metatarsal frontal portion of the foot is first amputated. Two to four weeks later, depending upon the condition of the patient and the wound, the remainder of the gangrenous area is excised.

2554. Läwen, A. On the operative treatment of gangrenous frostbite of the feet. [Abstract, in German]. *Deut. med. Wschr., v. 69, Jan. 22, 1943: 70.*

The author discusses the handling of 58 patients with 3rd degree freezing injuries and gangrenous frostbite of the feet. Treatment was conservative, soldiers with gangrenous frostbite being sent down from the front line to await a definite line of demarcation between the living and gangrenous tissue before amputation. The amputation and preparation of the amputation stump was then done in one or several operations depending on the level of the amputation site and other factors.

2555. Lang, K. Experiences on pedicle grafts of skin [In German]. *Chirurg, v. 16, June 1944: 212–224.*

Report is made of surgical treatment of frostbite cases with special reference to amputation at various levels. This study is based upon 219 patients with 392 frostbitten lower extremities on which 187 amputations were performed.

2556. Lorenz, A. Operative treatment of wartime freezing injury in the region of the feet [In German]. *Zschr. Orthop., v. 75, June 30, 1944: 118–126.*

Methods of amputation in cases of severe frostbite are described. There are short discussions of the use of the operative procedures of Sharpe, Lisfranc, Chopart, Pirogoff, and Syme according to the level of the amputation which is required.

---

* Original not seen.

2557.   Mangeim, A. E. Surgical treatment of 3rd and 4th degree frostbite injuries of the foot [In Russian]. *In: Sbornik nauchnykh rabot evakogospitaleĭ Narkomzdrava Tadzhikskoĭ SSR, p. 87–92. Stalinabad, Izdatel'stvo Narkomzdrava Tadzhikskoı SSR, 1945.*

As poor results had been obtained by conservative surgery, the author resorted to surgery earlier in 24 cases of frostbite. In 3rd and 4th degree frostbite of the feet, surgery should be begun as soon as a demarcation line has appeared in the soft tissue, without waiting for the appearance of necrosis and separation of the bone. Surgical procedures in the involvement of various parts and levels of the foot, are discussed. Injury to the soft tissues of the foot determines the level of the amputation. The healthy bone stump is covered by muscles and skin; the scar must be on the dorsal side. A plaster cast is necessary after amputation to prevent contractures of the foot. Early fitting and use of a prosthesis is indispensable in cases of high-level amputations.

2558.   Marziani, R. Consideration of 50 cases of plastic skin surgery in third degree frostbite of the foot [In Italian]. *Atti Accad. med. lombarda, v. 30, Nov. 2–17, 1941: 341–348.*

The value of plastic skin surgery in cases of severe freezing injuries, is discussed. Techniques of grafting and transplanting are described and illustrated.

2559.   Marziani, R. Indications and results of plastic skin surgery following 3rd degree freezing injury [In Italian]. *In: Atti Congresso Nazionale di Chirurgia di Guerra, May 24–26, 1942, p. 219–221. Roma, 1943.*

The techniques of the plastic surgery which may be required following amputation of limbs because of frostbite injury, are discussed.

2560.   Michelsson, F. Results with early amputations in freezing injuries [In German]. *Zbl. Chir., v. 71, Aug. 12, 1944: 997–1002.*

In cases of severe frostbite, amputation is recommended three to four weeks after development of dry gangrene. The lesion heals in six to eight weeks.

2561.   Osna, A. I. Plastic surgery in restoration of skin defects of the sole of the foot [In Russian]. *Khirurgiīa, Moskva, v. 1 (3), 1947: 37–43.*

The use of plastic surgery methods for restoration of fairly large areas of the sole of the foot, is recommended—rather than to resort to amputation—in cases of non-healing ulcers. Treatment by plastic surgery is described in 68 cases, in 39 of which the injury had been caused by frostbite. By use of a pedicle-type graft, it was possible to cover satisfactorily areas up to 100 cm³. Good results were reported for the group with all but a few of the patients walking freely without the use of a cane.

2562.   Peracchia, G. On the amputations of limbs in freezing injuries and in the wounds of war [In Italian]. *Arch. ital. chir., v. 69 (2), 1947: 143–170.*

Freezing injuries encountered in the course of military operations are discussed. Indications for the amputation of frozen limbs are given together with the surgical techniques required.

2563.   Peronato, G. Surgical treatment of frostbite of first and second degree [In Italian]. *Riforma med., v. 57, Feb. 8, 1941: 177–181.* Abstract, in Italian, in: *Minerva med., Tor., anno 32 (v. 1), Apr. 13, 1941: 374.*

In cases of mild frostbite injury, the making of beak-shaped incisions in affected toes promoted recovery and prevented complications.

2564.   Rivolta, E. Treatment of the grave results of third degree frostbite of the forefoot with transplantation of skin [In Italian]. *Atti Accad. med. lombarda. v. 31, Apr. 17, 1942: 217–221.*

Treatment of 21 cases of 3rd degree frostbite of the forefoot, is described. In cases of amputations of all toes, it was found necessary to provide skin grafts for a satisfactory result. The technique is described.

2565.   Sauerbruch, F., and A. Jung. Treatment of functionally or anatomically conditioned circulatory disturbances by means of cutting and scarification [In German]. *Deut. Zschr. Chir., v. 258 (6–8), 1944: 319–341.*

The author discusses the beneficial effects of cutting and scarification of the legs in frostbite cases, and in several other conditions of circulatory impairment. The series of small cuts allows the drainage of edematous fluid and toxic exudates and thereby retards sepsis and gangrene. It is, according to the author, a simple and easy method which fundamentally is one of interruption of the functions, in that area, of the sympathetic nervous system.

2566.   Schalek, D. Mutilation in frostbite of third degree [Abstract, in German]. *Wien. med. Wschr., v. 94, May 6, 1944: 212.*

A method of treatment of 3rd degree frostbite is presented, based on the experience from 400 cases, of which 99% were of the feet, and only 1% of the hands. Third degree frostbite is exclusively the province of the surgeon. His task lies in the correction of the stump, the prevention of contractures through active exercising of the neighboring articulation, and the fixation of the extremity in proper position, if infection or complications have occurred. Bohler's method, which prescribes immobilisation of the injured extremity in a raised position without a bandage, may be effective. Exclusion of sympathetic innervation has little value. The open treatment promotes rapid mummification and avoids the pain from changing the bandages. In cases of humid gangrene a gypsum splint has to be applied. Amputation should take place only 3–5 days after the appearance of the demarcation line, namely after complete mummification, and should be as conservative as possible. The importance of psychological influences is pointed out; the patient should be kept calm and rested in a special room, under specialized nursing care.

2567.   Schenk, N. A. The condition of the stumps after war-time amputations [In Russian]. *Sovet. med., v. 7 (5–6), 1943: 11–12.*

A great number of cases of amputation following frostbite were studied either 4–6 months after injury during the Finnish War, or 2 days to 2 months after injury during World War II. Of all the cases, 50% had sustained bilateral amputations; 39.5% had multiple injuries; 68% were of the lower extremities; 25.2% were of the fingers and hand. Complications through gaseous infection occurred only in cases involving bullet wounds. The trophic disturbances characteristic of frostbite sequelae in the stump, are enumerated. Defects in the stump included roentgenological bone alterations involving either degenerative atrophic processes or vitreous or varying osteoporosis. The latter condition was very common. After removal of necrotic tissue and re-amputation the wounds healed in 92.7% of the cases by primary intention. As seen from the cases of World War II, early surgery in a specialized hospital greatly shortened the hospital stay of frostbitten patients from 8–10 months to 2–3 months. The prostheses used after frostbite injury, though not differing from those used after other injuries, must be individually adjusted.

2568.   Shimanko, I. I. Types of surgery in gunshot wounds and frostbite of the fingers [In Russian]. *Hosp. delo, 1943 (2–3); 23–24.*

Finger amputations due to frostbite (40 cases) were performed after development of a clear line of demarcation. To hasten the healing, the wound was usually sewn up completely; in cases of abundant purulation only side stitches were used. The time of surgery was determined by the type of gangrene. In dry gangrene it is earlier than in moist gangrene; in the latter, it is done only after some pus resorption has been achieved. A healthy stump was obtained after

2 or 3 weeks; in 2 cases only, purulation lasted up to one month. Post-operative complications occurred in 3 cases.

2569. Silvestrini, L. On the surgical treatment of third degree freezing injury [In Italian]. *In: Atti Congresso Nazionale di Chirurgia di Guerra, May 24–26, 1942, p. 216–219. Roma, 1943.*

In the surgical treatment of 3rd degree frostbite lesions, an antiseptic powder (consisting of tannic acid, 40 parts; salicylic acid, 40 parts; rock alum, 10 parts; and zinc sulfate, 10 parts) is first applied. When the demarcation of the gangrenous area is complete, amputation is performed in such a way that the attachment of prosthetic aids will be facilitated.

2570. Studemeister, A. Contribution to the operative after-treatment of frozen stumps of the feet [In German]. *Deut. Zschr. Chir., v. 258, July 24, 1943: 49–54.*

A "Viesier plastic flap" was used on the stumps following amputation of frostbitten extremities, to promote quicker healing of the stump.

2571. Vicentini, F. Treatment of grave frostbite lesions of the foot and their sequelae [In Italian]. *Sperimentale, v. 98, Dec. 22, 1947: 632.*

This is a report on 465 cases of frostbite, 20 of which were treated surgically by Scagliatti's modification of Lisfranc's disarticulation.

2572. Vogl, A. The care of stump wounds after frostbite of the distal foot [In German]. *Deut. Zschr. Chir., v. 259, Aug. 7, 1944: 235–241.*

Conservative treatment of frostbite injuries is recommended. Where amputation was required the author used preparatory treatment with sulfonamides. Whole skin pedicle grafts, complete with subcutaneous fat, were successfully transplanted on the stumps.

2573. Watermann, H. Choice of amputation for the gangrene following frostbite [In German]. *Zbl. Chir., v. 70, Oct. 30, 1943: 1586–1596.*

In this discussion of indications for amputation—in gangrenous conditions following frostbite of an extremity—with arguments for and against various techniques, the author indicates his preference for Pirogoff's or Syme's procedures.

2574. Ziegler, F. Terminal treatment of severe freezing sequelae by plastic skin surgery [In German]. *Chirurg, v. 17–18, Aug. 1947: 505–507.*

Information is given on a group of 35 surgical operations employing skin grafts, performed on amputation stumps in cases of severe frostbite involving injury to the metatarsus.

See also items: 2143, 2494, 2502, 2624, 2665.

14. Prophylaxis

2575. Anon. Instructions for the prevention and treatment of frostbite [In Russian]. *Moskva, Medgiz, 1942. 63 p.*

These instructions from the Central Military Administration of the Red Army, deal with the etiology, pathogenesis, prophylaxis, and treatment of frostbite injuries. Prophylactic measures are detailed, including the provision of adequate footwear for additional warmth; special treatment of average and excessively perspiring feet; use of chemical heaters; and some simple types of wind protection under frontline conditions. Acclimatization exercises should be continued even in the frontline. The clinical aspects of the 4 degrees of frostbite, first aid, and treatment of frostbite and trench foot, and rules for surgical operation, are discussed in detail.

Early lengthwise incisions (in 2–3 stages) accelerate the determination of the demarcation line. Ointments (Mikulich or Vishnevskiĭ's) are widely used. Physiotherapeutical methods include the use of the Sollux and quartz lamps, or the use of ultraviolet rays, together with a vitamin-rich diet. Epithelization is best achieved under a paraffin layer (applied, first for 2–3, then for 24 hours or more) and is aided by arsonvalization. Final amputation should be performed at the stage of granulating scarification and epithelization. Novocain block, according to Visnnevskiĭ's method, has been found to accelerate healing. Because of the peculiar changes in the nervous system during 3rd and 4th degree frostbite paravertebral block at the level of the nerves serving the extremities, is also recommended. Treatment should then proceed by the open method during the whole hospital stay; periods of exposure in a heated case should be repeated 4–5 times daily.

2576. Anon. Army to use new foot powder to prevent cold injuries. *Med. Bull. Europ. Command, U. S., v. 8, Nov. 1951, 523.*

A new foot powder to reduce perspiration, developed through Army medical research, is said to have reduced foot sweating by as much as 24% during tests in the Artic. It is intended for use in the cold where military situations prevent the changing of socks and shoes. The preparation contains a powdered talc base with aluminum chloride and potassium alum (the anhidrotic agents), as well as boric acid, salicylic acid, and starch. The powder is to be issued to troops in Korea and other cold areas, made up in a series of 7 separate envelopes for a week's supply for the individual soldier. A combination of the foot powder with a new rubber-barrier sock has shown a 60% reduction in perspiration. Additional research is underway to incorporate the rubber-barrier sock into a new rubber boot to eliminate the need for the extra sock.

* 2577. Ar'ev, T. IÃ. The prophylaxis of frostbite [In Russian]. *Voen. med. zh., Moskva, Dec. 1946, (12): 3–8.*

"*Contains* a review article based on the experience of World Wars I and II, and dealing with the causes of frost injury: low-temperature, moisture, mechanical slowing of circulation (e.g., through tight clothing, footwear), general and local decrease of resistance. This is followed by a discussion and presentation of preventive measures of three kinds: (1) group prophylaxis (organization of hygienic field covers and quarters, proper food supply, etc.); (2) proper and hygienic clothing and footgear; (3) personal hygiene. The problem of foot-wear and foot-care is discussed in detail'—Arctic Bibl., v. 4, 1954: 51.

2578. Astaf'ev, A. D. Prevention of frostbite of the feet [In Russian]. *Voen. med. zh., Moskva, 1944, Jan.–Feb.: 76–79.*

In weather when felt boots are too warm and heavy, inner soles made of cloth, cloth socks, preferably a second foot-cloth, and outer shoe laps are recommended for increased warmth of shoes. Such foot-covering is said to yield enough warmth to prevent frostbite of the feet and to be little inferior to the felt boots.

2579. Büttner, K., A. Frank, and J. Bolze. Freezing of the skin on cold metal [In German]. *Deut. Militärarzt., v. 9, Jan. 1944: 18–20.*

The problem of freezing of ungloved hands in contact with cold metal is of considerable military significance. It was found that moist hands froze most readily in touching cold metal or a semi-conductor like glass. Coating the bare hands or the metal with a cold-stable oil was found to afford good protection.

2580. Büttner, K. Physical heat balance in man. *In: German aviation medicine, World War II, v. 2, p. 766–791. Washington, D. C., Department of the Air Force, [1950].*

The section of this chapter entitled Cold on the Extremities (p. 784–791) reports experiments on means of protecting the hand, especially the fingers, against injury from extreme cold (down to −45 °C). Ointments were tested, including various greases and oils, and ointment

---

* Original not seen.

containing histamine or related extracts which are supposed to have a direct dilating effecs on capillaries. Ordinary mittens were found to have little value, but double gloves with thick fur and wool linings were able to prevent abrupt temperature drop. Habituation, massage, preheating, and electrical or chemical heating of the pulse area were all effective. Experiments on protection against freezing fast to metals included tests of various greases, waxes, and cold-resistant oils.

2581. Burnazian, A. I. Provisions for sanitary care of a rifle battalion (forward group) during a march into battle during the winter [In Russian]. *Voen. san. delo, 1938 (1): 29–35.*

In preparation for a military march in winter (December 1937) at −16°C with expected battle activities, the regimental commander ordered the following measures for the prevention of frostbite injuries: (1) Handing out to each soldier of an additional pair of socks, of news-papers to wrap the feet, and of fats for use on exposed areas of the body and for the feet. (2) Checking and mending of the shoes and clothing, with the shoes being provided with an inner sole of felt or, if need be, of straw. (3) Mutual observations to be made for the first signs of frostbite. (4) Short stops to be avoided, with halts of 25–30 minutes and one of 2 hours to be made in inhabited places where the socks should be dried. (5) With the line of march against the direction of the wind, the men marching in the front and on the sides of the column should be changed often. The scouts on horseback to be relieved at least every hour. (6) The chief sanitary officers of every battalion to instruct the men on the measures of frostbite prevention and of first aid. (7) An entire squad never to be assembled in the open. (8) Socks and gloves were to be dried before the night's rest. Fatigue and loss of blood are known to contribute heavily to frostbite casualties. Covered cabs on wheels, provided with blankets and hay, were to be used for the evacuation of the sick, wounded, and those injured by cold. Sanitary in-structors were to check on the carrying out of these measures for frostbite prevention.

2582. Champy, C., A. Giroud, and R. Coujard. The part played by the deficiency of vitamin B in the freezing of feet [In French]. *Bull. Acad. méd., Par., v. 123 (9–10), 1940: 185–192.*

It is shown that a deficiency of vitamin B may be a predisposing factor in frostbite of the feet influencing local neuritic effects. Symptoms of freezing injuries, such as edema followed by discoloration and desquamation of the epidermis, began to appear in from 2 to 5 hours in chickens and pigeons kept in environmental temperatures of −4° to 1°C and −5° to −8°C when they also had a vitamin deficiency. Little or no symptoms appeared in the control room animals or in those kept at a good vitamin level in the cold.

2583. Eisberg, H. B. Some of the problems facing a naval medical officer in the Arctic. *Mil. Surgeon, v. 102, Apr. 1948: 278–283.*

A description of the conditions found in the Arctic, and the steps necessary to prevent cold injury (frostbite or immersion foot), and their treatment under field conditions.

2584. Gaulejac, R. de. Freezing injuries of the face found in aviators [In French]. *Bull. méd., Par., v. 52, Oct. 1, 1938: 705–707.*

Freezing injuries of the face of aviators seem to occur at elevations of about 4,000–5,000 meters and above, and at temperatures of −30° to −40°C and lower, with humid cold favoring their development. Injuries are especially prevalent across the bridge of the nose and on the cheeks where the metal of the oxygen inhaler rests on the face. The use of different types of face masks—some of which are warmed—and of various animal body oils is discussed.

* 2585. K., F. On the use of fats and ointments in cold-injury prevention [In Russian]. *Voen. san. delo, 1943 (2–3); 63–65.*

"*Contains* an historical note on the use of fats and salves for preventing frostbite in earlier wars; prescriptions of ointments used by the Soviet army during the Finnish Campaign (1939)

---

* Original not seen.

and during the winter of 1941–42. The components of these salves are evaluated, and practical results of their use are indicated."—Arctic Bibl., v. 4, 1954: 486.

* **2586. Kobzev, A.** Army activities in wintertime [In Russian]. *In: Enŝsiklopedicheskiĭ slovar' voennoĭ mediŝiny, v. 2: col. 803–814. Ed. by E. T. Smirnov. Moskva, 1947.*

"*Contains* an historical account of largely Russian winter campaigns, including those of World War II; discussion of the effect of winter on the tactical properties of terrain, on roads, light conditions, etc., the effect of the snow cover; special requirements for winter campaigns; effect of environmental conditions on armies and men; diseases prevalent during the Russo-Finnish war (1939–1940). Military medical work during winter actions is described: prevention of frostbite, first aid, night work, etc.; also search and transportation of wounded (with illus. of sleds, skis, toboggans, etc.). Special clothes for sick and wounded; emergency and temporary housing (with illus. of shelters, huts, snowhouses, etc.) care of medicine and instruments, etc. Bibliography (about 20 items)."—Arctic Bibl., v. 4, 1954: 531.

* **2587. Krotkov, F. G.** Prevention of frostbite among the troops [In Russian]. *Voen. san. delo, 1943 (11–12): 61–67.*

"*Contains* a general account dealing with Russian army directives on winter clothing, shoeing and care of feet; body areas most commonly affected by frostbite; personal care and hygiene; shelter and its heating; hot food; special precautions for snipers; chemical pocket heaters; belly-bands."—Arctic Bibl., v. 4, 1954: 555.

* **2588. Levin, A. I., and F. M. Khaletskaia.** Contribution to the problem of the pathogenesis of frostbite. (The role of local disturbances of the blood circulation.) [In Russian]. *Arkh. biol. nauk, v. 60 (3), 1940: 15–24.* Translation in: E. Hope. *Frostbite. Translations from the Russian of a collection of sixteen papers published between 1939 and 1944, p. 43–52. Ottawa, Defence Research Board, Canada, 1950.*

Local ischemia produced in the ears of rabbits rendered that ear very susceptible to frostbite. The authors conclude that the maintenance of an active peripheral circulation is of considerable importance in the prevention of cold injury.

2589. Loos, [H. O.]. On cold injuries [Abstract, in German]. *Klin. Wschr., v. 22, Mar. 13, 1943: 242.*

A study was made of the responses to local injury of the skin caused by frostbite. The varied results obtained suggest that there is an "inner factor" involved. A vasoactive histamine-like substance appears to play an important role in natural resistance to cold. Prophylactic results were encouraging when subjects, who had previously been given histamine, were exposed to cold.

2590. Lowy, A. D. The effect of antihistamine compound on the flare reaction produced by burning or freezing of the skin of normal human beings. (*Thesis, Univ. of Minn.*) *Minneapolis, Minn., Univ. of Minnesota, 1950. 76 p.*

The skin responses in small areas of experimental burning or freezing following pre-treatment of the area with intracutaneous injections of antihistamine (Pyribenzamine), are reported. The flare response of the skin (reddened area before formation of wheal) to freezing was definitely reduced but that to burning was unchanged. Some possible explanations of the mechanisms of the reactions are given.

---

* Original not seen.

2591. Macht, M. B., M. E. Bader, and J. Mead. The inhibition of frostbite wheals by the iontophoresis of antihistaminic agents. *J. Clin. Invest., v. 28, May 1949: 564–566.*

The formation of wheals in frostbitten areas of forearms and thighs of human subjects was inhibited in areas which had been previously treated with the histamine antagonists Pyribenzamine hydrochloride and Benadryl hydrochloride. No other effects of the antihistamines on the healing of the frostbite lesions were observed.

2592. Nechaeva-D'iakonova, A. K. The structure of the walls of the subcutaneous veins of lower limbs [In Russian]. *Khirurgiia, Moskva, v. 6, June 1948: 40–48.*

The great saphenous vein, on the anteriomedial aspect of the ankle, lies in a very superficial position dangerously exposed to cold. Because of this, the protection of the area by warm anklets is advised. Overcooling of this area can contribute decidedly to the fate of the great toe in frostbite.

2593. Novikov, V. Particular features of the work in the sanitary service in the army frontlines in the winter [In Russian]. *Voen. san. delo, 1938 (1): 1–35.*

The struggle against cold occupies a central place in the sanitary service of the army. From the danger of frostbite or general hypothermia arises the urgency of very rapid transportation of the wounded and sick. In the Kwantung army during the Manchurian operation in 1931–1933 there were 1941 frostbite cases out of 6943 incapacitated, 320 of these with 3rd degree injuries. Special attention must be directed toward warm clothing, especially to comfortable, well-greased boots, warm socks, and inner-soles. The feet must be kept dry. In great cold, an additional pair of felt shoes should be given each soldier to change into at the place of rest for the night. Such double footwear was found to safeguard against frostbite. The head and face should be protected underneath the helmet. Clothing and personal equipment should be carefully checked daily, dried and mended. Sufficient quantities of boiling water and hot foot must be ready for the arrival of the men at any halting place and in the trenches.

2594. Patterson, R. H. Effect of prolonged wet and cold on the extremities. *Bull. U. S. Army M. Dep., no. 75, Apr. 1944: 62–70.*

The clinical history, pathology, and treatment of frostbite cases in soldiers during the taking of Attu in the Aleutian Islands by American forces, are discussed. The period of exposure to both wet and cold varied from 3 to 14 days. Preventive measures, for both command and individuals, are outlined.

2595. Prudnikov, ... Experience concerning sanitary provisions for a 700 kilometer march-maneuver under winter conditions [In Russian]. *Voen. san. delo, 1939 (11): 23–35.*

An account is presented of sanitary measures to be observed during prolonged military marches in war time. Training by acclimatization to cold is of primary importance. This can be done by such methods as sleeping without night clothing, daily washing and friction of the torso with cold water, drilling in the cold of early morning, and taking walks in the evening without an overcoat. The gradual process of acclimatization is of primary importance. The drill should not permit the chilling of the body. Before retiring each evening the feet should be washed in cold water, then covered with a solution of alcohol and Formalin and powdered with boric acid. A sufficient amount of grease should be allotted for the annointing of the feet, fingers, and face (also for daily greasing of shoes). Drinking of cold water during winter marches is very harmful; hot strong tea should be used instead. Sufficient sleep is indispensable since exhaustion must be avoided. Frostbite casualties should be carried in heated sleighs. Further measures for sanitary organization in army marches during the winter are detailed.

2596. Richter, W. Prophylaxis and therapy in frostbite [In German]. *Derm. Wschr., v. 115 (43), 1942: 884–887.*

Prophylactic measures against frostbite consist of maintaining the best possible condition of blood circulation and body nourishment and of the recognition of individual sensitivity to cold. Overconsumption of fats is to be avoided as a strain on the vascular system; alcohol excesses and all tight clothing and shoes are also to be avoided. A victim of hypothermia should be placed in a room at 18°–20°C, covered by blankets warmed to 27°–30°C and gradually to 40°C, in order to raise the body temperature. Hot drinks, if possible, or hot enemas are to be given. The heart is to be supported by strophanthin-grape sugar, Cardiazol, etc.; metabolism to be aided by injection of grape sugar or "tutofuchsin" solution. Cold injuries of 1st or 2nd degree may be helped by frost salves but these should not be used in gangrene conditions. In gangrene, sulfonamide powder is useful and particular attention should be paid to the possibility of tetanus infection. In the more serious freezing injuries, vascular spasm must first be curtailed. The author advises waiting beyond the usual 3–4 weeks if possible before resorting to surgery.

2597. Sarkizov-Serazini, I. M. Prophylaxis of frostbite [In Russian]. *Leningrad, Gosudarstvennoe Izdatel'stvo "Fizkul'tura i Sport", 1941. 28 p.*

The etiology and prophylaxis of frostbite are discussed.

2598. Sarkizov-Serazini, I. M. The fundamentals of conditioning and prevention of frostbite [In Russian]. *Leningrad, Gosudarstvennoe Izdatal'stvo "Fizkul'tura i Sport", 1941. 216 p.*

Detailed information is given about the physical therapy of frostbite, as well as the preventive measures to be taken.

2599. Schultze, W. Subsequent treatment of freezing injury and contribution to its prevention [In German]. *Arch. Derm. Syph., Berl., v. 184, Jan. 15, 1943: 65–67.*

In the late management of freezing injuries, irradiation with a carbon-arc lamp is recommended. Where hyperhidrosis has developed, a spray of pure metallic zinc and diachylon is used. Prophylactic measures include the wearing of proper footwear, frequent bathing, and underwater massage.

2600. Sheeley, W. F. Frostbite . . . Eighth Air Force. *Air Surgeon Bull., v. 2, Jan. 1945: 23–25.*

The lack of knowledge about protection from frostbite in the crews of the first B-17's to arrive in Europe, and the methods instituted to combat such injury, are discussed. It was found that about ⅓ of these frostbite cases required hospitalization and even the mild cases were grounded for 4 to 14 days. In order to keep special clothing and equipment in good condition, an order from Headquarters U.S. Eighth Air Force created the Personal Equipment Officer. The arrival of B-17's and B-24's with closed windows helped further in reducing the incidence of frostbite and markedly reduced that of frostbite of the face.

2601. Starlinger, F. On the prophylaxis of freezing injuries in the field [In German]. *Zbl. Chir., v. 69, Nov. 7, 1942: 1779–1782.*

Prophylactic measures are discussed for the prevention of frostbite in troops in the field, together with recommendations for first aid treatment designed to minimize effects of freezing. Measures are discussed for keeping the men warm, dry, well-nourished, and not overly-fatigued. Protection of the feet to avoid cold and wet, is stressed. Prophylaxis, by pharmaco-dynamic methods, might well be afforded by the giving of various substances with some circulatory-stimulating action, such as nitroglycerin, Eupaverin, Priscoline, or hormone compounds such as Padutin, thyroxin, and some of the sex hormones. Casualties from the cold should be kept in a warm place and then transported in a warm ambulance as quickly as possible.

2602. Yoshimura, H. Studies on the training for frostbite-proof. I. [Abstract, in English]. *Jap. J. M. Sc., Biophysics, v. 9, 1944: 8†.*

The feet of subjects were encased in rubber boots and then were immersed in cold water of 0° to −5°C, for periods of 15 to 60 minutes in the course of a month. Temperature reactions of the big toe were measured by thermopile. This treatment by repeated immersions, increased slightly the endurance of the leg against frostbite, but individual variations of the effects were not conclusive.

2603. Zetler, G. Influence of general pre-treatment by antihistaminics on local frostbite [In German]. *Arch. exp. Path., Berl., v. 214, 1951: 316–332.*

Studies were made of the ears of 20 rabbits to establish whether rapid blood coagulation after cold injury can be delayed or removed by antihistaminics, and what influence such an intervention would have on the clinical aspect of the injured part. After depilation, the upper third of one ear was frozen by carbon dioxide snow for 1.5 minutes, while blood tests were taken from the other ear. The freezing of one-third of the rabbit's ear accelerated blood coagulation by 63%. An edema with vesicles appeared, followed by demarcation of the necrosis after 24 days, and finally by a hole 5–6 cm large. Injection of 45 mg/kg Antistin before the onset of frostbite induced a 21% delay in blood coagulation, considerably diminished the local and collateral edema and vesicles, prolonged the duration to the end of demarcation to 36 days, and produced a final defect 1.24 cm² in area. The frostbite injury always produced a severe endarteritis obliterans, and regenerative perichondral cartilage growth appeared, which had previously been unknown. It is deduced that histaminics play an important part in the development of frostbite.

See also items: 63, 574, 622, 673, 852, 1325, 1426, 1901, 1904, 1931, 1950, 2025, 2092, 2104, 2159, 2161, 2171, 2184, 2199, 2205, 2206, 2210, 2225, 2243, 2245, 2261, 2263, 2312, 2377, 2408, 2722, 2726.

15. Sequelae

2604. A., A. Painful late syndrome of light frostbite. *Minerva med., Tor., anno 31 (v. 2), Dec. 15, 1940: 596.*

The paper deals with the less serious freezing injuries suffered by an army division fighting in the Alps in June 1940, especially the painful late effects of such injuries. The injuries are discussed as to etiology, clinical forms, prophylaxis, and immediate and late therapy.

2605. Annovazzi, G., and R. Tosetti. The oscillometric behavior of the pressure and fragility of the capillaries of the limbs as a result of freezing injury [In Italian]. *Atti Accad. med. lombarda, v. 31, Apr. 17, 1942: 208–213.*

A follow-up study was made one year later of 25 cases of severe cold injury, from the Greco-Albanese front, together with an account of the oscillometric findings on the pressure and capillary fragility of several blood vessels of the legs. Persistance of a low oscillometric index of capillary fragility seemed characteristic of the group; capillary pressure did not seem to be greatly changed from the normal. Among the therapeutic measures used were: administration of vitamins (P-P, C, B₁), abolishment of smoking, and use of the pavex apparatus.

2606. Barre, J. A., . . . Juif, and M. Bernhardt. Extensive unilateral syringomyelic syndrome following freezing of a hand [In French]. *Rev. neur., Par., v. 80, Feb. 1948: 128–131.*

Description is given of a case of syringo-myelic syndrome occurring 5 years after frostbite of the hand.

2607. Birch-Jensen, A. An instance of frostbite in the lower extremities with subsequent vascular disease of long duration [In Danish]. *Ugeskr. laeger, v. 101, Mar. 30, 1939: 390–391.*

The author attributes the development of gangrene and vascular diseases, such as thromboangiitis obliterans and endarteritis, to the effects of cold injury. He cites the experience of Danish polar expeditions.

2608. Bollea, J., and A. Cirenei. Neurological and electrical observations on the sequelae of local lesions from cold [In Italian, summaries in Italian, French, English, and German]. *Rass. neuropsich., v. 2, Jan.–Feb. 1948: 84–113.*

A study, 5 years after the original injury, of 18 cases of local lesions from cold has shown in almost all cases some alterations of the different forms of superficial sensibility. No motor defects could be ascribed to lesions of the nerves. The authors conclude that although it is known that nerve tissue is susceptible to injury from cold the greatest damage appeared to be in its functioning in relation to circulatory alterations.

2609. Cirenei, A. Delayed results of local injuries due to cold [In Italian]. *Arch. ed Atti Soc. Chir. ital., v. 48, 1946: 524–526.*

On the basis of the clinical findings in a group of 250 patients, who had experienced various degrees of frostbite injury during the war of 1914–1918 or in subsequent wars, the author observed that secondary changes were still present after a period of many years.

* 2610. Davidenkov, S. N., and A. F. Verbov. Neuritis following frostbite. *Klin. med., Moskva, v. 21 (10–11), 1943: 18–25.*

"*Contains* a report on cases of neuritis often following frostbite. Their symptoms and characteristics (with case histories), types, pathology, etc. are given."—Arctic Bibl., v. 4, 1954: 222.

2611. Fuchsig, P. On endangiitis obliterans and frost gangrene [In German]. *Chirurg, v. 19, July 1948: 314–317.*

The author studied 36 patients with frostbite injuries which had occurred from 5 to 29 months earlier. The pulsations of arteries of the feet could be demonstrated in 69% of the cases. Hyperemia was tested in the legs by means of an Esmarch bandage. From these experiences, and a study of patients with endangiitis obliterans, the author could find no relationship between endangiitis and earlier frostbite injury.

2612. Giliberti, P. Cutaneous epithelioma as sequelae of frostbite [In Italian]. *Clin. chir., Milano, v. 17, n.s., May–June 1941: 397–411.*

A case history of an epithelioma following frostbite, is discussed in detail. A review of the literature is given on p. 409–411.

2613. Giliberti, P. On the sequelae of frostbite reported during the war period 1915–1918 [In Italian]. *Policlinico, sez. prat., v. 48, Oct. 27; Nov. 3, 1941: 1787–1799; 1836–1843.*

Eight out of 15 veterans of World War I still had symptoms of frostbite remaining after 10 to 23 years. Three of them had paresthesia, pain, and feeling of coldness in the affected part. In 3 others, ulcers were still present in the region of the scar. Periarterial sympathectomy was found to be most effective in treatment of the conditions.

2614. Gohrbandt, E. Rehabilitation of frostbite victims [In German]. *Zbl. Chir., v. 70, Oct. 30, 1943: 1584–1586.* Abstract, in English, in: *Bull. war med., v. 5, 1944–45: 552.*

Delayed or lasting frostbite damages, and the problem of drafting of previously frostbitten soldiers into active military duty, are discussed. Although such late damages depend on the severity of the original injury, even quite superficial and limited frostbite may induce a severe, lasting damage. Besides organic disturbances, functional disorders especially in the vascular system, may appear, with manifold clinical aspects. Clinical tests should be made after performance of muscular effort. The men who have suffered earlier cold injury should be divided into two groups: those who still have complaints and pathological changes, and those without them. The first group should not be drafted, or only for limited duty, and must be kept from

---

* Original not seen.

exposure to cold. Of the second group the majority may be drafted. Men who are especially susceptible to cold, namely those liable to autonomous disturbances, should be drafted only for duty in cold-free climates.

2615. Hasenbach, J. Carcinoma of the back of the hand after a calcium chloride-Lysol burn followed by frostbite [In German]. *Zbl. Chir., v. 68 (2), 1941: 67–68.*

A superficial burn of the dorsum of the hand, which had resulted from contact with a mixture of calcium chloride and Lysol, was covered by an improvised dressing. Several days later the same hand was frostbitten. When the wound would not heal, clinical examination revealed an extremely malignant epithelioma with rapid growth and accelerated metastases. The genesis of this type of carcinoma (very rare in limbs) was to be found in existent pathological changes of the skin. But it was undetermined which of the two injuries was the primary cause of the epithelioma. If it was the Lysol burn, then the frostbite injury had prevented the process of regeneration.

2616. Hueper, W. C. Frostbite. *In: Occupational tumors and allied diseases, p. 290–291. Springfield, Ill., Thomas, 1942.*

Frostbite as a possible predisposing factor in subsequent malignant growths is discussed briefly. Several cases are cited from the literature.

2617. Judmaier, F. Vascular modifications in old cases of frostbite injury [In German]. *Schweiz. med. Wschr., v. 80, Nov. 4, 1950: 1180–1183.*

Clinical symptoms and pathological anatomy are discussed, with presentation of 9 case histories, in 97 patients following arteriectomy in long-standing (3 to 22 months) frostbite injuries. Examination of the statistical information available indicated no clear relationship between symptoms and histological findings. Patients with frostbite injuries are considered to be suffering from chronic vascular disorders, and disturbance may continue to appear over a long period of time.

2618. Klykov, M. A. Phantom limb following amputation as a result of frostbite [In Russian]. *Nevropat. psikhiat., v. 19, July–Aug. 1950: 64.*

The statement of a number of authors that after frostbite amputations phantom sensations do not occur, is refuted. In 10 cases of amputation of fingers or toes following frostbite injuries, pronounced phantom sensations were felt, more marked in the hand than in the foot. The pain often presented all aspects of increased protoplastic sensitivity. These sensations resembled in every way those which may follow traumatic injury; they may be very persistent and last several years, often differing from those of the normal limb. In some cases the pain, and occasionally phantom sensations, were suppressed by Novocain block of sympathetic nerves.

2619. Mangeim, A. E. On the morphological and clinical aspects of non-healing ulcerous skin defects after various war injuries [In Russian]. *In: Sbornik nauchnykh rabot evakogospitaleĭ Narkomzdrava Tadzhikskoĭ SSR, p. 93–99. Stalinabad, Izdatel'stvo Narkomzdrava Tadzhikskoĭ SSR, 1945.*

Non-healing ulcerations were often found at the site of former war-wounds or burns, or on amputation stumps following frostbite injuries. Patients with these ulcerations often manifested a defective metabolism (avitaminosis, diathesis, dystrophy), disturbances of the central and peripheral nervous systems, etc. Histological examination of 30 ulcerous wounds showed an old inflammatory process beneath the epithelium, involving the connective tissue which contained a great number of fibroblastic elements. Surgical intervention removed the old connective tissue which had delayed normal healing, and stimulated regeneration in the remaining tissues. A basic condition for the success of this operation is the preparation of the wound tissue and the surgical technique used. Simple excision of the ulcer without secondary stitching was found to shorten the period needed for healing.

2620. Marziani, R. Malignant tumors as a late result of third degree frostbite [In Italian]. *Arch. ortop., Milano, v. 59, Apr.–June 1946: 115–121.*

An epithelioma is described which developed in an area of chronic ulceration on an amputation stump of the foot 20 years after an amputation which had been necessitated by severe frostbite injury.

2621. Maugery, G. The sequelae of freezing injuries, with special reference to disorders of the nerves treated by sympathectomy [In French]. *(Strasbourg Université, Faculté de Medecine. Thèse, No. 84, 1940.) Strasbourg, Clermont-Ferrand, 1940. 48 p.*

This doctoral thesis is based largely on a discussion of the literature on freezing injuries. The information deals with the clinical picture and the classification of frostbite into three degrees according to the severity of the lesion, and with theories regarding the pathogenesis (nervous, vascular, vasomotor, and vitamin lack). Included is a clinical history of the successful treatment by sympathectomy, of the sequelae following frostbite of the lower extremities which had occurred in an Algerian soldier. The soldier had suffered the injuries two and a half months earlier; sequelae included bilateral vasoconstriction, pain, and numbness. Examination of biopsy material taken from each leg following treatment was said to provide conclusive proof of nerve lesions without disclosing any histological evidence of vascular injury. Nevertheless, there existed a permanent vasomotor syndrome.

2622. Novozhilov, D. A. Mud-bath treatment for the sequelae of frostbite [In Russian]. *Vopr. kurort., 1941 (1): 59–62.* Also, in Russian, in: *Voen. san. delo, 1938 (11): 36–39.*

Experience at the Red Army sanatorium in the Sergievsk health resort convinced the author that treatment at a balneary was most effective for the sequelae from frostbite injuries. Roentgenological examination indicated in all cases the presence of osteoporosis, the extent of which directly related to the degree of neurotrophic disturbance, particularly to the degree of pain. For hyperalgesic cases mud baths were kept at 40°–42°C; saline sulfur baths at 42°–44°C. In all cases, a great improvement was achieved, consisting in the decrease or complete disappearance of pain and in increased or restored mobility of the fingers or toes. Osteoporosis was diminished. Trophic ulcers disappeared in 80% and fistulas were closed in 53% of the cases. The major role of the baths appeared to be their rather rapid pain-reducing effect which allowed for subsequent treatment by motion physiotherapy and massage and helped in diminishing trophic disturbances. The circulation was improved, and the process of regeneration, in particular of the nerve endings, was accelerated.

2623. Ollinger, ... Demonstrations from the surgical ward at the University of Bonn [In German]. *Zbl. Chir., v. 73 (3), 1948: 325–327.*

The case of a 38-year-old man is presented who, after frostbite, developed numerous subcutaneous tough nodes, varying in size from that of a pea to that of a walnut, on the dorsal and volar side of the fingers, hands, and forearms. Tough fibrous plates developed on the forearms and resulted in elephantiasis of the hand because of the deviated lymphatic flow. Histologically these nodes and plates consisted of tough, fibrous, connective tissue with inflammatory cellular foci of infiltrates of doubtful origin. The etiology and nature of this strange disease appeared to be unknown.

2624. Pässler, H. W. The treatment of frostbite sequelae [In German]. *Zbl. Chir., v. 70, Nov. 13, 1943: 1596–1606; 1671–1672.*

In a study of 900 cases of frostbite sequelae, 50 cases were found which were combined with endangiitis. In the winter and spring, old scars would break open not because of renewed cold or snow but after a change to warmer weather; in the summer, complaints about pain in amputation stumps would prevail. The x-ray picture showed mostly local damage to the bone, partly of mechanical but mostly of trophic origin, due to insufficient blood supply and to metabolic disturbances. The original surgery had, apparently, often been too conservative, as indicated by sensitivity to pressure, by hyperkeratosis, and by degenerative processes such as typical degeneration of the bone. Late disturbances in the autonomic nervous system consisted in hyperhidrosis, circulatory disorders in the limbs, bladder disorders, or great fatigue. After healing of the wounds, further surgery was performed. Various surgical procedures are discussed. Only general or lumbar anesthesia could be applied. "Echinacin" was helpful in the healing of the wounds. Orthopedic shoes were usually not necessary. The patients were released only after long exercise-marches. A condensation of the paper and a discussion follows on pages 1671–1672.

2625. Rosgen, W., and ... Mamier. On a case of scleroderma resulting from frostbite [In German]. *Münch. med. Wschr., v. 89, Oct. 16, 1942: 889–891.*

A case of frostbite is described with scleroderma, diminished blood calcium, swollen glands, persistent hypotension, and myocardial damage.

2626. Salsano, P. Late effects of frostbite of the leg in the light of radiological, oscillometric, and thermometric evidence [In Italian]. *Gior. med. mil., v. 90, June 1942: 421–434.*

A detailed case history is given of the residual pathological effects on the left leg of a patient who had suffered frostbite of the leg in 1917. X-ray studies were supplemented by observations on the circulation and on the heat-regulatory functions of the skin.

2627. Siegmund, H. Pathologico-anatomical considerations of frostbite with special reference to sequelae [In German]. *Zbl. Chir., v. 70, Oct. 30, 1943: 1558–1570.*

This histological study of frostbitten tissues is based upon extensive human material from cold casualties in the German Army in the winter campaigns of 1942. Tissues from the skin, muscular and vascular systems, and kidneys were studied with special reference to the late results of exposure to cold.

2628. Stenger, E. Differential diagnosis between Raynaud's gangrene and freezing sequelae. (*Dissertation, Univ. Leipzig*) *Leipzig, R. Noske, 1939. 28 p.*

The differential diagnosis of Raynaud's disease and sequelae following freezing injuries is the subject of this dissertation. Also discussed is the treatment of frostbite by short-wave therapy and by sympathectomy.

2629. Stolfi, G., and G. Barlozzino. Disturbances of sensitivity in frostbitten limbs [In Italian]. *Boll. Soc. ital. biol. sper., v. 16, Mar. 1941: 153–154.*

Observations were made on cases of anesthesia, hypoesthesia, paresthesia, and neuralgia in limbs that had been injured previously by frostbite.

2630. Woll, W. Purulent thrombophlebitis in wounds and frostbite of the limbs and its treatment [In German]. *Münch. med. Wschr., v. 90, Nov. 19, 1943: 650–651.*

Description is given of 3 cases of thrombophlebitis following frostbite. High ligation of the affected vein was claimed to have given good results.

See also items: 1895, 1899, 1908, 1942, 1949, 2029, 2036, 2038, 2046, 2047, 2055, 2060, 2062, 2067, 2107, 2114, 2138, 2148, 2162, 2180, 2184, 2199, 2226, 2284, 2311, 2395, 2475, 2498, 2687.

1. General and Mixed

2631.   Anon. Trench foot [In French]. *Gaz. hôp., v. 113, Jan. 31, 1940: 84–85.*

This is a general account of trench foot including information on the clinical signs and symptoms, and on treatment.

2632.   Anon. Trench foot. [*Gt. Brit.*] *Army M. Dep. Bull., No. 44, Feb. 1945: (item 335) 1–2.*

Trench foot, like immersion foot, results from prolonged exposure to cold and damp which is less severe than that producing freezing and frostbite. It causes some tissue damage (especially to skin, muscle, nerves and blood vessels) from transient ischemia to gangrene. The pathology and clinical appearance of trench foot are essentially similar to immersion foot. The earliest signs are swelling of the feet and numbness. It is suggested that if feet are affected, the limbs be kept dry and cool, and that the feet not be rubbed or warmed too fast. Bed rest (average period of 21 days) has been found very effective, but if symptoms persist patient should be referred to a center for treatment of blood vessel injuries.

2633.   Anon. Trench Foot. *Bull. U. S. Army M. Dep., No. 85, Feb. 1945: 1–3.*

Basic principles of a satisfactory control program for trench foot are outlined and discussed briefly under the headings of provisions of suitable equipment, avoidance of unnecessary risk, and enforcement of adequate individual hygiene. Loose-fitting, water-proof or water-resistant boots with felt innersoles, with plenty of clean, dry, socks; avoidance of cramped positions and prolonged immobility; and the cleaning and drying of feet with changes to dry footwear, are recommended. For its development trench foot does not require freezing temperatures but only cold and wet conditions. It is of military significance in that it almost invariably incapacitates front-line fighting troops, the greater proportion of whom will never be able to return to combat duty. Because there is usually a shortage of extra clothing and equipment in a front-line situation, particularly vigorous command action is necessary to enforce individual foot hygiene. Treatment consists essentially of rest, avoidance of local trauma and infection, and elevation of the feet to promote drainage of edema fluid and reduction of metabolism in the affected part. Because of the latter, and also because it may cause considerable pain, extra heat is to be avoided. Areas of necrosis and ulceration which may develop should be treated conservatively.

2634.   Anon. Progress on the trench foot problem. *Bull. U. S. Army M. Dep., v. 3 or No. 88, May 1945: 3.*

The improved conditions with regard to incidence of frostbite cases, in the Fifth Army on the Italian front in January 1945 (223 cases) over that of January 1944 (1,490 cases) are said to be due in large measure to better footgear but also to the greater emphasis on discipline. Experiments showed that footgear alone did not eliminate trench foot if the troops did not follow through with instructions on foot care. Unit responsibility has been adopted as a means of exterminating trench foot; instruction to officers and men in preventive measures are being successfully applied. Among the statistics which show the improvement in trench foot incidence is that of only 1.3% of total infantry strength being afflicted in the period October 1944–February 1945, as against 4% for the same period a year ago.

2635.   Alves Bastos, V. Trench foot [In Portugese]. *Rev. med. mil., Rio., v. 36, Jan.–Mar. 1947: 277–280.*

The etiology, pathogenesis, clinical symptoms, diagnosis, treatment, and prophylaxis of trench foot are discussed. The treatment of all but severe cases is general and local, consisting of elevating the feet, exposing them to air, and of massaging them with lanolin or vaseline. In the more severe cases sympathetic block, vasodilator drugs, tetanus toxoid, or antigangrene sera are suggested. Amputation is usually necessary in only a few cases.

2636. Block, M. Genesis of the gangrenous and reparative processes in trench foot. *Arch. Path., Chic.,* v. 46, July 1948: 1–34.

A study was made of the pathologic anatomy of amputated tissue from cases of trench foot.

2637. Boland, F. K., Jr., T. S. Claiborne, and F. P. Parker. Trench foot. *Surgery,* v. 17, Apr. 1945: 564–571.

The symptoms, clinical course, and etiologic factors are presented for 125 cases of trench foot. The patients were studied in a general hospital, 1 to 4 weeks after exposure and the onset of symptoms. Patients were hospitalized for an average of 61 days, and even the milder cases of trench foot were disabling.

2638. Burch, G. E., H. L. Myers, R. R. Porter, and N. Schaffer. Rate of water loss from the skin of the foot of normal and trench foot subjects. *Am. J. Physiol.* v. 146, July 1946: 370–375.

The rate of water loss from the plantar and dorsal surfaces of the feet of trench-foot patients was measured and compared with similar measurements made on the feet of normal subjects. No differences were noted. It is concluded that the rate of water loss cannot be used as a criterion for determining the return to normal in cases of mild trench foot.

2639. Burch, G. E., H. L. Myers, R. R. Porter, and N. Schaffer. Objective studies on some physiologic responses in mild chronic trench foot. *Bull. Johns Hopkins Hosp.,* v. 80, Jan. 1947: 1–70.

A group of 46 patients were studied in an attempt to find whether these patients who had formerly suffered from acutely active but uncomplicated trench foot still showed residual signs of active disease. Skin temperature measurements, rate of re-filling of pressure-emptied vessels of the skin, and the occlusion-reactive hyperemia test were used as methods for estimating the degree of mild and chronic, but active, trench foot. The results of these tests were sufficiently promising to warrant further observations on larger groups of patients.

2640. Cutler, E. C. Experiences of an Army doctor in the European Theater of war. *Am. J. Surg.,* v. 73, June 1947: 637–650.

Lack of appreciation of the significance of the disorder known as "trench foot" is said to have brought about the incapacitation of 45,000 soldiers in the European Theater [World War II].

2641. Dry, T. J. Experiences with late trench foot and frostbite. *Nebraska M. J.,* v. 31, Nov. 1946: 443–446.

During the period of Feb. 2, 1945 to July 29, 1945, 4,958 patients with trench foot and frostbite were admitted to the U. S. General Hospital, Camp Carson, Colorado. This review of the group of cases includes information on the clinical and pathological aspects, the effect of cold injuries on various systems of the body, and the phenomenon of pathological sweating. To avoid the orthopedic difficulties seen often as sequelae of cold injuries, active functional rehabilitation of the feet was stressed. The medical phase of the treatment of these cases involved orientation and re-education; exercise, either in groups or individually; foot hygiene; and adequate foot support, with shoes being fitted about one size larger than the accustomed size and often supplied with a metatarsal arch support.

2642. Edwards, J. C., M. A. Shapiro, and J. B. Ruffin. Trench foot; report of 351 cases. *Bull. U. S. Army M. Dep.,* No. 83, Dec. 1944: 58–66.

This is a general account of trench foot in World War II. Included is information on the clinical picture, grades of severity, pathology, treatment, and rehabilitation. The report is based upon a study of 351 cases observed in an American military hospital.

2643. Friedman, N. B. The pathology of trench foot. *Am. J. Path., v. 21, May 1945: 387–433.*

This elaborate study of the morbid anatomy of trench foot is based upon specimens from 14 cases sent to the Army Medical Museum in Washington, D. C. Clinical data, gross pathologic findings, roentgenologic data, and microscopic findings are given in detail. The conclusion is reached that all injuries due to exposure to cold show a common pattern resulting from a similar sequence of events. A bibliography of 115 references (p. 410–414) is preceded by 10 pages of illustrations.

2644. Knight, B. W. "Trench Foot" in civilians. *Brit. M. J., 1940 (v. 2), Nov. 2: 610–611.*

This brief note reports cases resembling trench foot observed in persons sitting up all night either at home or in an air-raid shelter.

2645. Krause, L. A. M., J. J. Wallace, and J. J. Silverman. The incidence of palpable pulsations in convalescent trench foot; an analysis of 500 patients at an Army general hospital. *Am. J. M. Sc., v. 211, June 1946: 729–732.*

No significant differences were found in the incidence of palpable dorsalis pedis and posterior tibial pulsations in 500 patients convalescent from trench foot, as compared with 906 infantrymen with no circulatory disorders of the extremities.

2646. Kreyberg, L. Trench foot. *In: Inter-Allied Conferences on War Medicine, London, 1942–1945, p. 139–140.* Ed. by H. L. TIDY *and* J. M. BROWNE KUTSCHBACH. *New York, Staples Press, 1947.*

Trench foot and allied disorders are discussed briefly, with special reference to the clinical terminology.

2647. Leigh, O. C. A report on trench foot and cold injuries in the European theater of operations, 1944–1945. *Ann. Surg., v. 124, Aug. 1946: 301–313.*

This information is taken from a report of November 15, 1944, from the Trench Foot Study Project initiated at the 108th (U. S.) General Hospital. It is based upon the study of about 500 cases. Etiological factors, clinical and pathological aspects, and treatment are given. Comparative casualties from trench foot among the various armies (British and French) in the European Theater are also mentioned.

2648. Martins Pereira, H. A. Influence of cold on the health of combatants [In Portuguese]. *Resenha med., Rio, v. 15, Jan.–Feb. 1948: 5–9.*

This article covers the etiology, clinical aspects, prophylaxis, and treatment of frostbite and trench foot.

2649. Michaël, P. R. Burns and cold injury [In Dutch]. *Geneesk. gids., v. 18, June 7, 1940: 494–498.*

The prophylaxis, prognosis, and therapy of frostbite and trench foot are discussed.

2650. Monsaigneon, A. Frostbite and trenchfoot [In French]. *Presse méd., v. 48, Feb. 7–10, 1940: 166–168.*

This is a general account of the etiology, clinical aspects, and treatment of frostbite and trench foot.

2651. Muñoz Calero, A. Freezing injuries [In Spanish]. *Madrid, Imprenta Provincial, 1945. 103 p.*

This monograph deals with general freezing injuries with special reference to frostbite and trench foot. An extensive bibliography appears on pages 93–103.

2652. Rabut, R. Trench foot [In French]. *Presse méd., v. 47, Dec. 27–30, 1939:
1683–1684.*

This general discussion of trench foot involves information on its etiology, pathology, clinical
signs, complications, diagnosis, and preventive and curative treatment.

2653. Ragan, C. A., and A. E. Schecter. Clinical observations on early trench
foot. *Bull. U. S. Army M. Dep., v. 4, Oct. 1945: 434–440.*

This study is based upon cases of trench foot observed during the Italian campaign. The
clinical picture and pathogenesis of early trench foot is described in detail.

2654. Redisch, W. Chronic trenchfoot; a problem in the care of World War
II veterans. *Mil. Surgeon., v. 101, Dec. 1947: 509–513.*

Based on clinical impressions of a fairly large group of patients seen at a Veterans Administration Regional Office, it was found that chronic trench foot presented itself as a clinical
entity which was peculiar to the Veteran group; men afflicted with this condition were suffering from a true physical handicap. It was suggested that these cases be regarded as having
an impaired regulation of the peripheral blood circulation and that their care should be in
peripheral vascular clinics.

2655. Schecter, A. E., and C. A. Ragan. Trench foot; the diagnostic value of
"ischemic pain." *Bull. U. S. Army M. Dep., v. 3 or No. 89, June 1945: 98–100.*

In patients with trench foot, the application of a standard sphygmomanometer around
the thigh with inflation to about arterial pressure, produced pain which appeared at the
base of the toes along the longitudinal arch of the foot. The speed of onset of the pain is believed
to be an indication of the severity of the trench foot. In the more severe cases, pain appeared
after a brief period of occlusion at rest; in the less severe, pain appeared after some delay at
rest or only after exercise. In general the pain appeared in the trench foot cases in about 1
minute; in control cases after 5 minutes. In the healthy control subjects the pain occurred
along the dorsum of the foot at the level of the malleoli and along the anterior surface of the
lower leg. It is suggested that the term "ischemic pain" be applied to this phenomenon and
the procedure be used in forward areas to determine accurately and promptly the diagnosis
of trench foot. If the reaction were found to be negative, the period of observation usually
needed for such a diagnosis could be eliminated. The response of the individual patient was
found to be constant despite temporary changes in the skin temperature of the foot.

2656. Silverman, J. J. An inquiry into the incidence of hyperhidrosis in convalescent trench foot. *Ann. Int. M., v. 25, Oct. 1946: 702–710.*

The incidence of hyperhidrosis was studied in 200 patients in various stages of convalescence
from trench foot. A group of 100 general medical patients were used as controls. The degree
of trench foot appeared to have no bearing on the incidence of excessive sweating. The author
concludes that hyperhidrosis has no diagnostic significance in trench foot and when present
other causes should be sought.

2657. Toone, E. C., and J. P. Williams. Trench foot; prognosis and disposition.
Bull. U. S. Army M. Dep., v. 5, Feb. 1946: 198–210.

An analysis of trench foot emphasizes the fact that it is, even in mild cases, a serious disabling
military disease. The importance of prevention is stressed. Experience of the authors is that
less than 10% of cases of trench foot can be returned to full duty after recovery.

2658. White, J. C. Trench foot, shelter foot, and immersion foot. *Am. J. Nurs.
v. 43, Aug. 1943: 710–713.*

A brief general account is given of the etiology, clinical and pathological features, and
treatment of trench foot, shelter foot, and immersion foot.

2659. White, J. C. Trench foot and immersion foot. *In: American Academy of Orthopaedic Surgeons. The American Academy of Orthopaedic Surgeons presents lectures on reconstruction surgery . . ., p. 100–107. [Ann Arbor, Mich., J. W. Edwards], 1944.*

This general account of immersion foot and trench foot is based upon experience with shipwreck survivors and casualties from the Battle of Attu. Etiology, pathological physiology, and treatment are discussed.

2660. White, J. C., and W. B. Scoville. Trench foot and immersion foot. *N. England J. M., v. 232, Apr. 12, 1945: 415–422.*

This is a general account of trench foot and its seagoing counterpart immersion foot. The report is based upon observations of more than 100 cases of immersion foot and the clinical records and experiences supplied by numerous medical officers who handled trench foot cases especially from the Aleution campaign. Pathological physiology, clinical picture, and treatment are given in detail.

See also items: 1764, 1910, 1922, 1929, 1936, 1937, 1952, 1975, 2188, 2717.

2. Prophylaxis and Therapy

2661. Anon. Medicine and the war; trench foot. *J. Am. M. Ass., v. 126, Nov. 4, 1944: 644.*

This editorial notes the revision in regulations for definitive treatment of trench foot, as issued by the War Department in the Technical Bulletin, Medicine, no. 81, of August 4, 1944 (item 2663). Only in the case of incipient gangrene should the bed patient suffering from trench foot have the feet elevated above heart level.

2662. Anon. The prevention of trench foot. *Bull. U. S. Army M. Dep., v. 3 or No. 87, Apr. 1945: 1–3.*

Proper footgear is important in the prevention of trench foot but alone will not solve the problem. The success of prevention depends on intelligent use of footgear coupled with proper foot care, and it rests with the individual soldier after he has been given the necessary instruction. During 1944 two items of instruction on prevention of trench foot were issued: War Department Circular No. 312 and Technical Bulletin TB Med. 81. Modifications made in the shoe pac have been made to improve its "ground-grip"; these pacs are to be fitted loosely enough for wear with one or two pairs of socks. Socks should be fitted comfortably loose, so there will be no constriction of circulation, but not loosely enough to wrinkle. A thin cardboard folder entitled Your Enemies; Germans and Trench Foot, has been issued to enlisted men of the 36th Infantry Division to give concise information on care of the feet. Daily care of feet even under adverse conditions can be carried out by removal of shoes and rubbing of the feet at least once a day with foot powder; exercise of the feet can be done by wiggling the toes or by pushing with them against the end of the trench. Changes to clean, dry, socks should be made as often as possible. If trench foot develops the soldier should be placed on his back with feet raised about 15 inches above his body; feet should be kept dry and cool— do not rub them—; and medical aid should be summoned.

2663. Anon. Trench foot. *War Dep. Tech. Bull., TB Med. 81, War Department, Washington, D. C. Aug. 4, 1944: 1–6. Also in: Bull. U. S. Army M. Dep., v. 4, Sept. 1945: 265–271.*

Trench foot is discussed under the headings of definition, pathogenesis and morbid anatomy, clinical manifestations, prophylaxis, and treatment both initial and definitive. During initial or emergency treatment the patient should not be allowed to walk on damaged feet, all constricting clothing or shoes should be removed, and great care exercised in handling the feet to avoid pressure necrosis or further trauma and infection. While it is desirable to warm the patient, the feet should be kept cool. The same general principles which underlie the initial treatment should be continued in definitive treatment. The patient should be kept in bed with the affected parts on a horizontal level or elevated, by use of pillows, only slightly above heart level. Later (item 2661) a correction of this wording was issued stating that elevation of the extremities should be done only if there is no evidence of inadequate circulation (incipient gangrene), otherwise they should be kept horizontally. The amount and subsidence of edema should determine the length of the period of bed rest. The body should be kept warm but the feet moderately cool (65°–70°F). Cooling by use of ice bags is especially helpful during periods of extreme hyperemia.

2664.   **Barskiĭ, A. V.** The treatment of the neuritic form of trench foot, by intra-neural block [In Russian]. *Khirurgiia, Moskva, 1944 (4): 69–70.*

Description is given of two types of trench foot (in addition to the severe form, which runs a course similar to 4th degree frostbite) as follows: (1) the so-called serous form, with edema, but free from necrosis, and (2) the neuritic form, which is accompanied by severe pain but is without edema or necrosis. The technique of intraneural block by Yasenetsky's method of regional anesthesia, using procaine infiltration anesthesia of the nerves of the foot, is given in detail.

2665.   **Bates, R. R.** Surgical aspects of trench foot. *Surg. Gyn. Obst., v. 83, Aug. 1946: 243–248.*

From February 7, 1945 to June 7, 1945, 4,892 soldiers with trench foot and frostbite passed through the U. S. Army General Hospital at Camp Carson, Colorado. Of this group, 264 had persistent gangrene and required treatment. This paper reviews the results of treatment in these cases. Surgery was generally delayed until the last possible spontaneous healing had occurred. Complications, sequelae, and prostheses are also described.

2666.   **Beecher, H. K.** Early care of the seriously wounded man. *J. Am. M. Ass., v. 145, 1951: 193–200.*

The early care of the wounded man from the time of injury up to the time of surgical repair, is summarized. Information is included on resuscitation, transfusion, preoperative procedures, narcotics, and anesthetics. The section on Care of men with specific wounds (p. 196–197) includes a paragraph entitled Trench Foot (Frostbite).

2667.   **Berson, R. C., and R. J. Angelucci.** Trench foot. *Bull. U. S. Army M. Dep., No. 77, June 1944: 91–99.* Also in: *Arch. Phys. Ther., v. 25, Aug. 1944: 483–487, 506.*

This discussion of trench foot is based upon experience in a U.S. Army hospital on 88 consecutive cases. One group of patients was given a regular hospital diet, absolute bed rest, and sufficient codeine to maintain them comfortably; another was given, in addition, Buerger's exercises four times daily; and a third group was given no exercise but was administered 50 mg thiamine chloride hypodermically twice daily. During 14 days of observation no significant differences in response to the therapies could be detected. Responses of patients to Novocain blockade of the lumbar sympathetic ganglia were very varied. Application of dry cold, by use of ice bags, to one or both feet, which were often gangrenous, brought about a marked analgesic effect and did no appreciable harm. Although the importance of slow thawing and the application of actual cooling during the period of thawing has been stressed, only 34 patients of the group had had such treatment on admittance to the hospital. The importance of considering trench foot as an emergency and beginning cooling at once, is stressed. Prohibition of walking, of any constrictive clothing or shoes, and of all warming agents directly to the feet, is advised. Sympathetic block should be avoided at this early stage. From a statistical study of case histories of other patients, presumptive evidence indicates that a past history of symptoms from exposure, a family history of diabetes and hypertension, and a past history of heavy smoking, are not predisposing factors.

2668. Bigelow, W. G. The modern conception and treatment of frostbite. *Canad. M. Ass. J., v. 47, Dec. 1942: 529–534.*

In this survey and discussion of the literature dealing with frostbite and trench foot, are included some information on the pathology and therapy. 27 refs.

2669. Gil y Gil, C. Methods employed and results obtained in the treatment of trench foot [In Spanish]. *Rev. espan. med. cir., v. 2 (5), 1939: 9–29.*

Treatment of a group of 309 soldiers with trench foot (97 of these by the author and his staff) is discussed. It was noted that many in the group were suffering from 3rd degree injuries. Therapy was of three types: medical, surgical, and physical. Medical treatment involved use of antiseptics (Rivanol, tryptoflavin), vasodilators (Padutin and acetylcholine), and a drug (Genergeno, whose active principle was ergotamine) acting on the sympathetic nervous system. Surgical treatment was by partial or total resection or periarterial sympathectomy. Physical methods employed careful use of heat, warm air, and short-wave diathermy. Injuries of the 1st and 2nd degree, in a fairly benign state, were treated medically and with bed rest. In case of pain, diathermy was used except for those few patients who suffered severe pain and cyanosis. Patients with 3rd degree injuries were treated by diathermy, which has a vasodilator action.

2670. Greene, R. The prophylaxis of trench foot. *Brit. M. J., 1945 (v. 1), Feb. 24: 270–271.*

The author states that trench foot is almost entirely preventable and that the incidence is usually an index of discipline, given proper training and equipment. He warns against dulling the role of the adrenal medulla, the thyroid, and the autonomic nervous system by being habitually overclad. He advises that no more clothing be worn than that which just prevents shivering, and that adaptation to cold be aided by short periods of exercise in a minimum of clothing in cold weather. Clothing should be water-proof, wind-proof, loose enough to prevent any vascular constriction, and layered to trap air in the interstices for insulation. He advises exercise, and periods of rest with feet above head, to prevent venous stagnation, and intracapillary pressure. Facilities to warm the feet are valuable, but the availability of hot food is even more important.

2671. Greene, R. Trench foot. *In: Inter-Allied Conferences on War Medicine, London, 1942–1945, p. 140–143.* Ed. by H. L. TIDY and J. M. BROWNE KUTSCHBACH. *New York, Staples Press, 1947.*

Preventive measures in the field are emphasized in this brief general statement on trench foot.

2672. Lake, N. C. Frostbite and trench foot. *In: Surgery of modern warfare, Part 2, p. 153–328.* Ed. by H. BAILEY. *Edinburgh, Livingstone, 1944.*

In Chapter XV, Frostbite and trench foot (p. 153–170), are discussed some of the general effects of exposure to cold together with some information on the prevention and treatment of frostbite and trench foot. Protective clothing should be in as many layers as possible and made of a heat-retaining material, wool still being the best. Clothing must not be tight. Although there is some question of the efficacy of oiling the skin, recent observations indicate that for severe exposures the method may be really protective since it may help to induce supercooling. In trench foot, protection from moisture is also essential since it is the moisture rather than the degree of cold which causes damage. In either frostbite or trench foot, treatment consists of slow and gentle thawing with the temperature kept only slightly above that of the frozen part. Body heat should be increased by hot drinks and food. Raising the limb to a considerable angle is a simple and easy method to help control exudation and edema formation. Immediate treatment with calcium and vitamins C and P should be instituted; giving of anti-tetanus serum is advisable. In the late stages, various physiotherapeutic methods, including the use of heat, are to be considered to combat inelasticity and rigidity of the injured area. Shelter foot and immersion foot probably bear some relationship to trench foot. Debility and malnutrition, especially a shortage of vitamins C and P, are again predisposing factors.

2673. Mallet-Guy, P., and J. J. Lieffring. Lumbar infiltration and sympathectomy in feet injured by cold [In French]. *Mém Acad. chir., Par., v. 66, Jan. 31, 1940: 136–140.* Abstract, in French, in: *Bull. méd., Par., v. 54, May 11, 1940: 235.*

The excellent results from Novocain infiltration of the sympathetic nerves or from lumbar sympathectomies, are noted in treatment of feet injured by cold. There was a disappearance of subjective, but not of objective, signs following such infiltration. Examination of the injured feet by oscillometric methods following hot and cold baths, showed the absence of normal vasometric reactions.

2674. Redisch, W., and O. Brandman. Use of vasodilator drugs in chronic trench foot. *Angiology, v. 1, Aug. 1950: 312–316.*

Clinical studies were made of the effects of 5 "vasodilator" drugs—aminophylline, papaverine, Etamon, Priscoline, and Roniacil tartrate—on 100 patients with chronic trench foot. Only Priscoline and Roniacil tartrate produced beneficial results. Priscoline was beneficial only if given parenterally, whereas nicotinic alcohol tartrate (Roniacil tartrate) was effective by mouth.

2675. Ryles, C. S. Trench foot. *In: Inter-Allied Conferences on War Medicine, London, 1942–1945, p. 143–145. Ed. by* H. L. TIDY *and* J. M. BROWNE KUTSCHBACH. *New York, Staples Press, 1947.*

Routine field measures for the prevention of trench foot are discussed as they are practiced in the British Army. The use of a foot powder (containing boric acid, camphor, and talc powder) and a foot soap (containing sodium borate and camphor), together with an outline of instructions for keeping the feet dry and clean, are credited with drastically decreasing the incidence of trench foot. Trench foot is caused by prolonged standing in cold water or wet mud, with moisture being more of a factor than is cold. Unclean feet, fatigue, want of exercise, and constriction at any point on the leg are predisposing factors. The main symptom is pain, with foot being cold, numb, swollen, and red. Boots should be loose and provision should be made for drying them; clean, dry, heavy woolen socks should be made available.

2676. Shumacker, H. B., Jr. The surgical treatment of gangrene in trench foot. *Surg. Gyn. Obst., v. 83, Oct. 1946: 513–520.*

Experience in the surgical management of gangrene in trench foot is reported. The problems of infection, vasoconstriction, amputation, skin grafting, and plastic surgery are discussed in detail and numerous illustrations are provided.

2677. Soupault, ..., and ... Orsoni. Cold-injured feet (Infiltration by lumbar sympathectomy). [In French]. *Mém. Acad. chir., Par., v. 66, Mar 13, 1940: 358–359.*

Treatment of trench foot by lumbar sympathetic infiltration with Syncaine solutions, is reported.

2678. Stricker, T., and F. Buck. Treatment of trench foot by infiltration of the lumbar sympathetic with Scurocaine. Influence on pain and ischemic phenomena [In French]. *Mém. Acad. chir., Par., v. 66, Feb. 28, 1940: 235–242.*

Severe and very painful cases of trench foot affecting both feet were successfully treated by by injection of Scurocaine into the lumbar sympathetic chain. In the discussion following the report, G. JEANNEY stated that the gangrenous condition found in trench foot is usually fairly superficial. He suggested the use of oscillometric methods to determine the extent of arterial damage, and then conservative treatment, hoping to avoid amputation. The use of lumbar infiltration, for both anesthetic and antiseptic reasons, and of perifemoral sympathectomy, is mentioned. BASSETT questioned the practicality of sympathetic infiltration in handling large groups of such casualties. Many cases of cold-injured feet and trench feet encountered in the army would usually recover quickly with rewarming and with bed rest.

2679. Teneff, S. Trench foot [In Italian]. *In:* O. UFFREDUZZI *and* S. TENEFF. *War surgery, p. 558–561. Torino, Unione Tipografico-Editrice Torinese, 1940.*

The pathogenesis and symptomatology of trench foot are discussed, distinguishing it from other cold injuries of the foot. Prophylaxis and general therapeutic measures are outlined. A bibliography appears on pages 560–561.

See also items: 732, 1572, 1767, 2239, 2249, 2545, 2725, 2732.

3. Sequelae

2680. Abramson, D. I., and H. B. Shumacker, Jr. Sequelae of trench foot and their treatment by lumbar sympathectomy [Abstract]. *J. Laborat. Clin. M., v. 31, Apr. 1946: 479–480.*

This discussion of the sequelae of trench foot and their management, is based on a study of 567 patients. Three categories were distinguished clinically, and the value of sympathectomy was reviewed.

2681. Abramson, D. I., D. Lerner, H. B. Shumacker, Jr., and F. K. Hick. Clinical picture and treatment of the later stage of trench foot. *Am. Heart. J., v. 32, July 1946: 52–71.*

A group of 633 cases of trench foot in American soldiers was studied. The cases were seen two to thirteen months after initial exposure. The clinical picture is described together with late sequelae; early treatment is evaluated. Follow-up studies were begun on 250 patients returned to civilian life.

2682. Block, M. Pathology of the late sequelae of trench foot. *Proc. Inst. M. Chicago, v. 16, Apr. 15, 1947: 370–372.*

The author discusses the histological changes in the epidermis, dermis, and subcutaneous tissues of biopsy specimens taken from specific areas of the ankle and lower leg of 19 patients with trench foot, suffered previously in the European Theater of Operation.

2683. Block, M. Histologic aspects of the skin in the late stages of trench foot. *Arch. Path., Chic., v. 44, Oct. 1947: 360–371.*

Studies were made on the pathology of trench foot based upon biopsy specimens from 15 patients with no complications and in late stages of the disease. Material from 8 normal controls was also studied. The biopsy specimens from these patients as a group failed to reveal any pathological changes when compared with the eight controls of the same age group.

2684. Kirtley, J. A. Experiences with sympathectomy in peripheral lesions. *Ann. Surg., v. 122, July 1945: 29–38.*

Vasospasms of the extremities are discussed as they were encountered in 38 patients in a general hospital in a theater of operations. A group of 17 cases of trench foot with sequelae are described. While vasospasm and gangrene may benefit from sympathectomy, continued pain following trench foot is not likely to be relieved by the operation.

2685. Krontiris, A. Experiences with sympathectomy for sequelae of trench feet [In English]. *Ann. Surg., v. 125, Apr. 1947: 505–507. Also, in Italian, in: An. cirug., B. Air., v. 6 (4), 1947: 515–516.*

Report is made on 27 cases of sequelae in trench foot, acquired by Greek soldiers in the Albanian campaign of 1941, and treated by lumbar sympathectomy. The author considers this operation to be generally satisfactory as regards pain and vasometric troubles but only a temporary and doubtful palliative for the healing of ulcers and other neurotrophic sequelae.

2686. Latimer, J. W. Postwar aspects of the trench foot problem. *Med. Clin. N. America, v. 30, Mar. 1946: 421–429.*

Current concepts of trench foot, its etiology, pathogenesis, clinical picture, and treatment are discussed. The information is based upon the literature and the author's personal observations on 250 cases. Emphasis is placed upon late stages of the disease since such cases were coming to the attention of civilian doctors as soldiers so afflicted were leaving the armed services.

2687. Mendelowitz, M., and H. A. Abel. Quantitative blood flow measured calorimetrically in human toe in normal subjects and in patients with residua of trench foot and frostbite. *Am. Heart J., v. 39, Jan. 1950: 92–98.*

The average blood flow in the foot of each of a group of 41 patients with residual symptoms of trench foot and frostbite, was significantly decreased from that of a group of healthy individuals. Organic obstruction or constriction of the small arteries of the foot is thought to be a probable cause for this decrease.

2688. Paddock, F. K. Chronic disability in mild cases of trench foot. *N. England J. M., v. 234, Mar. 28, 1946: 433–437.*

In a study of the late manifestations of trench foot of moderate severity, related observations of the arterioles, capillaries, and venules revealed that there was increased arteriolar tone, apparently secondary to increased sympathetic stimulation, but no evidence of arteriolar obstruction. The capillaries and venules appeared to be normal. Besides superficial hypalgesia, there was frequently diminution of temperature, vibration, and position sense; poor toe-flexion did not appear to result from any obvious structural abnormality; deep-seated sensitivity to cold tended to be absent. It would appear that the difficulties encountered in the late stages of mild trench foot are more dependent on neural than on vascular damage; microscopic examination of the tissue tends to confirm this concept.

2689. Redisch, W., O. Brandman, and S. Rainone. Chronic trench foot: a study of 100 cases. *Ann. Int. M., v. 34, May 1951: 1163–1168.*

A study of 100 cases in the late chronic phase of trench foot—the acute phase had occurred during the winter of 1944–45 in the European campaign—supported the concept that this condition was essentially characterized by a disturbance in regulation of the peripheral blood flow. An abnormal sensitivity to cold was the most incapacitating feature of the disease.

2690. Shumacker, H. B., Jr., and D. I. Abramson. Sympathectomy in trench foot. *Ann. Surg., v. 125, Feb. 1947: 203–215.*

The effects of lumbar sympathectomy in the treatment of sequelae of trench foot, are studied. Sympathectomy accelerated healing in patients with extensive gangrene; it was of aid in treating marked hyperhidrosis; and helped reduce cold sensitivity. It is a definite aid in certain cases of trench foot.

See also item: 2639.

F. IMMERSION FOOT

1. General

2691. Anon. Immersion foot. *Bull. U. S. Army M. Dep., no. 70, Nov. 1943: 26–33.*

Immersion foot is the term applied to the condition resulting from prolonged immersion of the feet in water, usually associated with dependency and immobility of the lower extremities and with constriction of the limbs by shoes or clothing. The condition usually follows immersion in very cold sea water but it may also occur in subtropical waters; it is essentially different from frostbite but similar to trench foot and shelter foot. It is conceivable that the increase of heat loss from the skin surface is the only specific action contributed by the immersion. The condition is discussed in some detail as to pathogenesis and morbid anatomy; classification; signs and symptoms; prophylaxis; treatment; first aid; and definitive treatment. Prophylactic measures involve keeping the feet as dry and warm as possible; avoiding cramped positions; keeping upper part of body dry and out of exposure to cold winds; avoiding tight clothing, socks, shoes, and garters; and of maintaining nutrition at as high a level as possible and avoiding alcoholic beverages. Treatment involves bed rest, avoidance of local trauma and infection, and elevation of feet to promote drainage of edema fluid and reduction of metabolism in the affected parts. The patient should be warmed but too rapid rewarming should be avoided; cooling by the careful use of ice bags may aid in the hyperemic stage. Massage or the application of local antiseptic solution should not be used. In cases of intractable edema and pain, Novacain block of the sympathetic ganglia can be done. Compression dressings or an elastic bandage may be cautiously applied even though the value of the method of treatment has not yet been established. Later, physiotherapy should be used if the movement of the toes has become limited by fibrosis or edema.

2692.   Blackwood, W., and H. Russell. Experiments in the study of immersion foot. *Edinburgh M. J., v. 50, July 1943: 385–398.*

Histological findings in the tails of rats after prolonged immersion in artificial sea water (4°–5°C), are reported. Slight lesions appeared after 48 hours, and marked lesions after 96 hours of exposure. Three series of rats were studied, each group being allowed to recover at a different rate. The injuries were confined to muscle and nerve, no injuries being evident in skin, subcutaneous tissue, and blood vessels. The findings from the experimental treatment confirm the clinical observations that immersion foot lesions should not be heated. Numerous microphotographs, and a short bibliography of 14 references, follow the paper.

2693.   Blackwood, W. Injury from exposure to low temperature: pathology. *Brit. M. Bull., v. 2 (7), 1944: 138–141.*

A brief summary is made of the pathological changes observed in immersion foot and in frostbite. Included are illustrations of the pathology of immersion foot as seen in human material and in experimental animals.

2694.   Blackwood, W. Studies in the pathology of human "immersion foot." *Brit. J. Surg., v. 31, Apr. 1944: 329–350.*

This account of the pathological anatomy of immersion foot is based upon detailed studies of tissues from 14 cases. Included are numerous black and white as well as colored illustrations of gross and microscopic specimens.

2695.   Blackwood, W., and H. Russell. Further experiments in the study of immersion foot. *Edinburgh M. J., v. 52, May 1945: 160–165.*

This paper follows an earlier study (item 2693) in which changes were observed in the tails of rats 90 to 365 days after exposure to wet and cold in artificial sea water. As in the earlier experiments, nerves and muscles in the rats' tails were found to be most directly affected by wet and cold. Nerves were found to make a slow progressive recovery, but muscles showed much variability.

2696.   [DeBakey, M., and J. C. White.] Immersion foot. *Air Surgeon Bull., v. 1, Apr. 1944: 14–17.*

This information on immersion foot was compiled from reports made by Major M. DeBakey and Commander J. White. Immersion foot is stated to be the term applied to the condition resulting from prolonged immersion of the feet in water and usually associated with dependency and immobility of the lower extremities with some constriction of clothing or shoes. Although it is usually associated with cold or icy water, the condition can also occur in subtropical regions. It is essentially different from frostbite but similar to trench foot and shelter foot. Three comparatively distinct stages in immersion foot have been observed after rescue. In the pre-hyperemic stage the foot is cold, somewhat swollen, discolored, and numb, with the peripheral arteries being almost pulseless. In the hyperemic stage, the foot is dry, red, hyperemic, and hot with a full and bounding peripheral pulse. Damage to the peripheral vessels is suggested by ulceration and gangrene. The numbness of the earlier stage is replaced by an intense paresthesia. The affected parts are made worse by warmth and dependency. In the post-hyperemic stage the clinical manifestations vary greatly depending on the degree of involvement and type of therapy. At the time of rescue from partial immersion, the patient should not attempt to walk but should be carried and placed in a bed with his legs slightly raised above heart level and free of pressure. The feet should be left uncovered and cool, if it is necessary to warm the body with blankets and hot drinks. Especially during intense hyperemia and severe neuritic pain the feet may be cooled by fans blowing cold air over them or by careful packing in ice. After hyperemia and edema have subsided, various vascular exercises should be begun gradually. Even though the value of these methods of treatment has not been definitely established, sympathetic block, compression dressings, or elastic bandages may be employed in intractable edema and pain.

2697. Fausel, E. G., and J. A. Hemphill. Study of the late symptoms of cases of immersion foot. *Surg. Gyn. Obst., v. 81, Nov. 1945: 500–503.*

Report is made on the late symptoms of a group of patients suffering from immersion foot as a result of the sinking of a transport in the North Atlantic in 1943. A group of 65 patients were still under observation 14 months after the sinking. Clinical histories and symptomatology of the late sequelae are given in detail.

2698. Friedman, N. B., K. Lange, and D. Weiner. Pathology of experimental immersion foot. *Arch. Path., Chic., v. 49, Jan. 1950: 21–26.*

In a group of rabbits one of the hind legs of each animal was kept in a circulating cold water (35°–39°F) bath for 3–4 days. Histopathological examinations of the tissues of the legs immediately or after 4–135 days following exposure, showed striking degenerative changes in the muscles and nerves which appeared to be the direct effect of cold. Vascular changes, such as those produced by exposure at temperatures below 32°F, were not observed. These findings lead the authors to the assumption that, at least in rabbits, there are essential differences between injuries produced by freezing and those produced by chilling.

2699. Goldstone, B. W., and H. V. Corbett. Aetiology of "Immersion foot." *Brit. M. J., 1944 (v. 1), Feb. 12: 218–219.*

Description is given of the immersion foot syndrome, as observed during treatment of rescued mariners. The authors quote Greene (item 1765) who had assumed that, clinically, immersion foot and trench foot were almost identical and that trench foot was probably identical with gradual frostbite. The authors state that immersion foot differs markedly from frostbite and that treatment therefore differs. They regard immersion foot or hand as the result of a massive chilling and ischemia of the tissues, and state that it commonly bears a striking resemblance to peripheral neuritis. In frostbite the injury is primarily from ice crystal formation bringing about simultaneous death of all tissues in the area irrespective of their relative hardihood. The foot in both conditions should be kept cool at first, but in immersion foot it is often beneficial to promote vasodilatation by the use of a heat cradle for the foot when the pain becomes severe. Mixed forms of the two conditions can occur.

2700. Hunt, T. C. Medical experiences in North Africa, 1943–44. *Brit. M. J., 1944 (v. 2), Oct.: 495–498.*

In the section of Immersion Foot (p. 497–498), the author discusses the treatment of soldiers with immersion foot. The injury had developed after the men had been forced by battle conditions to remain almost stationary in mud and rain for many days. Initial signs of injury had been coldness of foot and leg, followed by hyperemia and severe edema, with loss of most forms of skin sensation. Without further injury from warming of the extremity or other complication, the edema usually subsided in 1 or 2 weeks.

2701. Johnson, A. C. Immersion foot. *Med. J., Lond. (Can.), v. 14, Mar. 1944, 8–13.*

The clinical picture of immersion foot is described as an injury secondary to cold, manifesting itself as a sublethal injury to the chilled tissue cells, the vascular system, and nerve fibers. Details of treatment are given.

2702. Kreyberg, L. Experimental immersion foot in rabbits [In English]. *Acta path. microb. scand.*, *v. 26, 1949: 296–308.*

Experimental immersion foot was produced in rabbits by exposing extremities to moderate cold (2° to 5°C); the early circulatory changes were studied. The responses observed were vasoconstriction, moderate edema, increased vascular permeability with enhanced edema, then vascular spasm.

2703. Lange, K., D. Weiner, and L. J. Boyd. The functional pathology of experimental immersion foot. *Am. Heart J., v. 35, Feb. 1948: 238–247.*

Experimental immersion foot was produced in rabbits and it was found that the lesions so produced are basically different from those in frostbite. The former are mainly disturbances of muscular and nervous function and the intravascular agglutination generally associated with frostbite is absent. Circulation in exposed limbs continues during immersion, although at a slower rate, and edema occurs during exposure not afterwards as in frostbite. Gangrene in experimental immersion foot is extremely rare.

2704. Learmonth, J. R., C. C. Ungley, W. Blackwood, J. B. Gaylor, R. Greene, and T. Lewis. Discussion on immersion injuries and vasomotor disorders of the limbs in wartime. *Proc. R. Soc. M., Lond., v. 36, Aug. 1943: 515–522.*

Vasomotor disorders are classified by Learmonth into 3 groups: (a) resulting from trauma; (b) from organic vascular disease; and (c) from the local effects of cold. Ungley outlined the clinical features of immersion foot; Blackwood the pathology; and Gaylor some physiological aspects of the syndrome. Greene and Lewis both suggested that sympathectomy should be used with caution as its physiological basis was not yet fully established.

2705. Lesser, A. Report on immersion foot casualties from the battle of Attu. *Ann. Surg., v. 121, Mar. 1945: 257–271.*

Two groups (totaling 52 cases) of immersion foot, returned from combat duty on the island of Attu, are described. Etiology, clinical picture, and treatment are discussed. All tissues surgically removed were studied microscopically and findings are indicated.

2706. Lewis, T. Swelling of the human limbs in response to immersion in cold water. *Clin. Sc., Lond., v. 4, 1939: 349–360.*

Immersion of an extremity in cold water (5°C) appeared to injure directly the skin and subcutaneous tissue, the effect beginning at a skin temperature about 15° to 18°C. Swelling was due mainly to an edema of the tissues, as judged by its rapid development and relatively high protein content; the amount of imbibed water was very slight.

2707. Ogden, E., and C. E. Hall. Peripheral circulation. *Annual Rev. Physiol., v. 11, 1949: 435–468.*

The literature from July 1947 to July 1948 concerned with peripheral circulation is reviewed. Circulation in the extremities and vascular disorders of the extremities, including frostbite and immersion foot, are discussed on p. 442–445. 238 refs.

* 2708. Orlov, G. A. Chilling in water ("wet extremity") [In Russian]. *Khirurgīa, Moskva, Sept. 1949 (9): 17–25.*

"*Contains* information on the first mass appearance of cold immersion damage in the Soviet army in 1942; previous studies of the problem; differences from injuries by "dry" cold; pathology and clinical studies based on 34 cases, one of them a woman; case histories; therapy."— Arctic Bibl., v. 4, 1954: 767.

---

* Original not seen.

2709. Richards, R. L. The immersion foot syndrome. *In: The peripheral circulation in health and disease, p. 123–143. Baltimore, Williams & Wilkins, 1946.*

A general account of immersion foot is given based upon the author's personal experience. A series of case histories is presented together with a discussion of the origin and use of the term "immersion foot", the clinical picture, pathogenesis, treatment, and complications.

2710. [Solandt, D. Y., and M. L. Bunker.] "Immersion foot." *J. Canad. M. Serv., v. 3, May 1946: 340–342.*

The experiments of Surgeon Commander D. Y. Solandt and Lieutenant M. L. Bunker are described in which a condition resembling human immersion foot was induced in white rats. Use of vaseline-impregnated knitted woolen stockings, attached to a jacket-like device in which the animals were suspended, delayed the appearance of the syndrome. Addition of fat and yeast to the diet seemed to be effective in prolonging survival time. Life rafts and life boats of the Merchant Navy were provided with spirally-knit vaseline-impregnated stockings, but no report of their efficacy was received perhaps because a change in war conditions made it unnecessary to give them a trial under sea conditions.

2711. Ungley, C. C., and W. Blackwood. Peripheral vasoneuropathy after chilling: "immersion foot and immersion hand" with note on the morbid anatomy. *Lancet, Lond., v. 243, Oct. 17, 1942: 447–451.*

A detailed account is given of immersion foot based upon the study of more than 80 cases seen in Scotland over a period of 2½ years. The clinical features, morbid anatomy, prophylaxis, and treatment are discussed.

2712. Ungley, C. C. Discussion on immersion injuries and vasomotor disorders of the limbs in wartime. *Proc. R. Soc. M., Lond., v. 36, 1943: 518–521.*

After a summary of the main clinical findings and a discussion of the grades of severity seen, the vasomotor disorders of immersion foot are described. The short pre-hyperemic period is followed by a hyperemic period which increases in length of time with increase of injury. The hyperemia seems to be due, in part, to the destruction of vasoconstrictor fibers in peripheral nerves.

2713. Ungley, C. C. Immersion foot and immersion hand. *In: R. Maingot, E. G. Slesinger, and E. Fletcher. War wounds and injuries, p. 468–475. 2nd ed. Baltimore, Williams & Wilkins, 1943.*

This general account of immersion injury is based on personal observations of more than 100 cases seen in Scotland, and on the available literature from other areas where shipwrecked mariners were treated. The author discusses the clinical picture, differential diagnosis, morbid anatomy, pathogenesis, prevention, and treatment.

2714. Ungley, C. C. Immersion foot and immersion hand. (Peripheral vasoneuropathy after chilling). *Bull. War. M., Lond., v. 4, Oct. 1943: 61–65.*

This general account of immersion injury is based on the author's own clinical experience. The discussion covers the etiology, clinical picture and classes, pathogenesis, prevention, and treatment.

2715. Ungley, C. C., G. D. Channell, and R. L. Richards. Immersion foot syndrome. *Brit. J. Surg., v. 33, July 1945: 17–31.*

The clinical and pathological features of the immersion foot syndrome are discussed in a general manner. Recommendations for treatment emphasize the fact that measures employed should take into account the stage of injury encountered.

2716. Ungley, C. C. The immersion foot syndrome. *In: Advances in Surgery, v. 1, p. 269–336. New York, Interscience Publ., 1949.*

This comprehensive review of the problems of immersion foot is based not only on the literature but also on the extensive clinical experience of the author. Discussions follow under the headings of clinical features (during exposure, the pre-hyperemic stage, hyperemic stage, and post-hyperemic stage); vascular disturbances; cold-sensitive states; swelling, blisters, and gangrene; bones, joints, tendons; sensory, motor, and sudomotor disturbances; and other not as common clinical findings. Immersion hand is discussed on pages 293–295. Etiological factors are discussed with details outlined of the four levels of severity of injury of Grades A through D. Edema of the limbs in survivors from shipwreck in warm waters, the differentiation of frostbite from immersion foot, and details of morbid anatomy are discussed. Pathogenesis is considered in detail under the three main causal factors of direct effects of cold, effect of anoxia, and pressure and exudation of fluid into the tissues. The effect of cold on blood vessels and the therapeutic methods to be used are considered depending on the stage of injury. There are also short sections on the damage to skin (blisters and gangrene), damage to nerve and muscle, and disorders of sweating. Some preventive measures are outlined.

2717. Webster, D. R. Sequelae of local exposure to cold. *Canad. M. Ass. J., v. 58, Mar. 1948: 258–261.*

General summary is made of the author's experience with 150 cases of trench foot and immersion foot, mostly among rescued seamen injured during the Battle of the Atlantic, and seen in Canadian hospitals. The cases are classified into four groups depending on the degree of injury ranging from mild cases with little apparent damage to severe with extensive loss of tissue. Emphasis is placed on individual treatment.

2718. White, J. C. Painful edema of the extremities in shipwrecked mariners. A newly recognized syndrome occurring after prolonged dehydration, malnutrition, and vitamin deficiency in southern waters. *U. S. Nav. M. Bull., v. 41, Jan. 1943: 32–43.*

A group of 15 survivors from ships torpedoed in the South Atlantic in warm water (70°C) were adrift in lifeboats for nearly 2½ weeks. All developed conditions of swollen and painful feet which nevertheless differed markedly from the previously described "immersion foot" found among survivors of ship wreck in colder waters such as the North Atlantic. The author describes the clinical and pathological findings in this new syndrome. It is suggested that vitamin B and K deficiency attendant on malnutrition and dehydration may be of etiological significance.

2719. White, J. C. Vascular and neurologic lesions in survivors of shipwreck. I. Immersion foot syndrome following exposure to cold. II. Painful swollen feet secondary to prolonged dehydration and malnutrition. *N. England J. M., v. 228, Feb. 18; Feb. 25, 1943: 211–222; 241–247.* Also in: *Rehabilitation of the war injured,* p. 647–684. Ed. by W. B. DOHERTY and D. D. RUNES. New York, Philosophical Library, 1943. Also, same material slightly condensed in: Vascular and neurological lesions of the extremities in survivors of shipwreck. I. Thermal injury to the feet secondary to immersion in cold water. II. Painful swollen feet secondary to prolonged dehydration and malnutrition. *In: American Academy of Orthopedic Surgeons. Lectures on peace and war: orthopedic surgery,* p. 226–232; 232–238. Ed. by J. E. M. THOMSON. *Chicago, 1943.*

A resumé is given of observations on immersion foot occurring in men rescued from the North Atlantic, contrasted with 15 cases rescued after shipwreck in the South Atlantic. The author regards the latter cases as not true immersion foot and suggests that the symptoms may be a syndrome following prolonged dehydration and malnutrition.

2720. White, J. C., and S. Warren. Causes of pain in feet after prolonged immersion in cold water. *War Med., Chic., v. 5, Jan. 1944: 6–13.*

In the early stages of inflammation due to prolonged immersion, the intense pain which is felt is caused by oxygen deficiency. Cooling the legs lessens pain because it lowers cell metabolism, thus reducing oxygen requirements. Pain and rigidity which persist after the inflammation has subsided are shown to be caused by an increase in interstitial connective tissue and collagen, involving blood vessels, muscle fibers, and nerves.

See also items: 394, 1107, 1220, 1243, 1253, 1909, 2632, 2658, 2659, 2660.

2. Prophylaxis and Therapy

2721. Anon. First aid in the Royal Navy. *London, His Majesty's Stationery Office, 1943. 106 p.*

In chapter 7, Abandon ship; first aid for survivors, the prevention and first aid treatment of frostbite and immersion foot are discussed. In abandoning ship it is best to carry too much rather than too little clothing since the extra clothing will serve as protection against either cold or sun. When survivors have reached a raft or boat, clothing should be dried if possible in layers and effort made to change positions to avoid poor circulation. Since some degree of shock is often involved, the victims usually need aid in getting aboard. If there is injury from frostbite or immersion foot, walking should be prohibited after removal of wet clothing, bed rest with the body warm but the feet kept cool, is prescribed. In case of less severe frostbite, the fingers or toes may be placed in cold water or may be very gently rubbed. In immersion foot, while the patient is kept warm and at rest, the feet should be left uncovered and resting on a soft pillow with an electric fan blowing cool air over them.

2722. Anon. Medical Research Council (Gt. Brit.). Committee on the care of shipwrecked personnel. A guide to the preservation of life at sea after shipwreck. *London, H. M. Stationery Office, 1943. 21 p.*

Based largely on Medical Research Council War Memorandum No. 8, instructions are given to mariners on what to do in case of shipwreck. Under the heading Lifeboat ailments, p. 17–19, information is given on the prevention of frostbite and immersion foot. Treatment after rescue is described on page 21.

2723. Anon. How to survive on land and sea; individual survival. U. S. Navy Department. Office of Naval Operation. *Annapolis, Md., U. S. Naval Institute, 1943. 264 p.*

Brief information is given (p. 186–188) on immersion foot and on the effects of cold, with instructions on preventive measures. There are also hints on first aid if the symptoms of immersion foot or of cold injury appear.

2724. Anon. A guide to the preservation of life at sea after shipwreck. *Brit. M. Bull., v. 2 (6), 1944: 149–150.*

This is an announcement of a wartime memo known as Medical Research Council War Memorandum No. 8, London, 1943. A small section of the memorandum notes the essential clinical features of frostbite and immersion foot, and discusses the prevention and therapy of the two conditions.

2725. B., R. B. Injuries due to cold. *Bumed News Lett., Wash., v. 2, Sept. 17, 1943: 10.*

The author states that the retention of body heat by insulation with suitable clothing and the maintenance of circulation in the extremities and exposed areas (by use of exercise or application of heat) are the two basic methods of preventing injuries due to cold. He cites immersion foot and trench foot as examples of severe injuries by cold which occur without freezing of the tissues.

2726. B., R. B. Prevention of injuries by cold. *Bumed News Lett., Wash., v. 2, Sept. 17, 1943: 10–11.*

Because frostbite occurs more rapidly with a combination of moisture and low temperature, wet clothing should be removed immediately and dry covering be provided by some means. Immersion foot can be avoided by drying, covering, and elevating the feet, and by exercising to maintain circulation. Sleep is advisable, unless the person is exhausted and unprotected, since a rested condition will increase resistance to cold.

2727. B., R. B. Recognition and first aid treatment of injuries due to cold. *Bumed News Lett., Wash., v. 2, Sept. 17, 1943: 11.*

The author describes the clinical symptoms of frostbite and immersion foot. He suggests elevation of the affected extremity with slow rewarming as methods of treatment, and cautions against massage or rubbing of the area with snow.

2728. Baumann, J. Immersion foot (White's syndrome). [In French]. *Presse méd., v. 53, Jan. 20, 1945: 27–28.*

This brief general account of immersion foot covers etiology, clinical picture, pathology, and treatment. Emphasis is placed on pre- and post-ganglionic sympathectomies. Refrigeration therapy at 20°C for several weeks, together with a diet rich in proteins and vitamins, is also recommended.

2729. Bigelow, W. G., and E. C. G. Lan Yon. Some uses for dry cold therapy, and a proposed cooling cabinet. *Brit. M. J., 1944, (v. 1), Feb. 12: 215–217.*

Some therapeutic applications of dry cold are discussed, together with a description of a cooling cabinet. The use of the cabinet in the treatment of immersion foot and of frostbite is described.

2730. Fellowes, R. Nursing care of immersion foot. *Canad. Nurse, v. 39, Sept. 1943: 581–582.*

Some comments on the management of cases of immersion foot are given. The rapid application of cold, either through ice bags or fans, is advocated.

2731. Lake, N. C. "Immersion foot" and cold therapy. *Brit. M. J., 1944 (v. 1), Feb. 26: 301–302.*

Description is given of the immersion foot syndrome, as observed during treatment of rescued mariners. Reference is made to a paper by Goldstone and Corbett which quotes Greene (item 1765) as saying that frostbite and trench foot are probably synonymous terms. Lake agrees with Goldstone and Corbett (item 2699) that there is an essential difference between immersion foot and true frostbite, and that immersion foot resembles trench foot in clinical course. He disagrees with Goldstone and Corbett in their recommended use of vasodilatation in some phases of immersion foot, and recommends strongly the use of vasoconstrictors and refrigeration therapy in both immersion foot and frostbite. Because of the capacity of tissues for supercooling, there is a critical temperature of about $-5°C$ above which tissue will survive for long periods and below which death occurs because of protoplasmic disruption.

2732. Spealman, C. R. Wet cold. *In: Physiology of heat regulation and the science of clothing, p. 367–370. Ed. by* L. H. NEWBURGH. *Philadelphia, Saunders, 1949.*

The problems of protection of the feet against immersion foot and trench foot, are discussed in general. Painful and swollen feet may occur in survivors of shipwreck in equatorial waters as well as in northern waters. Whether or not the condition is the same regardless of the temperature of the water, is not a completely established fact. In general the injury does not occur in warm waters unless the period of immersion is a rather long one. Practical experience with survivors of shipwreck would indicate that feet are not injured quickly unless they are cooler than 8°C according to some authors, or 10°–15°C according to others. Keeping the body as a whole warm is an important consideration in keeping the feet warm. Rubber boots and overshoes which provide a water-tight barrier under normal circumstances, are inadequate on life rafts since the water gains entrance at the tops of the boots. The etiology of cold, on the other hand, seems to be clearly established in trench foot. The problem of providing water-tight footgear in trenches and foxholes is much less difficult than it is on rafts.

2733. **Stephenson, C. S., G. W. Mast, and J. F. Shronts.** First aid treatment for certain conditions common among shipwreck survivors. *Hosp. Corps Q.*, *v. 16. Jan. 1943: 1–13.*

This is a first aid manual for the use of those who may be concerned with the rescue of shipwrecked persons and is based upon experience and doctrines of the U. S. Navy. Immersion foot, frostbite, and prolonged exposure to cold are among the conditions discussed.

2734. **Ungley, C. C.** Treatment of immersion foot by dry cooling. *Lancet, Lond., v. 244, May 29, 1943: 681–682.*

Two case histories are given which illustrate the importance of cooling localized injured areas, either by fan or refrigeration. The author warns again of the necessity for avoiding use of heat.

2735. **Webster, D. R., F. M. Woolhouse, and J. L. Johnston.** Immersion foot. *J. Bone Surg., Am. Vol., v. 24, Oct. 1942: 785–794.*

Experiences in the treatment of 142 cases of immersion foot among survivors from North Atlantic naval and merchant vessels, are reported. Clinical features are described. Treatment was by cooling, either through use of ice bags, fans, or exposure of the feet to a cold room temperature. The aim was to reduce metabolic demands until local vascular conditions had returned to normal. Results were generally good. Rapid rewarming and sympathectomy were contraindicated.

2736. **White, J. C.** Immersion foot. *Mod. Concepts Card. Dis., v. 13, Feb. 1944: 1–2.*

This general account of the immersion foot syndrome, based upon experience with survivors of torpedoed vessels in the North Atlantic, includes a discussion of the pathological physiology and treatment.

See also items: 558, 732, 1557, 1607, 1615, 1637, 1662, 1669, 1680, 1767, 1877, 1913, 2160, 2187, 2527, 2583.

AUTHOR INDEX